London GCSE MATHEMATICS

INTERMEDIATE COURSE

1	Number	1
2	Simple functions	15
3	Probability 1	28
4	2-D and 3-D shapes	39
5	Measure 1	55
6	Approximation	70
7	Graphs of linear functions	81
8	Collecting and organizing data	98
9	Using and applying mathematics	110
10	Angles	121
11	Fractions	137
12	Measure 2	154
13	Quadratic functions	171
14	Properties of numbers	178
15	Pythagoras' theorem	193
16	Averages and spread	201
17	The tangent ratio	226

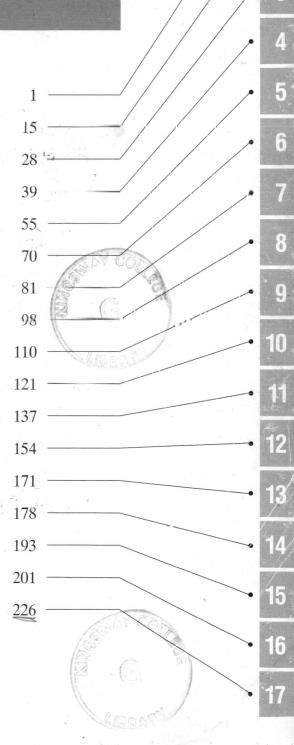

About this book

This book is designed to provide you with the best possible preparation for your London GCSE Mathematics Examination. The authors are examiners and coursework moderators themselves and have a good understanding of all the Examination Council's requirements.

Finding your way around

To help you find your way around when you are studying and revising use the:

- **edge marks** (shown on the front pages) – these help you get to the right unit quickly;
- **contents list** – this lists the headings that identify key syllabus ideas covered in the book so you can turn straight to them (Codes are included to show which part of the programmes of study and left-hand column of the syllabus these relate to. For example **S4d** means the content relates to Shape, space and measures section **4** understanding and using measures subsection **d**)

Remembering key ideas

We have provided clear explanations of the key ideas and techniques you need throughout the book. **Key points** you need to remember are listed in a **summary** at the end of each unit and marked like this where they appear in the units themselves:

■ **Each digit in a number has a face value and a place value.**

Exercises and examination questions

In this book questions are carefully graded so they increase in difficulty and gradually bring you up to examination standard.

- **past examination questions** are marked with an [L];
- **worked examples** and **worked examination questions** show you how to answer questions;
- **examination practice paper** – this is included to help you prepare for the examination itself;
- **answers** are included at the end of the book.

Investigations and information technology

Two units focus on particular skills required for your course and examination:

- **using and applying mathematics** (unit 9) – shows how investigative work is assessed, and the skills required to carry out such work;
- **calculators and computers** (unit 30) – shows you how to use a variety of methods of solving problems using calculators and computers.

18 Graphs of more complex functions 236

19 Probability 2 257

20 Lengths, areas and volumes 273

21 Algebraic expressions and formulae 291

22 Percentages 312

23 Transformations 333

24 Presenting data 355

25 Ratio and proportion 373

26 Accurate drawing, scales and loci 385

27 The sine and cosine ratios 398

28 Equations and inequalities 412

29 Interpreting data 431

30 Calculators and computers 438

Examination practice paper 456

Formulae sheet 461

Answers 462

Contents: Intermediate book

1 Number

1.1	**Digits and place value**	N2a	understanding place value in whole numbers	1–2
1.2	**Decimals**	N2a	place value and multiplication and division of decimal numbers by powers of ten	2–4
1.3	**Ordering numbers**	N2a	writing assorted numbers in order of size	5
1.4	**Working without a calculator**	N3b	long multiplication and long division without using a calculator	6–7
1.5	**Using negative numbers**	N2b	addition, subtraction, multiplication and division using negative numbers	7–13
	Summary of key points			13–14

2 Simple functions

2.1	**Using a number machine**	A2b	using two-box number machines as an introduction to functions	15–16
2.2	**Going backwards through a number machine**	A2b	using the inverse of each number machine instruction	16–17
2.3	**Equivalent number machines**	A2b	finding two-box number machines which always give the same result	17–18
2.4	**Using function notation**	A2b	converting a number machine into an algebraic function	18–19
2.5	**Input to output**	A2b	finding the outputs of different functions for various inputs	19–20
2.6	**Output to input**	A2b	using inverse functions	20–21
2.7	**Writing functions in the form $n \rightarrow bn + c$**	A2b	finding equivalent functions	21–23
2.8	**Finding functions to fit given inputs and outputs**	A2b	looking at number patterns in order to find functions	23–24
2.9	**Finding an expression for the *n*th term of a sequence**	A2b	finding the function to match a sequence of numbers	25–27
	Summary of key points			27

3 Probability 1

3.1	**What is probability?**	H3a	an introduction to the concept of probability	28
3.2	**Games and experiments**	H3a	using games and experiments to find estimated probabilities	29–31
3.3	**Equally likely outcomes**	H3d	looking at theoretical probabilities	32–34
3.4	**Mutually exclusive events**	H3a/H3d	when only one outcome is possible, it excludes all other possible outcomes	34–38
	Summary of key points			38

4 2-D and 3-D shapes

4.1	**Some reminders about polygons**	S2a	basic information about polygons	39–42
4.2	**Congruent and similar shapes**	S2b	comparing diagrams to find congruent shapes and similar shapes	42–45
4.3	**Looking at symmetry**	S2c	line symmetry and rotational symmetry of 2-D shapes	45–47
4.4	**Drawing 3-D shapes and their planes of symmetry**	S2a/S2c	using squared or isometric paper to draw 3-D shapes and their planes of symmetry	47–50
4.5	**Drawing nets of 3-D shapes**	S2a	drawing 2-D nets of 3-D shapes	50–53
Summary of key points				53–54

5 Measure 1

5.1	**Estimating**	S4a	the need to make estimates in everyday life	55
5.2	**Estimating length**	S4a	lengths used in everyday life	55–56
5.3	**Estimating capacity**	S4a	capacities used in everyday life	56
5.4	**Estimating weight (mass)**	S4a	weights of items used in everyday life	57–58
5.5	**Choosing appropriate units of measure**	S4a	choosing sensible units of measure in everyday life	58–59
5.6	**Measuring time**	S4a	using the 12-hour and the 24-hour clock systems	59–60
5.7	**Reading scales**	S4b	reading scales as accurately as possible	61–62
5.8	**Measuring lines**	S4b	using a centimetre ruler	62–63
5.9	**Calculating time**	S4a	adding and subtracting times	63–64
5.10	**Dealing with dates**	S4a	using a calendar	64–65
5.11	**Timetables**	S4a/H2a	using bus and train timetables	66–67
Summary of key points				68–69

6 Approximation

6.1	**Rounding a number**	N2a	rounding whole numbers to the nearest 10, 100 or 1000	70–71
6.2	**Rounding remainders**	N4d	rounding remainders sensibly in everyday life	71–72
6.3	**Rounding to a number of decimal places**	N2a	approximating to a given number of decimal places	73
6.4	**Rounding to a number of significant figures**	N2a	approximating to a given number of significant figures	74–75
6.5	**Checking and estimating**	N3f/N4c	writing numbers to one significant number in order to estimate or check answers	75–76
6.6	**Recognizing inaccuracy of measurements**	N4d	finding minimum and maximum values for rounded measurements	77–79
Summary of key points				79–80

7 Graphs of linear functions

7.1	**Graphs of linear functions with positive whole number inputs**	A2d	graphs of simple linear functions	81–83
7.2	**Graphs of linear functions with continuous positive inputs**	A2d	straight line graphs	83–87
7.3	**Investigating graphs of linear functions with positive and negative inputs**	A2d	graphs of $y = mx + c$ for various values of m and c	87–88
7.4	**Graphs of linear functions written in the form $y = mx + c$**	A2d	looking at the gradients and y-intercepts of various graphs	89–91
7.5	**Lines parallel to the y-axis**	A2d	graphs of equations such as $x = k$ and others	92
7.6	**Distance/time graphs**	A2c	graphs which illustrate journeys	93–96
	Summary of key points			97

8 Collecting and organizing data

8.1	**Two-way tables**	H2a	using two-way tables to sort out given data	98–100
8.2	**Other types of tables**	H2a	assorted tables to present data	101–102
8.3	**Databases**	H2a	organized collections of information	102–103
8.4	**Different types of data**	H2a	qualitative and quantitative data	103–104
8.5	**Tally marks and frequency distributions**	H2a	using tally marks on data capture sheets	104–105
8.6	**Grouped data**	H2a	using class intervals for recording data	105–106
8.7	**Data collection**	H2b	collecting different kinds of data	107
8.8	**Questionnaires**	H2b	looking at suitable questions for a questionnaire	107–108
	Summary of key points			109

9 Using and applying mathematics

	Coursework guidelines	UA1	investigating the number of diagonals that can be drawn in various polygons	110–120

10 Angles

10.1	**Calculating angles in triangles and quadrilaterals**	S2d	angle properties of triangles and quadrilaterals	121–125
10.2	**Calculating angles in polygons**	S2d	interior and exterior angles of polygons	126–128
10.3	**Calculating angles at parallel lines**	S2d	corresponding angles and alternate angles	129–131
10.4	**Calculating angles in circles**	S2b	angle properties in connection with circles	131–133
10.5	**Using three-figure bearings**	S2a	examples of three-figure bearings	134–135
	Summary of key points			135–136

11 Fractions

11.1	**Finding equivalent fractions**	N2b	using diagrams to find equivalent fractions	137–139
11.2	**Simplifying fractions**	N2b	cancelling fractions	139–140

11.3	**Improper fractions and mixed numbers**	N2b	interchanging improper fractions and mixed numbers	140–141
11.4	**Changing fractions to decimals**	N2b	interchanging fractions and decimals and using recurring decimals	142–144
11.5	**Adding and subtracting fractions**	N3c	using common denominators	144–147
11.6	**Multiplying and dividing fractions**	N3c	using fractions in problems involving multiplication and division	147–150
11.7	**Solving problems involving fractions**	N3c	assorted work on fractions	150–152

Summary of key points 153

12 Measure 2

12.1	**Converting units (metric)**	S4a	using metric units of measure	154–156
12.2	**Converting between metric and Imperial units**	S4a	using assorted units of measure	157–158
12.3	**Using unusual units**	S4a	using imaginary and outdated units	159
12.4	**Converting units of area and volume**	S4a	using metric and Imperial units of area and volume	159–160
12.5	**Accuracy of measurement**	S4b	degrees of accuracy of given measurements	160–162
12.6	**Choosing an appropriate degree of accuracy**	S4b	using sensible units for various measurements	162–163
12.7	**Using compound measures**	S4c	using speed and density formulae	163–166
12.8	**Changing units**	S4c	converting between various units of speed	167–168
12.9	**Comparing measurements**	S4c	changing units as necessary	168–170

Summary of key points 170

13 Quadratic functions

13.1	**Simple quadratic functions of the type $n \to an^2 + c$**	A2b	finding the value of c in various functions	171–172
13.2	**Using the method of differences**	A2b	finding the value of a in $n \to an^2 + c$	172–173
13.3	**Quadratic functions of the type $n \to an^2 + bn + c$**	A2b	finding the values of a, b and c	173–177

Summary of key points 177

14 Properties of numbers

14.1	**Types of numbers you should know**	N3a	even, odd and prime numbers and factors and multiples of numbers	178–179
14.2	**Square numbers and cube numbers**	N3a	calculating and recognizing square and cube numbers	179–180
14.3	**Finding squares and square roots of numbers**	N3c	squares and square roots of decimal numbers and squares of negative numbers	180
14.4	**Finding cubes and cube roots of numbers**	N3c	cubes and cube roots of decimal numbers and negative numbers	181

14.5	**Finding square roots and cube roots by trial and improvement**	N3c	using trial and improvement	182
14.6	**Calculating powers**	N2c	finding powers of whole numbers	183
14.7	**Multiplying and dividing powers of the same number**	N2c	obtaining the rules of adding and subtracting indices	184–185
14.8	**Prime factor form**	N3a	writing numbers in terms of their prime factors	185
14.9	**Finding the Highest Common Factor (HCF)**	N3a	using prime factors to find the HCF	185
14.10	**Finding the Lowest Common Multiple (LCM)**	N3a	using lists of multiples to find the lowest common multiple	186
14.11	**Standard form**	N2c	writing numbers in standard form	186–189
14.12	**Calculating with standard form**	N2c	using standard form in calculations	189–191

Summary of key points 192

15 Pythagoras' theorem

15.1	**Using Pythagoras' theorem to find the hypotenuse**	S2e	use Pythagoras' theorem to calculate the length of a hypotenuse	193–197
15.2	**Using Pythagoras' theorem to find one of the shorter sides of a triangle**	S2e	more work on Pythagoras' theorem	197–199

Summary of key points 200

16 Averages and spread

16.1	**The mean**	H2d	an example of the mean of a set of data	201
16.2	**The mode**	H2d	an example comparing the mean and the mode of a set of data	202
16.3	**The median**	H2d	an example comparing the mean, the mode and the median of a set of data	202–203
16.4	**The range**	H2e	using the range of a set of data	204
16.5	**The quartiles**	H2e	finding the quartiles for sets of data	205–206
16.6	**The interquartile range**	H2e	finding the inter-quartile range	206–207
16.7	**Averages from frequency distributions**	H2d	finding the mean, mode and median from frequency tables	207–209
16.8	**Spread from frequency distributions**	H2e	finding the range and inter-quartile range from a frequency table	209–211
16.9	**Averages from grouped data**	H2d	finding the mean, mode and median from grouped frequency tables	211–213
16.10	**Cumulative frequency**	H2d	estimating the median from a cumulative frequency table	214–215
16.11	**Cumulative frequency graphs**	H2c	drawing cumulative frequency graphs	216–218
16.12	**Using cumulative frequency graphs**	H2d/H2e	finding the median, quartiles and inter-quartile range from a cumulative frequency graph	218–225

Summary of key points 225

17 The tangent ratio

17.1	**Discovering the tangent ratio**	S2f	introducing the tangent ratio	226–227
17.2	**The tangent ratio on a calculator**	S2f	using a calculator for the tangent ratio	227–228
17.3	**Using the tangent ratio to find an angle**	S2f	calculating the size of an angle	229–231
17.4	**Using the tangent ratio to find a length**	S2f	assorted questions using the tangent ratio	231–234
	Summary of key points			235

18 Graphs of more complex functions

18.1	**Drawing graphs of simple quadratic functions**	A2d	graphs of functions $y = ax^2 + c$ where a and c can be positive or negative	236–240
18.2	**Solving simple quadratic equations**	A3d	using inverse number machines to solve equations such as $ax^2 + c = d$	240–241
18.3	**Drawing graphs of more complex quadratic functions**	A2d	graphs of functions $y = ax^2 + bx + c$	241
18.4	**Solving more complex quadratic equations**	A2d	using graphs to solve equations such as $ax^2 + bx + c = d$	242–243
18.5	**Solving problems involving quadratic equations**	A3d	using graphs to solve problems	243–244
18.6	**Graphs of functions involving x^3 and $\frac{1}{x}$**	A2d	graphs of cubic and reciprocal functions	244–247
18.7	**Drawing accurate graphs of more complex functions**	A2d	using graphs to solve cubic and reciprocal equations	247–248
18.8	**Solving equations by trial and improvement**	A3d	solving cubic equations non-graphically	249–250
18.9	**Graphs that describe real life situations**	A2c	assorted situations treated graphically	250–254
18.10	**Summary of graph shapes**			254–255
	Summary of key points			256

19 Probability 2

19.1	**Independent events**	H3e	possible outcomes of two independent events using space diagrams and tree diagrams	257–259
19.2	**Relative frequency**	H3c	using relative frequency to test the fairness of a coin or a dice	259–261
19.3	**The probability of combined events**	H3f	using the addition and multiplication rules of probability	261–263
19.4	**Tree diagrams**	H3e/H3f	using tree diagrams in probability questions	263–271
	Summary of key points			272

20 Lengths, areas and volumes

20.1	**Lengths and areas of rectangles, triangles and composite shapes**	S4d	perimeters and areas of triangles and quadrilaterals	273–276
20.2	**Circumference of a circle**	S4d	introducing π and the formula for the circumference of a circle	277–278
20.3	**Area of a circle**	S4d	develop the formula for the area of a circle	279
20.4	**Areas and volumes of 3-D shapes**	S4d	surface areas and volumes of prisms	281–284
20.5	**Considering dimensions**	S4d	deciding whether an algebraic expression represents a length, area or volume	285–289

Summary of key points 289–290

21 Algebraic expressions and formulae

21.1	**Evaluating algebraic expressions**	A3b	simple substitution	291–292
21.2	**Evaluating algebraic expressions involving squares**	A3b	substitution involving squaring	293–294
21.3	**Using indices**	A3c	manipulating expressions involving indices	294–296
21.4	**Removing brackets from algebraic expressions**	A3c	simple work on removing brackets	296–297
21.5	**Simplifying algebraic expressions**	A3c	multiplying out brackets	297–301
21.6	**Using formulae**	A3b	substitute numerical values into formulae	301–303
21.7	**Rearranging formulae**	A3c	changing the subject of a formula	304–307
21.8	**Factorizing**	A3c	factorizing trinomials and difference of two squares	307–310

Summary of key points 310–311

22 Percentages

22.1	**Percentages, fractions and decimals**	N2b	interchanging between percentages, fractions and decimals	312–314
22.2	**Finding a percentage of a quantity**	N3c	finding percentages and using percentages in problems	315–317
22.3	**Finding one quantity as a percentage of another**	N3c	finding percentage changes	317–319
22.4	**Finding the original amount before a percentage change**	N3d	finding 100% when another amount is known	319–320
22.5	**Dealing with profit and loss**	N3c	finding a percentage profit or loss	320–322
22.6	**Calculating VAT**	N3c	problems involving value added tax	322–323
22.7	**Buying on credit**	N3c	finding the added cost of buying goods on credit terms	323–324
22.8	**Calculating with simple and compound interest**	N4a	using the formulae for simple and compound interest	324–328
22.9	**Solving problems involving percentages**	N3c	assorted work on percentages	328–331

Summary of key points 331–332

23 Transformations

23.1	**Translations**	S3b	examples of translations	333–336
23.2	**Reflections**	S3b	examples of reflections	336–339
23.3	**Rotations**	S3b	rotations through given angles about particular points	339–343
23.4	**Enlargements**	S3b	stating the scale factor and centre of an enlargement	343–348
23.5	**Combining transformations**	S3b	combinations of translation, reflection, rotation and enlargement	348–353
	Summary of key points			353–354

24 Presenting data

24.1	**Pictograms**	H2c	an example of a pictogram	355
24.2	**Bar charts**	H2c	examples of bar charts	356–357
24.3	**Line graphs**	H2c	line graphs to illustrate continuous data	357
24.4	**Histograms**	H2c	histograms and other illustrations of data	357–359
24.5	**Frequency polygons**	H2c	assorted frequency polygons	360–362
24.6	**Pie charts**	H2c	using pie charts to illustrate data	362–366
24.7	**Scatter graphs**	H2c/H2f	looking at correlation between variables and drawing lines of best fit where possible	366–370
	Summary of key points			371–372

25 Ratio and proportion

25.1	**What is a ratio?**	N2b	an introduction to ratios	373–375
25.2	**Writing ratios in unitary form**	N2b	ratios as 1:n or as n:1	375–376
25.3	**Writing ratios as fractions**	N2b	writing ratios as fractions in order to solve problems	376–377
25.4	**Dividing quantities in a given ratio**	N3c	sharing in a given ratio	378
25.5	**Direct proportion**	N3d	examples in which increasing one quantity causes another quantity to increase in the same ratio	379–380
25.6	**Inverse proportion**	N3d	examples in which increasing one quantity causes another quantity to decrease in inverse proportion	381–383
	Summary of key points			384

26 Accurate drawings, scales and loci

26.1	**Making accurate drawings**	S2b	accurate constructions of triangles and quadrilaterals	385–387
26.2	**Using scales in accurate drawings**	S3d	scale drawings	387–389
26.3	**Finding the locus of an object**	S3e	perpendicular bisector of a line, bisector of an angle and other loci	390–392
26.4	**Using mathematical similarity**	S3d	scale drawings and similarity	392–396
	Summary of key points			396–397

27 The sine and cosine ratios

27.1	**Discovering the sine ratio**	S2f	an introduction to the sine ratio	398–399
27.2	**Using the sine ratio**	S2f	calculating lengths and angles	399–401
27.3	**Discovering the cosine ratio**	S2f	an introduction to the cosine ratio	401
27.4	**Connecting the sine and cosine ratios**	S2f	finding the relationship between the sine and cosine ratios	402
27.5	**Using the cosine ratio**	S2f	calculating lengths and angles	402–404
27.6	**Angles of elevation and depression**	S2f	numerical examples using angles of elevation or depression	405
27.7	**Using trigonometrical ratios**	S2f	assorted work using the trigonometrical ratios and Pythagoras' theorem	405–410
	Summary of key points			411

28 Equations and inequalities

28.1	**Using inverse number machines to solve problems**	A3b	forming and using simple formulae	412–413
28.2	**Solving linear equations using inverse number machines**	A3d	solving simple equations	413–414
28.3	**Solving linear equations by the balance method**	A3d	doing the same to both sides of an equation	415–419
28.4	**Using graphs to solve simultaneous linear equations**	A3d	an introduction to simultaneous equations and how to solve them graphically	420–422
28.5	**Solving simultaneous linear equations by substitution**	A3d	substitute for one unknown from one equation into the other equation	422–424
28.6	**Solving simultaneous linear equations by elimination**	A3d	eliminate one unknown by adding or subtracting equations	424–427
28.7	**Solving inequalities**	A3d	keeping the two sides of an inequality balanced	427–428
28.8	**Solving quadration equations by factorizing**	A3d	solving linear equations with whole number coefficients	428–430
	Summary of key points			430

29 Interpreting data

This unit illustrates the care that is needed when interpreting data based on averages, spread, interquartile range, and so on.	H2f	431–437
Summary of key points		437

30 Calculators and computers

30.1	**How well do you know your scientific calculator?**	N3e	becoming familiar with a scientific calculator	438–441
30.2	**Using memories to represent formulae on a graphics calculator**		calculating the area and perimeter of a rectangle	442–443
30.3	**Saving formulae so you can use them again**			444–445
30.4	**Solving problems and equations by trial and improvement**	N4b/A3d	finding the radius of a circle with a given area	445–447
30.5	**Using the Ans and EXE keys to produce number sequences**			447–448
30.6	**Drawing graphs on your calculator**	A2d	comparing groups of graphs	448–449
30.7	**Solving equations by drawing graphs on your calculator**	A2d	superimposing pairs of graphs in order to solve a given question	449–450
30.8	**Investigating number sequences with a spreadsheet**	A2b	using a spreadsheet to build up number sequences	450–451
30.9	**Problem solving with a spreadsheet**	N4b	finding measurements of enclosures that give maximum areas for given perimeters	451–453
30.10	**Trial and improvement on a spreadsheet**	A3d	using the area of a rectangle as an example	453–455

Examination practice paper 456–460

Formulae sheet 461

Answers 462

Index 494

Keith Pledger is **Project Director** for the London GCSE Mathematics series. He is subject officer for GCSE Mathematics at London Examinations and is also an OFSTED team inspector. Keith has worked in examining for over 21 years. Previously he was Head of Mathematics in three schools.

John Sylvester is **Series Editor** for the Foundation Book. He is an Examiner, Member of the Grading Committee and Coursework Moderator for GCSE Mathematics. He has been examining for over 25 years, chaired the subject committee and has been Head of Mathematics in two schools.

Christine Medlow is **Series Editor** for the Intermediate Book. She is Principal Examiner for GCSE Mathematics and has been examining with London for over 25 years. Christine has taught at a girls' grammar school, a co-educational comprehensive school and in adult education.

David Kent is **Series Editor** for the Higher Book. He is Chair of Examiners for GCSE Mathematics and Principal Moderator for Coursework. David has been a Head of Mathematics Departments and Adviser/ Inspector in three LEAs. He is at present an OFSTED team inspector.

Peter Jolly is **Consulting Editor** for the London GCSE Mathematics series. He is an Examiner, a member of the Subject Advisory and Grading Committees, and a Coursework Moderator for GCSE Mathematics at London Examinations. Peter has worked in both grammar and comprehensive inner city schools.

Author team

John Casson
Tony Clough
Gareth Cole
Ray Fraser
Barry Grantham
John Hackney
Karen Hughes
Trevor Johnson
Andrew Killick
Graham Newman
Sally Russell
Rob Summerson
Roy Woodward

Publishing team

Editorial
Philip Ellaway
Juliet Smith

Design
Phil Richards
Colette Jacquelin
Fiona Reynolds

Production
David Lawrence
Lucy Wallis

Heinemann Educational Publishers
Halley Court, Jordan Hill, Oxford OX2 8EJ
A Division of Reed Educational & Professional Publishing Ltd

OXFORD MELBOURNE AUCKLAND
JOHANNESBURG BLANTYRE GABORONE
IBADAN PORTSMOUTH (NH) USA CHICAGO

First published 1996

99 00 01 02 15 14 13 12 11

ISBN: 0435 53203 0

Produced by Gecko Limited, Bicester, Oxon

Printed in Spain by Mateu Cromo S.A. Pinto (Madrid)

Acknowledgements

The publisher's and author's thanks are due to London Examinations for permission to reproduce questions from past examination papers. These are marked with an [L]. The answers have been provided by the authors and are not the responsibility of the Examinations Council.

p28 and p165: Tony Stone Worldwide; p66: Colin Garratt; p67: Milepost; p134: Tony Stone Images; p146 and p356: Rex Features London; p162, p204, p324 and p355: Topham Picture Point; p336: Trevor Clifford Photography.

1 Number

1.1 Digits and place value

Nowadays most people use Arabic numbers. About fifteen hundred years ago they looked like this:

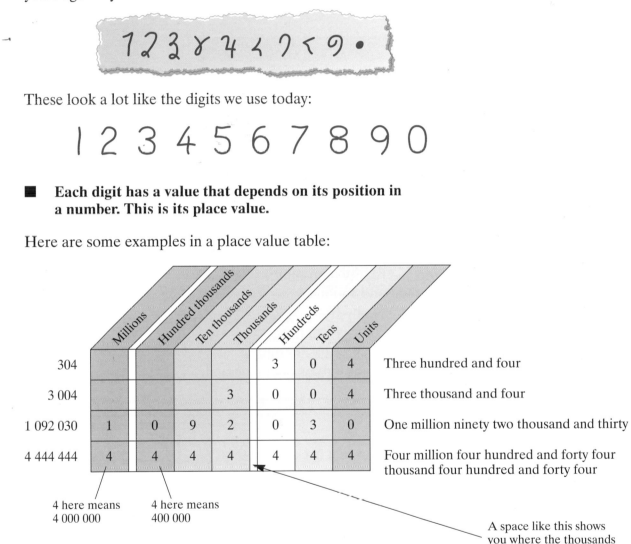

These look a lot like the digits we use today:

1 2 3 4 5 6 7 8 9 0

■ **Each digit has a value that depends on its position in a number. This is its place value.**

Here are some examples in a place value table:

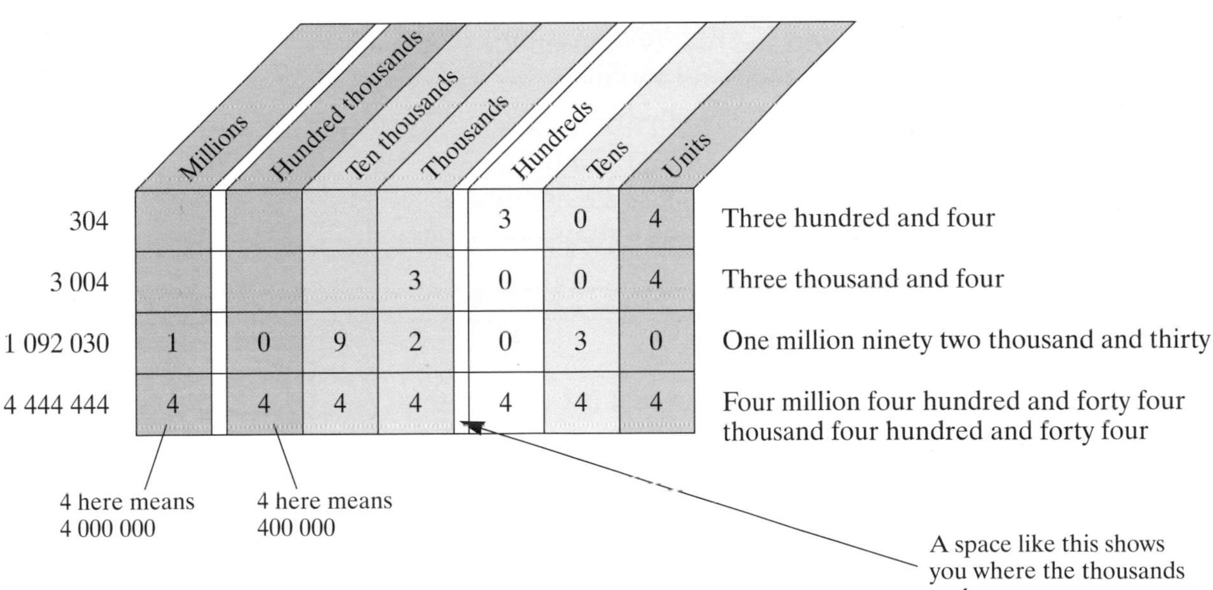

	Millions	Hundred thousands	Ten thousands	Thousands	Hundreds	Tens	Units	
304					3	0	4	Three hundred and four
3 004				3	0	0	4	Three thousand and four
1 092 030	1	0	9	2	0	3	0	One million ninety two thousand and thirty
4 444 444	4	4	4	4	4	4	4	Four million four hundred and forty four thousand four hundred and forty four

4 here means 4 000 000
4 here means 400 000
A space like this shows you where the thousands end.

Example 1

Write the number 1 804 603 in words.

To help you read a very large number the digits can be grouped in threes:

1 804 603 is	million	thousands	hundreds/tens/units		
	1	804	6	0	3

One *million*, eight hundred and four *thousand*, six *hundred* and three.

Example 2

Write these numbers using digits:

(a) half a million
(b) six thousand and twenty
(c) two million, fifty eight thousand, three hundred and six.

(a) half a million is 1 000 000 ÷ 2 = 500 000
(b) six thousand and twenty is 6020
(c) two million, fifty eight thousand, three hundred and six is 2 058 306.

Exercise 1A

In questions **1** and **2** write the numbers in words.

1 **(a)** 2 352 **(b)** 5 007 **(c)** 12 300
(d) 103 500 **(e)** 305 203 **(f)** 4 040 430

2 **(a)** 990 099 **(b)** 450 540 **(c)** 6 750 800
(d) 5 200 450 **(e)** 7 804 561 **(f)** 800 800 800

In questions **3** and **4** write the numbers with digits.

3 **(a)** one hundred thousand and twenty
(b) five hundred and fifty thousand, four hundred and ten
(c) one million, five hundred thousand and seventy
(d) five million, two thousand, four hundred and five
(e) four million, five hundred and twenty thousand
(f) nine hundred and ninety thousand and nine
(g) one million, ninety five thousand and four

4 **(a)** three million, three hundred thousand and thirteen
(b) one and a half thousand **(c)** two and a half million
(d) five and a quarter thousand **(e)** six and three quarter thousand

1.2 Decimals

■ **Decimals are used for parts of a number that are smaller than 1.**

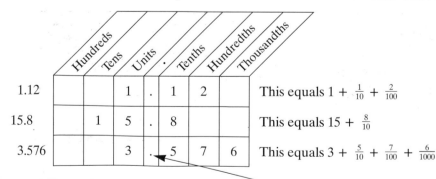

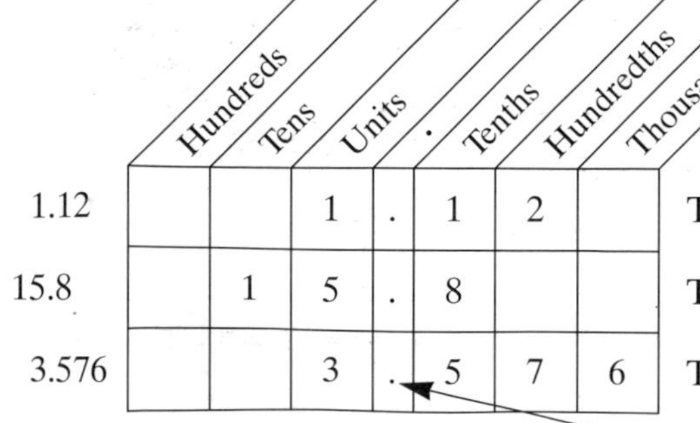

Hundreds
Tens
Units
.
Tenths
Hundredths
Thousandths
1.12
1 . 1 2
15.8
1 5 . 8
3.576
3 . 5 7 6

This equals $1 + \frac{1}{10} + \frac{2}{100}$

This equals $15 + \frac{8}{10}$

This equals $3 + \frac{5}{10} + \frac{7}{100} + \frac{6}{1000}$

This is a decimal point.
It separates the whole numbers from the part that is smaller than 1.

Example 3

Put the decimal 7.3208 into the table and write it in its separate parts.

You say "seven point three, two, nought, eight".

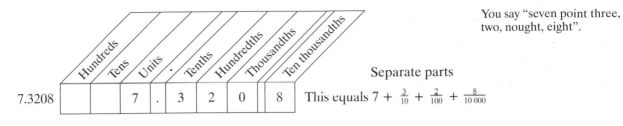

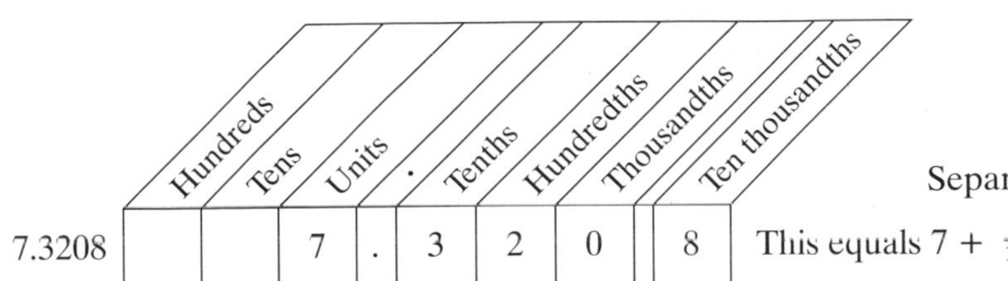

Separate parts

This equals $7 + \frac{3}{10} + \frac{2}{100} + \frac{8}{10\,000}$

Exercise 1B

Make a place value table with these headings:

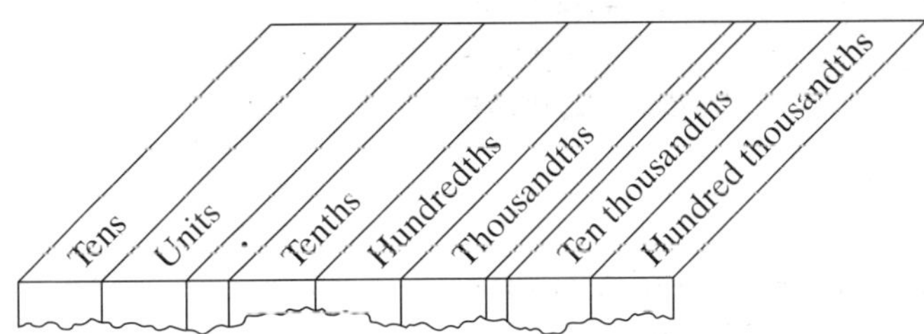

You will need room for sixteen answers.

Put each of the decimals into the table and write them in their separate parts.

(a) 0.26	**(b)** 1.79	**(c)** 38.24	**(d)** 14.8
(e) 0.0101	**(f)** 0.033	**(g)** 2.645	**(h)** 80.934
(i) 4.39852	**(j)** 0.0011	**(k)** 5.107	**(l)** 9.8302
(m) 7.457	**(n)** 13.0306	**(o)** 54.705	**(p)** 10.50301

Multiplying by 10

When numbers are multiplied by ten the digits move one place to the left like this:

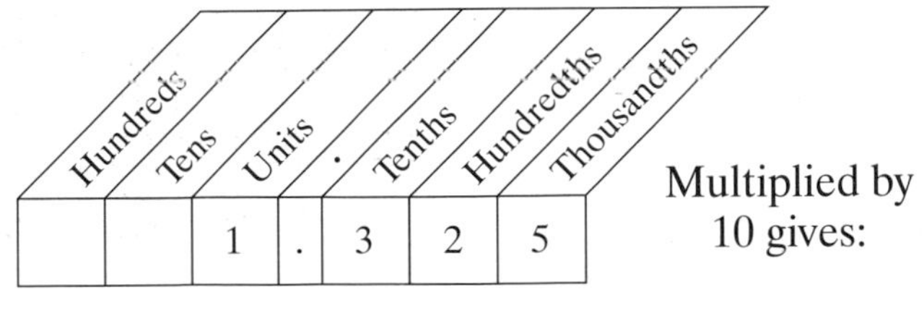

Multiplied by 10 gives:

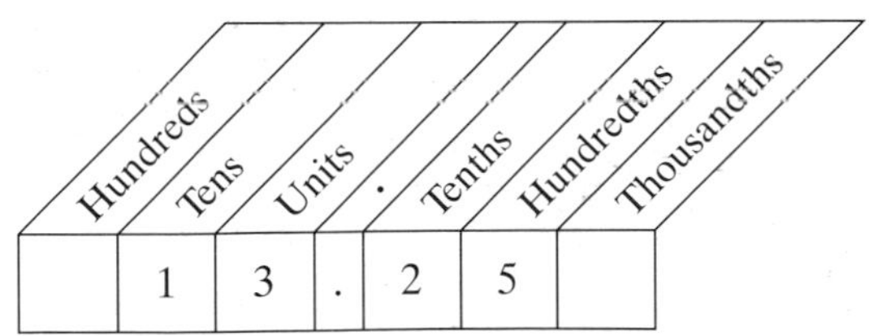

$1.325 \times 10 = 13.25$

Dividing by 100

When numbers are divided by a hundred the digits move two places to the right like this:

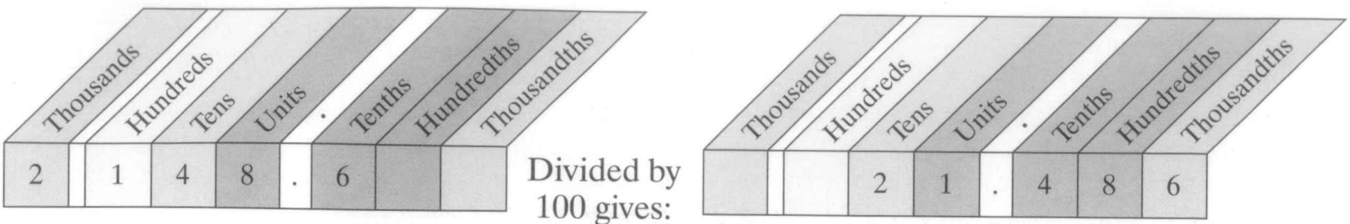

2148.6 ÷ 100 = 21.486

- **To multiply decimals by 10 move the digits one place to the left. To multiply by 100 move the digits two places to the left.**
- **To divide decimals by 10 move the digits one place to the right. To divide by 100 move the digits two places to the right.**

Example 4

Write down the answers to:

(a) $4.567 \div 100$ (b) 0.778×1000

(a) $4.567 \div 100 = 0.045\,67$
(b) $0.778 \times 1000 = 778$

Mental calculations

In your examinations you will sometimes be told not to use a calculator. All the work you do to find the answer should be shown on paper.

The next exercise is for practice in mental calculation. All the work you do to find the answer should be done in your head.

Exercise 1C

Write down the answers to the calculations in questions **1**, **2** and **3**.

Do not use a calculator.

1 **(a)** $21.2 \div 10$ **(b)** 4.121×100 **(c)** 0.401×10
(d) 0.27×100 **(e)** 0.213×1000 **(f)** 2.4×100

2 **(a)** 3.71×1000 **(b)** $21.31 \div 100$ **(c)** 4.92×1000
(d) $0.49 \div 100$ **(e)** 0.079×100 **(f)** $4.71 \div 10$

3 **(a)** $5.78 \div 10$ **(b)** 0.065×1000 **(c)** 9.54×10
(d) $133 \div 100$ **(e)** $45 \div 1000$ **(f)** 0.077×100
(g) 7.99×1000 **(h)** 0.0101×100

4 Now go back to questions **1, 2** and **3** and use a calculator to check your calculations.

1.3 Ordering numbers

You will often need to sort measurements and other numbers into size order. You need to be able to sort decimals as well as whole numbers.

Example 5

Rearrange these numbers in order of size, largest first.

$1.07, 1.7, 1\frac{7}{8}, 2, 1.085$

First write any fractions as decimals. Then compare whole numbers, then digits in the tenths place, then digits in the hundredths place, and so on.

$1\frac{7}{8} = 1.875$

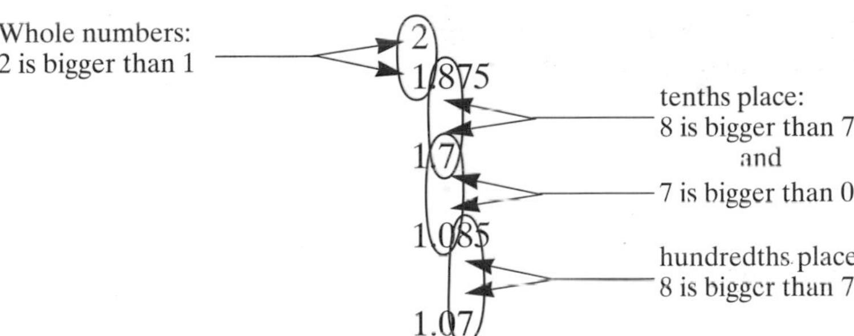
Whole numbers:
2 is bigger than 1
2
1.875
1.7
1.085
1.07
tenths place:
8 is bigger than 7
and
7 is bigger than 0
hundredths place:
8 is bigger than 7

So the order is 2, 1.875, 1.7, 1.085, 1.07

Exercise 1D

Rearrange the measurements in each question in order of size, largest first:

1. 4.101 m, 4.009 m, 4.0059 m
2. $\frac{1}{8}$ kg, 0.55 kg, 0.525 kg, 1.25 kg
3. 5.202 km, 5.305 km, 5.306 km, 5.204 km
4. $9\frac{9}{10}$ tonne, 9.904 tonne, 9.804 tonne, 9.99 tonne
5. Times taken in an experiment for a model car to roll down a slope: $5\frac{3}{4}$ s, 6.556 s, 5.623 s, 6.554 s.
6. The capacities of four containers: 2.02 cl, $\frac{1}{5}$ cl, 2.0 cl, 0.022 cl
7. Barry notes the distances he has run before losing breath: 6.202 km, 6.306 km, 6.204 km, 6.305 km
8. The weights of four lorries on a weighbridge: 4.512 tonne, 6.443 tonne, 6.448 tonne, 6.643 tonne
9. The widths of four machine parts: 1.08 cm, 9.8 cm, 9.08 cm, $10\frac{4}{5}$ cm
10. Four tubes have been made to these lengths: 8.701 m, 8.8 m, 8.88 m, 8.801 m

1.4 Working without a calculator

In some exam questions you need to do calculations without using a calculator. (However, you would be sensible to check your answer with a calculator.)

It is very important to show all your working, particularly when you do multiplication and division. It must be clear from your working that you have not used a calculator.

Example 6

Work out 418 × 37 without using a calculator.

Method 1

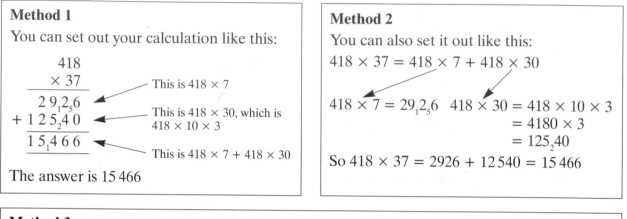

You can set out your calculation like this:

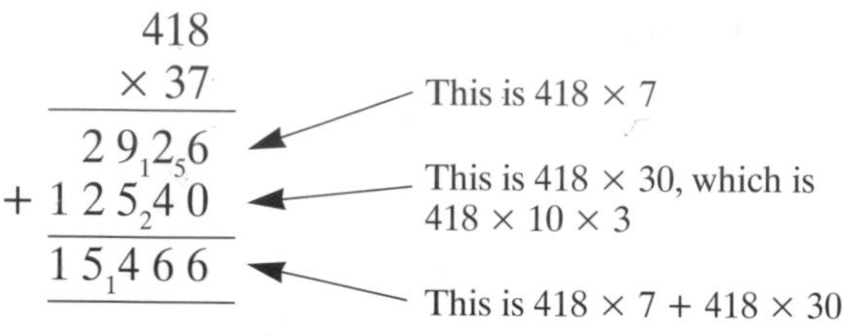

The answer is 15 466

Method 2

You can also set it out like this:

$418 \times 37 = 418 \times 7 + 418 \times 30$

$418 \times 7 = 29_{1}2_{5}6$ $\quad 418 \times 30 = 418 \times 10 \times 3$

$= 4180 \times 3$

$= 125_{2}40$

So $418 \times 37 = 2926 + 12\,540 = 15\,466$

Method 3

You could do this:

418 + 418 + 418 + …… + 418 but adding 37 lots of 418 together isn't a good idea!

Example 7

Work out 8704 ÷ 17 without using a calculator.

Here are 3 ways of setting out the calculation:

Method 1 By long division

Follow these steps:

17)8704

17 divides into 87
5 times remainder 2

```
     5
17)8704
  - 85
     2
```

17 divides into 20
1 time remainder 3

```
     51
17)8704
  - 85↓
     20
  -  17
      3
```

17 divides into 34
2 times exactly

```
     512
17)8704
  - 85
     20
  -  17↓
      34
      34
       0
```

So 17 divides into 8704 **512** times.

Method 2 By short division

This is a shorter way of setting out the steps in method 1:

```
    5 1 2
17)87²0³4
```

Method 3 By repeated subtraction

8704 – 17 = 8687

8687 – 17 = 8670 . . .

You would have to do this 512 times – not a practical method!

Exercise 1E

Work these out without using a calculator.

1 194 × 15 **2** 3178 ÷ 14 **3** 306 × 32

4 186 × 36 **5** 7421 ÷ 41 **6** 612 × 81

7 12 287 ÷ 91 **8** 547 × 51 **9** 32 638 ÷ 65

10 785 × 89 **11** 20 608 ÷ 28 **12** 35 344 ÷ 82

13 A lorry delivers 226 boxes of crisps. There are 48 packets in each box.
How many packets are there altogether?

14 A box contains 24 rubbers.
How many complete boxes can be filled with 8000 rubbers?

15 There are 12 items in one dozen.
How many items are there in 888 dozen?

You can check these answers using a calculator.

1.5 Using negative numbers

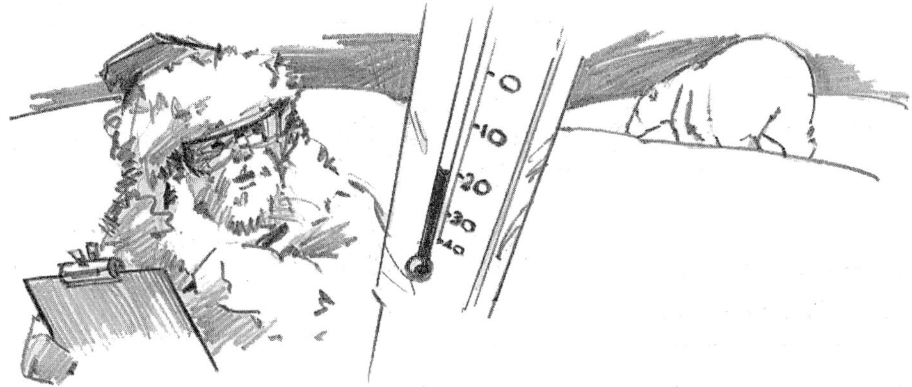

The thermometer shows that the temperature is negative 20 degrees. This is written –20 °C. The temperature represents 20 ° below freezing, or 20 °C below zero.

You need to be able to add and subtract negative numbers. To help you get used to working with subtraction signs and negative numbers they are written like this when they appear together in this section:

$^{-}5$ means negative 5, or 5 below zero

7 – 4 means 7 subtract 4

7 – $^{-}5$ means 7 subtract negative 5

Sometimes 3 is written $^{+}3$

■ **You can use negative numbers to describe quantities such as temperatures less than 0 °C. You can also use negative numbers in calculations.**

Example 8

(a) The temperature was 5 °C. It fell by 8°.
What is the new temperature?
(b) What is the difference in temperature from 4 °C to ⁻4 °C?

(a) From 5 °C count 8 degrees down to ⁻3 °C.
(b) From 4 °C count to ⁻4 °C. There are 8 degrees difference between the two temperatures.

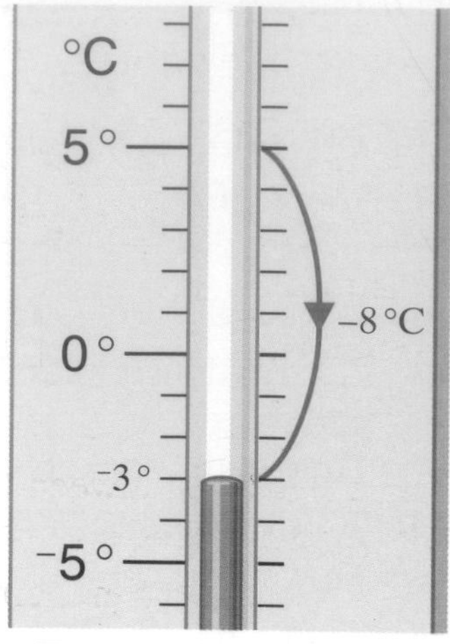

Temperature falls by 8 °

Worked exam question 1

The temperature during an Autumn morning went up from –3 °C to 6°C.

(a) By how many degrees did the temperature rise?

During the afternoon the temperature then fell by 8 degrees from 6 °C.

(b) What was the temperature at the end of the afternoon?

(a) Counting from –3 °C to 6 °C gives 9 degrees.
(b) Counting down 8 degrees from 6 °C gives –2 °C.

[L]

A full size – sign will be used to show negative numbers in your exam.

Exercise 1F

Draw a number line going from –10 °C to + 10 °C to help you with these questions.

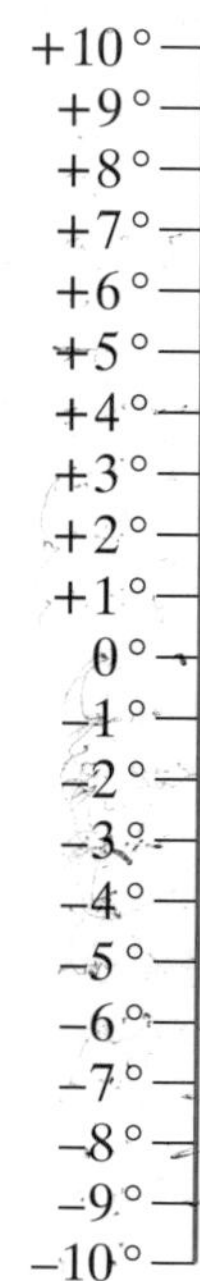

1 Find the number of degrees between each pair of temperatures:
(a) −3 °C, 2 °C **(b)** −4 °C, −1 °C **(c)** 2 °C, 8 °C
(d) −6 °C, 4 °C **(e)** 7 °C, −3 °C **(f)** 1 °C, 9 °C
(g) −3 °C, −8 °C **(h)** −7 °C, 6 °C

2 Find the temperature when:
(a) −4 °C rises by 2° **(b)** 4 °C falls by 7°
(c) 8 °C falls by 15° **(d)** −4 °C rises by 7°
(e) −5 °C rises by 8° **(f)** 4 °C falls by 10°
(g) −3 °C falls by 6°

3 Rearrange the temperatures in each question in numerical order, lowest temperature first:
(a) 4 °C, −5 °C, 2 °C, −12 °C, 7 °C, 0 °C, −7 °C, −1 °C, 9 °C
(b) 5 °C, −3 °C, 2 °C, 10 °C, −8 °C, −2 °C, 8 °C, 0 °C, −9 °C
(c) 7 °C, 3 °C, −7 °C, −4 °C, −1 °C, 8 °C, −6 °C, 5 °C, −3 °C
(d) −4 °C, 9 °C, 4 °C, −2 °C, 7 °C, −8 °C, 1 °C, −3 °C, 6 °C
(e) 5 °C, −5 °C, 7 °C, −7 °C, 4 °C, −9 °C, −3 °C, −1 °C, 8 °C, 0 °C

Subtracting negative numbers

This table shows lunchtime and evening temperatures in different parts of the world:

Place	Temperature at lunchtime in °C	Temperature in the evening in °C
Bahrain	20	15
London	5	−2
Alaska	−8	−14

The difference between the lunchtime temperature and the evening temperature in Bahrain can be written:

lunchtime temperature – evening temperature

$= {}^{+}20 - {}^{+}15 = {}^{+}5$ (or $20 - 15 = 5$)

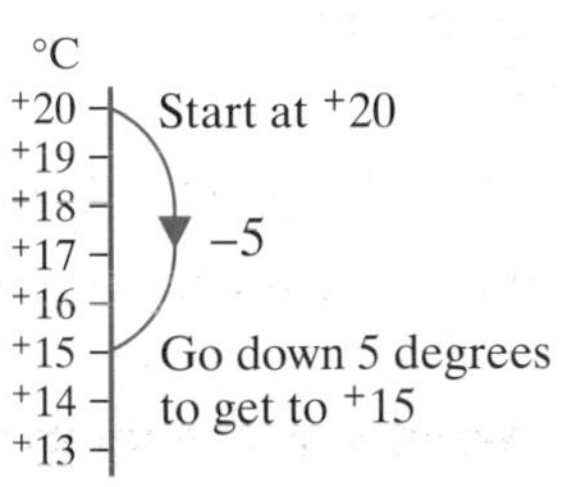

You can also think of this as $\quad {}^{+}20 + {}^{-}15 = {}^{+}5$

The difference in London is $\quad 5 - {}^{-}2 = {}^{+}7$

You also get 7 from working out $\quad 5 + {}^{+}2 = 7$

The difference in Alaska is $\quad {}^{-}8 - {}^{-}14 = 6$

You also get 6 from working out $\quad {}^{-}8 + {}^{+}14 = 6$

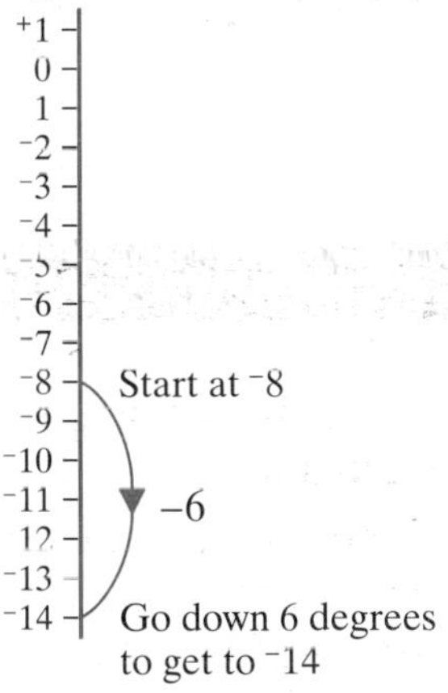

- **Subtracting a positive number is the same as adding the negative number.**

  Subtracting a negative number is the same as adding the positive number.

  $- {}^{+}4 = + {}^{-}4$

  $- {}^{-}3 = + {}^{+}3$

Example 9

Work out (a) $^{-}2 + {}^{+}3$ (b) $4 + {}^{-}2$ (c) $^{-}3 - {}^{+}5$ (d) $^{-}2 - {}^{-}6$

(a) Start at $^{-}2$ and go *up* 3 steps to get to $^{+}1$. $\quad {}^{-}2 + {}^{+}3 = {}^{+}1$

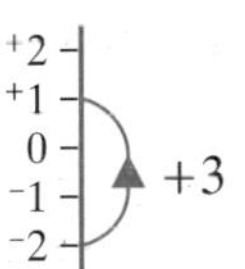

(b) Start at 4 and go *down* 2 steps to get to $^{+}2$. $\quad 4 + {}^{-}2 = {}^{+}2$

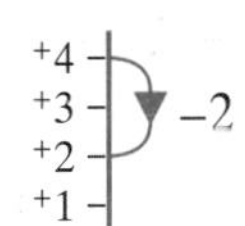

(c) $^{-}3 - {}^{+}5$ is the same as $^{-}3 + {}^{-}5$.
Start at $^{-}3$ and go *down* 5 steps to get to $^{-}8$.
$^{-}3 - {}^{+}5 = {}^{-}3 + {}^{-}5 = {}^{-}8$

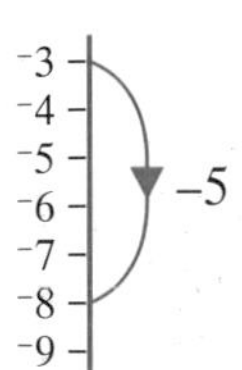

(d) $^{-}2 - {}^{-}6$ is the same as $^{-}2 + {}^{+}6$.
Start at $^{-}2$ and go *up* 6 steps to get to $^{+}4$.
$^{-}2 - {}^{-}6 = {}^{-}2 + {}^{+}6 = {}^{+}4$

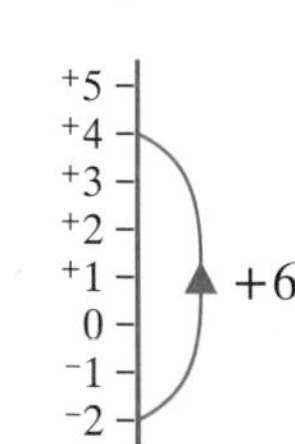

Full size – signs are used for negative numbers for the rest of this Unit.

Exercise 1G

Work out the answers:

1	**(a)** +3 + –3	**(b)** –4 + 0	**(c)** –9 – +5	**(d)** –9 + +5
2	**(a)** –5 – –6	**(b)** +12 – –5	**(c)** –10 + +8	**(d)** +6 – –4
3	**(a)** +8 + –13	**(b)** +5 – 0	**(c)** +13 – +15	**(d)** –2 + –4
4	**(a)** –3 – +8	**(b)** –3 + +6	**(c)** +11 – –6	**(d)** –12 + +7
5	**(a)** –7 + –7	**(b)** +4 – +1	**(c)** +3 + –8	**(d)** –3 – +6

Exercise 1H

Multiplication grid

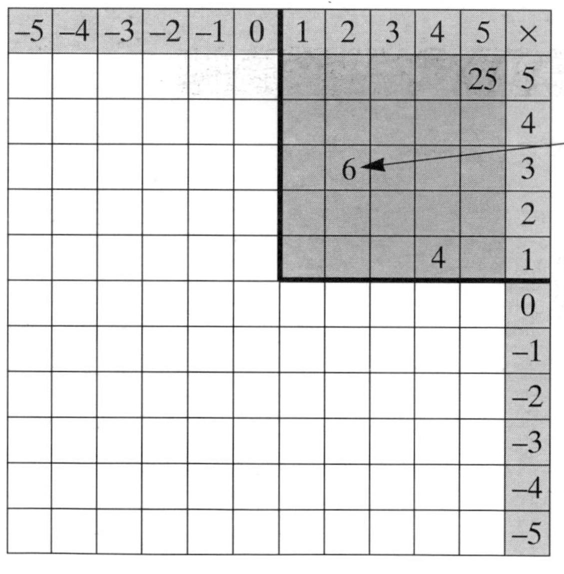

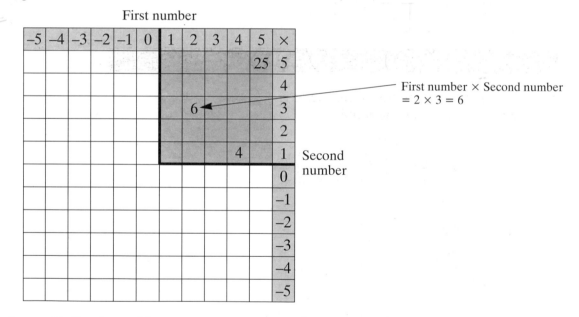

1. Copy the multiplication grid.
2. Complete the shaded square for numbers 1 to 5 on the grid.
3. Look at the patterns in the shaded square. Continue these patterns to complete all the horizontal and vertical rows in the table.
4. From your grid write down the values of:

(a) +5 × +2	**(b)** +4 × –3	**(c)** –2 × +4	**(d)** –3 × –5
(e) +3 × +1	**(f)** +2 × –3	**(g)** –5 × +4	**(h)** –4 × –1

- **When you multiply two numbers together this table shows the signs you get.**

+	×	+	=	+
+	×	–	=	–
–	×	+	=	–
–	×	–	=	+

Remember: when multiplying (or dividing) two like signs give a +, two unlike signs give a –.

–12 ÷ +4 is the same as –12 × + $\frac{1}{4}$ so the result is negative. (The answer is –3.)

- **When you divide one number by another, this table shows the signs you get.**

+	÷	+	=	+
+	÷	–	=	–
–	÷	+	=	–
–	÷	–	=	+

Note: the results are the same for multiplying and dividing.

Exercise 1I

1 Copy and complete this multiplication grid for first number × second number.

First number

	×	+5	+3	–6	–2
	+2				
Second number	+8				
	–3				
	–4				

2 Copy and complete this division grid for first number ÷ second number.

First number

	÷	+6	–12	–18	+24
	+3				
Second number	–2				
	–6				
	+1				

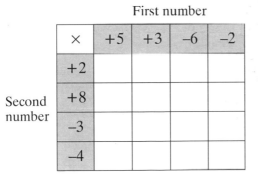

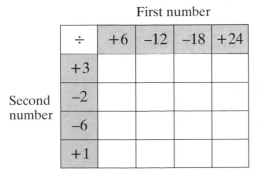

Example 10

Work out (a) $+5 \times -2$ (b) $+16 \div +2$ (c) $-1 \times +3$ (d) $-20 \div -5$

(a) $+5 \times -2 = -10$ (b) $+16 \div +2 = +8$
(c) $-1 \times +3 = -3$ (d) $-20 \div -5 = +4$

Exercise 1J

Work out:

1 **(a)** $+3 \times -1$ **(b)** $+24 \div -8$ **(c)** $+4 \div +1$
(d) $+2 \times +6$ **(e)** $-12 \div +3$ **(f)** $-3 \times +4$

2 **(a)** $-9 \times +10$ **(b)** $-32 \div -8$ **(c)** $-20 \div -4$
(d) $-2 \times +7$ **(e)** $+10 \div -5$ **(f)** -3×-4

3 **(a)** $-5 \times +4$ **(b)** $-16 \div -8$ **(c)** $-4 \times +5$
(d) $-18 \div -3$ **(e)** $+18 \div +2$ **(f)** $-6 \times +7$

4 **(a)** -8×-3 **(b)** $-30 \div +2$ **(c)** $-16 \div +4$
(d) -3×-9 **(e)** $+5 \times -8$ **(f)** $+24 \div +8$

5 **(a)** $-50 \div -5$ **(b)** $-7 \times +8$ **(c)** $+6 \times +6$
(d) -3×-7 **(e)** $-9 \div +3$ **(f)** $-7 \times +6$

Exercise 1K Mixed questions

1 Write in words the number 100 101.

2 Write with digits the number five and a half thousand.

3 Write with digits the number three and three quarters of a million.

4 Six cheques have these reference numbers:
374 214 735 102 542 372 539 999 390 002 642 137
Rewrite these numbers in numerical order, starting with the smallest.

5 Six distances have been recorded:
3.451 km, 3.506 km, 3.9 km, 3.008 km, 3.671 km, 3.91 km.
Rewrite these distances in numerical order, starting with the largest.

6 One hundred pupils each pay £8.75 towards a school trip. What is the total amount paid?

7 Prize money of £520 is to be shared equally by ten people. How much does each person receive?

8 Work out:
(a) $+4 - +7$ **(b)** $+4 \times -5$ **(c)** $-15 \div +3$
(d) $+3 - -8$ **(e)** -1×-1 **(f)** $-4 + -5$

9 A climber descends from the 6000 ft summit of one mountain, then climbs to the 4800 ft summit of the next mountain in the range. What is the difference in the heights of the two mountains?

10 The table below shows the maximum and minimum temperatures recorded in six cities one day last year.

City	Maximum	Minimum
Los Angeles	22 °C	12 °C
Boston	22 °C	−3 °C
Moscow	18 °C	−9 °C
Atlanta	27 °C	8 °C
Archangel	13 °C	−15 °C
Cairo	28 °C	13 °C

(a) Which city in the table had the lowest temperature?

(b) Work out the difference between the maximum temperature and the minimum temperature for Moscow. [L]

11 **Do not use your calculator for this question.**
Show all your working.
A school is planning a disco for 936 pupils. Each pupil will be given 1 can of drink. Cans of drink are sold in trays of 24.
Work out how many trays of drinks will be needed. [L]

12 A group of 29 teenagers is planning an activities holiday. The holiday will cost £118 per person.
Do not use a calculator.
Work out the total cost of the holiday for the group. Show all the stages in your working clearly.
Write down the answer. [L]

13 **In this question you MUST show all your working.**
Without using a calculator work out 148 × 23. [L]

Summary of key points

1 Each digit has a value that depends on its position in a number. This is its place value.

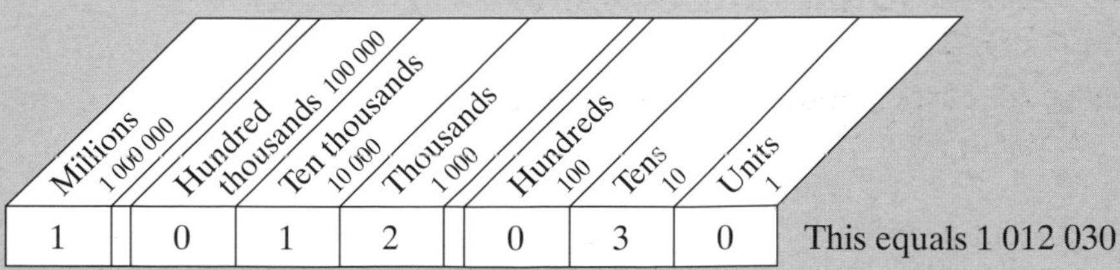

Millions 1 000 000
Hundred thousands 100 000
Ten thousands 10 000
Thousands 1 000
Hundreds 100
Tens 10
Units 1
1
0
1
2
0
3
0
This equals 1 012 030

2 Decimals are used for parts of a number that are smaller than 1.

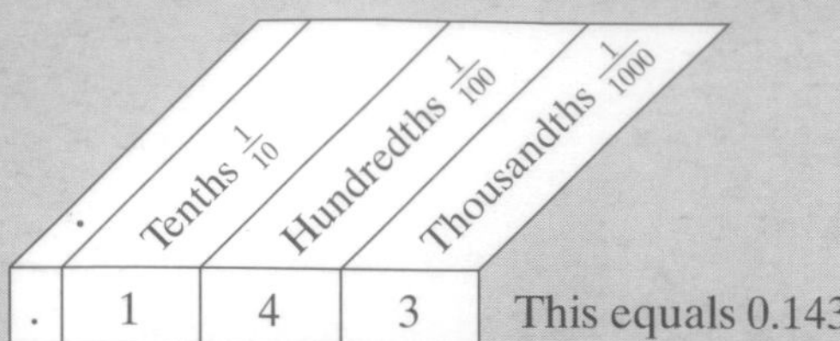

This equals 0.143

3 To multiply decimals by 10 move the digits one place to the left. To multiply by 100 move the digits two places to the left.

4 To divide decimals by 10 move the digits one place to the right. To divide by 100 move the digits two places to the right.

5 You can use negative numbers to describe quantities such as temperatures less than 0 °C. You can also use negative numbers in calculations.

6 Subtracting a positive number is the same as adding the negative number. $- +4 = + -4$

Subtracting a negative number is the same as adding the positive number. $- -3 = + +3$

7 When you multiply two numbers together, this table shows the signs you get:

+	×	+	=	+
+	×	−	=	−
−	×	+	=	−
−	×	−	=	+

Remember: when multiplying (or dividing) two like signs give a +, two unlike signs give a −.

8 When you divide one number by another, this table shows the signs you get:

+	÷	+	=	+
+	÷	−	=	−
−	÷	+	=	−
−	÷	−	=	+

Note: the results are the same for multiplying and dividing.

2 Simple functions

Sometimes you need to follow a set of instructions.
The instructions for cooking a turkey are:
Allow 45 minutes per kilogram then add an extra 30 minutes.
You could work out the time in minutes needed to cook a 3 kilogram turkey like this:

Start with 3.
Multiply 3 by 45 and you get 135.
Then add 30 and you get 165.

Exercise 2A

Work out the cooking times for a turkey that weighs:

(a) 4 kg **(b)** 7 kg **(c)** 10 kg **(d)** 2 kg
(e) 3.5 kg **(f)** 4.5 kg **(g)** 5 kg

2.1 Using a number machine

The instructions for cooking a turkey are very wordy.
They can be shown as a number machine diagram like this:
This is called a two-box **number machine**.

In → ×45 → +30 → Out

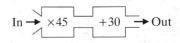

■ **A number machine shows instructions in a clear way.**

Exercise 2B

1 **(a)** Draw a two-box number machine for these instructions:
take a number, multiply it by 3 then subtract 1.

(b) Put each number into your number machine and calculate what comes out:

(i) 2 (ii) 4 (iii) 1 (iv) 0.5 (v) 2.5
(vi) –1 (vii) –2 (viii) –5 (ix) 1.25 (x) 2.75

2 **(a)** Draw a two-box number machine for these instructions:
take a number, add 4 then multiply by 2.

(b) Put each of these numbers into your number machine and calculate what comes out:

(i) 3 (ii) 6 (iii) 11 (iv) 0.5 (v) 2.5
(vi) 0.25 (vii) 1.25 (viii) –1 (ix) –6 (x) 0

3 **A game for 2 people**

Work in pairs.

One person, **A**, draws a two-box number machine but does not show it to person **B**. The number machine should not be too difficult.

B tells **A** a number to put into the number machine.

A calculates the number that comes out of the number machine and tells **B**.

B guesses what instructions are in the boxes of the machine.
If the guess is incorrect **B** tells **A** another number to put in.
B's score is the number of guesses taken to guess correctly.
A and **B** then swap roles.

The person with the lowest score wins the game.

4 **An investigation**

This is an investigation into the effect of swapping the order of boxes in a two-box number machine.

(a) Look at these two-box number machines. They contain the same instructions but in different orders.

(i) Choose some numbers to put into the first two-box number machine and calculate the numbers that come out.

(ii) Put the same numbers into the second two-box number machine and calculate the numbers that come out.

(iii) What do you notice?

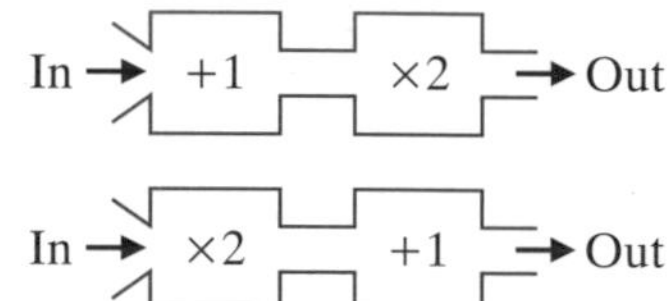

(b) Draw a two-box number machine of your own. Swap the order of the boxes over to make a second machine. Repeat part **(a)**.

(c) Find a two-box number machine for which swapping the boxes does not alter the way it changes numbers.

(d) (i) Explain what is special about the two-box number machines for which the order of the boxes does not matter.

(ii) Explain what is special about the two-box number machines for which the order of the boxes does matter.

2.2 Going backwards through a number machine

Example 1

Here is a two-box number machine:

If 13 comes out of the machine, what went in?

In → ×2 → +3 → Out

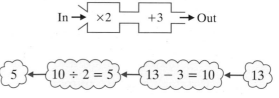

Send 13 backwards through the number machine.

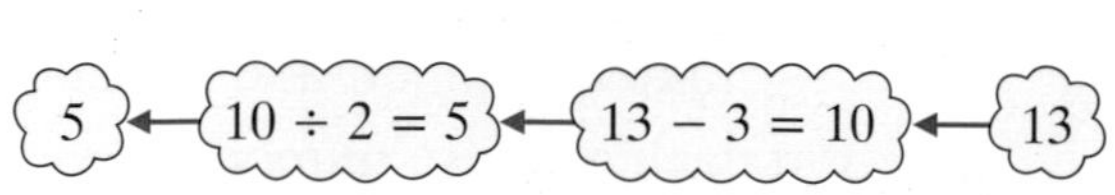

When you go backwards through a number machine you do the opposite to what the boxes contain.

Subtract 3 from 13 and you get 10.

Then divide 10 by 2 and you get 5.

So 5 went into the machine.

It is easier to do this if you first draw the **inverse number machine**.

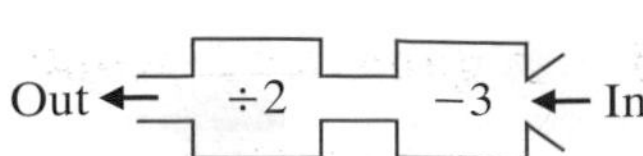

+3 and –3 are opposite instructions
×2 and ÷2 are opposite instructions

- **The inverse of a number machine goes in the opposite direction and each box contains the opposite instruction.**

Exercise 2C

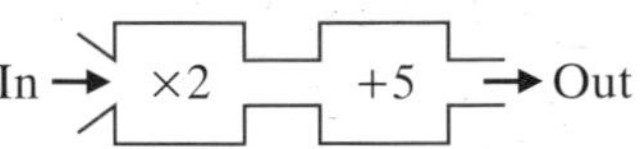

1 Here is a number machine:
  (a) Draw its inverse number machine.
  (b) What numbers went into the number machine for these numbers to come out?
  (i) 19 (ii) 9 (iii) 15 (iv) 7 (v) 8
  (vi) 12 (vii) –1 (viii) –3 (ix) –5 (x) 5.4

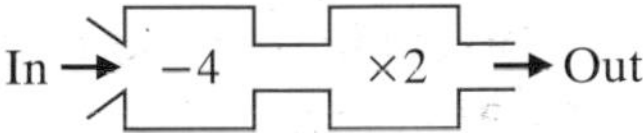

2 Here is a number machine:
  (a) Draw its inverse number machine.
  (b) What numbers went into the machine for these numbers to come out?
  (i) 6 (ii) 20 (iii) 14 (iv) 3 (v) 9
  (vi) –12 (vii) –2 (viii) 0 (ix) 2.5 (x) 10.5

2.3 Equivalent number machines

- **If two number machines have the same effect on any chosen number we say they are equivalent.**

Exercise 2D

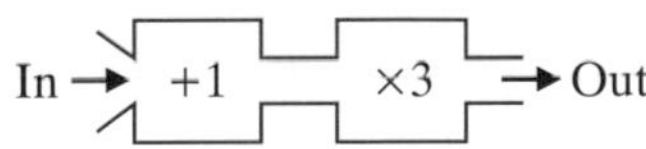

Number machine **A**

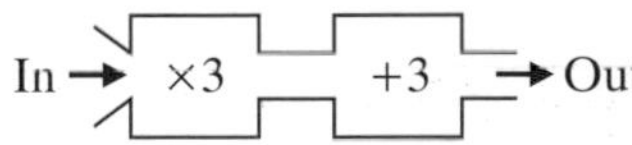

Number machine **B**

(a) Put 2 into each of these number machines. What comes out of (i) number machine **A** (ii) number machine **B**?

(b) Put 5 in. What comes out of (i) number machine **A** (ii) number machine **B**?

(c) Put some other numbers in. Make some of the numbers fractions and some negative.

(d) What do you notice about the numbers that come out of the different number machines when the same number is put in?

You should find that the two machines **A** and **B** have the same effect on any chosen number.

Exercise 2E

1 Put different numbers into each of these number machines. Use the numbers that come out to help you find and write down number machines that are equivalent.

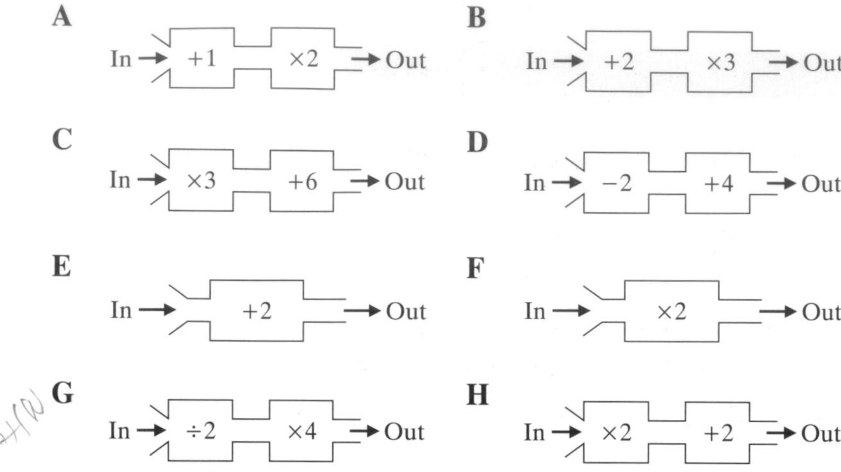

2.4 Using function notation

Here is a number machine:

You can show how it changes numbers like this:

You can let a letter n stand for any number and show how the machine changes it like this:

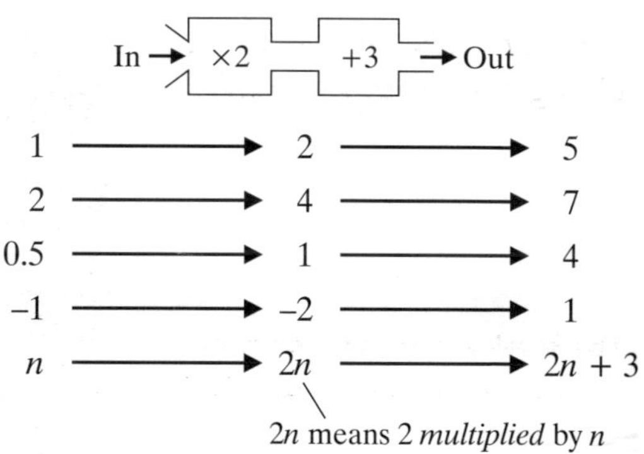

You don't need to draw the number machine.

You can just write: $n \to 2n + 3$

■ **$n \to 2n + 3$ is called a function. A function is a rule which shows how one set of quantities relates to another.**

Here are some more number machines and their functions:

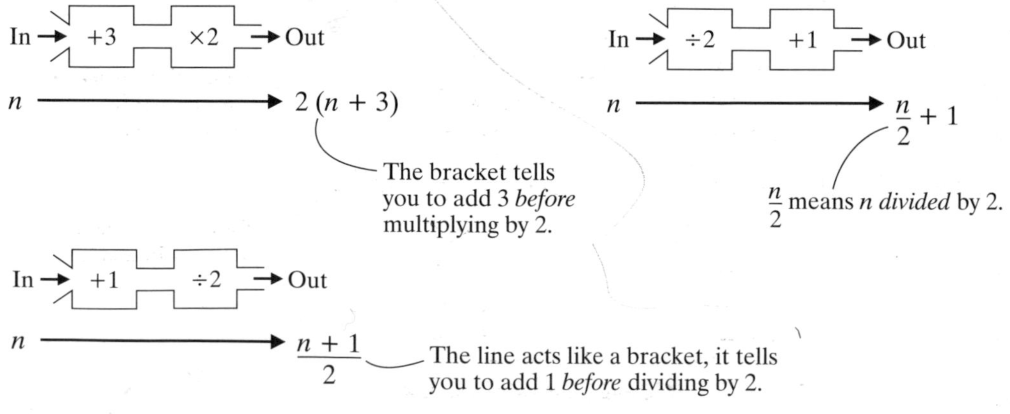

Exercise 2F

Write down the functions for the number machines in questions **1** and **2**.

1 **(a)** In → ×3 → +2 → Out **(b)** In → +2 → ×3 → Out

(c) In → ÷4 → −2 → Out **(d)** In → −3 → ÷3 → Out

2 **(a)** In → −1 → ×4 → Out **(b)** In → ÷3 → +5 → Out

(c) In → ×4 → −1 → Out **(d)** In → +2 → ÷3 → Out

3 Draw the number machines for these functions:

(a) $n \to 5n - 2$ **(b)** $n \to 4(n + 1)$ **(c)** $n \to 3n + 4$

(d) $n \to \frac{n}{4} + 3$ **(e)** $n \to \frac{n - 2}{2}$ **(f)** $n \to 6(n - 4)$

2.5 Input to output

You can show how a function changes numbers like this:

Input (Numbers put in)		Output (Numbers coming out)	
n	→	$2n + 3$	
1	→	5	$2 \times 1 + 3 = 5$
2	→	7	$2 \times 2 + 3 = 7$
3	→	9	$2 \times 3 + 3 = 9$
10	→	23	$2 \times 10 + 3 = 23$
0.5	→	4	$2 \times 0.5 + 3 = 4$

This is called a **mapping diagram**.
You can say that n **maps onto** $2n+3$.

Exercise 2G

1 Work out the outputs for each function using the inputs given:

(a) $n \to 2n - 2$
1 →
2 →
3 →
10 →

(b) $n \to 3n + 2$
1 →
2 →
3 →
10 →

(c) $n \to 2(n + 3)$
1 →
2 →
3 →
10 →

Remember: work out the part in brackets first.

(d) $n \to 3(n - 1)$
1 →
2 →
3 →
10 →

(e) $n \to \frac{n}{2} + 1$
1 →
2 →
3 →
10 →

Remember: divide by 2 first.

(f) $n \to \frac{n + 3}{2}$
1 →
2 →
3 →
10 →

Remember: the line acts as a bracket.

Exercise 2D on page 17 shows that these two number machines are equivalent:

In → +1 → ×3 → Out   Number machine **A**

In → ×3 → +3 → Out   Number machine **B**

The function for number machine **A** is $n \rightarrow 3(n + 1)$ and for machine **B** is $n \rightarrow 3n + 3$.

If you input the same number into these functions you will get the same output. So the functions are **equivalent**.

■ **Two functions are equivalent if they have the same effect on any chosen number.**

Exercise 2H

1 Write down the letters of the pairs of functions that are equivalent. Hint: look back at the equivalent number machines in **Exercise 2E**.

A $n \rightarrow n + 1$ **B** $n \rightarrow 2\,(n - 2)$ **C** $n \rightarrow 3\,(n - 1)$

D $n \rightarrow 2n - 4$ **E** $n \rightarrow 3n - 3$ **F** $n \rightarrow 2n + 2$

G $n \rightarrow 2\,(n + 1)$ **H** $n \rightarrow \dfrac{2n + 2}{2}$

2.6 Output to input

If you know a function's output how do you work out the input?

Example 2

When a number is put into the function $n \rightarrow 2n + 3$ the output is 15. What is the input?

$n \rightarrow 2n + 3$
$? \rightarrow 15$

Draw the number machine for the function:

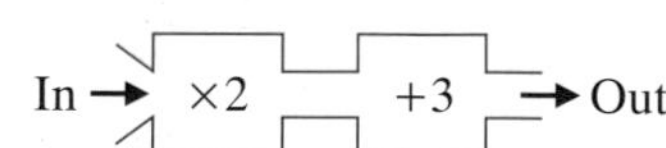

Draw the inverse number machine:

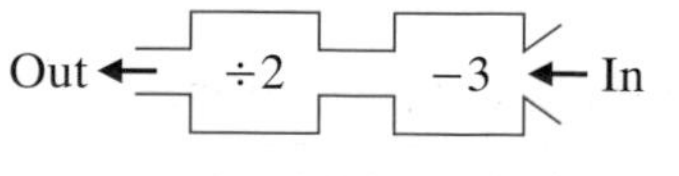

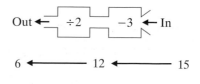

Send the output through the inverse number machine:

6 ← 12 ← 15

The input is 6.

Exercise 2I

1 Draw the inverse number machines for these functions and use them to work out the missing inputs:

(a) $n \to 3n - 2$
$\to 4$
$\to 13$
$\to 1$
$\to -1$

(b) $n \to 2n + 3$
$\to 11$
$\to 5$
$\to 8$
$\to -3$

(c) $n \to 3(n + 2)$
$\to 12$
$\to 9$
$\to 21$
$\to 6$

Think carefully what the last operation in the number machine is.

(d) $n \to 2\,(n - 2)$
$\to 4$
$\to 2$
$\to 0$
$\to 1$

(e) $n \to \frac{n}{2} - 1$
$\to 1$
$\to 3$
$\to 1.5$
$\to 0$

(f) $n \to \frac{n - 1}{2}$
$\to 2$
$\to 4$
$\to 7$
$\to -2$

Remember: $(n - 1)$ is all divided by 2.

2 Work out the missing inputs and outputs for these functions:

(a) $n \to 4n + 1$
$3 \to$
$5 \to$
$\to 9$
$\to 25$

(b) $n \to 5n - 3$
$4 \to$
$1 \to$
$\to 12$
$\to 22$

(c) $n \to 3(n + 1)$
$\to 9$
$\to 15$
$\to 21$
$\to 7$

(d) $n \to 4(n - 2)$
$3 \to$
$\to 12$
$1 \to$
$\to 20$

(e) $n \to \frac{n}{3} + 2$
$\to 6$
$\to 7$
$9 \to$
$4 \to$

(f) $n \to \frac{n + 1}{2}$
$\to 2$
$5 \to$
$\to 3.5$
$8 \to$

2.7 Writing functions in the form $n \to bn + c$

Exercise 2H shows that these functions are equivalent:

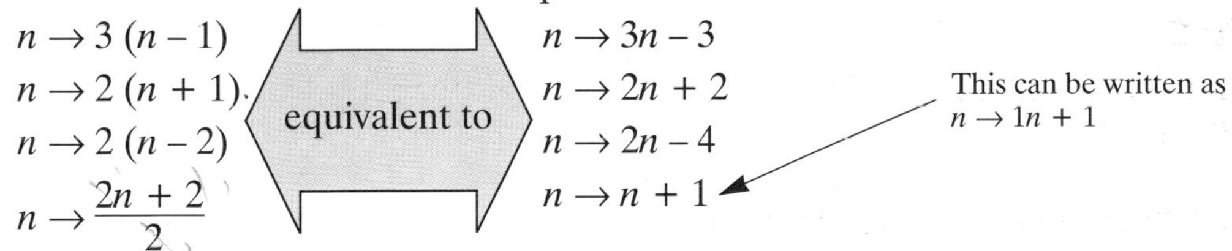

This can be written as $n \to 1n + 1$

All the functions we have looked at so far can be written as:

$$n \to bn + c$$

b and c are whole numbers or fractions and can be positive or negative.

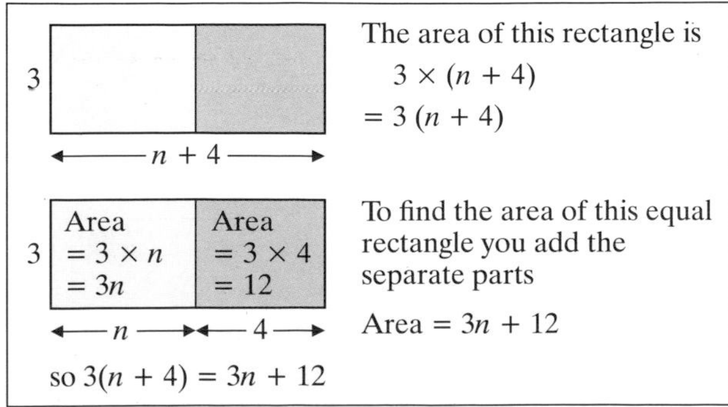

3
$n + 4$
The area of this rectangle is
$3 \times (n + 4)$
$= 3\,(n + 4)$
Area $= 3 \times n = 3n$
Area $= 3 \times 4 = 12$
n
4
To find the area of this equal rectangle you add the separate parts
Area $= 3n + 12$
so $3(n + 4) = 3n + 12$

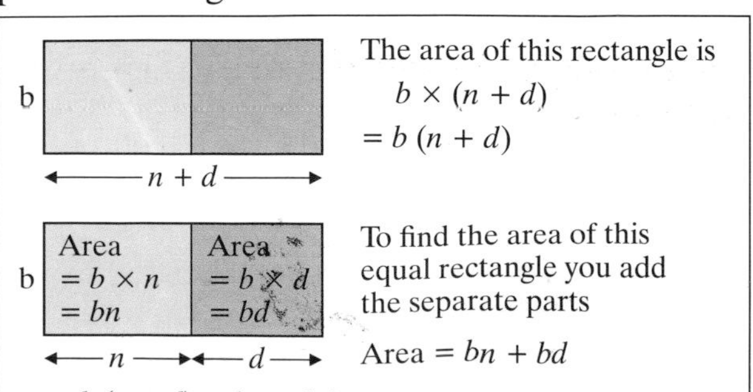

b
$n + d$
The area of this rectangle is
$b \times (n + d)$
$= b\,(n + d)$
Area $= b \times n = bn$
Area $= b \times d = bd$
n
d
To find the area of this equal rectangle you add the separate parts
Area $= bn + bd$
so $b\,(n + d) = bn + bd$

Example 3

Write $n \to 4(n + 2)$ in the form $n \to bn + c$

$4(n + 2)$ means $4 \times (n + 2)$

which means $4 \times n + 4 \times 2$

which is $4n + 8$

so $n \to 4(n + 2)$ can be written as $n \to 4n + 8$

You multiply everything inside the bracket by what is outside

$b(n + d) = b \times (n + d) =$

$b \times n + b \times d$

So

$b(n + d) = bn + bd$

Example 4

Write $n \to \frac{9n - 2}{3}$ in the form $n \to bn + c$

$\frac{9n - 2}{3}$ means divide $(9n - 2)$ by 3

which can be written as $\frac{1}{3}(9n - 2)$

which means $\frac{1}{3} \times 9n - \frac{1}{3} \times 2$

which is $3n - \frac{2}{3}$

so $n \to \frac{9n - 2}{3}$ can be written as $n \to 3n - \frac{2}{3}$

Exercise 2J

1 Write these functions in the form $n \to bn + c$

(a) $n \to 2(n + 3)$ **(b)** $n \to 5(n + 2)$ **(c)** $n \to 3(n - 2)$

(d) $n \to 4(n - 3)$ **(e)** $n \to 4(n + \frac{1}{2})$ **(f)** $n \to \frac{4n + 6}{2}$

(g) $n \to \frac{10n - 5}{5}$ **(h)** $n \to \frac{8n + 3}{4}$ **(i)** $n \to \frac{6n - 1}{3}$

2 Write down the letters of the pairs of equivalent functions.
Hint: first write each function in the form $n \to bn + c$

A $n \to \frac{4n - 6}{2}$ **B** $n \to \frac{n - 3}{3}$ **C** $n \to \frac{n + 4}{2}$

D $n \to \frac{2n - 6}{6}$ **E** $n \to \frac{2n + 8}{4}$ **F** $n \to \frac{6n + 18}{2}$

G $n \to 3(n + 3)$ **H** $n \to 2n - 3$

3 **A game for the whole class in two teams**
One person from team **A** writes part of a function on the board.
Members of team **B** take turns to give a number as input.
The person at the board gives the output and writes it on the board.
After each output is written team **B** may make one suggestion for what the function is.
The number of suggestions needed by team **B** to get the correct function is the score for team **A**.
The teams now change roles.
The winning team is the one with the highest score.

4 **A game for small groups**
One person thinks of a function and gives an input and its output for that function.
The rest of the group, working individually, have one minute to write down as many different functions as possible to fit the input and output given.
They score one point for each correct function written.
Each member of the group has a turn giving the input and output.
Everyone totals their points.
The winner is the person with the highest score.

2.8 Finding functions to fit given inputs and outputs

Look at this function: $n \to 2n + 3$

When the input is 0 the output is 3. $0 \to 3$

The input goes up in ones.
The output goes up in twos.

$1 \to 5$
$2 \to 7$
$3 \to 9$

Look at these functions:

$n \to 3n + 2$	$n \to 4n - 1$	$n \to n - 2$
$0 \to 2$	$0 \to -1$	$0 \to -2$
$1 \to 5$	$1 \to 3$	$1 \to -1$
$2 \to 8$	$2 \to 7$	$2 \to 0$
$3 \to 11$	$3 \to 11$	$3 \to 1$
$4 \to 14$	$4 \to 15$	$4 \to 2$

$1n - 2$

■ **For a function which can be written as $n \to bn + c$**
If the input is 0 the output is c
If the input goes up 1 the output goes up b.

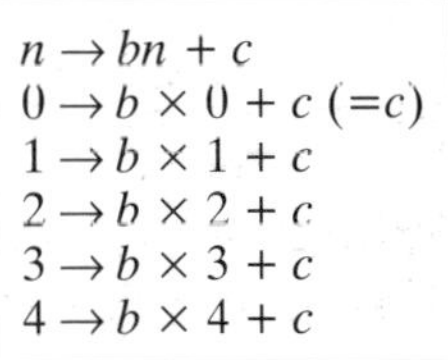
$n \to bn + c$
$0 \to b \times 0 + c\ (=c)$
$1 \to b \times 1 + c$
$2 \to b \times 2 + c$
$3 \to b \times 3 + c$
$4 \to b \times 4 + c$

Example 5

Find the function to fit this pattern of inputs → outputs.

When the input is 0 the output is 3 so c is 3.
When the input goes up 1 the output goes up 2, so b is 2.

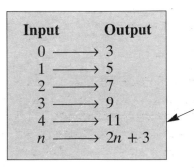

Input	Output
0 ⟶	3
1 ⟶	5
2 ⟶	7
3 ⟶	9
4 ⟶	11
n ⟶	$2n + 3$

The function is: $n \to 2n + 3$

Or you could say:
$0 \to 3$
so $b \times 0 + c = 3$
so $c = 3$
$1 \to 5$
so $b \times 1 + 3 = 5$
so $b = 2$

Example 6

Find the function to fit this pattern of inputs $\rightarrow$ outputs

When the input is 0 the output is -1 so c is -1.

When the input goes up 1 the output goes up 3, so b is 3.

The function is: $n \rightarrow 3n - 1$

Input		Output
0	$\longrightarrow$	-1
1	$\longrightarrow$	2
2	$\longrightarrow$	5
3	$\longrightarrow$	8
4	$\longrightarrow$	11
n	$\longrightarrow$	$3n - 1$

Or you could say:

$0 \rightarrow -1$

so $b \times 0 + c = -1$

so $c = -1$

$1 \rightarrow 2$

so $b \times 1 - 1 = 2$

so $b = 3$

Exercise 2K

1 Find the function to fit each pattern of inputs $\rightarrow$ outputs:

(a)	**(b)**	**(c)**	**(d)**
$0 \rightarrow 2$	$0 \rightarrow 6$	$0 \rightarrow -3$	$0 \rightarrow -1$
$1 \rightarrow 4$	$1 \rightarrow 9$	$1 \rightarrow -1$	$1 \rightarrow 0$
$2 \rightarrow 6$	$2 \rightarrow 12$	$2 \rightarrow 1$	$2 \rightarrow 1$
$3 \rightarrow 8$	$3 \rightarrow 15$	$3 \rightarrow 3$	$3 \rightarrow 2$
$4 \rightarrow 10$	$4 \rightarrow 18$	$4 \rightarrow 5$	$4 \rightarrow 3$

(e)	**(f)**	**(g)**	**(h)**
$0 \rightarrow 1$	$0 \rightarrow 0$	$0 \rightarrow -2$	$0 \rightarrow -0.5$
$1 \rightarrow 1.5$	$1 \rightarrow 4$	$1 \rightarrow 0$	$1 \rightarrow 0$
$2 \rightarrow 2$	$2 \rightarrow 8$	$2 \rightarrow 2$	$2 \rightarrow 0.5$
$3 \rightarrow 2.5$	$3 \rightarrow 12$	$3 \rightarrow 4$	$3 \rightarrow 1$
$4 \rightarrow 3$	$4 \rightarrow 16$	$4 \rightarrow 6$	$4 \rightarrow 1.5$

2 Find functions to fit these patterns of inputs $\rightarrow$ outputs.
Hint: you may need to rearrange the inputs first.

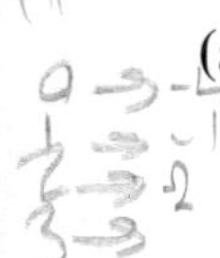

(a)	**(b)**	**(c)**	**(d)**
$3 \rightarrow 5$	$1 \rightarrow 3$	$0 \rightarrow 3$	$1 \rightarrow -3$
$1 \rightarrow -1$	$4 \rightarrow 9$	$5 \rightarrow 8$	$-1 \rightarrow -5$
$0 \rightarrow -4$	$2 \rightarrow 5$	$4 \rightarrow 7$	$3 \rightarrow -1$
$2 \rightarrow 2$	$3 \rightarrow 7$	$2 \rightarrow 5$	$4 \rightarrow 0$

3 **(a)** Which of these patterns of inputs $\rightarrow$ outputs cannot be written in the form $n \rightarrow bn + c$?

(b) Explain your answers.

(i)	**(ii)**	**(iii)**	**(iv)**
$1 \rightarrow 2$	$2 \rightarrow 8$	$1 \rightarrow -1$	$5 \rightarrow 20$
$3 \rightarrow 8$	$3 \rightarrow 9$	$4 \rightarrow 2$	$2 \rightarrow 11$
$2 \rightarrow 5$	$1 \rightarrow 5$	$2 \rightarrow 0$	$1 \rightarrow 8$
$4 \rightarrow 11$	$0 \rightarrow 3$	$0 \rightarrow -2$	$4 \rightarrow 17$
$0 \rightarrow -1$	$4 \rightarrow 11$	$5 \rightarrow 3$	$0 \rightarrow 5$

2.9 Finding an expression for the *n*th term of a sequence

The *n*th term of a sequence is the term in the *n*th position in the sequence. The *n*th term can often be written as an expression involving n. For example, to find the 7th term in the sequence you put n equal to 7 in the expression.

Example 7

A computer generates the following sequence of numbers:

5 8 11 14 17

Write down, in terms of n, an expression for the *n*th term in the sequence.

Think of the sequence as a pattern of inputs → outputs. The first term has output 5, the second term has output 8 and so on.

When the input goes up by 1 the output goes up by 3.
So the function is of the form $n \to bn + c$ and b is 3.

Input	Output
1 ⟶	5
2 ⟶	8
3 ⟶	11
4 ⟶	14
5 ⟶	17

To find c continue the pattern backwards like this:
When the input is 0 the output is 2, so the value of c is 2.

0 → 2 −3
1 → 5 −3
2 → 8 −3
3 → 11 −3
4 → 14 −3
5 → 17 −3

b is 3 and c is 2 so the function is $n \to 3n + 2$.

The *n*th term in the sequence is the output when the input is n, so the *n*th term is $3n + 2$.

Example 8

This is part of a sequence of shapes made from matchsticks.

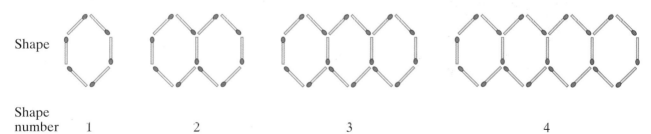

Shape

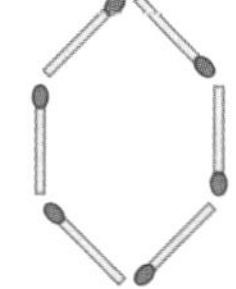

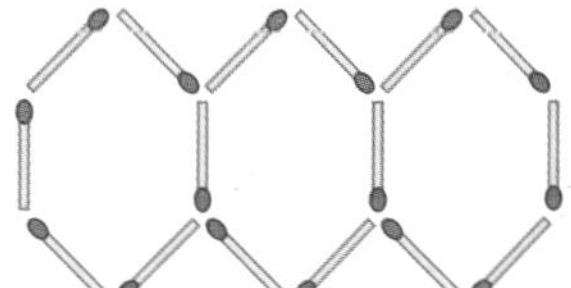

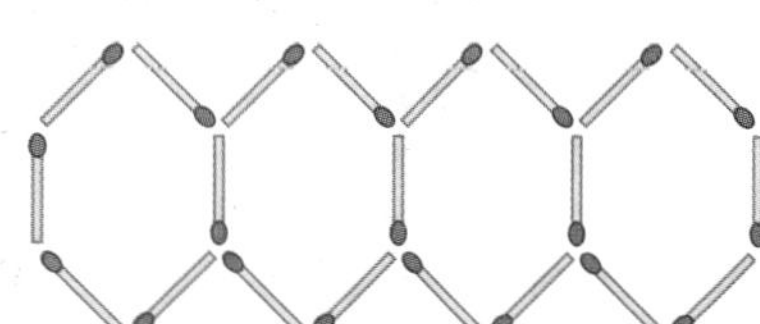

Shape number 1 2 3 4

Write down, in terms of n, an expression for the number of matches in the *n*th shape.

Write the sequence as a pattern of inputs $\rightarrow$ outputs.

When the input goes up by 1 the output goes up by 5.

So the function is of the form $n \rightarrow bn + c$ and b is 5.

Continue the pattern backwards to the input 0.
The value of c is 1.

b is 5 and c is 1 so the function is $n \rightarrow 5n + 1$.

Input (shape number)	Output (number of matches)
1 $\longrightarrow$	6
2 $\longrightarrow$	11
3 $\longrightarrow$	16
4 $\longrightarrow$	21
0 $\longrightarrow$	1
n $\longrightarrow$	$5n + 1$

$0 \rightarrow 6 - 5 = 1$

Or you could say:
$0 \rightarrow 1$
So $b \times 0 + c = 1$
so $c = 1$
$1 \rightarrow 6$
so $b \times 1 + 1 = 6$
so $b = 5$

The number of matches in the nth shape is $5n + 1$.

■ **If a sequence of numbers can be written as a function (for example: $n \rightarrow 5n + 1$) then the nth term of the sequence is the output of the function ($5n + 1$ in this example) when the input is n.**

Exercise 2L

You will need matchsticks, dotty isometric paper, dominoes and multilink cubes.

1 Write down, in terms of n, an expression for the nth term in each of these sequences:

(a) 7 9 11 13 15 17 **(b)** 4 7 10 13 16 19
(c) –3 1 5 9 13 17 **(d)** 0 4 8 12 16 20
(e) 3 6 9 12 15 18 **(f)** 1.5 2.5 3.5 4.5 5.5

The remaining questions in this exercise are practical activities which produce simple functions.

2 **Matchstick sequences**
Make some sequences of shapes from matchsticks.
For each sequence find an expression for the number of matchsticks used to make the nth shape.

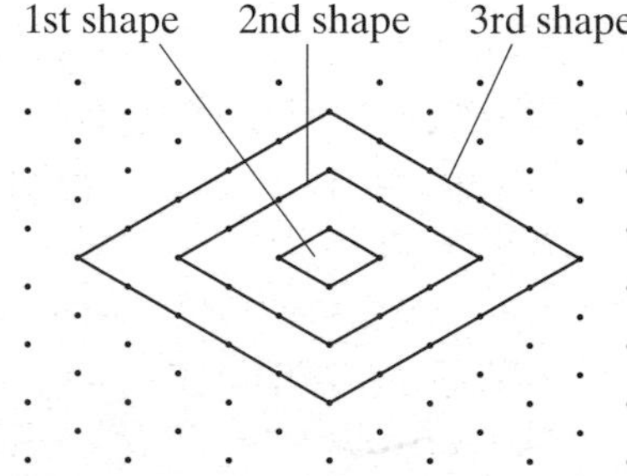

3 **Shapes on dotty paper**
Draw a shape on dotty paper.
Count the number of dots on its perimeter.
Draw bigger versions of the same shape.
Find an expression for the number of dots on the perimeter of the nth shape.

4 **Domino bridges**
Build a bridge using dominoes.
Find an expression for the number of dominoes needed to build a bridge of length n.
Repeat this using different types of bridge.

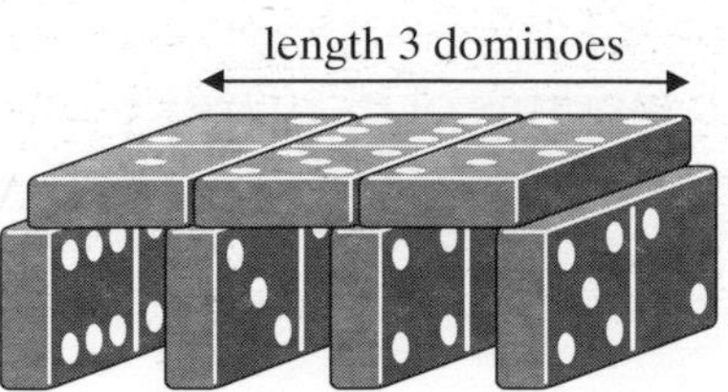

5 Surrounds

(a) Start with a single domino and surround it with layer after layer of dominoes like this:

Find an expression for the number of dominoes in the nth layer.

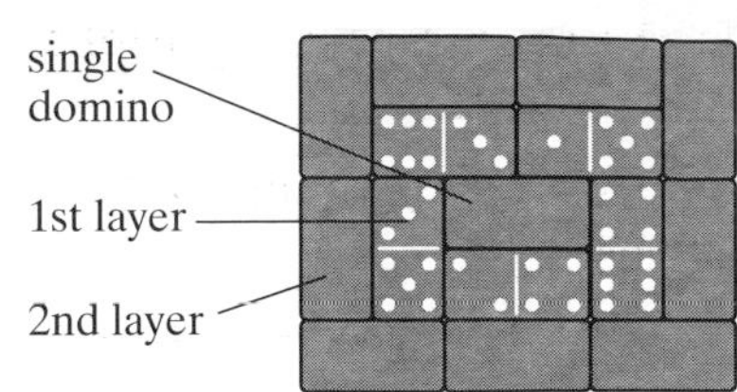

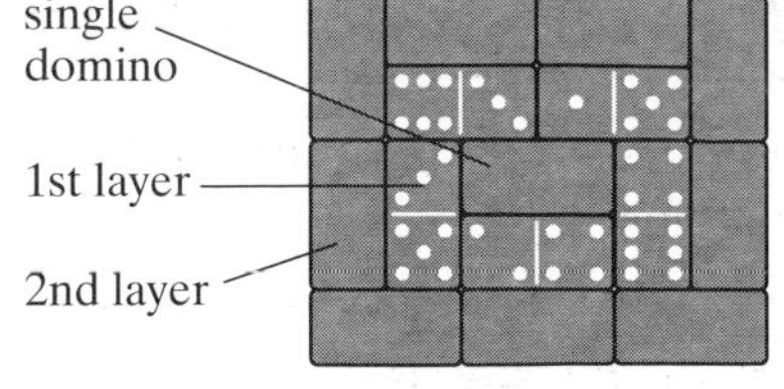

(b) Repeat part **(a)** starting with two dominoes in the centre.

or

(c) Repeat part **(a)** with other numbers of dominoes in the centre.

(d) Investigate surrounds using square tiles or any other tiles which tessellate.

Note: a shape tessellates if exact copies of it can be arranged on a flat surface so that all the space is filled leaving no gaps and with no overlaps.

6 Multilink towers

Build towers out of multilink cubes.

For each tower work out how many faces of the cubes can be seen.

Find an expression for the number of faces that can be seen for a tower of height n.

height of tower 5

21 faces can be seen (although not all at the same time)

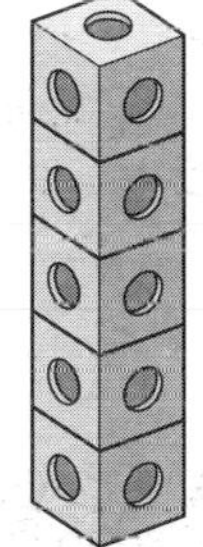

Summary of key points

1 A number machine shows instructions in a clear way like this:

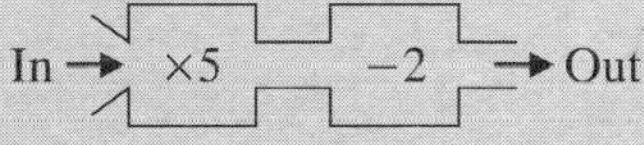

Think of a number, multiply it by 5 and subtract 2. What is the answer?
18? 33?

2 The inverse of a number machine goes in the opposite direction and each box contains the opposite instruction.

3 If two number machines have the same effect on any chosen number we say they are equivalent.

4 A function is a rule which shows how one set of quantities relates to another.

$n \to 5n - 2$ is a function

5 Two functions are equivalent if they have the same effect on any chosen number.

6 For a function which can be written as $n \to bn + c$
if the input is 0 the output is c
if the input goes up by 1 the output goes up by b.

7 If a sequence of numbers can be written as a function, (for example as $n \to 5n - 2$), then the nth term of the sequence is the output of the function ($5n - 2$ in this example) when the input is n.

3 Probability 1

3.1 What is probability?

Probability is used in business, commerce and industry to predict the chance of things happening in the future.

- a coin has a chance of showing heads when tossed
- the sun has a chance of shining for seven hours on Boxing Day
- your favourite pop group has a chance of being number one in the charts
- the roll of a dice has a chance of showing a four.

In probability work these are all called **events**.

■ **You can represent the chance that an event will happen as a number. This number is called the probability that the event will happen.**

■ **Probability is measured on a scale of 0 to 1.**

- A probability of 0 means the event is impossible.
- A probability of 1 means the event is certain.

impossible | unlikely | evens | likely | certain

0 | $\frac{1}{4}$ | $\frac{1}{2}$ | $\frac{3}{4}$ | 1

■ **You must write a probability as a fraction, a decimal or a percentage.**

Example 1

Mark on the probability scale an estimate of the probability of each of these events:

(a) a coin will show a Head when tossed
(b) the sun will shine for seven hours on Christmas Day
(c) the roll of a dice will give a four
(d) the sun will rise tomorrow
(e) tomorrow will be a school day.

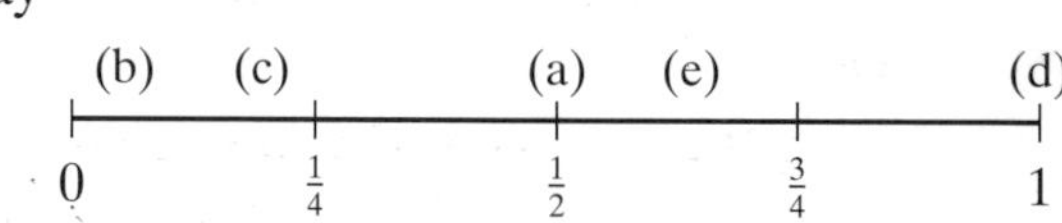

Exercise 3A

1 Draw a probability scale. Mark on your scale the probability of each event happening:
(a) this person wins a big prize in the lottery
(b) you will use a ruler today
(c) a pet dog will live forever
(d) you will have a drink today
(e) when a coin is tossed it will show a Tail
(f) the moon will rise tonight
(g) you will watch television this week.

2 Draw a probability scale. Mark on your scale the probability that when this spinner is spun it lands on:
(a) red **(b)** blue **(c)** yellow.

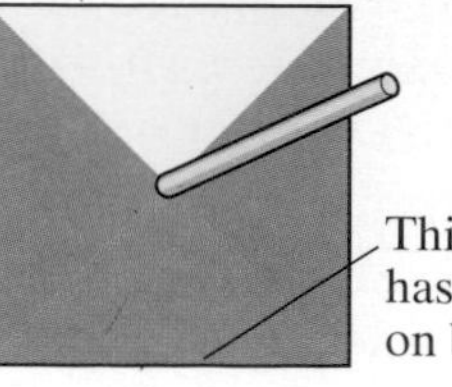
This spinner has landed on blue.

3.2 Games and experiments

You can use games and experiments to estimate the probability of an event happening.

Repeat the game or experiment several times and keep a record of:

- the number of successful trials (when the event happens)
- the total number of trials.

■ **The estimated probability of an event in a game or experiment is:**

$$\textbf{estimated probability} = \frac{\textbf{number of successful trials}}{\textbf{total number of trials}}$$

This is also called the **relative frequency** because the number of successful trials is being related to the total number of trials.

Example 2

(a) Roll a dice 100 times.
Record your results in a tally chart.

(b) Estimate the probability of scoring 6 when you roll a dice.

The score on this dice is 3.

(a) First draw up a tally chart.

Top face of dice	Tally	Frequency
six	~~IIII~~ ~~IIII~~ ~~IIII~~ IIII	19
not a six	~~IIII~~ ~~IIII~~ ~~IIII~~ ~~IIII~~ ~~IIII~~ ~~IIII~~ ~~IIII~~ ~~IIII~~ ~~IIII~~ ~~IIII~~ ~~IIII~~ ~~IIII~~ ~~IIII~~ ~~IIII~~ ~~IIII~~ ~~IIII~~ I	81

Next complete the tally chart for 100 throws of the dice (shown in red).

(b) Using the results of the tally chart

Estimated probability of throwing a six

$$= \frac{\text{number of successful trials}}{\text{total number of trials}}$$

$$= \frac{\text{number of sixes thrown}}{\text{total number of throws}}$$

$$= \frac{19}{100} \qquad = 0.19$$

This is called the **estimated probability** that the result will be a six.

Exercise 3B

You will need a coin, a pack of playing cards, a bag containing 6 red beads and 4 yellow beads and two dice.

1 You need a coin.

(a) Copy this tally chart.

Top face of coin	Tally	Frequency

(b) Toss a coin 100 times and record your results in the tally chart.

(c) Estimate the probability that the result will be a Head.

(d) Estimate the probability that the result will be a Tail.

2 You need a normal pack of playing cards. The experiment is to select a card, record it on a tally chart, then replace it. Repeat this a further 99 times.

(a) Copy the tally chart.

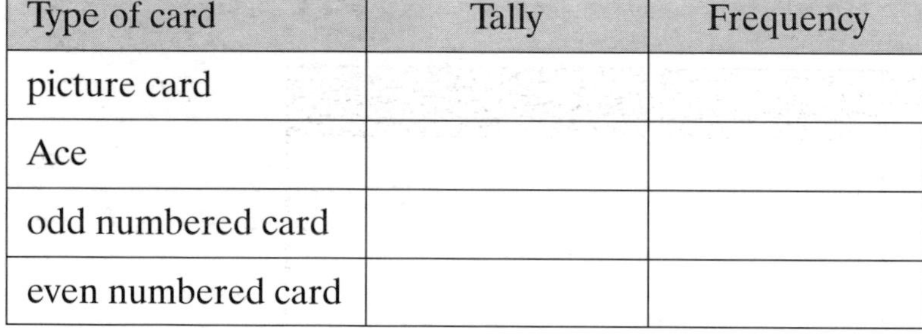

Type of card	Tally	Frequency
picture card		
Ace		
odd numbered card		
even numbered card		

(b) Guess the frequency for each of the four events.

(c) Carry out the experiment and record your results in your tally chart.
How good were your guesses?

(d) Estimate the probability that the result will be
(i) a picture card (ii) an Ace
(iii) an odd numbered card (iv) an even numbered card.

(e) Which event is most likely to happen?

(f) Which event is least likely to happen?

3 You need a bag containing 6 red beads and 4 yellow beads. (You can use other colours but the numbers of beads must be the same.)
Carry out an experiment to estimate the probability of a yellow bead being chosen.

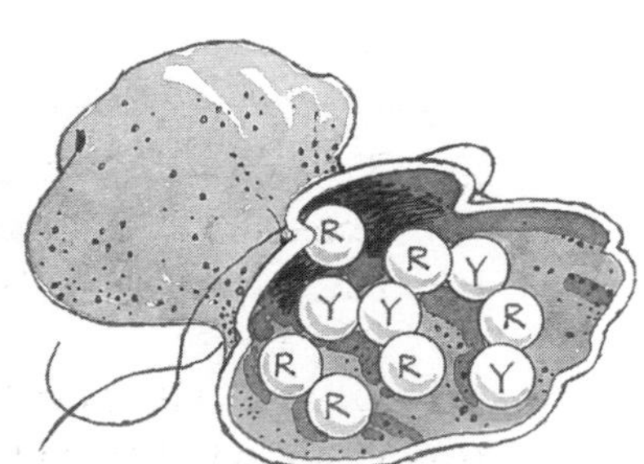

Remember: replace the bead each time, note the colour, draw up a tally chart.

4 Work in pairs.
You need a dice to play a game.
The rules are:

- The first person throws a dice. If a six is thrown the first person wins the game.
- If a six is not thrown the second person throws the dice. The second person wins the game if a six is thrown.
- Keep taking turns to throw the dice until someone wins the game.

For each game record:
(i) the winner
(ii) how many throws it took to win
(iii) how many throws the winner had.
Record your results in a tally chart.

Play the game 50 times.
The same person must start every game.
(a) Estimate the probability that the first person wins.
(b) Estimate the probability that the second person wins.
(c) Who is the most likely to win?
(d) How many times was the game won after two throws?
(e) What is the average number of throws needed to win the game?

5 You need two normal dice.
(a) Make a copy of this tally chart

Number	Tally	Frequency	Estimated probability
2			
3			
4			
5			
6			
7			
8			
9			
10			
11			
12			

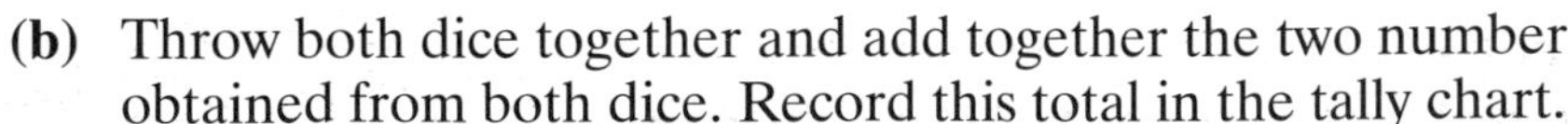

(b) Throw both dice together and add together the two numbers obtained from both dice. Record this total in the tally chart.
(c) Repeat **(b)** a further 99 times. Record all your results in the tally chart.
(d) Draw a bar chart to illustrate your results.
(e) Complete the column for estimated probability in the tally chart.
(f) Which total number are you most likely to get when you throw two dice?

There is more about bar charts in unit 24.

3.3 Equally likely outcomes

Section 3.2 shows how you can find an estimate of probability for different events by doing an experiment or playing games.

Sometimes the events are **equally likely** to happen.

For example:

- when you toss a coin, Head or Tail are the possible outcomes. These are equally likely.
- when you roll a dice there are six possible outcomes. The scores 1, 2, 3, 4, 5 or 6 are all equally likely.

The probability of an event can be found by calculation.

■ **The calculated probability of an event happening** $= \dfrac{\textbf{number of successful outcomes}}{\textbf{total number of possible outcomes}}$.

Example 3

Calculate the probability of a Tail when a coin is tossed.

There are two equally likely outcomes: Head or Tail.
The number of successful outcomes of a Tail is 1
The total number of possible outcomes is 2

$$\text{So, probability of a Tail} = \frac{\text{number of successful outcomes}}{\text{total number of possible outcomes}} = \frac{1}{2}$$

Instead of using the word probability you can use the letter P and say P (Tail) $= \frac{1}{2}$.

Example 4

A card is drawn from a pack of 52 playing cards.
What is the probability that the card will be an Ace?

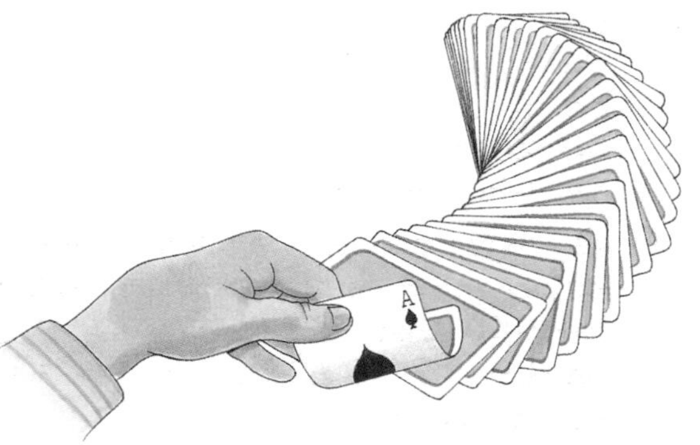

There are 52 equally likely outcomes.
There are 4 Aces giving 4 successful outcomes.

$$\text{So P (Ace)} = \frac{\text{number of successful outcomes}}{\text{total number of possible outcomes}} = \frac{4}{52} = \frac{1}{13}$$

To calculate the probability each outcome must have the same chance of being selected. We say the item is **selected or chosen at random**.

Example 5

A bag contains 3 yellow beads, 4 blue beads and 5 green beads. A bead is selected at random. What is the probability that the bead chosen is:

(a) blue (b) green?

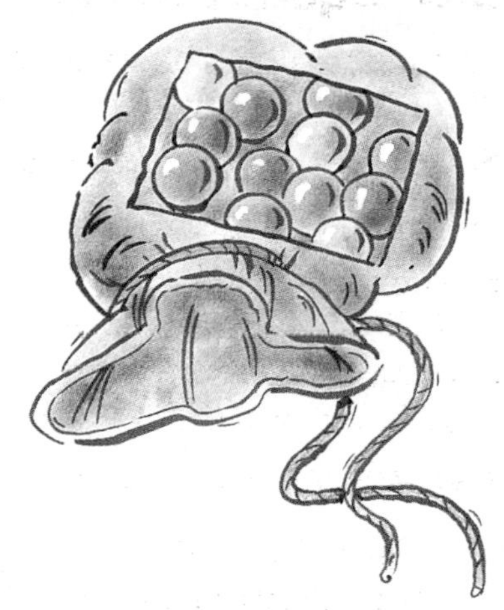

(a) The total number of possible outcomes is $3 + 4 + 5 = 12$. They are all equally likely.

$$\text{P (blue)} = \frac{\text{number of blue beads}}{\text{total number of beads}}$$

$$\text{P (blue)} = \frac{4}{12} = \frac{1}{3}$$

(b) $$\text{P (green)} = \frac{\text{number of green beads}}{\text{total number of beads}}$$

$$= \frac{5}{12}$$

Exercise 3C

1 Jessica is rolling a dicc.
What is the probability that she will roll:
(a) a five **(b)** a two **(c)** an even number
(d) a number less than 5 **(e)** a one or a three?

2 A bag contains 1 white, 3 black and 5 blue beads. Proshotam selects a bead at random. What is the probability that the bead he chooses is:

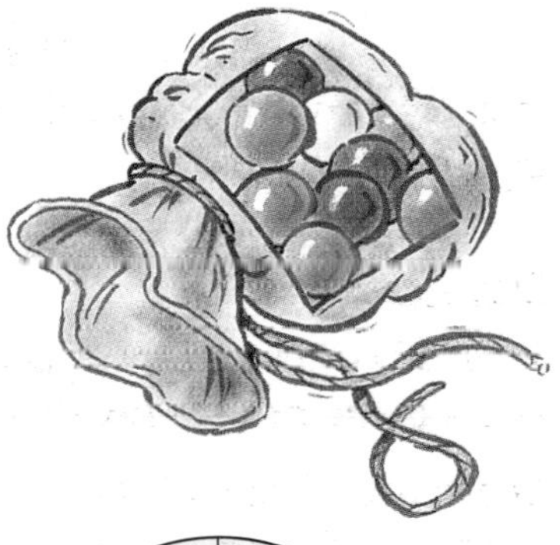

(a) white
(b) black
(c) blue
(d) not white
(e) white or black?

3 In a game at a fete a pointer is spun. You win the amount of money written in the sector where the pointer stops. Each sector is equally likely.
Work out the probability that you win:

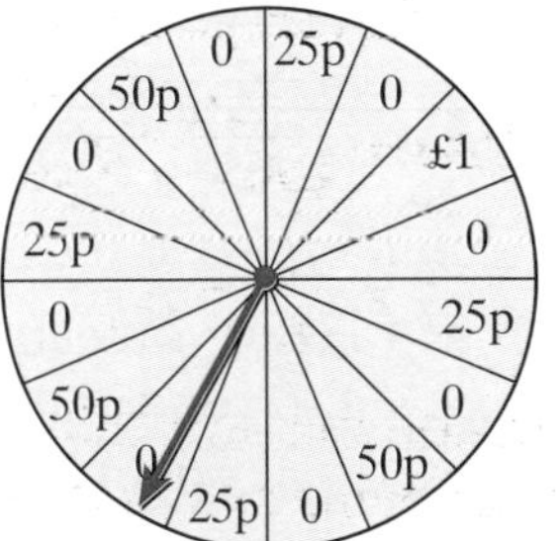

(a) no money
(b) 25p
(c) 50p
(d) 74p
(e) £1.

4 A card is drawn at random from a normal pack of 52 playing cards. What is the probability that the card will be:

(a) the nine of clubs **(b)** a diamond
(c) a red card **(d)** the Queen of spades
(e) a King **(f)** not a King
(g) a joker?

5 In a raffle 5000 tickets are sold. Jasmir buys 20, Karen buys 100, Lucy buys 50 and Winston buys 25 tickets. There is one winning ticket.
Work out the probability that:

(a) Jasmir wins
(b) Karen wins
(c) Lucy wins
(d) Winston wins.

6 A box of sweets contains 4 toffees, 3 mints, 5 bonbons, 6 eclairs, 2 wine gums and 10 sherbet lemons. One sweet is chosen at random.
Work out the probability that it will be:

(a) a toffee **(b)** a sherbet lemon
(c) a bonbon **(d)** a wine gum
(e) an eclair or a mint **(f)** not a sherbet lemon.

7 A set of coloured pencils contains 1 black, 1 white, 2 red, 3 green, 3 blue, 4 brown, 2 yellow, 1 pink and 1 purple pencil. If one pencil is selected at random, find the probability that it will be:

(a) white **(b)** red **(c)** green
(d) blue **(e)** brown **(f)** yellow
(g) pink **(h)** purple **(i)** not yellow
(j) not brown **(k)** red or green **(l)** mauve.

8 A letter is chosen at random from the word PROBABILITY.
Work out the probability that it will be:

(a) R **(b)** Y **(c)** B
(d) I or A **(e)** B or I.

3.4 Mutually exclusive events

When a coin is tossed it can show either a Head or a Tail.

If you toss a Head you cannot get a Tail.
If you toss a Tail you cannot get a Head.

These events are called mutually exclusive because if you get one outcome you cannot get the other outcome.

Three events or more can be mutually exclusive. For example, at the cross roads you can turn left, turn right or go straight across.

These three events are mutually exclusive.

■ **When one outcome prevents another outcome from happening, the outcomes are mutually exclusive.**

When you toss a coin you can get a Head (H) or a Tail (T).
The probability of a Head or a Tail is written P(H or T).
It is certain that you will get either a Head or a Tail. So P(H or T) = 1.

The probability of getting the outcome Head can be written P(H) for short.

$P(H) = \frac{1}{2}$ and $P(T) = \frac{1}{2}$

so $P(H) + P(T) = \frac{1}{2} + \frac{1}{2}$
$= 1.$

Notice: P(H or T) = 1 = P(H) + P(T).

■ **The probabilities of all the possible mutually exclusive events add up to 1.**

In general if two events A and B are mutually exclusive:

■ **P(A or B) = P(A) + P(B). This is called the OR rule.**

Example 6

A dice is rolled.

(a) List the six mutually exclusive events and their probabilities.
(b) What is the probability of a six?
(c) What is the probability of not getting six?

(a) $P(1) = \frac{1}{6}$, $P(2) = \frac{1}{6}$, $P(3) = \frac{1}{6}$
$P(4) = \frac{1}{6}$, $P(5) = \frac{1}{6}$, $P(6) = \frac{1}{6}$

Notice that all these probabilities add up to 1.

(b) $P(6) = \frac{1}{6}$

(c) P(not a six)
$= P(1) + P(2) + P(3) + P(4) + P(5)$
$= \frac{1}{6} + \frac{1}{6} + \frac{1}{6} + \frac{1}{6} + \frac{1}{6}$
$= \frac{5}{6}$

Notice that this is the same as $1 - P(6)$ or $1 - \frac{1}{6} = \frac{5}{6}$

Rule 1

■ **If the probability of an event happening is *p* then the probability of it not happening is $1 - p$.**

When a dice is rolled
P(1, 2, 3, 4 or 5)
= P(not a 6)
= 1 – P(6)

Rule 2

■ **If there are *n* mutually exclusive events all equally likely the probability of one event happening is $\frac{1}{n}$**

Rule 3

■ **If there are *n* mutually exclusive events and *a* successful outcomes the probability of a successful outcome is $\frac{a}{n}$**

Example 7

A dice is rolled.
What is the probability of:

(a) a five (b) not a five
(c) an odd number (d) not an odd number
(e) a 3 or a 4 (f) a 1 or a 2 or a 3 or a 4?

(a) There are six equally likely outcomes: 1, 2, 3, 4, 5 or 6.
So $n = 6$

Using Rule 2: $P(5) = \frac{1}{n} = \frac{1}{6}$

(b) Using Rule 1: $P(\text{not } 5) = 1 - P(5)$
$= 1 - \frac{1}{6}$
$= \frac{5}{6}$

(c) Using Rule 3:
There are 3 odd numbers on a dice.
So the number of successful outcomes is 3 and $a = 3$
Remember: there are six equally likely outcomes so $n = 6$.

So $P(\text{odd number}) = \frac{a}{n} = \frac{3}{6} = \frac{1}{2}$

(d) Using Rule 1:
$P(\text{not odd number}) = 1 - P\ (\text{odd number})$
$= 1 - \frac{1}{2}$
$= \frac{1}{2}$

(e) Using Rule 3:
The number of successful outcomes is 2, so $a = 2$
The total number of equally likely outcomes is 6

So $P(3 \text{ or } 4) = \frac{a}{n} = \frac{2}{6} = \frac{1}{3}$

(f) Using Rule 3:

$P(1 \text{ or } 2 \text{ or } 3 \text{ or } 4) = \frac{a}{n} = \frac{4}{6} = \frac{2}{3}$

Exercise 3D

1 A dice is rolled.
What is the probability of getting:
(a) a 2 **(b)** not a 2 **(c)** a 3 **(d)** not a 3?

2 This spinner is spun.
What is the probability of getting:
(a) a 1 **(b)** not a 1
(c) an odd number **(d)** not an odd number?

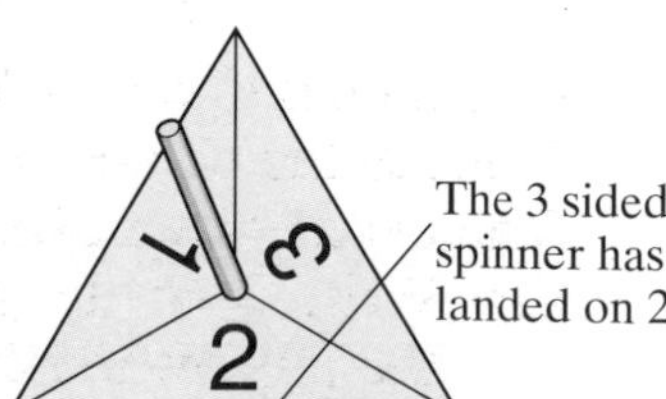

3 Nine counters numbered 2 to 10 are put in a bag. One counter is selected at random.
What is the probability of getting a counter with:
(a) a number 5 **(b)** an odd number
(c) not an odd number **(d)** a prime number
(e) a square number **(f)** a multiple of 3?

4 A bag contains 20 coloured balls. 8 are red, 6 are blue, 3 are green, 2 are white and 1 is brown. A ball is chosen at random from the bag.
What is the probability that the ball chosen is:
(a) blue **(b)** not blue **(c)** brown
(d) not brown **(e)** blue or red
(f) red or green **(g)** green or white or brown?

5 A card is drawn at random from a normal pack of playing cards.
What is the probability that the card will be:
(a) a King **(b)** not a King
(c) a picture card **(d)** not a picture card
(e) a 2 or a 3?

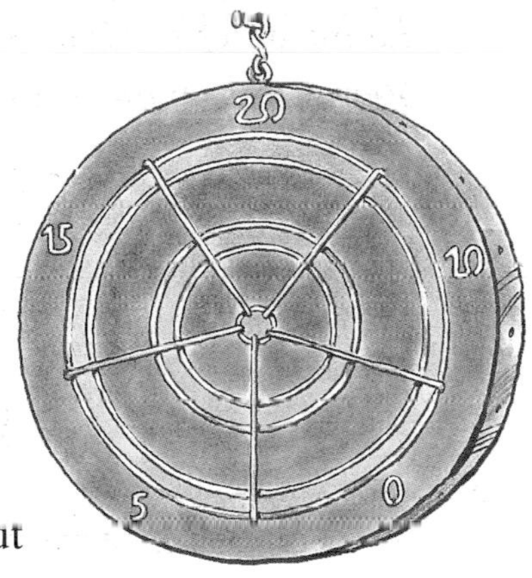

6 The probability of Jane scoring a 20 in darts is $\frac{1}{5}$.
What is the probability of Jane not scoring 20?

7 A bag contains 20 balls. There are three different colours: green, red and blue. A ball is chosen at random from the bag.
The probability of a green ball is $\frac{1}{4}$.
The probability of a red ball is $\frac{2}{5}$.
(a) What is the probability of a blue ball?
(b) How many balls are red?
(c) How many balls are green?
(d) How many balls are blue?

8 A survey was carried out in Mathstown High School to find out how long it takes the pupils to travel to school.
The results of the survey are shown in the table.

Time, t minutes, to travel to school	Number of pupils in Year 10	Number of pupils in Year 11
$0 < t \leq 10$	15	14
$10 < t \leq 20$	14	12
$20 < t \leq 30$	17	19
$30 < t \leq 40$	1	5
Totals	47	50

The names of all the **Year 10** pupils in the survey are put into a bag. All the names are different.
The headteacher picks one out without looking.
(a) Write down the probability that the headteacher will pick the pupil who takes over 30 minutes to travel to school.

The names of all the **Year 11** pupils in the survey are now put into another bag. All the names are different.
The headteacher picks one out without looking.

(b) Write down the probability that the headteacher will pick a pupil who takes over 30 minutes to travel to school.

[L]

9 Jean is going on an activities holiday. Each activity lasts a whole day. She can only do one activity a day.
The probability that she will go pony-trekking on any one day is 0.6.

(a) Work out the probability that Jean will **not** go pony-trekking on the first day.

The probability that Jean will go windsurfing on any one day is 0.25.

(b) Work out the probability that Jean will **either** go windsurfing **or** pony-trekking on the first day. [L]

Summary of key points

1 You can represent the chance that something will happen as a number. This number is called the **probability** that the event will happen.

2 Probability is measured on a scale of 0 to 1.
- A probability of 0 means the event is impossible.
- A probability of 1 means the event is certain.

3 You must write a probability as a fraction, a decimal or a percentage.

4 The estimated probability of an event in a game or experiment

$$= \frac{\text{number of successful trials}}{\text{total number of trials}}$$

This is also called the relative frequency.

5 The calculated probability of an event happening

$$= \frac{\text{number of successful outcomes}}{\text{total number of outcomes}}$$

6 When one outcome prevents another outcome from happening the outcomes are mutually exclusive.

7 The probabilities of all the possible mutually exclusive events add up to 1.

8 For two events A and B which are mutually exclusive P(A or B) = P(A) + P(B). This is called the OR rule.

9 If the probability of an event happening is p then the probability of the event not happening is $1 - p$.

10 If there are n mutually exclusive events all equally likely, the probability of one event happening is $\frac{1}{n}$

11 If there are n mutually exclusive events and a successful outcomes the probability of a successful outcome is $\frac{a}{n}$

4 2-D and 3-D shapes

This unit looks at 2-D and 3-D shapes. It shows you how to use their properties to solve problems.

You should know some of these properties already:

A straight line is **one dimensional** (1-D). It has only *length*.

A rectangle and a circle are **two dimensional** (2-D) shapes. They have *area*.
All points on 2-D shapes are in the same **plane** (or flat surface).

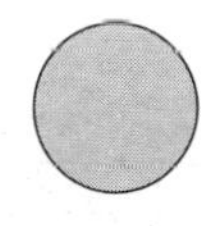

A cube and a football are **three dimensional** (3-D) objects. They have *volume* (or capacity).

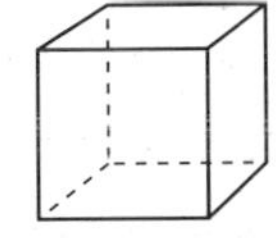

An **angle** is a measure of **turn** (or change of direction).

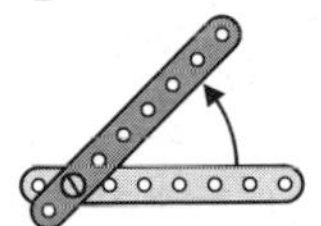

The darker geo strip has turned through an angle

Two lines are **parallel** if they are in the same direction.

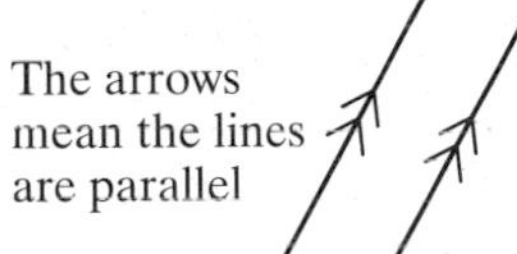
The arrows mean the lines are parallel

Two lines are **perpendicular** if they are at right angles to each other.

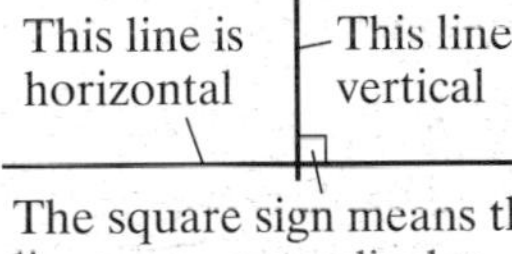
This line is horizontal
This line is vertical
The square sign means the lines are perpendicular

4.1 Some reminders about polygons

■ **A *polygon* is a 2-D shape with any number of straight *sides*.**

This table shows the special names used for polygons depending on the number of sides.

Number of sides	Name of polygon
3	triangle
4	quadrilateral
5	pentagon
6	hexagon
7	heptagon
8	octagon
9	nonagon
10	decagon

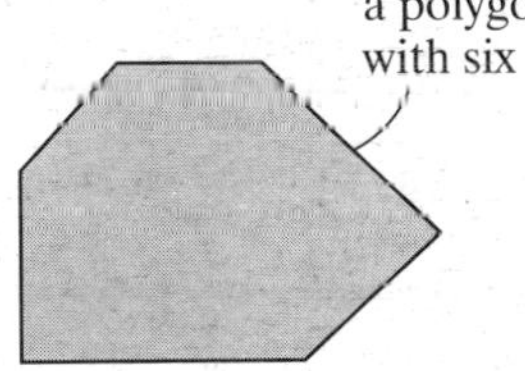
a polygon with six sides

A hexagon

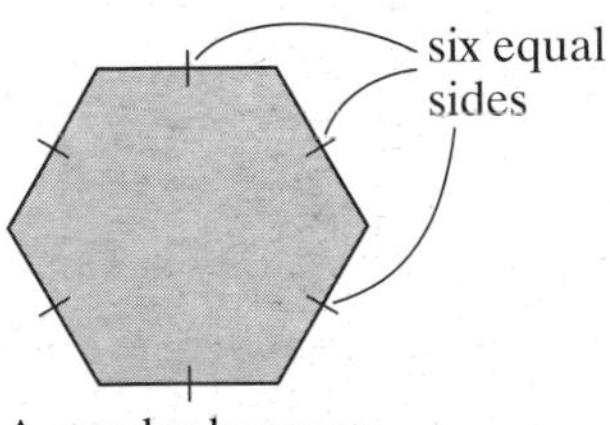
six equal sides

A regular hexagon

■ **A polygon is *regular* if all its sides and all its angles are equal.**

You can show that sides are equal on a shape by using the same mark on the equal sides.

- The point where two sides meet is called a **corner** or **vertex**. The plural of vertex is **vertices**.
- The **angle** at a vertex is a measure of the turn between the two sides that meet there. Angles are usually measured in **degrees**.

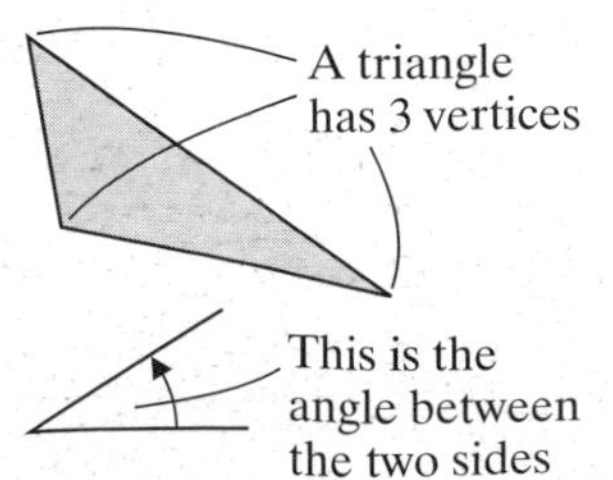
A triangle has 3 vertices
This is the angle between the two sides

Special triangles

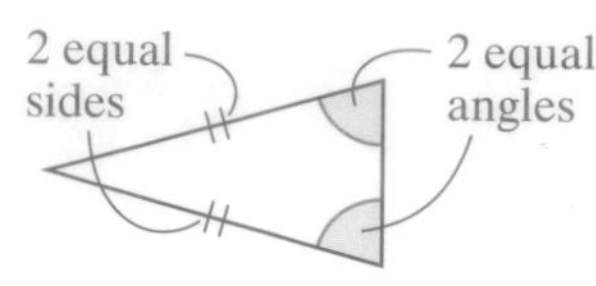

An **isosceles triangle** has:
- two equal sides
- two equal angles

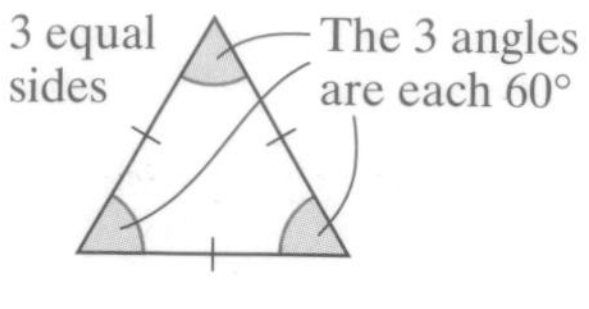

An **equilateral triangle** has:
- three equal sides
- three 60° angles

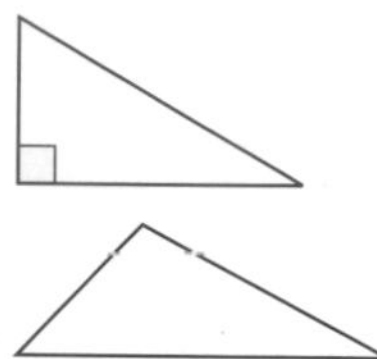

A **right angled triangle** has:
- a right angle as one of its angles

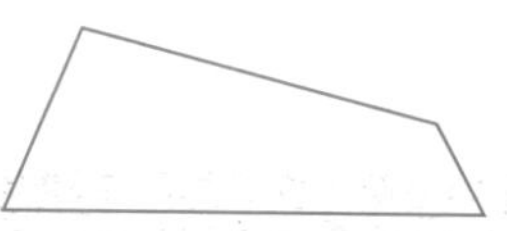

A **scalene triangle** has:
- no equal sides
- no equal angles

Special quadrilaterals

A **quadrilateral** has:
- four sides
- angles that add up to 360°

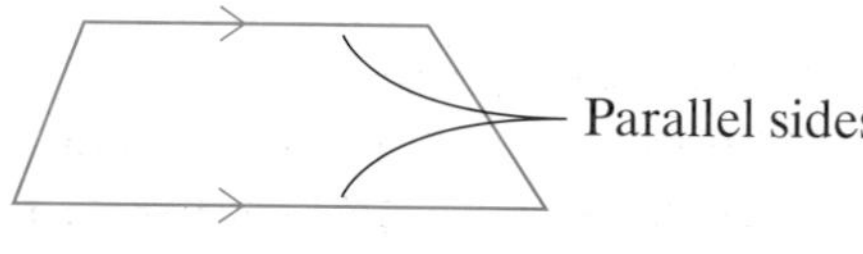

A **trapezium** has:
- one pair of opposite sides parallel

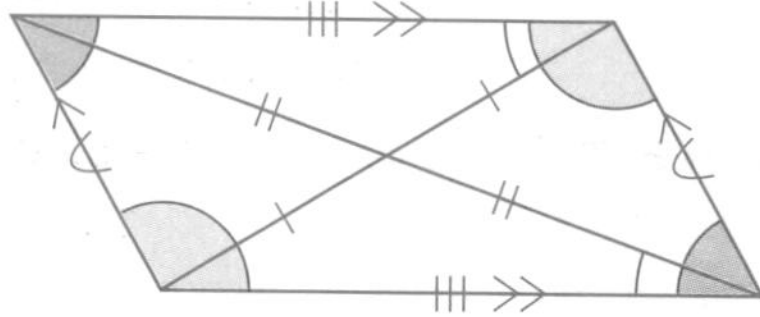

A **parallelogram** has:
- both pairs of opposite sides parallel
- opposite sides equal
- opposite angles equal
- diagonals that bisect each other

Bisect means divides exactly into two equal parts.

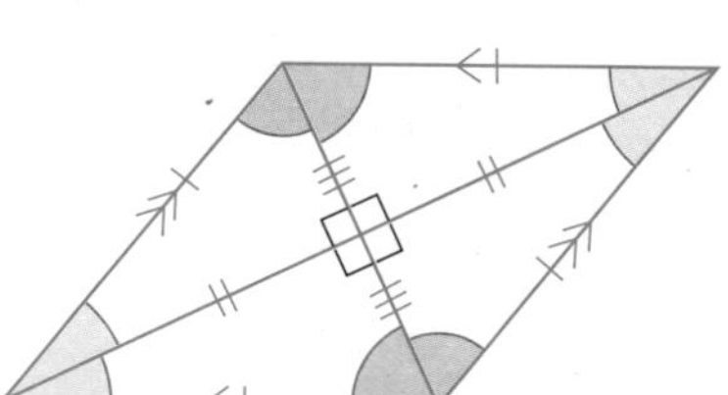

A rhombus is a special parallelogram.

A **rhombus** has:
- all sides equal
- both pairs of opposite sides parallel
- opposite angles equal
- diagonals that bisect each other at right angles
- diagonals that bisect the angles at the vertices.

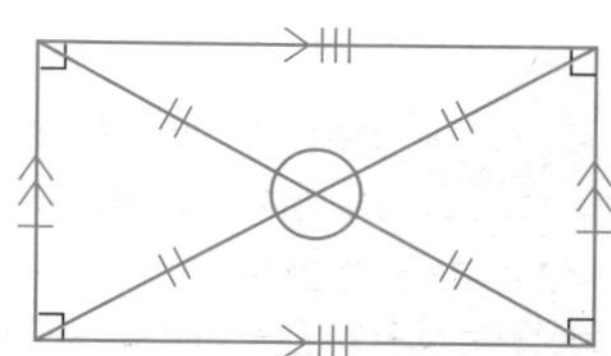

A **rectangle** has:
- both pairs of opposite sides parallel
- four 90° angles
- equal diagonals that bisect each other
- opposite sides equal

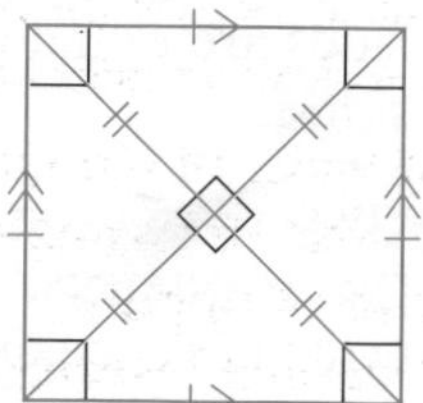

A **square** has
- all sides equal
- four 90° angles
- both pairs of opposite sides parallel
- equal diagonals that bisect each other at right angles
- diagonals that bisect the angles at the vertices

A **kite** has:

- two pairs of adjacent sides equal
- one pair of opposite angles equal
- diagonals that cross at right angles
- one of its diagonals bisected by the other diagonal

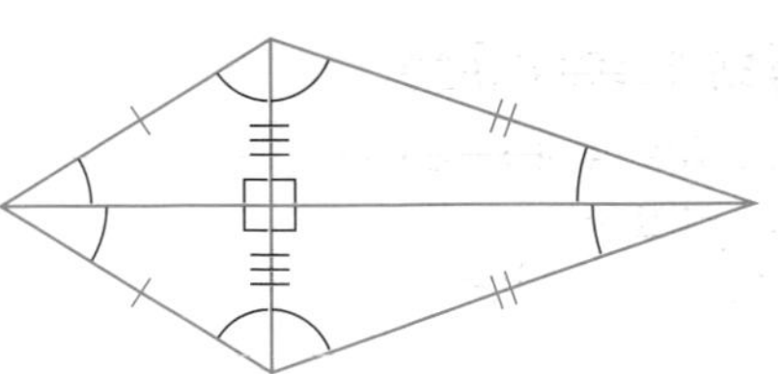

Naming angles

Angles can be named using letters. For example:

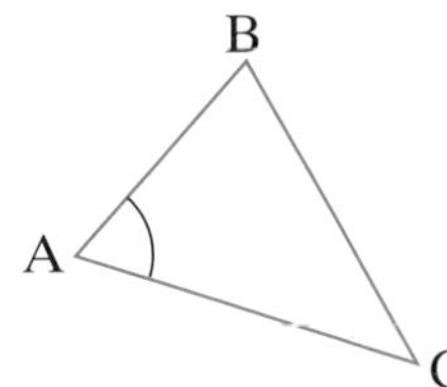

The angle marked is angle BAC or in short form $B\hat{A}C$ or $\angle$ BAC.
It could also be called angle CAB or in short $C\hat{A}B$ or $\angle$ CAB.

Exercise 4A

1 Here is a list of the names of some shapes:

hexagon	rhombus	isosceles triangle
rectangle	trapezium	parallelogram
octagon	pentagon	right angled triangle
square	kite	equilateral triangle

Use the list to help you write down the names of these:

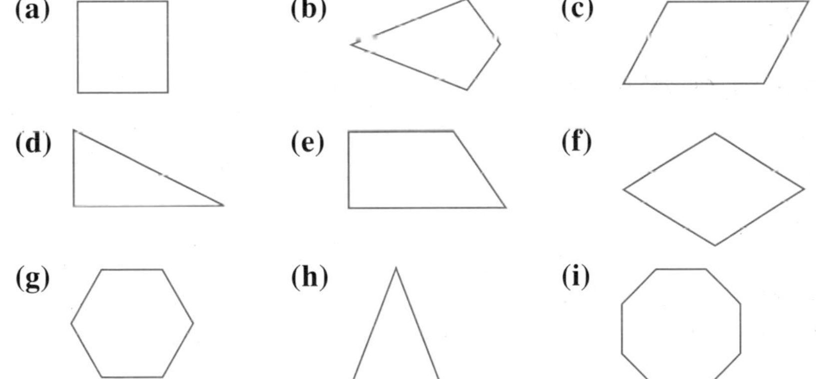

2 Write down the special names of these shapes:

(a) a triangle with all its sides equal
(b) a polygon with five sides
(c) a polygon with eight equal sides and all its angles equal
(d) a triangle with two of its sides equal
(e) a polygon with ten vertices.

3 Write down the name of a quadrilateral with:

(a) all its sides and all its angles equal
(b) only one pair of opposite sides parallel
(c) only one diagonal bisected by the other diagonal.

4 Write down the names of all the quadrilaterals which have:
(a) all their angles equal
(b) two pairs of opposite sides parallel
(c) all their sides equal
(d) two pairs of equal sides but not all their sides equal.

5 Write down the names of all the quadrilaterals which have:
(a) the diagonals equal
(b) the diagonals bisecting each other
(c) the diagonals meeting at right angles
(d) the diagonals bisecting each other at right angles
(e) at least one pair of opposite sides parallel.

6 In the parallelogram:
(a) write down the value of a
(b) calculate
(i) b
(ii) c.

(Note: the angles of a quadrilateral add to 360°.)

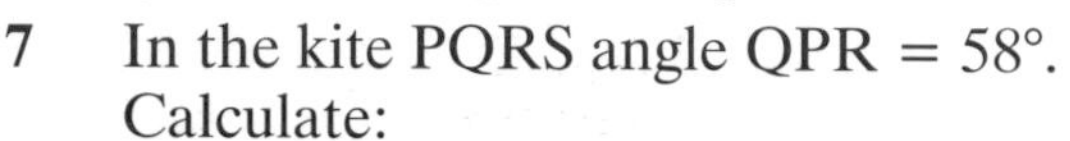

7 In the kite PQRS angle QPR = 58°.
Calculate:
(a) angle PQS
(b) angle PQR.

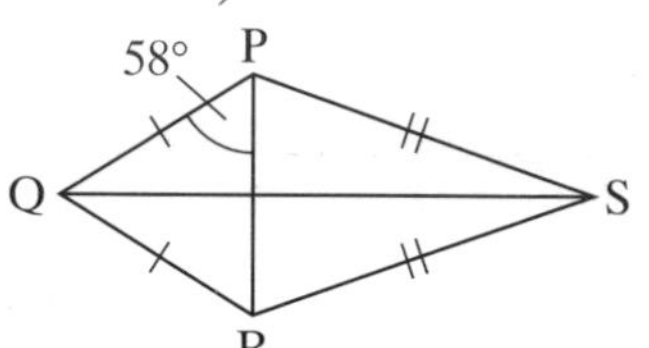

8 In the rhombus AC = 6 cm and BD = 10 cm.
Work out the area of:
(a) triangle ABD
(b) the rhombus ABCD.
(Note: the area of a triangle is $\frac{1}{2}$ × base × height.
You can read more about this on page 274.)

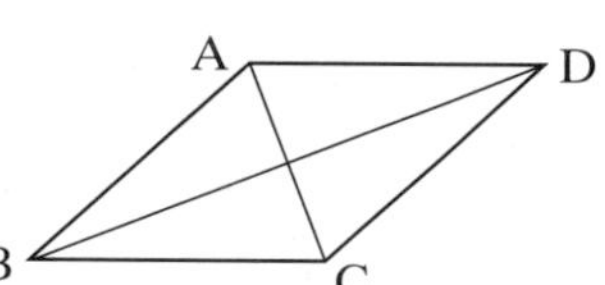

4.2 Congruent and similar shapes

■ ***Congruent*** **shapes are *exactly the same shape* and the *same size*. This means they are identical.**

If you draw congruent shapes on paper and cut them out they will fit exactly over each other. You might need to turn over some of the cut out shapes.

- All the corresponding angles are equal.
- All the corresponding lengths are equal.

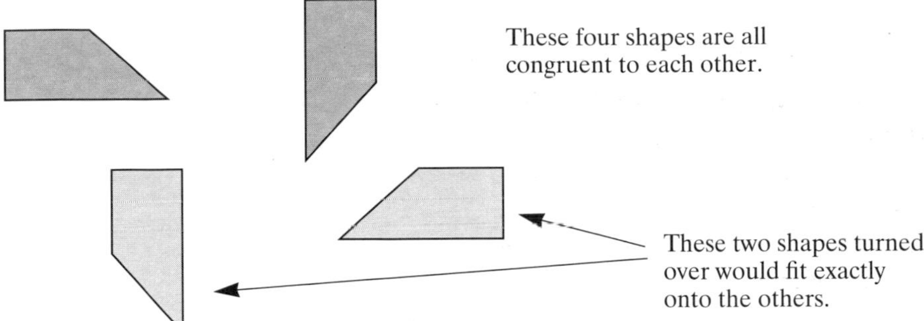

These four shapes are all congruent to each other.
These two shapes turned over would fit exactly onto the others.

■ ***Similar* shapes in maths have the *same shape*.**

- All the corresponding angles are equal.
- All the corresponding lengths are in the same ratio. (There is more about ratio on page 373.)

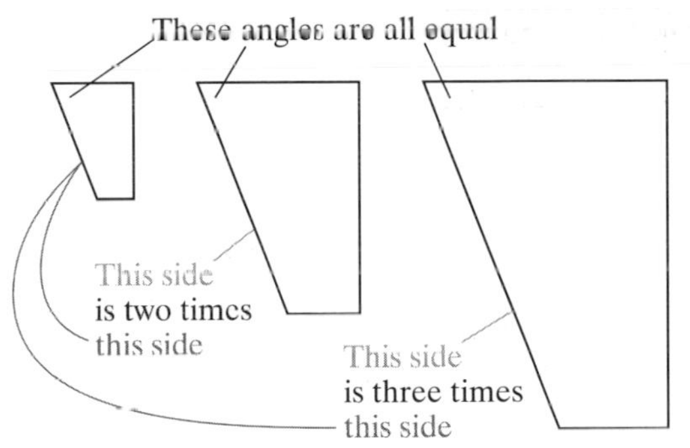

This side is two times this side
This side is three times this side

These three shapes are all similar to each other.

That's my younger sister
Mrs Green says I am similar to my sister
You are not mathematically similar to her as you are not an exact scale version of her

Example 1

Write down the letters of two pairs of congruent shapes.

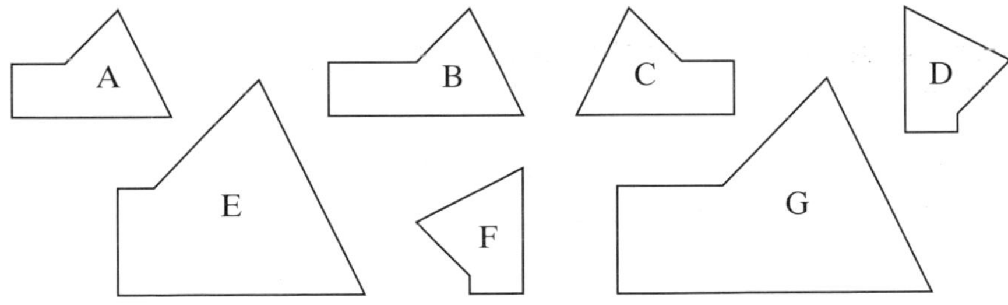

Shapes **A** and **C** are congruent.
Shapes **D** and **F** are congruent.
(They are the same shape and size.)

Example 2

Write down the letters of the similar shapes.

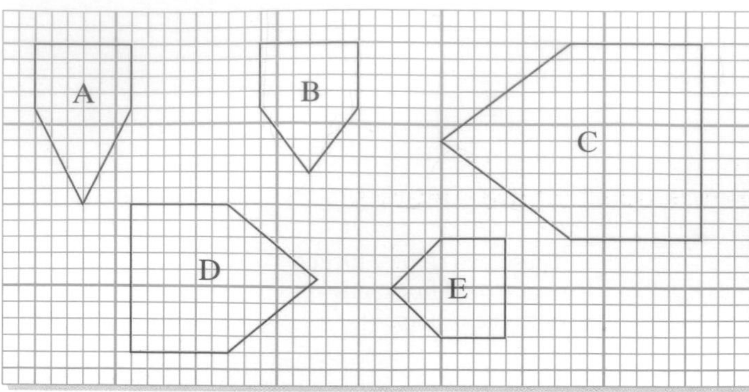

Shapes **B**, **C** and **D** are similar to each other.
(They are the same shape.)

Exercise 4B

You need a ruler, protractor and squared paper to answer these questions.

1

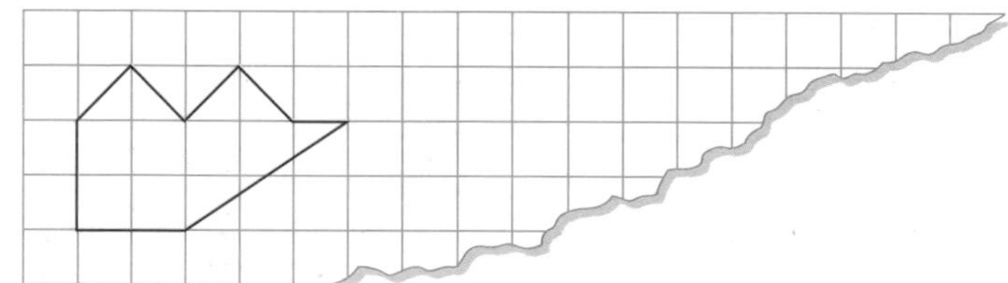

Copy the shape on to squared paper.
On the same paper draw two shapes that are congruent to the given one, but turned round into a different position.

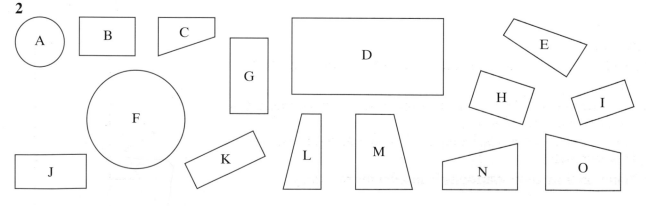

2

Write down the letters of two pairs of congruent shapes.
(Hint: measure the lengths and the angles carefully.)

3 Write down the letters of two pairs of similar shapes in question **2**.

4

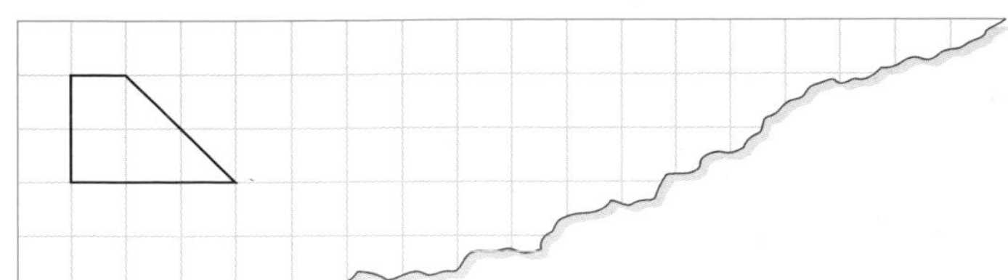

Copy the shape on to squared paper.
On the same paper draw two different shapes that are similar to the given one.

4.3 Looking at symmetry

Line symmetry

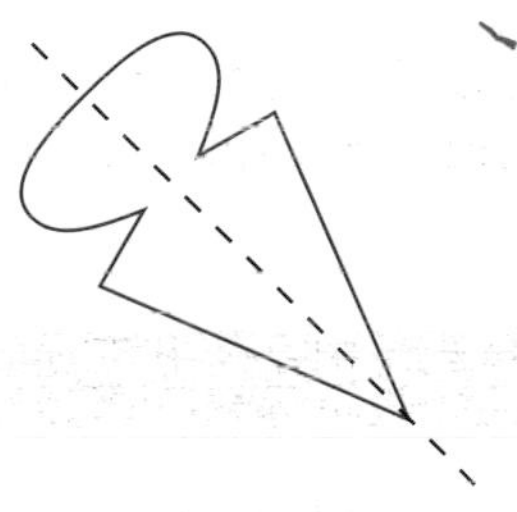

This shape is **symmetrical** about the dotted line.
The shape has **one line of symmetry** (or **axis of symmetry**).

One half of the shape is the mirror image of the other half. One half of the shape is congruent to the other half. So corresponding lengths are equal and corresponding angles are equal.

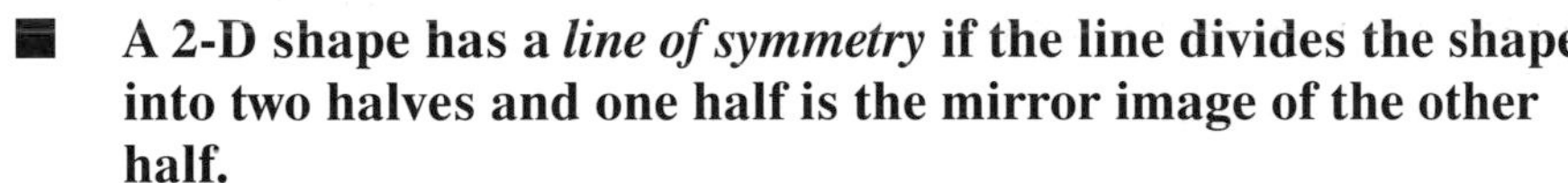

- **A 2-D shape has a *line of symmetry* if the line divides the shape into two halves and one half is the mirror image of the other half.**

This shape has four lines of symmetry.

Example 3

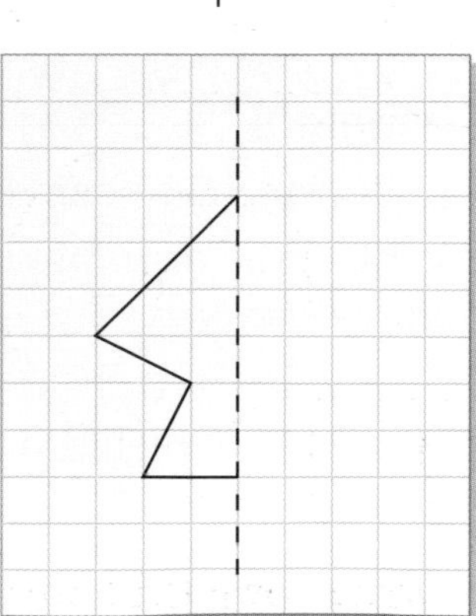

Complete this drawing so that the dotted line is the axis of symmetry.

The mirror image of a point is the same distance from the axis of symmetry as the original point.
The line joining a point to its mirror image is at right angles to the axis of symmetry.

A point on the axis of symmetry is its own mirror image.

First you mark the mirror images of B, C and D at B′, C′ and D′. Then you join up the points A′B′C′D′E′.

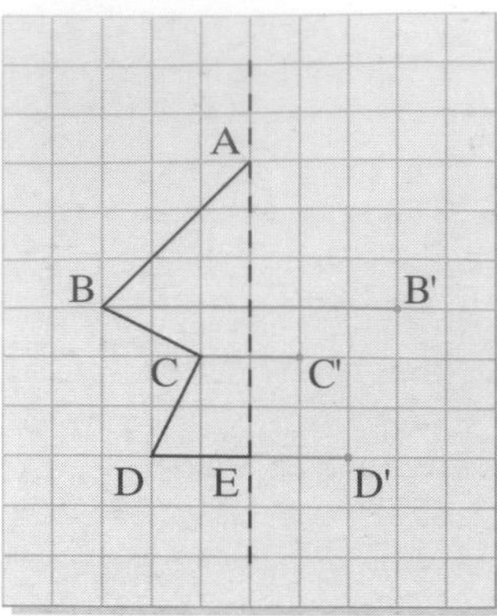

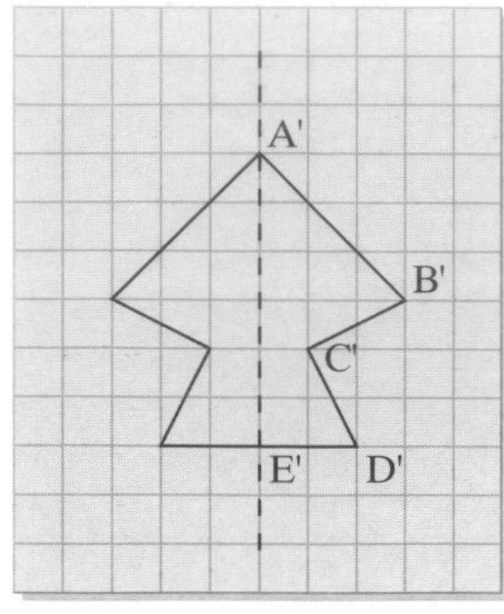

This is the completed shape.

Rotational symmetry

This shape can be **turned** (rotated), holding the centre point fixed.

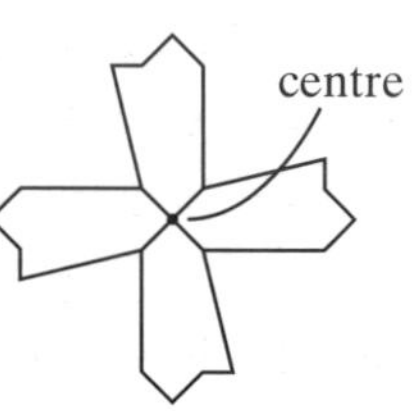

- **A 2-D shape has rotational symmetry if it fits onto itself two or more times in one turn.**
- **The order of rotational symmetry is the number of times a shape fits onto itself in one turn.**

This shape will fit onto itself four times in one turn.

It has **rotational symmetry of order 4**.

Example 4

Write down the order of rotational symmetry of this shape.

This shape will fit onto itself three times when rotated. If the point P is at any of the three positions P, Q or R the shape will look exactly the same.
The shape has rotational symmetry of order 3.

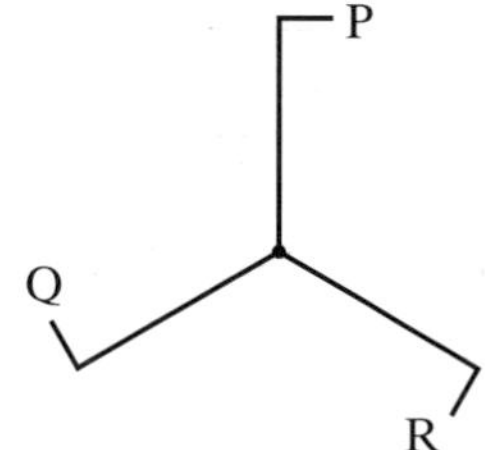

Example 5

This drawing has been torn in half.

Complete the drawing so that the whole shape has rotational symmetry of order 2.

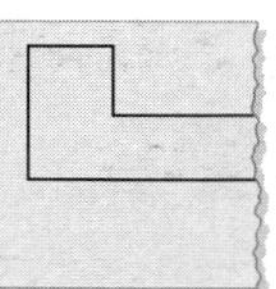

This is the completed shape.

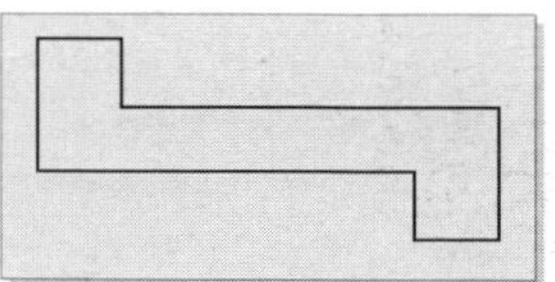

Exercise 4C

You can use tracing paper for this exercise to copy the shapes and check symmetry.

1 Copy these shapes and draw with dotted or coloured lines all the lines of symmetry, if any.

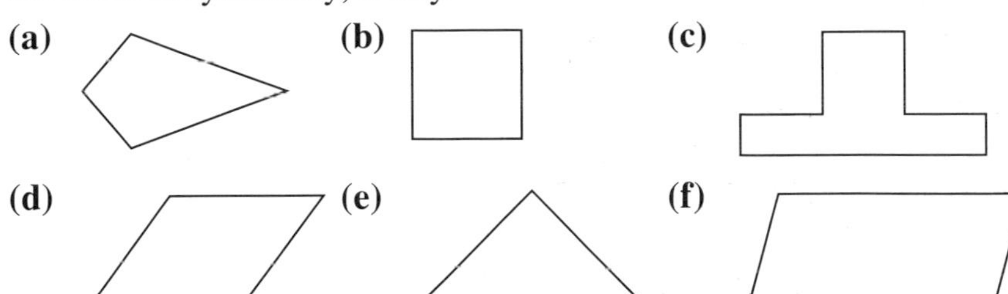

2 The arrowhead shape ABCD is a type of kite. AB = BC and AD = DC. Copy the diagram and draw any lines of symmetry.

3 Draw a shape that is symmetrical about one line. Show the line of symmetry with a dotted or coloured line.

4 Draw a shape that has four lines of symmetry. Show the lines of symmetry with dotted or coloured lines.

5 Write down the order of rotational symmetry, if any, of these shapes:

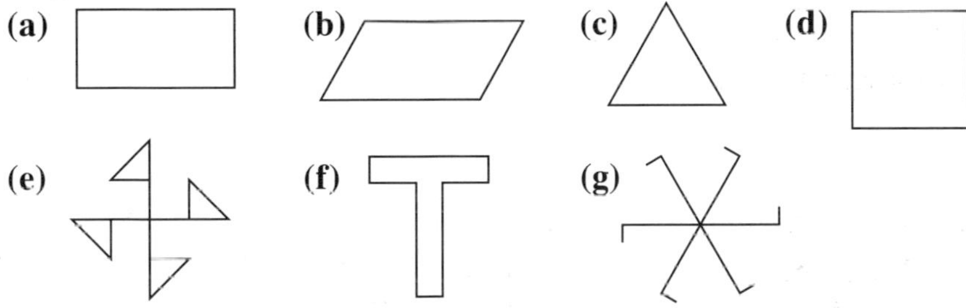

6 Draw a shape that has rotational symmetry of order:
(a) 2 (b) 4 (c) 3 (d) 1 (e) 8

One way to represent a cuboid

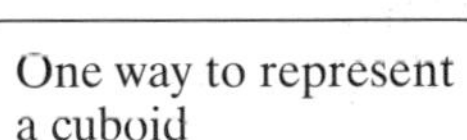

Start with a rectangle

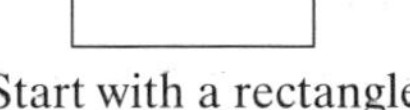

Draw an identical rectangle just above and to the right

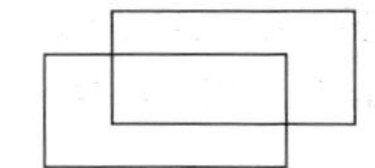

Join up the corners and make the hidden edges dotted

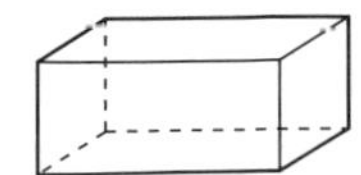

4.4 Drawing 3-D shapes and their planes of symmetry

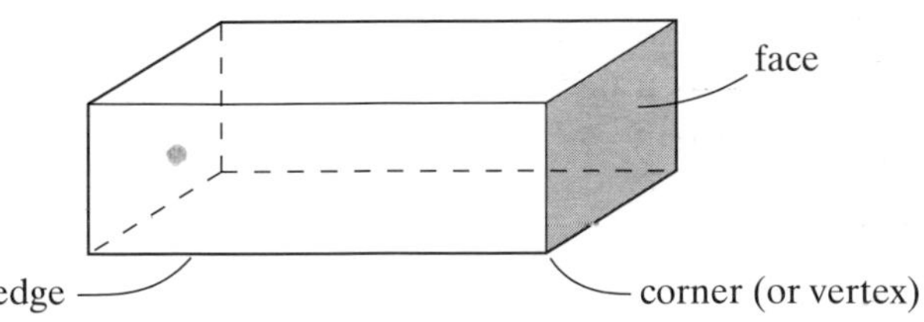

A **cuboid** has **8 vertices (corners)**. It has **12 edges** and **6 faces**. The faces of a cuboid are all rectangles. Some do not look like rectangles in the drawing.

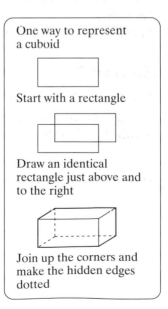

- **When a 3-D shape is *represented* by a 2-D drawing *vertical lines* are always represented by vertical lines. *Parallel lines* should always look parallel. A *horizontal line* can be drawn in any direction except vertically.**

- **A *prism* is a 3-D shape with the same cross-section all along its length. For example, a cylinder is a prism whose cross-section is a circle.**

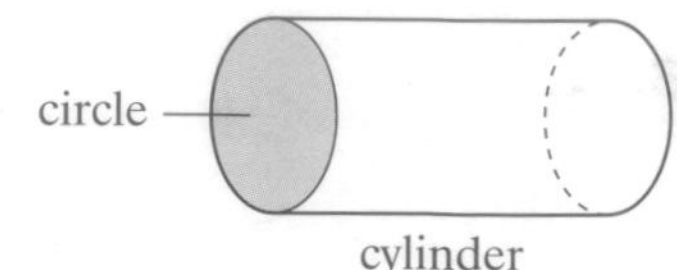

Usually you will use right prisms. In these the length (or height) is at right angles to the base.

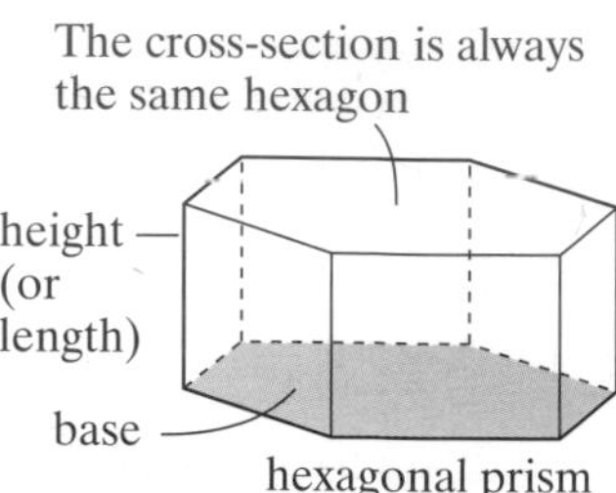

You can represent 3-D shapes on isometric paper. This paper lets you draw lengths in three perpendicular directions on the same scale. The faces do not appear as their true shape.

Example 6

On isometric paper draw a diagram of a prism with a T-shaped cross-section. (Note: all the edges must be drawn along the printed lines.)

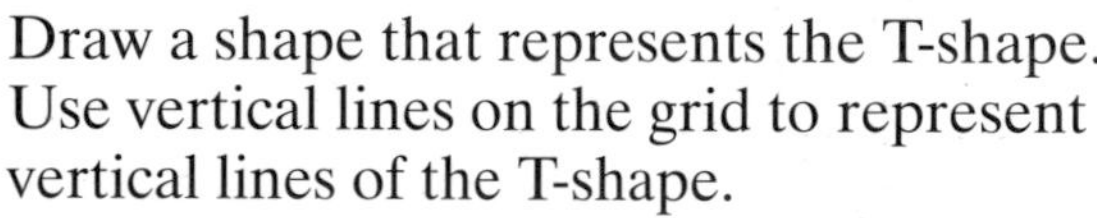

Draw a shape that represents the T-shape. Use vertical lines on the grid to represent vertical lines of the T-shape.

From each vertex draw the length of the prism along the printed lines. Here it is the same length as three triangle sides, but it could be any length.

Complete the T-shaped cross-section at the other end of the prism. Make parallel lines look parallel.

Join corresponding points to form the remaining edges. Use dotted lines for hidden edges.

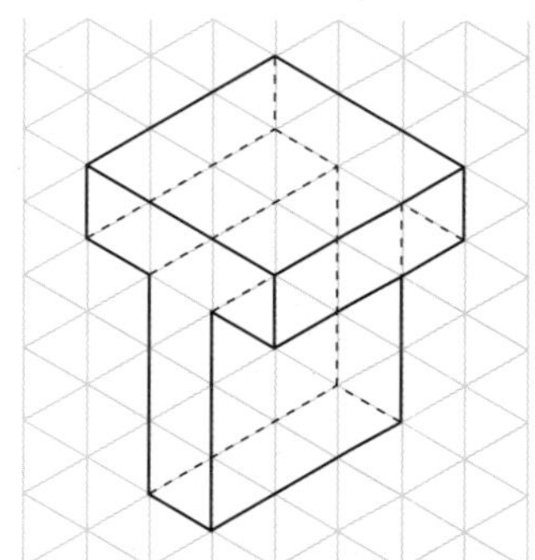

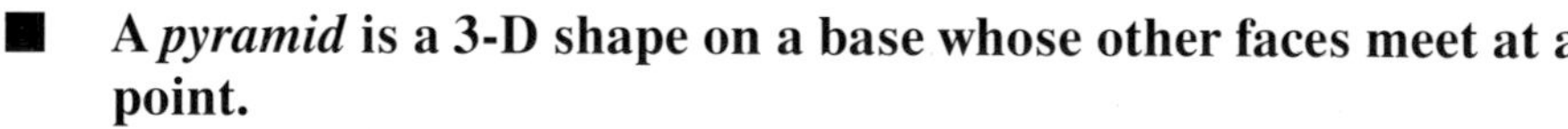

- **A *pyramid* is a 3-D shape on a base whose other faces meet at a point.**

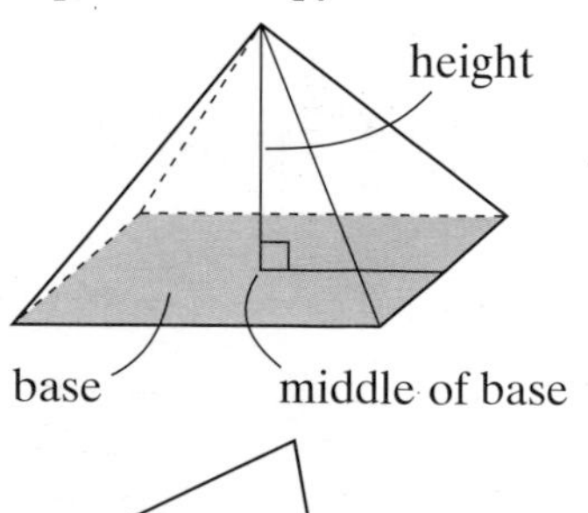

Usually you will use **right** pyramids. In these the height from the point is at right angles to the base.

- The base of a **square based pyramid** is a square.
- A **cone** is a pyramid whose base is a circle.

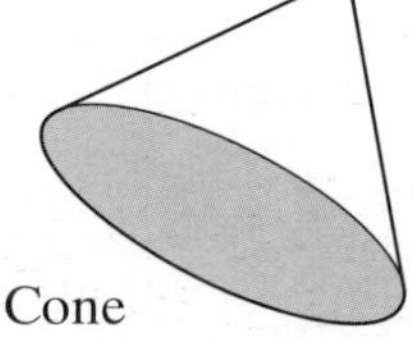

Planes of symmetry

You can also represent 3-D shapes on squared paper.
This cuboid is symmetrical about each of the shaded planes.

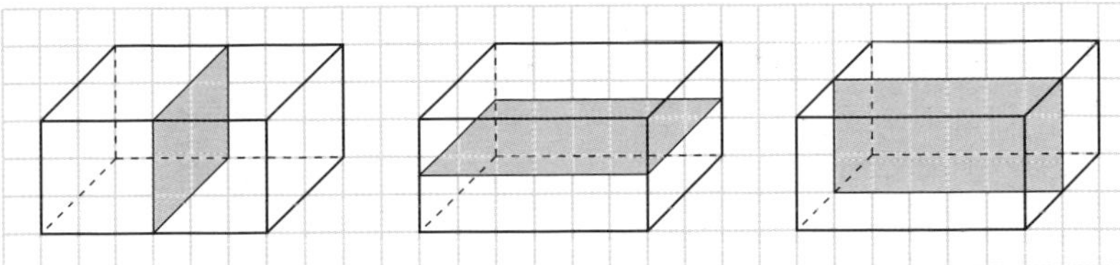

It has 3 **planes of symmetry**.

■ **A 3-D shape has a *plane of symmetry* if the plane divides the shape into two halves and one half is the mirror image of the other half.**

Example 7

Copy this house shape and draw all its planes of symmetry on separate diagrams.
There are two planes of symmetry.

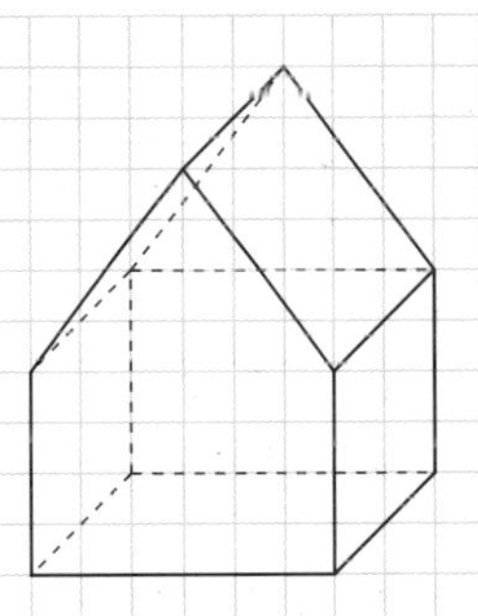

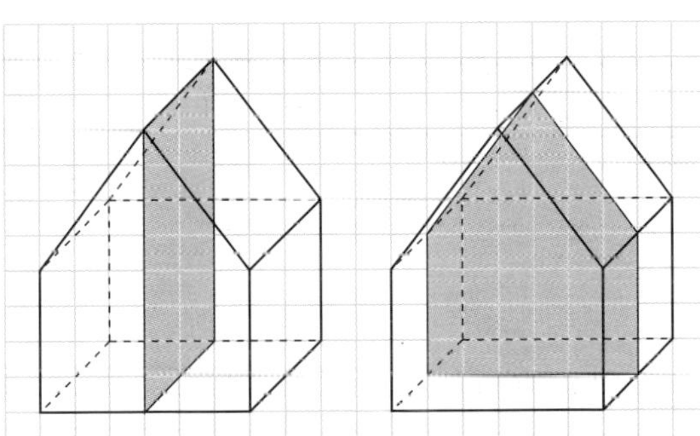

Exercise 4D

You need isometric paper and squared paper to answer these questions.

1 On isometric paper draw a diagram of
  (i) a cube
  (ii) a cuboid
  (iii) a prism with an 'L' shaped cross-section.

2

Copy this hexagonal prism twice. On each of your diagrams draw a different plane of symmetry of the prism.

3 Copy these shapes that represent 3-D objects and draw all their planes of symmetry on separate diagrams:

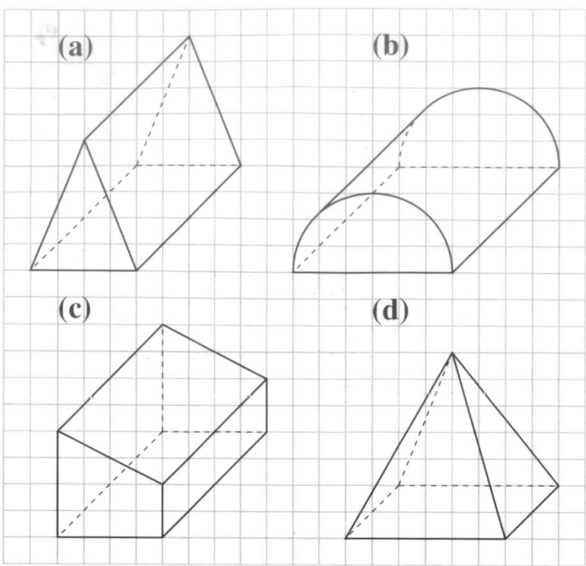

4.5 Drawing nets of 3-D shapes

■ **The *net* of a 3-D shape is the 2-D shape that is folded to make the 3-D shape.**

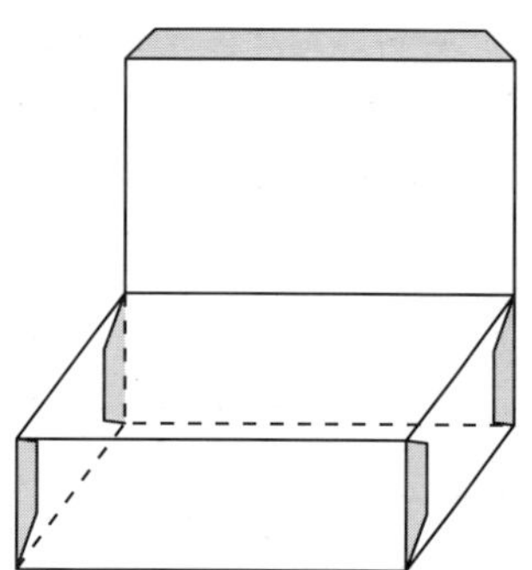

Follow these steps to understand the idea:

Step 1: find an empty packet that is a cuboid.
Step 2: open out the packet so that it lies flat.
Step 3: cut off the tabs (shaded in the picture).
Step 4: on paper draw the opened out shape.

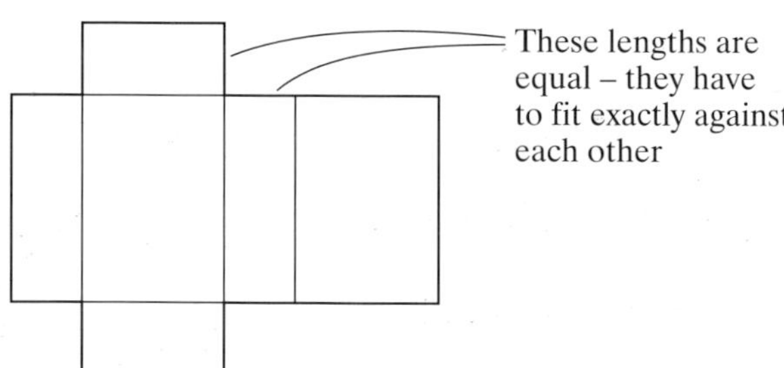

These lengths are equal – they have to fit exactly against each other

The shape is called the **net** of the cuboid.

To construct a 3-D shape

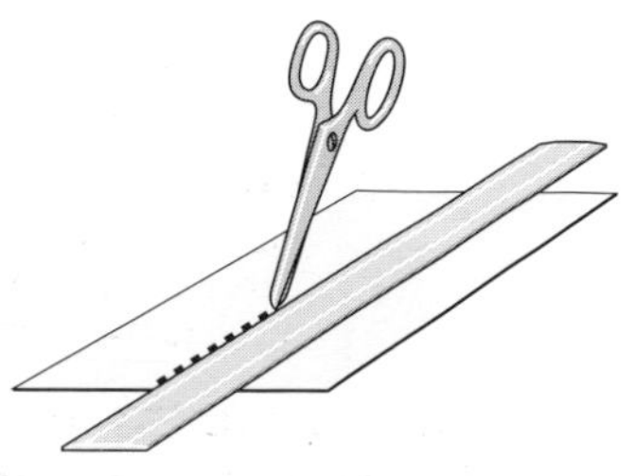

Step 1: draw the net of the shape.
Step 2: score along the edges using scissors against a ruler.
Step 3: fold the net to form the 3-D shape.
Step 4: stick the edges together with sticky tape.

For a neater finish you can include tabs on the net. They should be wide enough to hold the shape together firmly when they are glued.

Example 8

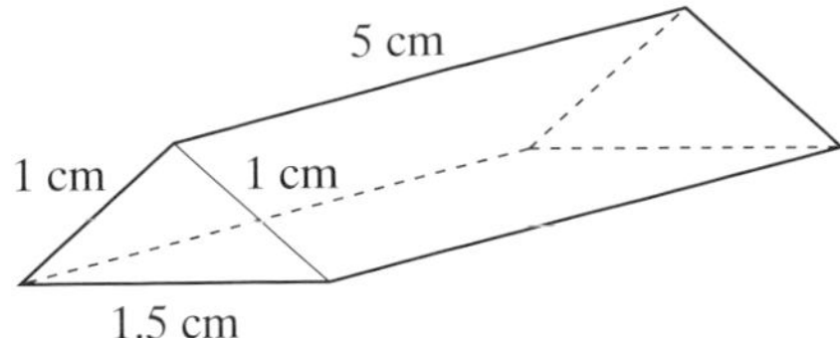

Draw a full size net of the triangular prism.

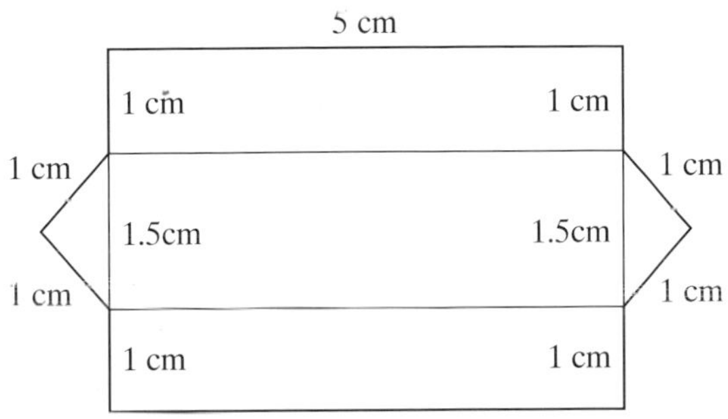

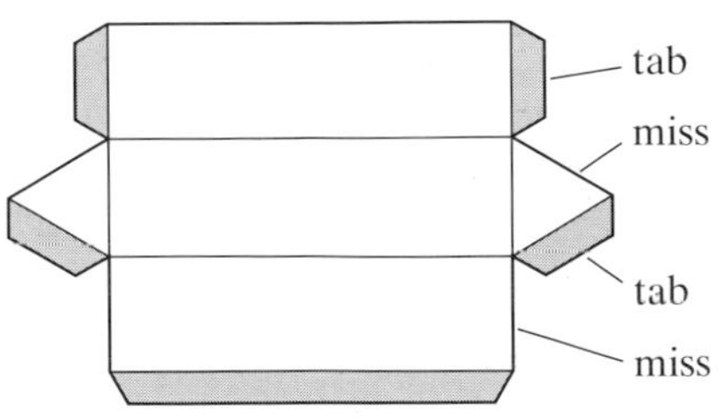

If you want to stick the prism you could use tabs. Put a tab on every other side

Exercise 4E

You will need a ruler, protractor and compasses to answer these questions. Read about accurate constructions in unit 26.

1 Draw full size nets of the 3-D shapes represented:

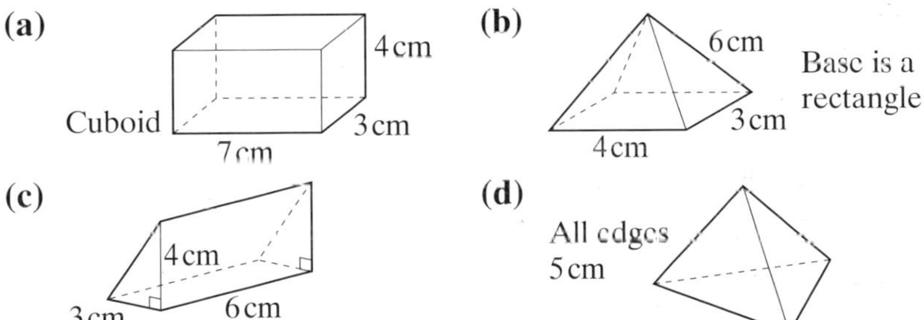

2 The base of the pyramid is a square of side 4 cm. The sloping edges are all 5 cm.

(a) On paper or card draw a full size net of the pyramid with tabs.

(b) Fold the net and stick the edges to make the pyramid.

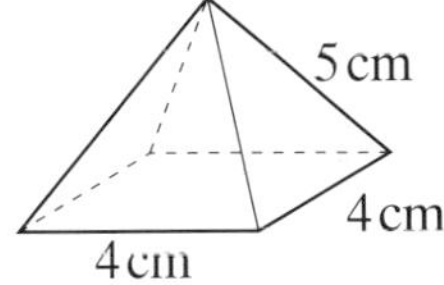

3

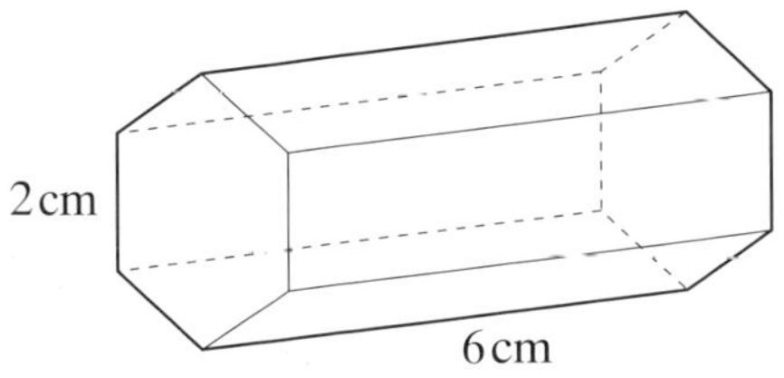

The base of this prism is a regular hexagon with each edge 2 cm. The height of the prism is 6 cm.

(a) On paper or card draw a full size net of the prism with tabs.

(b) Fold the net and stick the edges to make the prism.

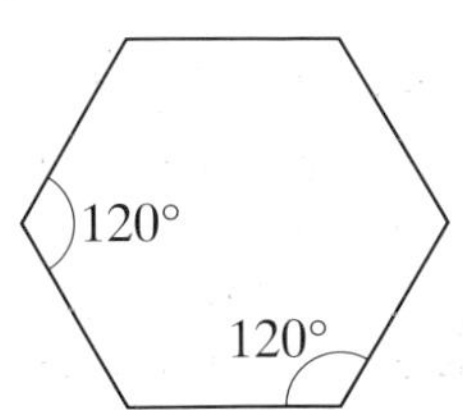

Each angle of a regular hexagon is 120°

H/W 1–9

Exercise 4F Mixed questions

You will need a ruler, compasses and squared paper to answer these questions.

1 Write down the letters of two pairs of congruent shapes:

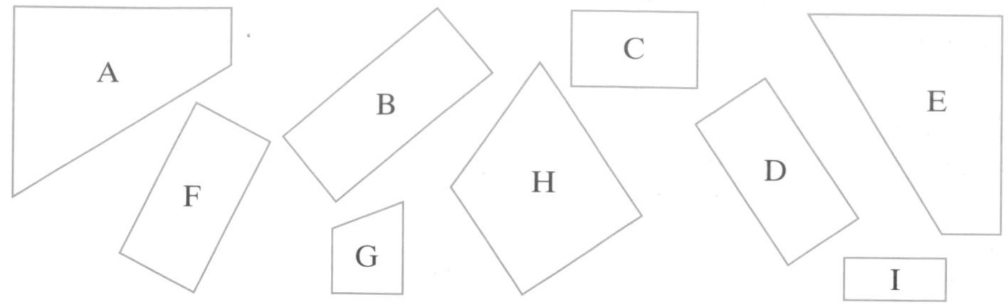

2 Write down the letters of two pairs of similar shapes in question **1**.

3

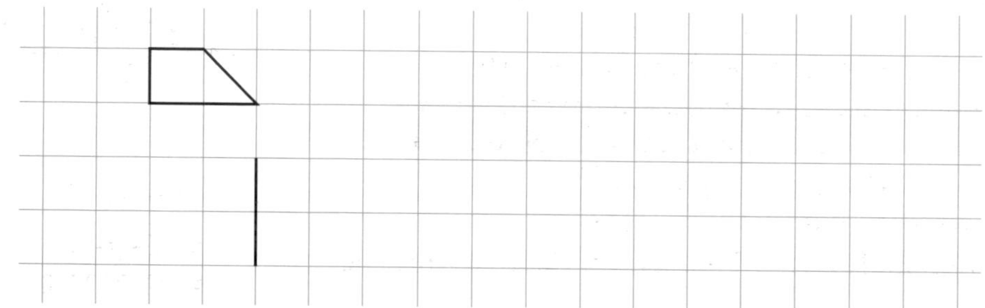

(a) Copy the shape on to squared paper.

One edge of a similar shape has been drawn.

(b) Complete the similar shape on your paper.

4 Draw a shape that has two lines of symmetry.
Show the lines of symmetry with dotted or coloured lines.

5

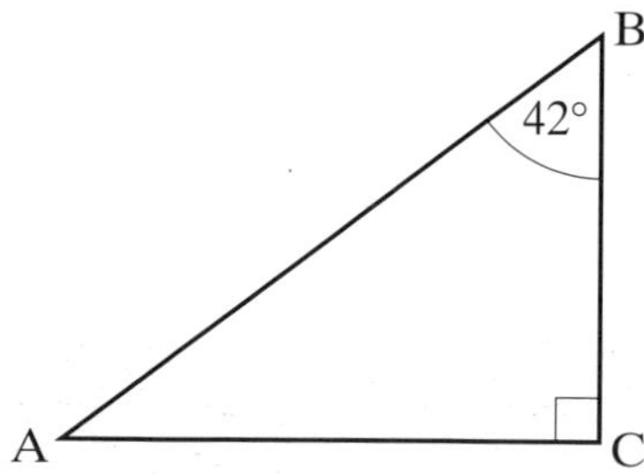

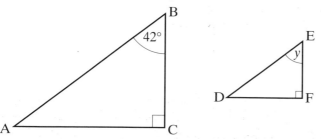

Diagram NOT drawn accurately

Triangle DEF is similar to triangle ABC.
The length of EF is half the length of BC.
Write down the value of y.

6 The diagram shows a regular hexagon.

Write down the order of rotational symmetry of the hexagon.

[L]

7 Here are the names of some quadrilaterals:

square	rectangle	rhombus
parallelogram	trapezium	kite

(a) Write down the names of the quadrilaterals which have two pairs of parallel sides.

(b) Write down the names of the quadrilaterals which must have two pairs of equal sides. [L]

8 The diagram represents a prism. The cross-section (shaded region) of the prism is a right angled isosceles triangle.
Copy the diagram and draw one plane of symmetry of the prism. [L]

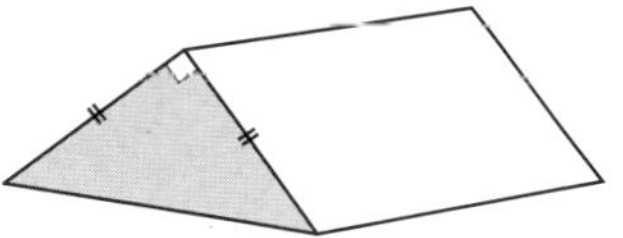

9 The circle ABCD has centre O. AOD is a straight line. Angle AOB = angle COD = 60°.

(a) Write down three of the lines which are equal to AO.

(b) What type of triangle is triangle ABO?

(c) What is the mathematical name of the shape ABCD?

(d) Name one triangle which is congruent to triangle ABO.

(e) Some pairs of lines in the diagram are parallel to each other. Write down three pairs of parallel lines.

Shape ABCD is to be reflected in the line AD.

(f) Copy the diagram and sketch the image of ABCD after the reflection.

(g) What is the mathematical name of the shape formed by ABCD together with its reflection in the line AD?

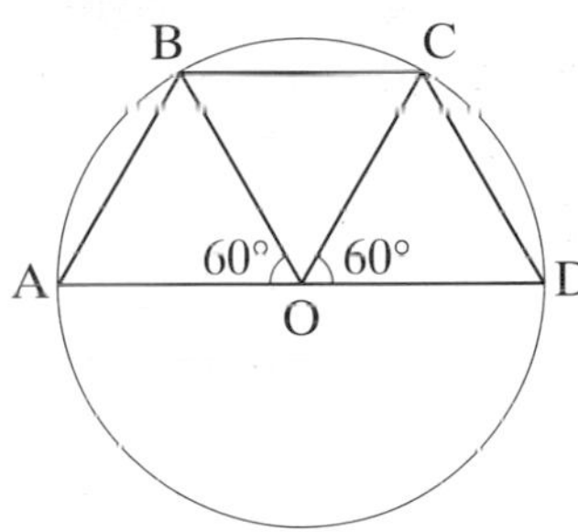

The diagram is a scale drawing

10

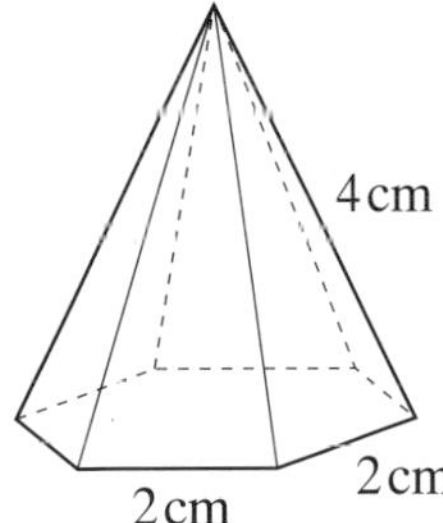

The base of the pyramid is a hexagon with each edge 2 cm.
The sloping edges are all 4 cm.
Draw a full size net of the pyramid.

Summary of key points

1 A **polygon** is a 2-D shape with any number of straight sides.

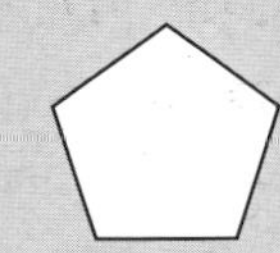

A pentagon

2 A polygon is **regular** if all its sides and all its angles are equal.

A regular pentagon

3 **Congruent** shapes are exactly the *same shape* and the *same size*. This means they are identical.

These shapes are congruent

4 **Similar** shapes have the *same shape*.

These shapes are similar

5 A 2-D shape has a **line of symmetry** if the line divides the shape into two halves and one half is the mirror image of the other half.

6 A 2-D shape has **rotational symmetry** if it fits onto itself two or more times in one turn.

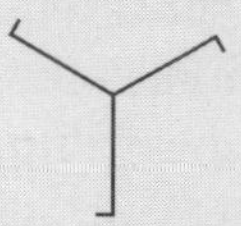

7 The order of rotational symmetry is the number of times a shape fits onto itself in one turn.

This shape has rotational symmetry of order 3

8 When a **3-D shape** is **represented** by a **2-D drawing** *vertical lines* are always represented by vertical lines. *Parallel lines* should always look parallel. A *horizontal line* can be drawn in any direction except vertically.

Dotted lines are hidden

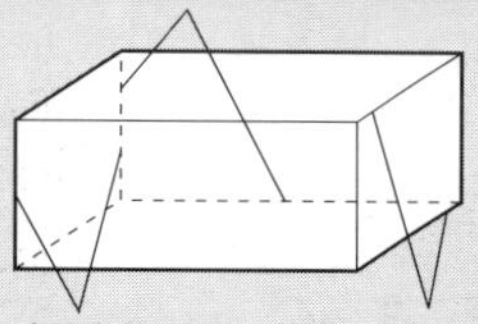

Vertical lines look vertical

Parallel lines look parallel

9 A **prism** is a 3-D shape with the same cross-section all along its length.

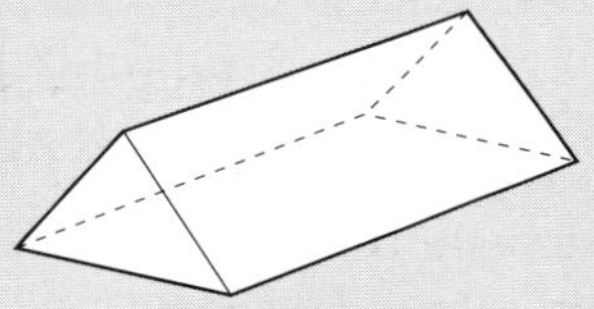

A prism

10 A **pyramid** is a 3-D shape on a base whose other faces meet at a point.

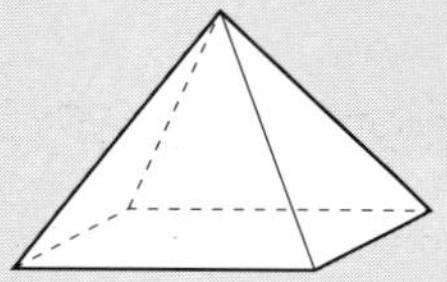

A pyramid

11 A 3-D shape has a **plane of symmetry** if the plane divides the shape into two halves and one half is the mirror image of the other half.

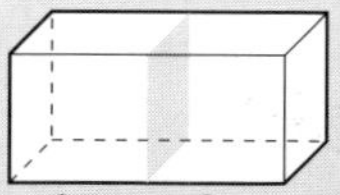

One plane of symmetry of this cuboid

12 The **net of a 3-D shape** is the 2-D shape that is folded to make the 3-D shape.

The net of a triangular prism

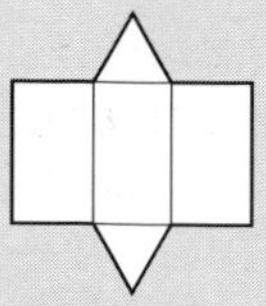

5 Measure 1

5.1 Estimating

Estimation is a key skill in everyday life. You are estimating distances, time and lots of other measures when you ask questions such as:

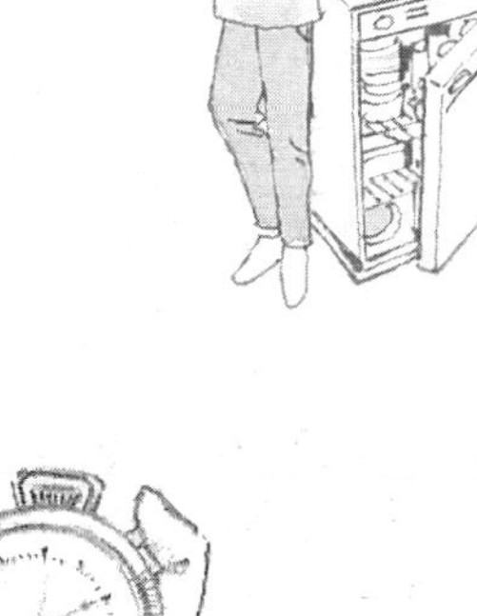
Just about enough for a cup of tea.

- Will this book fit in my bag?
- How long will it take me to walk to the shops?
- Have I got time for another cup of tea?
- Is there enough milk in the fridge for the rest of the week?

Here are some measures that you have to estimate in real life.

Length

Capacity

Weight

Time

This section is about estimating these measures.

It involves using measures in metric units and Imperial units (the old style units) such as miles, pounds, gallons and pints. You need to be able to convert Imperial units to approximate metric values.

5.2 Estimating length

Here are some basic estimates of distances in real life.

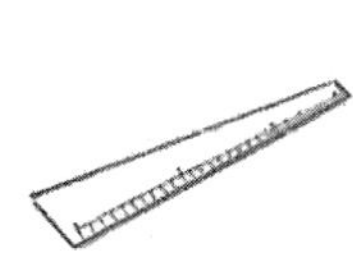

■ **A 30 cm ruler is about 1 foot**

A door is 2 m high or about $6\frac{1}{2}$ feet

A long stride is 1 m long or about 3 feet

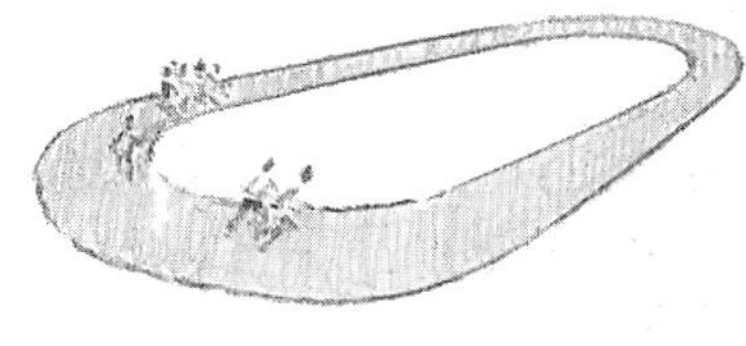

$2\frac{1}{2}$ times around the track is 1 km or about $\frac{5}{8}$ mile

Exercise 5A

Look at the picture and write down an estimate for each measurement.

1 The height of the:
(a) man **(b)** girl **(c)** bus **(d)** car

2 The length of the:
(a) car **(b)** bus **(c)** wall

3 The height of the:
(a) house **(b)** tree **(c)** wall

4 The width of the:
(a) drive **(b)** garage **(c)** house

5.3 Estimating capacity

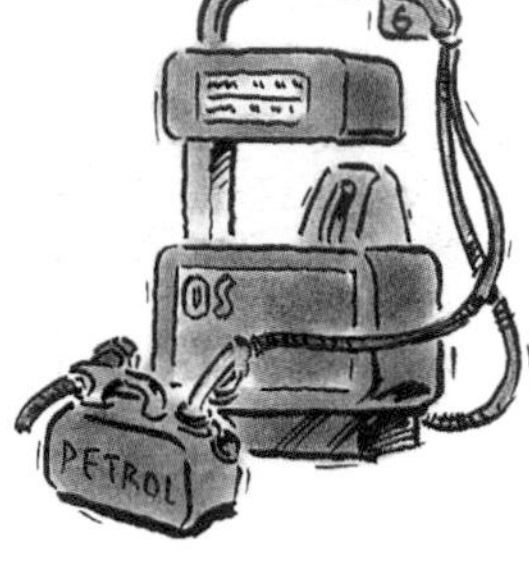

■ **A milk carton holds 1 pint or about $\frac{1}{2}$ litre (500 m*l*)**

A petrol can holds 1 gallon or 4.5 litres

A mug and a can of cola each hold about $\frac{1}{2}$ pint or about 300 m*l*

A medicine spoon and a teaspoon hold about 5 m*l*

Exercise 5B

Copy the table into your book.
Look at the picture and write down an estimate for each item. Give your answers in metric and Imperial units.

Amount of	Metric	Imperial
(a) milk in a full bottle		
(b) milk in the bottle		
(c) cola in a full can		
(d) cola in the glass		
(e) coffee in the jug		
(f) petrol in a full tank		
(g) water in a full bucket		
(h) water in a full paddling pool		

5.4 Estimating weight (mass)

You are really dealing with the *mass* of these quantities. However in everyday life you talk about the *weight* of a quantity so that word is used here.

■ **A $\frac{1}{4}$ pound packet of tea weighs about 100 g**

A 1 kg bag of sugar weighs about 2.2 pounds

A 50 kg bag of cement weighs about 110 pounds

Exercise 5C

Copy the table into your book.
Look at the picture and write down an estimate for each item. Give your answer in metric and Imperial units.

Weight of the	Metric	Imperial
(a) bag of potatoes		
(b) block of butter		
(c) bag of apples		
(d) packet of coffee		
(e) loaf of bread		
(f) packet of cereal		
(g) bottle of squash		
(h) packet of biscuits		
(i) packet of crisps		
(j) box of soap powder		

Making sensible estimates

You need to be able to make sensible estimates. For example, few people in the world can run 100 m in less than 10 seconds. So 8 seconds is not a sensible estimate for the time of the school's 100 m race on Sports Day.

Example 1

My car is 20 m long. Is this a sensible estimate?

This is not very sensible because it means the car's length would be about the same as 10 men lying head to toe or about as long as an articulated lorry.

Exercise 5D

For each of these statements say whether the estimate is sensible. If the statement is not sensible then give a reasonable estimate for the measurement.

(a) My teacher is 20 m tall.

(b) My father is 20 cm tall.

(c) The classroom measures 2 m by 3 m.

(d) I bought 2 g of potatoes at the supermarket.

(e) A can of cola holds 3 *l* of liquid.

(f) A house is 10 m high.

(g) The tallest boy in school is 2 m tall.

(h) John can just lift 50 kg.

(i) Jandeep has to walk 1 km to school each day.

(j) A cup full of tea contains 2 *l* of liquid.

(k) The river Thames is 20 km long.

(l) A 50 p piece weighs 0.5 kg.

(m) A box of chocolates weighs 500 g.

(n) A 50 cc moped can travel at 150 miles per hour.

(o) A pint glass will hold 1 *l* of liquid.

(p) The capacity of the petrol tank in my car is 5 *l*.

(q) My new sports car can travel at 100 miles per hour.

(r) The Eiffel Tower in Paris is more than 200 m high.

(s) The capacity of the petrol tank in my car is 50 gallons.

(t) A packet of tea weighs 50 g.

5.5 Choosing appropriate units of measure

When you want to measure something you must first decide what units to use.

For example, to measure how long it takes to run 100 m you use seconds. To measure how long it takes to run a marathon (26 miles) you would use hours, minutes and seconds.

Exercise 5E

Copy this table into your book.
Write down appropriate units of measurement for each item. Give your answers in metric and Imperial units.

Units of measurement for the	Metric	Imperial
(a) length of your classroom		
(b) width of this book		
(c) distance of Edinburgh from London		
(d) length of a double decker bus		
(e) weight of a sack of potatoes		
(f) weight of a packet of sweets		
(g) weight of a lorry full of sand		
(h) amount of petrol in a car's petrol tank		
(i) amount of liquid in a full cup of tea		
(j) amount of medicine in a medicine spoon		
(k) amount of water in a raindrop		
(l) amount of water in a reservoir		
(m) time it takes to boil an egg		
(n) time it takes to run 400 metres		
(o) time it takes to walk 20 miles		
(p) time it takes to sail from Southampton to New York		
(q) length of a piece of wood		
(r) thickness of a page in this book		
(s) weight of 30 of these books		
(t) time it takes to travel from Earth to Mars		

5.6 Measuring time

Only another 5 minutes
I wonder when this lesson ends?

Of all the measures used in everyday life, time is probably used most often. After all, you always want to know when your maths lesson will finish!

You need to be able to tell the difference between the times in the morning and times in the afternoon and evening.

There are two ways of doing this:

- use am for morning and pm for afternoon and evening
- use the 24-hour clock system that is used on bus and train timetables.

■ This table shows some times of day under both systems:

Using am and pm	Using the 24-hour clock
12:00 midnight	00:00 or 24:00
9 am	09:00
12:00 noon	12:00
3:30 pm	15:30
12:00 midnight	24:00 or 00:00

am is short for ante meridiem (before midday).

pm is short for post meridiem (after midday).

In the morning the time shown by these clocks is

9:25 am or 09:25 or twenty five past nine in the morning.

In the afternoon the time shown by these clocks is

1:35 pm or 13:35 or twenty five to two in the afternoon.

When the time is after 12 noon you add 12 to the hour number to get the 24-hour clock time.

You say "twenty five past nine in the morning"

You say "twenty five to two in the afternoon"

Exercise 5F

1 Write these times as you would say them:
(a) 11:00 **(b)** 9:15 **(c)** 22:50
(d) 3:05 **(e)** 15:40 **(f)** 12:20

2 Change these times from am and pm to 24-hour clock times:
(a) 10:00 am **(b)** 10:00 pm **(c)** 9:30 am
(d) 9:30 pm **(e)** 8:20 pm **(f)** 8:20 am
(g) 7 am **(h)** 8 pm **(i)** 3:30 pm
(j) 4:40 am **(k)** 1:08 am **(l)** 1:08 pm

3 Write these times using the 24-hour clock:
(a) 5:50 pm **(b)** 5:50 am **(c)** 11 pm **(d)** 8 am
(e) quarter past 8 in the morning
(f) quarter to 9 in the evening
(g) five to three in the afternoon
(h) twenty to seven in the morning.

4 Change these times from 24-hour clock times to am or pm:
(a) 08:00 **(b)** 09:20 **(c)** 21:30 **(d)** 13:10
(e) 12:10 **(f)** 00:20 **(g)** 01:40 **(h)** 08:00
(i) 15:45 **(j)** 18:00

5 Write these times using am or pm:
(a) 16:30 **(b)** 21:10 **(c)** 23:55 **(d)** 14:02
(e) 06:25 **(f)** 00:00 **(g)** 24:00 **(h)** 12:00
(i) 10:55 **(j)** 20:55

5.7 Reading scales

As well as being able to read a time scale (clock) you often need to be able to read other scales, for example: a measuring scale (ruler), a weight scale (cookery scales) and liquid measure scales (measuring jug).

Here are some examples of reading scales:

- The line ends between the 5 and the 6. There are 10 spaces between the 5 and the 6 so each mark shows $\frac{1}{10}$ or 0.1.
  As the line ends on the third mark it must be 0.3 or $\frac{3}{10}$.
  The line is 5.3 units long.

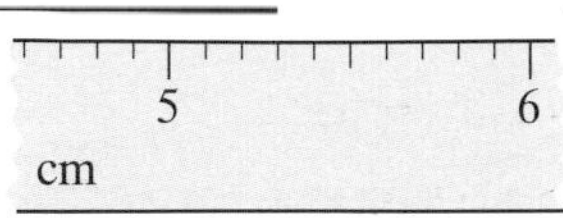

- The pointer lies between 20 and 30. There are 10 spaces between 20 and 30 so each mark shows 1 unit.
  As the pointer is on the seventh mark it must be 7.
  The reading is 27 units.

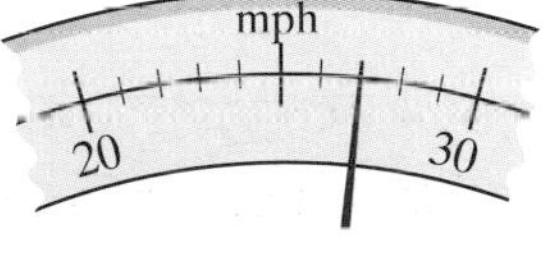

- The reading lies between 150 and 200. There are 5 spaces marked between 150 and 200 so each mark shows 10 units.
  The reading is 170 units.

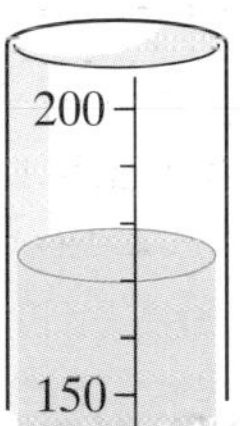

Exercise 5G

Write down the readings on these scales.

1

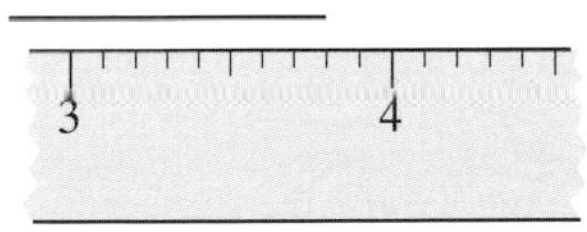

2

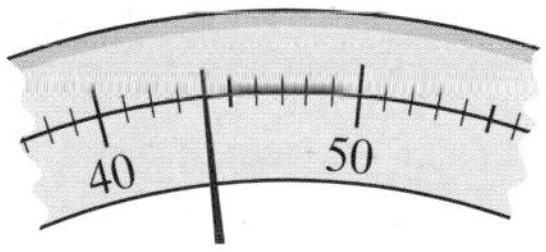

3

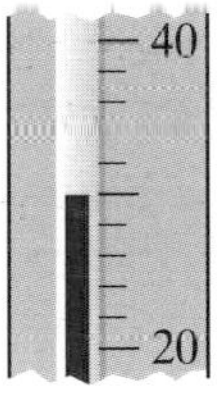

4

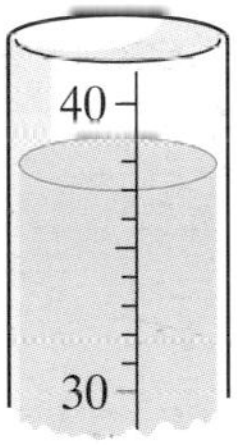

5

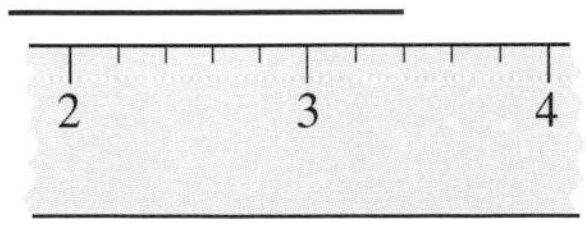

6

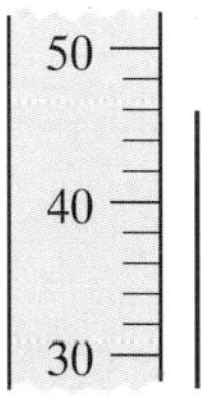

7

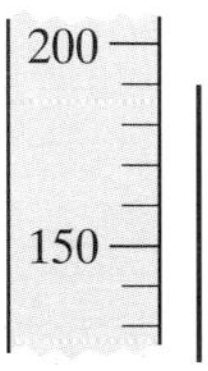

8

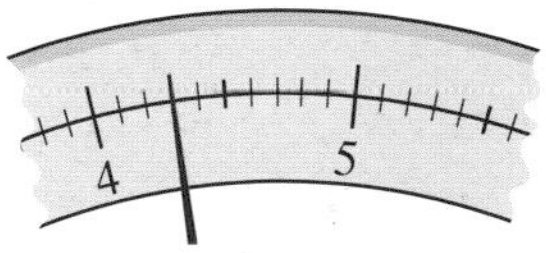

Estimating from scales

Sometimes scales have no helpful marks on them so you have to estimate the readings.

- The only point marked on this scale is halfway between 4 and 5, at 4.5. The pointer is slightly further than halfway between 4.5 and 5 so we estimate the reading to be 4.8 units.

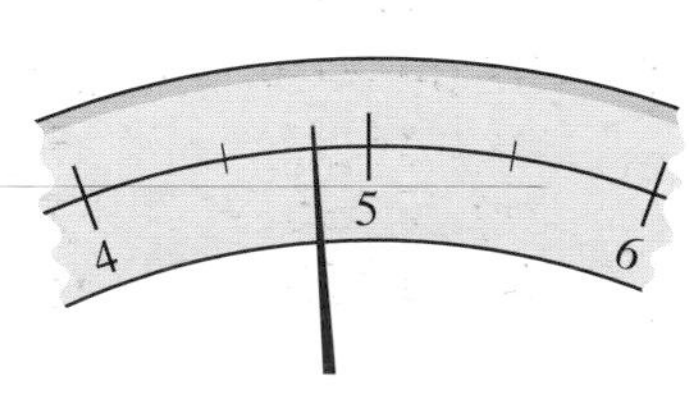

Exercise 5H

Estimate the measurements on these scales.

1 ______

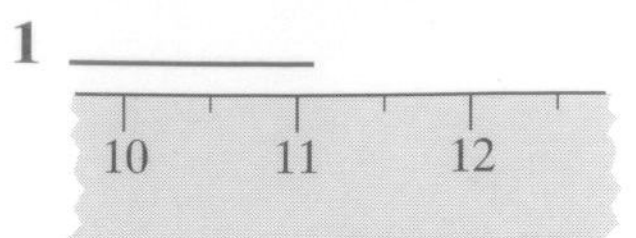

2 ______

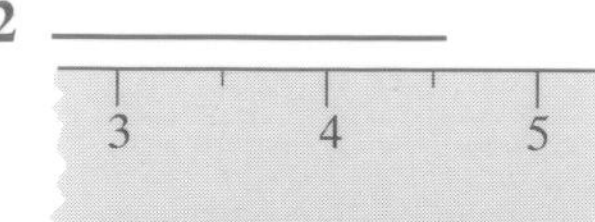

3

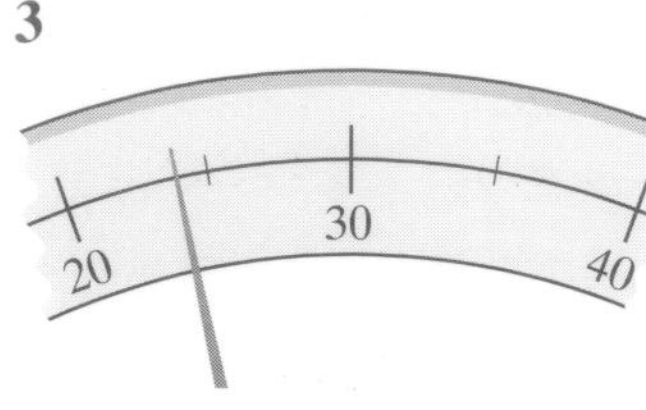

4

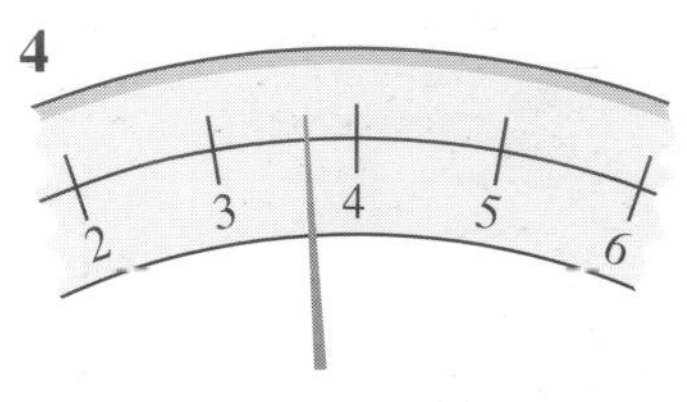

5 ______

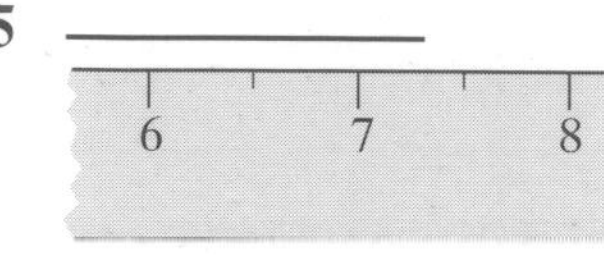

6

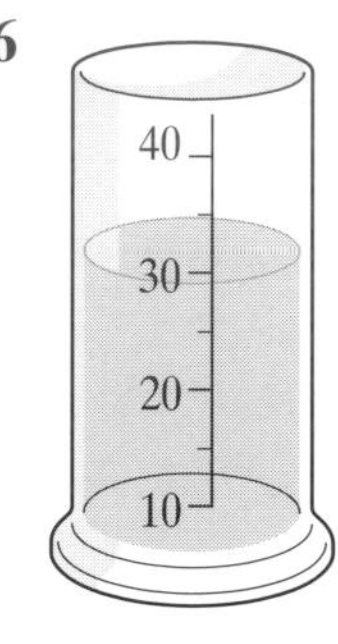

7 ______

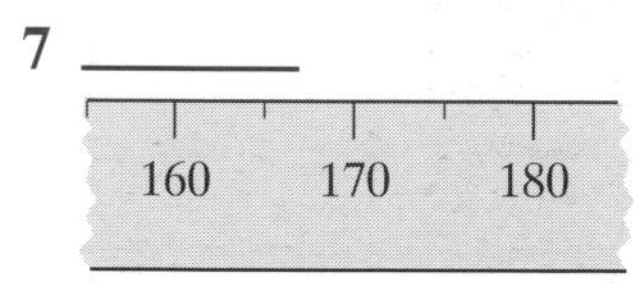

8

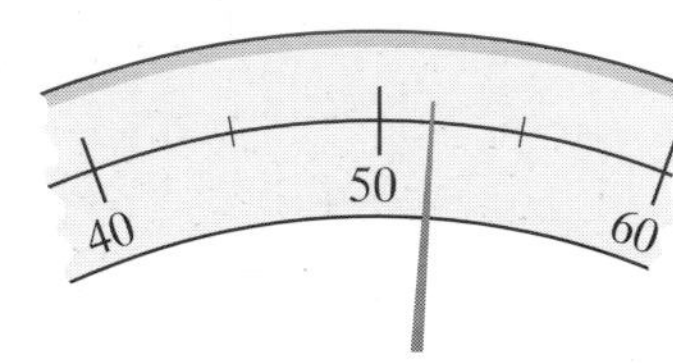

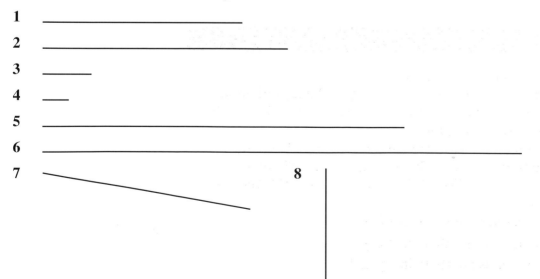

5.8 Measuring lines

When you measure the length of a line, don't forget to start measuring from 0 on the scale you are using and not from the end of the ruler.

This line measures 3.7 cm

Exercise 5I

You will need a centimetre ruler.

Measure and write down the length of these lines in centimetres:

1 ______

2 ______

3 ______

4 ______

5 ______

6

7

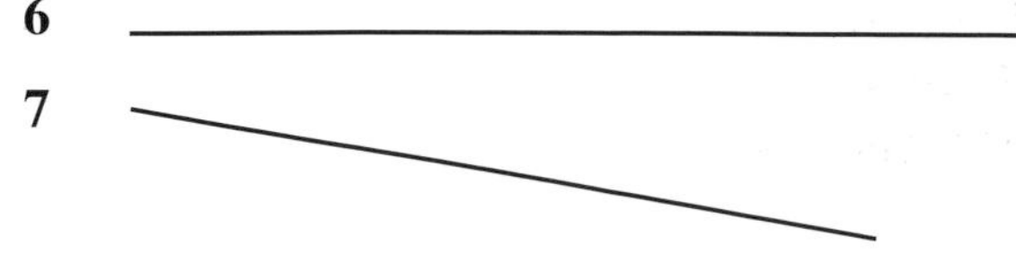

8

Exercise 5J

You will need a centimetre ruler.
Draw and label lines with lengths:

(a) 4 cm **(b)** 6 cm **(c)** 2.5 cm **(d)** 5.7 cm **(e)** 4.8 cm
(f) 50 mm **(g)** 43 mm **(h)** 8 mm **(i)** 18 mm **(j)** 39 mm

5.9 Calculating time

■ **You need to know these:**

60 seconds = 1 minute
60 minutes = 1 hour
24 hours = 1 day
365 days = 1 year
366 days = 1 leap year

Example 2

(a) Change 135 minutes to hours and minutes.
(b) How many minutes are there in 3 hours?

(a) $135 \div 60 = 2.25$ hours

Do NOT write this as 2 hours 25 minutes as this would be wrong.

To change the 0.25 hours to minutes you must multiply 0.25 by 60 because there are 60 minutes in an hour.

$0.25 \times 60 = 15$ minutes

so 135 minutes is 2 hours 15 minutes

(b) 3 hours $= 3 \times 60$ minutes $= 180$ minutes

Exercise 5K

1 Change these times into minutes:
(a) 2 hours **(b)** 5 hours **(c)** 2 hours 30 minutes
(d) $5\frac{1}{2}$ hours **(e)** $6\frac{1}{4}$ hours **(f)** 5 hours 15 minutes

2 Change these times into hours:
(a) 180 minutes **(b)** 240 minutes **(c)** 75 minutes
(d) 260 minutes **(e)** 325 minutes **(f)** 90 minutes
(g) 3 days **(h)** $5\frac{1}{2}$ days **(i)** 500 minutes
(j) 1 week

3 How many seconds are there in 1 hour?

4 How many minutes are there in 1 day?

5 How many seconds are there in a year?

When you make calculations with time values you have to be careful with the 'carry' digit.

Example 3

(a) Add $2\frac{1}{2}$ hours to the time of 10:40.
(b) Take 3 hours 15 minutes away from 11:10.

(a)
```
  10:40
   2:30 +
  13:10  <—— 40 + 30 = 70 minutes or 1 hour 10 minutes
  1  <—— The 'carry' digit represents 1 lot of 60 minutes
```

Don't forget 60 minutes make 1 hour.
So
70 minutes = 1 hour 10 minutes

(b)
```
  11:10   You have to 'borrow' 60 minutes so 70 – 15 gives 55.
   3:15 –
   7:55
```

You might find it easier to write 11:10 as 10:70 to do this calculation.

Exercise 5L

1 Add 15 minutes to each of these times:
(a) 10:30 **(b)** 09:45 **(c)** 11:40 **(d)** 09:55

2 Add 50 minutes to each of these times:
(a) 09:00 **(b)** 10:30 **(c)** 11:40 **(d)** 08:05

3 Add 2 hours 40 minutes to each of these times:
(a) 09:40 **(b)** 10:45 **(c)** 11:50 **(d)** 06:10

4 Add 12 hours 45 minutes to each of these times:
(a) 02:30 **(b)** 07:15 **(c)** 12:50 **(d)** 16:45

5 Subtract 15 minutes from each of these times:
(a) 09:55 **(b)** 11:40 **(c)** 08:10 **(d)** 09:05

6 Subtract 50 minutes from each of these times:
(a) 08:55 **(b)** 11:40 **(c)** 10:30 **(d)** 09:00

7 Subtract 2 hours 30 minutes from each of these times:
(a) 09:55 **(b)** 11:40 **(c)** 08:10 **(d)** 09:05

8 Subtract 12 hours 45 minutes from each of these times:
(a) 14:50 **(b)** 17:30 **(c)** 12:00 **(d)** 08:30

5.10 Dealing with dates

To work out dates you need to know the number of days in each month. This rhyme will help.

■ **30 days have September,**
April, June and November.
All the rest have 31
except for February alone
which has just 28 days clear
and 29 in each leap year.

Example 4

Jolene has agreed to go out with Sam in 10 days' time. Today is Tuesday 23rd April.
When is their date?

	April					May				
Monday	1	8	15	22	29		6	13	20	27
Tuesday	2	9	16	23	30		7	14	21	28
Wednesday	3	10	17	24		1	8	15	22	29
Thursday	4	11	18	25		2	9	16	23	30
Friday	5	12	19	26		3	10	17	24	31
Saturday	6	13	20	27		4	11	18	25	
Sunday	7	14	21	28		5	12	19	26	

If you start at 23 and count 10 days on you get to Friday 3rd May.
So their date is on Friday 3rd May.

Exercise 5M

1 Count on 10 days from:
(a) 1st Jan (b) 2nd March (c) 3rd June
(d) 5th July (e) 10th Sept (f) 20th May
(g) 25th June (h) 27th Aug

2 Count on 14 days from:
(a) 2nd Feb (b) 3rd March (c) 3rd April
(d) 7th Dec (e) 15th Nov (f) 18th Sept
(g) 23rd March (h) 25th Nov

3 Count on 30 days from:
(a) 5th April (b) 6th June (c) 17th May
(d) 1st Sept (e) 7th June (f) 20th May
(g) 30th Nov (h) 5th Dec

Use the calendar in Example **4** to answer questions **4** to **10**.

4 What day and date is 5 days after 5th April?

5 Which day and date is 5 days after 27th April?

6 Which day and date is 7 days before 20th May?

7 What is the day and date 10 days before 5th May?

8 Write down the day and date two weeks after 19th April.

9 How many days are there between 5th April and 8th May?

10 How many days are there between 23rd April and 5th May?

11 Calculate the number of days between 1st July and 5th August.

12 Find the number of days between 25th February 1996 and 5th March 1996.

5.11 Timetables

Bus and train timetables are often used in GCSE examinations to test your knowledge of time and your skill in reading tables.

The time when a train starts its journey is shown at the top of the timetable. Its stopping times at stations on the journey are shown underneath. The time it leaves a station can be read off opposite the place name.

Example 5

Find how long it takes for the 8:15 am train from Swindon to get to London (Paddington).

You first have to find the 08:15 train from Swindon. It's in the third column along.
Follow that column down to the bottom to find the arrival time in London 09:10.

Bristol	07:10	07:25	07:40	07:55
Bath	07:30	07:45	08:00	08:10
Swindon	07:45	08:00	08:15	08:25
Didcot	08:05	08:20	08:35	08:45
Reading	08:15	08:30	08:45	08:55
London (Paddington)	08:40	08:55	09:10	09:20

07:10 train from Bristol arrives in London at 08:40

08:15 train from Swindon

arrives in London at 09:10

In Example **3** part (b) we used a subtraction sum to take 3 hours 15 minutes from 11:10. It involved 'borrowing' 60 minutes from the hour column.
Here is another way of dealing with the problem that you may find easier.

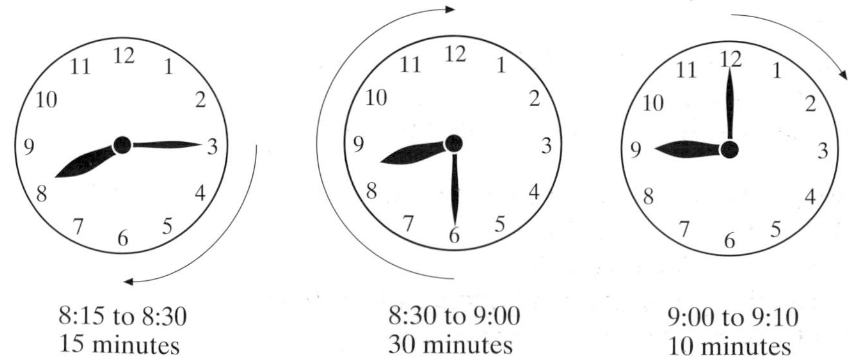

8:15 to 8:30
15 minutes

8:30 to 9:00
30 minutes

9:00 to 9:10
10 minutes

Total time 15 + 30 + 10 = 55 minutes

It takes the 08:15 train from Swindon 55 minutes to get to London.

Exercise 5N

Use these timetables to answer the questions.

Swindon bus timetable

Coate	07:05	07:35	08:05
Piper's Way	07:10	07:40	08:10
Old Town	07:20	07:50	08:20
Drove Road	07:25	07:55	08:25
New Town	07:30	08:00	08:30
Bus Station	07:35	08:05	08:35

Train timetable

Bristol	07:10	07:25	07:40	07:55
Bath	07:30	07:45	08:00	08:15
Swindon	07:45	08:00	08:15	08:30
Didcot	08:05	08:20	08:35	08:50
Reading	08:15	08:30	08:45	09:00
London (Paddington)	08:40	08:55	09:10	09:25

1 At what time does:
- **(a)** the 7:35 bus from Coate arrive at Drove Road
- **(b)** the 07:40 train from Bristol arrive at Didcot
- **(c)** the 08:30 train from Reading start from Bristol
- **(d)** the 08:00 bus from New Town start at Piper's Way?

2 Buses from Coate depart every half hour. Continue the bus timetable for the next three buses. Assume that each bus takes the same amount of time between stops as shown in the timetable.

3 Trains from Bristol depart every quarter of an hour. Continue the train timetable for the next three trains. Assume that each train takes the same amount of time between stops as shown in the timetable.

4 Rashmi arrives at the train station in Bath at 07:35. What time is the next train he could catch to London?

5 Claude arrives at the train station in Didcot at 08:25. What time is the next train he could catch to London?

6 Cecile arrives at the train station in Swindon at 09:10. What time is the next train she could catch to Reading?

7 Sophia arrives at the train station in Bristol at 08:00. What time is the next train she could catch to Bath?

8 How long should it take to travel:
- **(a)** by bus from Coate to the Bus Station
- **(b)** by bus from Piper's Way to New Town
- **(c)** by train from Bristol to London Paddington
- **(d)** by train from Swindon to Reading
- **(e)** by train from Bath to Didcot?

9 The bus timetable is for a bus route in Swindon. It takes five minutes to walk from the bus station to the train platform.
Use both timetables to work out which bus and train these people should catch:
- **(a)** Gareth, from Piper's Way to be in London Paddington at 09:00
- **(b)** Susan, from Coate to be in Reading at 08:30
- **(c)** Mario, from Old Town to be in Didcot at 09:00
- **(d)** Claudette, from Drove Road to be in London Paddington by 10:00
- **(e)** Bridget, from Old Town to be in Reading at 09:35
- **(f)** Which bus did Katrina catch from Drove Road if she arrived in Reading at 08:45?

Summary of key points

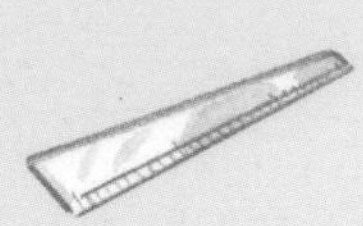

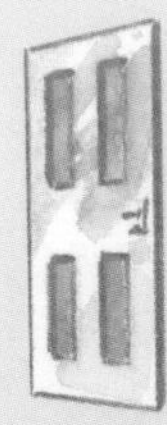

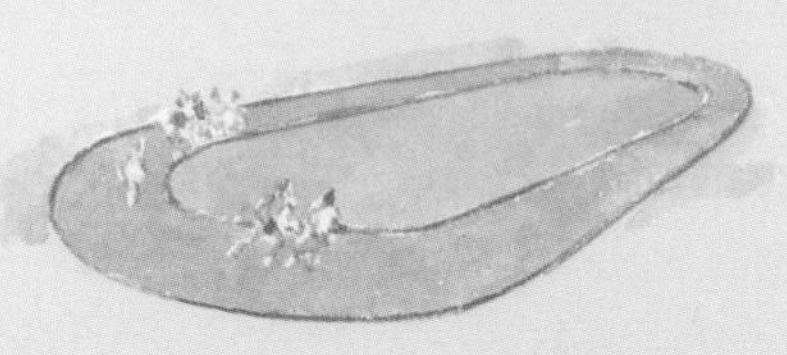

1 A 30 cm ruler is about 1 foot

A door is 2 m high or about $6\frac{1}{2}$ feet

A long stride is 1 m long or about 3 feet

$2\frac{1}{2}$ times around the track is 1 km or about $\frac{5}{8}$ mile

2 A milk carton holds 1 pint or about $\frac{1}{2}$ litre (500 m*l*)

A petrol can holds 1 gallon or 4.5 litres

A mug and a can of cola each hold about $\frac{1}{2}$ pint or about 300 m*l*

A medicine spoon and a teaspoon each hold about 5 m*l*

3 A $\frac{1}{4}$ pound packet of tea weighs about 100 g

A 1 kg bag of sugar weighs about 2.2 pounds

A 50 kg bag of cement weighs about 110 pounds

4 This table shows some times of day under both systems

Using am and pm	Using the 24-hour clock
12:00 midnight	00:00 or 24:00
9 am	09 :00
12:00 noon	12:00
3:30 pm	15:30
12:00 midnight	24:00 or 00:00

5 60 seconds = 1 minute
60 minutes = 1 hour
24 hours = 1 day
365 days = 1 year
366 days = 1 leap year

6 30 days have September,
April, June and November.
All the rest have 31
except for February alone
which has just 28 days clear
and 29 in each leap year.

6 Approximation

If you write down numbers exactly with all their digits it can be confusing.

An approximate answer is often as useful as an exact one.

The population of Colchester is 148 724 … plus 2!

Better to say 148 700 or 149 000.

6.1 Rounding a number

The attendance at a pop concert was 12 134, the exact number of tickets sold.

12 134 can be rounded to the nearest ten, hundred, thousand, and so on . . .

to the nearest ten:	to the nearest hundred:	to the nearest thousand:
12 130	12 100	12 000

Useful number for catering department (12 100)

Number used by newspaper reporter (12 000)

The newspaper headline gives an idea of how many people were there. The extra 134 in the audience is very small compared to 12 000.

Page 4 The Daily News
12 000 attend concert

■ **Large numbers are often rounded to the nearest ten, hundred, thousand . . .**

Example 1

Round the amount £46 476 to the nearest:

(a) £10 (b) £100 (c) £1000.

(a) £46 476 is between £46 470 and £46 480.
Since £76 is nearer to £80 than £70, £46 476 to the nearest £10 is £46 480.

(b) £46 476 is between £46 400 and £46 500.
Since £476 is nearer £500 than £400, £46 476 to the nearest £100 is £46 500.

(c) £46 476 is between £46 000 and £47 000.
Since £6476 is nearer £6000 than £7000, £46 476 to the nearest £1000 is £46 000.

■ **In rounding, halves or 5s are usually rounded upwards.**

7.5 = 8 (to the nearest whole number).

Example 2

Round the measurement 555 mm:

(a) to the nearest 10 mm
(b) to the nearest 100 mm.

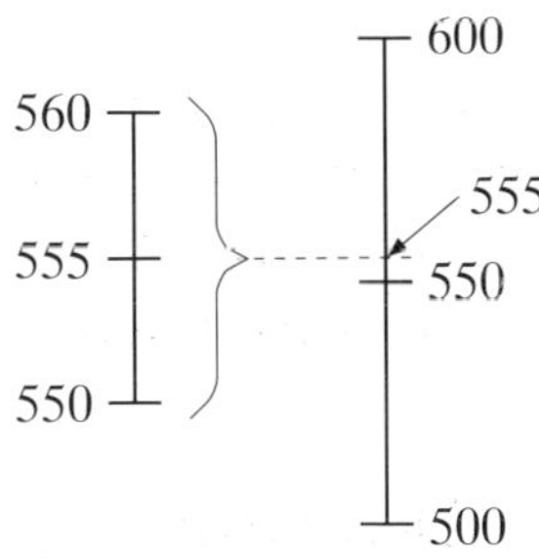

(a) 555 mm is exactly halfway between 550 mm and 560 mm. When rounding to the nearest 10 mm, 555 mm rounds upwards to become 560 mm.

(b) 555 mm is between 500 mm and 600 mm, but nearer to 600 mm. When rounding to the nearest 100 mm, 555 mm becomes 600 mm.

Exercise 6A

1 Round these:
(i) to the nearest 10 (ii) to the nearest 100
(iii) to the nearest 1000.

(a) 3412	**(b)** 6940	**(c)** 5374	**(d)** 6100
(e) 11 362 m	**(f)** £31 297	**(g)** 86 305 km	**(h)** 63 942 t
(i) £48 189	**(j)** £33 733	**(k)** 1300.9 m	**(l)** 1175.6 m*l*

2 The attendance at an athletics meeting was 12 937.
Write this figure to the nearest 100.

3 During the summer season the number of visitors to a heritage centre was 18 894.
Write this figure to the nearest 1000.

4 The estimated cost of a school extension is £24 980.
Write this estimate to the nearest £1000.

6.2 Rounding remainders

There are times when you work out problems and a remainder is left. Sometimes the remainder will need rounding up or rounding down to give an answer that is appropriate.

I've worked out that I need 1½ tins of paint for my bedroom

You can't buy half a tin of paint!

Example 3

There are 220 pupils in a year group. They are planning to go on a school trip.

The coaches that they are using have a maximum capacity of 50 people.

How many coaches are needed?

220 ÷ 50 = 4 coaches, remainder 20 pupils

But the 20 pupils cannot be left behind!
Although 20 is nearer to 0 than to 50, in this case the number of coaches needs to be rounded up.

The number of coaches needed is 5.

Example 4

One hundred eggs are to be packed into boxes. Each box contains 6 eggs.
How many boxes can be filled?

$100 \div 6 = 16$, remainder 4

The 4 eggs remaining cannot be sold in a box which should contain 6 eggs. Although 4 is closer to 6 than 0, in this case the number of boxes needs to be rounded down.

The number of complete boxes that can be filled is 16.

■ **You can round answers with remainders upwards or downwards. You need to decide which is appropriate.**

Exercise 6B

1 An empty tank has a capacity of 55 litres.
Work out how many 8 litre containers of water can be emptied into the tank before the tank overflows.

2 The greatest number of people allowed in a lift at one time is 10.
Work out the least number of trips the lift must make to carry 52 people.

3 Mahmood has 225 pens. He packs them in boxes of ten.
How many boxes can he fill?

4 Winnie needs 76 tiles for her kitchen wall. The tiles come in boxes of 5.
How many boxes will she need?

5 A transporter can carry 7 cars on one trip.
Work out the least number of trips needed to deliver 90 cars.

6 Paint is sold in 5 litre tins. Josie needs 21 litres of paint.
How many tins must she buy?

7 Barry has £9.90. He needs 50 p coins for his electricity meter.
How many 50 p coins will he get for £9.90?

8 A&B Cabs hire out taxis that take 5 passengers. A day trip out is planned for 51 disabled children from a school with 10 helpers.
How many taxis will be needed?

9 Bread rolls are sold in bags of eight. Paul needs 35 bread rolls for a party.
How many bags must he buy?

10 Peat for the garden is sold in 4 kg bags. Bill needs 23 kg of peat.
How many bags must he buy?

6.3 Rounding to a number of decimal places

There are times when you work something out on your calculator and the number fills the whole display. The answer is far more accurate than you need. Instead of using all the digits you can round the number to a given number of decimal places.

Reminder: $14.576 = 14 + \frac{5}{10} + \frac{7}{100} + \frac{6}{1000}$

Each of the digits 5, 7 and 6 in the number 14.576 represents a quantity which is less than 1. They are decimal values.

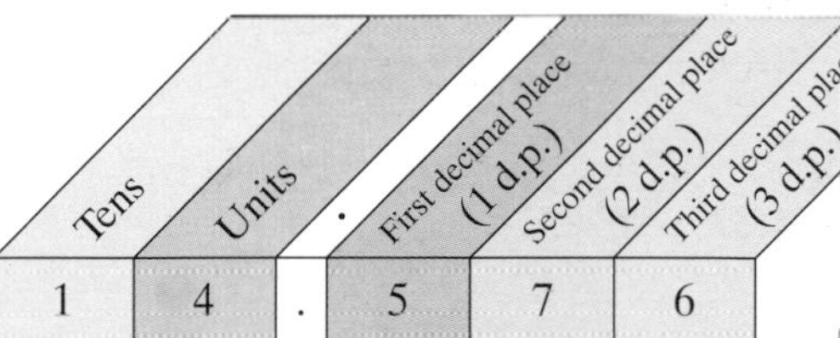

14.57¦6 = 14.58 (correct to 2 d.p.).

- **You can round (or correct) numbers to a given number of decimal places (d.p.).**
  The first decimal place is the first number (zero or non-zero) after the decimal point.

Oh dear! You have truncated 5.28 to 5.2 instead of rounding it to 5.3

Count the number of places from the decimal point. Look at the next digit after the one you want. If it is 5 or more you need to round upwards.

Example 5

Round these (i) to 3 d.p. (ii) to 2 d.p.:
(a) 4.4315 (b) 7.3962

Decimal places and d.p.
You can write it like this: 4.4315 = 4.432 (correct to 3 decimal places) or 4.4315 = 4.432 (to 3 d.p.).

(a) (i) In the number 4.4315 the next digit after the 3rd d.p. is 5. So round up and the 1 becomes 2.
4.4315 rounded to 3 d.p. is 4.432.
(ii) In the number 4.4315 the next digit after the 2nd d.p. is 1, so you round down and the 3 remains the same.
4.4315 to 2 d.p. is 4.43.

(b) (i) 7.3962 to 3 d.p. is 7.396
(ii) 7.3962 to 2 d.p. is 7.40
The 6 makes the 9 round up to 10 and this changes the 3 to a 4.

Note: the final zero is important in the 7.40 because 2 d.p. means that two decimal digits need to be shown. In this case the 4 and the 0 must be written down.

Exercise 6C

In questions **1** to **4** round each number (i) to 3 d.p. (ii) to 2 d.p.:

1 **(a)** 4.2264 **(b)** 9.7868 **(c)** 0.4157 **(d)** 0.058 38

2 **(a)** 10.5167 **(b)** 7.5034 **(c)** 21.7295 **(d)** 9.088 95

3 **(a)** 15.5978 **(b)** 0.4081 **(c)** 7.2466 **(d)** 6.050 77

4 **(a)** 29.1582 **(b)** 0.054 86 **(c)** 13.3785 **(d)** 5.9976

5 Round to the number of decimal places given in brackets:
(a) 5.6166 (3 d.p.) **(b)** 0.0112 (1 d.p.)
(c) 0.923 98 (4 d.p.) **(d)** 0.8639 (2 d.p.) **(e)** 9.6619 (1 d.p.)

6.4 Rounding to a number of significant figures

You will often be asked to round answers to '2 significant figures' or '3 significant figures'. 'Significant' means 'important'.

When you are estimating the number of people at a hockey match you don't need to say that there were exactly 8742 people there. You can give your answer to two significant figures:

First significant figure	Second significant figure	Third significant figure	Fourth significant figure
8	7	4	2

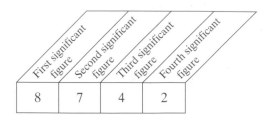

There were about 8700 people (to 2 s.f.).

This is called 'correcting to two significant figures'.

■ **You can round (or correct) numbers to a given number of significant figures (s.f.).**
The first significant figure is the first non-zero digit in the number, counting from the left.

Rounding to a significant figure which is on the right of the decimal point is like the process you used in rounding to decimal places. You look at the next digit after that significant figure.

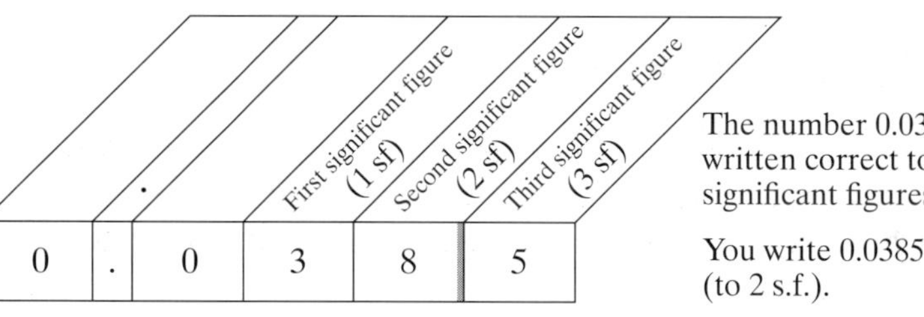

The number 0.0385 written correct to 2 significant figures is 0.039.

You write 0.0385 = 0.039 (to 2 s.f.).

Example 6

Round 642.803: (a) to 1 s.f. (b) to 2 s.f. (c) to 3 s.f. (d) to 4 s.f. (e) to 5 s.f.

	1 s.f.	2 s.f.	3 s.f.	.	4 s.f.	5 s.f.	6 s.f.									
(a)	6	4	2	.	8	0	3	=	6	0	0					(to 1sf)
(b)	6	4	2	.	8	0	3	=	6	4	0					(to 2sf)
(c)	6	4	2	.	8	0	3	=	6	4	3					(to 3sf)
(d)	6	4	2	.	8	0	3	=	6	4	2	.	8			(to 4sf)
(e)	6	4	2	.	8	0	3	=	6	4	2	.	8	0		(to 5sf)

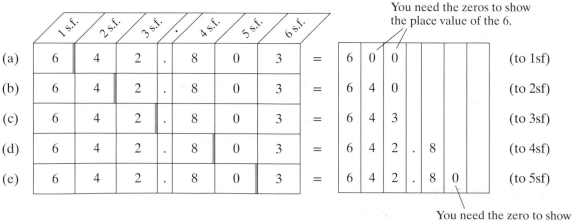

You need the zeros to show the place value of the 6.

You need the zero to show **5** significant figures.

Exercise 6D

In questions **1** to **5** round these numbers (i) to 1 s.f. (ii) to 3 s.f.:

1 **(a)** 0.061 75 **(b)** 0.1649 **(c)** 96.303 **(d)** 41.475

2 **(a)** 734.56 **(b)** 0.079 47 **(c)** 5.6853 **(d)** 586.47

3 **(a)** 0.014 48 **(b)** 2222.8 **(c)** 76.249 **(d)** 0.3798

4 **(a)** 8.3846 **(b)** 35.959 **(c)** 187.418 **(d)** 0.066 63

5 **(a)** 94.746 **(b)** 851.126 **(c)** 6.2534 **(d)** 0.062 62

6 Write these to the number of significant figures given in the brackets:
(a) 0.098 12 (2 s.f.) **(b)** 54.875 (4 s.f.) **(c)** 7.6542 (1 s.f.)
(d) 3125.4 (2 s.f.) **(e)** 5942.7 (1 s.f.) **(f)** 52.973 (3 s.f.)

6.5 Checking and estimating

Get into the habit of checking the answers to your calculations. Sometimes a wrong answer is obvious: 4.2 metres for the average height of a man in a survey or 0.02 km for the distance travelled by a car on a motorway in a day are clearly incorrect.

Once you notice that an answer is obviously wrong you can repeat the calculation to try and find the correct answer.

Working backwards

Another method of checking answers is to work backwards from the answer reversing each step in the calculation.
To do this you need to use the **inverse** of each operation:

operation:	+	–	×	÷
inverse operation:	–	+	÷	×

Example 7

Write down a suitable calculation you could use to check the answer:

(a) $2115 \div 5 = 423$

(b) $2346 - 89 = 2267$

(a) To check $2115 \div 5 = 423$ use 423×5. This gives 2115 so the answer is correct.

(b) To check $2346 - 89 = 2267$ use $2267 + 89$. This gives 2356 so the answer is not correct. You need to do the calculation 2346 – 89 again.

Making an estimate

Another way of checking a calculation is to make an estimate. Round all the numbers to one significant figure. Then do the calculation with the rounded numbers.

Example 8

Estimate the answer to:

(a) 5.12×2.79 (b) $19.67 \div 2.8$ (c) $\dfrac{2.75 \times 8.33}{5.23 + 2.74}$

(a) Round all numbers to 1 significant figure:
5.12×2.79 becomes $5 \times 3 = 15$ as an estimate. (Actual answer: 14.2848)

(b) Round all numbers to 1 significant figure:
$20 \div 3 = 6\frac{2}{3} = 7$ (to 1 significant figure). (Actual answer: 7.025)

(c) Round all numbers to 1 significant figure:
$\dfrac{3 \times 8}{5 + 3} = \dfrac{24}{8} = 3$ as an estimate. (Actual answer: $22.9075 \div 7.97 = 2.874$)

Worked exam question

$$\frac{10.25 + 29.75}{0.2 \times 45}$$

Show how you would estimate the answer to this expression without using a calculator. Write down your estimate. [L]

Round all numbers to 1 s.f.: $\dfrac{10 + 30}{0.2 \times 50} = \dfrac{40}{10} = 4$ *as an estimate*

■ **To estimate answers round all numbers to 1 significant figure and do the simpler calculation.**

Exercise 6E

1 (i) Write down and use a suitable calculation to check each answer shown. Hint: use inverse operations.
(ii) If the answer shown is incorrect, work out the correct answer to the original problem.

(a) $1638 \div 7 = 234$ **(b)** $269 \times 8 = 2152$
(c) $687 + 362 = 1049$ **(d)** $1053 - 97 = 966$
(e) $9.9095 - 8.462 = 0.533$ **(f)** $1.236 \div 1.2 = 1.003$

In each of questions **2** to **13**:
(a) write down a calculation that could be used to estimate the answer
(b) work out an estimated answer
(c) use a calculator to work out the exact answer.

2 7.86×8.27 **3** $13.89 \div 6.73$ **4** 8.37×24.5

5 $36.8 \times (5.73 + 6.42)$ **6** $\dfrac{6.95 \times 92.8}{0.175}$ **7** 48.13×3.33

8 $\dfrac{192.4 \times 85.3}{53.8}$ **9** $2.28 \times (2.96 - 0.49)$ **10** $(1095 \times 403) + 287$

11 $\dfrac{33.5 + 42.4}{0.0237}$ **12** $\dfrac{0.743 \times 0.0286}{0.0326}$ **13** $\dfrac{0.897 \times 8.114}{4.401 \times 0.310}$

6.6 Recognizing inaccuracy of measurements

Suppose you use a ruler marked in millimetres to measure a line as 85mm, correct to the nearest mm.

The true length could be anywhere between 84.5 mm and 85.5 mm.

So the true length could be anywhere in a range 0.5 mm below and 0.5 mm above the recorded value:

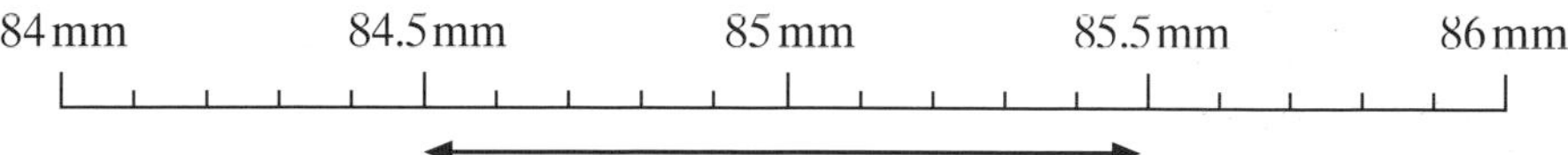

Any measurement given correct to the nearest mm can be up to 0.5 mm less than or 0.5 mm more than the given measurement.

■ **Measurements expressed to a given unit have a possible error of half the unit.**

Example 10

A time is given as 3.27 seconds correct to the nearest hundredth of a second. Write down:

(a) the minimum time it could be

(b) the maximum time it could be.

3.27 is written to the **nearest hundredth of a second** so the 'unit' used is 0.01 s. Half a 'unit' is 0.005 s.

(a) minimum time = 3.265 s ← 3.27 – 0.005

(b) maximum time = 3.275 s ← 3.27 + 0.005

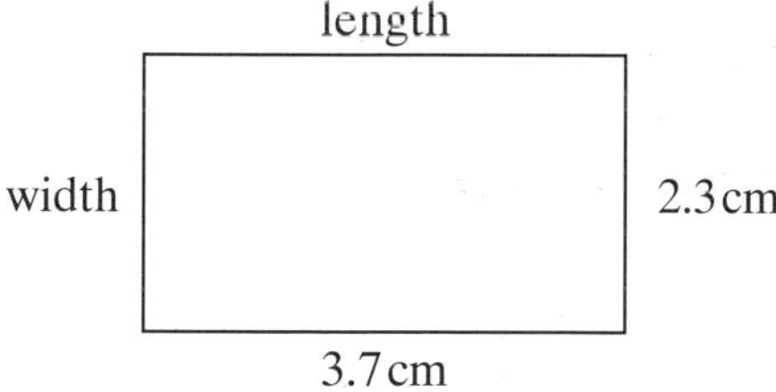

Worked exam question

The dimensions of the rectangle are given correct to one decimal place.

Write down the smallest possible length of the rectangle. [L]

Length = 3.7 cm

Smallest length (minimum) = 3.65 cm ← −0.05

The 'unit' is 0.1 so half a 'unit' is 0.05.

Exercise 6F

For each measurement in questions **1** to **4** write down:

(i) the minimum it could be
(ii) the maximum it could be.

1 These measurements are given correct to the nearest whole number:
(a) 34 cm **(b)** 65 g **(c)** 154 m **(d)** 20 *l*

2 These measurements are given correct to one decimal place:
(a) 64.7 cm **(b)** 17.6 m*l* **(c)** 49.1 g **(d)** 44.0 *l*

3 These measurements are given correct to two decimal places:
(a) 9.02 km **(b)** 6.11 s **(c)** 7.23 kg **(d)** 0.43 s

4 These measurements are given correct to three decimal places:
(a) 0.324 km **(b)** 0.139 s **(c)** 0.455 kg **(d)** 0.895 km

Exercise 6G Mixed questions

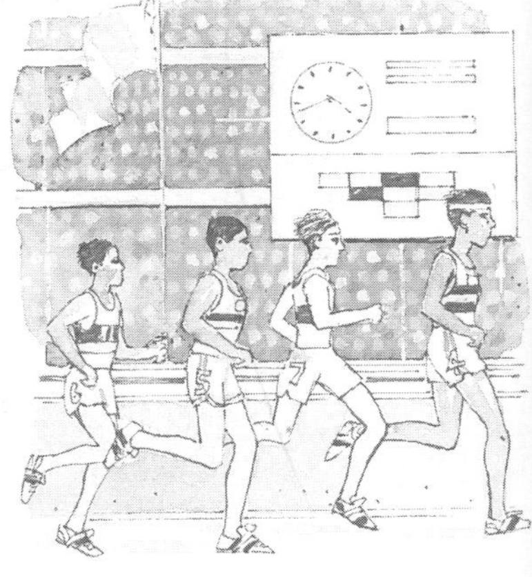

1 The attendance at an athletics meeting was 9482.
What is 9482 rounded to the nearest 100?

2 The number of people at a football match was 11 937.
Write 11 937 rounded to the nearest 1000.

3 700 pigeons are to be transported in carriers which hold a maximum of 30 pigeons each.
How many carriers are needed?

4 Twelve counters are needed to make a board game. Amina has 200 counters.
Work out the number of board games she can make.

5 Round these to the number of decimal places given in brackets:
(a) 10.4912 (1 d.p.) **(b)** 0.0555 (3 d.p.)
(c) 6.599 (2 d.p.) **(d)** 3.5943 (3 d.p.)

6 Round these to the number of significant figures given in brackets:
(a) 532.59 (3 s.f.) **(b)** 124.72 (4 s.f.)
(c) 469.52 (2 s.f.) **(d)** 893.13 (1 s.f.)

7 Write down a suitable calculation to check the answers shown:
(a) $3.256 \times 1.5 = 4.884$ **(b)** $56.25 \div 1.25 = 45$
(c) $56.21 + 19.78 = 75.99$ **(d)** $109.46 - 83.27 = 26.19$

8 **(a)** Write down the numbers you could use to get an approximate answer to 59×32.
(b) Write down your approximate answer.
(c) Using a calculator find the difference between your approximate answer and the exact answer. [L]

9 Trudie uses the expression $a = \dfrac{118.07 - 17.76}{4.8}$

Trudie estimates the value of a without using her calculator.

(a) Write down the numbers Trudie could use to estimate the value of a.

(b) Write down the estimate these numbers would give for the value of a. [L]

10 The distance of a buoy from a coastguard station is 14 km to the nearest km.

(a) Write down the maximum distance it could be.

(b) Write down the minimum distance it could be. [L]

11 You want to estimate the value of 21.2×31.2.
Each number must be written to 1 significant figure.

(a) Write down a suitable calculation which could be used.

(b) State the value of this estimate. [L]

12 A distance of 5.2 km has been rounded to 1 decimal place.
Write down the minimum distance it could be. [L]

Summary of key points

1 Large numbers are often rounded to the nearest ten, hundred, thousand . . .

- 13 542 is 13 540 (to the nearest 10)
- 13 542 is 13 500 (to the nearest 100)
- 13 542 is 14 000 (to the nearest 1000).

2 In rounding, halves or 5s are usually rounded upwards.

7.5 = 8 (to the nearest whole number).

3 You can round answers with remainders upwards or downwards. You need to decide which is appropriate.

4 You can round (or correct) numbers to a given number of decimal places (d.p.).
The first decimal place is the first number (zero or non-zero) after the decimal point.

9.1¦57 = 9.2 (rounded to 1 d.p.).

5 You can round (or correct) numbers to a given number of significant figures (s.f.).
The first significant figure is the first non-zero digit in the number, counting from the left.

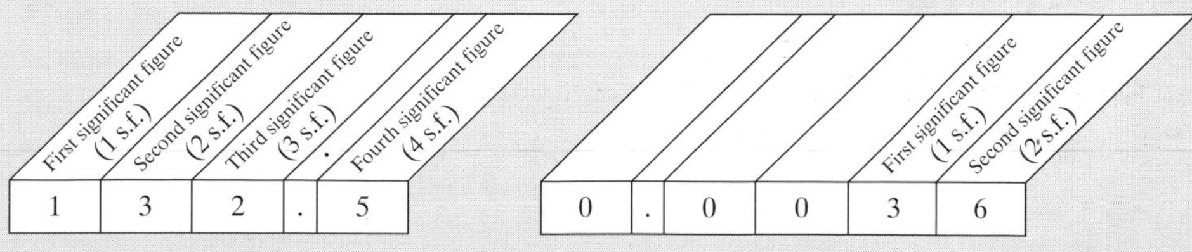

6 You should check answers to make sure they are reasonable. The answer should make sense in the context of the question.

7 You can use inverse operations to check calculations.

$241 \times 25 = 6025$?

Check by working out $6025 \div 25$ ($\div$ is the inverse of $\times$)
Does this give 241?

8 To estimate answers round all numbers to 1 significant figure and do the simpler calculation.

$1.56 \times 0.428 \approx 2 \times 0.4 = 0.8$

9 Measurements expressed to a given unit have a possible error of half the unit.

For example, a length is measured as 2.5 km (correct to 1 d.p.). The minimum the length could be is 2.45 km. The maximum the length could be is 2.55 km.

7 Graphs of linear functions

7.1 Graphs of linear functions with positive whole number inputs

Before starting this unit make sure you understand the ideas in Unit 2 Simple functions.

Here is a simple function: $n \rightarrow 2n + 1$

Another way to look at a function is to let x stand for the input and y stand for the output, so: $x \rightarrow y$

But using $n \rightarrow 2n + 1$ we know that: $x \rightarrow 2x + 1$

So y and $2x + 1$ must be worth the same and we can write: $y = 2x + 1$

■ **$y = 2x + 1$ is called an equation. The value of y is always equal to the value of $2x + 1$.**

We now have two ways of showing the same rule or function:

$n \rightarrow 2n + 1$ or $y = 2x + 1$

$0 \rightarrow 1$

$1 \rightarrow 3$

$2 \rightarrow 5$

$3 \rightarrow 7$

$4 \rightarrow 9$

$5 \rightarrow 11$

x	0	1	2	3	4	5
y	1	3	5	7	9	11

This is called a **table of values.**

We can show the numbers in the table of values as a graph.

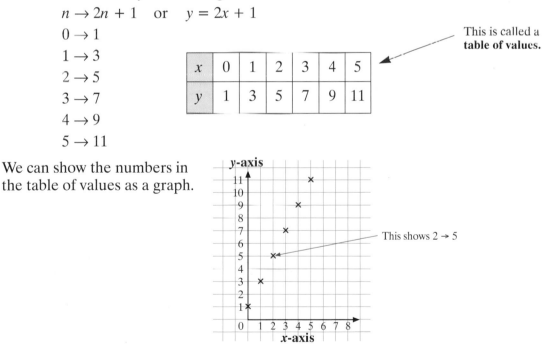

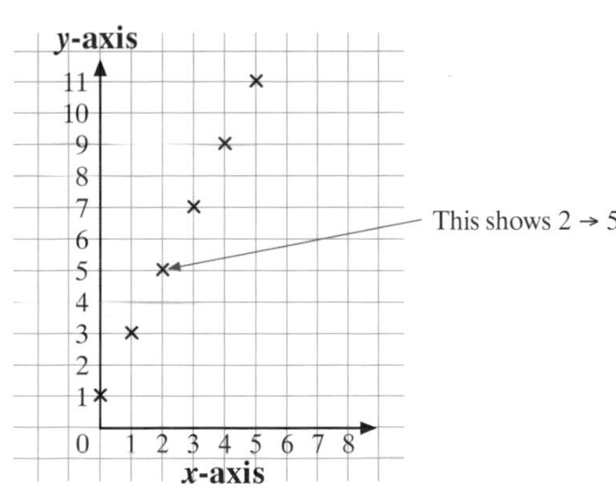

To help you plot the points the values of x are written along a line called the x-axis and the values of y along the y-axis.

The word **axis** means line. The plural of axis is **axes**.

Exercise 7A

You will need 5 mm squared paper.

1 (a) Write the function $n \rightarrow n + 2$ as an equation using x and y.
(b) Make a table of values for your equation using the values 0, 1, 2, 3, 4, 5 for x.
(c) Draw a graph to show the numbers from your table of values.

2 Do the same as in question **1** for each of these functions:
(a) $n \rightarrow n + 4$ (b) $n \rightarrow 2n + 3$
(c) $n \rightarrow 3n + 2$ (d) $n \rightarrow 2n$

3 (a) Complete the table of values for this sequence of matchstick patterns.

Number of squares x	1	2	3	4	5
Number of matchsticks y	4	7			

(b) Draw the graph for this table of values.
(c) Write down the equation of the graph.

4 (a) Complete the table of values for this sequence of matchstick patterns.

Number of triangles x	1	2	3	4	5
Number of matchsticks y	3				

(b) Draw the graph for the table of values.
(c) Write down the equation of the graph.

5 (a) Invent and draw a sequence of matchstick patterns for each of these graphs.
Hint: draw up a table of values for each graph.

(i)

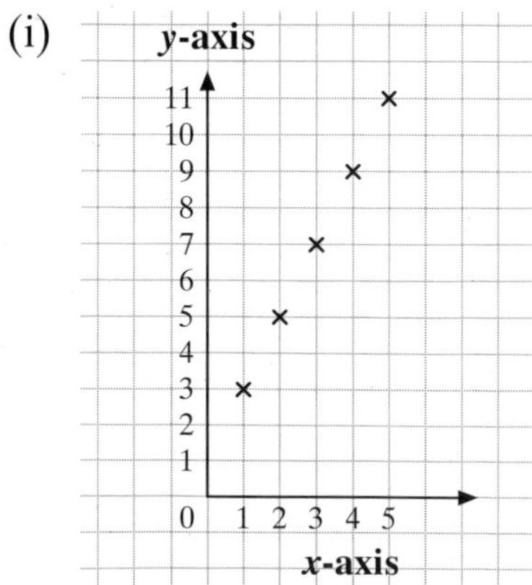

(ii)

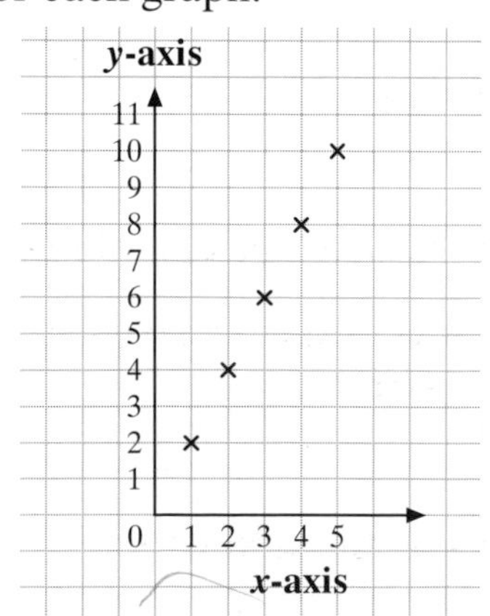

(b) Write the equation for each graph in part **(a)**.

6 **(a)** Invent and draw a sequence of matchstick patterns for each of these tables of values.

(i)

x	1	2	3	4	5
y	4	8	12	16	20

(ii)

x	1	2	3	4	5
y	6	11	16	21	26

(b) Draw the graph for each table in part **(a)**.

7.2 Graphs of linear functions with continuous positive inputs

In questions **3**, **4** and **5** of Exercise **7A** x could take only whole number values. We could not join the points in those graphs because there are no values of x and y between those points.

If x can take any values, either whole numbers or decimals, we say x is **continuous**.

■ **The input values of x are continuous if x can take any value (whole numbers or decimals).**

Look at the graph for $y = 2x + 1$ on page 81.

The points lie on a straight line.

We can draw the straight line in this graph because x is continuous.

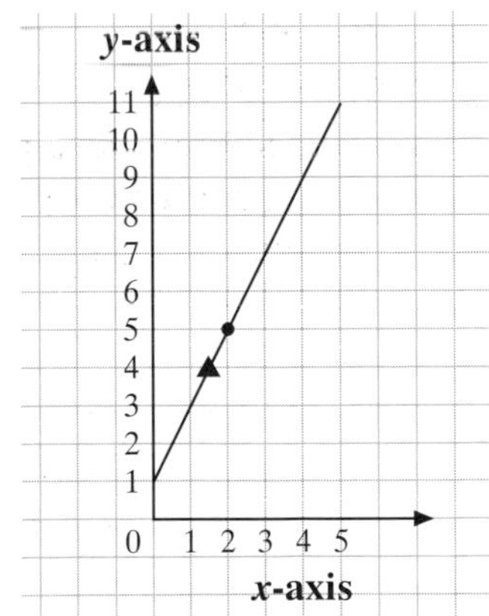

The x and y values for the point marked • are 2 and 5.
So the point • has coordinates (2, 5).

If you put $x = 2$ into the equation $y = 2x + 1$
you get $y = 2 \times 2 + 1 = 5$
So when $x = 2, y = 5$.

We say the coordinates (2, 5) 'satisfy' the equation $y = 2x + 1$.

Look at the point ▲ which has coordinates $(1\frac{1}{2}, 4)$.
Put $x = 1\frac{1}{2}$ in the equation $y = 2x + 1$.
You get $y = 2 \times 1\frac{1}{2} + 1 = 4$
So when $x = 1\frac{1}{2}, y = 4$.

Do the same for other points on the straight line.

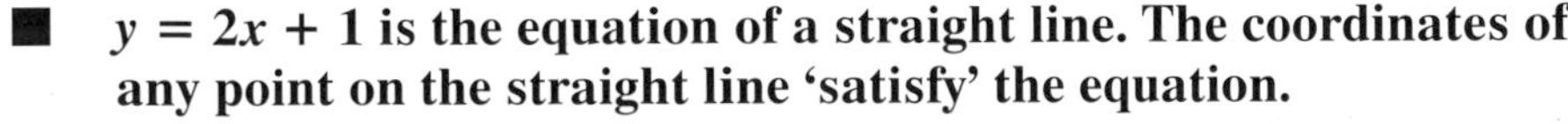

■ **$y = 2x + 1$ is the equation of a straight line. The coordinates of any point on the straight line 'satisfy' the equation.**

■ **$x \rightarrow 2x + 1$ is called a linear function because its graph is a straight line.**

Example 1

Water flows steadily from a pipe into a storage tank. Every minute the depth of the water in the tank increases by 2 cm. When the water starts to flow the depth of water in the tank is already 3 cm.

(a) Draw a graph to show the relationship between the depth, y cm, of the water in the tank and the time, x minutes, after the water starts to flow.

(b) Use the graph to find the depth of water $3\frac{1}{2}$ minutes after the water starts to flow.

(a) Draw up a table of values for whole number values of x.

Time in minutes x	0	1	2	3	4
Depth in cm y	3	5	7	9	11

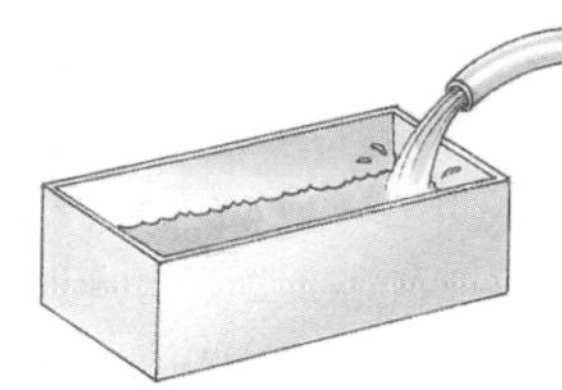

Draw the graph.

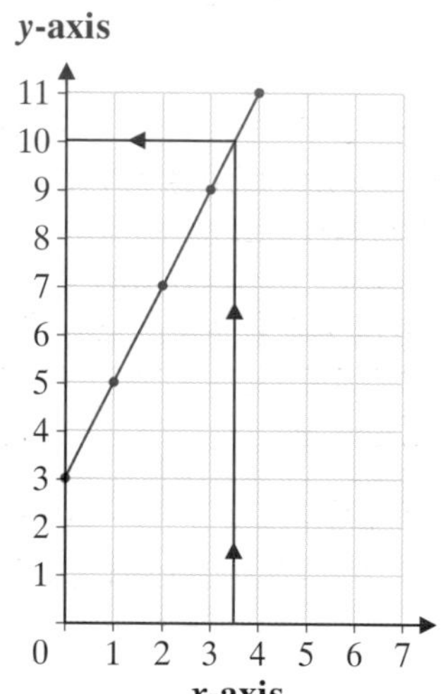

(b) Find $3\frac{1}{2}$ on the x-axis.
Go up to the line and across to find the corresponding value of y, which is 10.
The depth of the water $3\frac{1}{2}$ minutes after the water starts to flow is 10 cm.

Exercise 7B

You will need 5 mm squared paper.

1 A longboat travels on a canal at a speed of 4 miles per hour.

(a) Complete this table of values:

Time travelled in hours x	0	1	2	3	4
Distance travelled in miles y	0	4			

(b) Draw the graph for the table of values.

(c) Use your graph to find how far the boat travels in $3\frac{1}{2}$ hours.

2 In Britain miles are used to measure large distances. In the rest of Europe kilometres are used. A good approximation to use to change miles into kilometres is 5 miles = 8 kilometres.

(a) Complete this table of values:

Distance in miles x	0	5	10	15	20	25
Distance in kilometres y	0	8				

(b) Draw the graph for the table of values.

(c) Use your graph to find how many kilometres are the same as 13 miles.

(d) How many miles are the same as 14 kilometres?
Hint: find 14 on the y-axis, go across to the line and down to the x-axis.

3 Mortar is used to stick bricks together. To mix mortar you put 1 bucket of cement with 3 buckets of sand.

(a) Complete this table of values:

Buckets of cement x	0	1	2	3	4	5	6
Buckets of sand y	0	3					

(b) Draw the graph for the table of values.

(c) Use your graph to find how many buckets of cement you should put with 14 buckets of sand.

4 A cookery book gives this rule for cooking joints of lamb:

Cook for half an hour per 500 g of weight plus half an hour.

(a) Complete this table of values:

Weight in kg x	$\frac{1}{2}$	1	$1\frac{1}{2}$	2	$2\frac{1}{2}$	3	$3\frac{1}{2}$
Cooking time in hours y	1	$1\frac{1}{2}$					

(b) Why isn't it sensible to start the values of x at 0?
What is the biggest value you think it would be sensible to put for x?

(c) Draw the graph for the table of values.

(d) Use your graph to estimate how long it would take to cook a 2.3 kg joint of lamb.

Drawing accurate graphs

In Exercise **7B** you used 5 mm squared paper for your graphs.
For more accurate readings from your graph you can use graph paper.
Label the axes with letters or words that relate to the problem.

Example 2

Cloth is cut from a roll. The cost of the cloth is £1.60 per metre of length.

(a) Draw a graph to show the relationship between the length, L metres, of a piece of the cloth and its cost, C pounds.

(b) Use your graph to find the cost of 3.5 metres of the cloth.

L metres

(a) Draw up a table of values for whole number values of L.

Length in metres L	0	1	2	3	4	5
Cost in pounds C	0	1.6	3.2	4.8	6.4	8

Draw the graph.

(b) Find 3.5 on the L-axis.
Go up to the line and across to find the corresponding value of C, which is 5.6

The cost of 3.5 metres of cloth is £5.6 which we write as £5.60.

Notice that the axes are labelled with letters that relate to the problem.

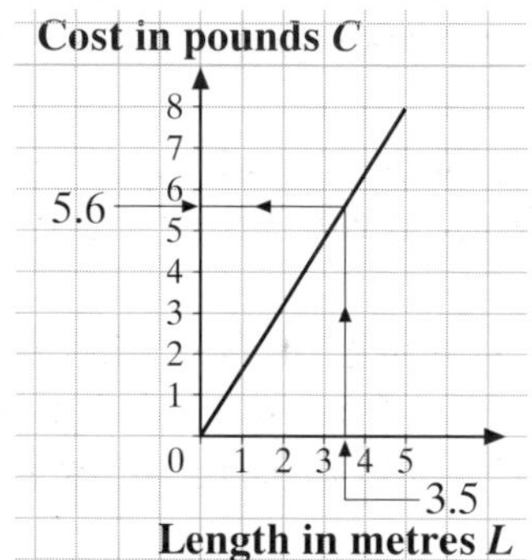

Exercise 7C

You will need graph paper.

1 A garage sells petrol at £0.65 per litre.

(a) Draw a graph which can be used to work out the cost of any amount of petrol up to 40 litres.
Hint: put the number of litres bought on the x-axis and label it L (for litres). Put the cost on the y-axis and label it C (for cost).

(b) Use your graph to answer these questions.

(i) What is the cost of 23 litres of petrol?

(ii) How much petrol can I buy with £12?

2 In Britain we use two different scales to measure temperature: Fahrenheit (F) and Celsius (C). The equation that connects the temperatures in the two scales is: $f = 1.8c + 32$

(a) Complete this table of values:

c	0	20	40	60	100
f	32	68			

(b) Draw the graph for this table of values.

(c) Use your graph to answer these questions.

(i) The hottest temperature last year in London was 33 °C. What is 33 °C in Fahrenheit?

(ii) The normal body temperature of a human being is 98.4 °F. What is 98.4 °F in Celsius?

3 **Activity: the length of a spring**

Investigate the relationship between the length of a spring and the mass of a weight hung from it.

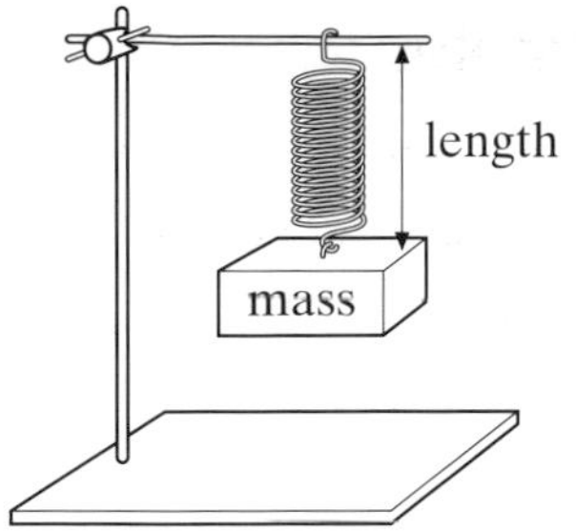

4 **Activity: a pendulum swinging**

The diagram shows a very easily constructed pendulum being held in its starting position.

The pendulum consists of a piece of string of length L, and a bob of weight W.

At the start the string makes an angle of $x°$ with the vertical.

When you let the bob go the pendulum will swing back and forth.

The **period** of the swing is the time it takes for the pendulum to swing from its starting position, across to the other side and back again.

Your task is to investigate what happens to the **period** of the swing when you have different weights, starting angles and lengths.

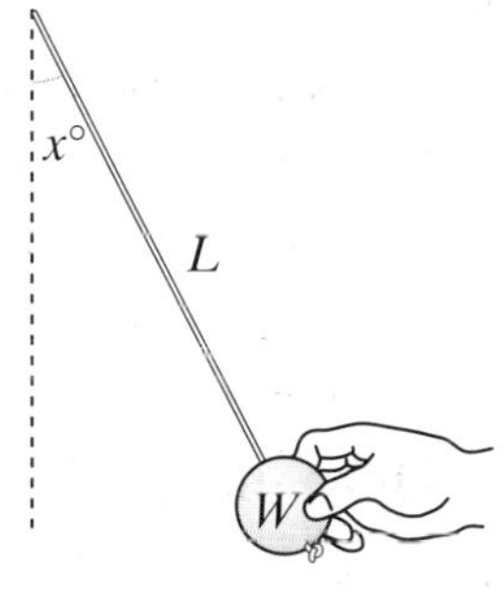

(a) Make a pendulum.
Make sure that the length of the string is at least half a metre and that the bobs are of a small volume. When you swing the pendulum it is best if the starting angle is less than 30 degrees to the vertical.

(b) Investigate what happens to the period of swing
(i) when you change the length of the string
(ii) when you change the starting angle
(iii) when you change the weight of the bob.

(c) Record your results in the form of tables and graphs.

(d) Comment on your results.

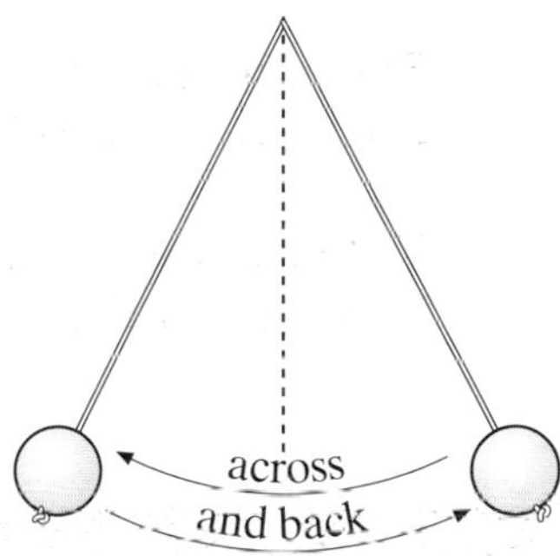

The **period** is the time taken for a complete swing of the pendulum.

7.3 Investigating graphs of linear functions with positive and negative inputs

Section 7.2 shows the graph for $y = 2x + 1$ for positive values of x.

We can also let x take negative values and draw the graph for these values.

x	−3	−2	−1	0	1	2
y	−5	−3	−1	1	3	5

The graph continues as a straight line.

Before going on to the next section you should try at least questions **1** and **2** of Exercise **7D**.

We often label the x and y axes like this

We usually write the equation near the graph

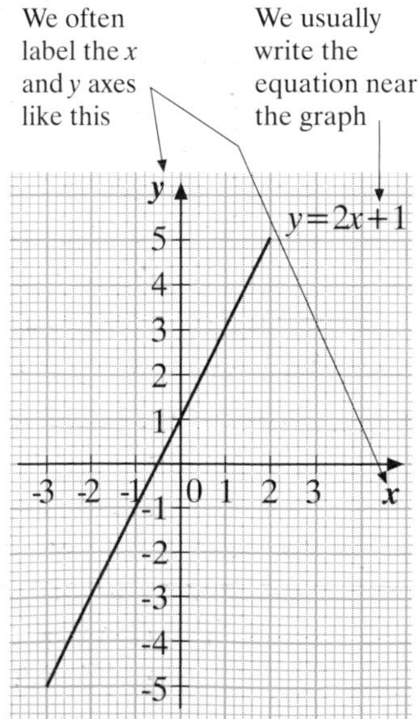

Exercise 7D

It is best to use a graphics calculator or a graph drawing program on a computer for this exercise.

If you do not have these, draw your graphs on graph paper.

1 **(a)** Draw graphs of $y = mx + 1$ for different values of m. For example, if you put $m = 2$ you get $y = 2x + 1$ and the graph on page 87.
Now put $m = 3$ and draw the graph of $y = 3x + 1$, then put $m = 4$ and so on.
Try giving m negative values, fractional values and the value zero.
(b) What effect does the value of m havc on the graphs you have drawn?
(c) Do the graphs have anything in common?

2 **(a)** Draw the graphs of $y = 2x + c$ for different values of c. For example, if you put $c = 1$ you get $y = 2x + 1$ and the graph on page 87.
Now put $c = 2$ and draw the graph of $y = 2x + 2$, and so on.
Try giving c negative values, fractional values and the value zero.
(b) What effect does the value of c have on the graphs?
(c) Do the graphs have anything in common?

3 **(a)** Draw the graphs of $y = mx + c$ where m and c have the same value for each graph.
For example, draw the graph of $y = 1x + 1$, draw the graph of $y = 2x + 2$ and so on.
Try negative values as well, for example $y = (-2x) + (-2)$.
(b) What do you notice?

4 **(a)** Draw the graphs of $y = mx + c$ where the value of m is twice the value of c for each graph.
For example, draw the graphs of $y = 2x + 1$, $y = 4x + 2$, $y = 6x + 3$ and so on.
Remember negative values: for example $y = (-4x) + (-2)$
(b) Write down anything that you notice.

5 **(a)** Draw the graphs of $y = mx + c$ where the value of c is one greater than the value of m.
For example, draw the graphs of $y = 1x + 2$, $y = 2x + 3$, $y = 3x + 4$.
(b) Write down anything that you notice.

6 Try variations of questions **3**, **4** and **5** using different relationships between m and c to see what you can discover.

7.4 Graphs of linear functions written in the form $y = mx + c$

Questions **1** and **2** of Exercise **7D** showed the following points about straight line graphs and their equations.

- The graphs for equations of the type $y = mx + c$, where m and c are each given a value, are all straight lines.
  For example $y = 3x + 2$, $y = 0.5x + 1$ and $y = -2x + 0.5$ are all straight lines.

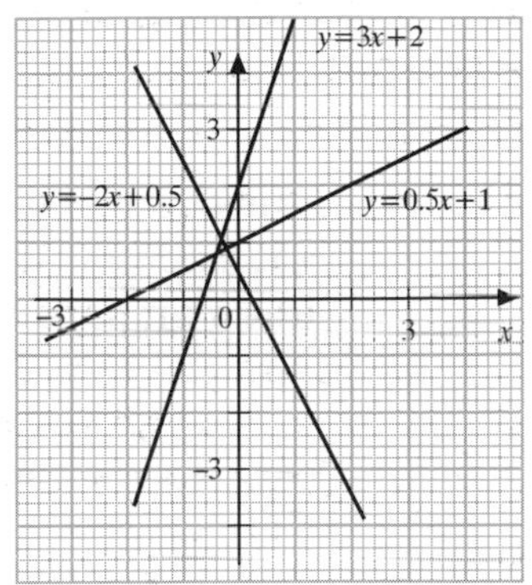

- Fixing m and giving c different values produces a family of parallel straight lines. Each line cuts the y-axis at the point $(0, c)$.
  As c increases the lines cut the y-axis further up.
  As c decreases the lines cut the y-axis further down.

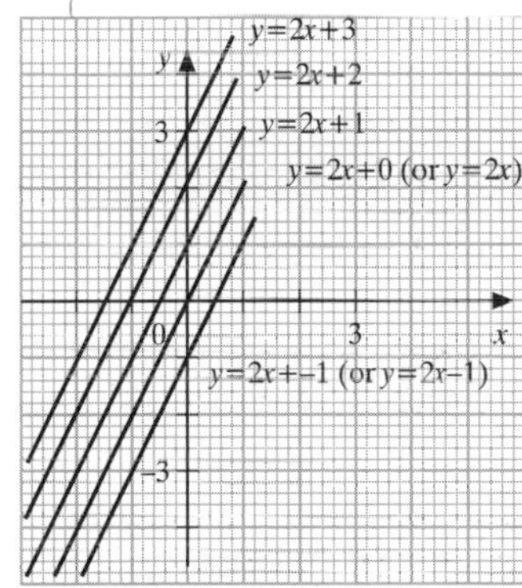

- Fixing c and giving m different values produces a family of straight lines passing through the point $(0, c)$.
  As m increases the lines become steeper.
  If m is positive the line slopes forwards.
  If m is negative the line slopes backwards.
  If $m = 0$ the line is parallel to the x-axis.

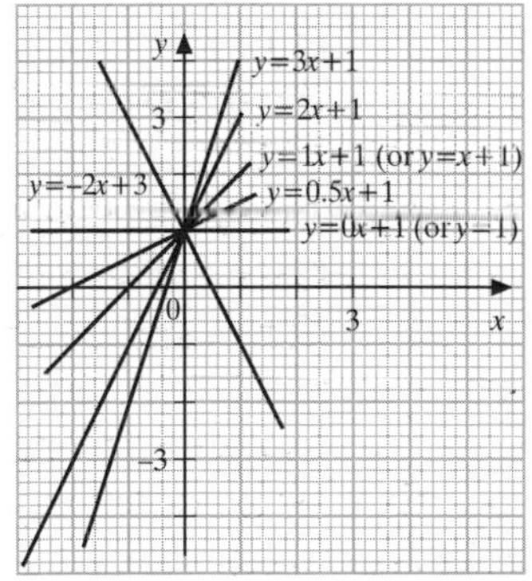

m is called the **gradient** of the line. If a point moves along the line a distance of 1 in the direction of the x-axis it will have moved a distance of m in the direction of the y-axis.

c is called the **intercept** on the y-axis. It is the distance from the point (0, 0) to the point where the line cuts the y-axis at $(0, c)$.

■ **The general form for the equation of a straight line is $y = mx + c$.**
m is called the gradient.
c is called the intercept on the y-axis.
The greater the value of m the steeper the line is.

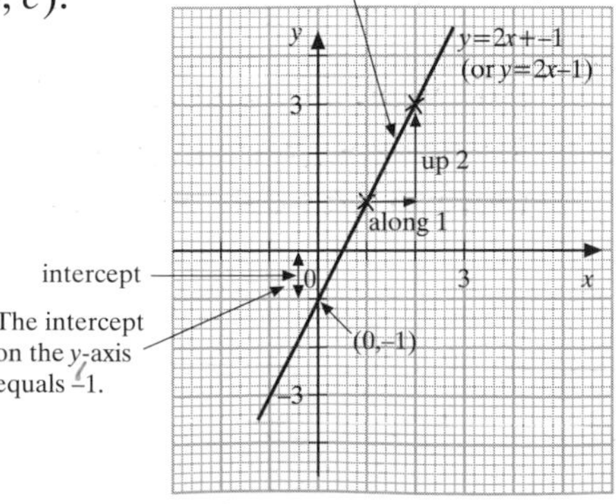

Example 3

Find the equation of the line shown.

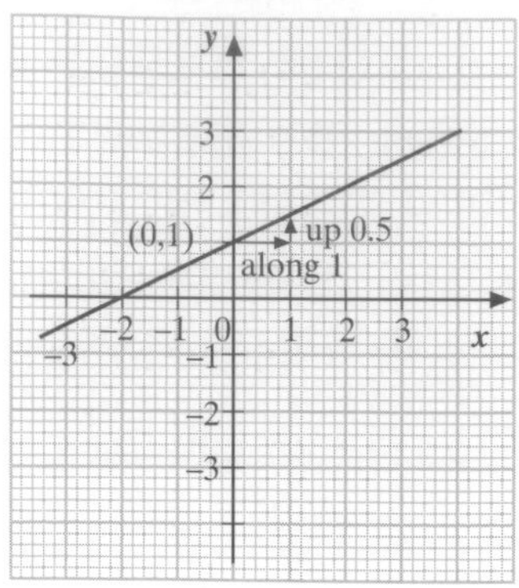

The equation for a straight line can be written as $y = mx + c$
The line cuts the y-axis at $(0, 1)$ so $c = 1$
If a point moves across 1 it moves up 0.5, so $m = 0.5$
The equation of the line is $y = 0.5x + 1$

Notice that if you were given the equation of the line you could reverse the process to draw the line without first drawing up a table of values.
$y = 0.5x + 1$. Here $c = 1$ so the line goes through the point $(0, 1)$
The value of $m = 0.5$ so from $(0, 1)$ keep going in steps along 1 and up 0.5 to find other points on the line.

Exercise 7E

You will need graph paper.

1 Find the equation of the straight line in each of these diagrams:

(a)

(b)

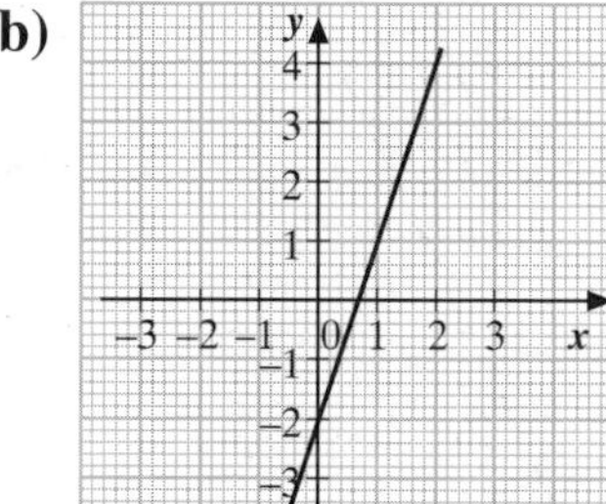

(c)

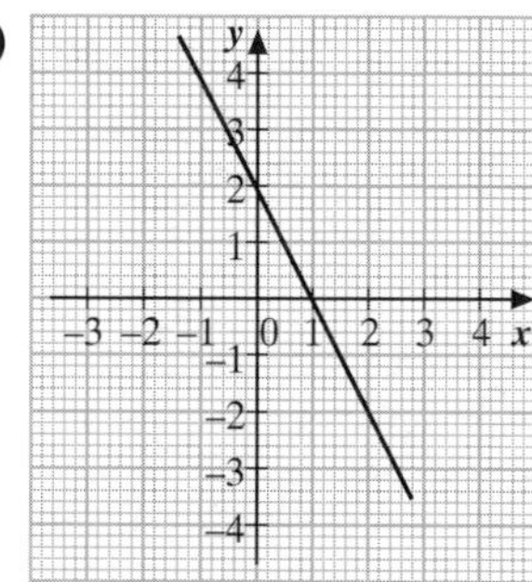

(d)

(e)

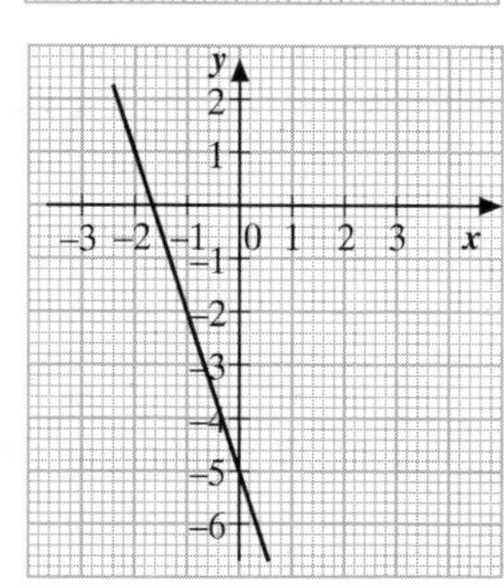

(f)

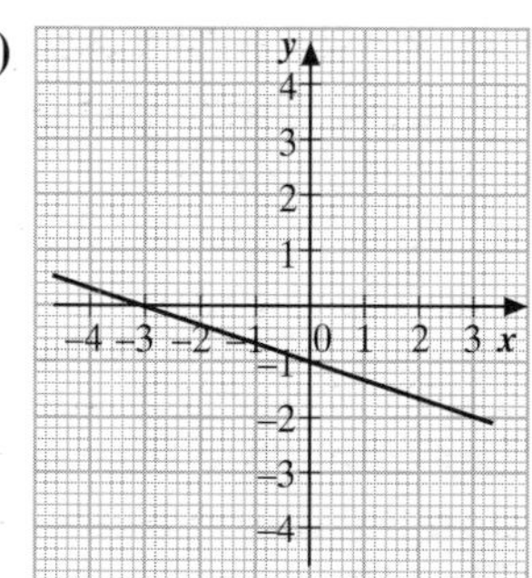

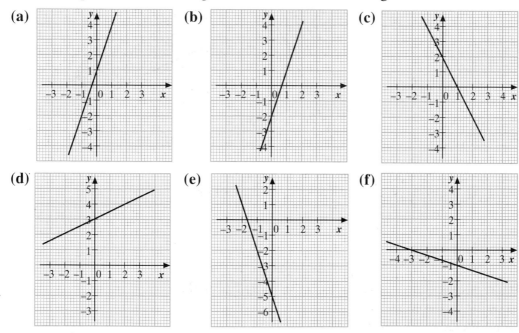

2 Use the values of m and c to draw the graphs for these equations written in the form $y = mx + c$.
Do not draw up a table of values first.

(a) $y = 4x + 2$ **(b)** $y = 3x + (-4)$ **(c)** $y = -2x + 1$
(d) $y = 0.25x + 2$ **(e)** $y = 3x$ **(f)** $y = 3x - 3$

3 Repeat question **2** for these equations:

(a) $y = 4$ **(b)** $y = x$ **(c)** $y = -3x - 4$
(d) $y = 0.5x + 4$ **(e)** $y = -0.5x - 1$ **(f)** $y = -2$

4 The equations of five straight lines are:
$y = x - 2$ $y = 2x + 3$ $y = 3x + 2$ $y = 5x + 2$ $y = 3x - 3$
Two of the lines go through the point (0, 2).
(a) Write down the equations of these two lines.

Two of the lines are parallel.
(b) Write down the equations of these two lines. [L]

5 **(a)** Complete this table of values for $y = 2x - 1$.

x	−2	−1	0	1	2	3
y			−1			

Draw a pair of axes with the x-axis going from −4 to 4 and the y-axis from −5 to 5.
(b) Plot the points represented by the values in your table. Join the points with a straight line.
(c) Use your graph to find the value of x when $y = \frac{1}{2}$. [L]

6 Write the equation for each of the lines shown in the following diagrams.
Take care: some of the scales on the x and y axes are different!

(a) 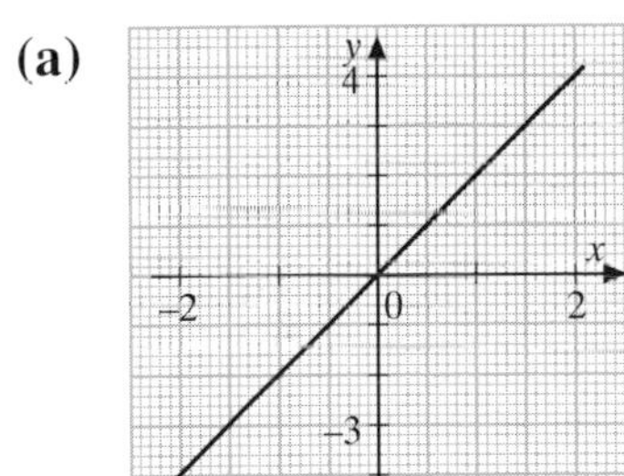

(b) 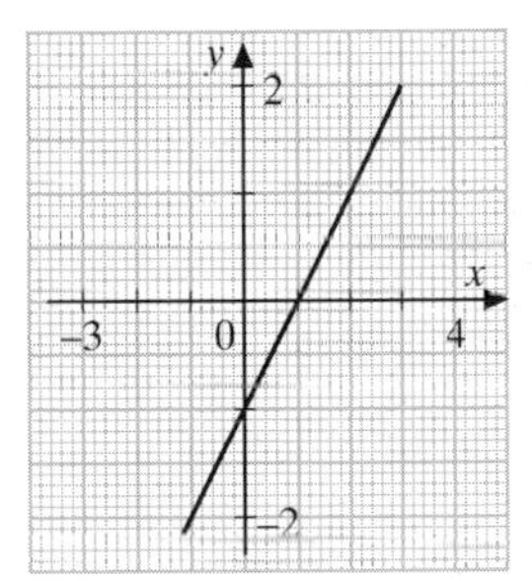

(c) 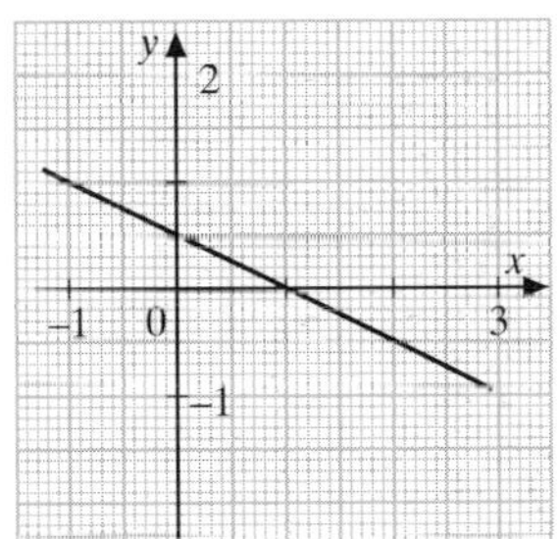

7 Draw a pair of axes with x and y each going from 0 to 6.
(i) Draw the lines that go through the point (2, 3) and have the following gradients:
(a) 1 **(b)** 2 **(c)** −1 **(d)** 0 **(e)** 0.5 **(f)** −0.5
(ii) Find the equations of the lines.

8 Draw a pair of axes with x and y each going from −5 to 5.
(a) (i) Draw the line that goes through the point (2, 5) and is parallel to the line $y = 2x + 3$
(ii) Find the equation of the line.
Repeat part **(a)** for the given point and the given line:
(b) (4, 3) and the line $y = 0.5x + 3$
(c) (2, 1) and the line $y = -2x + 1$
(d) (−3, 1) and the line $y = x$
(e) (−1, −3) and the line $y = -x$

7.5 Lines parallel to the y-axis

Every point on this line has its x-coordinate equal to 3. The equation $x = 3$ describes every point on the line so $x = 3$ is the equation of the line.

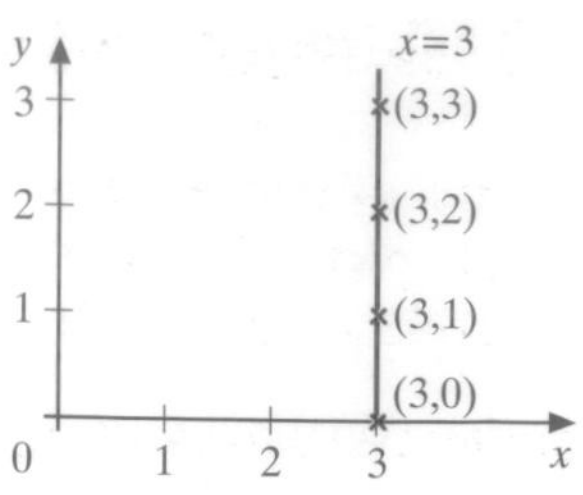

The equations of lines parallel to the y-axis cannot be written in the form $y = mx + c$.

Every point on a line parallel to the y-axis has its x-coordinate equal to a fixed value k. The equation of the line is $x = k$.

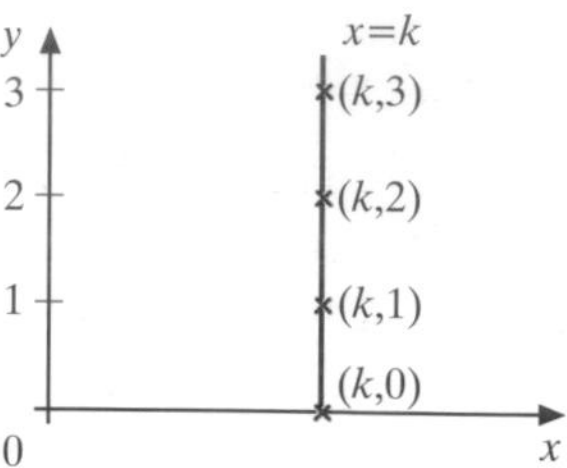

■ **Lines parallel to the y-axis have equations of the form $x = k$.**

Exercise 7F

You will need graph paper.

1 **(a)** Write down the equation of the line parallel to the y-axis that passes through the point (5, 6).

Repeat part **(a)** for these points:

(b) (2, 7) **(c)** (0.5, 2.5) **(d)** (−3, 4) **(e)** (3, −4)

2 Write down the equations of all the lines that have been used to produce these patterns.

(a)

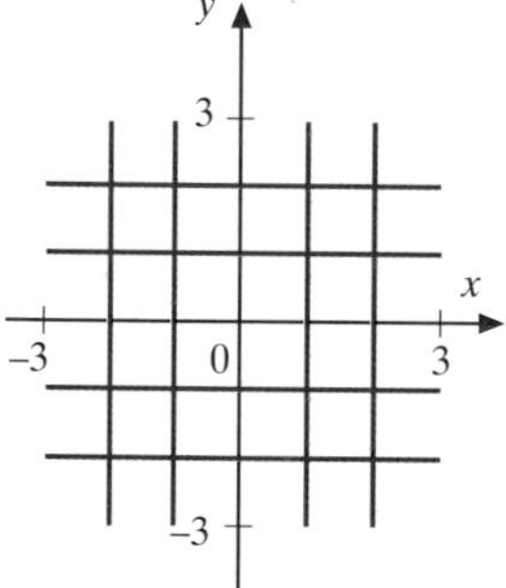

(b)

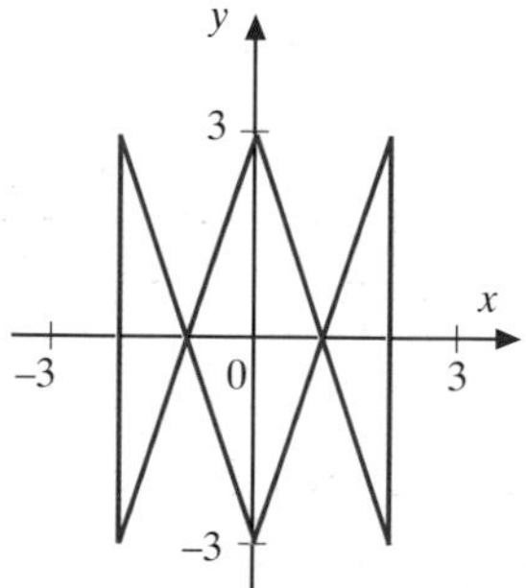

(c)

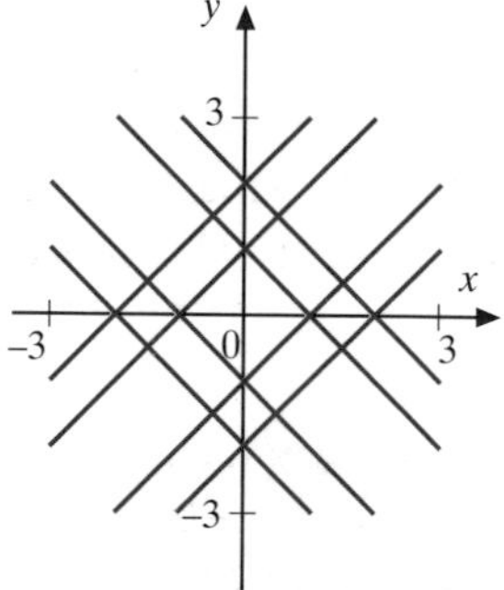

3 Draw a pair of axes with x and y each going from −6 to 6.

(a) Find the equation of the line that joins the point (1, 3) to the point (4, 6).

Repeat part **(a)** for these pairs of points:

(b) (2, 2) and (6, 4) **(c)** (−3, −5) and (−1, 1)

(d) (−1, −4) and (2, −1) **(e)** (−4, −1) and (4, −3)

7.6 Distance/time graphs

■ **You can solve problems involving distance and time by drawing graphs. The position of an object (for example, a train or a cyclist) can be shown by a point on the graph.**

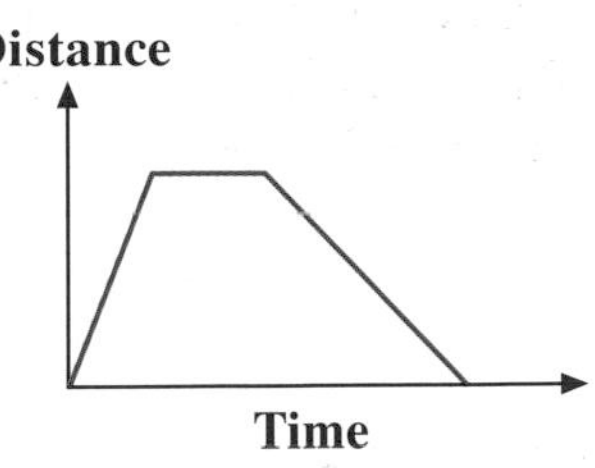

Usually the horizontal axis represents the time and the vertical axis represents the distance travelled.

Example 4

Seamus leaves his home in Belfast at 10:00 and rides his motor bike at an average speed of 72 km h^{-1}. He goes to Newry, 60 km away. Seamus stays at Newry for 30 minutes and then rides back to Belfast along the same road.

He arrives home at 12:50.

(a) Draw a graph to represent Seamus's journey.

(b) Use your graph to find:
  (i) the time Seamus arrived at Newry
  (ii) the average speed of Seamus's return journey home.

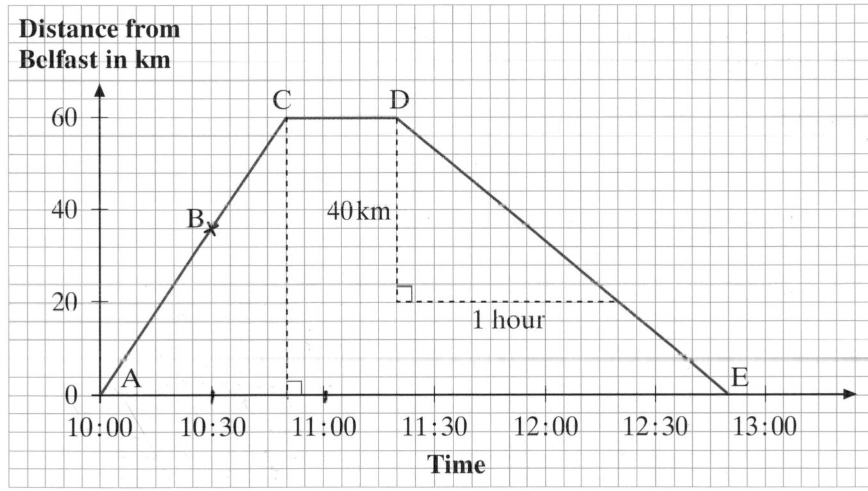

(a) Use 12 squares to represent 1 hour along the time axis, starting at 10:00. So 1 square represents 5 minutes.
Use 5 squares to represent 20 km along the distance axis, starting at 0. So 1 square represents 4 km.
Seamus begins his journey at 10:00 in Belfast, so plot the point (10:00, 0) and label it A.
He travels 72 km h^{-1}. In 1 hour he goes 72 km, so in half an hour he goes 36 km. Plot the point (10:30, 36) and label it B. Join AB and continue the line until it reaches C, where the distance from Belfast is 60 km.
He remains in Newry 30 minutes. He is still 60 km from Belfast, so draw a line horizontally for 6 squares to D.
He arrives home at 12:50 so plot the point E (12:50, 0) and join DE with a straight line.

(b) (i) Draw a line down from C to the x axis. The line meets the x axis 5 squares horizontally from A. This represents 50 minutes.
So Seamus arrives in Newry at 10:50.
(ii) Draw a right angled triangle somewhere along DE making the horizontal length represent 1 hour. Reading the vertical distance on the triangle the distance travelled in 1 hour is 40 km. So the average speed of Seamus's journey home is $40\,\text{km}\,\text{h}^{-1}$.

■ **On a distance/time graph the gradient gives the speed.**

Example 5

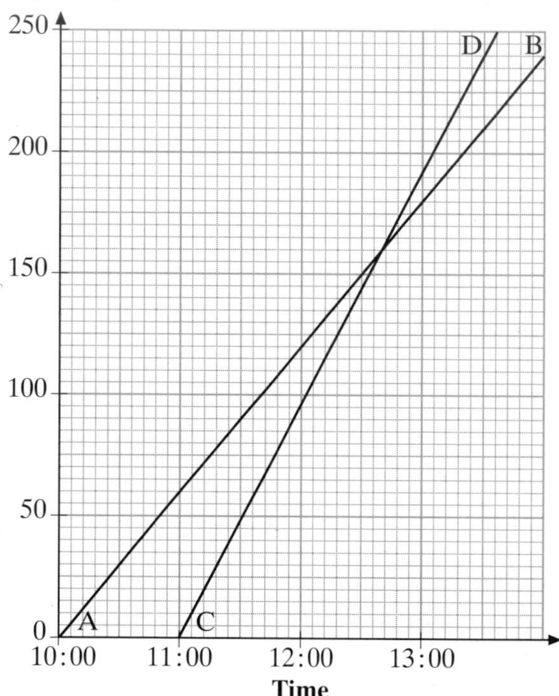

On the graph the line AB represents part of the journey of a slow train from London to Carlisle and the line CD represents part of the journey of a faster train on the same route.

(a) How far are the trains from London when the faster train overtakes the slower train?

(b) What is the speed of the slower train?

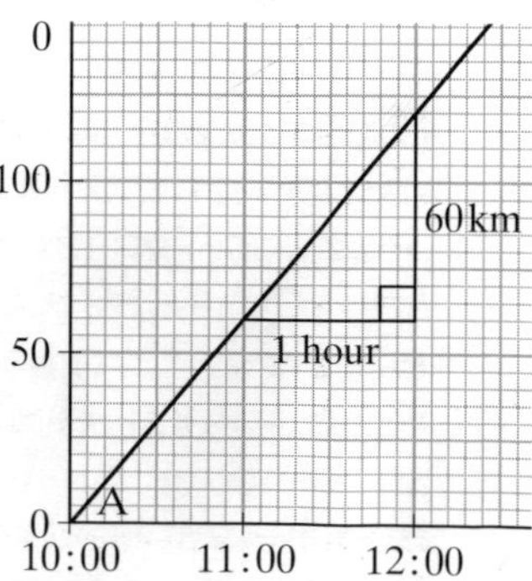

(a) Where the faster train overtakes the slower one they are the same distance from London at the same time. So they are at the place represented by the point where AB crosses CD. Reading from the vertical axis, the distance from London is 160 km.

(b) Draw a right angled triangle along the line AB, making the horizontal length represent 1 hour.
From the vertical scale, the distance travelled in 1 hour is 60 km.
So the speed of the slower train is $60\,\text{km}\,\text{h}^{-1}$.

Exercise 7G

You will need squared paper and graph paper.

1 A cyclist wants to ride from Braintree to Great Sampford, 20 km away.
He rides at $16\,\text{km}\,\text{h}^{-1}$ until his bicycle breaks down after he has travelled 12 km. He tries to fix it for 10 minutes and then walks the rest of the way at $8\,\text{km}\,\text{h}^{-1}$.
Draw a distance/time graph and use it to find the time the cyclist takes for the whole journey. Use a scale of 1 cm to represent 10 minutes and 1 cm to represent 2 km.

2

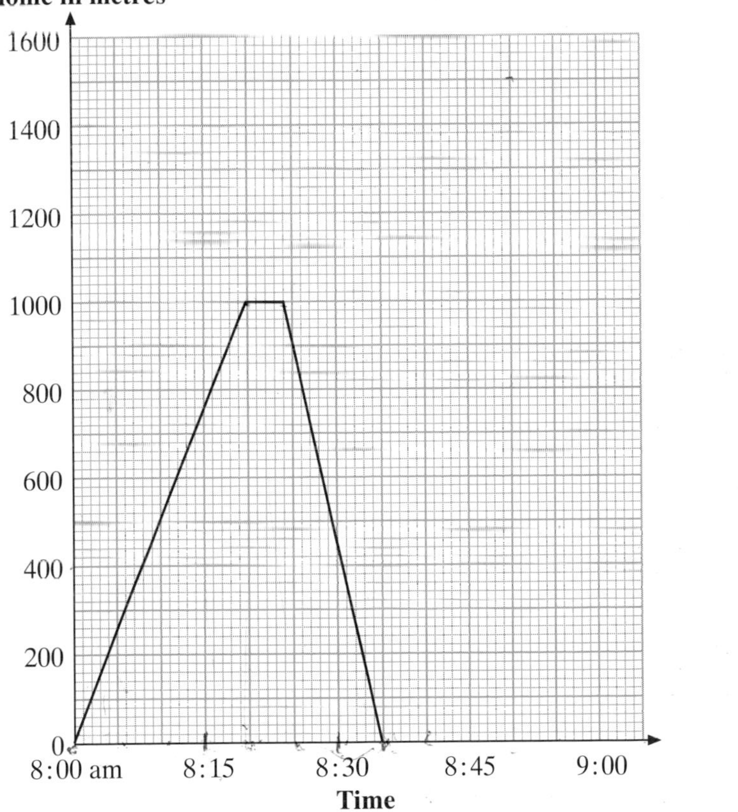

On his way to school, Jeremy stops to buy some sweets. He realizes that he has forgotten his money and so he returns home to collect his dinner money. The distance/time graph for his journey is shown.

(a) How far is the sweet shop from Jeremy's home?

(b) How long, in minutes, does Jeremy spend in the sweet shop?

Jeremy then leaves home at 8:40 am. He runs to school which is 1500 m from his home at a constant speed of 9 kilometres per hour.

(c) Copy the graph and draw on the grid the line which represents Jeremy's journey to school. Show your working clearly. [L]

3

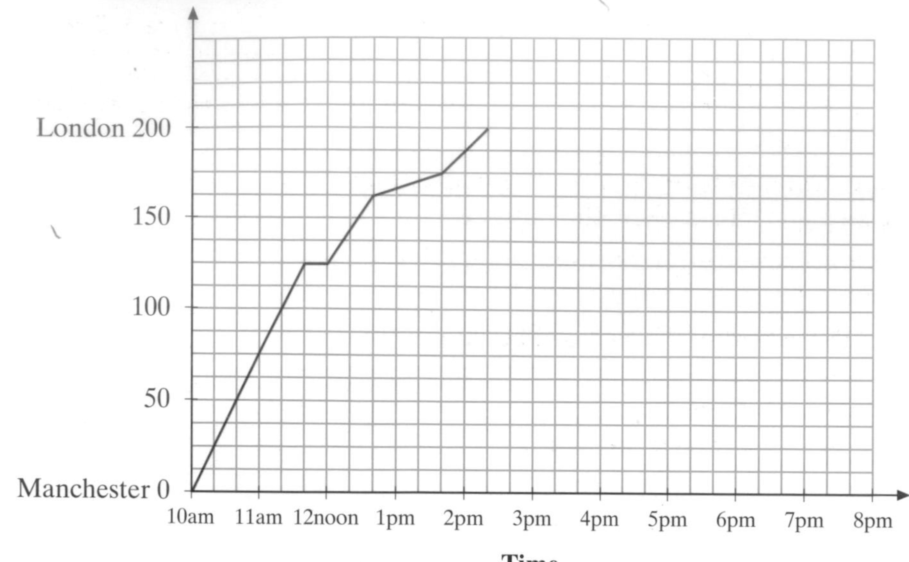

The graph represents Mrs Hinton's journey from Manchester to London. Mrs Hinton stopped for a rest at a service station.

(a) (i) Write down the time at which she stopped.

(ii) For how long did she stop?

For part of her journey Mrs Hinton had to slow down because of a traffic queue.

(b) For how many miles did she travel at this slower speed?

Mrs Hinton spent an hour at a meeting in London. She then returned home to Manchester, travelling at an average speed of 50 miles an hour.

(c) Copy the graph and use this information to complete the graph of her journey.

[L]

4 Natalie leaves Framwellgate Moor at 14:00 and cycles 5 km to Edmondsley at an average speed of $15\,\text{km}\,\text{h}^{-1}$.
She spends 30 minutes in Edmondsley and then rides home along the same road and reaches Framwellgate Moor at 15:05.

(a) Draw a distance/time graph of Natalie's journey.

(b) Work out the average speed at which she cycles home.

5 The distance from Oxford to Bicester is 24 km. Heather leaves Oxford at 09:00 and walks to Bicester at $8\,\text{km}\,\text{h}^{-1}$.
George leaves Bicester at 10:00 and cycles to Oxford at $16\,\text{km}\,\text{h}^{-1}$.
Draw a distance/time graph and find the time when George and Heather meet.

Summary of key points

1 $y = 2x + 1$ is called an equation. The value of y is always equal to the value of $2x + 1$.

The coordinates (2, 5) satisfy the equation $y = 2x + 1$ so the point (2, 5) is on the line whose equation is $y = 2x + 1$.

2 The input values of x are continuous if x can take any value (whole numbers or decimals).

3 $y = 2x + 1$ is the equation of a straight line. The coordinates of any point on the straight line 'satisfy' the equation.

4 $x \rightarrow 2x + 1$ is called a linear function because its graph is a straight line.

5 The general form for the equation of a straight line is $y = mx + c$.
m is called the gradient.
c is called the intercept on the y-axis.
The greater the value of m the steeper the line is.

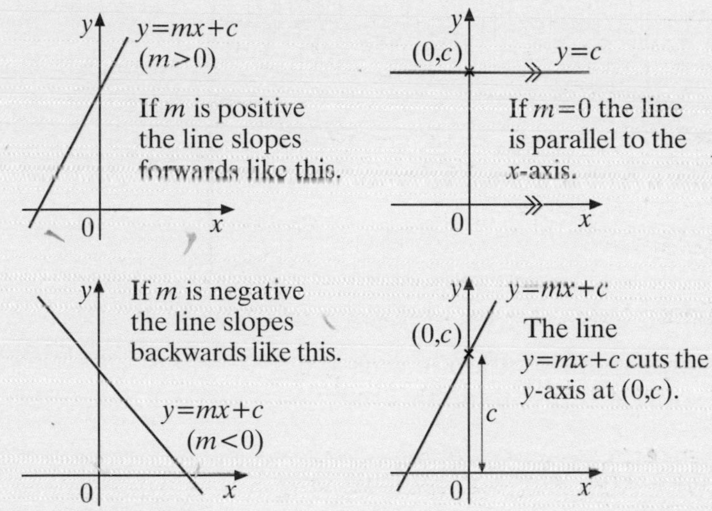

6 Lines parallel to the y-axis have equations of the form $x = k$.

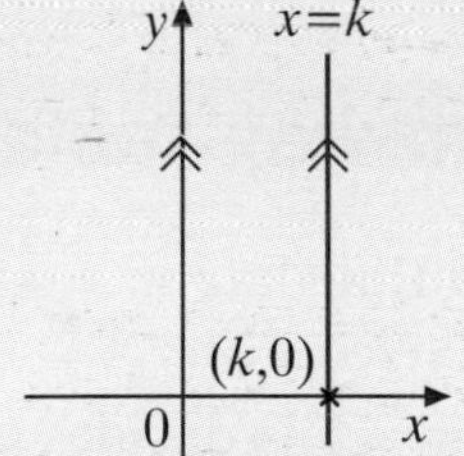

7 You can solve problems involving distance and time by drawing graphs. The position of an object (for example, a train or a cyclist) can be shown by a point on the graph.

8 On a distance/time graph the gradient gives the speed.

The gradient on a distance/time graph gives the speed

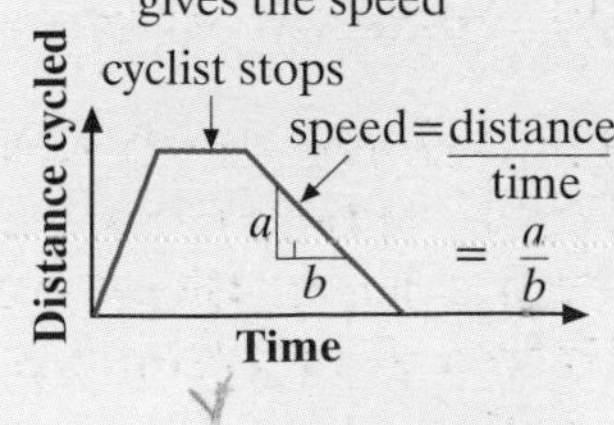

8 Collecting and organizing data

Every day you are bombarded with information:

This unit is about collecting and recording information in ways that make it easier to work with, and to spot patterns. To do this the information must be organized.

We call the information we collect **data**. One way of organizing data is to put it in rows and columns in a **table**.

8.1 Two-way tables

■ **Presenting data in a table can give you more information than you started with.**

For example, Zala decides to classify her music collection.

- She has a total of 84 cassettes and CDs.
- Of these, 58 are pop music.
- Only 2 of her 50 cassettes are classical.

The information is about cassettes and CDs which have been classified as classical or pop music. You can organize it in a two-way table like this:

	Cassettes	CDs	Totals
Classical			
Pop			
Totals			

The **two-way table** presents **two** types of information about the music collection:

→ This way it shows the format: cassette or CD.

↓ This way it shows the type of music: pop or classical.

The original information gives you four numbers to go into the table.

- The total of 84 cassettes and CDs.
- The total of 58 popular cassettes and CDs.
- 2 classical cassettes out of 50.

You can put these in and fill some gaps like this:

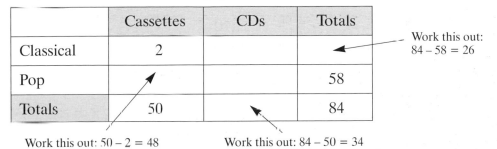

	Cassettes	CDs	Totals
Classical	2		
Pop			58
Totals	50		84

Work this out: 84 – 58 = 26

Work this out: 50 – 2 = 48

Work this out: 84 – 50 = 34

Now you can work out the data for the CDs.

	Cassettes	CDs	Totals
Classical	2		26
Pop	48		58
Totals	50	34	84

Work this out: 26 – 2 = 24

Work this out: 58 – 48 = 10

The final table is:

	Cassettes	CDs	Totals
Classical	2	24	26
Pop	48	10	58
Totals	50	34	84

Notice that in the original information there was no detail given about the CDs.
In the final table it is all there.
In this example you needed 4 pieces of information to work out the rest.

- If the information is in percentages then you only need 3 pieces of information. The 4th piece is that percentages add up to 100.
- Similarly, if the information is in probabilities you know that the overall total will be 1.

Exercise 8A

1 Copy and complete this two-way table for activities chosen by 74 youngsters on an adventure holiday.

	Rock climbing	Mountain walking	Totals
Boys		5	
Girls	7	20	
Totals			

2 As an experiment, Peter throws a dice and spins a coin. He repeats this 150 times, noting the results. He records a head 71 times and a six 21 times. On 68 occasions he is unable to record a head or a six.
Use a suitable two-way table to work out all the outcomes.

	6	Not a 6
Head		
Tail		

Peter's table

3 The members of a tennis club are classified according to sex and whether they are over or under 18.
Only 12% of the members are female under 18. 53% are male and over 18. 60% of members are male.
Use a two-way table to find what percentage are female over 18.

4 A market research company interviewed people travelling by train or bus.
88 out of 120 train travellers had made journeys over 50 miles.
Of the 300 people interviewed, 205 had travelled under 50 miles.
How many of the people had made a bus journey under 50 miles?

5 One hundred people arriving home from holiday were asked what type of accommodation they had stayed in. Part of the information is given in the table.

	Hotel	Caravan	Camping	Other	Totals
July	11	4	3		
August		14		6	
September			4	3	30
Totals	49		15	11	100

(a) Copy and complete the table.
(b) How many of these people
(i) went on holiday in August
(ii) stayed in a hotel in September?

8.2 Other types of tables

Here are some more ways of presenting data in tables:

This is part of a train timetable.
It shows the times when trains start or stop at different stations.

Reading – Basingstoke				Monday – Friday					
Reading	07:24	07:50	08:06	08:10	08:35	08:55	09:08	09:20	09:50
Reading West	07:27	07:53		08:13	08:38	08:58		09:23	09:53
Mortimer	07:35	08:01		08:21	08:46	09:06		09:31	10:01
Bramley	07:40	08:06		08:26	08:51	09:11		09:36	10:06
Basingstoke	07:48	08:14	08:25	08:34	08:59	09:19	09:28	09:44	10:14

A gap in the table means that the train does not stop at that station.

Here are two different ways of presenting a school's SATs results:

This table shows the National Curriculum Levels achieved by boys and girls in three subjects.

		Levels								
		1	2	3	4	5	6	7	8	A
	Boys	2	5	13	32	29	12	6	1	0
Mathematics	Girls	2	6	11	35	30	14	2	0	0
	Totals	4	11	24	67	59	26	8	1	0
	Boys	3	7	14	31	30	11	4	0	0
English	Girls	1	5	15	36	23	15	4	1	0
	Totals	4	12	29	67	53	26	8	1	0
	Boys	4	6	13	35	30	9	3	0	0
Science	Girls	3	7	13	34	28	12	3	0	0
	Totals	7	13	26	69	58	21	6	0	0

The table shows that 34 girls achieved Level 4 in Science.

You could organize the same data differently in a table with these headings:

	Boys			Girls			Totals		
	Maths	English	Science	Maths	English	Science	Maths	English	Science
Levels 1									
2									
3									
4									

There are other ways of organizing this data. You need to choose which is best for the data you are presenting.

Exercise 8B

Design tables which could show this information:

1 A list of hotels, different periods of the year, prices for adults and children.

2 Microwave ovens by manufacturer, capacity, features.

3 Holiday resorts, month, weather (rainfall, hours of sunshine, average temperature).

4 Accidents by category (death, serious, slight), place (home, work, road, other) and age (under 10, 10–18, over 18).

5 Swimming races.
Use 100 m, 200 m, 400 m; Freestyle, Breast stroke, Back stroke; Boys, Girls; under 12, under 14, under 16, under 18.

6 Theatre.
Use Weekday, Weekend; Adults, Children; Matinee, Evening; Front stalls, Rear stalls, Balcony.

7 Do you think your tables from questions **5** and **6** are easy to understand? Explain your answer.

8.3 Databases

■ **A database is an organized collection of information. It can be stored on paper or in a computer.**

Here is a table of data from a database of exam results:

Name	Maths		English		Science	History	French
	paper 1	paper 2	paper 1	paper 2			
Peter	34	41	53	46	57	29	43
Ahmed	73	85	60	58	63	52	46
Lucy	49	60	74	83	48	60	52
Chandra	55	38	46	40	62	45	36
Cita	61	65	50	44	71	58	52
Glenys	17	24	38	55	30	47	19

This is part of a database created using Microsoft Access.

A computer database allows you to obtain information quickly and in a variety of forms, for example:

- in alphabetical order
- in numerical order
- girls' results only
- pupils scoring over 60 in one subject only . . .

Exercise 8C

Here is a database for Adventure Holidays:

Location	Activities	Age	Length	Cost
North Wales	Mountain biking, Climbing, Canoeing, Archery	14+	10 days	£300
Lake District	Watersports, Hang gliding, Mountain biking	18+	7 days	£250
Northumberland	Orienteering, Climbing	18+	7 days	£200
Cornwall	Watersports	14+	7 days	£220
New Forest	Horse-riding, Mountain biking, Archery	14+	7 days	£210
Peak District	Climbing, Archery, Shooting, Canoeing	18+	10 days	£350
Devon	Horse-riding, Watersports, Archery, Orienteering	14+	7 days	£220

1 Sandeep is 15 and interested in archery. Which holidays can he go on?

2 Alix can afford £230 and she does not like watersports. Which holidays could she choose?

3 Which holidays offer canoeing and archery?

4 Which holidays offer four activities?

5 How many holidays cost under £230?

6 Which activities are not available to 15-year-olds?

7 A 16-year-old is really keen on mountain biking. Which holiday would you recommend and why?

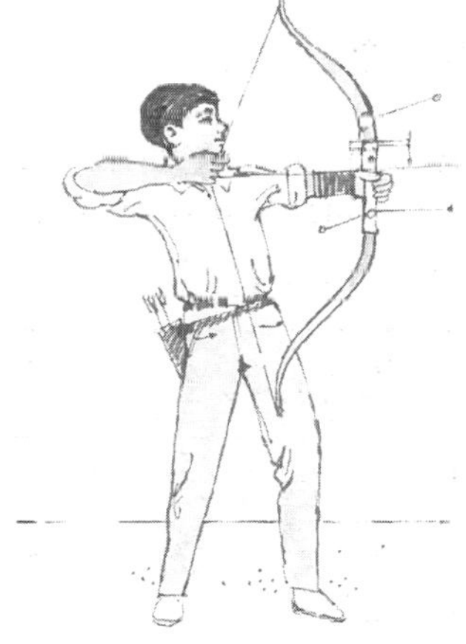

8.4 Different types of data

The Adventure Holidays database at the top of this page contains data in words and numbers.

A set of data is called a **distribution**. A set of data which shows the number of times each value occurs is called a **frequency distribution**.

There are two main types of data:

■ **Qualitative data is described using words:**

Place names such as North Wales, activities such as mountain biking, and colours such as red and green are **qualitative data**.

■ **Quantitative data consists of numbers:**

Data that can be counted or measured, such as the number of days in a holiday, temperatures, and weights are **quantitative data**.

Quantitative data can be **discrete** or **continuous**.

■ **Discrete data can only take particular values.**

For example, you can buy shoes in these sizes:

6 $6\frac{1}{2}$ 7 $7\frac{1}{2}$ 8

These values are **discrete** (meaning separate).
There are **no** values in between them.
Discrete data has an *exact* value.

■ **Continuous data can take any value.**

For example, your foot could be:

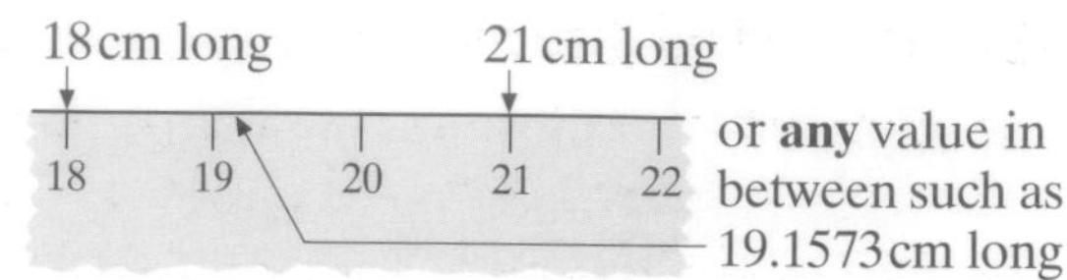

Continuous data *cannot be measured exactly*. The accuracy of a measurement depends on the accuracy of the measuring device.

Exercise 8D

For each type of data write down whether it is qualitative, quantitative and discrete, or quantitative and continuous:

(a) length of a nail
(b) colour of a flower
(c) time taken to play a record
(d) weight of a packet of sugar
(e) number of goals scored in a hockey match
(f) age of a tree
(g) taste of a drink
(h) smell of a scent
(i) number of buses per day
(j) score on a dice
(k) temperature of an oven

8.5 Tally marks and frequency distributions

It is easy to lose count while you are collecting information. One way of avoiding this is to use **tally marks** like this:

	I	II	III	IIII	~~IIII~~	~~IIII~~ I
Standing for	1	2	3	4	5	6

So 12 would look like: ~~IIII~~ ~~IIII~~ II

Here are the results of an eye colour survey carried out by members of a class:

Eye colour	Tally	Frequency
Brown	~~IIII~~ ~~IIII~~ I	11
Blue	~~IIII~~ ~~IIII~~ III	13
Hazel	~~IIII~~ I	6
		30

Adding the tallies gives the frequency of each eye colour.

There is one tally mark for each pupil.

■ **The frequency is the total number of times a result occurred.** You could say it shows 'how frequently a result happened'.

The table above is called a **frequency distribution table** or frequency table for short.

You can prepare a blank frequency distribution table to record data from a survey or experiment as you collect it. This is called a **data capture sheet**.

Exercise 8E

Design data capture sheets to carry out these experiments:

1 **(a)** Throw a single dice and keep a record of the scores.
(b) Throw two dice and record the differences in the scores.

2 **(a)** Find which letters are used most in written English.
f, v, x or z are unlikely, but a, e, i, o, n, s, t, r are strong candidates.
(b) Find out whether books, magazines and newspapers give similar results for part **(a)**.
(c) Investigate the sentence lengths in a passage from a book.
(d) Investigate the lengths of words used by two different authors.

A greater number of results is likely to give a more reliable estimate. You can achieve this by combining your results for Exercise **8E** with the results of a friend. You can get a more reliable estimate by combining the results of the whole class.

8.6 Grouped data

When data has a very wide range of values it makes sense to group sets of values together. This makes it easier to record the data, and to spot any patterns or trends.

For example, scores out of 50 in a test might be grouped:

0 – 10, 11 – 20, 21 – 30, and so on up to 41 – 50.

It often makes life easier if the groups are the same size, but they do not have to be. In this case the first group has 11 members and the others have 10.

We call the groupings 0 – 10, 11 – 20 ... **class intervals**.

- **Class intervals are groupings of quantitative data.**

Here is a frequency distribution table for the test:

The class intervals must not overlap. Each score can only be in one class interval.

The test scores are discrete data. You can score 31 or 32, but *not* 31.4.

Score	Tally	Frequency
0–10	II	2
11–20	𝍸 III	8
21–30	𝍸 𝍸 IIII	14
31–40	𝍸	5
41–50	I	1

Here is a frequency distribution table for some continuous data – the heights of students in the class:

This class interval includes any height greater than or equal to 1.4 m and less than 1.5 m. It does not include 1.5 m.

Height h in metres	Tally	Frequency
$1.3 \leq h < 1.4$		0
$1.4 \leq h < 1.5$	II	2
$1.5 \leq h < 1.6$	𝍸 𝍸	10
$1.6 \leq h < 1.7$	𝍸 𝍸 𝍸 II	17
$1.7 \leq h < 1.8$	I	1

Ideally, you should use no more than ten class intervals to group your data.

Exercise 8F

1 As part of his Geography fieldwork, Tony took measurements of the steepness of slopes. The steepness was measured as the angle the slope made with the horizontal. Tony's results are shown below.

15°, 16°, 9°, 21°, 32°, 37°, 25°, 36°, 40°, 8°, 32°
13°, 21°, 32°, 29°, 32°, 29°, 32°, 7°, 4°, 18°, 17°

Copy and complete the frequency distribution table below, using 4 equal class intervals.

Class interval (steepness in °)	Tally	Frequency
1 – 10		

[L]

2 Forty people took part in a clay pigeon shooting competition. The points they scored are shown below.

18 24 19 3 24 11 25 10 25 14 25 14 25 9
16 26 21 27 13 23 5 26 22 12 27 20 7 28
21 20 22 16 12 25 7 25 19 17 15 8

(a) Using class intervals 1–5, 6–10, 11–15, 16–20, 21–25, 26–30 construct the frequency table.

(b) Use the same data to construct a frequency table with ten class intervals.

(c) Which of your answers do you think is best? Why?

3 Neville weighed 3 dozen hens' eggs to see if there was much difference between them. They all came from boxes marked size 2. These are his results.

63.1 g 65.4 g 61.9 g 62.2 g 63.4 g 65.1 g 61.7 g 62.2 g

64.9 g 63.5 g 67.1 g 62.8 g 61.9 g 62.6 g 63.1 g 64.3 g

65.0 g 63.7 g 65.2 g 61.8 g 62.1 g 63.5 g 65.1 g 66.3 g

64.4 g 62.3 g 61.5 g 63.7 g 64.7 g 65.1 g 62.3 g 62.8 g

64.7 g 62.2 g 63.6 g 61.4 g

(a) Use class intervals 61.0–61.9, 62.0–62.9, 63.0–63.9, 64.0–64.9, 65.0–65.9, 66.0 and over, to construct a frequency table.

(b) The true class interval for 61.0–61.9 is $60.95 \leqslant x < 61.95$. Why is this?

8.7 Data collection

There are lots of reasons for collecting data. For example:

- market research prior to launching a new product
- quality control to make sure a product is up to standard
- collecting information for reference

Market research

A company is about to launch a new product, for example a new soap powder.
It wants to know what to call its product and which type of advertising campaign is most likely to be successful.
It conducts a survey using interviews and a questionnaire.

Quality control

A fireworks company needs to be sure that its products will perform well.
Every day they take a batch of 20 of each of their range and test them. The fireworks are graded excellent, good or poor.
The production manager studies the results and decides what action to take.

Information and reference

A hotel in a holiday resort keeps daily records of sunshine, rainfall and maximum and minimum temperatures.
This may be useful in the hotel's brochure.

8.8 Questionnaires

One way of collecting data is to use a **questionnaire**.

■ **When you are writing questions for a questionnaire:**

- be clear about what you want to find out, and what data you need.
- ask short, simple questions.

Here are some good examples:

This has a clear choice of two answers.

Are you:

Male ☐
Female ☐

What age are you:

under 21 ☐
21–40 ☐
41–60 ☐
over 60 ☐

Which of these do you like:

Soul ☐
Rock ☐
Pop ☐
Classical ☐

These both offer four choices.

- avoid questions which are too vague, too personal, or which may influence the answer.

Do you go running:

sometimes ☐ occasionally ☐ often ☐

Sometimes, occasionally and often may mean different things to different people.

Have you ever stolen anything from a shop:

Yes ☐ No ☐

Even a hardened criminal is unlikely to answer this question honestly!

Do you agree that running is good for you:

Yes ☐ No ☐

This question suggests that the right answer is Yes. It is **biased**.

Test your questionnaire on a few people first to see if it works or needs to be improved. This is called a **pilot survey**.

Exercise 8G

1 Say, with reasons, whether each of the following is a good or bad question for a questionnaire:

(a) Do you like chips?

(b) How do you feel about school?

(c) What kind of books do you read?

(d) Why do you watch TV?

(e) How old are you?

2 Rewrite the bad questions from question **1** so that they could be used in a questionnaire.

3 Design a questionnaire with no more than five questions to obtain information on a topic of your choice.

Summary of key points

1. Organizing data in a **table** can give you more information than you started with.
2. A **database** is an organized collection of information. It can be stored on paper or in a computer.
3. There are two main types of data:
   - **Qualitative data** is described using words. Examples are:
     place names such as: Sheffield, Swansea
     colours such as: red, green
   - **Quantitative data** consists of numbers. Examples are:
     data that can be counted such as: the number of animals in a zoo
     data that can be measured such as: temperatures and weights.
4. Quantitative data can be discrete or continuous:
   - **Discrete data** can only take particular values. Examples are:
     shoe sizes: 6 $6\frac{1}{2}$ 7 $7\frac{1}{2}$ 8 $8\frac{1}{2}$ . . .
     the number of goals scored in a football match: 0 1 2 3 . . .
     Discrete data has an exact value.
   - **Continuous data** can take any value. Examples are:
     lengths: 1.2 m 2.75 m 17.684 m
     times: 7 s 0.0004 s 27.35 s
     Continuous data cannot be measured exactly. The accuracy of the measurement depends on the accuracy of the measuring instrument.
5. Quantitative data can be grouped into **class intervals** making it easier to record and spot any patterns or trends.
6. In a survey or experiment the **frequency** of an answer or result is the number of times it occurred.
7. The results of a survey or experiment can be collected in a **frequency distribution table**. A blank table used to record data is called a **data capture sheet**.
8. When you are writing questions for a **questionnaire**:
   - be clear what you want to find out and what data you need
   - ask short, simple questions
   - avoid questions which are too vague, too personal, or which may influence the answer.

9 Using and applying mathematics

In your GCSE course you will be using and applying mathematics all the time.

For your GCSE exam, using and applying mathematics is sometimes tested through coursework and sometimes through an examination. Whichever way it is tested the basic ideas are the same.

This unit uses an **investigative task** to show you how to tackle this type of work. Here is the task:

Diagonals

The diagram below shows a regular hexagon.

A diagonal of any shape is a line which joins any two of the vertices (corners) of the shape but which is not an edge of the shape.

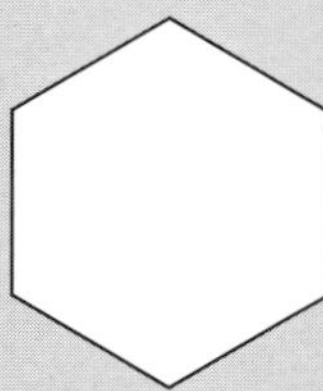

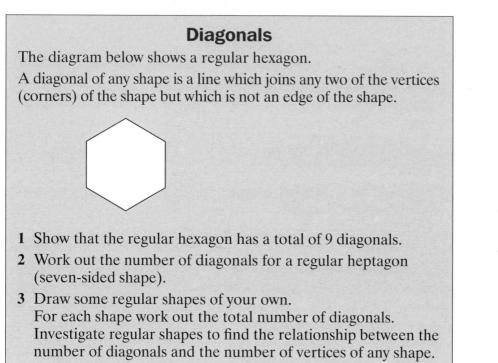

1 Show that the regular hexagon has a total of 9 diagonals.

2 Work out the number of diagonals for a regular heptagon (seven-sided shape).

3 Draw some regular shapes of your own.
For each shape work out the total number of diagonals.
Investigate regular shapes to find the relationship between the number of diagonals and the number of vertices of any shape.

How investigative tasks are marked

Your work will be marked on three qualities which can be described as:

Doing **Showing** **Explaining**

Doing means carrying out the investigation.

Showing means writing down your results so that others can understand what you have done. Tables and diagrams are good ways of showing your results.

Explaining means giving reasons for your answers.

It is important that your work contains all three qualities.

What to do in an investigation

Here is a list of things you should try to do during an investigation *and* things you should provide evidence of in your final report.

Don't worry if you don't understand it all yet. The rest of this unit will help.

If you are doing an investigative task as coursework you can refer to this list.

- Make sure you understand the problem.
- Check to see if you have worked on a similar problem. If you have, try to make use of this experience.
- Try some simple and special cases.
- Plan your work in an ordered way. Have a strategy.
- Record what you are trying to do.
- Record your observations.
- Use appropriate diagrams and forms of communication.
- Record and tabulate any findings and results.
- Predict what you think may happen and test it. This is called testing a conjecture.

For more advanced work you should try to do some or all of this list:

- Try to find and make use of any counter examples.
- Generalize, especially in symbols, if you can.
- Comment on any generalizations.
- Explain or justify your generalizations.
- Try to prove any generalizations.

The rest of this unit shows you how the task called **Diagonals** could be investigated.

Understanding the problem

You need to understand the main idea of the task:

You are being asked to investigate the number of diagonals there are in regular shapes in two dimensions.

An answer to question **1** about the regular hexagon will help to show that you understand the basic idea of the problem.

Remember:
A diagonal is a line from one corner to another that is not a side of the shape.

1 Show that the regular hexagon has a total of 9 diagonals.

Here are the 9 diagonals drawn on the hexagon:

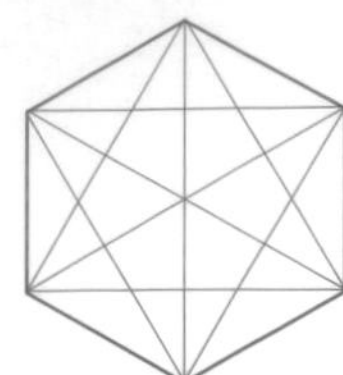

If you label the six vertices of the regular hexagon as:

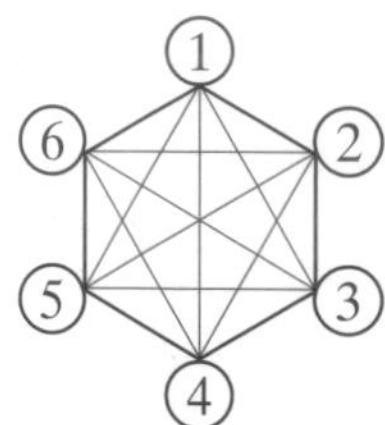

then you can record the 9 diagonals as:

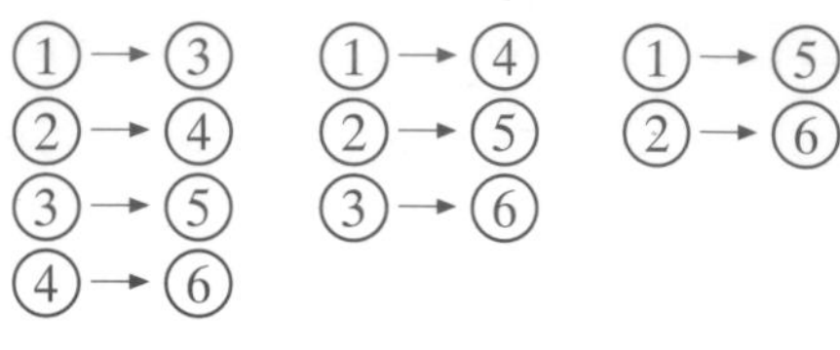

This way of recording the results for the regular hexagon may help at a later stage.

Have you worked on a similar problem?

Only you can answer this but it is quite likely that you have done similar work before.

Compare the way the diagonals of the regular hexagon are recorded:

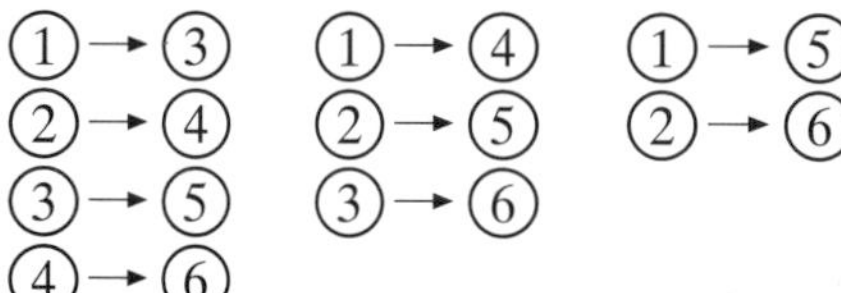

with an array of dots like this:

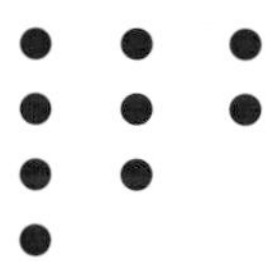

You may have seen similar dot patterns when dealing with number patterns such as the triangular numbers or the square numbers. This may help later.

Question **2** helps to develop your understanding of the problem:

> **2** Work out the number of diagonals for a regular heptagon (seven-sided shape).

Here are the diagonals, the recording of them and the dot pattern:

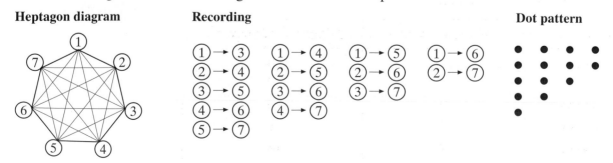

Heptagon diagram

Recording

1 → 3	1 → 4	1 → 5	1 → 6
2 → 4	2 → 5	2 → 6	2 → 7
3 → 5	3 → 6	3 → 7	
4 → 6	4 → 7		
5 → 7			

Dot pattern

Try some simple and special cases

You could just keep exploring different shapes but it is more sensible to choose an order in which to investigate them. For example: start with a triangle, square and pentagon, increasing the number of sides by one each time.

Here are the results in diagrams, the record of them and the dot patterns:

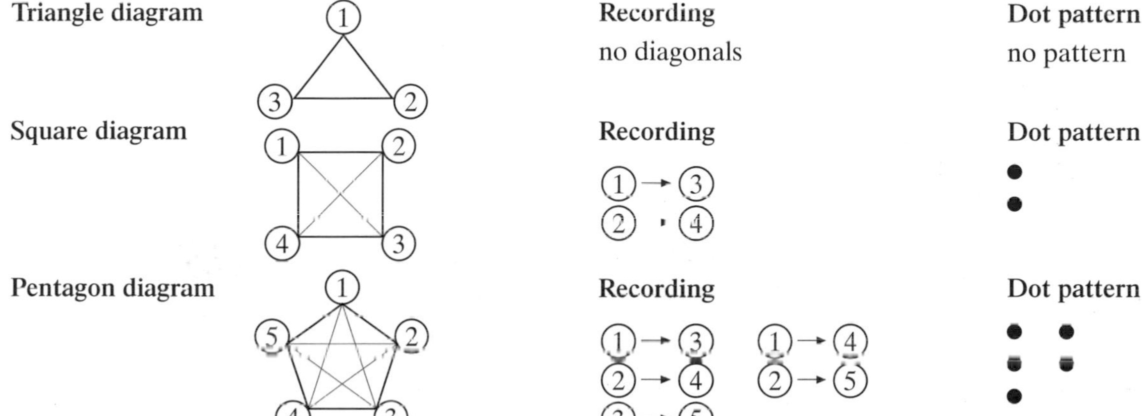

Strategies

It is always worth writing a sentence or two to explain what you have done and how you have done it.

The strategy used so far has been:

Step 1 Draw the shape.

Step 2 Number the vertices.

Step 3 Join up the diagonals starting with those that go from 1; then those that go from 2 and so on.

Step 4 Make a record of the diagonals.

Step 5 Draw the dot pattern.

Once ① → ③ is drawn you do not need to draw ③ → ① in the opposite direction. This is an important part of the strategy.

Recording and tabulating observations and results

You are now at a stage where you can record the results of the investigation so far in a table:

Shape	Number of vertices	Number of diagonals
Triangle	3	0
Square	4	2
Pentagon	5	5
Hexagon	6	9
Heptagon	7	14

Forms of communication

Several forms of **communication** have been used so far: diagrams, the ① ② ③ labelling system, dot patterns and numbers and the table of results.

Now you can look for any pattern in the number of diagonals of the regular shapes.

Observations and predictions

Without the shape names the table of results looks like this:

Vertices	3	4	5	6	7
Diagonals	0	2	5	9	14

You can make many comments or **observations** about this sequence of results.

At a very basic level you might observe that the larger the number of vertices the larger the number of diagonals.

At a higher level you might observe that the numbers of diagonals follow a pattern of:

even, even, odd, odd, even

You might **predict** that for 8 vertices there would be an even number of diagonals.

Remember:
Write down any observations you try out even if they don't work.

Using differences to find patterns

One of the best ways of finding patterns about which you can make observations is the method of **differences**.

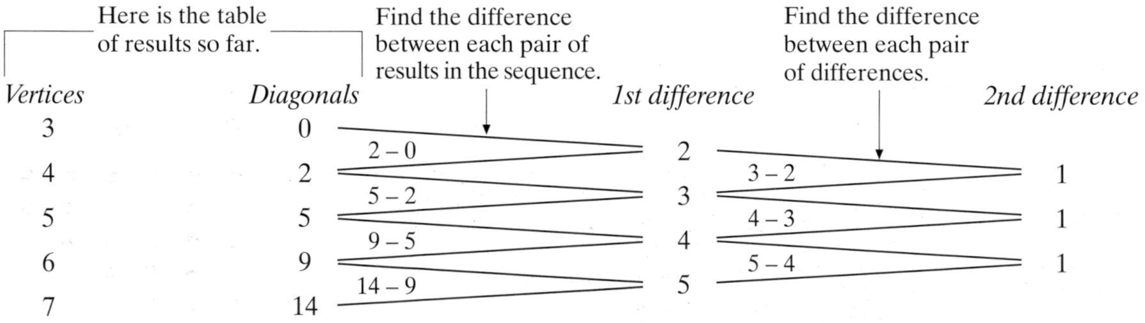

Vertices	*Diagonals*		*1st difference*		*2nd difference*
3	0				
		2 – 0	2		
4	2			3 – 2	1
		5 – 2	3		
5	5			4 – 3	1
		9 – 5	4		
6	9			5 – 4	1
		14 – 9	5		
7	14				

You might now notice that the numbers under the 1st difference column follow a very simple pattern. The numbers under the second difference column are all the same and equal to 1.

This is very useful information as it *suggests* that the pattern of results can be continued as:

Vertices	*Diagonals*		*1st difference*		*2nd difference*
3	0				
			2		
4	2				1
			3		
5	5				1
			4		
6	9				1
			5		
7	14				1
			6	5 + 1	
8	20	14 + 6			1
			7	6 + 1	
9	27	20 + 7			

Making and testing predictions

The method of differences allows you to **predict** (or **conjecture**) that the number of diagonals for a regular shape with 8 vertices is 20 and for a regular shape with 9 sides is 27.

It also tells you that if this is correct you may have found a general pattern.

You can **test** your predictions or conjectures using the diagrams, and the recording and dot pattern method used on page 112:

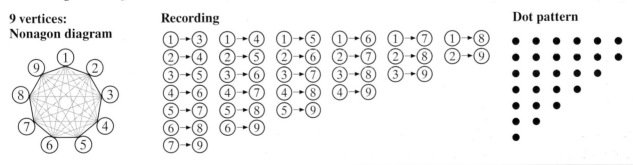

8 vertices:
Octagon diagram

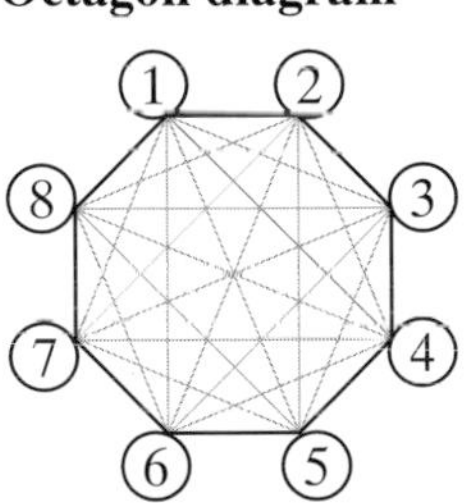

Recording

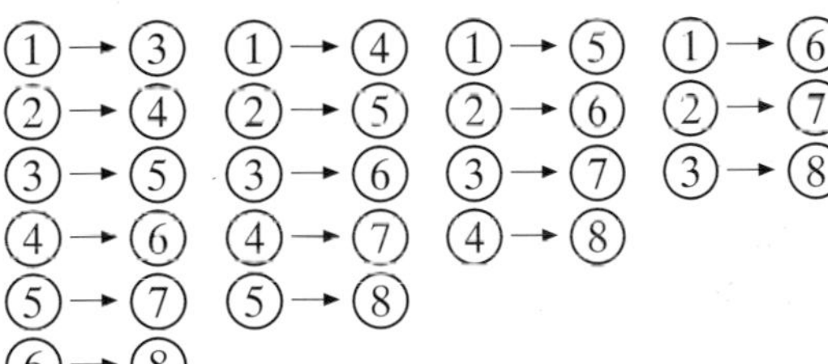

Dot pattern

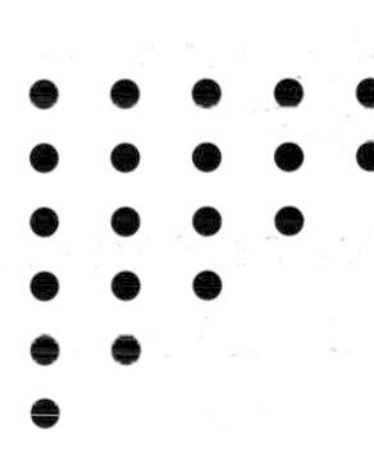

Counting the diagonals confirms the result of 20.

9 vertices:
Nonagon diagram

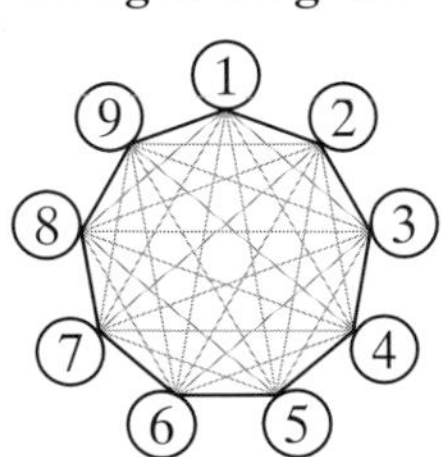

Recording

①→③ ①→④ ①→⑤ ①→⑥ ①→⑦ ①→⑧
②→④ ②→⑤ ②→⑥ ②→⑦ ②→⑧ ②→⑨
③→⑤ ③→⑥ ③→⑦ ③→⑧ ③→⑨
④→⑥ ④→⑦ ④→⑧ ④→⑨
⑤→⑦ ⑤→⑧ ⑤→⑨
⑥→⑧ ⑥→⑨
⑦→⑨

Dot pattern

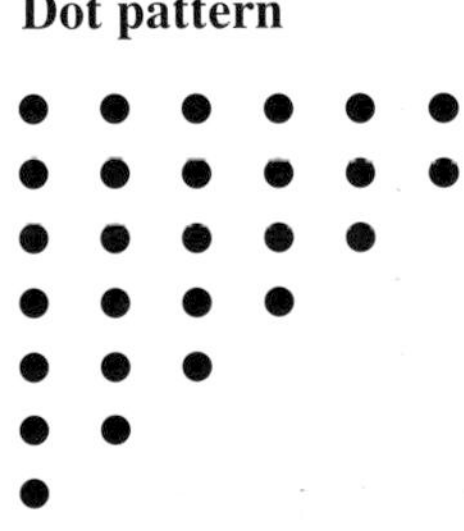

Counting the diagonals confirms the result of 27.

Counter examples
Sometimes your results will *not* confirm your predictions.

Results like these are called **counter examples**. Include them with your other results and use them to help make another prediction.

Making and testing generalizations

When you can explain a pattern with a **general rule** for finding other numbers in the pattern you are **generalizing** or **making a generalization**.

Look at the results and the first differences again:

Vertices	3		4		5		6		7		8		9
Diagonals	0		2		5		9		14		20		27
1st difference		2		3		4		5		6		7	

You can see that the 1st differences follow the sequence of **natural numbers** (apart from 1): 2, 3, 4, 5, 6, 7 and so on. This is a generalization. You can use it to extend the table of results like this:

	10		11		12
	35		44		54
8		9		10	

Generalizing in symbols

The next stage in developing this investigation is to try to put the generalization in **symbolic** (or **algebraic**) **form**. The correct use of **symbols** is usually a very important step on the road to achieving the higher GCSE grades (C to A*).

Sometimes it is quite easy to spot a general rule, but this one is a bit harder. One of the keys here is to see that we have:

Vertices	Diagonals
3	$0 = 3 \times 0$
5	$5 = 5 \times 1$
7	$14 = 7 \times 2$
9	$27 = 9 \times 3$

which suggests that with 11 vertices the number of diagonals $= 11 \times 4 = 44$. This does work – it is a result we have already obtained.

Now look again at the full set of results:

Vertices	Diagonals
3	$0 = 3 \times 0 \quad = 3 \times \frac{0}{2}$
4	$2 = 4 \times \frac{1}{2} \quad = 4 \times \frac{1}{2}$
5	$5 = 5 \times 1 \quad = 5 \times \frac{2}{2}$
6	$9 = 6 \times 1\frac{1}{2} \quad = 6 \times \frac{3}{2}$
7	$14 = 7 \times 2 \quad = 7 \times \frac{4}{2}$
8	$20 = 8 \times 2\frac{1}{2} \quad = 8 \times \frac{5}{2}$
9	$27 = 9 \times 3 \quad = 9 \times \frac{6}{2}$
10	$35 = 10 \times 3\frac{1}{2} = 10 \times \frac{7}{2}$
11	$44 = 11 \times 4 \quad = 11 \times \frac{8}{2}$

This suggests that the **general rule** is:

Diagonals = Vertices × ((Vertices – 3) ÷ 2)

Writing:

D for the number of diagonals
V for the number of vertices

the **symbolic form** of the general rule is

$$D = V \times \frac{(V - 3)}{2}$$

or $D = \frac{1}{2}V(V - 3)$

Test your generalization

You can test the generalization in one of two ways.

One way is to use values of V and D for which you know the result. If you put V equal to 6 in the rule you get:

$$D = \tfrac{1}{2}V(V - 3)$$
$$D = \tfrac{1}{2}6\,(6 - 3)$$
$$= 3\,(3) = 9$$

which agrees with the results and so confirms the rule.

Another way is to test the rule for a new value of V and check the result by using the dot pattern or extending the table of results. For example, $V = 12$.

$$D = \tfrac{1}{2}(12)\,(12 - 3)$$
$$= 6 \times 9$$
$$= 54$$

Using the rule you expect D to be 54 in a 12-sided shape.

If you check this either by extending the table of results or by drawing, recording and dot patterns you should find that when V is 12 then D is 54.

So you have now tested your generalization in two ways.

Explaining or justifying your generalizations

Now that you have found a formula, the next stage is to justify it. You can do this in at least two ways.

Justification using differences

Unit 13, page 174, shows you how to use differences to find a function. You can use that method here.

The set of results and 1st and 2nd differences is:

Vertices (V)	3		4		5		6		7		8		9
Diagonals (D)	0		2		5		9		14		20		27
1st difference		2		3		4		5		6		7	
2nd difference			1		1		1		1		1		

Because the 2nd differences are constant, the formula is quadratic. So it must be of the type:

$$D = aV^2 + bV + c$$

The formula found is $D = \frac{1}{2}V(V - 3)$

If you multiply out the brackets you get:

$$D = \tfrac{1}{2}V^2 - 1\tfrac{1}{2}V$$

So your formula is of the expected type with $a = \frac{1}{2}$, $b = 1\frac{1}{2}$ and $c = 0$

The 2nd difference is equal to $2a$.

So $2a = 1$ and $a = \frac{1}{2}$.

You could say that the number you multiply V^2 by (called the coefficient of V^2) is half the 2nd difference.

All you need to do with a quadratic formula is check that it works in 3 cases. Try $V = 3$, 4 and 5:

V	D	
3	$\frac{1}{2}(3)(3-3) = 1\frac{1}{2} \times 0 = 0$	checked
4	$\frac{1}{2}(4)(4-3) = 2 \times 1 = 2$	checked
5	$\frac{1}{2}(5)(5-3) = 2\frac{1}{2} \times 2 = 5$	checked

So these 3 successful checks mean that you have justified the general rule as a quadratic formula and that it is:

$$D = \tfrac{1}{2}V(V - 3)$$

Justification using the dot pattern

You can justify the generalization in a more sophisticated way – leading to a better GCSE grade – using the dot pattern.

To do this look at the dot patterns for 6 and 7 vertices. These are:

6 vertices

● ● ●
● ● ●
● ●
●

7 vertices

● ● ● ●
● ● ● ●
● ● ●
● ●
●

Putting one more dot on the top row of each pattern would have given the triangular numbers pattern – for 7 vertices:

● ● ● ● ●
● ● ● ●
● ● ●
● ●
●

So for 7 vertices the number of diagonals is 1 less than the 5th triangular number. The formula for the nth triangular number is $\frac{1}{2}n(n + 1)$

The dot pattern approach tells us that the rule is:

Vertices	**Diagonals**
V	$(V-2)$th triangular number minus 1

Since the nth triangular number is $\frac{1}{2}n\ (n+1)$ the $(V-2)$th triangular number is:

$$\begin{aligned} &\tfrac{1}{2}(V-2)(V-2+1) \quad (\text{using } n = V-2) \\ &= \tfrac{1}{2}(V-2)(V-1) \\ &= \tfrac{1}{2}(V^2 - V - 2V + 2) \\ &= \tfrac{1}{2}(V^2 - 3V + 2) \end{aligned}$$

so for V vertices, the number of diagonals, D, is:

$$\begin{aligned} D &= \tfrac{1}{2}(V^2 - 3V + 2) - 1 \\ &= \tfrac{1}{2}V^2 - 1\tfrac{1}{2}V + 1 - 1 \\ &= \tfrac{1}{2}V^2 - 1\tfrac{1}{2}V \\ D &= \tfrac{1}{2}(V^2 - 3V) \quad (\text{or } D = \tfrac{1}{2}V(V-3)) \end{aligned}$$

This has really justified the general rule in a strong way, because it has gone back to the geometry of the problem.

Proving your generalization

To do this, think of a general regular polygon with V vertices, labelled from 1 to V:

Starting at any vertex, for example ①, the number of diagonals will be $(V-3)$, because the lines drawn will go to all but ① itself and the two vertices either side of ①.

The same will be true for every other vertex.

For each vertex there are $(V-3)$ diagonals and there are V vertices.

So the total number of diagonals is:

$$V(V-3)$$

But this gives the diagonals going in both directions. So it really gives double the number of different diagonals.
Hence the actual number of diagonals is:

$$\tfrac{1}{2}V(V-3)$$

This proves the result.

Extending the investigation

The process outlined in this unit is sufficient to achieve the top grade at GCSE. However, unlike textbook exercises and examination questions, a mathematical investigation is never finished. One of the things you can always do is extend the investigation.
Here are suggestions of two extensions of 'Diagonals' which you might like to see as a future challenge.

Extension 1

What happens in the case when the shape is not regular, looking in particular at concave shapes such as:

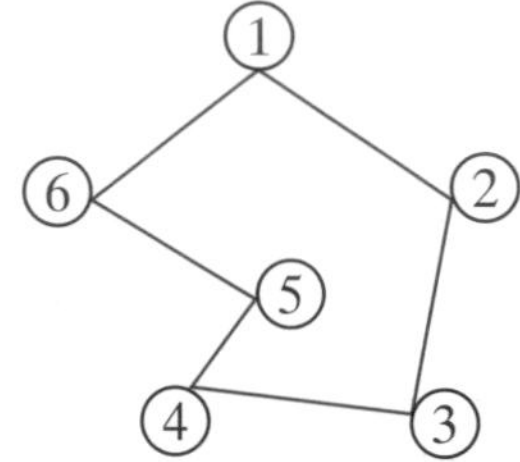

The angle at corner ⑤ is bigger than 180° so the hexagon is concave.

or special cases such as:

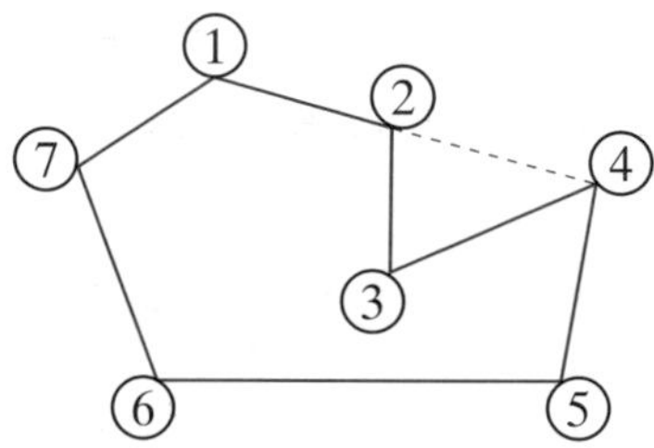

If you continue the side from corner ① to ② it passes through corner ④.

Extension 2

Try to obtain a general rule for shapes in three dimensions, such as:

a cube:

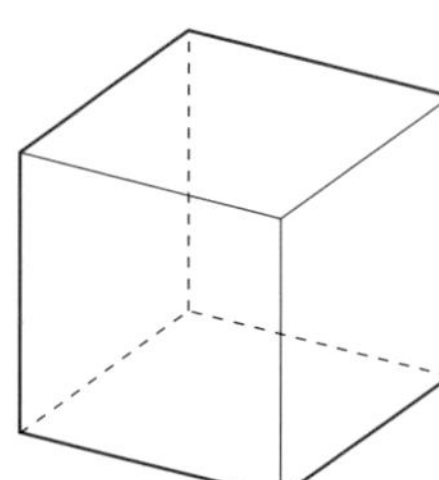

an octahedron:

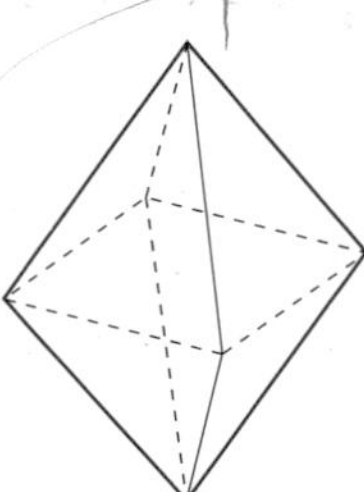

Neither of these extensions is easy. The solutions require mathematical skills beyond the GCSE syllabus. However, there is nothing to stop you having a go.

10 Angles

This unit is about angles and how to use them in calculations and to show directions.

An angle is a measure of turn. The turn can be **clockwise** ↷ or **anti-clockwise** ↺ .

Angles are usually measured in degrees (° for short). A complete turn is 360°.

You need to know the names of these types of angles:

An angle of 90° is a quarter-turn or **right angle**

A right angle is usually marked with this symbol.

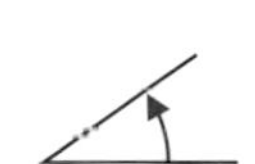

An angle between 0° and 90° is an **acute angle.**

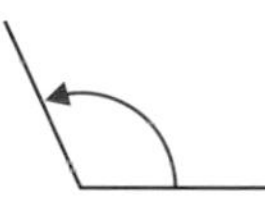

An angle between 90° and 180° is an **obtuse angle.**

An angle between 180° and 360° is a **reflex angle.**

Angle D can be described as angle CDE, angle EDC or in these three ways:

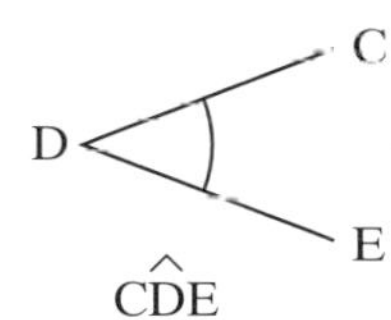

$\hat{CDE}$

...with a 'hat'

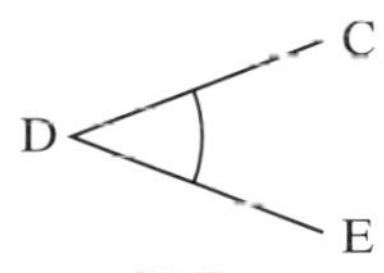

∠CDE

...with an angle sign

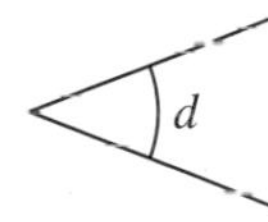

...with a letter

10.1 Calculating angles in triangles and quadrilaterals

If you place two right angles together they make a straight line. A right angle is 90°, so if any number of angles are placed together and make a straight line the angles must add up to $2 \times 90° = 180°$.

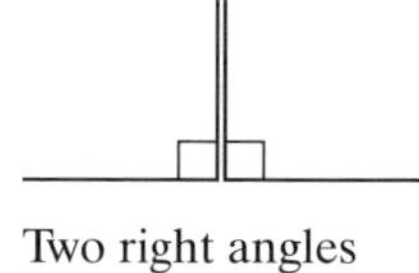

Two right angles make a straight line.
$2 \times 90° = 180°$

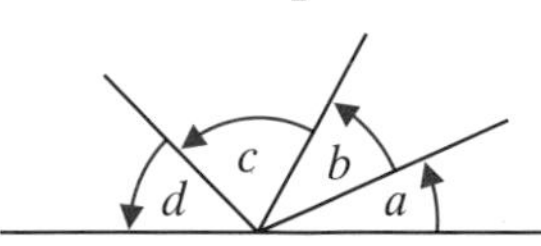

These angles make a straight line.
So $a + b + c + d = 180°$

■ **Angles on a straight line add up to 180°**

These four angles placed together at the point make four right angles or 360°

■ **Angles at a point add up to 360°**

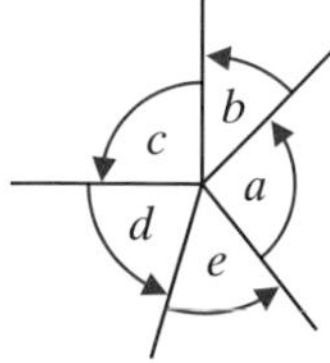

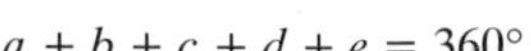

$a + b + c + d + e = 360°$

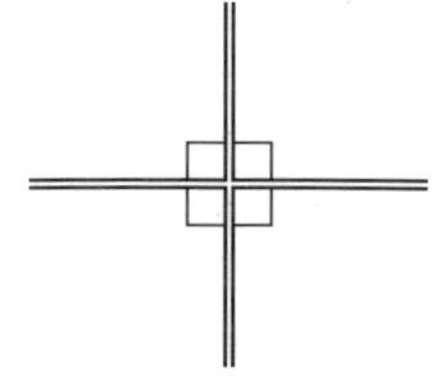

$4 \times 90° = 360°$

Where the two straight lines meet:

$$a + b = 180° \quad \text{(angles on a straight line)}$$

and

$$a + d = 180° \quad \text{(angles on a straight line)}$$

$$\text{so } b = d$$

The angles b and d are called **vertically opposite angles**.

In the same way $\quad a = c$

$a = c$

$d = b$

■ **Vertically opposite angles are equal.**

Interior angles of a triangle

Step 1: draw any triangle on paper and cut it out.
Step 2: colour each angle of the triangle with a different colour.
Step 3: draw a straight line on paper.
Step 4: tear each angle from the triangle and place the angles together against the straight line.
Step 5: write down what you notice.

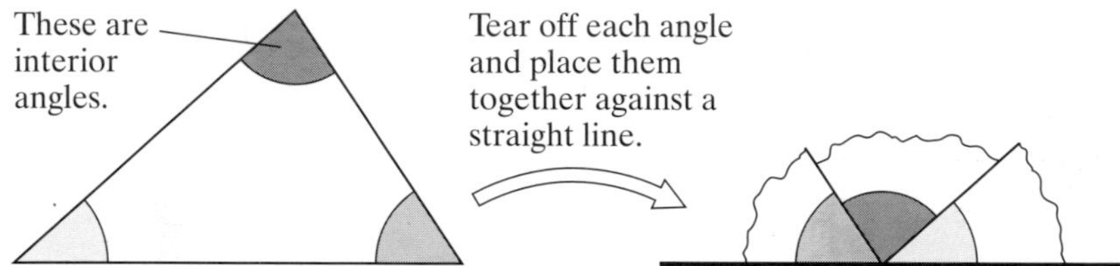

The angles placed together make a straight line so they add to 180°. Try this yourself with a different triangle.

■ **The sum of the interior angles of a triangle is 180°.**

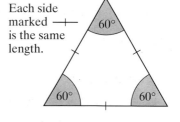

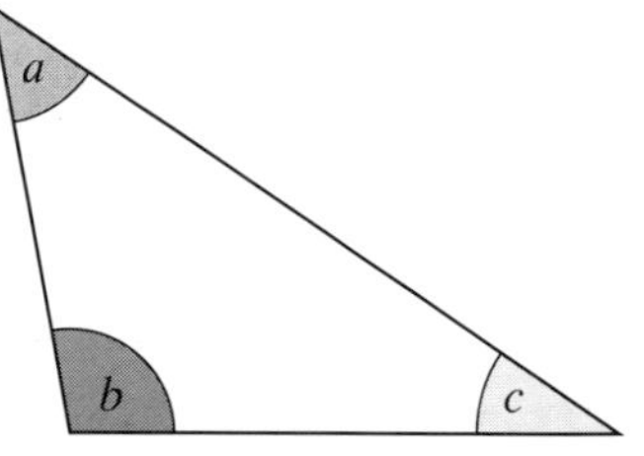

$a + b + c = 180°$

An **equilateral triangle** has rotational symmetry of order 3 so its interior angles are all equal to each other. The angles add to 180° so each angle is 180° ÷ 3 or 60°.

Each side marked —+— is the same length.

60°

■ **Each interior angle of an equilateral triangle is 60°.**

The height of an **isosceles triangle** is a line of symmetry so the two base angles are equal.

Line of symmetry

The sides marked —++— are the same length.

■ **The base angles of an isosceles triangle are equal.**

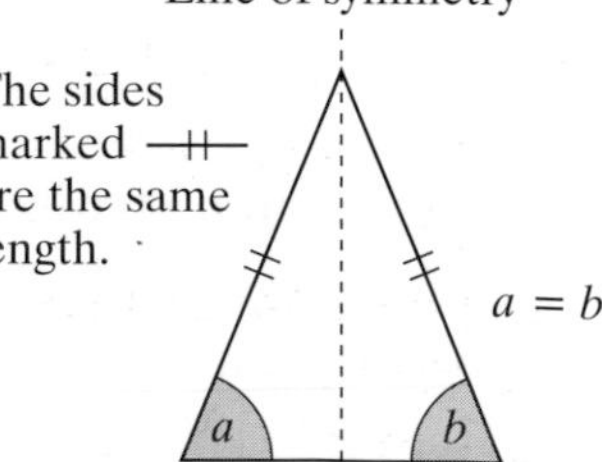

Interior angles of a quadrilateral

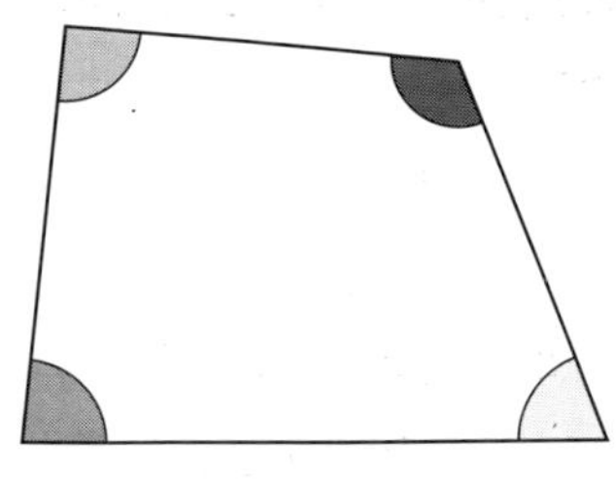

Step 1: draw any quadrilateral on card or paper and cut it out.
Step 2: colour each angle of the quadrilateral differently.
Step 3: on paper draw round the outline of the quadrilateral and colour the angles the same as in step 2.
Step 4: starting at one corner of the outline, place the cut out quadrilateral in different positions so that it makes a tessellation.
(A **tessellation** is an arrangement of a shape or a set of shapes on a flat surface so that *all the space is filled, with no gaps and no overlaps*.)
Step 5: draw the outline of the quadrilateral in these positions and colour the angles the same as in step 2.

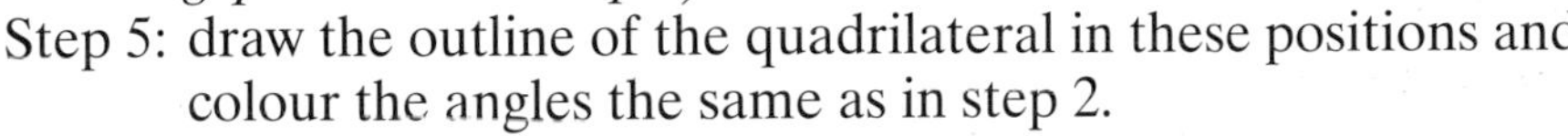

Step 6: repeat steps 4 and 5 until the first outline is completely surrounded.
Step 7: write down what you notice about the angles at each corner.

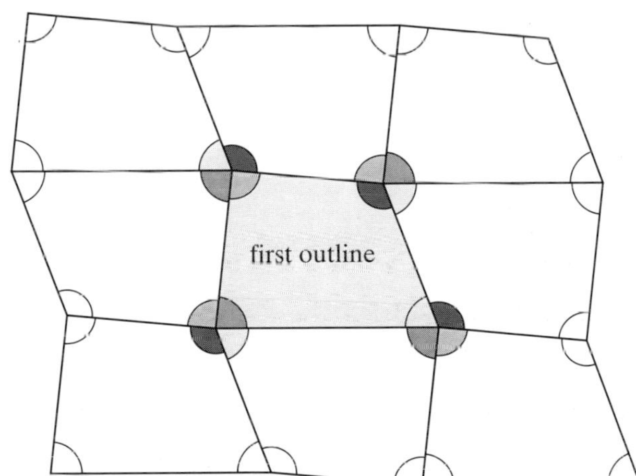

At each corner point the four different angles of the quadrilateral appear. There are no gaps so the angles add to 360°.

Try this yourself with a different quadrilateral.

■ **The sum of the interior angles of a quadrilateral is 360°.**

Example 1

Work out the lettered angles, giving reasons.

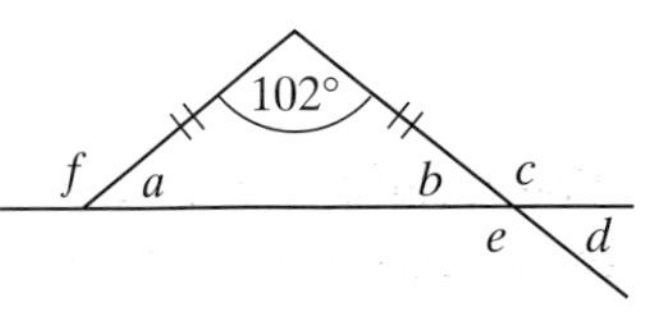

The sides marked —+|— are the same length.

$a + b + 102° = 180°$ (sum of angles of triangle)

so $a + b = 180° - 102° = 78°$

$a = 78° \div 2 = 39°$ (base angles of isosceles triangle)
$b = 39°$

$c = 180° - 39° = 141°$ (angles on a straight line)
$d = 39°$ (vertically opposite angles)
$e = 141°$ (vertically opposite angles)
$f = 180° - 39° = 141°$ (angles on a straight line)

Worked examination question

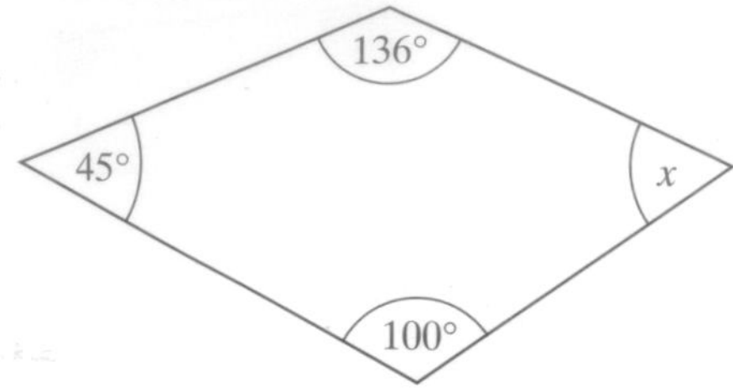

Diagram NOT accurately drawn.

[L]

Work out the value of x.

$x + 136° + 45° + 100° = 360°$ (sum of angles of quadrilateral)

$x + 281° = 360°$

so $x = 360° - 281° = 79°$

Worked examination question

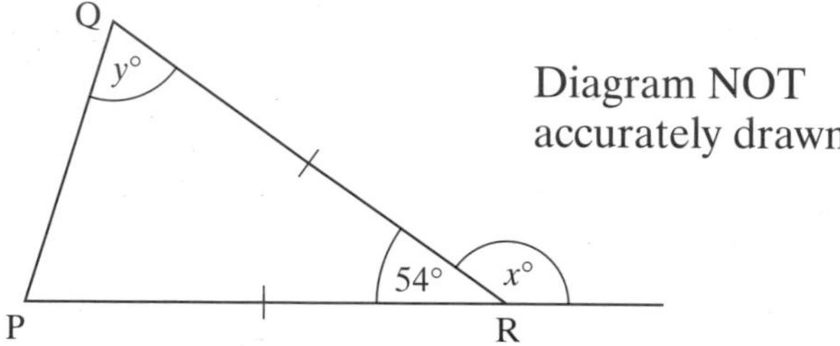

Diagram NOT accurately drawn.

PR = QR and angle PRQ = 54°.

(a) Work out the value of x.

Triangle PQR is a special type of triangle.

(b) Write down the mathematical name of this type of triangle.

(c) Work out the value of y. [L]

(a) $x° = 180° - 54°$ (angles on a straight line)

$x = 126$

(b) Triangle PQR has two equal sides so it is an isosceles triangle.

(c) Angle P + $y°$ + 54° = 180° (sum of angles of triangle)

so Angle P + $y°$ = 126°

Angle P = $y°$ (base angles of isosceles triangle)

so $y° = 126° \div 2$

$y = 63$

Exercise 10A

Work out the lettered angles, giving reasons.

1

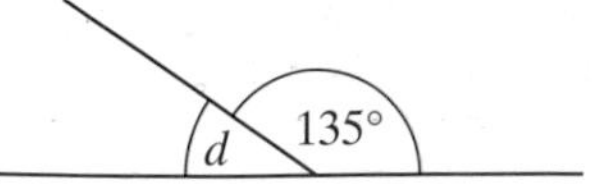

2

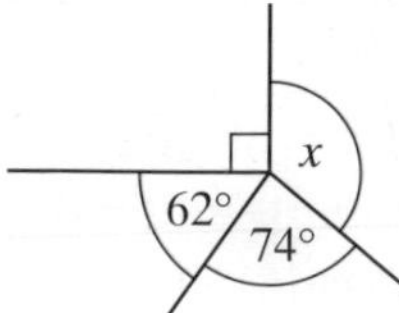

3

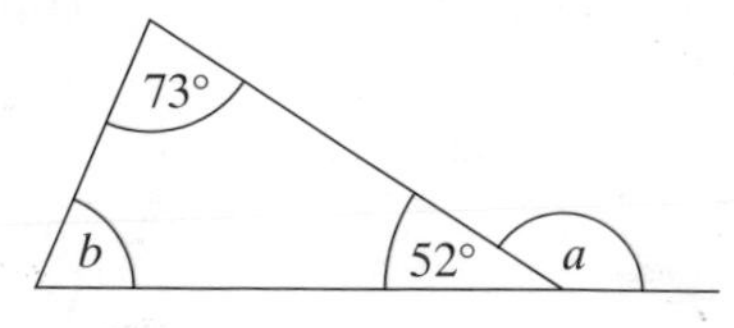

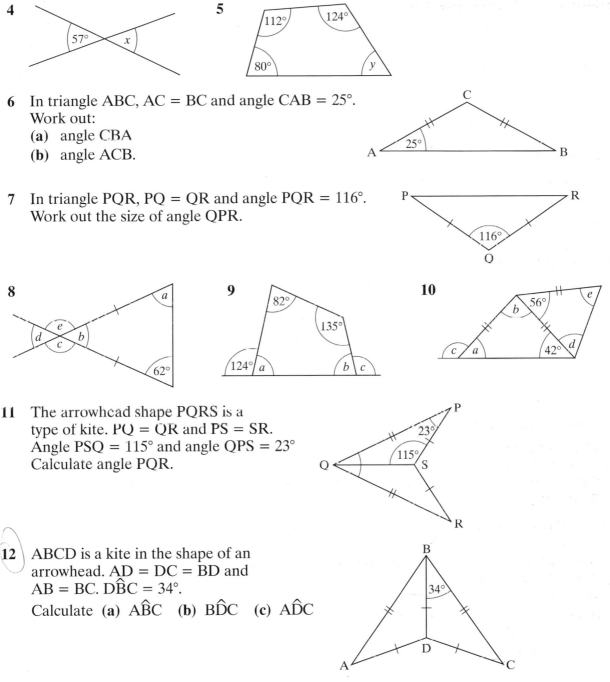

4

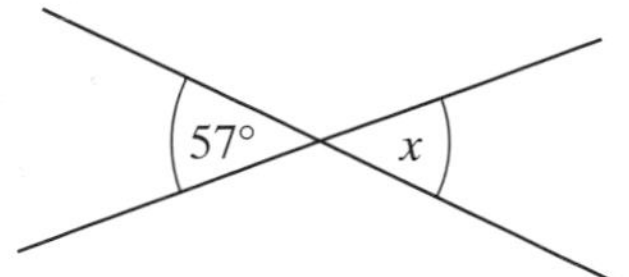

5

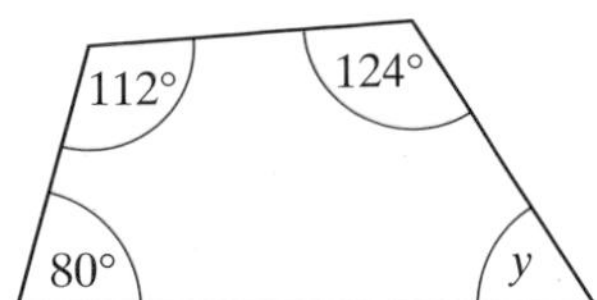

6 In triangle ABC, AC = BC and angle CAB = 25°.
Work out:
(a) angle CBA
(b) angle ACB.

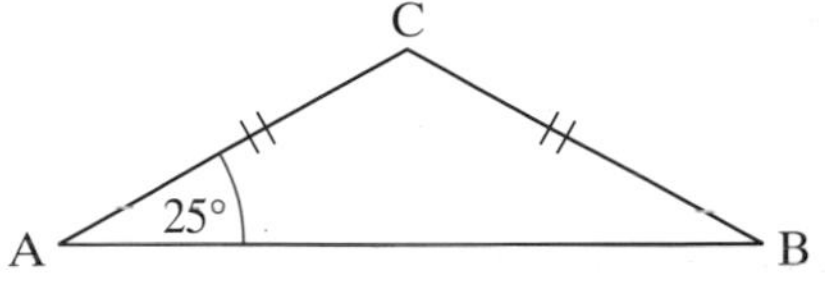

7 In triangle PQR, PQ = QR and angle PQR = 116°.
Work out the size of angle QPR.

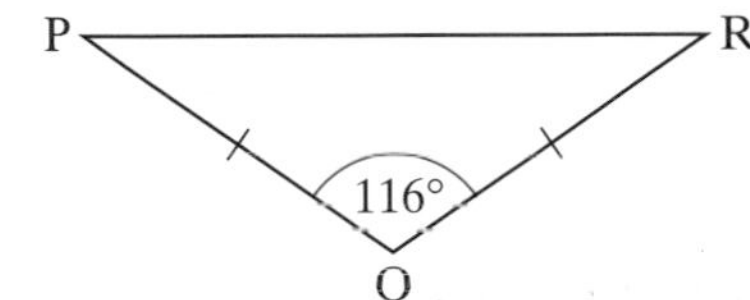

8

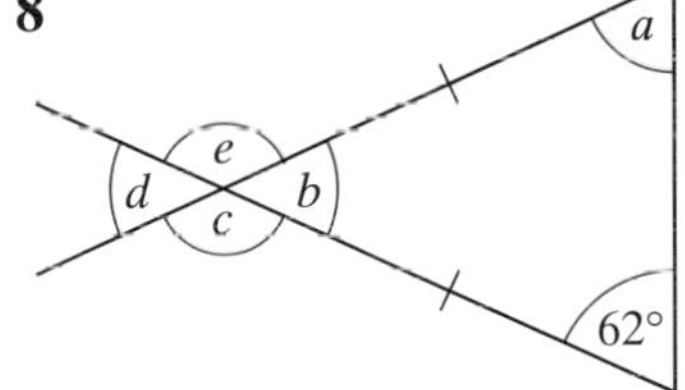

9

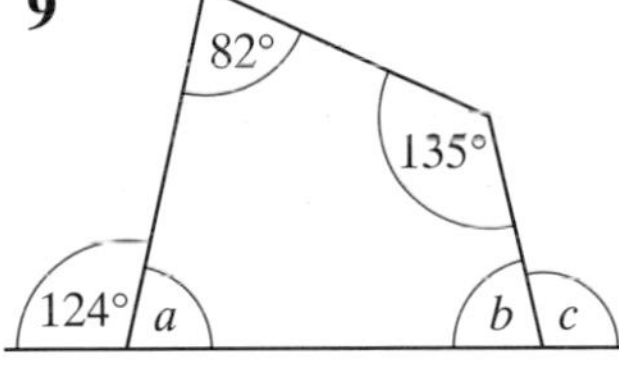

10

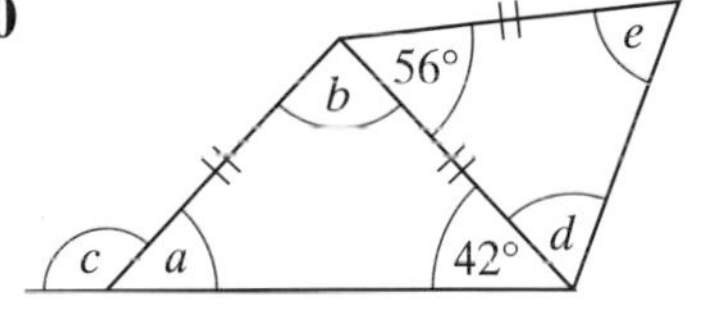

11 The arrowhead shape PQRS is a type of kite. PQ = QR and PS = SR. Angle PSQ = 115° and angle QPS = 23° Calculate angle PQR.

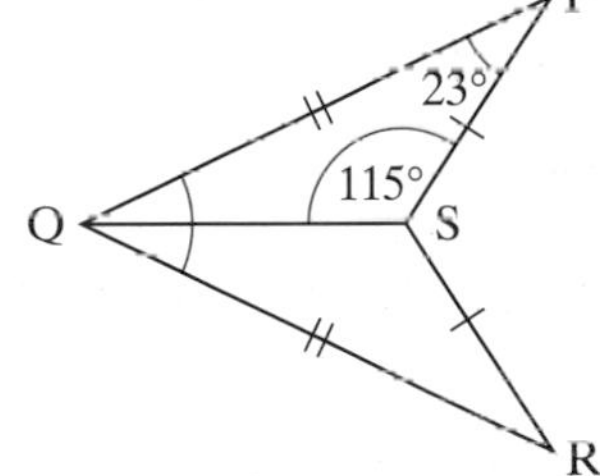

12 ABCD is a kite in the shape of an arrowhead. AD = DC = BD and AB = BC. $D\hat{B}C = 34°$.
Calculate **(a)** $A\hat{B}C$ **(b)** $B\hat{D}C$ **(c)** $A\hat{D}C$

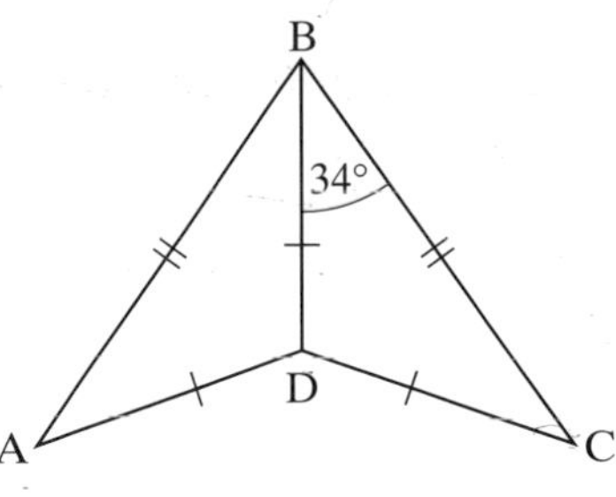

13

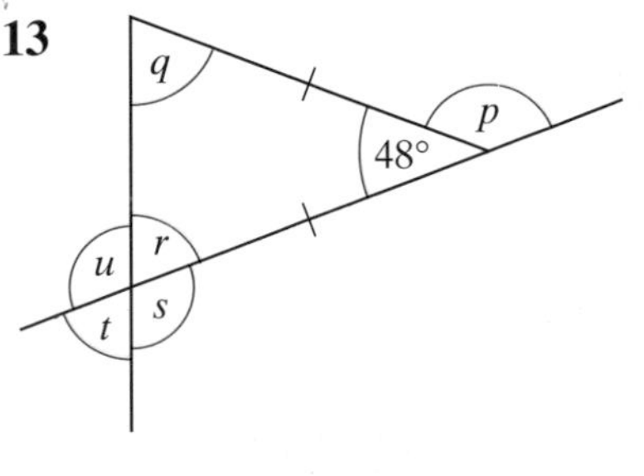

14

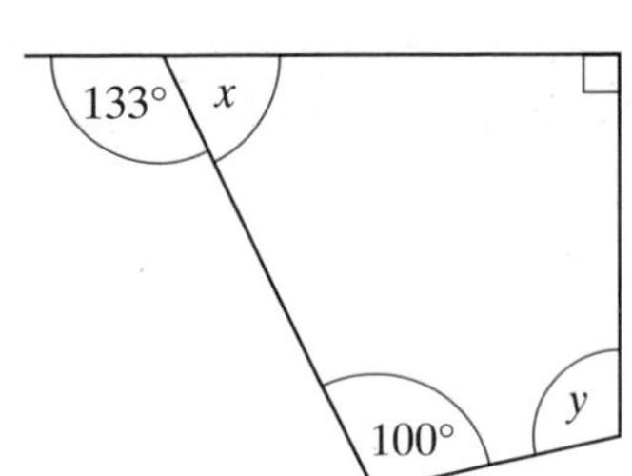

15

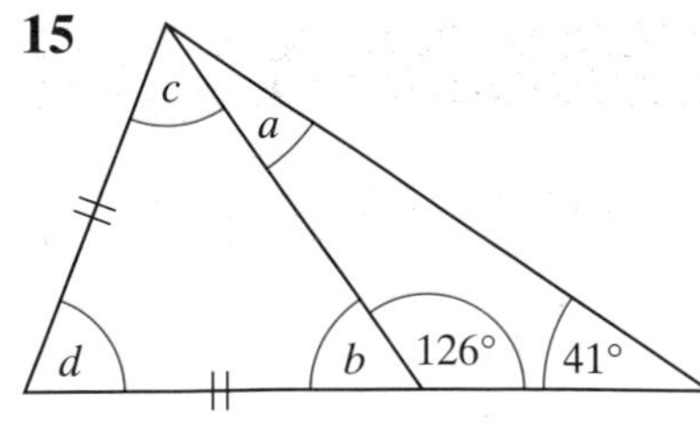

10.2 Calculating angles in polygons

Sum of exterior angles

Step 1: draw a polygon (with each angle less than 180°) on paper.
Step 2: extend each side of the polygon to form the **exterior angles**.
Step 3: label each exterior angle with a different letter.
Step 4: cut out the exterior angles leaving some paper.
Step 5: place the angles together at a point.
Step 6: write down what you notice.

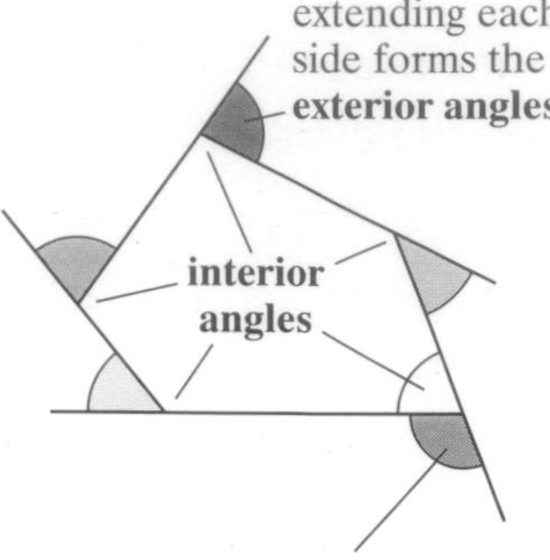
extending each side forms the **exterior angles**
interior angles

At each vertex: interior angle + exterior angle = 180°

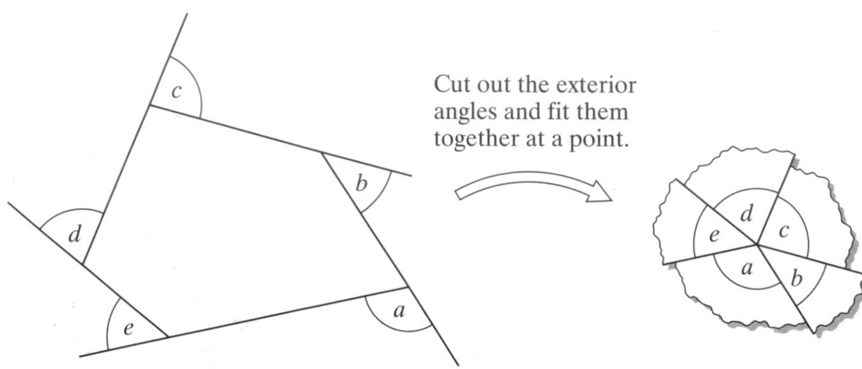
c
b
d
e
a
Cut out the exterior angles and fit them together at a point.
d
c
e
a
b

The exterior angles fit together at a point with no gaps, so they add to 360°.

Try this yourself with a polygon with a different number of sides.

- **The sum of the exterior angles of any polygon is 360°.**
- **At each vertex of a polygon the sum of the interior angle and the exterior angle is 180°.**

Sum of interior angles

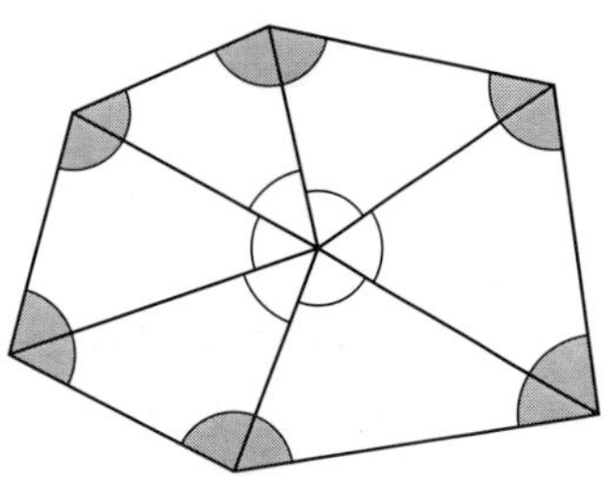

In this hexagon the six vertices are joined to a point inside to make six triangles.

The sum of the interior angles of the hexagon and the angles at the point inside equals the sum of the angles of six triangles, so:

sum of interior angles of a hexagon + 360° = 6 × 180°
so: sum of interior angles of a hexagon = (6 × 180°) – 360°
= 720°

To find the sum of the interior angles of a polygon with n sides join all the vertices to a point in the centre to make n triangles.

- **The sum of the interior angles of a polygon with n sides is $(n \times 180°) - 360°$ usually written $(n - 2) \times 180°$**

If the polygon is regular, each interior angle is the sum of all the interior angles divided by the number of sides.

Example 2

Work out the size of an interior angle of a regular nonagon.
Remember: a nonagon has 9 sides.

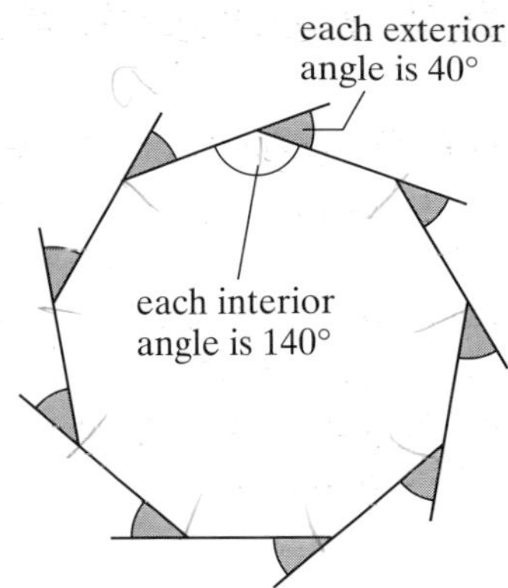

First method, using exterior angles

The nine exterior angles add to 360°.
All the exterior angles of a regular nonagon are equal
one exterior angle is 360° ÷ 9 = 40°
so one interior angle is 180° – 40° = 140° (angles on a straight line)
An interior angle of a regular nonagon is 140°.

Second method, using interior angles

A regular nonagon has nine equal sides.
Join all the vertices to the centre, O, of the nonagon.
The sum of all the angles at O is 360°

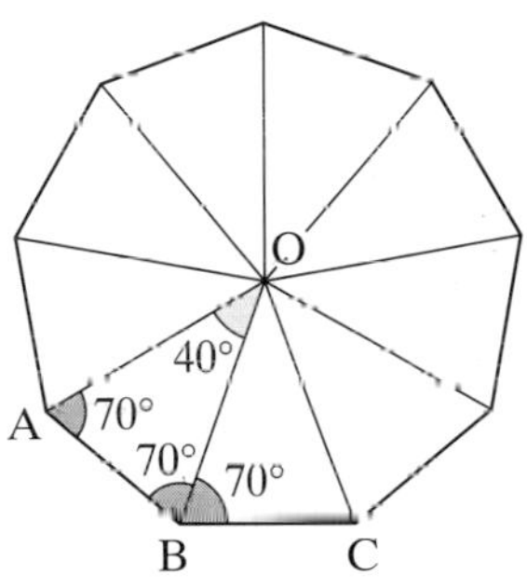

so angle AOB = 360° ÷ 9 = 40°
Angle ABO + angle BAO = 140° (sum of angles of triangle)
Angle ABO = angle BAO = 70° (base angles of isosceles triangle)

Angle CBO = 70° (by symmetry) so angle ABC is 140°

An interior angle of a regular nonagon is 140°.

Example 3

Calculate x.

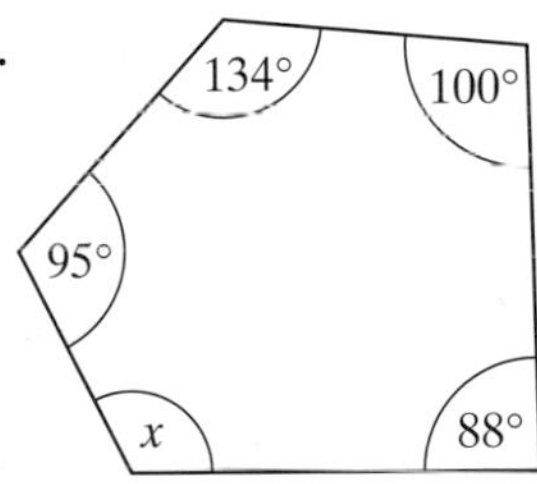

First method, using exterior angles

Four of the exterior angles are:

180° – 88° = 92°
180° – 100° = 80°
180° – 134° = 46°
180° – 95° = 85°

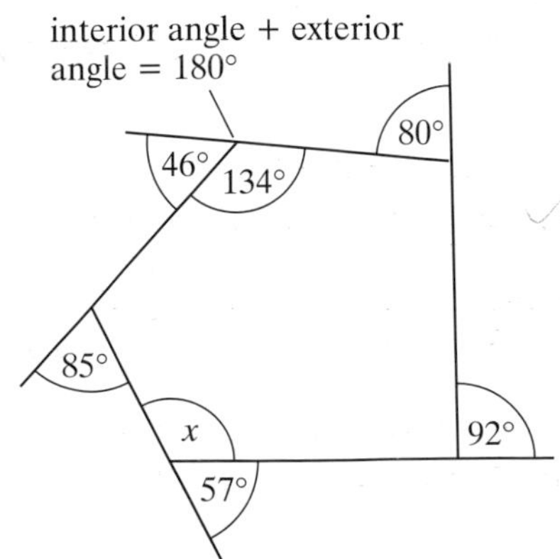

These four angles add to 303°.
The exterior angles of a polygon add to 360°.
So the exterior angle next to x is 360° – 303° = 57°

and x = 180° – 57° = 123°

Second method, using interior angles

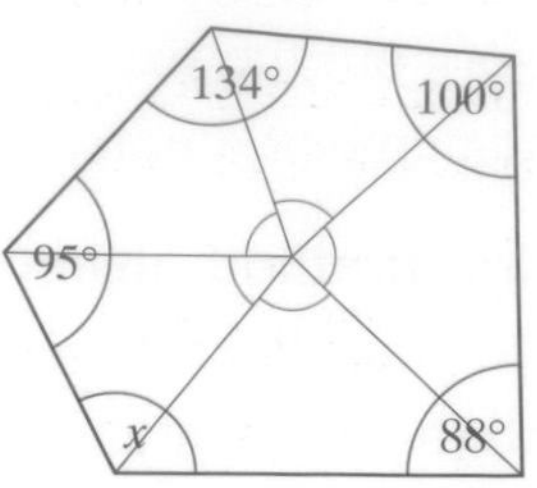

Join all the vertices to a point inside the pentagon to make five triangles.

The sum of all the angles in five triangles is $5 \times 180° = 900°$
This includes 360° at the point.

So the sum of all the interior angles of the pentagon is $900° - 360° = 540°$

Adding all the interior angles:

$$88° + 100° + 134° + 95° + x = 540°$$

so $x = 540° - 417° = 123°$

Exercise 10B

In each question give reasons for your answers.

1 Calculate:
(a) p
(b) q

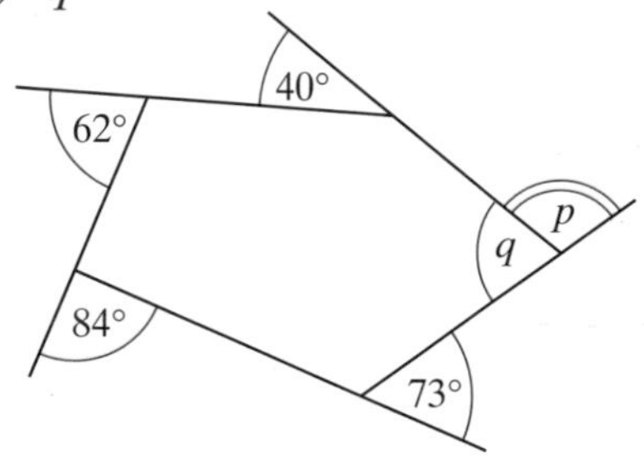

2 Calculate m

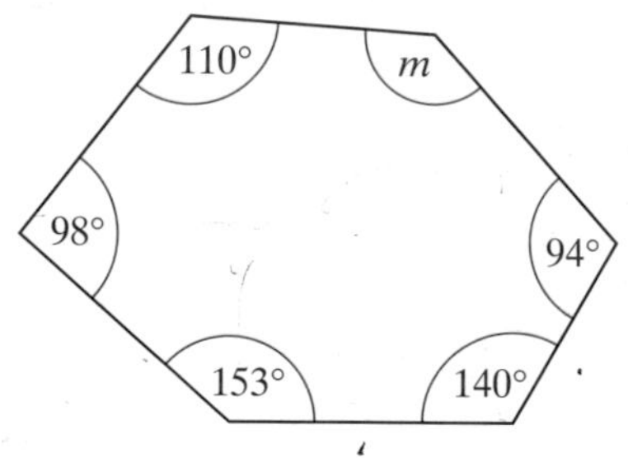

3 Calculate the size of one interior angle of a regular decagon.

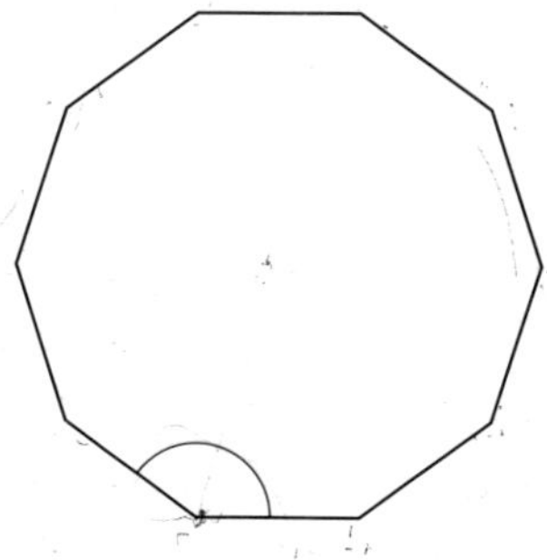

4 ABCDE is a regular pentagon.
O is the centre of the pentagon.
Work out the value of:
(a) x
(b) y

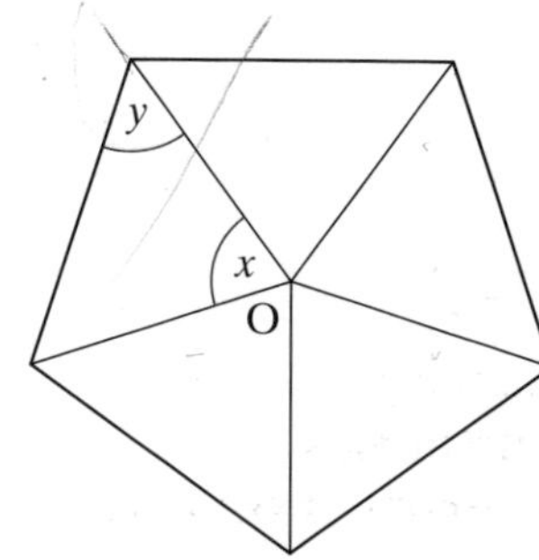

10.3 Calculating angles at parallel lines

When a straight line crosses a pair of parallel lines **corresponding angles** are formed:

Parallel lines are the same distance apart all along their length.
Lines marked —>— are parallel.

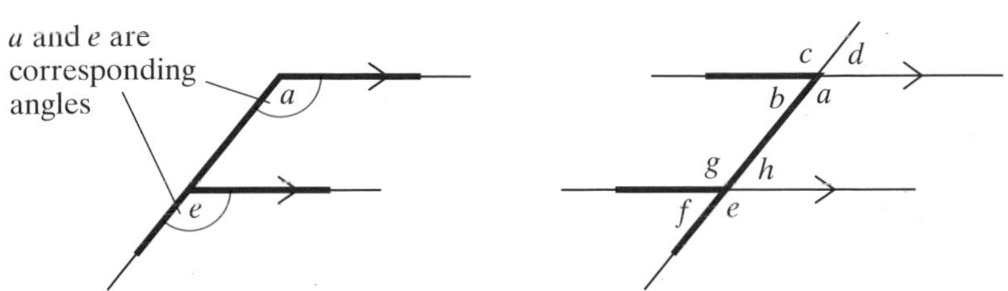

If you cut out the angle e it would fit exactly over angle a.
So $a = e$
Also, angle $b = f$, angle $c = g$ and angle $d = h$.
These are all corresponding angles as well.

They are called corresponding angles because they are on corresponding sides of the parallel lines and the line crossing them.

Sometimes they are called **F** angles, because the shape of the lines makes the letter **F**.

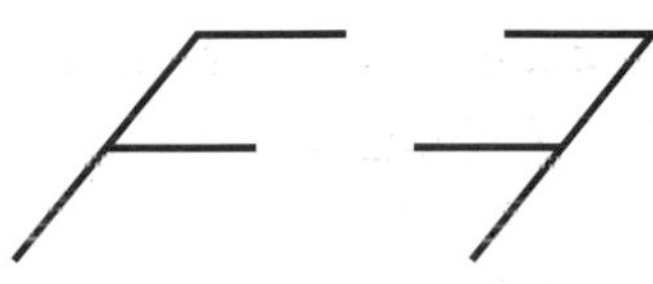

■ **Corresponding angles are equal.**

This drawing can be rotated so that angle x fits exactly over angle y.

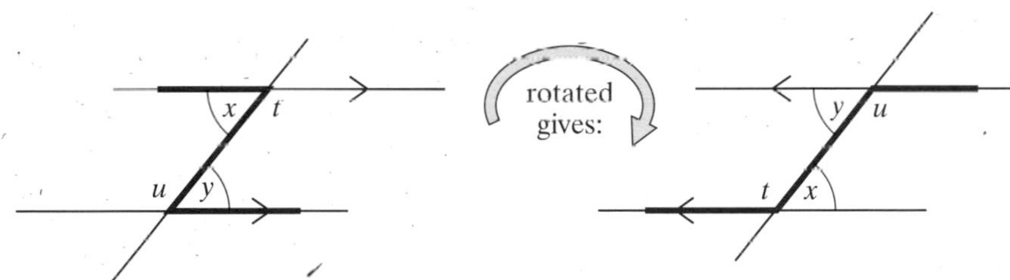

So $x = y$
They are called **alternate angles**.
Also angle $t = u$, because these are alternate angles as well.
They are called alternate angles because they are on alternate sides of the parallel lines and the line crossing them.

Sometimes they are called **Z** angles because the shape of the lines makes a letter **Z**.

■ **Alternate angles are equal.**

Example 4

Calculate a, b and c, giving reasons.

$a = 56°$ (alternate angles)
$b = 72°$ (alternate angles)
$a + b + c = 180°$ (sum of angles of triangle)

So:

$56° + 72° + c = 180°$
$c = 180° - 128° = 52°$

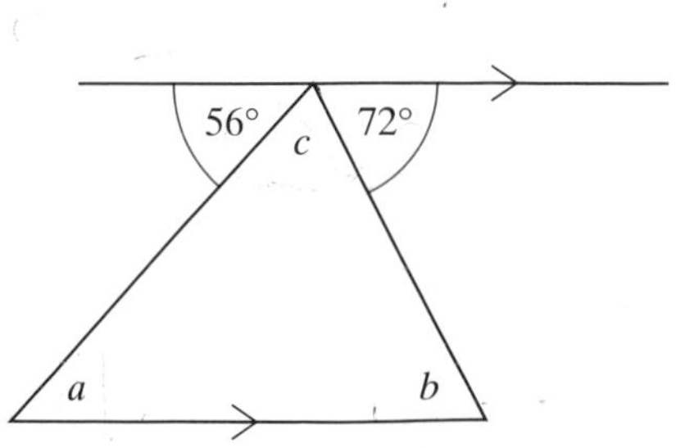

Worked examination question

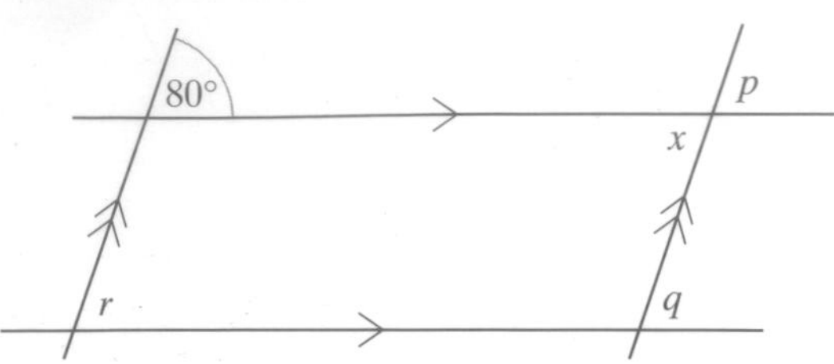

Diagram NOT accurately drawn.

The diagram has two pairs of parallel lines.
Angles marked p and q are equal.

(a) What geometrical name is given to equal angles of this type?
(b) Write down the size of angle r.
(c) (i) Write down the size of angle x.
(ii) What geometrical name is given to the pair of angles x and q?

[L]

(a) The angles p and q are called corresponding angles.
(b) Angle $r = 80°$ (angle r and 80° are corresponding angles).
(c) (i) Angle $x = 80°$ (angle x and 80° are alternate angles).
(ii) The pair of angles x and q are called alternate angles.

Exercise 10C

Calculate the named angles, giving reasons.

1 **(a)**

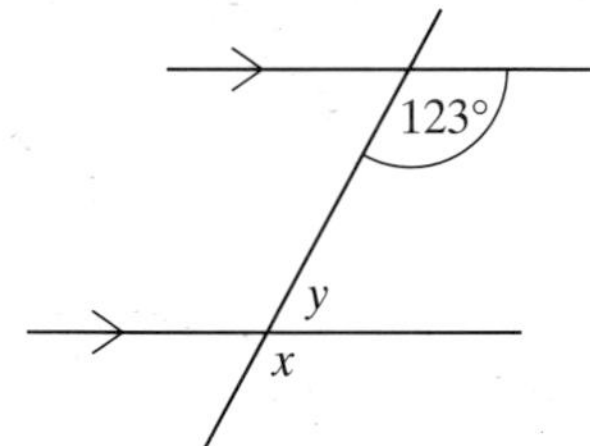

(b)

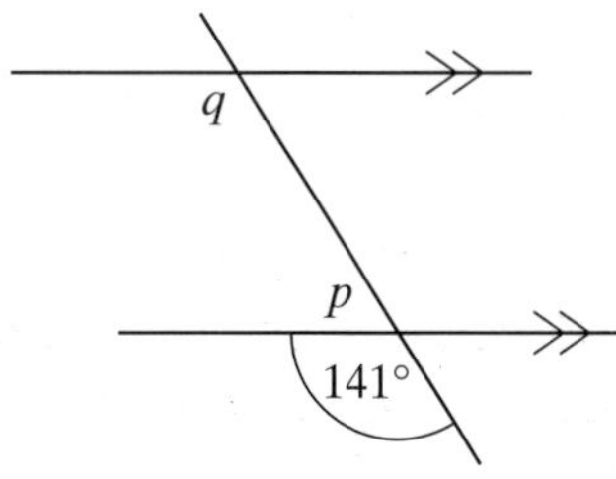

(c)

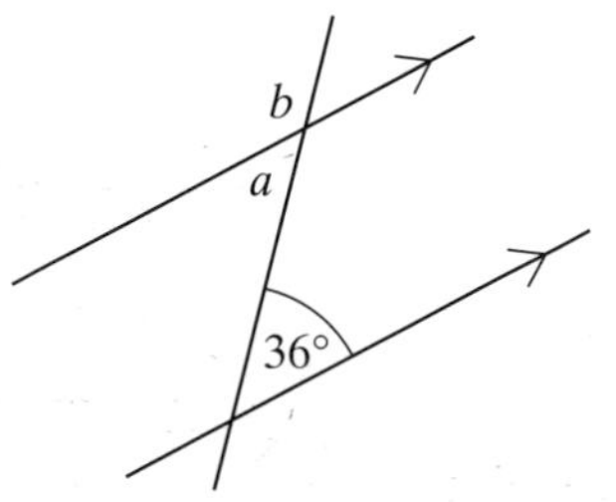

(d)

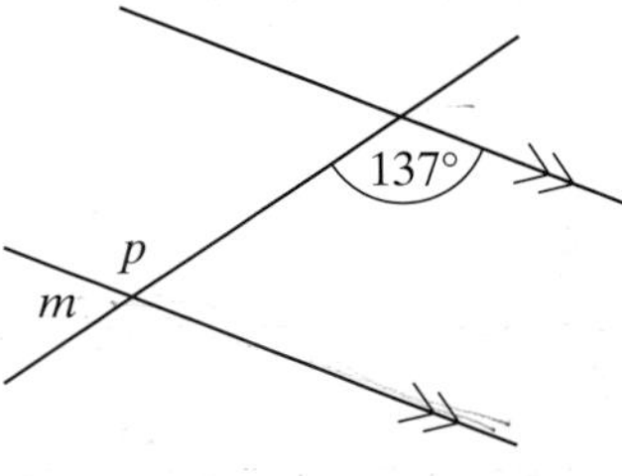

2 **(a)**

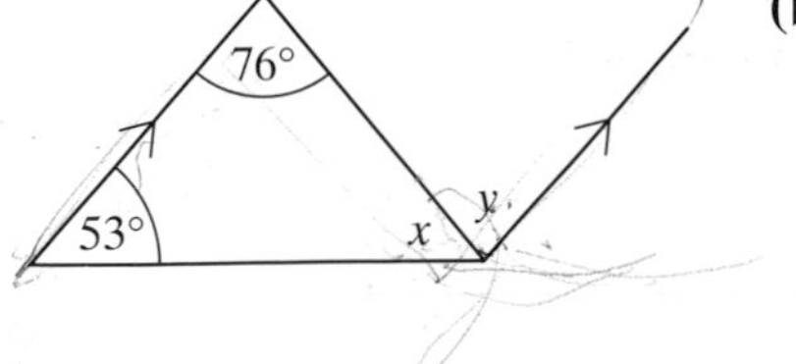

(b)

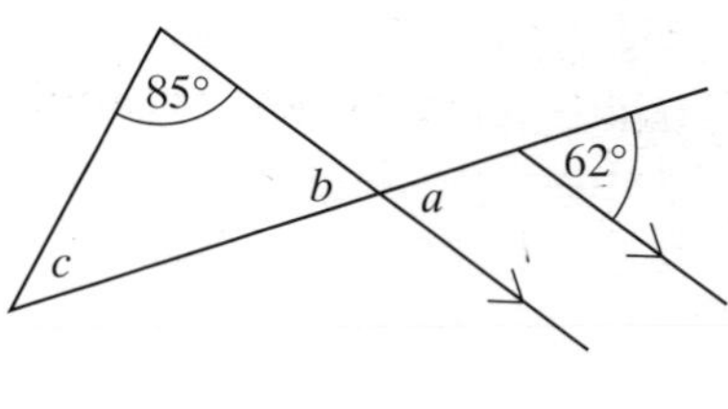

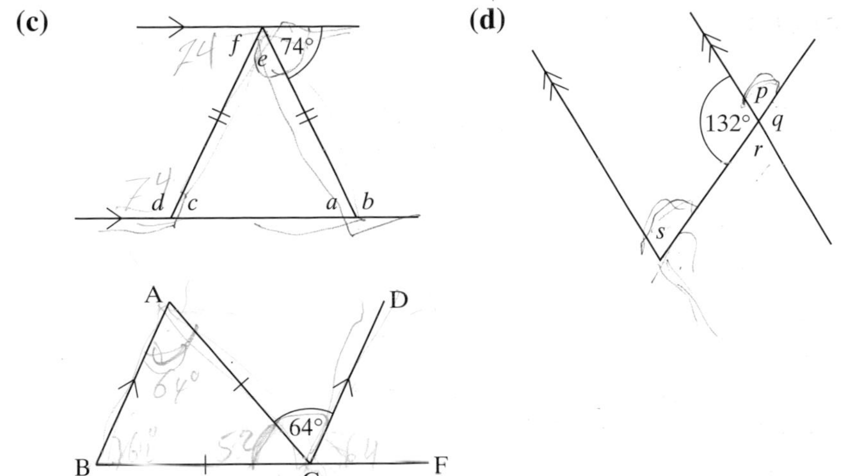

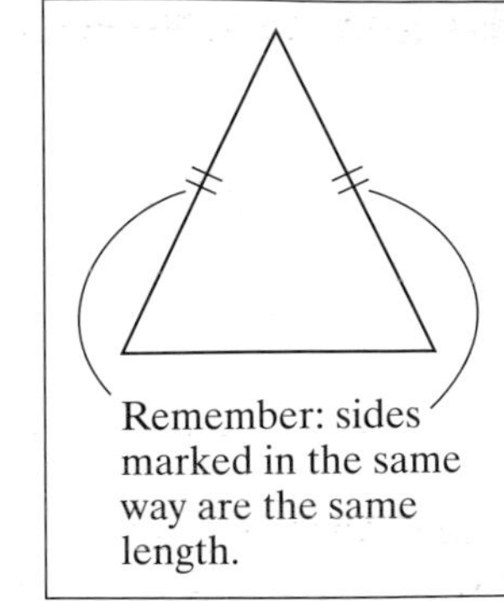

Remember: sides marked in the same way are the same length.

3 The diagram shows the following information:
BA is parallel to CD, CA = CB, angle $A\hat{C}D = 64°$
Find the size of (i) angle $B\hat{A}C$
(ii) angle $B\hat{C}A$. [L]

10.4 Calculating angles in circles

You need to know the names given to different parts of a circle.

The length round the edge of a circle is called the **circumference**.
A straight line going from a point on the circumference of a circle through the centre to the opposite point on the circumference is called a **diameter**.
A straight line from the centre to a point on the circumference is called a **radius**.
A diameter of a circle is **twice** the length of a radius.

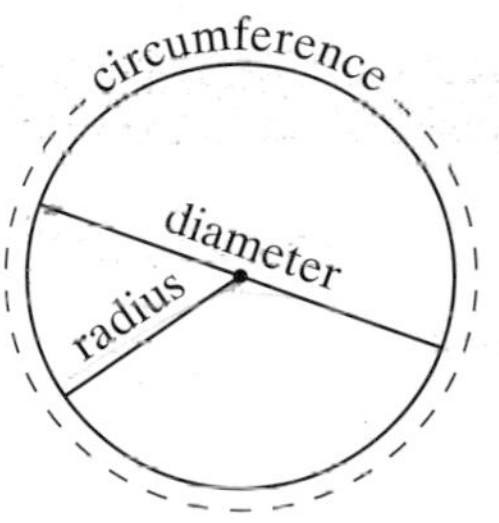

Part of the circumference of a circle is called an **arc**.
A straight line from one point on the circumference to another and which does not pass through the centre is called a **chord**.
A straight line that touches a circle is called a **tangent**.

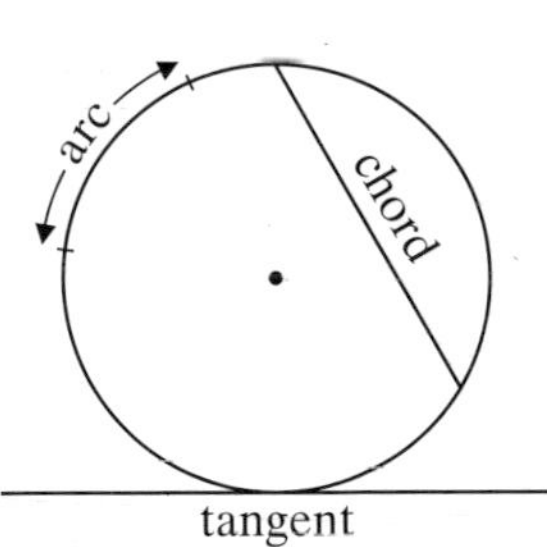

There are some useful angle properties concerning chords and tangents of circles.

A line is drawn from the centre of the circle to the middle point of a chord.

The line is a line of symmetry so it is perpendicular to the chord.

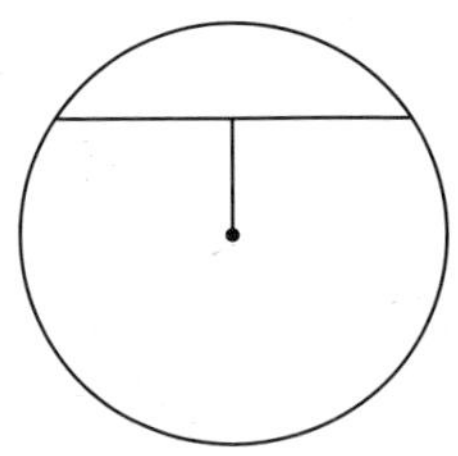

- **A line drawn from the centre of a circle to the middle point of a chord is perpendicular to the chord.**

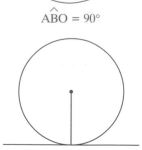

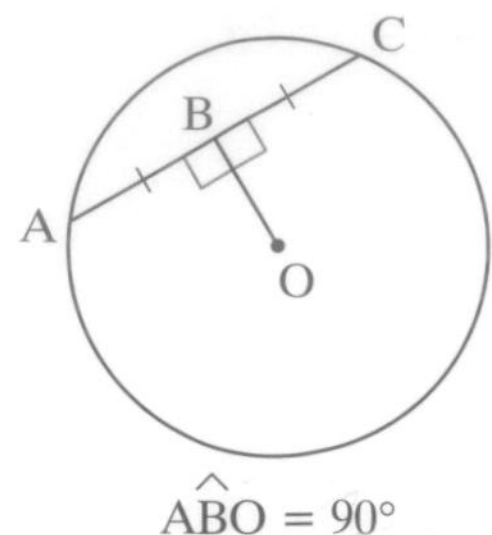

$A\hat{B}O = 90°$

A radius is drawn from the point where a tangent touches the circle.
The radius is a line of symmetry so it is perpendicular to the tangent.

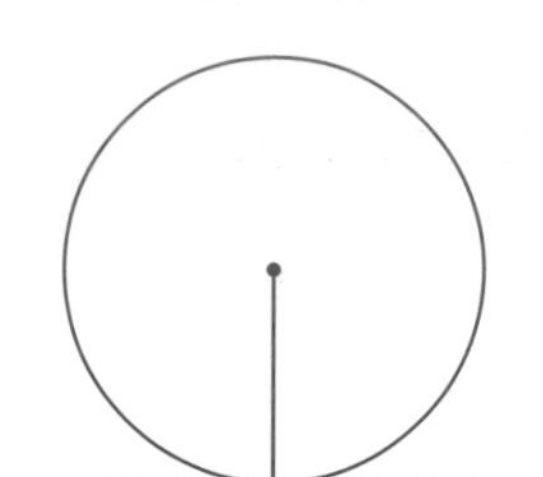

- **A radius drawn from the point where a tangent touches a circle is perpendicular to the tangent.**

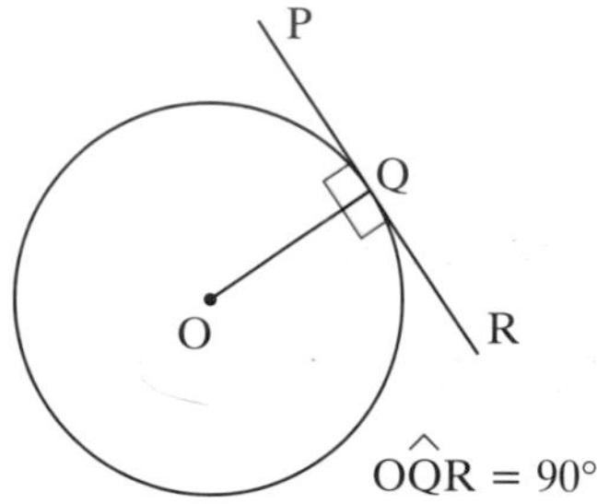

$O\hat{Q}R = 90°$

Example 5

TS is a tangent to the circle and AB is a diameter.
Work out the size of (i) x
(ii) y, giving reasons for your answers.

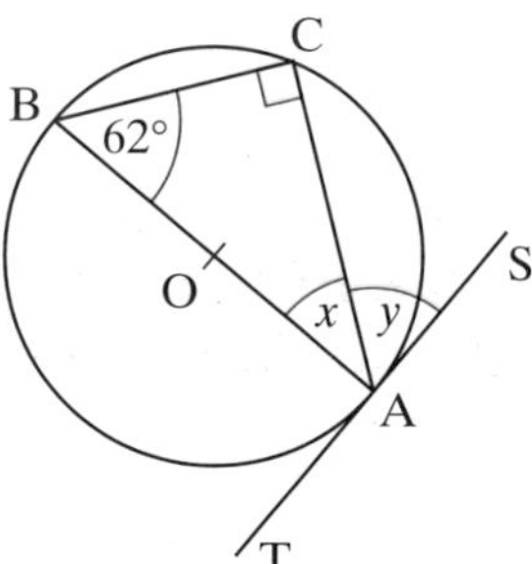

(i) $x + 62° + 90° = 180°$ (sum of angles of triangle)

so $x = 180° - 62° - 90°$

$x = 28°$

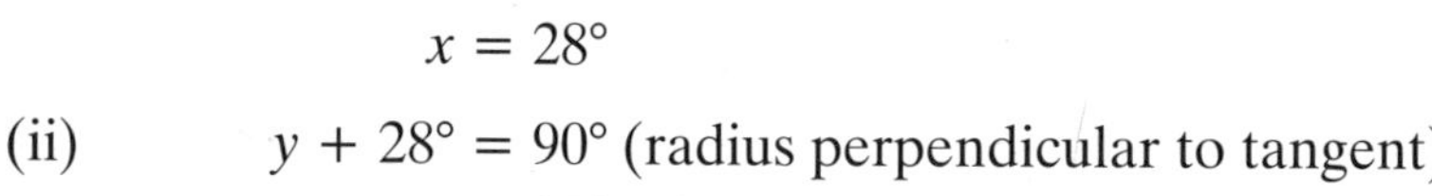

(ii) $y + 28° = 90°$ (radius perpendicular to tangent)

so $y = 90° - 28° = 62°$

Exercise 10D

In all the questions O is the centre of the circle.

1 C is the middle point of the chord AB
Angle $O\hat{B}C = 47°$
Calculate angle $C\hat{O}B$

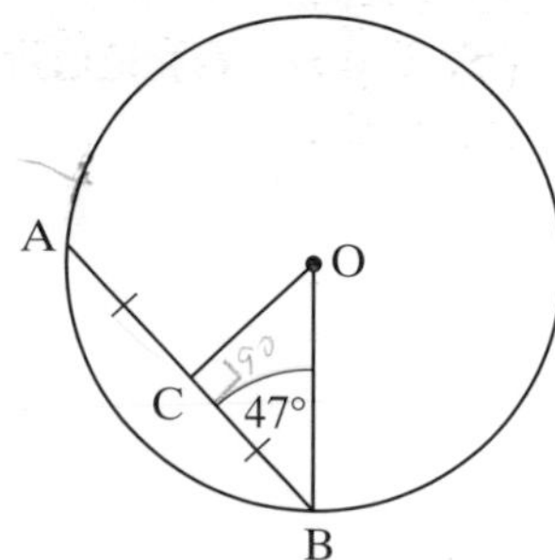

2 CD is the tangent at B to the circle.
$A\hat{B}C = 61°$
Calculate $A\hat{B}O$.

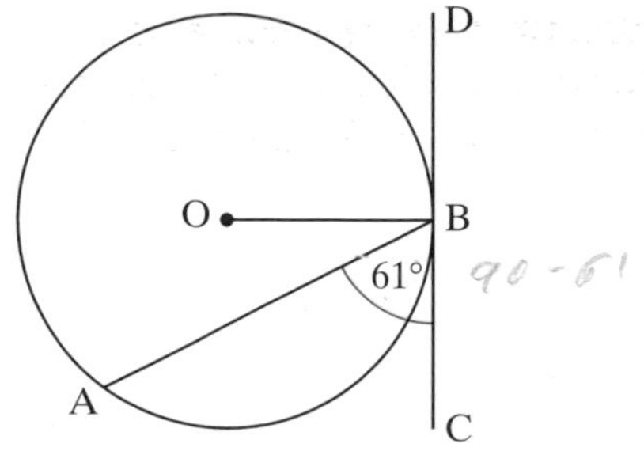

3 N is the middle point of the chord PQ.
Angle $Q\hat{O}N$ is 52°.
Calculate angle $N\hat{Q}O$

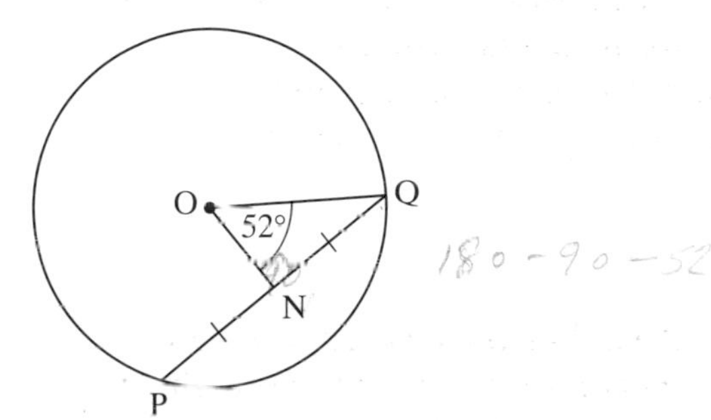

4 BC is the tangent at B to the circle.
$O\hat{B}A = 24°$
Calculate **(a)** $A\hat{B}C$ **(b)** $O\hat{A}B$.

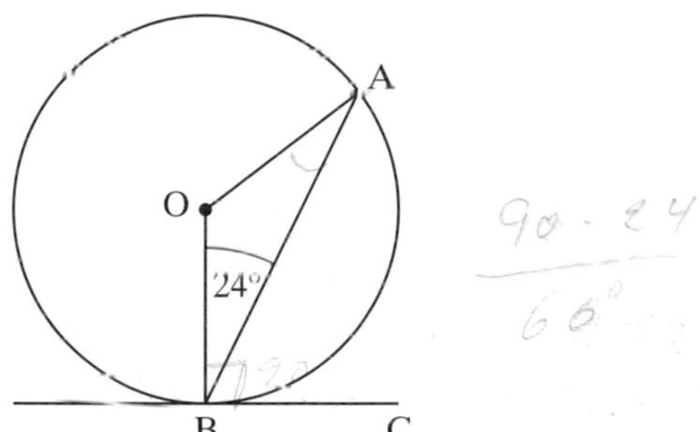

5 PQ is a diameter of the circle. TS is the tangent at P. $P\hat{R}Q = 90°$ and $P\hat{Q}R = 34°$.
Calculate **(a)** $R\hat{P}Q$ **(b)** $R\hat{P}T$

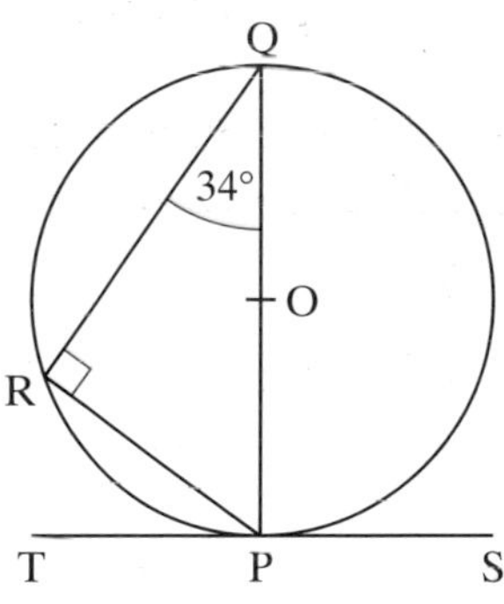

6 DE is the tangent at B to the circle.
AO is parallel to BC. $O\hat{B}A = 56°$
Calculate **(a)** $A\hat{B}D$ **(b)** $O\hat{A}B$ **(c)** $A\hat{O}B$
(d) $O\hat{B}C$ **(e)** $C\hat{B}E$

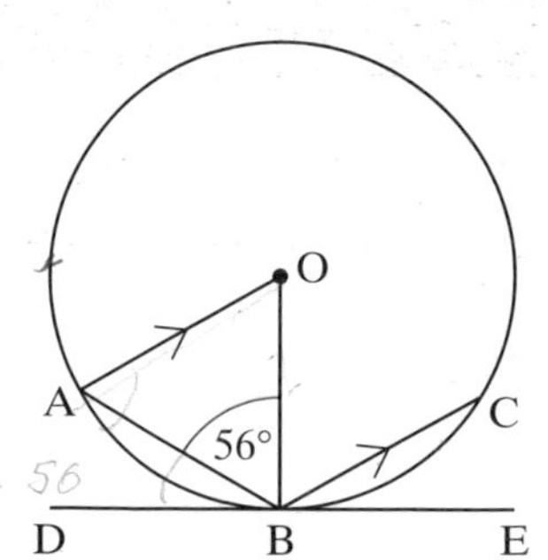

10.5 Using three-figure bearings

Remember: to describe a **direction** you can use the compass bearings North, South, East and West.

Another method is to use **three-figure bearings**.

Aircraft pilots use bearings. Nowadays computer navigation equipment can calculate these automatically

■ **A three-figure bearing gives a direction in degrees. It is an angle measured clockwise from the North.**

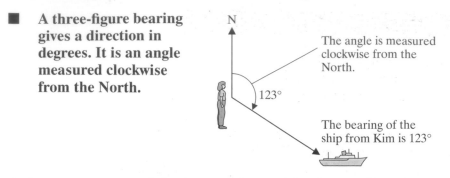

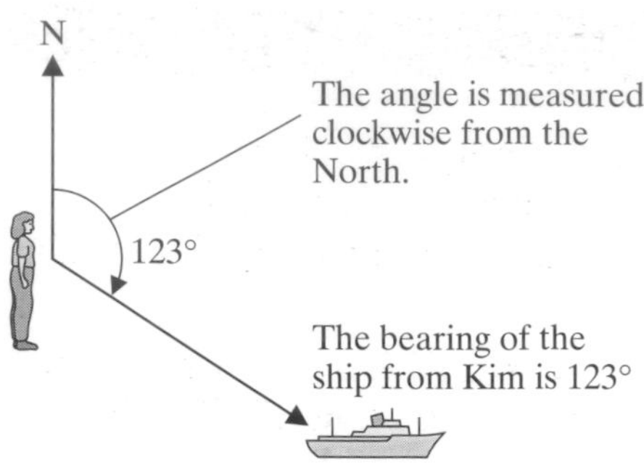

As its name suggests, it is always written with 3 figures (digits).

Example 6

Write down the three-figure bearing of P from Q.

(a)

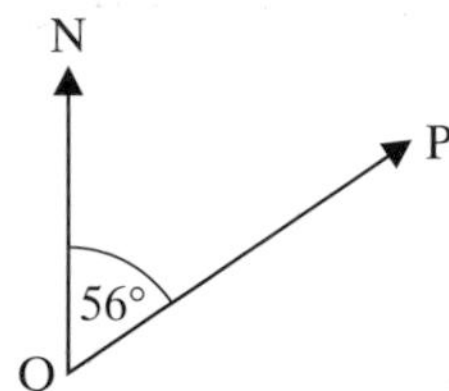

(b)

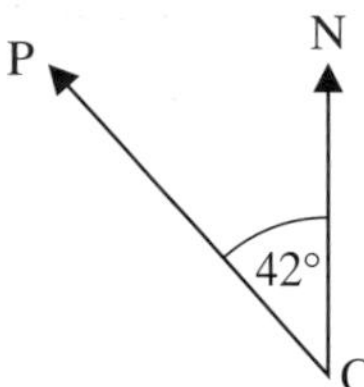

(a) The bearing of P from Q is 056°.
(Note: the zero is included to make three digits.)

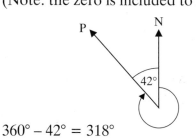

(b)

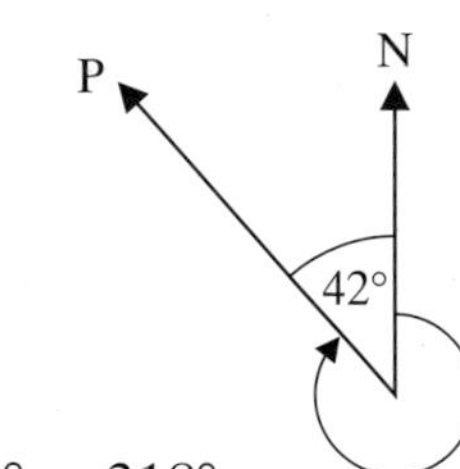

$360° - 42° = 318°$

The bearing of P from Q is 318°.

Exercise 10E

1 Write down the three-figure bearing of A from O.

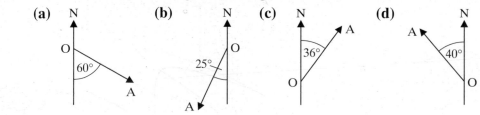

(a) N O 60° A

(b)

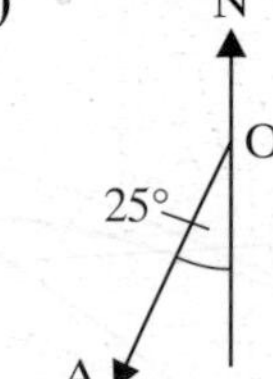

(c) N A 36° O

(d)

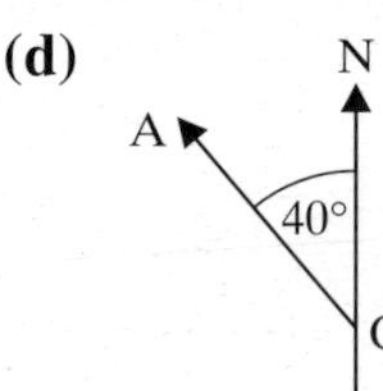

2 Draw diagrams like those in question **1** to illustrate these three-figure bearings:

(a) 072° **(b)** 250° **(c)** 160° **(d)** 290°

Exercise 10F Mixed questions

1 Each interior angle of a regular polygon is 144°.

(a) Calculate the number of sides of this polygon.

(b) Calculate the **sum** of the interior angles, in degrees, of a polygon which has 7 sides. [L]

2 The diagram shows a triangle ABC with a line XY drawn parallel to BC. Angle BAC = 45° and angle BYC = 70°. Given that the line XY bisects the angle AYB:

(a) Calculate the sizes of the following angles:

(i) angle AYX (ii) angle AXY (iii) angle YCB (iv) angle ABY

(b) (i) Write down the letters of the three points which form an isoceles triangle in the diagram.

(ii) Name the equal sides of this triangle. [L]

3 In the diagram PQ is parallel to TS. PQ = PT and angle PQT = 53°.

(a) Write down the size of angle QTS.

(b) Write down the size of angle QTP.

(c) Calculate the size of angle QPT. [L]

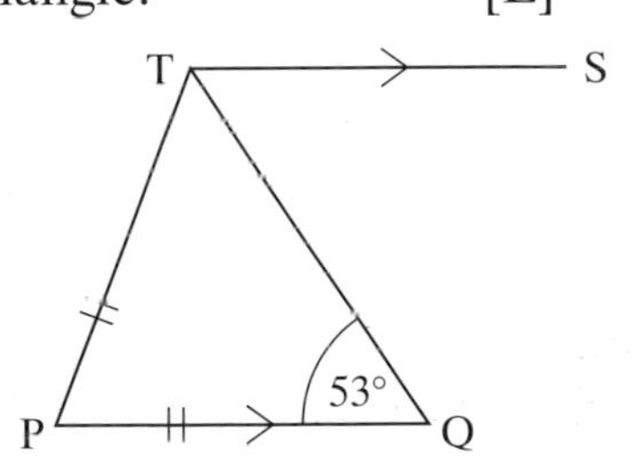

4 BD is a diameter of the circle with centre O. AC is the tangent at B. $A\hat{B}E = 66°$ and $B\hat{E}D = 90°$. Calculate **(a)** $E\hat{B}D$ **(b)** $B\hat{D}E$.

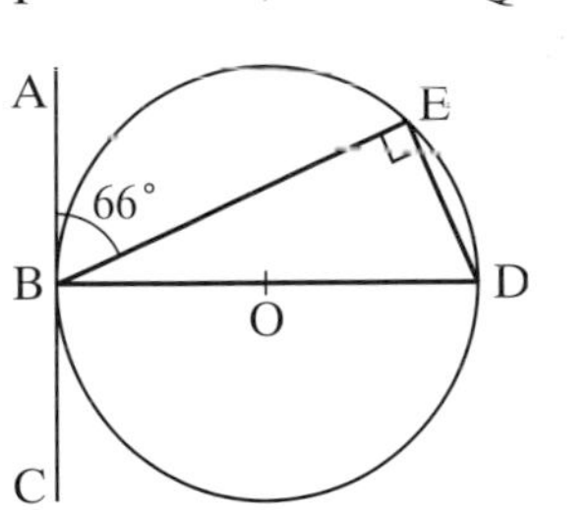

Summary of key points

1 Angles on a straight line add up to 180°.

$a + b + c + d = 180°$

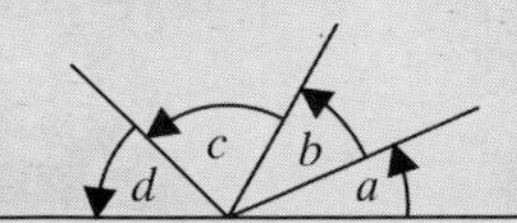

2 Angles at a point add up to 360°.

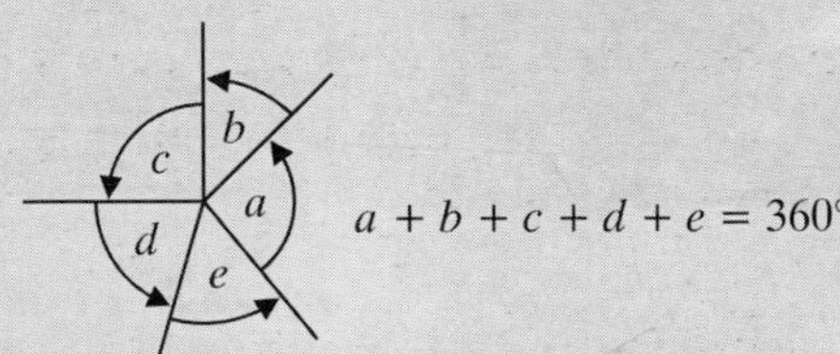

3 Vertically opposite angles are equal.

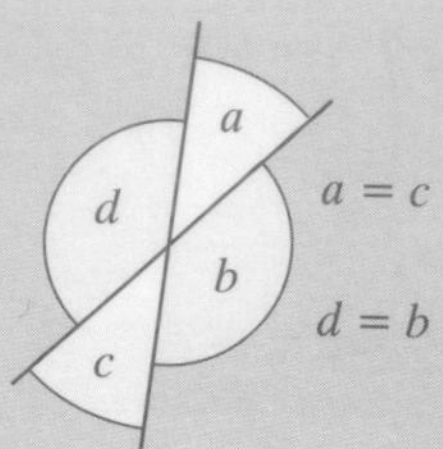

4 The sum of the interior angles of a triangle is 180°.

$a + b + c = 180°$

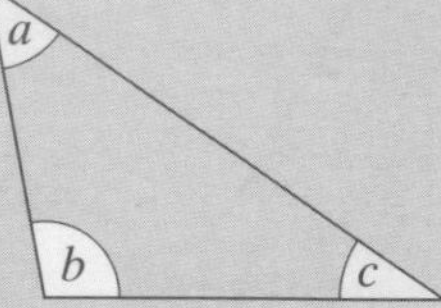

5 Each interior angle of an equilateral triangle is 60°.

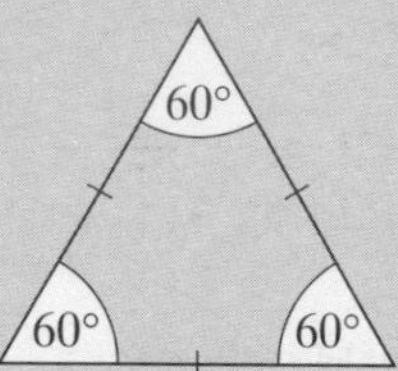

6 The base angles of an isosceles triangle are equal.

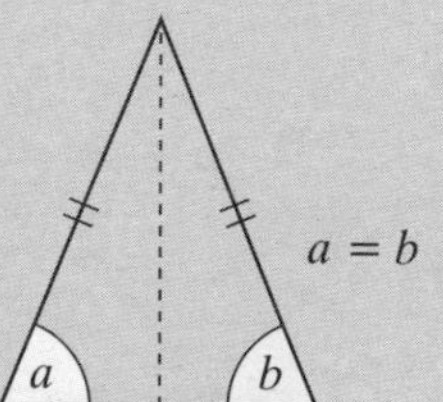

7 The sum of the interior angles of a quadrilateral is 360°.

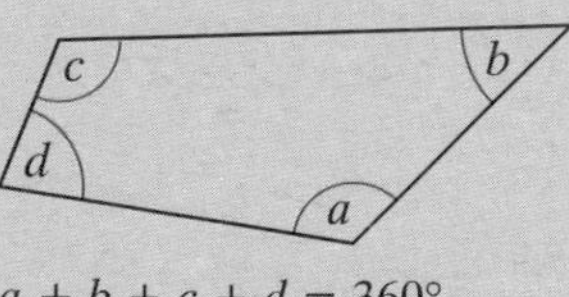

$a + b + c + d = 360°$

8 The sum of the exterior angles of any polygon is 360°.

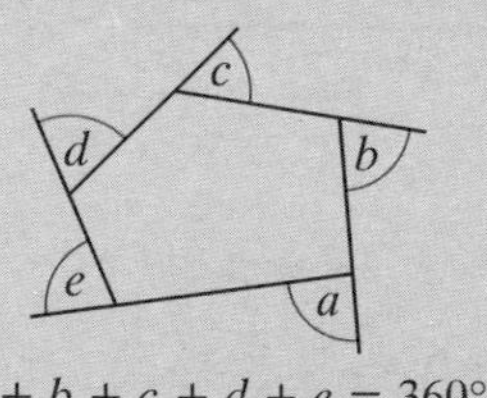

$a + b + c + d + e = 360°$

9 At each vertex (point) of a polygon the sum of the interior angle and the exterior angle is 180°.

10 The sum of the interior angles of a polygon with n sides is:

$$(n - 2) \times 180°$$

11 Corresponding angles are equal.

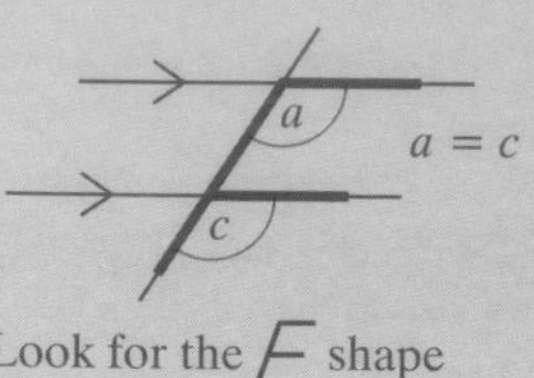

Look for the F shape

12 Alternate angles are equal.

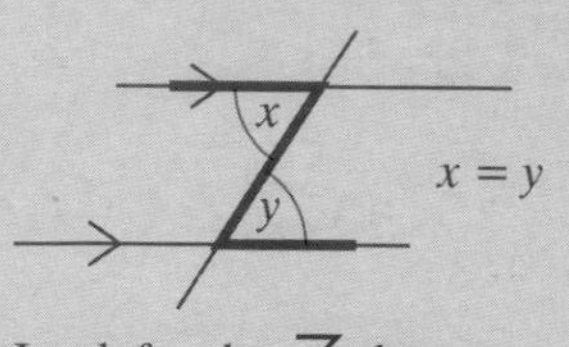

Look for the Z shape

13 A point drawn from the centre of a circle to the middle point of a chord is perpendicular to the chord.

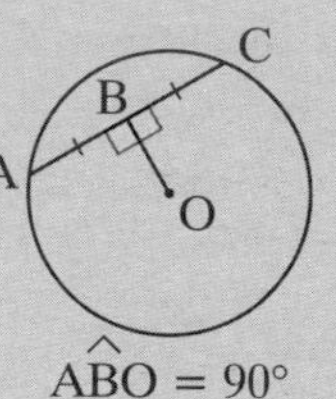

$A\hat{B}O = 90°$

14 A radius drawn from the point where a tangent touches a circle is perpendicular to the tangent.

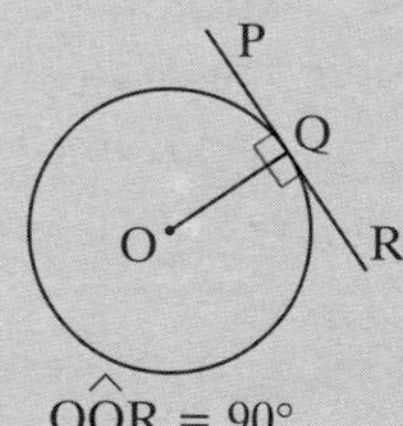

$O\hat{Q}R = 90°$

15 A three-figure bearing gives a direction in degrees. It is an angle measured clockwise from the North.

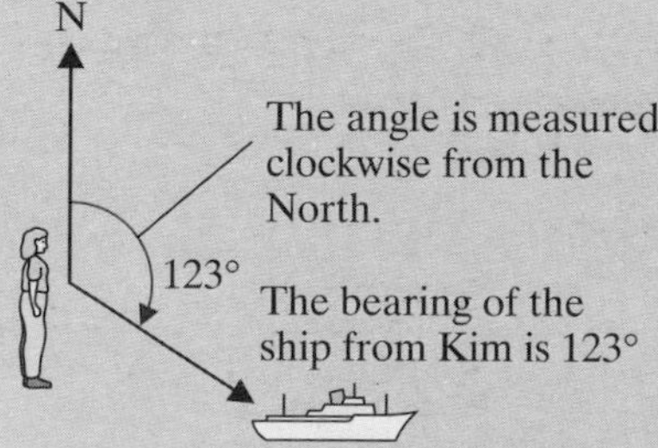

11 Fractions

All these things can be divided into parts called **fractions**:

A football pitch has two halves. Each part is $\frac{1}{2}$ the pitch.

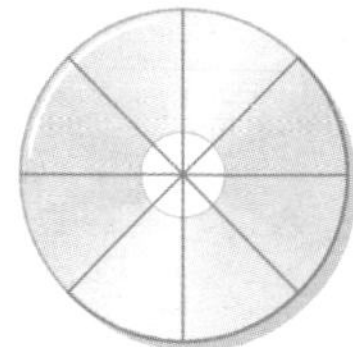

This computer disc has eight equal sectors. Each sector is $\frac{1}{8}$ of the disc.

A chessboard has 64 equal squares. Each square is $\frac{1}{64}$ of the board.

A fraction is a package of information. For example, if $\frac{3}{8}$ of my computer disc is full of data:

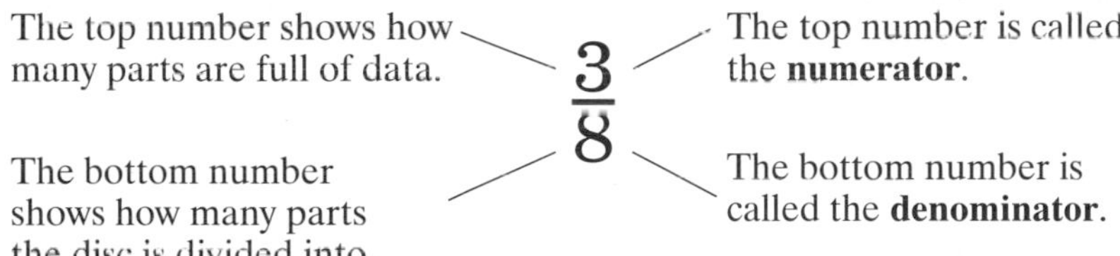
The top number shows how many parts are full of data.
The bottom number shows how many parts the disc is divided into.
3
8
The top number is called the **numerator**.
The bottom number is called the **denominator**.

In your examination fractions will usually appear in the context of a number problem, or in questions on probability, areas or volumes.

This unit shows you how to add, subtract, multiply and divide fractions.

11.1 Finding equivalent fractions

This circle is divided into 8 parts.

Each part is $\frac{1}{8}$ (or one eighth) of the whole circle.

The shaded area is $\frac{2}{8}$ of the whole circle.

The shaded area is also $\frac{1}{4}$ (or one quarter) of the whole circle.

$\frac{2}{8}$ and $\frac{1}{4}$ represent the same area of the circle. They are called **equivalent fractions**.

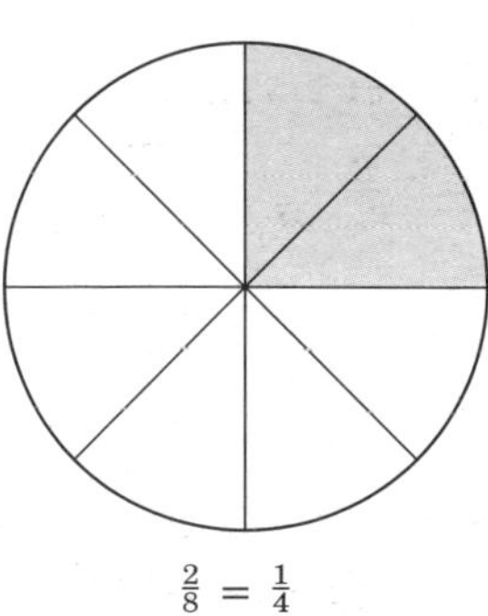

$\frac{2}{8} = \frac{1}{4}$

Example 1

What fraction of the rectangle is shaded?

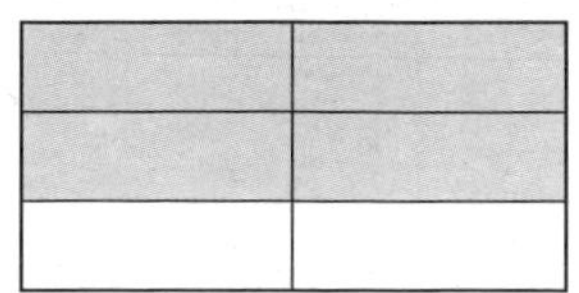

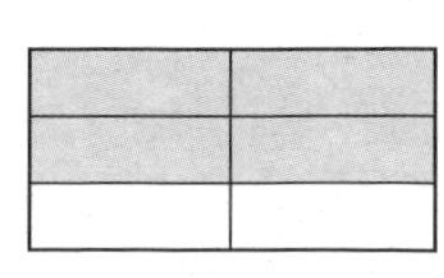

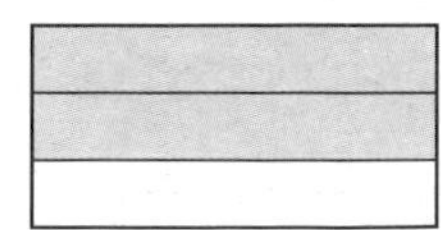

$\frac{4}{6} = \frac{2}{3}$

The fraction shaded is $\frac{4}{6}$ or $\frac{2}{3}$.

Exercise 11A

For each of these diagrams write down at least two equivalent fractions that describe the fraction shaded.

1 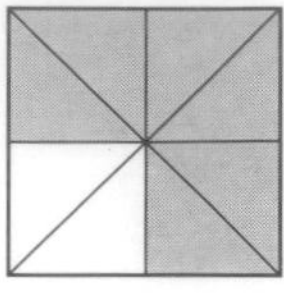

2 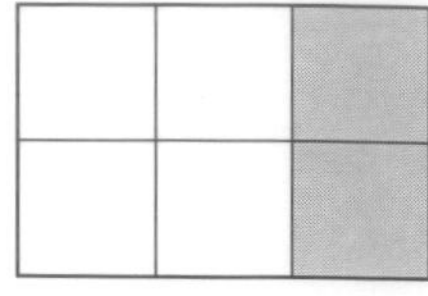

3 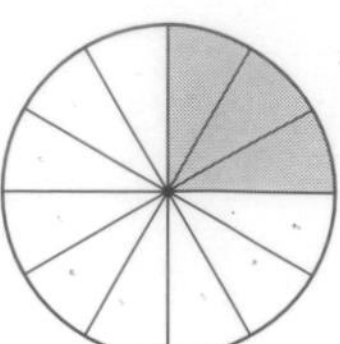

4 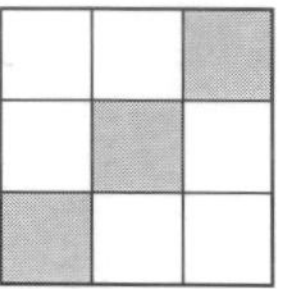

5 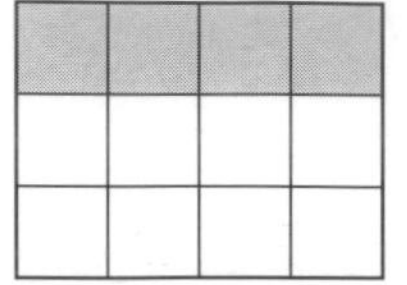

6 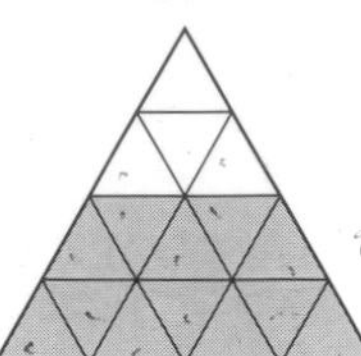

7 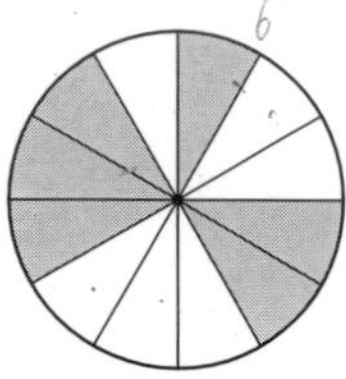

8 

9 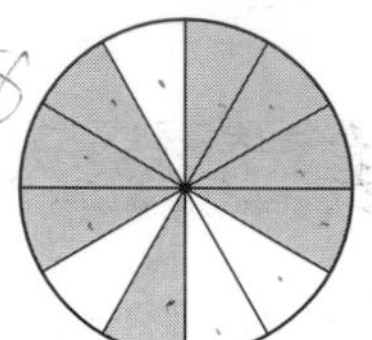

10 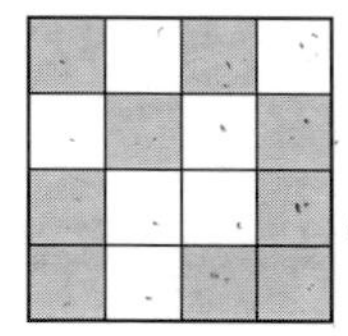

- **You can find equivalent fractions by multiplying (or dividing) the top and bottom of a fraction by the same number.**

Here are three examples:

$$\frac{3}{5} \underset{\times 2}{\overset{\times 2}{=}} \frac{6}{10}$$

so $\frac{3}{5}$ and $\frac{6}{10}$ are equivalent

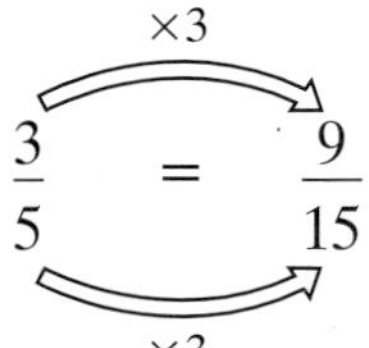

$$\frac{3}{5} \underset{\times 3}{\overset{\times 3}{=}} \frac{9}{15}$$

so $\frac{3}{5}$ and $\frac{9}{15}$ are equivalent

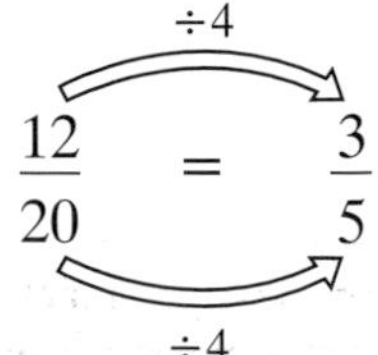

$$\frac{12}{20} \underset{\div 4}{\overset{\div 4}{=}} \frac{3}{5}$$

so $\frac{12}{20}$ and $\frac{3}{5}$ are equivalent

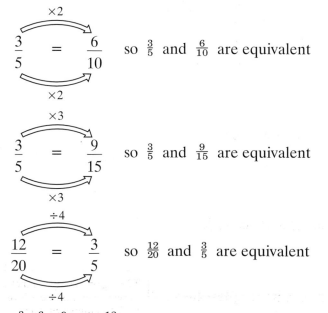

So $\frac{3}{5}$, $\frac{6}{10}$, $\frac{9}{15}$ and $\frac{12}{20}$ are all equivalent fractions.

Example 2

Find the first five equivalent fractions of $\frac{5}{7}$.

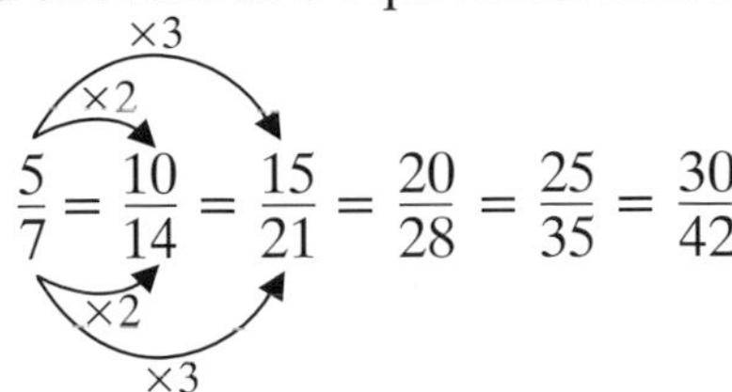

Example 3

Complete: (a) $\frac{3}{8} = \frac{?}{16}$ (b) $\frac{4}{5} = \frac{?}{10} = \frac{?}{25}$

(a) $\frac{3}{8} = \frac{?}{16}$ so $\frac{3}{8} = \frac{6}{16}$ (b) $\frac{4}{5} = \frac{?}{10} = \frac{?}{25}$ so $\frac{4}{5} = \frac{8}{10} = \frac{20}{25}$

×2 ×2 ×5

Exercise 11B

Copy and complete these sets of equivalent fractions:

1 **(a)** $\frac{3}{4} = \frac{}{8} = \frac{}{12} = \frac{}{16} = \frac{}{20} = \frac{}{24}$ **(b)** $\frac{2}{7} = \frac{}{14} = \frac{}{21} = \frac{}{28} = \frac{}{35} = \frac{}{42}$

(c) $\frac{4}{5} = \frac{}{10} = \frac{}{15} = \frac{}{20} = \frac{}{25} = \frac{}{30}$ **(d)** $\frac{3}{9} = \frac{}{18} = \frac{}{27} = \frac{}{36} = \frac{}{45} = \frac{}{54}$

2 **(a)** $\frac{1}{6} = \frac{}{18}$ **(b)** $\frac{3}{7} = \frac{}{14}$ **(c)** $\frac{3}{8} = \frac{}{48}$ **(d)** $\frac{4}{7} = \frac{}{21}$

(e) $\frac{5}{6} = \frac{}{36}$ **(f)** $\frac{2}{3} = \frac{6}{}$ **(g)** $\frac{4}{9} = \frac{24}{}$ **(h)** $\frac{5}{7} = \frac{}{56}$

3 **(a)** $\frac{9}{10} = \frac{90}{}$ **(b)** $\frac{3}{5} = \frac{}{15}$ **(c)** $\frac{2}{5} = \frac{}{20}$ **(d)** $\frac{5}{8} = \frac{}{40}$

(e) $\frac{8}{9} = \frac{40}{}$ **(f)** $\frac{7}{12} = \frac{84}{}$ **(g)** $\frac{7}{8} = \frac{49}{}$ **(h)** $\frac{2}{9} = \frac{}{81}$

11.2 Simplifying fractions

■ **A fraction can be simplified if the numerator (top) and denominator (bottom) have a common factor.**

For example:

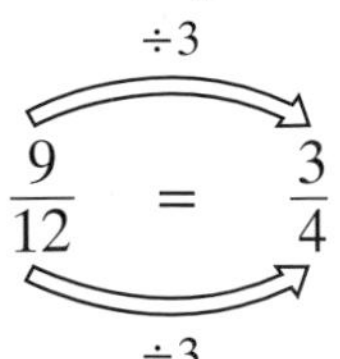

The numerator and denominator of the fraction $\frac{9}{12}$ have a common factor of 3.

$\frac{3}{4}$ cannot be simplified any more. The fraction is in its **simplest form**.

To get straight to the simplest form divide the numerator and denominator by the largest factor they have in common – **the highest common factor**.

> The highest common factor of two given numbers is the largest number which is a factor of the two numbers. Read about this on page 185.

Example 4

Write these fractions in their simplest form:

(a) $\frac{21}{28}$ (b) $\frac{22}{55}$ (c) $\frac{36}{84}$

(a) The highest common factor of 21 and 28 is 7.

Divide top and bottom by 7: $\frac{21}{28} = \frac{3}{4}$

(b) The highest common factor of 22 and 55 is 11.

Divide top bottom by 11: $\frac{22}{55} = \frac{2}{5}$

(c) The highest common factor of 36 and 84 is 12.

Divide top and bottom by 12: $\frac{36}{84} = \frac{3}{7}$

Exercise 11C

1 Write each fraction in its simplest form:

(a) $\frac{12}{18}$ **(b)** $\frac{9}{15}$ **(c)** $\frac{20}{35}$ **(d)** $\frac{18}{24}$ **(e)** $\frac{14}{21}$

2 Write these in their lowest terms:

(a) $\frac{6}{8}$ **(b)** $\frac{30}{36}$ **(c)** $\frac{40}{48}$ **(d)** $\frac{35}{49}$ **(e)** $\frac{25}{45}$

'in their lowest terms' means in their simplest form.

3 Write these in their lowest terms:

(a) $\frac{20}{32}$ **(b)** $\frac{48}{64}$ **(c)** $\frac{21}{27}$ **(d)** $\frac{24}{60}$ **(e)** $\frac{48}{72}$

11.3 Improper fractions and mixed numbers

Fractions bigger than 1 can be written in two ways, as mixed numbers and as improper fractions. It is useful to be able to change a fraction from a mixed number to an improper fraction and from an improper fraction to a mixed number.

This picture represents the fraction $\frac{5}{2}$ (or five halves).

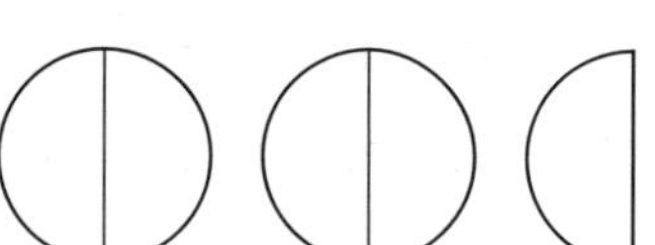

$\frac{5}{2}$ is sometimes called a *top-heavy* fraction because 5 is greater than 2.

■ **$\frac{5}{2}$ is called an improper fraction.**

$\frac{5}{2}$ is also equivalent to two whole circles and one half, which is written $2\frac{1}{2}$.

■ **$2\frac{1}{2}$ is called a mixed number because it contains a whole number part and a fractional part smaller than 1.**

■ **Mixed numbers can be written as improper fractions and improper fractions can be written as mixed numbers.**

Example 5

Change these mixed numbers to improper fractions:

(a) $1\frac{3}{4}$ (b) $2\frac{2}{3}$

(a) Change the mixed number $1\frac{3}{4}$ to quarters:
1 can be written as $\frac{4}{4}$
so $1\frac{3}{4} = \frac{4}{4} + \frac{3}{4} = \frac{7}{4}$

(b) Change $2\frac{2}{3}$ to thirds:
$2 = \frac{6}{3}$
so $2\frac{2}{3} = \frac{6}{3} + \frac{2}{3} = \frac{8}{3}$

Exercise 11D

Change to improper fractions:

1 **(a)** $1\frac{3}{5}$ **(b)** $1\frac{1}{6}$ **(c)** $4\frac{5}{6}$ **(d)** $2\frac{3}{5}$
(e) $3\frac{2}{3}$ **(f)** $3\frac{4}{9}$ **(g)** $4\frac{1}{5}$ **(h)** $5\frac{1}{2}$

2 **(a)** $5\frac{2}{3}$ **(b)** $1\frac{5}{9}$ **(c)** $5\frac{7}{10}$ **(d)** $4\frac{7}{8}$
(e) $7\frac{3}{4}$ **(f)** $8\frac{4}{5}$ **(g)** $6\frac{3}{10}$ **(h)** $2\frac{2}{5}$

■ **Improper fractions in their simplest form are written as mixed numbers.**

You should write answers as mixed numbers rather than improper fractions.

Example 6

Change these improper fractions to mixed numbers:

(a) $\frac{11}{4}$ (b) $\frac{17}{5}$

(a) Arrange $\frac{11}{4}$ into as many groups of four quarters as possible.

$\frac{11}{4} = \frac{4}{4} + \frac{4}{4} + \frac{3}{4} = 2\frac{3}{4}$

(b) Arrange $\frac{17}{5}$ into as many groups of five fifths as possible.

$\frac{17}{5} = \frac{5}{5} + \frac{5}{5} + \frac{5}{5} + \frac{2}{5} = 3\frac{2}{5}$

$\frac{4}{4} = 1$

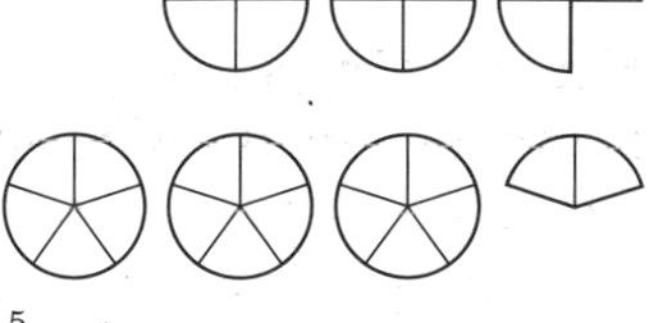

$\frac{5}{5} = 1$

Exercise 11E

Write each fraction in its simplest form by changing it to a mixed number:

1 **(a)** $\frac{9}{2}$ **(b)** $\frac{9}{4}$ **(c)** $\frac{7}{3}$ **(d)** $\frac{17}{5}$ **(e)** $\frac{11}{4}$

2 **(a)** $\frac{49}{8}$ **(b)** $\frac{21}{4}$ **(c)** $\frac{37}{10}$ **(d)** $\frac{71}{9}$ **(e)** $\frac{53}{11}$

3 **(a)** $\frac{29}{5}$ **(b)** $\frac{59}{12}$ **(c)** $\frac{30}{7}$ **(d)** $\frac{40}{11}$ **(e)** $\frac{52}{7}$

11.4 Changing fractions to decimals

You can use both fractions and decimals to show parts of whole numbers. It is useful to be able to change a fraction to a decimal and a decimal to a fraction.

A fraction such as $\frac{3}{4}$ can be thought of as $3 \div 4$. You can change fractions into decimals easily using a calculator:

You can check this:

$$0.75 \text{ is equal to } \frac{75}{100}$$

$$\frac{75}{100} \text{ simplifies to the equivalent fraction } \frac{3}{4}$$

So the decimal 0.75 is equivalent to the fraction $\frac{3}{4}$.

■ **You can convert a fraction to a decimal by dividing the numerator by the denominator.**

Example 7

Convert these fractions to decimals:

(a) $\frac{3}{8}$ (b) $4\frac{1}{5}$

(a) $\frac{3}{8} = 3 \div 8 = 0.375$

(b) $4\frac{1}{5} = 4 + \frac{1}{5}$.

$\frac{1}{5} = 1 \div 5 = 0.2$

So $4\frac{1}{5} = 4 + 0.2 = 4.2$

Exercise 11F

Write these fractions as decimals:

1 **(a)** $\frac{4}{5}$ **(b)** $\frac{3}{4}$ **(c)** $1\frac{1}{8}$ **(d)** $\frac{19}{100}$

(e) $3\frac{3}{5}$ **(f)** $\frac{13}{25}$ **(g)** $\frac{5}{8}$ **(h)** $3\frac{17}{40}$

2 **(a)** $\frac{7}{50}$ **(b)** $4\frac{3}{16}$ **(c)** $3\frac{3}{20}$ **(d)** $4\frac{5}{16}$

(e) $\frac{7}{1000}$ **(f)** $1\frac{7}{25}$ **(g)** $15\frac{15}{16}$ **(h)** $2\frac{7}{20}$

■ **You can convert a decimal to a fraction.**

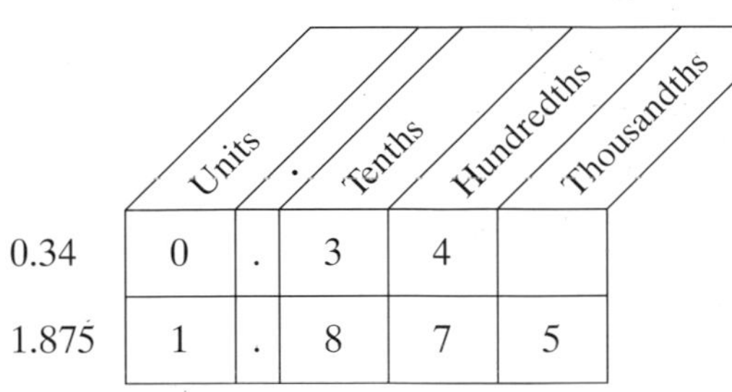

Last significant figure is a hundredth so $0.34 = \frac{34}{100}$

Last significant figure is a thousandth so $1.875 = 1\frac{875}{1000}$

You can write 0.34 as $\frac{34}{100}$ which simplifies to $\frac{17}{50}$.
1.875 is $1\frac{875}{1000}$ which simplifies to $1\frac{7}{8}$.

Example 8

Write these decimals as fractions in their simplest form:

(a) 0.204 (b) 1.17 (c) 2.4375

(a) $0.204 = \frac{204}{1000} = \frac{51}{250}$
(b) $1.17 = \frac{117}{100}$ (cannot simplify further)
(c) $2.4375 = 2\frac{4375}{10\,000} = 2\frac{175}{400} = 2\frac{7}{16}$

Exercise 11G

Write these decimals as fractions in their simplest form:

1	**(a)** 0.48	**(b)** 0.25	**(c)** 1.7	**(d)** 3.406	**(e)** 4.003
2	**(a)** 2.025	**(b)** 0.049	**(c)** 4.875	**(d)** 3.75	**(e)** 10.101
3	**(a)** 0.625	**(b)** 2.512	**(c)** 0.8125	**(d)** 14.14	**(e)** 9.1875

Recurring decimals

Not all fractions have an exact equivalent decimal.

The fraction $\frac{2}{3}$ is $2 \div 3 = 0.666\,666\,6\ldots$ This is called a *recurring* decimal since one of the digits recurs (repeats).

0.6666667

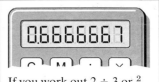

If you work out $2 \div 3$ or $\frac{2}{3}$ on a calculator the result on the display could be 0.6666667. The result has been corrected to 7 s.f. by the calculator.

You usually put a dot over the digits that repeat:

$\frac{2}{3} = 0.666\,666\,6\ldots = 0.\dot{6}$ $\frac{5}{12} = 0.416\,666\,6\ldots = 0.41\dot{6}$

$\frac{1}{3} = 0.333\,333\,3\ldots = 0.\dot{3}$ $\frac{3}{11} = 0.272\,727\,2\ldots = 0.\dot{2}\dot{7}$

You need two dots here since both the 2 and the 7 repeat.

$\frac{7}{9} = 0.777\,777\,7\ldots = 0.\dot{7}$

$\frac{1}{7} = 0.142\,857\,142\,857\,142\,857\ldots = 0.\dot{1}4285\dot{7}$

The two dots show that all the digits from 1 to 7 repeat.

■ **Recurring decimal notation:**
$0.\dot{3}$ means 0.333 333 3 recurring and
$0.\dot{1}\dot{7}$ means 0.171 717 17 recurring.

Example 9

Write these fractions as recurring decimals:

(a) $\frac{6}{11}$ (b) $3\frac{8}{9}$

Write your answers:

(i) as shown on the calculator display
(ii) using recurring decimal notation.

(a) (i) $\frac{6}{11} = 6 \div 11 = 0.545\,454\,5$
(ii) $0.\dot{5}\dot{4}$

(b) (i) $3\frac{8}{9} = 3 + (8 \div 9) = 3.888\,888\,8$ (or $3.888\,888\,9$)
(ii) $3.\dot{8}$

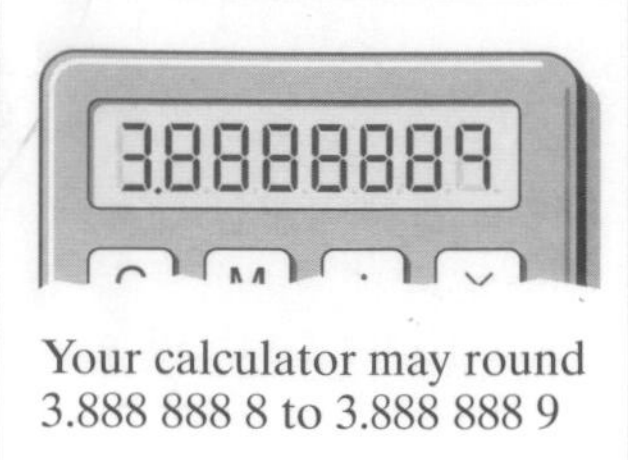

Your calculator may round 3.888 888 8 to 3.888 888 9

Exercise 11H

Write these fractions as recurring decimals.
Write your answers:

(i) as shown on the calculator display
(ii) using recurring decimal notation.

1	$\frac{5}{6}$	**2**	$1\frac{2}{9}$	**3**	$3\frac{1}{6}$	**4**	$\frac{11}{12}$	**5**	$5\frac{5}{9}$
6	$4\frac{9}{11}$	**7**	$\frac{3}{44}$	**8**	$2\frac{7}{11}$	**9**	$9\frac{21}{22}$	**10**	$\frac{25}{30}$

11.5 Adding and subtracting fractions

Adding fractions with the same denominator

It is easy to add fractions when each denominator (bottom) is the same. To do this you add the numerators. You must not add the denominators.

Why you don't add denominators

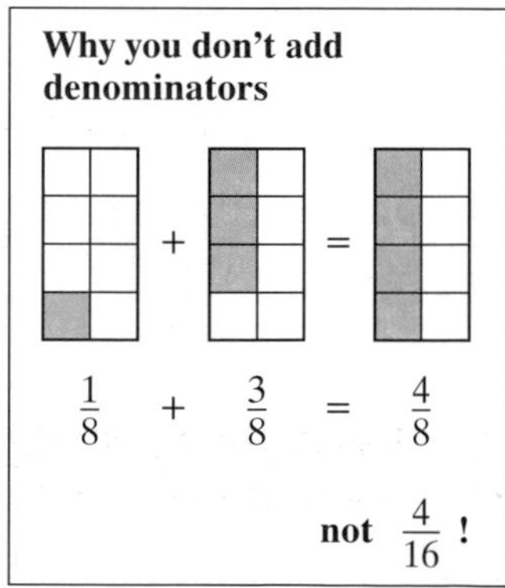

Example 10

Work out:

(a) $\frac{4}{9} + \frac{1}{9}$ (b) $\frac{7}{8} + \frac{5}{8}$ (c) $1\frac{1}{5} + 2\frac{3}{5}$

add the top numbers only

(a) $\frac{4}{9} + \frac{1}{9} = \frac{4+1}{9} = \frac{5}{9}$

(b) $\frac{7}{8} + \frac{5}{8} = \frac{7+5}{8} = \frac{12}{8} = \frac{3}{2} = 1\frac{1}{2}$ ← change to a mixed number

simplify

(c) $1\frac{1}{5} + 2\frac{3}{5} = 3 + \frac{1}{5} + \frac{3}{5} = 3 + \frac{1+3}{5} = 3\frac{4}{5}$

add the whole numbers first

Adding fractions with different denominators

$\frac{3}{4} + \frac{1}{8} = ?$

The denominators of these fractions are different.

■ **To add fractions find equivalent fractions that have the same denominator (bottom).**

Example 11

Work out:

(a) $1\frac{3}{4} + 2\frac{1}{8}$ (b) $\frac{2}{3} + \frac{1}{5}$ (c) $\frac{1}{6} + \frac{3}{4}$

add the whole numbers separately

(a) $1\frac{3}{4} + 2\frac{1}{8} = 3 + \frac{3}{4} + \frac{1}{8}$

To add $\frac{3}{4}$ and $\frac{1}{8}$ find equivalent fractions with the same denominators.

$\frac{3}{4}$ is equivalent to $\frac{6}{8}$.

$\frac{3}{4} + \frac{1}{8} = \frac{6}{8} + \frac{1}{8} = \frac{7}{8}$

So $1\frac{3}{4} + 2\frac{1}{8} = 3\frac{7}{8}$

(b) $\frac{2}{3} + \frac{1}{5}$

The smallest number that is a multiple of both 3 and 5 is 15, so change both the $\frac{2}{3}$ and the $\frac{1}{5}$ to equivalent fractions with denominators of 15.

$\frac{2}{3}$ is equivalent to $\frac{10}{15}$ $\frac{1}{5}$ is equivalent to $\frac{3}{15}$.

$\frac{2}{3} + \frac{1}{5} = \frac{10}{15} + \frac{3}{15} = \frac{13}{15}$

(c) $\frac{1}{6} + \frac{3}{4} = \frac{2}{12} + \frac{9}{12} = \frac{11}{12}$

The smallest number that is a multiple of both 6 and 4 is 12 so change both fractions to equivalent fractions with denominators of 12. You could use any multiple of 12 as the denominator.

Exercise 11I

Work out:

1 **(a)** $\frac{1}{8} + \frac{3}{8}$ **(b)** $\frac{2}{7} + \frac{4}{7}$ **(c)** $\frac{2}{5} + \frac{4}{5}$ **(d)** $\frac{9}{10} + \frac{7}{10}$
(e) $\frac{7}{9} + 2\frac{4}{9}$ **(f)** $\frac{5}{6} + 1\frac{5}{6}$ **(g)** $\frac{3}{4} + \frac{3}{4} + \frac{1}{4}$ **(h)** $\frac{3}{8} + \frac{5}{8} + \frac{7}{8}$

2 **(a)** $\frac{5}{8} + \frac{1}{4}$ **(b)** $1\frac{1}{2} + 2\frac{1}{8}$ **(c)** $\frac{1}{2} + \frac{7}{8}$ **(d)** $2\frac{3}{4} + 3\frac{7}{8}$
(e) $1\frac{3}{4} + 2\frac{5}{16}$ **(f)** $\frac{3}{4} + 3\frac{5}{8}$ **(g)** $\frac{3}{8} + \frac{11}{16}$ **(h)** $2\frac{9}{16} + 1\frac{5}{8}$

3 **(a)** $\frac{1}{5} + \frac{3}{8}$ **(b)** $\frac{1}{5} + \frac{1}{6}$ **(c)** $1\frac{3}{10} + 1\frac{2}{3}$ **(d)** $\frac{2}{3} + \frac{2}{7}$
(e) $3\frac{1}{6} + \frac{2}{7}$ **(f)** $2\frac{5}{6} + 1\frac{1}{7}$ **(g)** $3\frac{2}{5} + 2\frac{7}{15}$ **(h)** $1\frac{2}{3} + 1\frac{2}{9}$

4 Tim travelled $2\frac{3}{4}$ miles to one village then a further $4\frac{1}{3}$ miles to his home.
What is the total distance Tim travelled?

5 Work out the perimeter of this photograph.

6 Two pieces of wood are fixed together. One piece has thickness $2\frac{3}{8}$ inch and the other has thickness $1\frac{5}{16}$ inch.
What is the total thickness of the two pieces of wood?

7 In a class $\frac{1}{6}$ of the pupils own one pet, and $\frac{2}{5}$ of the pupils own more than one pet.
What total fraction of the pupils own at least one pet?

8 A bag weighs $\frac{3}{7}$ lb. The contents weigh $1\frac{1}{5}$ lb.
What is the total weight of the bag and its contents?

Subtracting fractions

You can subtract fractions in the same way as adding them.

Example 12

Work out:

(a) $\frac{7}{8} - \frac{11}{16}$ (b) $7\frac{3}{5} - 3\frac{1}{2}$

(a) $\frac{7}{8} - \frac{11}{16}$

Here there are different denominators. Change the eighths ($\frac{7}{8}$) to sixteenths to match the $\frac{11}{16}$.

$\frac{7}{8} - \frac{11}{16} = \frac{14}{16} - \frac{11}{16} = \frac{3}{16}$

$\frac{7}{8}$ is equivalent to $\frac{14}{16}$

(b) $7\frac{3}{5} - 3\frac{1}{2}$

Subtract the whole numbers first.
$7 - 3 = 4$

$= 7 - 3 + \left(\frac{3}{5} - \frac{1}{2}\right)$

Change both the $\frac{3}{5}$ and the $\frac{1}{2}$ to equivalent fractions with a denominator of 10. The lowest number that is a multiple of both 5 and 2 is 10.

$= 4 + \left(\frac{6}{10} - \frac{5}{10}\right) = 4\frac{1}{10}$

$\frac{3}{5}$ is equivalent to $\frac{6}{10}$ $\frac{1}{2}$ is equivalent to $\frac{5}{10}$

Exercise 11J

Work out:

1 **(a)** $\frac{3}{4} - \frac{1}{4}$ **(b)** $\frac{5}{8} - \frac{3}{8}$ **(c)** $\frac{15}{16} - \frac{7}{16}$ **(d)** $\frac{6}{7} - \frac{3}{7}$

2 **(a)** $\frac{1}{2} - \frac{3}{8}$ **(b)** $\frac{7}{8} - \frac{1}{2}$ **(c)** $\frac{7}{8} - \frac{3}{4}$ **(d)** $4\frac{5}{8} - 2\frac{1}{4}$

3 **(a)** $2\frac{3}{4} - \frac{3}{5}$ **(b)** $4\frac{4}{5} - 2\frac{2}{7}$ **(c)** $8\frac{2}{3} - 3\frac{2}{5}$ **(d)** $4\frac{5}{8} - 1\frac{2}{9}$

4 **(a)** $4\frac{7}{8} - 1\frac{2}{3}$ **(b)** $5\frac{7}{9} - 3\frac{1}{3}$ **(c)** $3\frac{4}{5} - \frac{3}{8}$ **(d)** $7\frac{4}{7} - 4\frac{2}{5}$

5 A box containing tomatoes has a total weight of $5\frac{7}{8}$ kg. The box when empty has a weight of $1\frac{1}{4}$ kg.
What is the weight of the tomatoes?

6 A tin contains $7\frac{1}{2}$ pints of oil. From the tin $4\frac{3}{8}$ pints are poured out.
How much oil remains?

7 A plank of wood is $6\frac{1}{2}$ feet long. A $4\frac{3}{8}$ foot length is cut from one end of the plank.
What length of wood remains?

8 Carol spends $\frac{2}{3}$ of her salary on food. She spends $\frac{1}{4}$ of her salary on bills.
What fraction of her salary is left?

9 Amarjit travels $5\frac{3}{8}$ km due North in her car, then $3\frac{1}{4}$ km due South.
How far is she from her starting point?

11.6 Multiplying and dividing fractions

How to multiply two fractions:

multiply the numerators (top)

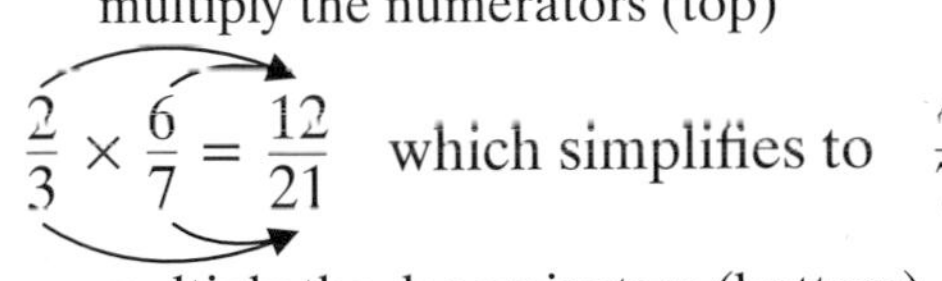

multiply the denominators (bottom)

Finding $\frac{2}{3}$ of $\frac{6}{7}$

This represents $\frac{6}{7}$:

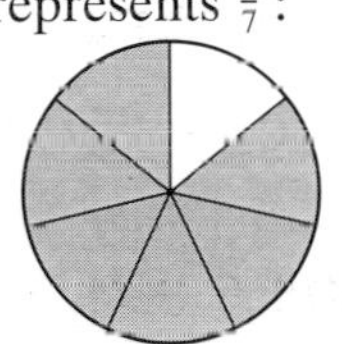

$\frac{2}{3}$ of the shaded part is $\frac{2}{3}$ of $\frac{6}{7}$:

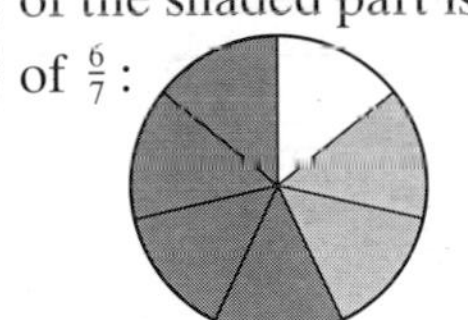

So $\frac{2}{3}$ of $\frac{6}{7}$ is the same as $\frac{4}{7}$

■ **To multiply two fractions, multiply the numerators (top) then multiply the denominators (bottom).**

Another way of doing this is to simplify the fractions before you multiply them:

$$\frac{2}{3} \times \frac{6}{7} = \frac{2 \times 6}{3 \times 7}$$

Simplify by dividing top and bottom by 3.

$$\frac{(2 \times 6) \div 3}{(3 \times 7) \div 3} = \frac{2 \times 2}{7} = \frac{4}{7}$$

This method is sometimes called **cancelling**.

Here, the word **of** means multiplied by

$\frac{1}{2}$ of 8 is $\frac{1}{2} \times 8 = 4$

■ **When you multiply or divide mixed numbers you must change them to improper (top-heavy) fractions first.**

Example 13

(a) Find the weight of a quarter of a $\frac{3}{5}$ kg packet of biscuits.
(b) Work out $2\frac{1}{2} \times 1\frac{2}{5}$

(a) $\frac{1}{4}$ of $\frac{3}{5}$ kg is $\frac{1}{4} \times \frac{3}{5}$ kg $= \frac{3}{20}$ kg

First multiply the numerators, then multiply the denominators.

(b) $2\frac{1}{2} \times 1\frac{2}{5} = \frac{5}{2} \times \frac{7}{5}$

First change mixed numbers to improper fractions.

$= \frac{(5 \times 7) \div 5}{(2 \times 5) \div 5}$

Simplify by dividing top and bottom by 5.

$= \frac{7}{2} = 3\frac{1}{2}$

Always write the answer in its simplest form.

Exercise 11K

Work out:

1 (a) $\frac{1}{2} \times \frac{3}{8}$ (b) $\frac{4}{5} \times \frac{2}{3}$ (c) $\frac{4}{7} \times \frac{1}{3}$ (d) $\frac{2}{3} \times \frac{2}{5}$
(e) $\frac{2}{7} \times \frac{1}{5}$ (f) $\frac{2}{3} \times \frac{5}{7}$ (g) $\frac{1}{2} \times \frac{3}{4}$ (h) $\frac{3}{5} \times \frac{1}{3}$

2 (a) $\frac{1}{3} \times \frac{6}{7}$ (b) $\frac{6}{7} \times \frac{5}{12}$ (c) $\frac{1}{2} \times \frac{4}{5}$ (d) $\frac{2}{3} \times \frac{1}{4}$
(e) $\frac{3}{7} \times \frac{2}{6}$ (f) $\frac{6}{5} \times \frac{1}{3}$ (g) $5 \times \frac{7}{10}$ (h) $\frac{9}{10} \times \frac{13}{18}$

3 (a) $\frac{2}{3} \times 1\frac{1}{3}$ (b) $\frac{2}{5} \times 2\frac{1}{3}$ (c) $1\frac{1}{2} \times \frac{1}{4}$ (d) $1\frac{1}{2} \times 2\frac{1}{2}$
(e) $2\frac{1}{2} \times \frac{1}{4}$ (f) $1\frac{2}{5} \times 1\frac{1}{3}$ (g) $6 \times 2\frac{2}{3}$ (h) $2\frac{1}{7} \times 1\frac{2}{5}$

4 A melon weighs $2\frac{1}{2}$ lb.
Work out the total weight of $8\frac{1}{4}$ melons.

5 Ivor takes $2\frac{1}{4}$ minutes to clean one window.
How long will it take him to clean $6\frac{1}{2}$ windows of a similar size?

6 A mechanic can do a car service in $1\frac{1}{3}$ hours. One week he has to service 15 cars.
How long will it take him?

7 Sharon can paint a garage door in $1\frac{2}{5}$ hours.
How long will it take her to paint 7 garage doors?

8 Find the area of this rectangle.
Leave your answer as a fraction.

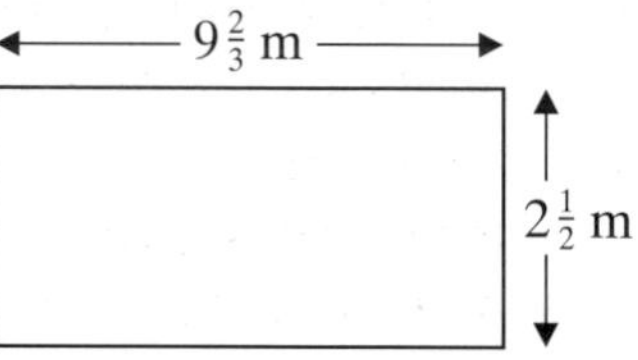

How to multiply a fraction by a whole number

To work out $\frac{7}{10} \times 4$

first write 4 as the top-heavy (or improper) fraction $\frac{4}{1}$.

$$\frac{7}{10} \times \frac{4}{1} \text{ is } \frac{7 \times 4}{10 \times 1} = \frac{28}{10}$$

So $\frac{7}{10} \times 4 = \frac{28}{10}$ This is usually written as a mixed number: $2\frac{8}{10}$
which simplifies to $2\frac{4}{5}$

Example 14

Find $\frac{2}{5}$ of 65 metres

$$\frac{2}{5} \text{ of } 65\text{ m is } \frac{2}{5} \times \frac{65}{1} = \frac{2 \times 65}{5 \times 1}$$

Simplify by dividing top and bottom by 5

$$= \frac{(2 \times 65) \div 5}{(5 \times 1) \div 5} = \frac{2 \times 13}{1} = 26\text{ m}$$

Worked examination question

Work out $\frac{3}{8}$ of 6 metres. [L]

$$\frac{3}{8} \times \frac{6}{1} = \frac{(3 \times 6) \div 2}{(8 \times 1) \div 2} = \frac{9}{4} = 2\frac{1}{4} \text{ or } 2.25 \text{ metres}$$

Exercise 11L

Work out:

1 (a) $\frac{1}{8}$ of 72 (b) $\frac{5}{6}$ of 36 (c) $\frac{4}{9}$ of 63 litres
(d) $\frac{7}{16}$ of 48 pints

2 (a) $\frac{1}{12}$ of £180 (b) $\frac{4}{5}$ of 4.63 kg (c) $\frac{2}{3}$ of £3.96
(d) $\frac{17}{20}$ of 73 litres

3 (a) $\frac{3}{4}$ of 36 lb (b) $\frac{2}{5}$ of £5.55 (c) $\frac{11}{12}$ of 714 km
(d) $\frac{4}{7}$ of 490 people

4 (a) $\frac{4}{9}$ of £38.25 (b) $\frac{4}{15}$ of 630 toys (c) $\frac{4}{9}$ of 1620 cars
(d) $\frac{5}{7}$ of £52.01

5 Barry earns £130.60 in one week. He pays $\frac{1}{4}$ of this in tax.
How much money does he pay in tax each week?

6 Sara receives £2.70 pocket money each week. She saves $\frac{2}{5}$ of it.
How much money does she save each week?

7 During a 28-week holiday season $\frac{2}{7}$ of the days were wet.
How many dry days were there?

8 Jomo delivers 56 newspapers on his round. On Fridays $\frac{3}{8}$ of the newspapers have a supplement each.
How many supplements does he deliver?

How to divide by a fraction

Here is a problem that you can solve if you divide by a fraction:
The length of a relay race is 2 laps of a running track. Each member of a team runs $\frac{1}{5}$ of a lap.
How many runners are there in a team?

You can easily work out in your head that there are 10 runners in a team. To show your method you need to find how many fifths of a lap there are in 2 whole laps.
You could work this out by dividing $2 \div \frac{1}{5}$.

To get the answer 10 you could work out $\frac{2}{1} \times \frac{5}{1}$.

You get this expression from $\frac{2}{1} \div \frac{1}{5}$ if you turn the second fraction upside down and change the ÷ sign to a × sign.

Why inverting works
A fraction like $\frac{3}{4}$ is the same as:
$3 \div 4$
or $3 \times \frac{1}{4}$
But $\frac{1}{4}$ is $\frac{4}{1}$ inverted.
So dividing is the same as multiplying by the inverted number.
$12 \div 3 = 4$
$12 \times \frac{1}{3} = 4$ too

Example 15

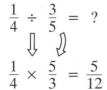

$$\frac{1}{4} \div \frac{3}{5} = ?$$

Turn the fraction you are dividing by upside down.

Change the ÷ sign to a × sign.

$$\frac{1}{4} \times \frac{5}{3} = \frac{5}{12}$$

This is called **inverting** the fraction.

So $\frac{1}{4} \div \frac{3}{5} = \frac{5}{12}$

■ **To divide by a fraction: invert the dividing fraction (turn it upside down) and change the division sign to multiplication.**

Example 16

Work out:

(a) $\frac{2}{5} \div \frac{1}{2}$ (b) $\frac{4}{9} \div 6$ (c) $3\frac{1}{2} \div 2\frac{2}{3}$

(a) $\frac{2}{5} \div \frac{1}{2} = \frac{2}{5} \times \frac{2}{1} = \frac{4}{5}$

The $\frac{1}{2}$ becomes $\frac{2}{1}$; the ÷ becomes ×.

(b) $\frac{4}{9} \div 6 = \frac{4}{9} \div \frac{6}{1}$

$= \frac{4}{9} \times \frac{1}{6} = \frac{4}{54} = \frac{2}{27}$

The 6 can be written $\frac{6}{1}$, which becomes $\frac{1}{6}$ when you invert it.

(c) $3\frac{1}{2} \div 2\frac{2}{3} = \frac{7}{2} \div \frac{8}{3}$

First write the mixed numbers as improper fractions.

$= \frac{7}{2} \times \frac{3}{8} = \frac{21}{16} = 1\frac{5}{16}$

Remember to simplify the final answer.

Exercise 11M

Work out:

1 **(a)** $\frac{2}{9} \div \frac{1}{2}$ **(b)** $\frac{2}{5} \div \frac{3}{4}$ **(c)** $\frac{3}{8} \div \frac{2}{3}$ **(d)** $\frac{1}{2} \div \frac{1}{4}$

2 **(a)** $\frac{8}{9} \div 4$ **(b)** $\frac{2}{3} \div 6$ **(c)** $4\frac{2}{3} \div 4$ **(d)** $5\frac{1}{4} \div 3$

3 **(a)** $1\frac{1}{3} \div 1\frac{1}{2}$ **(b)** $2\frac{1}{2} \div \frac{1}{3}$ **(c)** $4\frac{3}{5} \div \frac{2}{3}$ **(d)** $2\frac{1}{5} \div 1\frac{1}{3}$
(e) $1\frac{1}{3} \div 2\frac{2}{9}$ **(f)** $2\frac{2}{3} \div 2\frac{2}{5}$ **(g)** $3\frac{1}{3} \div 7\frac{1}{2}$ **(h)** $4\frac{4}{5} \div 5\frac{1}{3}$

4 A tin holds $10\frac{2}{3}$ litres of methylated spirit for a lamp. How many times will it fill a lamp holding $\frac{2}{3}$ litre?

5 A metal rod is $10\frac{4}{5}$ metres long. How many short rods $\frac{3}{10}$ metres long can be cut from the longer rod?

6 Tar & Stone Ltd can resurface $2\frac{1}{5}$ km of road in a day. How many days will it take to resurface a road of length $24\frac{3}{5}$ km?

11.7 Solving problems involving fractions

In this section you are given various problems to solve. Fractions are used in many different situations and these problems introduce you to the types of questions that are included in GCSE examinations.

Example 17

A bag of flour weighs 2.25 kg. More flour is added, and the weight of the bag of flour is increased by three fifths.

What is the new weight of the bag of flour?

$\frac{3}{5}$ of 2.25 kg is $\frac{3}{5} \times 2.25 = \frac{3 \times 2.25}{5} = \frac{6.75}{5} = 1.35$ kg

The new weight is 2.25 kg + 1.35 kg = 3.6 kg

Example 18

A 5 litre tin of paint is filled with blue and yellow paint to make a shade of green. The tin contains $1\frac{1}{2}$ litres of blue paint.
What fraction of the paint in the 5 litre tin is blue?

The fraction of paint that is blue is:

$$\frac{\text{blue paint}}{\text{whole tin}} = \frac{1\frac{1}{2}}{5}$$

$$= 1\frac{1}{2} \div \frac{5}{1} = \frac{3}{2} \times \frac{1}{5} = \frac{3}{10}$$

Exercise 11N

1 A loaded lorry has a total weight of 13.2 tonnes. This weight is decreased by five eighths when the load is removed.
Find the weight of the lorry without the load.

2 Last year 204 Japanese cars were imported by a garage. This year the number of cars imported has increased by five twelfths.
How many cars have been imported this year?

3 Of 144 rail passengers surveyed, 32 claimed their train was regularly late.
What fraction of the total number of passengers was this?

4 There are 225 houses on an estate. Of these houses 85 have no garages.
What fraction of houses have no garages?

5 Find the difference between $\frac{3}{5}$ of 36 miles and $\frac{2}{3}$ of 30 miles.

6 A tin contains approximately 440 beans. The manufacturer increases the volume of the tin by three eighths.
Approximately how many beans would you expect to find in the larger tin?

7 A newspaper has 14 columns of photographs and 18 columns of advertisements.
What fraction of the paper is advertisements?

8 On an Intercity train there are 216 men, 144 women and 80 children.
What fraction of the total number is made up of children?

Exercise 11O Mixed questions

1 Complete these sets of equivalent fractions:

(a) $\frac{5}{9} = \frac{?}{18} = \frac{?}{27} = \frac{?}{36} = \frac{?}{45}$ **(b)** $\frac{2}{5} = \frac{?}{10}$

(c) $\frac{3}{?} = \frac{24}{64}$ **(d)** $\frac{?}{7} = \frac{40}{35}$

2 Express these fractions in their simplest form:

(a) $\frac{24}{30}$ **(b)** $\frac{19}{3}$ **(c)** $\frac{5}{60}$ **(d)** $\frac{50}{15}$ **(e)** $\frac{72}{18}$ **(f)** $\frac{13}{169}$

3 Express these fractions as decimals:

(a) $\frac{7}{8}$ **(b)** $2\frac{3}{4}$ **(c)** $4\frac{9}{25}$ **(d)** $\frac{7}{9}$ **(e)** $2\frac{5}{6}$

4 Express these decimals as fractions:

(a) 0.04 **(b)** 2.725 **(c)** 5.68 **(d)** 0.3 **(e)** 0.45

5 Find the difference between $\frac{2}{3}$ of 15 kg and $\frac{3}{5}$ of 18 kg.

6 Two pipes of length $4\frac{5}{8}$ ft and $3\frac{3}{4}$ ft are put end to end. What is their total length?

7 One route between two towns is of length $14\frac{1}{4}$ miles. Another route is of length $10\frac{3}{8}$ miles. Find the difference between the lengths of the two routes.

8 A length of wire is $5\frac{7}{8}$ feet long. A length of $1\frac{3}{16}$ feet is cut off. What length of wire is left?

9 There are 70 ounces of sweets in a jar. How many $4\frac{1}{4}$ ounce bags can be filled from the jar?

10 Derek spent £2 on motor oil and £16 on petrol. What fraction of the total amount did he spend on petrol?

11 Two rods are fixed together to make a part for a motor.

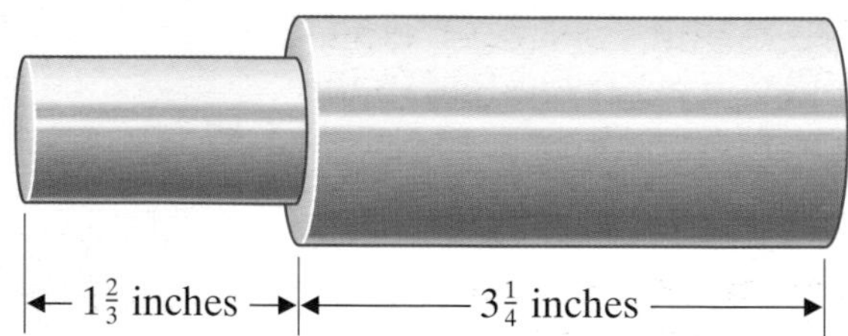

Work out the total length of the two rods.
Write your answer as a mixed number in its simplest form. [L]

12 A personal stereo was priced at £48. In a sale it was reduced to £42.
By what fraction was the original price reduced? [L]

13 Work out $\frac{3}{4}$ of £24. [L]

Summary of key points

1 You can find equivalent fractions by multiplying (or dividing) the top and bottom of a fraction by the same number.

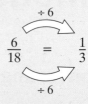

2 A fraction can be simplified if the numerator (top) and denominator (bottom) have a common factor.

$$\frac{6}{18} \overset{\div 6}{=} \frac{1}{3}$$

3 $\frac{5}{2}$ is called an improper or top-heavy fraction.

4 $2\frac{1}{2}$ is called a mixed number because it contains a whole number part and a fractional part smaller than 1.

5 Mixed numbers can be written as improper fractions and improper fractions can be written as mixed numbers.

$1\frac{3}{4} = \frac{7}{4}$

$\frac{9}{4} = 2\frac{1}{4}$

6 Improper fractions in their simplest form are written as mixed numbers.

7 You can convert a fraction to a decimal by dividing the numerator by the denominator.

$\frac{4}{5} = 4 \div 5 = 0.8$

8 You can convert a decimal to a fraction:

$1.32 = 1\frac{32}{100} = 1\frac{8}{25}$

9 0.666 666 6... is called a recurring decimal since one of the digits recurs (repeats).

Recurring decimal notation:

$0.\dot{3}$ means 0.333 333 3 recurring

$0.\dot{1}\dot{7}$ means 0.171 717 17 recurring

$0.\dot{2}15\dot{4}$ means 0.215 421 542 154 recurring.

10 To add fractions find equivalent fractions that have the same denominator (bottom).

$$\frac{1}{2} + \frac{2}{6} = \frac{3}{6} + \frac{2}{6} = \frac{3+2}{6} = \frac{5}{6}$$

equivalent fraction

11 To multiply two fractions multiply the numerators (top), then multiply the denominators (bottom):

$$\frac{3}{4} \times \frac{1}{7} = \frac{3 \times 1}{4 \times 7} = \frac{3}{28}$$

12 When you multiply or divide mixed numbers you must change them to improper (top heavy) fractions first.

13 To divide by a fraction: invert the dividing fraction (turn it upside down) and change the division sign to multiplication.

$$\frac{1}{4} \div \frac{2}{5} = \frac{1}{4} \times \frac{5}{2} = \frac{1 \times 5}{4 \times 2} = \frac{5}{8}$$

12 Measure 2

12.1 Converting units (metric)

This section shows you how to convert (or change) measurements from one metric unit to another. To do this you need to be able to multiply and divide whole numbers and decimals by 10, 100 and 1000 (covered on pages 000 to 000).

You need to know these facts:

■ **10 mm = 1 cm** **1000 mg = 1 g** **1000 m*l* = 1 *l***
100 cm = 1 m **1000 g = 1 kg** **1000 cm^3 = 1 *l***
1000 m = 1 km **1000 kg = 1 tonne**

Remember:

- when you change from small units to large units you divide.
- when you change from large units to small units you multiply.

Example 1

Change 2 kilometres to metres.

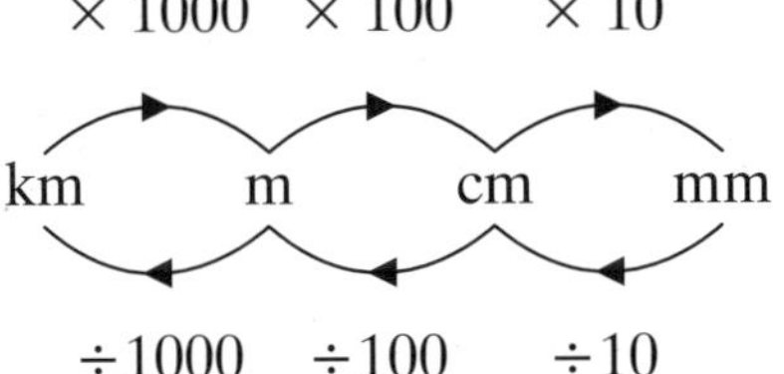

Kilometres are larger units than metres. Multiply by the number of metres in a kilometre, which is 1000.

2 km = 2 × 1000 m = 2000 m

Example 2

Change 250 mm to cm.

Millimetres are smaller units than centimetres. Divide by the number of millimetres in a centimetre, which is 10.

250 mm = 250 ÷ 10 cm = 25 cm

Exercise 12A

1 Change these lengths to centimetres:
(a) 3 m **(b)** 30 mm **(c)** 6 m **(d)** 100 mm

2 Change these lengths to millimetres:
(a) 2 cm **(b)** 5 cm **(c)** 20 cm

3 Change these lengths to metres:
(a) 5 km **(b)** 300 cm **(c)** 10 km **(d)** 2000 cm
(e) 60 km

4 Change these weights to grams:
(a) 5 kg **(b)** 40 kg **(c)** 250 kg

5 Change these volumes to litres:
(a) 3000 m*l* **(b)** 8000 m*l* **(c)** 50 000 m*l*

6 Change these volumes to millilitres:
(a) 6 *l* **(b)** 40 *l* **(c)** 350 *l*

7 Change these lengths to kilometres:
(a) 3000 m **(b)** 45 000 m

8 Change these weights to kilograms:
(a) 2000 g **(b)** 3 tonnes **(c)** 50 000 g

9 Jim's lorry weighs 8 tonnes. How many grams is this?

10 Jeremy walks 10 kilometres. How many centimetres is this?

11 Gerry has an average pace length of 75 cm. How many paces does she take in 3 km?

12 Write down the number of milligrams in 1 kilogram.

Exercise 12B

1 Put these lines in order, smallest first:

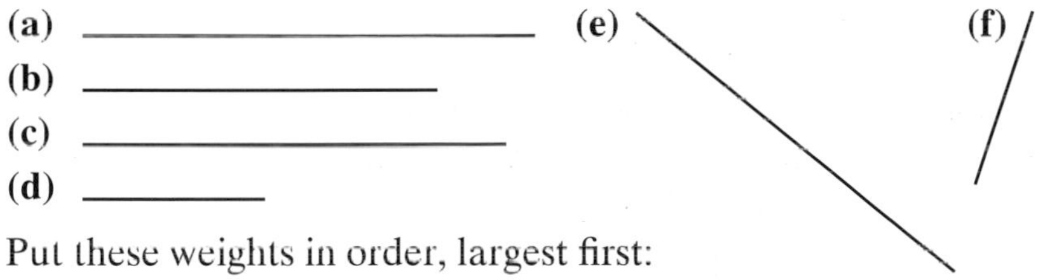

2 Put these weights in order, largest first:
250 g 25 g 2 kg 250 kg 3000 g

3 Put these lengths in order, smallest first:

3 m	5 mm	20 cm	3 km	50 mm
75 cm	3000 mm	2 m	4000 m	4 cm

4 Put these volumes in order, smallest first:
200 m*l* 5 *l* 600 m*l* 2000 m*l* 1 *l*

So far all of the answers in this section have been whole numbers. From now on you will find it easier if you use your calculator. Don't forget to **check whether your answer is sensible**.

Example 3

Change 450 g to kg.

450 g = 450 ÷ 1000 kg = 0.45 kg

Small units to larger so divide.
1 kg = 1000 g so divide by 1000.

Example 4

Change 2.4 *l* to m*l*.

2.4 *l* = 2.4 × 1000 m*l* = 2400 m*l*

Large units to smaller so multiply.
1 *l* = 1000 m*l* so multiply by 1000.

Exercise 12C

1 Change these lengths to metres:
(a) 250 cm (b) 3.6 km (c) 75 cm (d) 0.005 km
(e) 0.04 km (f) 5 mm

2 Change these weights to grams:
(a) 4.5 kg (b) 0.4 kg (c) 0.03 kg (d) 0.005 kg

3 Change these lengths to centimetres:
(a) 350 mm (b) 2.5 m (c) 5 mm (d) 0.08 m
(e) 0.8 m (f) 35 mm

4 Change these volumes to millilitres:
(a) 3.5 *l* (b) 15.4 *l* (c) 0.05 *l* (d) 0.003 *l*

5 Change these lengths to millimetres:
(a) 3.5 cm (b) 0.7 cm (c) 0.08 cm (d) 0.005 m

6 Write these lengths in kilometres:
(a) 300 m (b) 50 m (c) 1250 m (d) 75 m

7 Change these volumes to litres:
(a) 250 m*l* (b) 100 m*l* (c) 50 m*l* (d) 3500 m*l*

8 Write these weights in tonnes:
(a) 3500 kg (b) 450 kg (c) 50 kg (d) 3000 g

9 How many 75 m*l* glasses can be filled from a bottle holding 1.5 *l* of cola?

10 How many 50 mm pieces of wood can be cut from a piece of wood of length 3 m assuming there is no waste?

11 It takes 150 g of flour to make a batch of rock cakes.
How many batches of rock cakes can be made from 1.5 kg of flour?

Comparing measurements

Sometimes you have to compare measurements. First change all the measurements to the same units. You can only compare like with like.

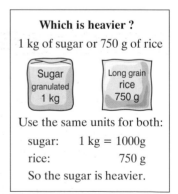

Which is heavier ?

1 kg of sugar or 750 g of rice

Use the same units for both:

sugar: 1 kg = 1000g
rice: 750 g
So the sugar is heavier.

Exercise 12D

1 Write these lengths in order, smallest first:
(a) 25 mm, 3 cm, 2.4 cm, 50 mm, 6 cm, 57 mm
(b) 30 cm, 0.4 m, 270 mm, 1.2 m, 500 mm, 45 cm
(c) 2 m, 340 cm, 4000 mm, 4 m, 370 cm, 3500 mm
(d) 5 cm, 45 mm, 36 cm, 0.3 m, 55 mm, 0.2 cm, 4 mm

2 Write these weights in order, smallest first:
(a) 250 g, 0.3 kg, 500 g, 0.05 kg
(b) 5000 g, 3000 g, 4 kg, 4.5 kg, 0.5 tonnes, 400 kg

3 Write these volumes in order, smallest first:
(a) 300 m*l*, 0.4 *l*, 500 m*l*, 250 m*l*, 0.3 *l*
(b) 500 m*l*, 450 m*l*, 0.4 *l*, 360 m*l*, 0.05 *l*, 45 m*l*

12.2 Converting between metric and Imperial units

You need to be able to convert measurements from metric units to Imperial units (the old style units) and from Imperial to metric. To do this it helps to memorize these approximate Imperial and metric equivalents:

	Metric	Imperial
*	1 kg	2.2 pounds
	25 g	1 ounce
*	1 l	$1\frac{3}{4}$ pints
*	4.5 l	1 gallon
*	8 km	5 miles
*	1 m	39 inches
*	30 cm	1 foot
	2.5 cm	1 inch

You will be expected to know the items with a star (*) by them for your exam.

Example 5

Change 10 km to miles.

8 km is approximately 5 miles

so 1 km = 5 ÷ 8 miles = 0.625 miles

and 10 km = 0.625 × 10 miles = 6.25 miles

Exercise 12E

The Evans family are going on holiday to Scotland. The family consists of Mr and Mrs Evans and their three children, Glenys, Eira and Gareth.

1 Mr Evans works out the distance from their home in London to Scotland. He makes it 400 miles.
What is this distance in kilometres?

2 Mrs Evans packs a 3 litre bottle of lemonade for the trip.
How many pints is 3 litres?

3 The petrol tank of the family's car holds 15 gallons.
How many litres is this?

4 Glenys estimates the weight of all the luggage as 100 kg.
Work out the weight of the luggage in pounds.

5 Gareth puts 1 pint of water in the radiator.
What is 1 pint in litres?

6 Mr Evans puts 30 litres of petrol in the car.
How many gallons is that?

7 Mrs Evans puts $0.5\,l$ of oil in the engine.
Change $0.5\,l$ to pints.

8 The family stop at a service station 150 km from home.
How many miles is that?

9 Eira buys an 800 g bar of chocolate.
Change 800 g to pounds.

10 When they get to Scotland there is half a bottle of lemonade left.
Work out the amount of lemonade left, in pints.

Exercise 12F

The pupils in Class 11E decide to raise money for charity by holding a cola morning.

1 Claire cooks 72 cakes. The amounts needed for her recipe are 24 ounces of fat, 40 ounces of flour and 32 ounces of dried fruit.
Claire only has a metric set of scales.
How many grams of each ingredient should she use?

2 Charlene buys ten $3\,l$ bottles of cola.
How many gallons is this?

3 Harjit buys 20 packets of biscuits. Each pack weighs 1 pound.
How many kilograms is this?

4 Jonathan brings plates that are 4 inches across.
How many centimetres is this?

5 The trays the class use are 24 inches long and 15 inches across.
Change these measurements to centimetres.

6 The tables the class use are circular with a diameter of 48 inches.
Will a tablecloth with a 1.2 m diameter cover a table?

7 Nilmini makes sandwiches. She uses 5 one-kilogram loaves and 500 g of spread.
Change these weights to pounds.

8 At the end of the cola morning there are 5 pints of cola left.
How many litres is this?

9 In the 'guess the weight of the cake' competition the correct answer is 5 pounds. Robin says the weight is 5.1 pounds and Hazel says 2.3 kilograms.
Work out which of these two answers is nearer the correct one.

10 The total weight of the cakes Claire sells is 3.5 kilograms.
How many pounds is that?

12.3 Using unusual units

Sometimes you may be given relationships between strange units to test your understanding of changing units.

Example 6

There are 5 groms in a nuti and 6 nutis in a bolta. How many groms are there in 10 boltas?

	1 nuti	= 5 groms
so	1 bolta	= 6 nutis or $6 \times 5 = 30$ groms
and	10 boltas	$= 10 \times 30 = 300$ groms.

Exercise 12G

1 If there are 7 spongs in a delta and 4 deltas in a rova, how many
(a) spongs in 5 deltas **(b)** deltas in 8 rovas **(c)** spongs in 12 rovas?

2 If there are 12 dolts in a ping and 20 pings in a pong, how many
(a) dolts in 6 pings **(b)** pings in 4 pongs **(c)** dolts in 5 pongs?

3 There were 4 farthings in an old penny, 4 old pennies in a groat and 6 groats in a florin. How many
(a) farthings in 5 old pennies **(b)** old pennies in 5 groats
(c) groats in 4 florins **(d)** farthings in 12 groats
(e) old pennies in 5 florins **(f)** farthings in 10 florins?

12.4 Converting units of area and volume

You can measure areas in square centimetres (cm^2), square metres (m^2), square kilometres (km^2) and so on.

To help convert from square metres to square centimetres here are two pictures of the same square:

1 m
sides measured in metres
1 m
area = 1 m × 1 m
= 1 m^2

100 cm
sides measured in centimetres
100 cm
area = 100 cm × 100 cm
= 10 000 cm^2

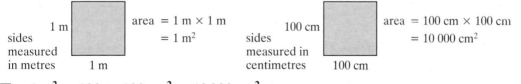

■ $\mathbf{1\ m^2 = 100 \times 100\ cm^2 = 10\,000\ cm^2}$

You can measure volumes in cubic centimetres (cm^3), cubic metres (m^3) and so on.

To help convert from cubic metres to cubic centimetres here are two pictures of the same cube:

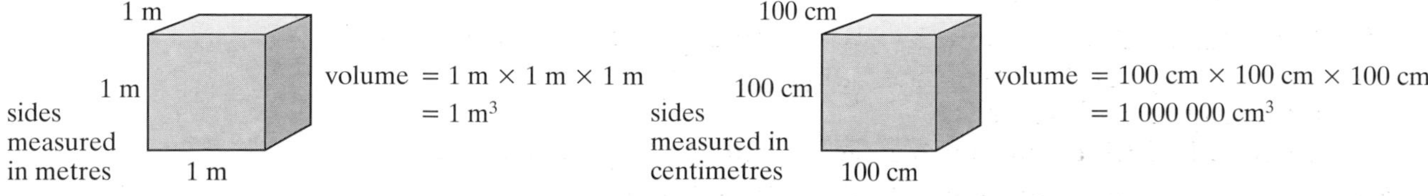

■ $\mathbf{1\ m^3 = 100 \times 100 \times 100\ cm^3 = 1\,000\,000\ cm^3}$

You can use the same method to convert units in other measurement systems.

Example 7

There are 12 inches in one foot.

Find the number of:

(a) square inches in a square foot (inches^2 in 1 foot^2)
(b) cubic inches in a cubic foot (inches^3 in 1 foot^3).

12 inches
square foot
12 inches

12 inches
12 inches
cubic foot
12 inches

(a) 1 square foot $= 12 \times 12$ square inches $= 144$ square inches.
(b) 1 cubic foot $= 12 \times 12 \times 12$ cubic inches $= 1728$ cubic inches.

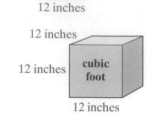

Exercise 12H

1 Calculate the number of:
(a) m^2 in 1 km^2 **(b)** mm^2 in 1 m^2 **(c)** mm^3 in 1 cm^3
(d) mm^3 in 1 m^3

2 There are 3 feet in 1 yard. Calculate how many:
(a) square feet in a square yard
(b) cubic feet in 1 cubic yard.

3 Barbara measures her living room in yards and works out that she needs 16 square yards of carpet. She knows that 1 yard is approximately 0.91 metres.
(a) Change 1 square yard to square metres.
(b) Work out the amount of carpet, in square metres, that Barbara needs for her living room.

4 Brian completely fills his fish tank with water. The tank is 24 inches long by 16 inches wide by 10 inches deep.
(a) Calculate the volume of the tank in cubic inches.

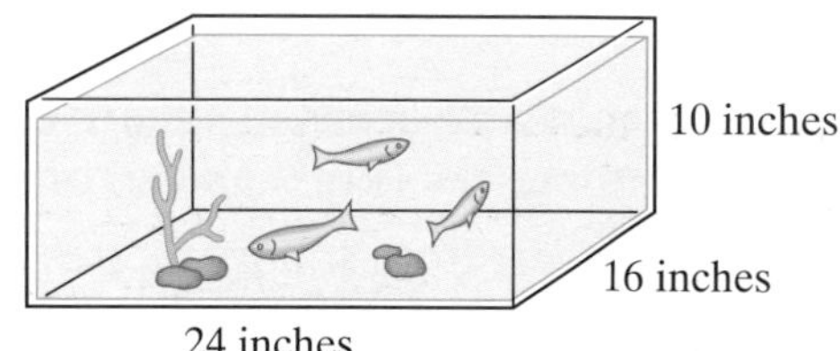

There are 2.54 cm in 1 inch.
(b) Work out the number of cm^3 in a cubic inch.
(c) Find the volume of the tank in cm^3.
There are 1000 cm^3 in a litre.
(d) Calculate the amount of water in the tank in litres.

12.5 Accuracy of measurement

Here are two different types of measurements a confectionery company can make on its boxes of chocolates:

Counting – a discrete measure

They can count the number of sweets in each box exactly. There may be:

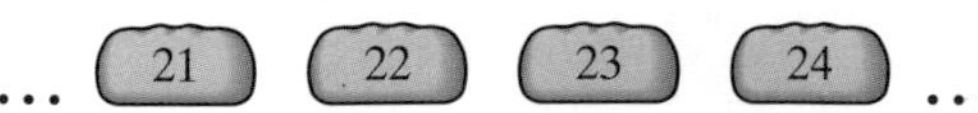

The possible values are **discrete** (or separate) from each other – there are no values in between them (such as 22.375).

Weighing – a continuous measure

They can weigh each box. A box could weigh any of these values:

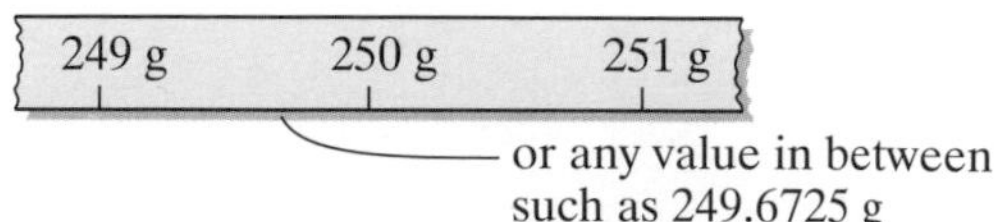

The possible values are **continuous**.

The accuracy of the measurement depends on the accuracy of the measuring instrument.

■ **Quantities that can be counted are called discrete measures.**

For example, the number of spectators at a swimming gala can be counted so it is a discrete measure.

■ **When you use a measuring instrument the measurements you make are called continuous measures.**

When you measure the height of a person, the weight of a parcel or the time it takes to run a race you are using continuous measures.

■ **Continuous measurements cannot be exact. They are only as accurate as the instruments you are using to carry out the measurement.**

Describing the accuracy of a measurement

Suppose you use a ruler marked in millimetres to measure a line as 237 mm correct to the nearest mm.

The true length could be anywhere between 236.5 mm and 237.5 mm.

So the true length could be anywhere in a range 0.5 mm below and 0.5 mm above the recorded value:

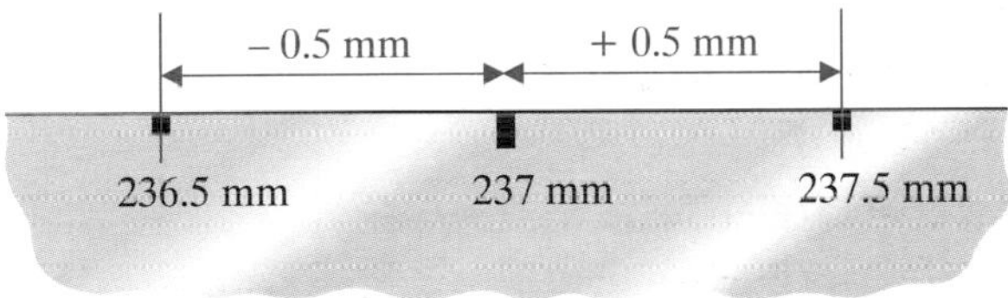

Here is another example:

The time taken to walk down some stairs is measured as 10 seconds to the nearest second. The time could be between 9.5 and 10.5 seconds.

If the time is measured as 10.3 seconds to the nearest tenth of a second, it could be between 10.25 and 10.35 seconds.

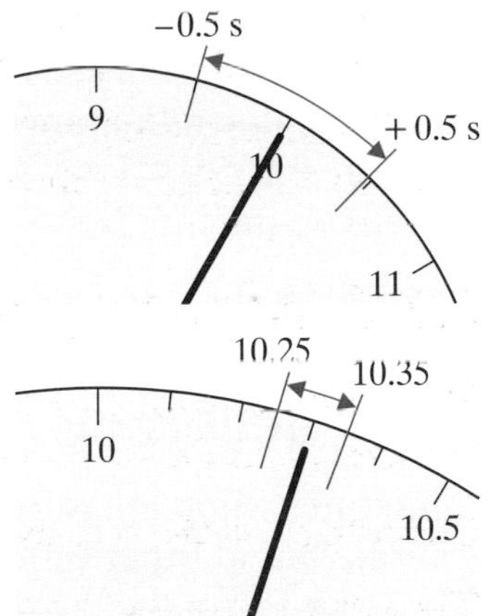

For any measurement you make:

■ **If you make a measurement correct to a given unit the true value lies in a range that extends half a unit below and half a unit above the measurement.**

Exercise 12I

1 Write down which of these is a discrete measure and which is a continuous measure:
(a) the number of bricks in a wall
(b) the number of nails in a box
(c) the height of a door
(d) the number of tiles in the bathroom
(e) the weight of sand on a lorry
(f) the time taken to unload the lorry
(g) the cost of a bag of potatoes
(h) the length of a piece of wood
(i) the number of door handles in a school
(j) the length of a roll of sticky tape.

2 These lengths are all measured to the nearest millimetre. Write down the smallest length they could be and the largest length they could be:
(a) 2.7 cm (b) 3.9 cm (c) 10.5 cm
(d) 12 mm (e) 25 mm (f) 36 mm

3 These lengths have all been measured to the nearest centimetre. Write down the smallest length they could be and the largest length they could be:
(a) 2.45 m (b) 5.34 m (c) 4.00 m
(d) 23 cm (e) 14 cm (f) 50 cm

4 Iain was measuring the time it took to run 100 m. His watch was accurate to the nearest tenth of a second and he measured the time as 12.1 seconds.
Write down the range of times between which the time could lie.

5 At a race meeting these times were measured to the nearest hundredth of a second.
Write down the range of times between which the times could lie.
(a) 22.35 s (b) 43.67 s (c) 10.02 s
(d) 2 min 45.34 s (e) 45.00 s (f) 50 s

12.6 Choosing an appropriate degree of accuracy

Sometimes when measurements are made they need to be very accurate but at other times a high degree of accuracy is not needed.

For example, the time for running the 100 metres in an international competition needs to be measured to the nearest hundredth of a second. However the time needed to drive the 400 miles from London to Scotland for a holiday does not need that degree of accuracy. A measurement to the nearest half hour would be sufficient.

If you measure the length of this book the most sensible unit of measure would be millimetres. Using centimetres is too inaccurate and using tenths of a millimetre is too accurate.

Exercise 12J

In questions **1** to **4** write down the most appropriate unit you could use to measure each quantity.

1 The time taken to:
(a) run a 200 m race (b) walk to school
(c) travel from London to Manchester by car
(d) run 1000 m (e) walk 20 miles (f) watch a film.

2 (a) The height of a door (b) The thickness of this book
(c) The length of your class room (d) The lengths of your fingers
(e) The height of a large tree (f) The width of a pencil.

3 The area of:
(a) a leaf (b) the school playing fields
(c) the British Isles (d) the school hall.

4 The volume of liquid in:
(a) a can of cola (b) a car's petrol tank (c) a large lake.

5 Abdul and Nia are measuring the perimeter of the school field.
(a) Write down the units they should use to measure it.
(b) What measuring instrument should they use?
(c) To what degree of accuracy should they give their answer?

6 Mario and Dara are carrying out an experiment with bouncing spheres. They drop spheres made from different materials from the first floor of the school building. They then measure the times the spheres take to fall and the heights to which they bounce.
(a) Write down the units they should use to measure (i) the times taken and (ii) the heights of bounce.
(b) What measuring instruments should they use?
(c) To what degree of accuracy should they give their answers?

12.7 Using compound measures

Speed

Sometimes you need to work with two units at the same time. For example, the speed of an ice hockey puck can be measured in metres per second – a measurement involving a unit of length and a unit of time.

The puck moves a distance of 63 metres in 3 seconds at a **constant speed.**

$$\text{distance moved in 3 seconds} = 63 \text{ metres}$$

$$\text{distance moved in 1 second} = \frac{63}{3} = 21\,\text{m}$$

So the speed of the puck is 21 metres each second or 21 metres per second ($21\,\text{m}\,\text{s}^{-1}$ or 21 m/s).

- **For an object moving at a constant speed:**
  $$\textbf{speed} = \frac{\textbf{distance}}{\textbf{time}} \qquad \textbf{time} = \frac{\textbf{distance}}{\textbf{speed}}$$
  $$\textbf{distance} = \textbf{speed} \times \textbf{time}$$

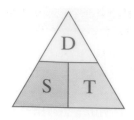

You can use this triangle to help you remember the formulae.

Typical units of speed are:
miles per hour (mph) and metres per second (m/s or ms^{-1}).
Over a long journey the speed of a vehicle is not constant for the whole journey so you use the average speed.

- $$\textbf{average speed} = \frac{\textbf{total distance travelled}}{\textbf{total time taken}}$$

Example 8

What speed does my car average if I travel 90 miles in 3 hours?

$$\text{average speed} = \frac{\text{distance}}{\text{time}}$$

$$\text{average speed} = 90 \div 3 = 30 \text{ miles per hour}$$

Example 9

How long does it take to travel 410 miles at an average speed of 50 miles per hour?

$$\text{time} = \frac{\text{distance}}{\text{speed}}$$

$$\text{time} = 410 \div 50 = 8.2 \text{ hours} = 8 \text{ hours and } 12 \text{ minutes}$$

$0.2\,\text{h} = 0.2 \times 60$ minutes
$= 12$ minutes

Example 10

How far can you go if you travel for 3 hours at an average speed of 10 miles per hour?

$$\text{distance} = \text{speed} \times \text{time}$$

$$\text{distance} = 10 \times 3 = 30 \text{ miles}$$

Exercise 12K

1. Elizabeth walked for 3 hours at an average speed of 4 miles per hour. How far did she walk?
2. Andrew drove 100 miles in 4 hours. At what average speed did he travel?
3. Syeda drove 300 miles at an average speed of 60 miles per hour. How long did it take her?
4. David was travelling by canal boat and went 30 miles in 8 hours. Calculate the average speed of the boat.
5. Amanda rode her bike for 3 hours and travelled 21 miles. Work out her average speed.
6. Gerry ran for 2 hours and covered 16 miles. Calculate his average speed.

7 Brigit swam for 3 hours and travelled 4 miles. What was her average speed?

8 Assad set off in his car at 8 am. He drove 200 miles and arrived at 11 am. Calculate his average speed in miles per hour (mph).

9 Jason set off for work at 07:55. He arrived at work at 08:10. If he lives 5 miles from work, what was his average speed?

10 Frances was using a keep fit treadmill. She ran for 40 minutes and travelled the equivalent of 20 kilometres. Calculate her average speed in kilometres per hour (km h^{-1}).

Density

Density is another compound measure. The density of a substance is defined as the mass per unit volume. It is worked out by the formula:

■ **density** $= \dfrac{\textbf{mass}}{\textbf{volume}}$

The formula can be rearranged to give:

volume $= \dfrac{\textbf{mass}}{\textbf{density}}$ **mass = volume × density**

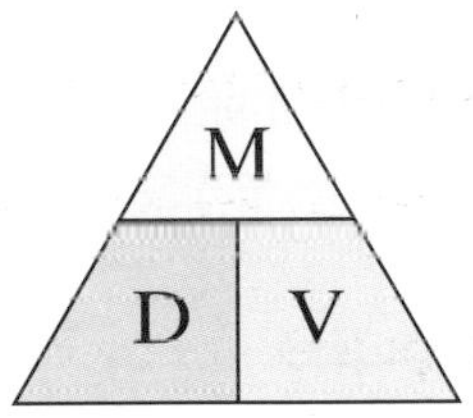

You can use this triangle to help you remember the formulae.

If the mass is measured in kilograms and the volume is measured in cubic metres the density is measured in kilograms per cubic metre. This can be abbreviated to kg/m^3 or kg m^{-3}.

Example 11

Calculate the density of a piece of metal that has a mass of 2000 kilograms and a volume of 0.5 cubic metres.

$$\text{density} = \frac{2000}{0.5} = 4000\,\text{kg m}^{-3}$$

Exercise 12L

Calculate the densities of the following materials.

Substance	Mass in kg	Volume in m^3
1 Aluminium	5400	2
2 Copper	12 000	1.34
3 Gold	3000	0.155
4 Nickel	450	0.0506
5 Silver	2700	0.257
6 Sodium	3900	4.02
7 Tin	4000	0.547
8 Zinc	30 000	4.21
9 Lead	1	0.000 088 1
10 Uranium	10	0.000 528

Using the density formula to calculate mass or volume

If you are given the density of a material and are asked to calculate the mass or the volume then you can substitute the values into the density formula.

Example 12

Calculate the volume of a piece of oak with a density of 720 kg per m^3 and a mass of 25 kg.

$$\text{density} = \frac{\text{mass}}{\text{volume}}$$

$$720 = \frac{25}{\text{volume}}$$

Multiply both sides by volume

$$720 \times \text{volume} = 25$$

Divide both sides by 720

$$\text{volume} = \frac{25}{720} = 0.035\,\text{m}^3$$

Example 13

Calculate the mass of a piece of aluminium that has a volume of 1.5 m^3 and a density of 2700 kg per m^3.

$$\text{density} = \frac{\text{mass}}{\text{volume}}$$

$$\text{so } 2700 = \frac{\text{mass}}{1.5}$$

Multiply both sides by 1.5

$$\text{mass} = 2700 \times 1.5$$
$$= 4050\,\text{kg}$$

There is another way to work out the answers to Examples 12 and 13. You can substitute the values into the rearrangements of the density formula written on page 165.

Exercise 12M

Copy this table and calculate the missing values:

Substance	Mass in kg	Volume in m^3	Density in kg m^{-3}
1 Steel	2.5		7700
2 Douglas fir (wood)		1.5	600
3 Balsa wood		1	200
4 Common brick	50		1600
5 Breeze block	100		1400
6 Concrete		3.5	2300
7 Polypropylene		4	900
8 Iron	1000		7860
9 Magnesium	0.5		174
10 Platinum	0.05		2145

12.8 Changing units

You need to be able to change units of speed between kilometres per hour, metres per second and miles per hour.

Example 14

Change 10 metres per second to kilometres per hour.

First of all you need to find how many metres are travelled in 1 hour. So you need to multiply by 60×60 or 3600.

> There are $60 \times 60 =$ 3600 seconds in 1 hour

In 1 second distance travelled = 10 m

In 1 hour distance travelled = $10 \times 3600 = 36\,000$

Divide by 1000 to change m to km

In 1 hour distance travelled $= \frac{36\,000}{1000} = 36$ km

So the speed in kilometres per hour is 36 km per hour (or 36 kmh^{-1})

Example 15

Change 60 miles per hour to **(a)** kilometres per hour **(b)** metres per second.

(Use 5 miles = 8 km)

> 5 miles = 8 km
>
> so 1 mile $= \frac{8}{5}$ km

(a) In 1 hour distance travelled = 60 miles

$$= 60 \times \frac{8}{5}\text{ km} = 96\text{ km}$$

So the speed is 96 km per hour (or 96 kmh^{-1})

(b) In 1 hour distance travelled = 96 km = 96 000 m

In 1 second distance travelled $= \frac{96\,000}{3600}$ m $= 26.66$ m

So the speed is 26.7 m/s (or 26.7 ms^{-1}) (to 3 s.f.)

Exercise 12N

In questions **1** to **6** change:

1 20 metres per second to metres per hour
2 30 km per hour to metres per second
3 60 miles per hour to miles per minute
4 15 metres per second to km per hour
5 20 metres per second to kilometres per hour
6 80 km per hour to metres per minute.
7 Sybil travels 80 kilometres in 4 hours. What is her average speed in metres per second?
8 A electron travels at 600 000 metres per second. What is this speed in km per hour?

9 A rocket must travel at 11 000 metres per second to escape the gravitational pull of the Earth. What is this speed in kilometres per hour?

10 The fastest land animal can travel at 98 km per hour. What is this speed in metres per second?

12.9 Comparing measurements

To compare two measurements that are not in the same units you have to change one measurement's units to the same units as the other.

Example 16

1 tonne of coal takes up a volume of $4\,\text{m}^3$.
13 kg of sand takes up a volume of $0.06\,\text{m}^3$.
Which material has the greater density?

You have to compare like with like. To compare the speed of an electron with the speed of a rocket you need to change both speeds to the same units.

$$\text{density} = \frac{\text{mass}}{\text{volume}}$$

$$\text{density of coal} = \frac{1000}{4} = 250\,\text{kg per m}^3$$

$$\text{density of sand} = \frac{13}{0.06}\,\text{kg per m}^3$$

$$= 216.\dot{6} = 217\,\text{kg per m}^3 \text{ (to 3 s.f.)}$$

so coal has a greater density than sand.

Exercise 12O

Where needed use 5 miles = 8 km.

1 Which car is travelling the faster, one at 40 miles per hour or one at 50 kilometres per hour?

2 The speed limit in France is 100 km per hour and in England it is 70 miles per hour. Which is the faster speed?

3 An electron travels at 600 000 metres per second. What is this speed in miles per hour?

4 The fastest land animal can travel at 98 km per hour. What is this speed in miles per hour?

5 A car is travelling on a motorway at 70 miles per hour. A bird can travel at 40 metres per second.
  (a) Change 70 miles per hour to metres per second.
  (b) Which is faster – the car or the bird?

6 In 1977 the land speed record was 283 metres per second and the water speed record was 330 miles per hour.
(a) Change 283 metres per second to miles per hour.
(b) How many times faster was the land speed record than the water speed record?

7 The density of gold is 19 320 kg m^{-3}. Work out the mass, in grams, of 1 cm^3 of gold.

8 The density of oak is 720 kg m^{-3}. Calculate the mass of a rectangular block of oak measuring 6 m by 0.7 m by 0.12 m.

9 The density of red cedar is 380 kg m^{-3}. Calculate the volume in m^3 of a block of red cedar with mass 212 kg.

10 The speed of light in a vacuum is 3×10^8 metres per second. The speed of a neutron is 4500 miles per hour.
(a) Change 3×10^8 metres per second to miles per hour.
(b) How many times faster is the speed of light than the speed of a neutron?

Exercise 12P Mixed questions

1 The diagram shows a man and a dinosaur called a velociraptor.
The man is 6 feet tall.
Estimate the height of the velociraptor in metres.

[L]

2 One day in 1995 the exchange rate was £1 = 1.51 US dollars.
(a) Change £425 to US dollars. **(b)** Convert 92.64 US dollars to £.

3 Light travels at 298 000 kilometres in 1 second. A light year is the distance travelled by light in 1 year.
Calculate, in kilometres, how far light travels in a year of 365 days. Give your answer correct to 3 s.f.

4 Given that 1 cm^3 of brass weighs 8.45 grams, calculate the weight of a solid cylinder of brass whose radius is 1.3 cm and whose height is 9.0 cm.

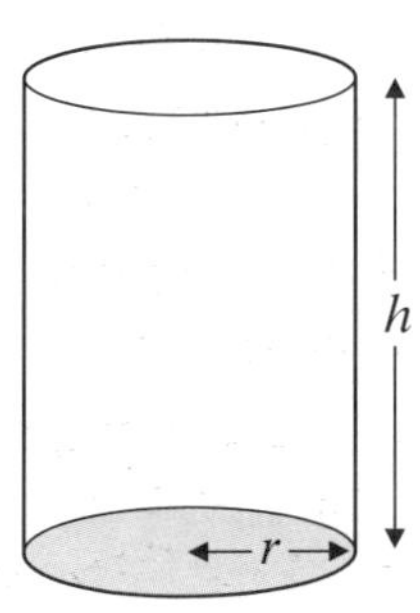

Volume of a cylinder
$= \pi r^2 h$
There is more about this on page 282

5 Stephanie ran 100 metres.
The distance was correct to the nearest metre.
(a) Write down the shortest distance Stephanie could have run.
Stephanie's time for the run was 14.8 seconds.
Her time was correct to the nearest tenth of a second.
(b) Write down
(i) her shortest possible time for the run,
(ii) her longest possible time for the run. [L]

6 In the 1988 Olympic Games, Carl Lewis ran 100 m in 9.92 s. Calculate Lewis' average speed in kilometres per hour correct to 3 significant figures. [L]

Summary of key points

1 10 mm = 1 cm, 100 cm = 1 m, 1000 m = 1 km; 1000 mg = 1 g, 1000 g = 1 kg, 1000 kg = 1 tonne; 1000 ml = 1 l, 1000 cm^3 = 1 l

2

Metric	Imperial
* 1 kg	2.2 pounds
25 g	1 ounce
* 1 l	$1\frac{3}{4}$ pints
* 4.5 l	1 gallon
* 8 km	5 miles
* 1 m	39 inches
* 30 cm	1 foot
2.5 cm	1 inch

You need to memorize the items with a star (*) for your exam.

3 $1\,m^2 = 100 \times 100\,cm^2 = 10\,000\,cm^2$

4 $1\,m^3 = 100 \times 100 \times 100\,cm^3 = 1\,000\,000\,cm^3$

5 Quantities that can be counted are called discrete measures.

6 When you use a measuring instrument the measurements you make are called continuous measures.

7 Continuous measurements cannot be exact. They are only as accurate as the instruments you are measuring with.

8 If you make a measurement correct to a given unit the true value lies in a range that extends half a unit below and half a unit above the measurement.

9 For an object moving at a constant speed:

$\text{speed} = \frac{\text{distance}}{\text{time}}$ $\quad$ distance = speed × time $\quad$ $\text{time} = \frac{\text{distance}}{\text{speed}}$

$\text{average speed} = \frac{\text{total distance travelled}}{\text{total time taken}}$

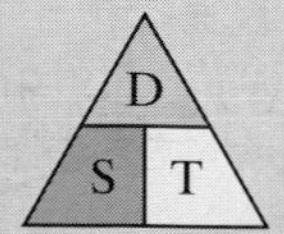

You can use this triangle to help you remember the formulae.

10 $\text{density} = \frac{\text{mass}}{\text{volume}}$ $\quad$ $\text{volume} = \frac{\text{density}}{\text{mass}}$ $\quad$ density × volume = mass

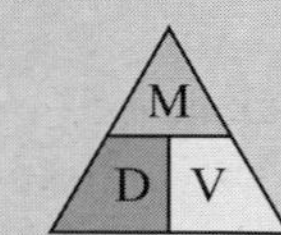

You can use this triangle to help you remember the formulae.

13 Quadratic functions

Unit 2 introduces linear functions of the type $n \to bn + c$ and shows how to use them to find the nth term of a sequence of numbers.

This unit extends these ideas to functions of the type $n \to an^2 + bn + c$ that have n^2 as the highest power of the input n. These are called **quadratic functions.**

■ **A quadratic function includes a square as its highest power.**
For example $n \to 2n^2 + 3n + 1$ is a quadratic function.
It does not contain any reciprocal terms like $\frac{5}{n}$.

13.1 Simple quadratic functions of the type $n \to an^2 + c$

Here is a three-box number machine:

input → multiply by itself → ×3 → +1 → output

It changes numbers like this:

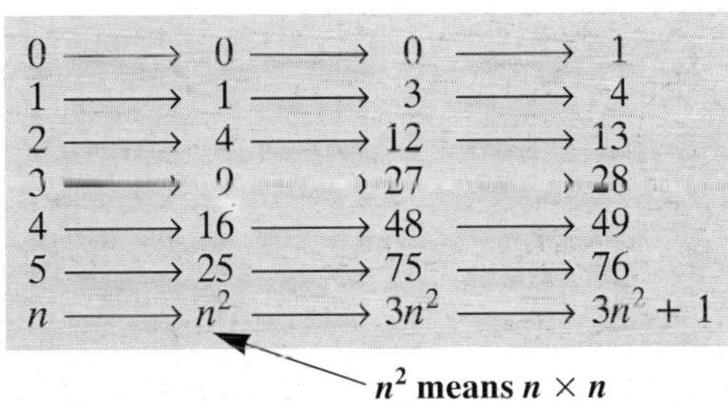

0 → 0 → 0 → 1
1 → 1 → 3 → 4
2 → 4 → 12 → 13
3 → 9 → 27 → 28
4 → 16 → 48 → 49
5 → 25 → 75 → 76
n → n² → 3n² → 3n² + 1
n² means n × n
n² is called n squared or
n to the power of 2

You can write the function as $n \to 3n^2 + 1$

Exercise 13A

1 Write down the functions for each of these number machines:

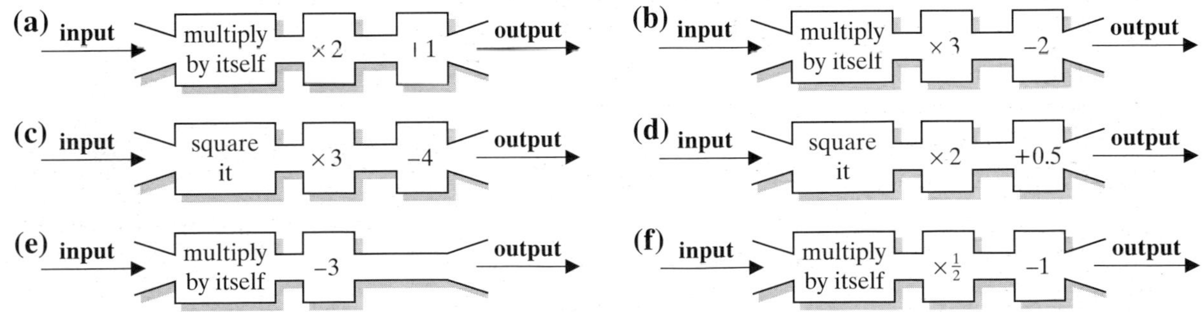

2 Work out the output for each of these functions using the inputs given.

(a) $n \to n^2 + 1$	**(b)** $n \to 3n^2$	**(c)** $n \to 3n^2 + 2$	**(d)** $n \to 2n^2 - 1$
$0 \to$	$0 \to$	$0 \to$	$0 \to$
$1 \to$	$1 \to$	$1 \to$	$1 \to$
$2 \to$	$2 \to$	$2 \to$	$2 \to$
$3 \to$	$3 \to$	$3 \to$	$3 \to$
$4 \to$	$4 \to$	$4 \to$	$4 \to$
$5 \to$	$5 \to$	$5 \to$	$5 \to$

3 Work out the outputs for each of these functions using the same inputs as in questions **2**.

(a) $n \to 2n^2 + 3$ **(b)** $n \to 4n^2 + 1$

(c) $n \to \frac{1}{2}n^2 + 3$ **(d)** $n \to n^2 + \frac{1}{2}$

4 **(a)** Put 0 (zero) into each of these functions and write down the result:

(i) $n \to n^2$ (ii) $n \to 3n^2$ (iii) $n \to 2n^2$
(iv) $n \to \frac{1}{2}n^2$ (v) $n \to 1.5n^2$ (vi) $n \to 4n^2 + 1$
(vii) $n \to 2n^2 + 5$ (viii) $n \to n^2 + 1$ (ix) $n \to 2n^2 + \frac{1}{2}$
(x) $n \to 2n^2 + 1.5$ (xi) $n \to 4n^2 - 1$ (xii) $n \to 2n^2 - 5$
(xiii) $n \to n^2 - 1$ (xiv) $n \to 2n^2 - \frac{1}{2}$ (xv) $n \to n^2 - 2.5$

(b) What do you notice about your answers to part **(a)**?

Finding the value of c

Question 4 of Exercise 13A shows that:

- For a quadratic function of the type $n \to an^2 + c$ if the input is 0 the output is c.

13.2 Using the method of differences

You can use the method of differences to help you to find the value of a in a quadratic function like $n \to an^2 + c$

Unit 2 shows how to find the value of b in linear functions of the type $n \to bn + c$

The value of b is found by putting the inputs 0, 1, 2, 3, 4, 5 into the function. b is the amount by which the output goes up when the input goes up by 1.

This is called the **first difference**

For a linear function the first difference stays the same when the input goes up by 1.

$n \to 3n + 4$	**1st difference**
$0 \to 4$	
$1 \to 7$	$7 - 4 = 3$
$2 \to 10$	$10 - 7 = 3$
$3 \to 13$	$13 - 10 = 3$

For this linear function the first difference is always 3.

Here is a quadratic function of the type $n \to an^2 + c$

For a quadratic function the first difference changes when the input goes up by 1.

$n \to 3n^2 + 1$	**1st difference**	**2nd difference**
$0 \to 1$		
$1 \to 4$	$4 - 1 = 3$	
$2 \to 13$	$13 - 4 = 9$	$9 - 3 = 6$
$3 \to 28$	$28 - 13 = 15$	$15 - 9 = 6$
$4 \to 49$	$49 - 28 = 21$	$21 - 15 = 6$
$5 \to 76$	$76 - 49 = 27$	$27 - 21 = 6$

The **second difference** is the amount by which the first difference goes up when the input goes up by 1.

The next exercise will help you see the relationship between the second difference and the value of a.

Exercise 13B

1 Put the values 0, 1, 2, 3, 4, 5 into each of these quadratic functions.
Draw a mapping diagram of your results.
Work out the 1st and 2nd differences.
The first one has been started for you.

(a) $n \to 2n^2 + 1$ (b) $n \to 3n^2 - 1$
(c) $n \to 2n^2 + 2$ (d) $n \to 2n^2 - 1$
(e) $n \to n^2 + 4$ (f) $n \to 3n^2$
(g) $n \to 4n^2 - 2$ (h) $n \to n^2 + \frac{1}{2}$
(i) $n \to \frac{1}{2}n^2 - \frac{1}{2}$ (j) $n \to -2n^2$

Mapping diagram

$n \to 2n^2 + 1$	**1st difference**	**2nd difference**
$0 \to 1$		
	2	
$1 \to 3$		4
	6	
$2 \to 9$		
$3 \to$		

2 For each function in question **1** look at the output when the input is 0. What do you notice?

3 Look at the second difference for each function in question **1**. What do you notice?

13.3 Quadratic functions of the type $n \to an^2 + bn + c$

It is difficult to use a number machine to work out the mapping diagram for a function of this type. Instead you can use a different method.

For example, put the value $n = 3$ into the function $n \to 2n^2 + 4n - 3$
The output is $2 \times 3^2 + 4 \times 3 - 3 = 18 + 12 - 3 = 27$.

This is the mapping diagram using inputs of 0, 1, 2, 3, 4 and 5.

Mapping diagram

$n \longrightarrow 2n^2 + 4n - 3$
$0 \longrightarrow -3$
$1 \longrightarrow 3$
$2 \longrightarrow 13$
$3 \longrightarrow 27$
$4 \longrightarrow 45$
$5 \longrightarrow 67$

Exercise 13C

1 Put the values 0, 1, 2, 3, 4, 5 into each of these larger quadratic functions.
Draw a mapping diagram and work out the first and second differences.

(a) $n \to 2n^2 + 3n + 2$ (b) $n \to 3n^2 + 2n + 1$
(c) $n \to \frac{1}{2}n^2 - 2n + 6$ (d) $n \to -n^2 + 4n + 8$

2 Look at the second differences for each function in question **1**. What do you notice?

Exercise 13C shows that:

- **For a quadratic function of the type $an^2 + bn + c$ if the input is O the output is c.**
- **For a quadratic function of the type $n \to an^2 + bn + c$ the second difference always has the same value. That value is equal to $2a$.**

Finding the value of *a*

Example 1

This pattern of inputs and outputs was formed by a quadratic function of the form $n \to an^2 + c$

Find the values of a and c.

Input	Output
0 ⟶	1
1 ⟶	5
2 ⟶	17
3 ⟶	37
4 ⟶	65
5 ⟶	101

If the input is 0 the output is c.

$0 \to 1$ so $c = 1$

Or you could say:
$0 \to 1$
Put $n = 0$ in $an^2 + c$
So
$a \times 0 + c = 1$
$c = 1$
Also $1 \to 5$
Put $n = 1$ in $an^2 + 1$
So
$a \times 1 + 1 = 5$
$a = 4$

To find a calculate the first and second differences.
The second difference is 8 so:

$2a = 8$

and: $a = 4$

The function is $n \to 4n^2 + 1$

	1st difference	2nd difference
$0 \to 1$		
	4	
$1 \to 5$		8
	12	
$2 \to 17$		8
	20	
$3 \to 37$		8
	28	
$4 \to 65$		8
	36	
$5 \to 101$		

■ **When the second difference is always the same (but not zero) the function is a quadratic function of the type $an^2 + bn + c$. The second difference is $2a$ and $0 \to c$.**

Example 2

Find the function that produced this sequence of numbers:

7 16 29 46 67

Write the sequence as inputs → outputs starting with $1 \to 7$.
Work out the first and second differences.

Work backwards using the second differences, then the first differences to get the numbers in bold. These show that $0 \to 2$.

Input	Output	1st difference	2nd difference
0 ⟶	**2**		
		5	
1 ⟶	7		−4
		9	
2 ⟶	16		4
		13	
3 ⟶	29		4
		17	
4 ⟶	46		4
		21	
5 ⟶	67		4

(−5 between 2 and 7; −4 between 5 and 9)

The same

The second difference is always 4 so try a quadratic function with $a = 2$.

$n \to 2n^2 + bn + c$

If the input is 0 the output is c so $c = 2$.

So the function is $n \to 2n^2 + bn + 2$

To find b put 1 into this function:

$1 \to 2 + b + 2 = 4 + b$ so $1 \to 4 + b$

But you know from the Input → Output table that $1 \to 7$

so $4 + b = 7$
$b = 3$

The function is $n \rightarrow 2n^2 + 3n + 2$

Check that the function gives the correct output for other inputs.

Check: $3 \rightarrow 2 \times 9 + 3 \times 3 + 2 = 29$
$4 \rightarrow 2 \times 16 + 3 \times 4 + 2 = 46$
$5 \rightarrow 2 \times 25 + 3 \times 5 + 2 = 67$

The values 29, 46 and 67 are equal to the outputs for the inputs of 3, 4 and 5.

Another method

Or you could say:
$0 \rightarrow 2$

Put $n = 0$ in $an^2 + bn + c$

So $a \times 0 + b \times 0 + c = 2$
$c = 2$

$1 \rightarrow 7$

Put $n = 1$ in $an^2 + bn + 2$

So $a \times 1 + b \times 1 + 2 = 7$
$a + b = 5$

$2 \rightarrow 16$
So $a \times 4 + b \times 2 + 2 = 16$
$4a + 2b = 14$
$2a + b = 7$

By trial and improvement you find that
$a = 2$ and $b = 3$
satisfies both equations, so
$n \rightarrow 2n^2 + 3n + 2$

Read how to solve simultaneous equations like this on page 425.

Exercise 13D

For some of these questions you need multilink cubes and isometric and square dotty paper.

1 Each of these patterns of inputs → outputs has been produced by a quadratic function of the type $n \rightarrow an^2 + c$
Find the function for each pattern.

(a)	**(b)**	**(c)**	**(d)**
$0 \rightarrow 0$	$0 \rightarrow 4$	$0 \rightarrow 1$	$0 \rightarrow 1$
$1 \rightarrow 2$	$1 \rightarrow 7$	$1 \rightarrow 6$	$1 \rightarrow 1.5$
$2 \rightarrow 8$	$2 \rightarrow 16$	$2 \rightarrow 21$	$2 \rightarrow 3$
$3 \rightarrow 18$	$3 \rightarrow 31$	$3 \rightarrow 46$	$3 \rightarrow 5.5$
$4 \rightarrow 32$	$4 \rightarrow 52$	$4 \rightarrow 81$	$4 \rightarrow 9$
$5 \rightarrow 50$	$5 \rightarrow 79$	$5 \rightarrow 126$	$5 \rightarrow 13.5$

(e)	**(f)**	**(g)**	**(h)**
$0 \rightarrow 0$	$0 \rightarrow -3$	$0 \rightarrow 2$	$0 \rightarrow 0.5$
$1 \rightarrow 4$	$1 \rightarrow -2$	$1 \rightarrow 2.5$	$1 \rightarrow 3.5$
$2 \rightarrow 16$	$2 \rightarrow 1$	$2 \rightarrow 4$	$2 \rightarrow 12.5$
$3 \rightarrow 36$	$3 \rightarrow 6$	$3 \rightarrow 6.5$	$3 \rightarrow 27.5$
$4 \rightarrow 64$	$4 \rightarrow 13$	$4 \rightarrow 10$	$4 \rightarrow 48.5$
$5 \rightarrow 100$	$5 \rightarrow 22$	$5 \rightarrow 14.5$	$5 \rightarrow 75.5$

2 Find the function for each of these patterns of inputs → outputs.

(a)	**(b)**	**(c)**	**(d)**
$0 \rightarrow 1$	$0 \rightarrow 2$	$0 \rightarrow -1$	$0 \rightarrow -2$
$1 \rightarrow 5$	$1 \rightarrow 3$	$1 \rightarrow 2$	$1 \rightarrow 0$
$2 \rightarrow 11$	$2 \rightarrow 8$	$2 \rightarrow 7$	$2 \rightarrow 8$
$3 \rightarrow 19$	$3 \rightarrow 17$	$3 \rightarrow 14$	$3 \rightarrow 22$
$4 \rightarrow 29$	$4 \rightarrow 30$	$4 \rightarrow 23$	$4 \rightarrow 42$
$5 \rightarrow 41$	$5 \rightarrow 47$	$5 \rightarrow 34$	$5 \rightarrow 68$

3 A computer was used to generate the following sequences.
Write down an expression for the nth term of each sequence.

(a) 6 16 32 54 82 **(b)** 9 15 25 39 57
(c) 7 10 15 22 31 **(d)** −2 4 14 28 46
(e) 2.5 7 14.5 25 38.5 **(f)** −4 −3 2 11 24

Here **expression** means an algebraic expression.
$4n - 2$ and $3n^2 + 2n + 1$ are examples of algebraic expressions.

4 Use multilink cubes to build this series of staircases.
Find an expression for the number of cubes in the nth staircase.
Then look again at your staircases and explain your expression.

5 Draw the next two shapes in this sequence on isometric dotty paper. Find an expression for the number of small equilateral triangles in the nth shape.
Then look again at your shapes and explain your expression.

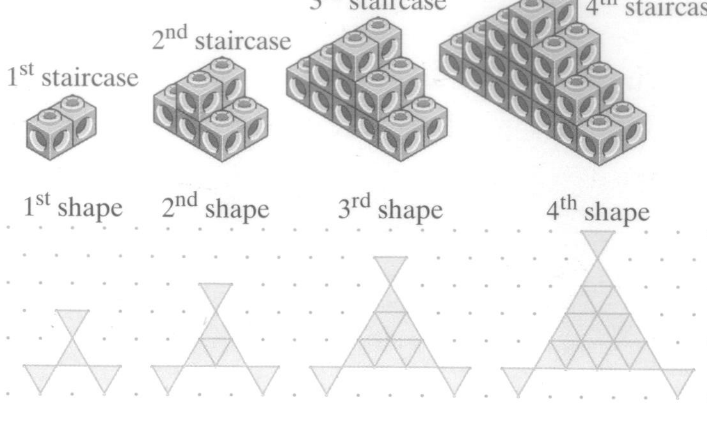

6 **Growing shapes**

Grow families of shapes on dotty paper.

For each family find an expression for the area of the nth shape.

Explain your expressions.

Exercise 13E Mixed questions

For some of these questions, you need matchsticks, multilink cubes, counters, and square and isometric dotty paper.

1 A computer was used to generate the following sequences. Write down, in terms of n, an expression for the nth term of each sequence.

(a) 13 43 93 163 253 **(b)** 6 15 30 51 78
(c) 8 24 50 86 132 **(d)** –1 2 9 20 35
(e) –3 –9 –19 –33 –51 **(f)** –2.5 –1 1.5 5 9.5

2 Draw the next two shapes in this sequence on square dotty paper. Find an expression for the number of small squares in the nth shape.

Explain your expression.

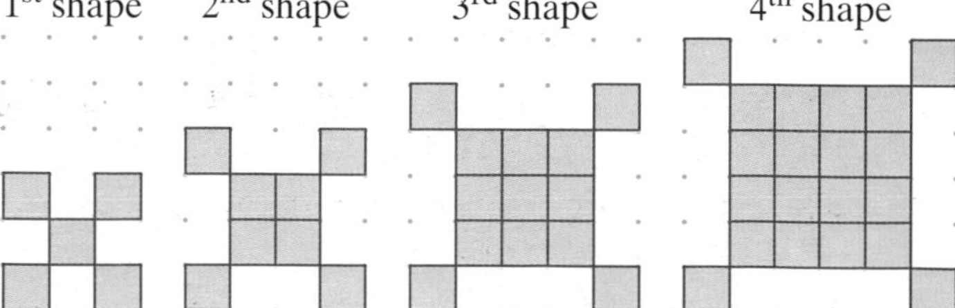

3 **Matchstick shapes**

Make sequences of shapes using matchsticks.

Find an expression for the number of matchsticks in the nth shape in each sequence.

Try to explain each expression by looking again at the shapes.

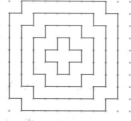

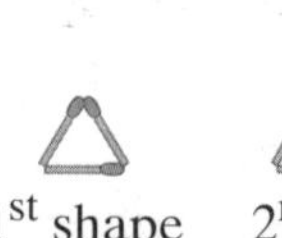
1st shape

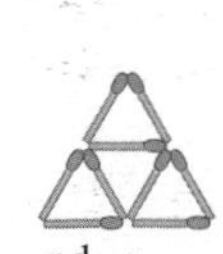
2nd shape

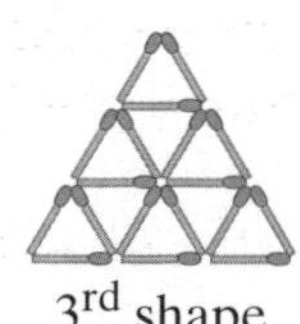
3rd shape

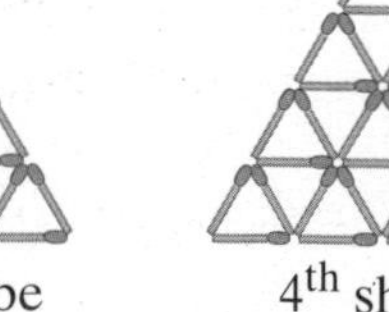
4th shape

4 Tower

Use multilink cubes to build towers as shown in the picture.

Find an expression for the number of cubes in a tower of height n cubes.

Do the same for other designs of tower.

5 Cutting a circle

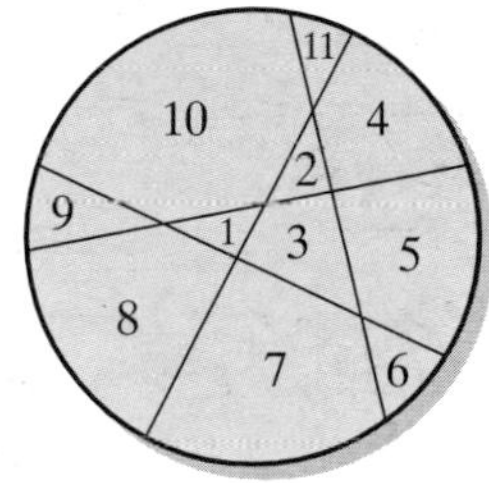

What is the maximum number of pieces a circle can be cut into using 4 straight cuts?

Find an expression for the maximum number of pieces the circle can be cut into using n straight cuts.

6 Counter populations

A population of counters consists of white and black counters. The population grows according to the following rules:

1. The population starts with a white counter.
2. Each white counter generates one white counter and one black counter.
3. Each black counter generates one black counter only.

Investigate the growth of this population.
In your investigation you should consider:

1. the number of counters in each generation;
2. the total number of counters in the population as it reaches different generations;
3. the proportions of white and black counters in each generation;
4. the proportion of white and black counters in the total population.

You should attempt to generalise each result.
(Hint: this means consider the nth generation.) [L]

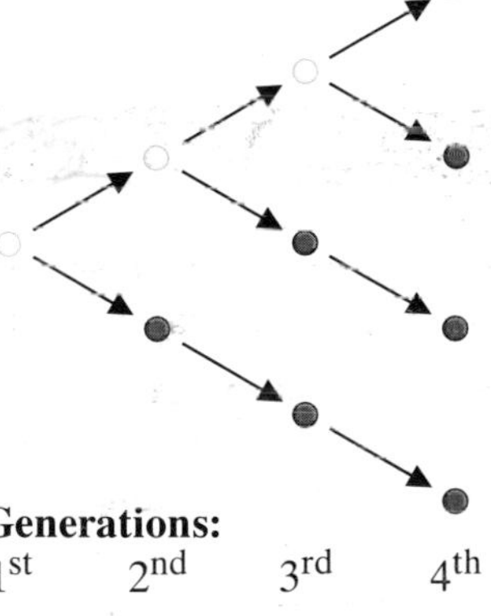

Summary of key points

1. A quadratic function includes a square as its highest power. For example $n \to 2n^2 + 3n + 1$ is a quadratic function.
2. For a quadratic function of the type $n \to an^2 + bn + c$ if the input is 0 the output is c.
3. For quadratic functions of the type $n \to an^2 + bn + c$ the second difference always has the same value. That value is equal to $2a$.
4. When the second difference is always the same (but not zero) the function is a quadratic function of the type $n \to an^2 + bn + c$.
   The second difference is $2a$ and $0 \to c$.

14 Properties of numbers

You will need to use and apply numbers in a wide variety of situations throughout your GCSE course. You also need to know many terms that describe numbers and their properties. This unit will help you remember them.

14.1 Types of numbers you should know

There are many different types of numbers. You should be able to recognize all of these:

- **Even numbers are whole numbers which divide exactly by 2.**
- **Odd numbers are whole numbers which do not divide exactly by 2.**
- **The factors of a number are whole numbers that divide exactly into the number. The factors include 1 and the number itself.**
- **Multiples of a number are the results of multiplying the number by a positive whole number.**

15 is a **multiple** of 3 — $15 = 3 \times 5$ — 3 is a **factor** of 15

15 is also a **multiple** of 5 — 5 is a **factor** of 15

308 is a **multiple** of 4, 7, and 11 — $308 = 4 \times 7 \times 11$ — 4, 7, and 11 are all **factors** of 308

- **A prime number is a whole number greater than 1 which has only two factors: itself and 1.**

The only factors of 7 are 1 and 7, so 7 is a **prime number**.

Example 1

Write down all the multiples of 4 between 20 and 50.

The word 'between' means that 20 and 50 are not included even if they are multiples of 4.
So the multiples are 24, 28, 32, 36, 40, 44 and 48.

Example 2

4, 8, 12, 14, 19, 31, 35, 36

From the list write down:
(a) two factors of 24 (b) two multiples of 7
(c) two prime numbers (d) the odd numbers.

(a) The two factors of 24 in the list are 4 and 8.
(b) The two multiples of 7 in the list are 14 and 35.
(c) The two prime numbers are 19 and 31.
(d) The odd numbers are 19, 31 and 35.

Exercise 14A

1 Write down all the odd numbers between **(a)** 30 and 40 **(b)** 120 and 130.
2 Write down all the even numbers between **(a)** 60 and 70 **(b)** 150 and 160.
3 Write down all the multiples less than 60 of **(a)** 6 **(b)** 8.
4 Write down all the factors of **(a)** 18 **(b)** 24 **(c)** 50.
5 Write down all the prime numbers between **(a)** 10 and 20 **(b)** 40 and 50.
6 From the list 8, 9, 11, 15, 23, 32, 45, 49 write down:
(a) all the even numbers **(b)** numbers which are multiples of 3
(c) numbers which are factors of 45 **(d)** prime numbers.

14.2 Square numbers and cube numbers

These numbers sometimes occur in number patterns in investigations.

■ **Square numbers are the result of multiplying a whole number by itself.**

Square numbers:

$1 \times 1 = 1$ 1st square number
$2 \times 2 = 4$ 2nd square number
$3 \times 3 = 9$ 3rd square number
$4 \times 4 = 16$ 4th square number
$x \times x = x^2$ the square of any number x

4 × 4 can also be written:
- the square of 4
- 4 squared
- 4^2

Square numbers can be shown as a square pattern of dots.

■ **Cube numbers are the result of multiplying a whole number by itself then multiplying by the number again.**

Cube numbers:

$1 \times 1 \times 1 = 1$ 1st cube number
$2 \times 2 \times 2 = 8$ 2nd cube number
$3 \times 3 \times 3 = 27$ 3rd cube number
$4 \times 4 \times 4 = 64$ 4th cube number
$x \times x \times x = x^3$ the cube of any number x

4 × 4 × 4 can also be written:
- the cube of 4
- 4 cubed
- 4^3

1 •
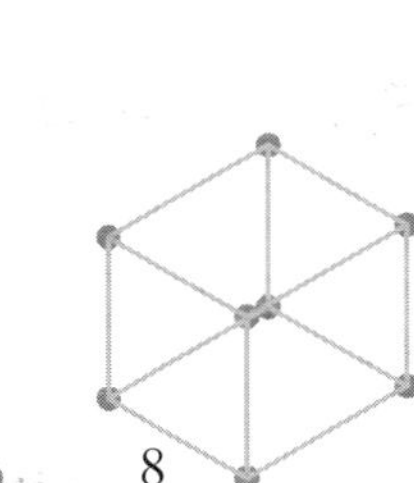

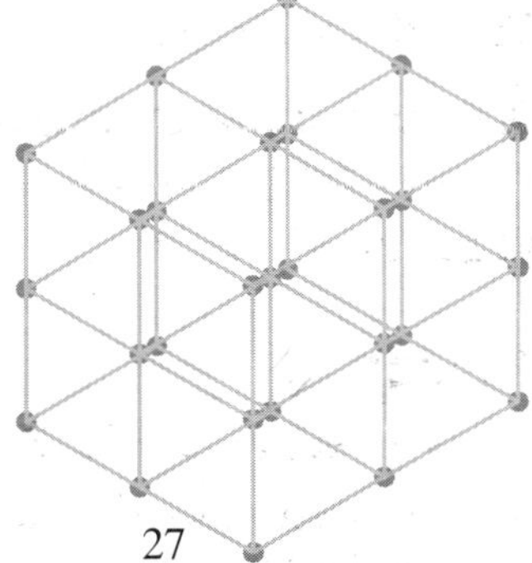

Example 3

1, 3, 4, 6, 8, 13, 16, 18, 24, 27, 30

From the list write down: (a) the square numbers (b) the cube numbers.

(a) 1, 4, 16 (b) 1, 8, 27

Exercise 14B

1 Write down:
(a) the 8th square number
(b) the 7th cube number
(c) the 12th square number
(d) the 10th cube number
(e) the first 12 square numbers
(f) the first 8 cube numbers.

2 From the list write down all the numbers which are:
(i) square numbers (ii) cube numbers.
(a) 50, 20, 64, 30, 1, 80, 8, 49, 9
(b) 10, 21, 57, 4, 60, 125, 7, 27, 48, 16, 90, 35
(c) 137, 150, 75, 110, 50, 125, 64, 81, 144
(d) 90, 180, 216, 100, 81, 75, 140, 169, 125

14.3 Finding squares and square roots of numbers

You need to find squares of numbers and square roots of numbers when you use Pythagoras' theorem (page 193).

Squares

■ **To find the square of any number multiply the number by itself.**

The square of 3.7 = $3.7^2 = 3.7 \times 3.7 = 13.69$

The square of –6.2 = $-6.2^2 = -6.2 \times -6.2 = 38.44$

Square roots

$4 \times 4 = 16$ so we say that 4 is a **square root** of 16; it is a number which multiplied by itself gives 16.

You can write the square root of 16 as $\sqrt{16}$

$1.5 \times 1.5 = 2.25$

So 1.5 is a square root of 2.25, written $\sqrt{2.25}$

In general, for any number A:

■ **If $x \times x = A$ then x is the square root of A, written $\sqrt{A}$**

Notice that

$-4 \times -4 = 16$

so –4 is also a square root of 16.

$\sqrt{16} = \pm 4$

Square roots are often not whole numbers. You can find the square root of any positive number. Most calculators have a function key that finds the square root of a number. You often need to round the answer or the calculator display. For example: $\sqrt{18} = 4.2426406 \ldots$ = 4.24 (to 2 d.p.)

Remember:
$\sqrt{18}$ can also be – 4.24 if that is a sensible answer to the problem you are solving.

14.4 Finding cubes and cube roots of numbers

Cubes

■ **To find the cube of any number multiply the number by itself then multiply by the number again.**

The cube of 5.3 = $5.3^3 = 5.3 \times 5.3 \times 5.3 = 148.877$

The cube of –2.1 = $-2.1^3 = -2.1 \times -2.1 \times -2.1 = -9.261$

Cube roots

$2 \times 2 \times 2 = 8$ so we say that 2 is the **cube root** of 8: it is a number which multiplied by itself, then multiplied by itself again gives 8.

You can write the cube root of 8 as $\sqrt[3]{8}$

$3.4 \times 3.4 \times 3.4 = 39.304$

So 3.4 is the cube root of 39.304, written $\sqrt[3]{39.304}$

In general, for any number A:

■ **If $y \times y \times y = A$ then y is the cube root of A,** written $\sqrt[3]{A}$

Cube roots are often not whole numbers. You can find the cube root of any positive or negative number. Some calculators have a cube root function key to find the cube root of numbers. As with square roots, you often have to round the answer. For example $\sqrt[3]{18} = 2.6207413\ldots = 2.62$ (to 2 d.p.)

Remember: $\sqrt[3]{-64} = -4$ because $-4 \times -4 \times -4 = -64$.

square root   cube root

Page 440 shows how to use the square root and cube root functions on a calculator.

Exercise 14C

Use your calculator to work out:

1 (a) 13^2 (b) 3.5^2 (c) 40^2
(d) 8.7^2 (e) 19.6^2 (f) $(-57.4)^2$

2 (a) 6^3 (b) 2.4^3 (c) 20^3
(d) $(-1.3)^3$ (e) 13.4^3 (f) 36.2^3

3 (a) $\sqrt{121}$ (b) $\sqrt{225}$ (c) $\sqrt{16900}$
(d) $\sqrt{2.89}$ (e) $\sqrt{0.49}$ (f) $\sqrt{33.64}$

4 In this question give your answers correct to 2 d.p.
(a) $\sqrt{253}$ (b) $\sqrt{2341}$ (c) $\sqrt{18.4}$
(d) $\sqrt{8476}$ (e) $\sqrt{29.44}$ (f) $\sqrt{1825963}$

5 In this question give your answers correct to 3 s.f.
(a) $\sqrt[3]{68}$ (b) $\sqrt[3]{3654}$ (c) $\sqrt[3]{26.5}$
(d) $\sqrt[3]{-9.2}$ (e) $\sqrt[3]{882.5}$ (f) $\sqrt[3]{6547812}$

14.5 Finding square roots and cube roots by trial and improvement

You can also find square roots and cube roots by **trial and improvement**.

Example 4

Use a trial and improvement method to find $\sqrt[3]{20}$ (the cube root of 20), correct to 2 decimal places.

	Try this number	Cube of the number	Bigger or smaller than 20?
Start by trying whole numbers of about the right size.	2	$2 \times 2 \times 2 = 8$	smaller
	3	$3 \times 3 \times 3 = 27$	bigger
Next try a value between 2 and 3, try 2.5.	2.5	$2.5 \times 2.5 \times 2.5 = 15.625$	smaller
Next try 2.8, bigger than 2.5	2.8	$2.8 \times 2.8 \times 2.8 = 21.952$	bigger
Next try 2.7, smaller than 2.8	2.7	$2.7 \times 2.7 \times 2.7 = 19.683$	smaller
Next try a value between 2.7 and 2.8, try 2.75	2.75	$2.75^3 = 20.796$	bigger
	2.71	$2.71^3 = 19.902$	smaller
The solution is between 2.71 and 2.72, so try the value halfway between 2.71 and 2.72, try 2.715	2.72	$2.72^3 = 20.123$	bigger
	2.715	$2.715^3 = 20.012\,876$	bigger

The solution is between 2.71 and 2.715. Any number in this range corrects to 2.71 (to 2 d.p.); so an approximate value for $\sqrt[3]{20}$ is 2.71 (correct to 2 d.p.).

Remember: Show all your attempts and working when you have used a trial and improvement method: it gives evidence of the methods you have used.

Exercise 14D

Use a trial and improvement method to find these roots correct to two decimal places. Use a calculator to check your answers.

1 $\sqrt{7}$ **2** $\sqrt[3]{15}$ **3** $\sqrt[3]{12}$ **4** $\sqrt{10}$

5 $\sqrt{20}$ **6** $\sqrt{32}$ **7** $\sqrt[3]{30}$ **8** $\sqrt[3]{42}$

9 $\sqrt{13}$ **10** $\sqrt[3]{50}$ **11** $\sqrt{28}$ **12** $\sqrt[3]{33}$

14.6 Calculating powers

There is a short way of writing repeated multiplication by the same number. For example, the factors of 32 can be written in the long way as $2 \times 2 \times 2 \times 2 \times 2$ or in the short way as 2^5. The ^{5} is the **index** (plural: indices).

You say 2^5 is '2 to the power 5'.

Any number can be raised to a power. For example 6^4 is 6 raised to the power 4 (or 6 to the power 4).

$6^4 = 6 \times 6 \times 6 \times 6$

Example 5

Work out (a) 3^2 (b) 5^3 (c) 2^6.

(a) $3^2 = 3 \times 3 = 9$
(b) $5^3 = 5 \times 5 \times 5 = 125$
(c) $2^6 = 2 \times 2 \times 2 \times 2 \times 2 \times 2 = 64$

Example 6

Find the value of x:

(a) $8^x = 64$ (b) $3^x = 81$

(a) $8 \times 8 = 64$ so $8^2 = 64$ and $x = 2$
(b) $3 \times 3 \times 3 \times 3 = 81$ so $3^4 = 81$ and $x = 4$

Example 7

Work out (a) $3^3 \times 4^2$ (b) $\frac{8^3}{2^3}$ (c) $5^2 + 3^3$

(a) $3^3 \times 4^2 = 27 \times 16 = 432$

(b) $\frac{8^3}{2^3} = \frac{512}{8} = 64$

(c) $5^2 + 3^3 = 25 + 27 = 52$

Exercise 14E

Work out:

1 **(a)** 3^2 **(b)** 2^4 **(c)** 5^6 **(d)** 1^4
2 **(a)** 3^6 **(b)** 5^5 **(c)** 0^2 **(d)** 9^4
3 **(a)** 15^3 **(b)** 7^4 **(c)** 6^6 **(d)** 10^3
4 **(a)** 4^2 **(b)** 6^3 **(c)** 9^5 **(d)** $4^3 + 3^2$
5 **(a)** 12^3 **(b)** 3^4 **(c)** 14^2 **(d)** $8^4 \div 2^3$

Find the value of x:

6 **(a)** $3^x = 243$ **(b)** $2^x = 8$ **(c)** $10^x = 100\,000$
7 **(a)** $6^x = 1296$ **(b)** $5^x = 125$ **(c)** $4^x = 256$
8 **(a)** $13^x = 169$ **(b)** $4^x = 4096$ **(c)** $11^x = 1331$
9 **(a)** $2^x = 1024$ **(b)** $9^x = 729$ **(c)** $15^x = 225$

14.7 Multiplying and dividing powers of the same number

Sometimes you need to write the product of two or more powers of a number as a single power of the same number.

$$2^2 \times 2^3 = (2 \times 2) \times (2 \times 2 \times 2) = 2^5$$
$$3^3 \times 3^4 = (3 \times 3 \times 3) \times (3 \times 3 \times 3 \times 3) = 3^7$$

Notice that:
$2^2 \times 2^3 = 2^{2+3} = 2^5$
$3^3 \times 3^4 = 3^{3+4} = 3^7$

You can use a similar method when you divide one power of a number by another power of the same number.

$$5^6 \div 5^2 = \frac{5 \times 5 \times 5 \times 5 \times 5 \times 5}{5 \times 5} = 5 \times 5 \times 5 \times 5 = 5^4$$

$$4^5 \div 4^2 = \frac{4 \times 4 \times 4 \times 4 \times 4}{4 \times 4} = 4 \times 4 \times 4 = 4^3$$

Notice that:
$5^6 \div 5^2 = 5^{6-2} = 5^4$
$4^5 \div 4^2 = 4^{5-2} = 4^3$

- **To multiply powers of the same number add the indices.**
  In general: $x^a \times x^b = x^{a+b}$
- **To divide powers of the same number subtract the indices.**
  In general: $x^a \div x^b = x^{a-b}$

Example 8

Write as a single power of the number:

(a) $3^2 \times 3^3$ (b) $5^3 \times 5$ (c) $7^5 \div 7^4$ (d) $3^4 \times 3^2 \times 3^6$

(a) $3^2 \times 3^3 = 3^{2+3} = 3^5$
(b) $5^3 \times 5 = 5^{3+1} = 5^4$
(c) $7^5 \div 7^4 = 7^{5-4} = 7$
(d) $3^4 \times 3^2 \times 3^6 = 3^{4+2+6} = 3^{12}$

Finding x^1 and x^0

Notice that: $\dfrac{3^3}{3^2} = \dfrac{3 \times 3 \times 3}{3 \times 3} = 3$ and $\dfrac{3^3}{3^2} = 3^{3-2} = 3^1$

There is more about x^0 on page 295

So $3^1 = 3$. In general:

- **Any number raised to the power 1 is equal to the number itself:**
  $6^1 = 6$ and $x^1 = x$

Notice too that: $\dfrac{3^2}{3^2} = 1$ and $\dfrac{3^2}{3^2} = 3^{2-2} = 3^0$

So $3^0 = 1$. In general:

- **Any number, not zero, raised to the power 0 is equal to 1:**
  $6^0 = 1$ and $x^0 = 1$ if x is not zero

Exercise 14F

Simplify by writing as a single power of the number:

1 **(a)** $6^8 \times 6^3$ **(b)** $8^3 \times 8^5$ **(c)** $2^4 \times 2^2$

2 **(a)** $4^3 \div 4^2$ **(b)** $6^6 \div 6^3$ **(c)** $7^5 \div 7$

3 **(a)** $4^2 \times 4^3$ **(b)** $5^3 \div 5$ **(c)** $3^9 \div 3^8$

4 **(a)** $5^6 \times 5^4 \times 5^3$ **(b)** $2^3 \times 2^7 \times 2$

5 **(a)** $10^2 \times 10^2 \times 10$ **(b)** $9^4 \div 9$

6 **(a)** $6^3 \times 6^7 \times 6$ **(b)** $5^2 \times 5^2 \times 5^2$

7 **(a)** $3^5 \times 3 \times 3^2$ **(b)** $\frac{4^7 \times 4^5}{4^6}$

8 **(a)** $\frac{6^8}{6^2 \times 6^3}$ **(b)** $\frac{5^8 \times 5^4}{5^7}$ **(c)** $\frac{4^9}{4^2 \times 4^5}$

14.8 Prime factor form

You can write any number as the product of its simplest factors. The simplest factors are prime numbers. Start with the lowest prime number first, like this:

The product of 8 and 4 is 8×4 which is 32.

$$\begin{aligned} 720 &= 2 \times 360 \\ &= 2 \times 2 \times 180 \\ &= 2 \times 2 \times 2 \times 90 \\ &= 2 \times 2 \times 2 \times 2 \times 45 \\ &= 2 \times 2 \times 2 \times 2 \times 3 \times 15 \\ &= 2 \times 2 \times 2 \times 2 \times 3 \times 3 \times 5 \end{aligned}$$

This can be written as: $720 = 2^4 \times 3^2 \times 5$

Here 720 is in **prime factor form**

2, 3, and 5 are **prime factors** of 720

- **A number written as the product of prime numbers is written in prime factor form.**

14.9 Finding the highest common factor (HCF)

Sometimes you will need to find the largest factor two numbers have in common, called the **highest common factor** or **HCF**. For example, to find the highest common factor of 720 and 84:

First write each number in prime factor form:

$$\begin{aligned} 720 &= 2 \times 2 \times 2 \times 2 \times 3 \times 3 \times 5 \\ 84 &= 2 \times 2 \times 3 \times 7 \end{aligned}$$

Then pick out the common factors: those that appear in *both* numbers. These are:

$$2 \times 2 \times 3$$

The highest common factor of 720 and 84 is $2 \times 2 \times 3 = 12$

- **The highest common factor (HCF) of two numbers is the highest factor common to both of them.**

14.10 Finding the lowest common multiple (LCM)

The multiples of 6 are: 6 21 18 24 30 36 42 48 54 60 66 72 …
The multiples of 8 are: 8 16 24 32 40 48 56 64 72 80 88 96 …

6 and 8 have some common multiples

The lowest (smallest) of these is 24 so the lowest common multiple of 6 and 8 is 24.

■ **The lowest common multiple (LCM) of two numbers is the lowest number that is a multiple of them both.**

Exercise 14G

1 Write these numbers in prime factor form:
(a) 24 **(b)** 32 **(c)** 18 **(d)** 13

2 Find the highest common factor of:
(a) 4 and 8 **(b)** 9 and 12 **(c)** 18 and 24 **(d)** 18 and 30
(e) 21 and 35.

3 Find the lowest common multiple of:
(a) 3 and 4 **(b)** 4 and 6 **(c)** 7 and 14 **(d)** 6 and 15.

4 Find the lowest common multiple of:
(a) 12 and 15 **(b)** 36 and 16 **(c)** 50 and 85

14.11 Standard form

Very large numbers are difficult to use and cannot always be shown in a calculator display. Standard form is an alternative way of writing very large or very small numbers.

Dinosaurs roamed the Earth about 140 000 000 years ago. Instead of writing long strings of zeros you can write this number in standard form. The number 140 000 000 can be written 1.4×10^8.

You can show numbers in a place value table:

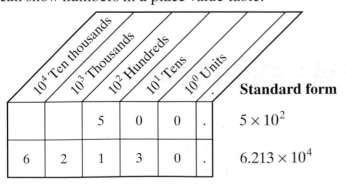

10^4 Ten thousands	10^3 Thousands	10^2 Hundreds	10^1 Tens	10^0 Units	.	**Standard form**
		5	0	0	.	5×10^2
6	2	1	3	0	.	6.213×10^4

The number 62 130 is written as 6.213×10^4 in standard form. The power of 10 is 4 since the most significant figure (6) is in the place value of 10^4.

■ **A number is in standard form when it is written like this:**

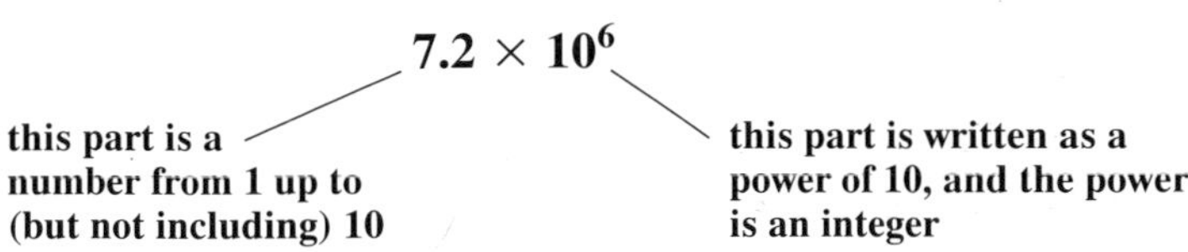

7.2 × 10^6
this part is a number from 1 up to (but not including) 10
this part is written as a power of 10, and the power is an integer

Example 9

Write in standard form:
(a) 2 568 000 (b) 74 500

The decimal point goes after the first significant figure.

	10^6	10^5	10^4	10^3	10^2	10^1	10^0	.	Standard form
2 568 000	2	5	6	8	0	0	0	.	2.568×10^6
74 500			7	4	5	0	0	.	7.45×10^4

(a) $2\,568\,000 = 2.568 \times 10^6$
(b) $74\,500 = 7.45 \times 10^4$

The power of 10 is the place value of the first significant figure.

Example 10

Write as ordinary numbers:
(a) 5.147×10^5 (b) 1.102×10^6 (c) 8.755×10^2

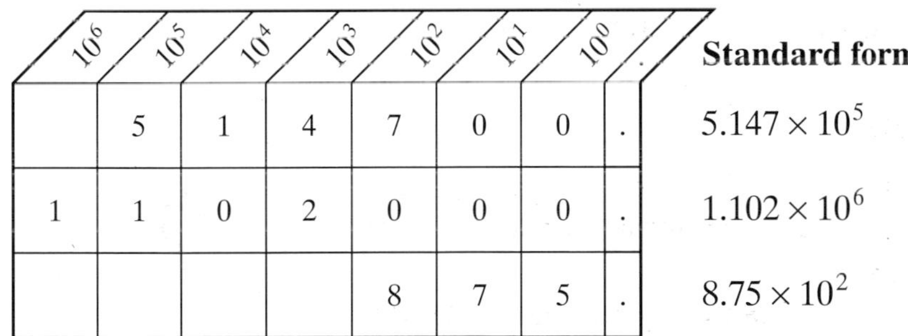

10^6	10^5	10^4	10^3	10^2	10^1	10^0	.	Standard form
	5	1	4	7	0	0	.	5.147×10^5
1	1	0	2	0	0	0	.	1.102×10^6
				8	7	5	.	8.75×10^2

(a) $5.147 \times 10^5 = 514\,700$
(b) $1.102 \times 10^6 = 1\,102\,000$
(c) $8.755 \times 10^2 = 875.5$

When you multiply by a positive power of 10 think of the digits moving to the left of the decimal point. The power of ten is the number of places the digits need to move to make an ordinary number.

Exercise 14H

Write in standard form:

1 **(a)** 600 000 **(b)** 35 000 **(c)** 5400

2 **(a)** 25 000 **(b)** 7000 **(c)** 236 000

3 **(a)** 40 000 000 **(b)** 1 210 000 **(c)** 54 000

Write as ordinary numbers:

4 **(a)** 3.24×10^5 **(b)** 5.75×10^4 **(c)** 8.04×10^3

5 **(a)** 2×10^6 **(b)** 2.56×10^5 **(c)** 3.06×10^4

6 **(a)** 2.7×10^6 **(b)** 1.6×10^7 **(c)** 8.09×10^3

Numbers less than 1

To write numbers less than 1 in standard form you need to know these powers of 10:

$$0.1 = \frac{1}{10} = \quad = 10^{-1}$$

$$0.01 = \frac{1}{100} = \frac{1}{10 \times 10} = 10^{-2}$$

$$0.001 = \frac{1}{1000} = \frac{1}{10 \times 10 \times 10} = 10^{-3}$$

$$0.0001 = \frac{1}{10\,000} = \frac{1}{10 \times 10 \times 10 \times 10} = 10^{-4}$$

From the work on powers on page 184:

$$\frac{10^0}{10^1} = \frac{1}{10} = 0.1$$

and:

$$\frac{10^0}{10^1} = 10^{0-1} = 10^{-1}$$

So $0.1 = 10^{-1}$

You can show numbers smaller than 1 in a place value table:

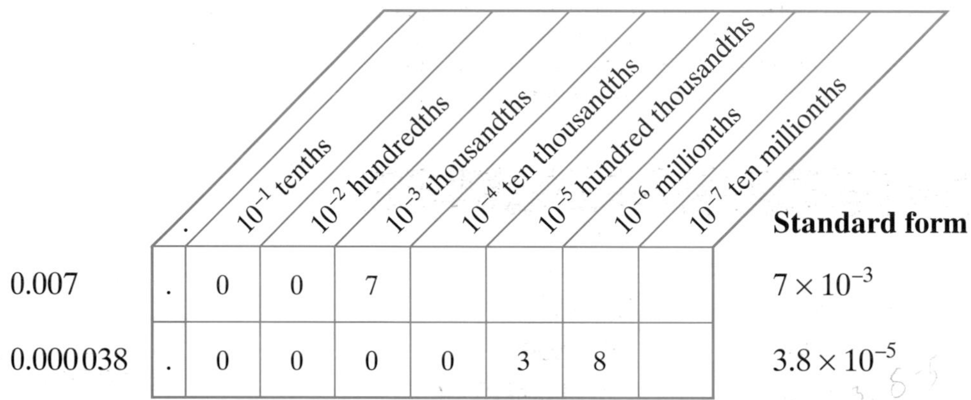

	.	10^{-1} tenths	10^{-2} hundredths	10^{-3} thousandths	10^{-4} ten thousandths	10^{-5} hundred thousandths	10^{-6} millionths	10^{-7} ten millionths	Standard form
0.007	.	0	0	7					7×10^{-3}
0.000038	.	0	0	0	0	3	8		3.8×10^{-5}

The number 0.000 038 is written as 3.8×10^{-5} in standard form. The power of 10 is –5 since the most significant figure (3) is in the place value of 10^{-5}.

Example 11

Write in standard form:

(a) 0.0013 (b) 0.0327 (c) 0.000 004

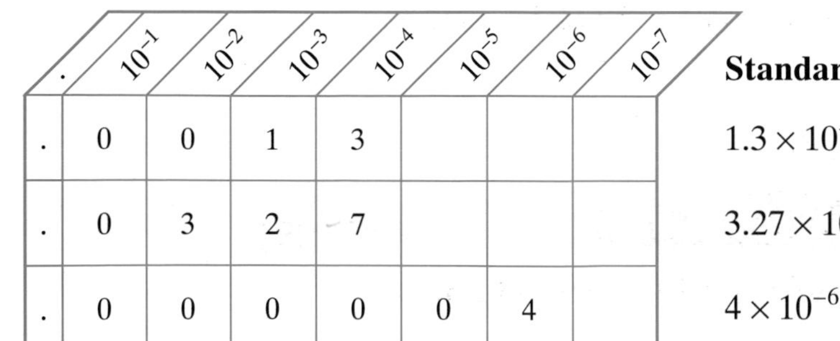

	.	10^{-1}	10^{-2}	10^{-3}	10^{-4}	10^{-5}	10^{-6}	10^{-7}	Standard form
0.0013	.	0	0	1	3				1.3×10^{-3}
0.0327	.	0	3	2	7				3.27×10^{-2}
0.000004	.	0	0	0	0	0	4		4×10^{-6}

The decimal point goes after the first significant figure.

The power of 10 is the place value of the first significant figure.

As the ordinary number is smaller than one the power of ten is negative.

(a) $0.0013 = 1.3 \times 10^{-3}$
(b) $0.0327 = 3.27 \times 10^{-2}$
(c) $0.000\,004 = 4 \times 10^{-6}$

Example 12

Write as ordinary numbers:

(a) 9×10^{-3} (b) 1.005×10^{-2} (c) 7.8×10^{-6}

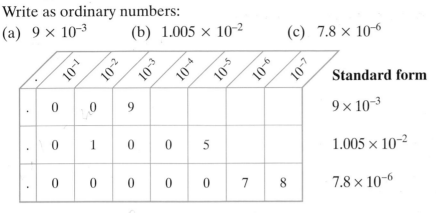

.	10^{-1}	10^{-2}	10^{-3}	10^{-4}	10^{-5}	10^{-6}	10^{-7}	Standard form
.	0	0	9					9×10^{-3}
.	0	1	0	0	5			1.005×10^{-2}
.	0	0	0	0	0	7	8	7.8×10^{-6}

(a) $9 \times 10^{-3} = 0.009$
(b) $1.005 \times 10^{-2} = 0.01005$
(c) $7.8 \times 10^{-6} = 0.000\,007\,8$

When you multiply by a negative power of 10 think of the digits moving to the right of the decimal point. The power of ten is the number of places the digits need to move to make an ordinary number.

Exercise 14I

Write in standard form:

1 **(a)** 0.009 **(b)** 0.08 **(c)** 0.45
2 **(a)** 0.000 43 **(b)** 0.038 **(c)** 0.0096
3 **(a)** 0.000 009 4 **(b)** 0.0008 **(c)** 0.000 077 7

Write as ordinary numbers:

4 **(a)** 9×10^{-3} **(b)** 7.4×10^{-4} **(c)** 2.8×10^{-3}
5 **(a)** 9.82×10^{-4} **(b)** 4.65×10^{-5} **(c)** 5.61×10^{-3}
6 **(a)** 5.5×10^{-7} **(b)** 1.34×10^{-4} **(c)** 6.502×10^{-3}

14.12 Calculating with standard form

You sometimes need to work out problems involving numbers written in standard form.

Worked examination question

The number 10^{100} is called a googol.
Write the number 50 googols in standard form. [L]

First write each part of 50×10^{100} in strict standard form:
$(5.0 \times 10^1) \times (1.0 \times 10^{100})$
Then multiply the numbers 5.0 and 1.0 and the powers 10^1 and 10^{100} separately:
$(5.0 \times 1.0) \times (10^1 \times 10^{100}) = 5.0 \times 10^{101}$

So 50 googols is 5.0×10^{101} in standard form.

In the worked examination question the numbers 5.0×10^{-1} and 1.0×10^{100} are multiplied so you can multiply the numbers 5.0 and 1.0 and the powers 10^1 and 10^{100} separately. The same applies when you divide two numbers in standard form.

If you add or subtract two numbers in standard form you need to change them to ordinary numbers.

For example,

$7.8 \times 10^{-6} - 3.2 \times 10^4$

$= 7\,800\,000 - 32\,000 = 7\,768\,000 = 7.768 \times 10^6$

Example 13

Work out:

(a) $(4.5 \times 10^4) \times (7 \times 10^{-2})$
(b) $(5.3 \times 10^7) + (3.6 \times 10^5)$

(a) $(4.5 \times 10^4) \times (7 \times 10^{-2}) = (4.5 \times 7) \times (10^4 \times 10^{-2})$
$= 31.5 \times 10^2$
$= 3.15 \times 10^1 \times 10^2$
$= 3.15 \times 10^3$ in standard form

(b) $(5.3 \times 10^7) + (3.6 \times 10^6) = 53\,000\,000 + 3\,600\,000$
$= 56\,600\,000$ or 5.66×10^7 in standard form

Exam tips:
In exam questions show your working so the examiner knows what you are trying to do, even if you make a calculation error. Make sure the answer is written in the way the question describes: sometimes the question will ask for the answer to be written in standard form.

Example 14

Work these out, giving your answer in standard form:

(a) $(9.5 \times 10^3) \times (8.72 \times 10^7)$
(b) $(1.632 \times 10^6) \div (9.6 \times 10^3)$

(a) $(9.5 \times 10^3) \times (8.72 \times 10^7) = (9.5 \times 8.72) \times (10^3 \times 10^7) = 82.84 \times 10^{10}$
$= 8.284 \times 10^1 \times 10^{10}$
$= 8.284 \times 10^{11}$

(b) $(1.632 \times 10^6) \div (9.6 \times 10^3) = (1.632 \div 9.6) \times (10^6 \div 10^3) = 0.17 \times 10^3$
$= 1.7 \times 10^{-1} \times 10^3$
$= 1.7 \times 10^2$

Exercise 14J

Work these out giving your answers in standard form.

1 **(a)** $(6.3 \times 10^3) + (8.5 \times 10^2)$ **(b)** $(1.23 \times 10^6) - (1.24 \times 10^5)$
(c) $(7.2 \times 10^{-7}) \times (8.4 \times 10^3)$ **(d)** $(1.3 \times 10^3) \times (6.1 \times 10^{-7})$
(e) $(4 \times 10^8) \times (6 \times 10^{-3})$ **(f)** $(3.8 \times 10^3) \times (7.9 \times 10^{-4})$

2 **(a)** $\dfrac{5.4 \times 10^{11}}{4.9 \times 10^7}$ **(b)** $\dfrac{2.4 \times 10^8}{7.1 \times 10^4}$ **(c)** $\dfrac{6.1 \times 10^7}{1.5 \times 10^4}$

3 The mass of one atomic group of particles is 2.275×10^{-14} grams. Calculate the total mass of 2000 groups of particles.

4 Light travels at a speed of 3×10^8 metres per second. Work out how far, in metres, light will travel in 10 000 years. Take one year as $365\frac{1}{4}$ days. Give your answer in standard form.

Exercise 14K Mixed questions

1 4, 5, 8, 9, 12, 14, 16, 20, 27, 35, 36, 37

From the list write down:

(a) all the odd numbers **(b)** all the multiples of 3
(c) all the factors of 48 **(d)** all the prime numbers
(e) all the square numbers **(f)** all the cube numbers.

2 Work out the highest common factor of:
(a) 45 and 60 **(b)** 30 and 36 **(c)** 35 and 42

3 Work out the lowest common multiple of:
(a) 4 and 5 **(b)** 6 and 9 **(c)** 18 and 30

4 By a trial and improvement method find: **(a)** $\sqrt{19}$ **(b)** $\sqrt[3]{24}$

5 Work out: **(a)** 13^3 **(b)** 25^2 **(c)** 6^5 **(d)** 7^4

6 Simplify: **(a)** $4^5 \times 4^4$ **(b)** $4^5 \div 4^2$ **(c)** $4^5 \times 4^6$

7 The Mean distance of the Earth from the Sun is 149.6 million kilometres.

(a) Write the number 149.6 million in standard form.

(b) The Earth travels a distance, D km, in one day. The value of D is given by the formula:

$$D = \frac{2\pi \times \text{Mean distance of Earth from Sun}}{365}$$

Calculate the value of D, giving your answer in standard form. [L]

8 A nanometre is 10^{-9} metres.
Write 50 nanometers in metres. Give your answer in standard form. [L]

9 Write down two prime numbers between 10 and 20. [L]

10 The mass of the moon is 7.343×10^{19} tonnes. The Earth has a mass 81 times bigger than that of the moon.

(a) Work out the mass of the Earth, giving your answer in standard form.

(b) The mass of a meteorite is 3.61×10^7 kg.
Write 3.61×10^7 as an ordinary number. [L]

11 Work out the value of $(4.6 \times 10^{-2}) \times (8.3 \times 10^4)$ giving your answer in standard form. [L]

12 The mass of a neutron is 1.675×10^{-24} grams.
Calculate the total mass of 1500 neutrons. Give your answer in standard form. [L]

Summary of key points

1 Even numbers are whole numbers which divide exactly by 2. — 2, 4, 6, 18, 24 are even numbers.

2 Odd numbers are whole numbers which do not divide exactly by 2 . — 1, 9, 15, 23, 27 are odd numbers.

3 Multiples of a number are the results of multiplying the number by a positive whole number. — Some multiples of 3 are 3, 6, 9, 12, 15, 18, 21, 24.

4 The factors of a number are whole numbers that divide exactly into the number. The factors include 1 and the number itself. — The factors of 12 are 1, 2, 3, 4, 6 and 12.

5 A prime number is a whole number greater than 1 which has only two factors, itself and 1. — The first ten prime numbers are 2, 3, 5, 7, 11, 13, 17, 19, 23, 29.

6 Square numbers are the result of multiplying a whole number by itself. — The first six square numbers are 1, 4, 9, 16, 25, 36.

7 Cube numbers are the result of multiplying a whole number by itself then multiplying by the number again. — The first six cube numbers are 1, 8, 27, 64, 125, 216.

8 To find the square of any number multiply the number by itself.

9 If $x \times x = A$ then x is the square root of A, written $\sqrt{A}$. — $\sqrt{36} = \pm 6$

10 To find the cube of any number multiply the number by itself then multiply by the number again.

11 If $y \times y \times y = A$ then y is the cube root of A, written $\sqrt[3]{A}$ — $\sqrt[3]{125} = 5$

12 To multiply powers of the same number add the indices. In general: $x^a \times x^b = x^{a+b}$ — $162^4 \times 162^3 = 162^{4+3} = 162^7$

13 To divide powers of the same number subtract the indices. In general: $x^a \div x^b = x^{a-b}$ — $43^{29} \div 43^{24} = 43^{29-24} = 43^5$

14 Any number raised to the power 1 is equal to the number itself. — $67^1 = 67 \quad x^1 = x$

15 Any number, not zero, raised to the power 0 is equal to the number 1. — $129^0 = 1 \quad x^0 = 1$ if x is not zero.

16 A number written as the product of prime numbers is written in prime factor form.

17 The highest common factor (HCF) of two numbers is the highest factor common to both of them.

18 The lowest common multiple (LCM) of two numbers is the lowest number that is a multiple of them both.

19 A number is in standard form when it is written like this: — Standard form: $a \times 10^n$ where $1 \leqslant a < 10$ and n is an integer.

$$7.2 \times 10^6$$

this part is a number from 1 up to (but not including) 10

this part is written as a power of 10, and the power is an integer

15 Pythagoras' theorem

This unit shows you how to calculate the lengths of sides of right angled triangles. This topic is always included in GCSE exams.

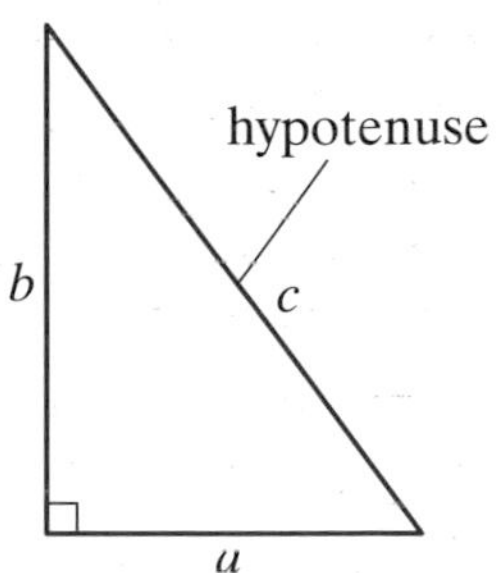

15.1 Using Pythagoras' theorem to find the hypotenuse

The longest side of a right angled triangle is the one opposite the right angle. It is called the **hypotenuse**.

Exercise 15A

1

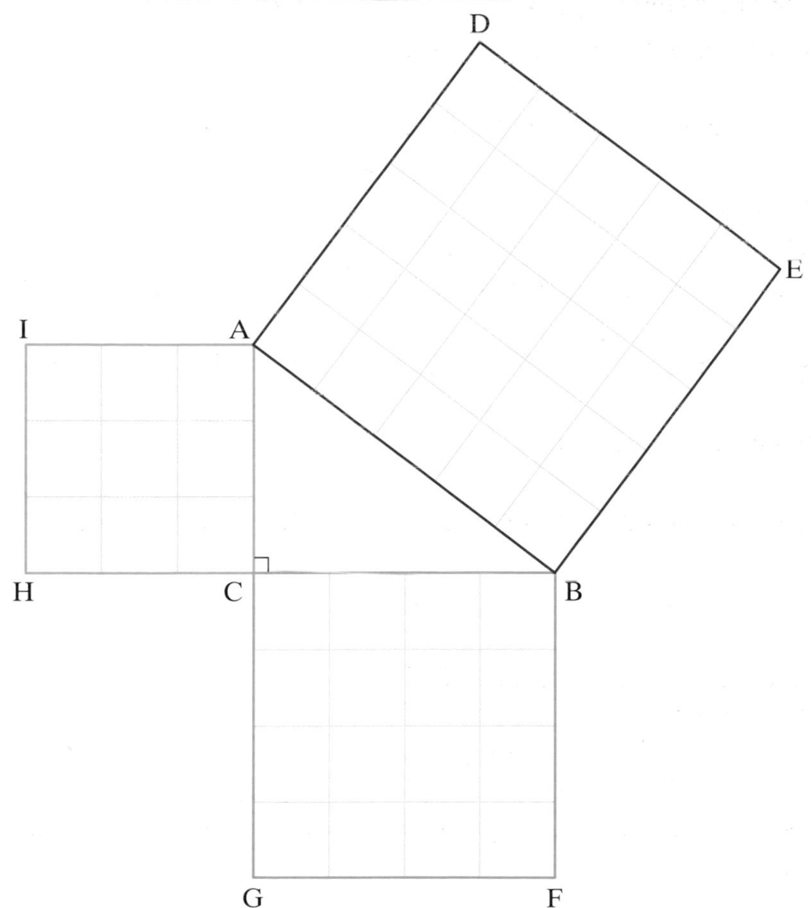

The right angled triangle ABC has sides 3 cm, 4 cm and 5 cm. Squares have been drawn on each of its sides.

(a) Find the number of small squares in:
   (i) the square CBFG
   (ii) the square ACHI
   (iii) the square BADE.

(b) Add your answers for **(a)** (i) and **(a)** (ii).

(c) Write down what you notice.

2

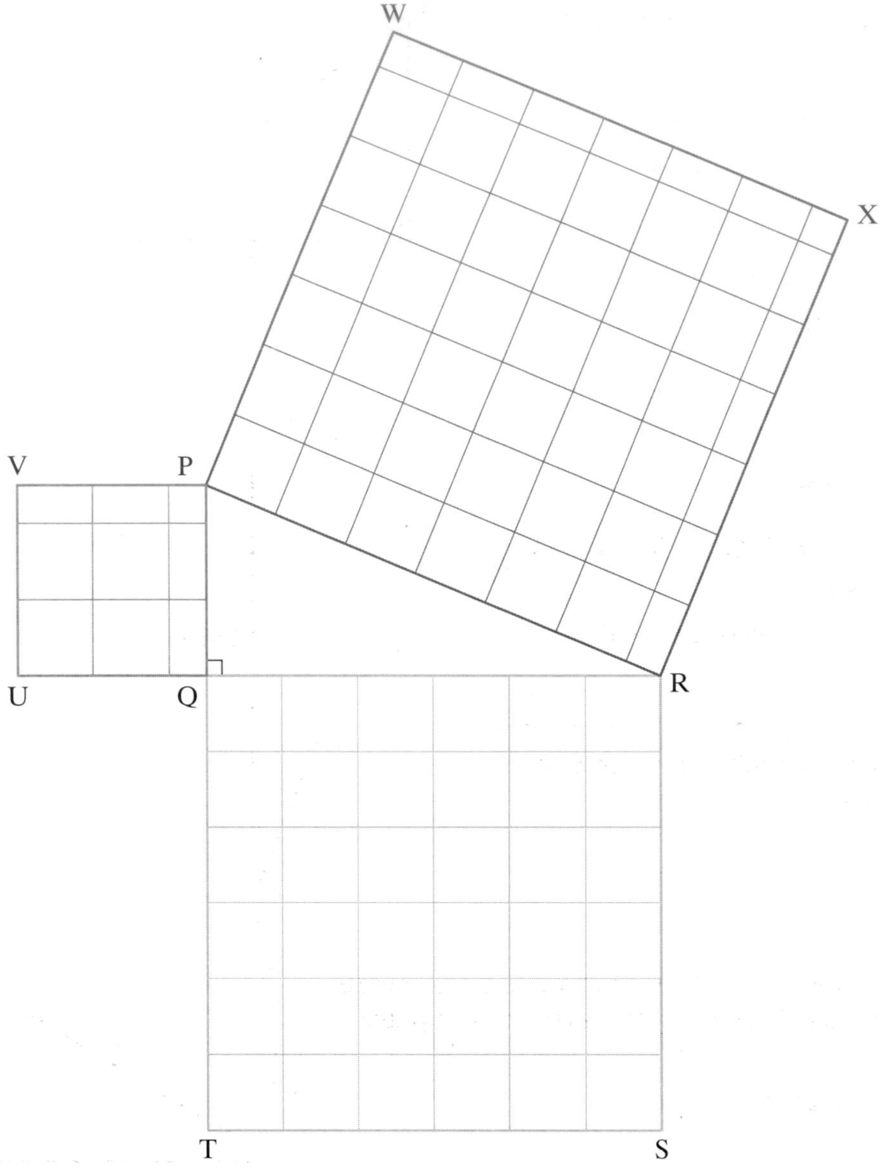

The right angled triangle PQR has sides 2.5 cm, 6 cm and 6.5 cm. Squares have been drawn on each side of the triangle.

(a) Count the number of small squares in:

(i) the square PQUV

(ii) the square QRST

(iii) the square RPWX.

(b) Add your answers for **(a)** (i) and **(a)** (ii).

(c) Write down what you notice.

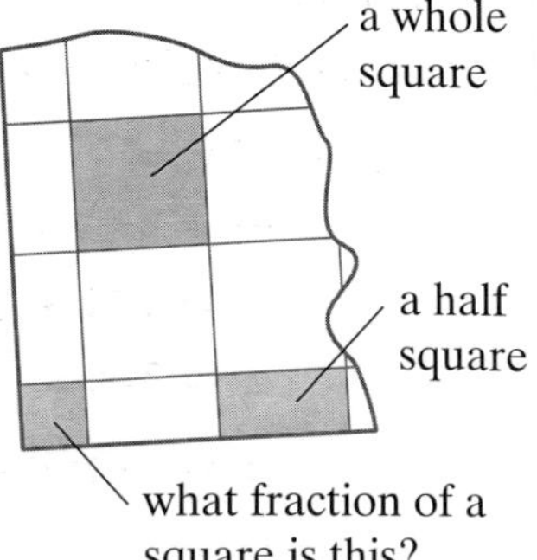
a whole square
a half square
what fraction of a square is this?

A relationship between areas

Exercise 14A shows that there is a relationship between squares drawn on the sides of a right angled triangle.

Another way to see the relationship is to calculate the areas of the squares.

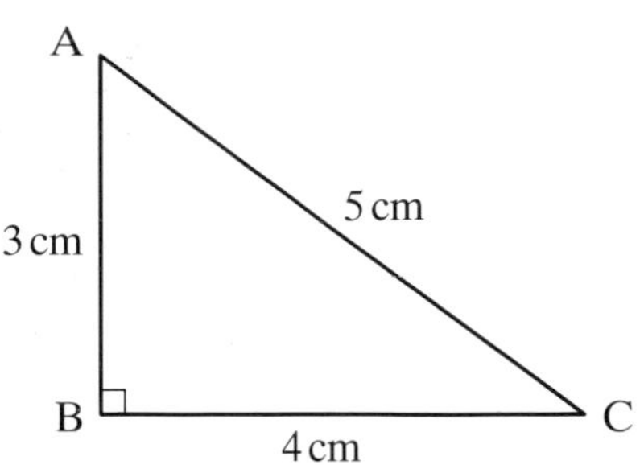

...le ABC the square on the hypotenuse is:

$= \mathbf{5^2} = \mathbf{25}$

...of the squares on the other two sides is:

$+ BC^2 = \mathbf{3^2 + 4^2} = 9 + 16 = \mathbf{25}$

$\mathbf{5^2 = 3^2 + 4^2}$

...quared = three squared + four squared)

$AC^2 = AB^2 + BC^2$

In triangle PQR the square on the hypotenuse is:

$PR^2 = \mathbf{6.5^2} = \mathbf{42.25}$

The sum of the squares on the other two sides is:

$PQ^2 + QR^2 = \mathbf{2.5^2 + 6^2} = 6.25 + 36 = \mathbf{42.25}$

so $\mathbf{6.5^2 = 2.5^2 + 6^2}$

(6.5 squared = 2.5 squared + 6 squared)

and $PR^2 = PQ^2 + QR^2$

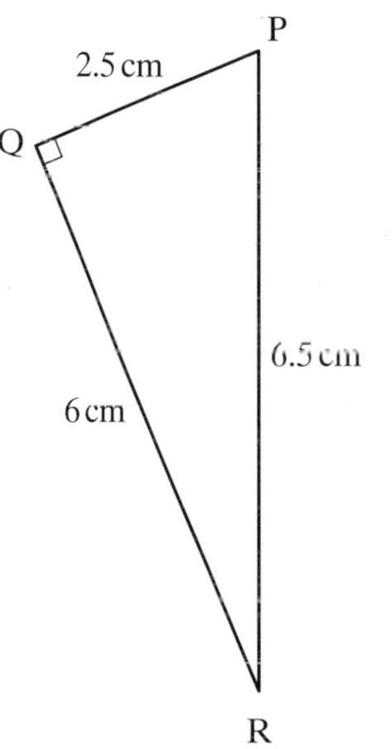

These are examples of a result, called a **theorem**, that was proved by **Pythagoras**, a Greek philosopher and mathematician who lived around 500 BC.

- **Pythagoras' theorem states that in a right angled triangle the square on the hypotenuse is equal to the sum of the squares on the other two sides.**
  $\mathbf{c^2 = a^2 + b^2}$ **or** $\mathbf{a^2 + b^2 = c^2}$

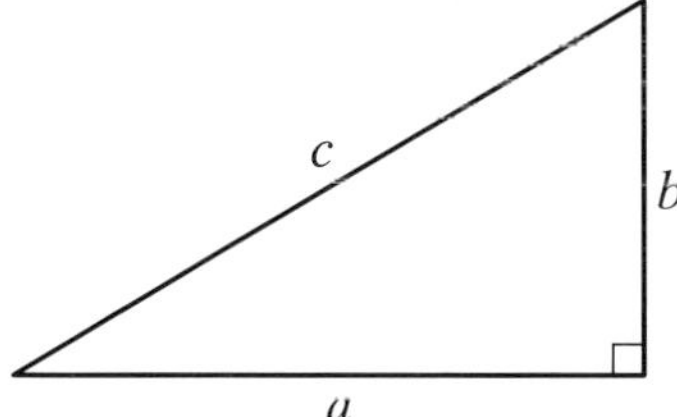

Example 1

In the right angled triangle calculate the length of the side marked z.

$$a^2 + b^2 = c^2$$
$$z^2 = 12^2 + 5^2$$
$$= 144 + 25$$
$$= 169$$

so $z = \sqrt{169} = 13\text{ cm}$

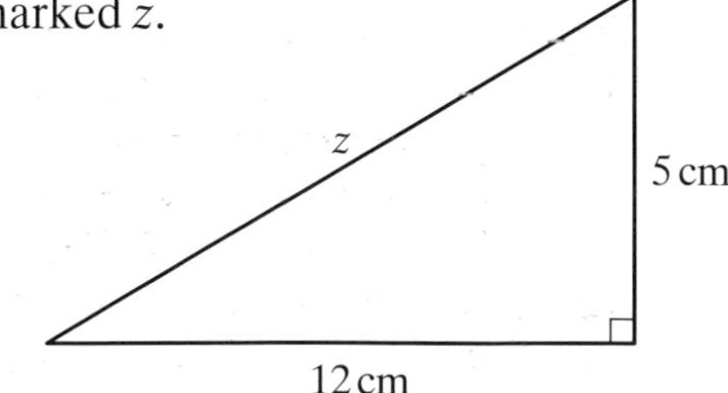

Example 2

In triangle LMN, angle N = 90°, LN = 18.3 cm and MN = 7 cm. Calculate LM correct to one decimal place.

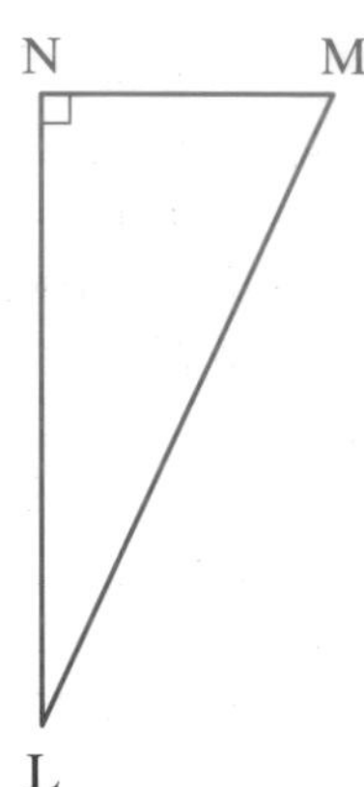

$$c^2 = a^2 + b^2$$
$$LM^2 = NM^2 + NL^2$$
$$= 7^2 + 18.3^2$$
$$= 49 + 334.89$$
$$= 383.89$$

so $\quad LM = \sqrt{383.89} = 19.59\ldots$ cm

$= 19.6$ cm (to 1 d.p.)

Exercise 15B

1 Calculate the lengths marked with letters in these triangles:

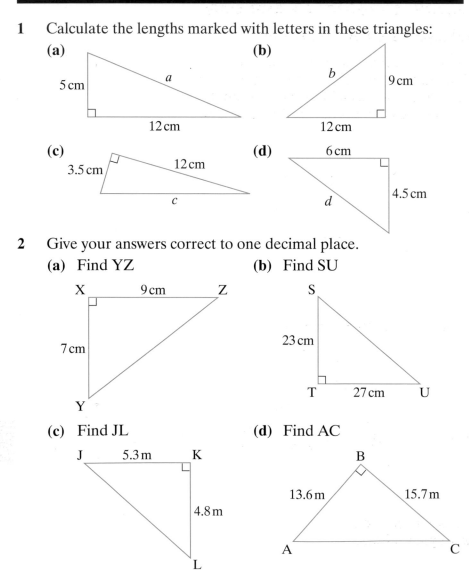

(a)

5 cm
a
12 cm

(b)

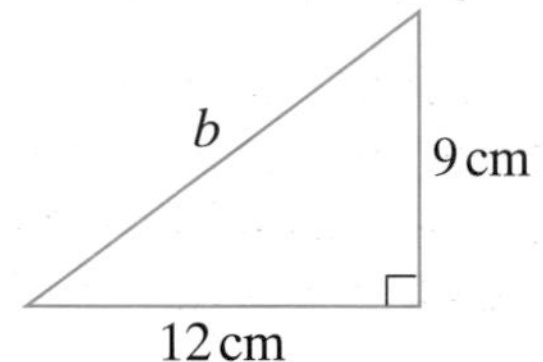

(c)

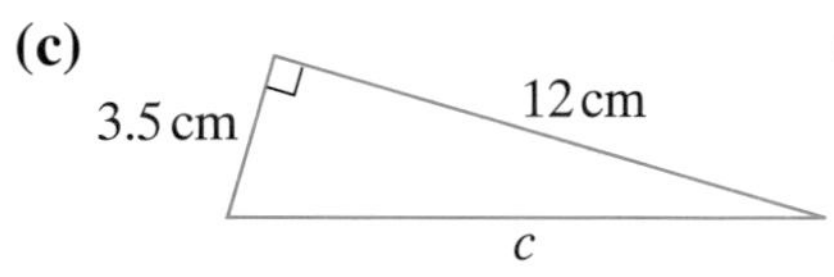

(d)

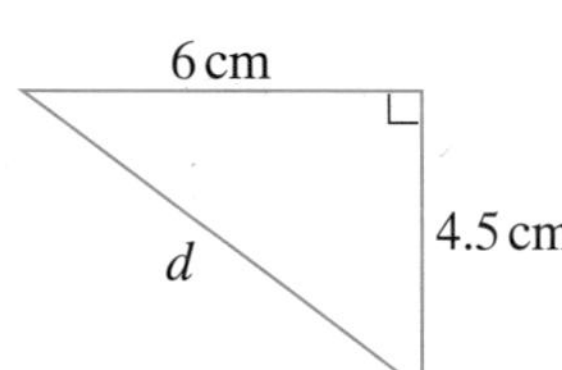

2 Give your answers correct to one decimal place.

(a) Find YZ

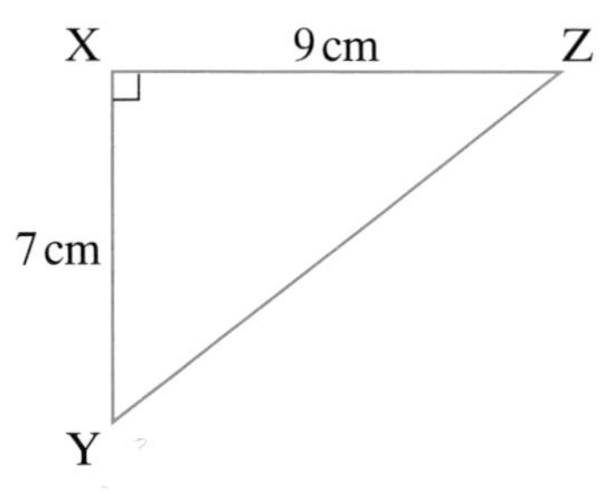

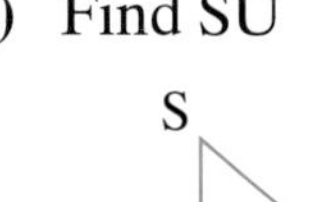

(b) Find SU

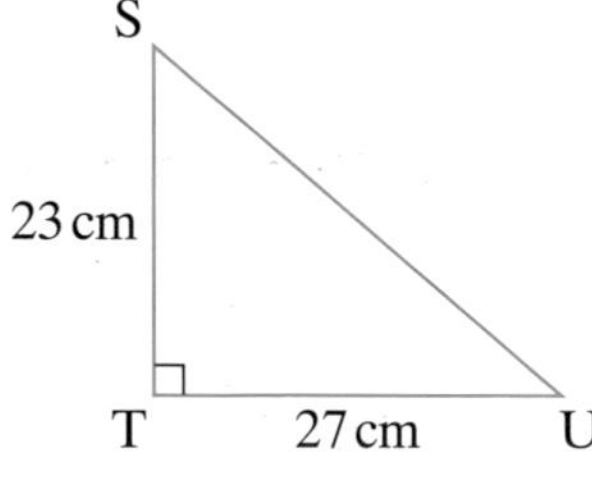

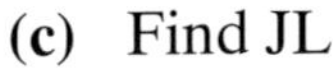

(c) Find JL

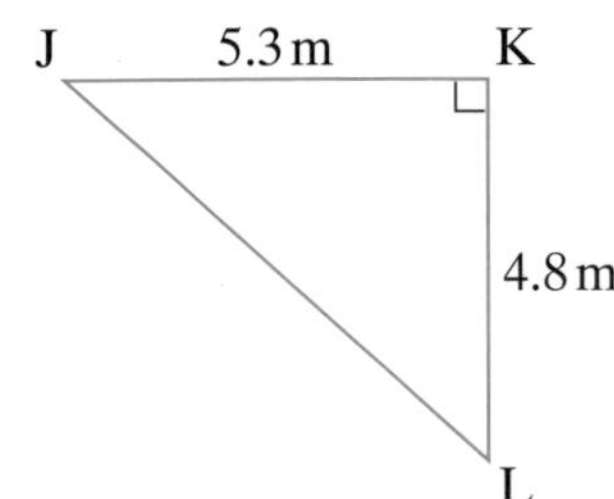

(d) Find AC

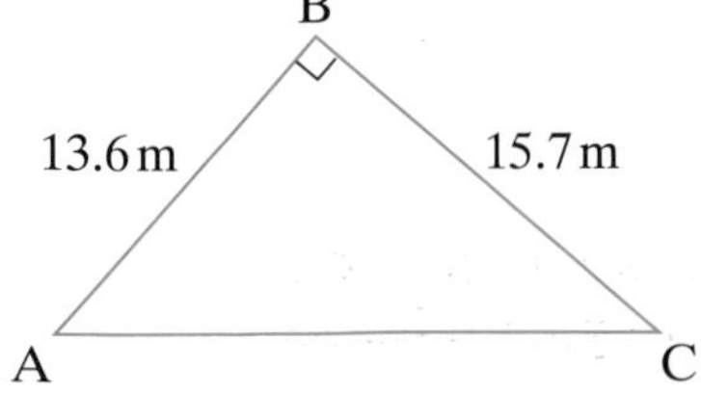

3 A rectangle is 13 cm long and 7 cm wide.
Work out the length of a diagonal of the rectangle.

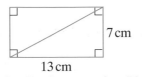

7 cm

13 cm

4 A boat leaves Broadstairs and sails due east for 5 km. The boat then changes course and sails due south for 3 km.
Calculate the final distance of the boat from Broadstairs, giving your answer correct to one decimal place.

5 Paul's boat is on a rock 35 m from the base of a vertical cliff. A coastguard stands on the cliff, 42 m above sea level. He uses a rocket to send a rope to the boat. Work out the length of the rope from the coastguard to the boat, assuming the rope is straight.

15.2 Using Pythagoras' theorem to find one of the shorter sides of a triangle

With the formula $a^2 + b^2 = c^2$ you can calculate the longest side c of a right angled triangle. If you need to find one of the shorter sides (a, for example) it is easier to change the formula so that a^2 is on its own on one side. (This is sometimes called 'making a^2 the subject of the formula'.)

Pythagoras' theorem states:

$$a^2 + b^2 = c^2$$

Subtract b^2 from both sides:

$$a^2 + b^2 - b^2 = c^2 - b^2$$

■ $$\mathbf{a^2 = c^2 - b^2}$$

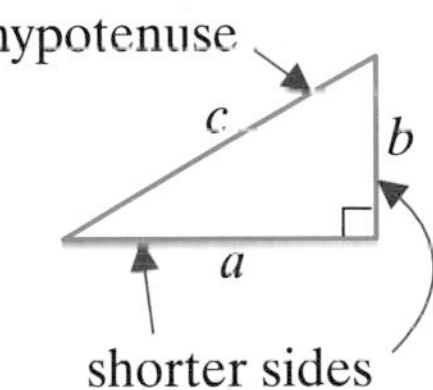

Example 3

In triangle DEF, angle F is a right angle, DF = 7.5 cm and DE = 12.5 cm.

Calculate the length of EF.

$$a^2 = c^2 - b^2$$

$$EF^2 = 12.5^2 - 7.5^2$$

$$= 156.25 - 56.25$$

$$= 100$$

so $$EF = \sqrt{100}$$

$$= 10\text{ cm}$$

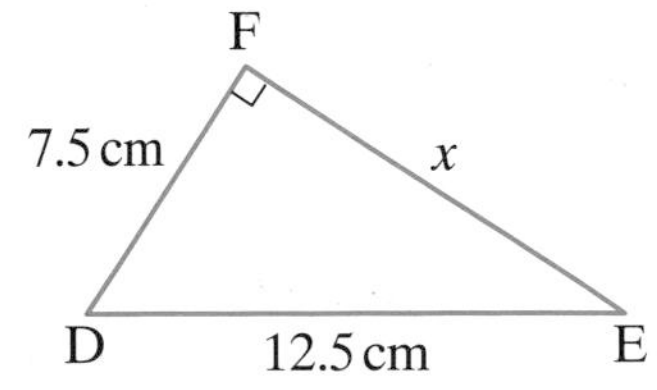

Hint: always check that the hypotenuse is still the longest side. If not, look for your mistake.

Example 4

An isosceles triangle PQR has PQ = 14.3 cm, PR = 14.3 cm and QR = 9.8 cm.

Calculate the height of the triangle correct to 1 d.p.

For a reminder about isosceles triangles see page 40.

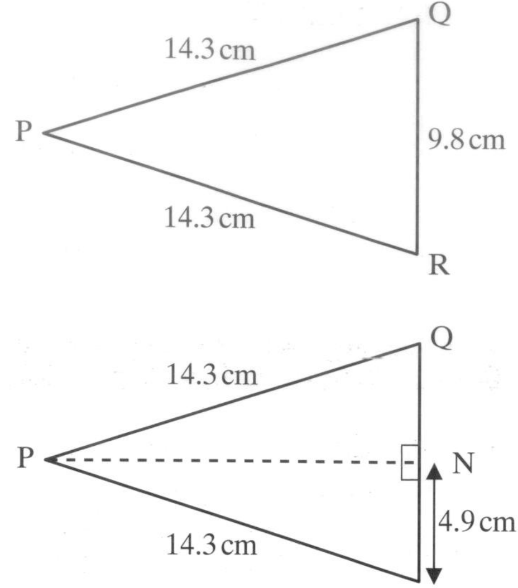

In this diagram PN is the height of the triangle.
PN is a line of symmetry so QN = NR.

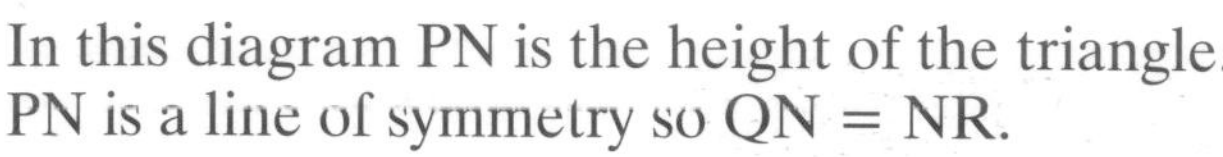

$$NR = \tfrac{1}{2} \times 9.8 = 4.9\,\text{cm}$$

Triangle PNR has a right angle at N so you can use Pythagoras' theorem.

$$a^2 = c^2 - b^2$$

$$PN^2 = 14.3^2 - 4.9^2$$
$$= 204.49 - 24.01$$
$$= 180.48$$

so $$PN = \sqrt{180.48}$$
$$= 13.43...$$

The height of the triangle is 13.4 cm correct to 1 d.p.

Exercise 15C

1 Calculate the lengths marked with letters in these triangles:

(a)

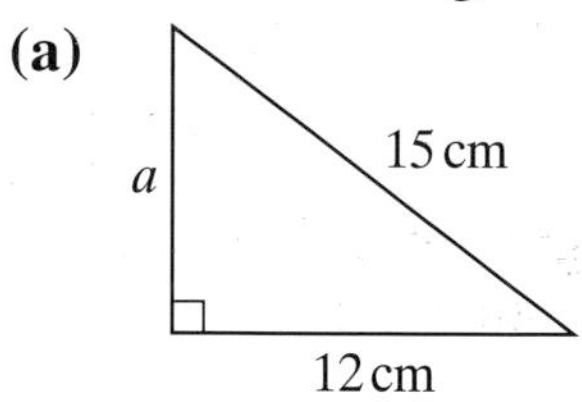

(b)

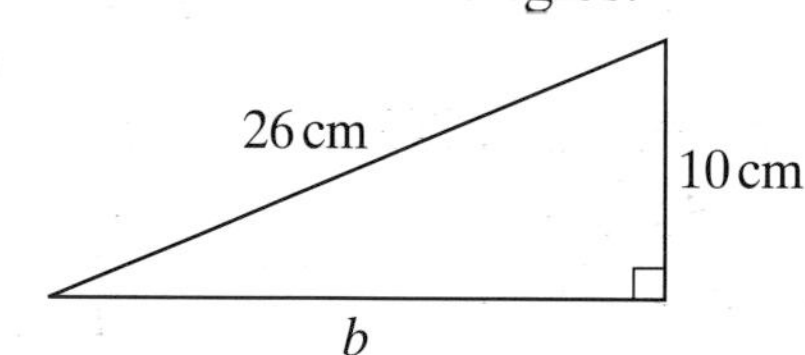

(c)

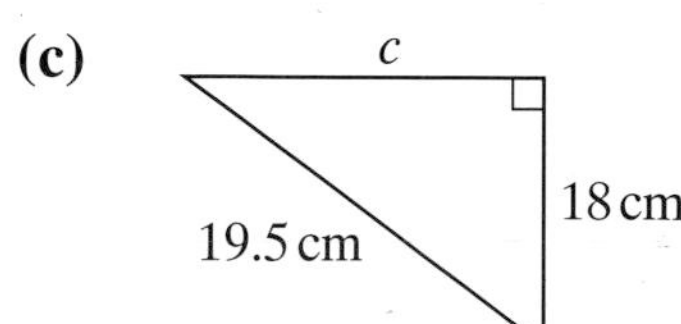

(d)

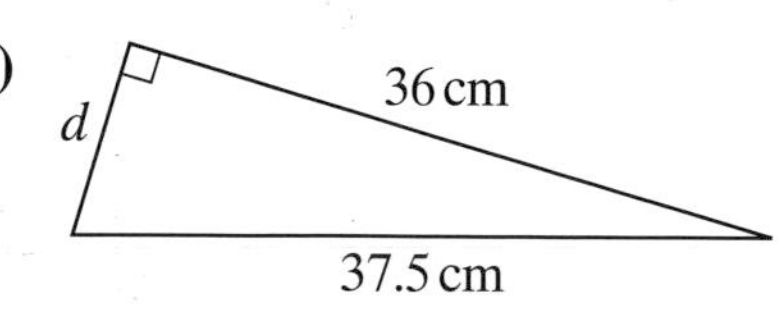

2 Give your answers correct to one decimal place.

(a) Find ON

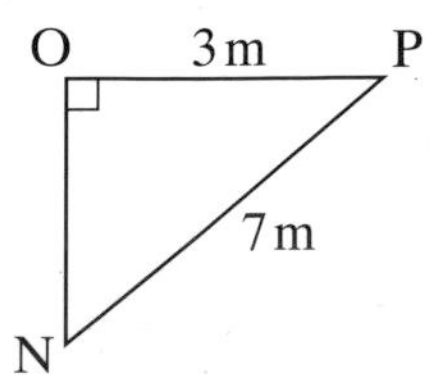

(b) Find RS

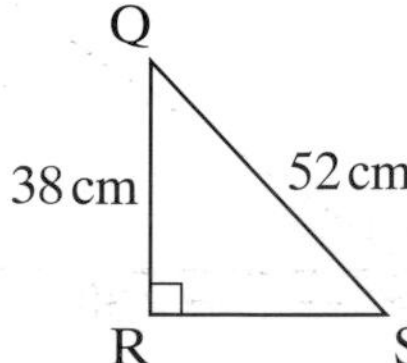

(c) Find TV

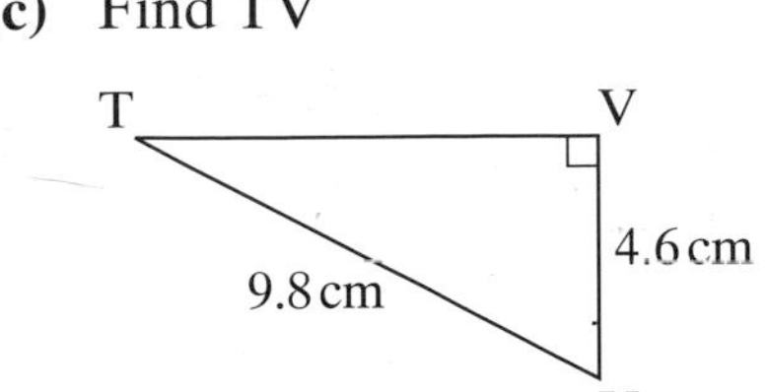

(d) Find XY

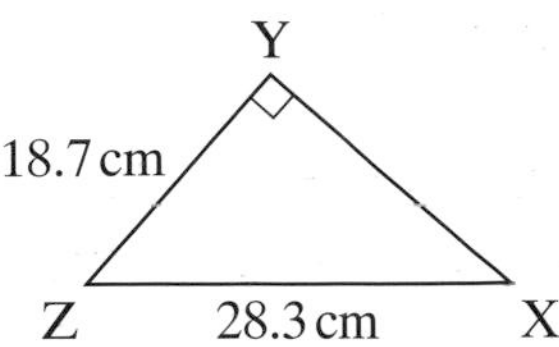

Exercise 15D Mixed questions

1 A ladder is 5 metres long. It leans against a wall with one end on the ground 1 metre from the wall. The other end of the ladder just reaches a windowsill.
Calculate the height of the windowsill above the ground.

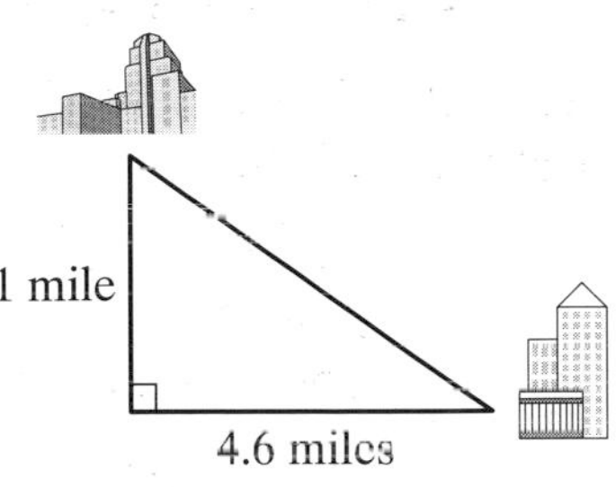

2 Rowena is in her helicopter above the Canary Wharf tower. She flies due west for 4.6 miles and then due north for 1 mile. She is then above Senate House.
Calculate the direct distance, in miles, of the Canary Wharf tower from Senate House.

3 An isosceles triangle ABC has AB = 9.5 cm and BC = 9.5 cm.
The height of the triangle is BD and BD = 7.2 cm.
Work out the length of AC.

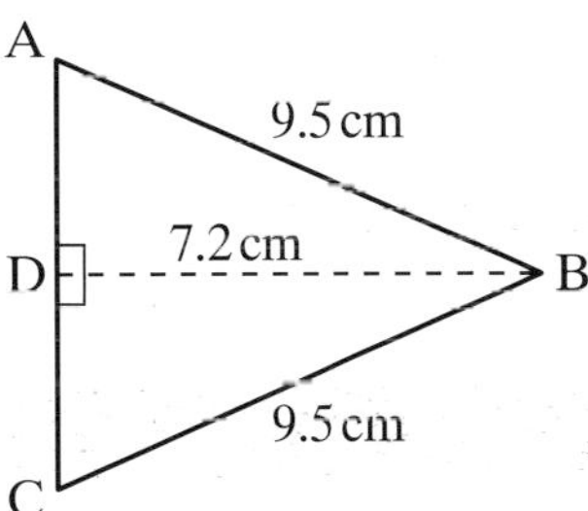

4 An isosceles triangle XYZ has XY = 26 cm, ZX = 26 cm and ZY = 18 cm.
Calculate the height of triangle XYZ.

5 ABC is a right angled triangle.
AB is of length 4 m and BC is of length 13 m.
Calculate the length of AC. [L]

Diagram NOT accurately drawn

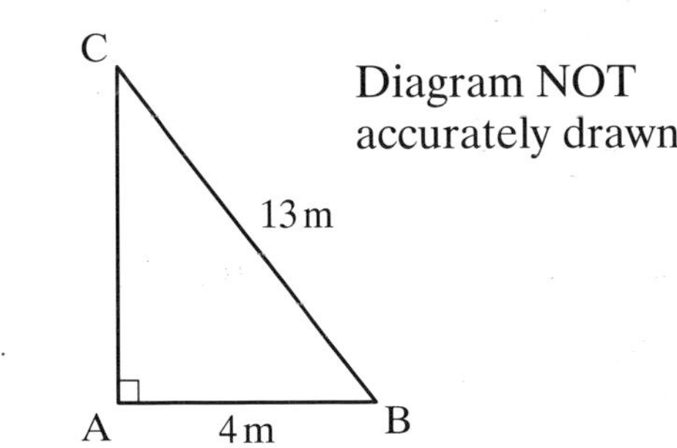

6 Work out the length, in metres, of side AB of the triangle. [L]

Diagram NOT accurately drawn

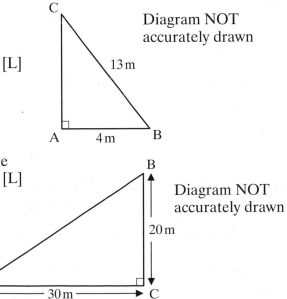

Summary of key points

Pythagoras' theorem states that in a right angled triangle the square on the hypotenuse is equal to the sum of the squares on the other two sides.

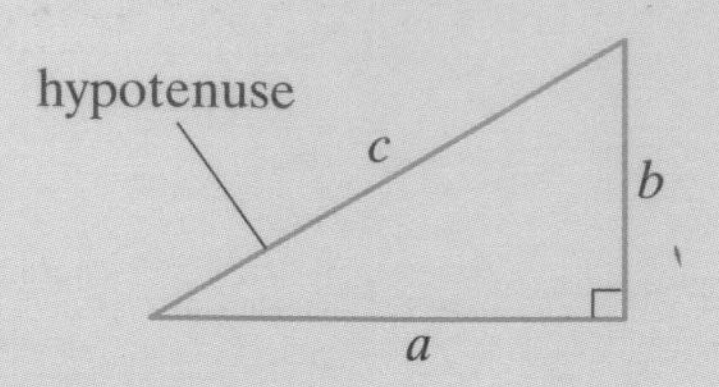

Use $a^2 + b^2 = c^2$ to calculate the hypotenuse
Use $a^2 = c^2 - b^2$ to calculate one of the shorter sides

16 Averages and spread

The word average is often used. Think about these statements:

Jenny is of average height.
A centre forward averages a goal a game.
Teenagers in Britain spend an average of £3 a week on hair care products.

Here the word average means that something is typical, or describes something that typically happens.

In mathematics an average is usually a single value which is used to represent a set of data. It is in some way typical of the data and gives an idea of what the data is like.

Three different averages are commonly used:

- the mean
- the mode
- the median

This unit shows you how each one is found and introduces some other ways of describing data.

On average a family size box contains 500 g of cereal. The weight of cereal is only allowed to vary within a very small range.

16.1 The mean

The students in the picture are talking about an average. This average is the **mean** – the score everyone would get if all the marks were shared equally.

■ **The mean of a set of data is the sum of the values divided by the number of values:**

$$\textbf{mean} = \frac{\textbf{sum of values}}{\textbf{number of values}}$$

Example 1

(a) Work out the mean of these 6 amounts of money in £:

13, 17, 19, 19, 23, 11.

(b) When a new amount is added the mean of the 7 amounts is £16. Calculate the new amount.

(a) Add the values to get £13 + 17 + 19 + 19 + 23 + 11 = £102

So the mean is $£\frac{102}{6} = £17$

(b) The mean of 7 amounts is £16
so the total of 7 amounts is £16 × 7 = £112
The seventh amount is £112 – 102 = £10

Because it is a calculated value the mean is quite likely to be a decimal even when the individual data values are whole numbers.

16.2 The mode

The **mode** is another type of average.

■ **The mode of a set of data is the value which occurs most often.**

Example 2

A small advertising company has a staff of nine. Their annual salaries are:

£16 000	£17 000	£17 000	£17 000	
£18 000	£19 000	£22 000	£64 000	£80 000

(a) What is the mean salary?
(b) What is the mode salary?
(c) Which of the mode and mean best describes the typical salary of someone working for the company?

(a) The mean is £270 000 ÷ 9 = £30 000.
(b) The mode is £17 000.
(c) The mean is £30 000. Nobody earns exactly this amount, and most people earn less. The mode is the best description of the typical salary because most people earn about this amount.

16.3 The median

There is a third average which you can use. It is called the **median**.

■ **The median is the middle value when the data is arranged in order of size.**

Example 3

A small engineering business has a work force of nine. Their annual wages are:

£14 000	£14 000	£16 000	£17 000	£18 000
£19 000	£20 000	£52 000	£100 000	

(a) Find the mean, mode and median wage.
(b) Which gives the best idea of the average wage?

(a) The mean is £270 000 ÷ 9 = £30 000.
The mode is £14 000. Most people (but only two) earn this.
The wages are already in order of size. To find the middle wage number these 1st to 9th. The middle one is the 5th, so the median is £18 000.

1st 2nd 3rd 4th 5th 6th 7th 8th 9th

middle value of nine

(b) Most people in the business earn less than the mean, more than the mode, and close to the median. So the median is the best statement of average wages for the business.

How to find the position of the median

An easy way to find the position of the median value in a set of data is to add 1 to the number of values, then divide the result by 2.

In Example 3 there are 9 wages:

$\frac{9+1}{2} = 5$ so the median wage is the 5th value when they are placed in order of size

Example 4

In a tournament a snooker player has breaks of 5, 23, 56, 102, 13, 26, 31, 67, 24 and 29. Work out the median value.

Put the numbers in order of size:

5, 13, 23, 24, 26, ↑ 29, 31, 56, 67, 102

There are 10 players so the middle value is the $(10 + 1) \div 2 = 5\frac{1}{2}$th.
There is no '$5\frac{1}{2}$th' value so you find the value half way between the 5th and 6th values. The 5th value is 26 and the 6th value is 29.

Half way between 26 and 29 is 27.5

So the median value is 27.5

Exercise 16A

1 Find the mean, mode and median of these quantities:
- **(a)** 3, 7, 4, 2, 3, 5, 3, 4, 9
- **(b)** 17 kg, 23 kg, 14 kg, 17 kg, 14 kg, 24 kg, 23 kg, 14 kg
- **(c)** 2.1 cm, 2.7 cm, 1.9 cm, 2.2 cm, 2.7 cm, 1.8 cm, 2.3 cm
- **(d)** £18.50, £19.50, £6.25, £7.75, £3.20

2 The total cost of 8 articles is £123.
A 9th article costs £93. What is the mean cost of the nine articles?

3 A Goal Shooter has scores of 14, 18, 10, 24, 32, 26, 32 in seven games.
How many must she score in the 8th game to bring her mean score up to 24?

4 The mean content of 11 boxes of matches is 46.
How many matches are there altogether?
The next box checked contains 49 matches.
What is the mean content when this box is included?

5 Four boys have a mean height of 160 cm. Seven girls have a mean height of 154 cm.
What is the mean height of the eleven young people?

6 The mean of 15, 17, x, 28 and 19 is 16.
What is the value of x?

7 What mark could Leo get in his next test to get the median stated:
- **(a)** marks so far: 1, 8, 5, 2 : median 5
- **(b)** marks so far: 8, 2, 4, 5, 3, 8, 4, 2, 9 : median 4

16.4 The range

Weather stations like this record the maximum and minimum temperature each day

Sometimes you need to compare two sets of data. One way of doing this is to see how spread out the values are.

■ **The range of a set of data is the difference between the highest and lowest values:**

range = highest value – lowest value

The way the range is calculated means that one extreme (very high or very low) value can have a big effect on the size of the range.

Example 5

At a quiz evening the individual scores of the 6 members in each team are:

Team A 22, 25, 29, 29, 33, 36
Team B 1, 15, 29, 29, 43, 57

Compare their scores.

For Team A and Team B the mode, median and mean are all 29. On their own the averages do not reveal any difference between the teams.

The range for Team A is 36 – 22 = 14.

The range for Team B is 57 – 1 = 56.

The ranges show that the Team A results are quite close together, but the Team B results are much more spread out.

Exercise 16B

1 In Form 4C the numbers staying for school dinner vary each day. The numbers for April were:

16 23 19 17 21 24 15 15 18 20
19 13 17 21 20 23 16 21 17 23

Find **(a)** the median number **(b)** the range of the numbers.

2 Five students were asked how long they spent on homework over the weekend. Their answers were:

10mins $1\frac{1}{2}$ hrs 2hrs 50mins $2\frac{1}{2}$ hrs

What is the range of the times?

3 Second-hand Ford Escorts in a car yard are priced at:

£8500 £7200 £6300 £7000 £7900 and £6250

What is the range of the prices?

4 A set of five numbers has a range of 12.
The numbers are all different and their median is 10.
Two of the values are 8 and 19.
What are the other three values? List all the possibilities.

5 Construct a list of seven numbers. The numbers must have a range of 4 and a mean of 6. The mode must also be 6.

16.5 The quartiles

The median divides a set of data arranged in ascending order of size into two halves. The data can also be divided into four quarters.

■ **When the data is arranged in ascending order of size: the lower quartile is the value one quarter of the way into the data the upper quartile is the value three quarters of the way into the data**

For example, here are the results of asking fifteen people how many cousins they have. The data is arranged in ascending order of size:

Number of cousins 0 2 4 5 7 8 10 12 12 12 13 14 14 15 16

- 5: the lower quartile is the 4th value
- 12: the median is the 8th value
- 14: the upper quartile 12th value

So the lower quartile is 5 cousins, the median is 12 cousins, and the upper quartile is 14 cousins.

For a set of 100 data values arranged in ascending order of size:

lower quartile $= \left(\dfrac{100+1}{4}\right)$th value

$= 25\frac{1}{4}$th value

median $= \left(\dfrac{100+1}{2}\right)$th value

$= 50\frac{1}{2}$th value

upper quartile $= \dfrac{3(100+1)}{4}$ th value

$= 75\frac{3}{4}$th value

For a set of n data values arranged in ascending order of size:

lower quartile $= \left(\dfrac{n+1}{4}\right)$th value

median $= \left(\dfrac{n+1}{2}\right)$th value

upper quartile $= \dfrac{3(n+1)}{4}$ th value

Example 6

The total prize money in £ paid in a school lottery for 11 consecutive months was:

63 96 67 99 87 68 61 85 91 102 89

Work out: (a) the lower quartile (b) the upper quartile

(a) Amounts in order of size:

61 63 67 68 85 87 89 91 96 99 102

The lower quartile is the $\left(\dfrac{11+1}{4}\right)$ = 3rd value, so it is £67.

(b) The upper quartile is the $\dfrac{3(11+1)}{4}$ = 9th value, so it is £96.

Example 7

Work out: (a) the median (b) the lower quartile (c) the upper quartile of these lengths in cm:

9 7 8 4 6 6 3 9 7

(a) First arrange the values in ascending order of size:

3 4 6 6 7 7 8 9 9

There are 9 values.

The median is the $\left(\frac{9+1}{2}\right) = 5$th value, so it is 7 cm.

(b) The lower quartile is the $\left(\frac{9+1}{4}\right) = 2\frac{1}{2}$th value.

You treat this as being the value halfway between the 2nd value (4 cm) and 3rd value (6 cm), so the lower quartile is 5 cm.

(c) The upper quartile is the $\frac{3(9+1)}{4} = 7\frac{1}{2}$th value.

You treat this as being the value halfway between the 7th value (8 cm) and the 8th value (9 cm), so the upper quartile is 8.5 cm.

Exercise 16C

Work out: **(a)** the median **(b)** the lower quartile **(c)** the upper quartile for the data in these questions:

1 The number of apples picked from 11 trees in one year:

155 152 173 150 160 130 155 160 152 155 158

2 The number of good work stars gained by 15 students in one month:

4 5 3 8 12 15 23 29 22 13 9 7 2 6 11

3 The number of letters delivered to each of the 19 houses in Wheatash Road:

1 0 6 0 1 5 2 3 1 2 2 2 0 1 0 5 7 4 2

4 The amounts in £ collected by 13 students from the sale of £1 raffle tickets:

231 205 194 240 217 203 229 235 227 232 186 216 225

16.6 The interquartile range

The quartiles are useful because together they can be used to give a better idea of the spread of a set of data than the range can.

■ **The interquartile range is the difference between the upper and lower quartiles:**

interquartile range = upper quartile – lower quartile

Unlike the range, the interquartile range is not distorted by extreme (very large or very small) data values. It also tells you whether the data values are spread evenly throughout the range, or concentrated in the middle half of the range. (There is more about this on page 433.)

Example 8

Work out the interquartile range for the data given in Example 7.

In Example 7 the lower quartile is 5 cm and the upper quartile is 8.5 cm.

interquartile range = upper quartile – lower quartile
= 8.5 – 5 = 3.5 cm

Exercise 16D

Work out the interquartile range for the data given in each question of Exercise 16C.

16.7 Averages from frequency distributions

Unit 8 (page 104) shows the convenience of collecting large amounts of data in a frequency distribution table.

This section shows you how to find the mean, mode and median where the information is given in a frequency table.

Example 9

A survey counted the number of eggs in seagulls' nests in June. These are the results:

Find
(a) the mode
(b) the median
(c) the mean number of eggs.

Number of eggs x	Frequency f
0	17
1	12
2	23
3	37
4	18
Total:	107

(a) The mode is the value which occurs most often. In a frequency table this is the item of data which has the highest frequency. For this data the mode is 3 eggs. There are more nests with 3 eggs than any other number of eggs.

(b) The median is the middle value of the data. There are 107 nests altogether. From the method for finding the position of the median (page 203) the middle nest would be value $(107 + 1) \div 2$ = value 54.

Nests 1 – 17 have 0 eggs
Nests 18 – 29 have 1 egg
Nests 30 – 52 have 2 eggs
Nests 53 – 89 have 3 eggs

so nest 54 is a 3 egg nest. The median is 3 eggs.

(c) The mean is the total number of eggs divided by the total number of nests (the total frequency):

Number of eggs x	Frequency f	Frequency × number of eggs $f \times x$
0	17	0
1	12	12
2	23	46
3	37	111
4	18	72
Totals:	107	241

The number of eggs in 2 egg nests is $23 \times 2 = 46$.

The total number of eggs is the sum of all the $f \times x$ values.

The mean = Total number of eggs ÷ Total Frequency

$= \frac{241}{107} = 2.25$ eggs

The mean of a frequency distribution

A short way of writing the mean uses the Greek letter sigma Σ to represent the sum of a set of values:

■ **For a frequency distribution:**

$$\textbf{mean} = \frac{\Sigma fx}{\Sigma f}$$

Σfx ← the sum of all the $(f \times x)$ values in the distribution

Σf ← the sum of the frequencies

Exercise 16E

1 Calculate the mean, mode and median number of cars per household using a table like this:

Cars per household x	Frequency f	$f \times x$
0	6	
1	20	
2	13	
3	4	
4	2	
Totals:		

The frequency tables in the next questions are written sideways in rows. You might find it easier to rewrite them in columns.

2

Dice score	1	2	3	4	5	6
Frequency	23	17	24	22	19	15

Dice score x	Frequency f	$f \times x$
1	23	23

Work out the mode, median and mean dice score.

3 A factory takes random samples of 102 items and tests them for faults.
(This is their method of maintaining standards. It is called Quality Control.)
Here are their results for last week.

Number of faults per sample	0	1	2	3	4	5
Number of samples	76	13	6	3	3	1

Work out the mode, median and mean number of faults per sample.

Hint: 'per sample' tells you that you need to divide the total number of faults by the total number of samples. So the 'number of samples' is the frequency.

4 Samir asked 24 people how many packets of crisps they ate last week. The results are shown in the table.

Number of packets of crisps	0	1	2	3	4	5	6	7	8
Number of people (frequency)	4	0	6	5	3	2	1	3	0

(a) Write down the mode number of packets.
(b) Work out the median number of packets.
(c) Calculate the mean number of packets, correct to 1 d.p.

5 Some teachers were asked how many National Lottery tickets they bought last week. The results are shown in the table.
(a) Which number of tickets is the mode?
(b) Work out the mean number of tickets.
(c) Find the median number of tickets. [L]

Number of tickets	Number of teachers
0	2
1	7
2	5
3	2
4	0
5	3
6	1

16.8 Spread from frequency distributions

This section shows you how to work out the interquartile range from information given in a frequency table.

Example 10

In a school stars are awarded for very good work. The number of stars awarded to each of 95 students is shown in this frequency table.

Number of stars	3	4	5	6	7	8	9	10	11	Total
Frequency	1	2	4	7	17	23	24	16	1	95

Work out: (a) the range (b) the interquartile range of the speeds

(a) Range = highest value – lowest value = 11 – 3 = 7 stars

(b) The lower quartile is the $\left(\frac{95 + 1}{4}\right) = 24$th value.

Adding up the frequencies in order:
$1 + 2 + 4 + 7 = 14$
and $1 + 2 + 4 + 7 + 17 = 31$

As the 24th value is between the 14th and 31st values, it is one of the 17 values recorded as 7 stars. So the lower quartile is 7 stars.

Using the same method, the upper quartile is the

$\frac{3(95 + 1)}{4} = 72$nd value.

Adding up the frequencies in order:
$1 + 2 + 4 + 7 + 17 + 23 = 54$
and $1 + 2 + 4 + 7 + 17 + 23 + 24 = 78$

As the 72nd value is between the 54th and 78th values, it is one of the 24 values recorded as 9 stars. So the upper quartile is 9 stars.

The interquartile range is:

upper quartile – lower quartile = 9 – 7 = 2 stars

Exercise 16F

Work out: **(a)** the range **(b)** the interquartile range for the data shown in the frequency table in each question.

1 The number of letters delivered to each house in a road of 39 houses:

Number of letters	0	1	2	3	4	5	6	7
Frequency (number of houses)	8	13	9	7	1	0	0	1

2 The marks gained by 63 pupils in an examination:

Mark	10	20	30	35	40	45	50	65
Frequency	0	4	8	13	16	10	7	5

3 The number of whole months over the age of 15 years of 29 pupils in a class:

Number of months over 15 years	0	1	2	3	4	5	6	7	8	9	10	11
Frequency	1	0	1	2	3	3	3	1	2	4	5	4

4 The amounts received from the sale of £1 concert tickets to 100 people:

Amount (£)	0	1	2	3	4	5	6	7	8
Frequency	5	17	25	19	13	12	5	2	2

In questions **5** to **8** use the data from Exercise 16E.

5 Use question **1** **6** Use question **2**

7 Use question **3** **8** Use question **4**

16.9 Averages from grouped data

Unit 8 (page 105) also shows you how to group large amounts of data in class intervals. What averages can be found from grouped data?

The manager of a small business checks the cost of telephone calls by looking at the number of units used per call. She summarizes the data from the telephone company in a frequency table, grouping it in class intervals.

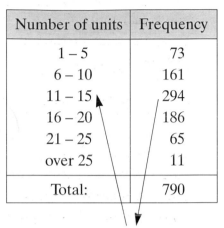

Number of units	Frequency
1 – 5	73
6 – 10	161
11 – 15	294
16 – 20	186
21 – 25	65
over 25	11
Total:	790

The $395\frac{1}{2}$th value is in this class interval.

The median: There were 790 phone calls so the position of the median data value is $(790 + 1) \div 2 = 395\frac{1}{2}$th value. It is in the class interval 11 – 15.
You cannot give an exact value for the median.

■ **You can state the class interval that contains the median.**

The modal class: The class interval 11 – 15 units per call has the highest frequency.

■ **The class interval with the highest frequency is the modal class.**

The modal class only makes sense as a measure of average if the class intervals are the same.

The mean: Each class interval contains calls using different numbers of units, so you have not got the exact data you need to calculate the mean. You can calculate an **estimate of the mean**. This is *not* a guess, but a calculation. Here is how to do it.

Assume each call in a class interval uses the number of units given by the middle value of the class interval the call is in.

Number of units used per call	Middle value x	Frequency f	$f \times x$
1 – 5	3	73	219
6 – 10	8	161	1288
11 – 15	13	294	3822
16 – 20	18	186	3348
21 – 25	23	65	1495
over 25	28	11	308
	Totals:	790	10 480

the middle value of the class interval 1 – 5 is 3

the middle value of class interval 6 – 10 is 8 and so on.

the 161 calls did not all use 8 units each. The errors made by overestimating approximately balance those made by underestimating.

A middle value must be chosen for calls over 25 units. This is a matter of judgement. Here 28 is used.

Now you can calculate an estimate of the mean in a similar way to that for ungrouped data (page 208):

$$\text{estimate of mean} = \frac{\text{sum of (middle values} \times \text{frequencies)}}{\text{sum of frequencies}} = \frac{\Sigma fx}{\Sigma f} = \frac{10\,480}{790} = 13.3$$

■ **With grouped data you can calculate an estimate of the mean using the middle value of each class interval.**

In the telephone calls example the data is discrete. You use exactly the same method to find an estimate of the mean of continuous data. The method works even if the class intervals are not the same size and the middle values are not whole numbers.

Exercise 16G

1 The students at Loovilla College decided to have a biscuit eating competition. A random sample of 25 students was taken. The table shows the numbers of students eating different numbers of biscuits in 4 minutes.

Number of biscuits eaten in 4 minutes	Middle value x	Frequency f	$f \times x$
1 – 5		2	
6 – 10		8	
11 – 15		7	
16 – 20		5	
21 – 25		2	
26 – 30		1	
	Totals:	25	

(a) Calculate an estimate of the mean number of biscuits eaten in 4 minutes.
(b) Write down the modal class interval.
(c) 250 students entered the competition. Estimate how many of them will eat more than 20 biscuits in the 4 minutes. [L]

2 In a five-leg darts match a record is kept of the scores for each throw of three darts.

Score	1 – 20	21 – 40	41 – 60	61 – 100	101 – 140	141 – 180
Frequency	3	17	25	56	8	3

(a) What is the modal class?
(b) Calculate an estimate of the mean score.

3 In 1992 a record was kept of the duration of marriages that ended in divorce.

Length of marriage in completed years	0 – 2	3 – 4	5 – 9	10 – 14	15 – 19	20 – 24	25 – 29	30–40
Frequency as a %	9	14	27	18	13	10	5	4

Work out an estimate for the mean length of a marriage that ended in a divorce.

4 The heights of students in a class are measured. These are the results.

Height interval (h cm)	Number of students
$150 \leqslant h < 155$	4
$155 \leqslant h < 160$	4
$160 \leqslant h < 165$	8
$165 \leqslant h < 170$	7
$170 \leqslant h < 175$	5
$175 \leqslant h < 180$	2

(a) What is the modal class?
(b) Work out an estimate of the mean height.

5 Ian looked at a passage from a book. He recorded the number of words in each sentence in a frequency table using class intervals of 1 – 5, 6 – 10, 11 – 15, etc.

Class interval	Frequency f	Middle value x	$f \times x$
1 – 5	16		48
6 – 10	28		
11 – 15	26	13	
16 – 20	14		
21 – 25	10		230
26 – 30	3		
31 – 35	1		
36 – 40	0		
41 – 45	2		86
Total:		Total:	

(a) Copy and complete the table.
(b) Write down the modal class interval.
(c) Write down the class interval in which the median lies.
(d) Work out an estimate for the mean number of words in a sentence. [L]

16.10 Cumulative frequency

Here is the data for the number of eggs in seagulls' nests from Example 9 on page 207. Notice that this data is discrete.

It is useful to find the cumulative frequency of this data to help calculate measures of average and spread.

- **The cumulative frequency is the running total of the frequency up to the end of each class interval.**

Number of eggs	Frequency
0	17
1	12
2	23
3	37
4	18

Number of eggs	Cumulative frequency
0	17
up to and including 1	29
up to and including 2	52
up to and including 3	89
up to and including 4	107

This column is a running total of the frequency so far.

There are 52 nests (17 + 12 + 23) altogether with 2 eggs or less in them.

There are 107 nests altogether so the position of the median is the (1+ 107) ÷ 2 = 54th nest.

It is easy to see from the **cumulative frequency** column that the 54th nest is a 3 egg nest. So the median number of eggs is 3.

You can also find the cumulative frequency for grouped data. Here are the students' heights from question 4 on page 213. Notice that this data is both grouped and continuous:

Height interval (h cm)	Frequency
$150 \leqslant h < 155$	4
$155 \leqslant h < 160$	4
$160 \leqslant h < 165$	8
$165 \leqslant h < 170$	7
$170 \leqslant h < 175$	5
$175 \leqslant h < 180$	2

Height interval (h cm)	Cumulative frequency
$150 \leqslant h < 155$	4
$150 \leqslant h < 160$	8
$150 \leqslant h < 165$	16
$150 \leqslant h < 170$	23
$150 \leqslant h < 175$	28
$150 \leqslant h < 180$	30

There are 8 students with heights in the range:

$150 \leqslant h < 160$

There are 30 students altogether so the position of the median is the $(30 + 1) \div 2 = 15\frac{1}{2}$th.

There is no $15\frac{1}{2}$th student but from the cumulative frequency column you can see that the median must be in the class interval $160 \leqslant h < 165$. This is the class interval in which the median lies.

Exercise 16H

1 **(a)** Copy and complete the cumulative frequency table for the number of children in each family in a small village:

Number of children	Frequency
0	2
1	7
2	6
3	4
4	2
5	1

Number of children	Cumulative frequency
0	2
up to and including 1	9
up to and including 2	
up to and including 3	
up to and including 4	
up to and including 5	

(b) Work out the median number of children per family.

2 **(a)** Copy and complete the cumulative frequency table for this frequency distribution:

Examination mark	Frequency
0 – 10	9
11 – 20	17
21 – 30	34
31 – 40	7
41 – 50	2

Examination mark	Cumulative frequency
up to and including 10	9
up to and including 20	
up to and including 30	
up to and including 40	
up to and including 50	

(b) Find the class interval in which the median lies.

3 Copy and complete the cumulative frequency table for this frequency distribution:

Weight (w kg)	Frequency
$100 \leqslant w < 120$	21
$120 \leqslant w < 140$	42
$140 \leqslant w < 160$	64
$160 \leqslant w < 180$	21
$180 \leqslant w < 200$	2

Weight (w kg)	Cumulative frequency
$100 \leqslant w < 120$	
$100 \leqslant w < 140$	
$100 \leqslant w < 160$	
$100 \leqslant w < 180$	
$100 \leqslant w < 200$	

16.11 Cumulative frequency graphs

You can display cumulative frequency data in a **cumulative frequency graph**. This allows you to estimate some useful statistical measures.

Example 11

Draw a cumulative frequency graph for this test data. (Notice that this is **discrete data**.)

To draw the graph:

- choose a suitable scale for each axis
- always use the vertical axis for the cumulative frequency
- plot the points (Mark, Cumulative frequency):
  (0, 1), (1, 5), (2, 11) and so on . . .
- draw a smooth curve through the points.

Mark	Frequency
0	1
1	4
2	6
3	19
4	27
5	31
6	22
7	16
8	13
9	2
10	1

Mark	Cumulative frequency
0	1
up to and including 1	5
up to and including 2	11
up to and including 3	30
up to and including 4	57
up to and including 5	88
up to and including 6	110
up to and including 7	126
up to and including 8	139
up to and including 9	141
up to and including 10	142

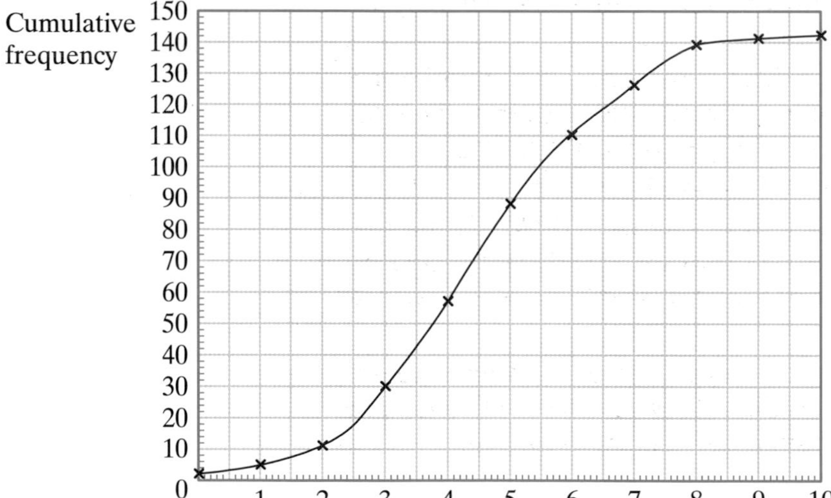

The resulting curve is nearly always a gentle S shape. Another name for a cumulative frequency graph is an **ogive**.

Grouped and continuous data

You can draw cumulative frequency graphs for grouped and continuous data in a similar way.

Here is a cumulative frequency table for the marks obtained in a test by 93 pupils:

Mark	1–10	1–20	1–30	1–40	1–50	1–60
Cumulative frequency	7	23	51	73	91	93

The marks are **discrete data**, but they have been recorded in **groups**.

To draw the cumulative frequency graph you would plot the points (10, 7), (20, 23), (30, 51), and so on.

Here is a cumulative frequency table for data on the heights of 360 plants. The heights were measured correct to the nearest centimetre, and recorded using the class intervals 1 to 3, 4 to 6, 7 to 9, and so on:

Height of plant (cm)	1 to 3	1 to 6	1 to 9	1 to 12	1 to 15	1 to 18	1 to 21	1 to 24	1 to 27
Cumulative frequency	3	24	84	143	205	278	330	357	360

This is **continuous data**, although there are gaps between the class intervals as the heights have been corrected to the nearest centimetre. However, there could be a plant with an actual height between 3 cm and 4 cm for example.

The true class intervals are 0.5 to 3.5, 3.5 to 6.5, 6.5 to 9.5 and so on. This is because the least value that a measurement given as 1 cm to the nearest cm could be is 0.5 cm, and the greatest value that a measurement given as 3 cm to the nearest cm could be is 3.5 cm.

To draw the cumulative frequency graph you should plot the points (3.5, 3), (6.5, 24), (9.5, 84), and so on. However, plotting the points (3, 3), (6, 24), (9, 84), and so on consistently would be accepted in an examination.

For the continuous data in question 3 of Exercise 16H there are *no gaps between the class intervals*. So the values 120, 140, 160 and so on should be used for the first coordinate of each point on the cumulative frequency graph.

Exercise 16I

You need graph paper for this exercise.

1 Draw a cumulative frequency graph using the data in question **1** of Exercise 16H.

2 **(a)** Make a cumulative frequency table for this test data:

Mark	0	1	2	3	4	5	6	7	8	9	10
Frequency	2	5	9	13	21	24	33	27	18	4	1

(b) Draw a cumulative frequency graph for the data.

In questions **3** and **4** use the data from Exercise **16H** to draw a cumulative frequency graph.

3 Use question **2** **4** Use question **3**

5 This frequency table groups the heights of some students measured to the nearest centimetre:

(a) Make a cumulative frequency table for this data.

(b) Draw a cumulative frequency graph. (Remember to plot the points at (145.5, 7), (150.5, 19) and so on.)

Height (cm)	Frequency
141–145	7
146–150	12
151–155	15
156–160	36
161–165	45
166–170	28
171–175	13
176–180	7

16.12 Using cumulative frequency graphs

A cumulative frequency graph can be used to estimate some useful statistical measures.

Estimating the median

A set of data arranged in class intervals is called a **distribution**.

■ **The median is the middle value of the distribution.**

To estimate the median from a cumulative frequency graph:

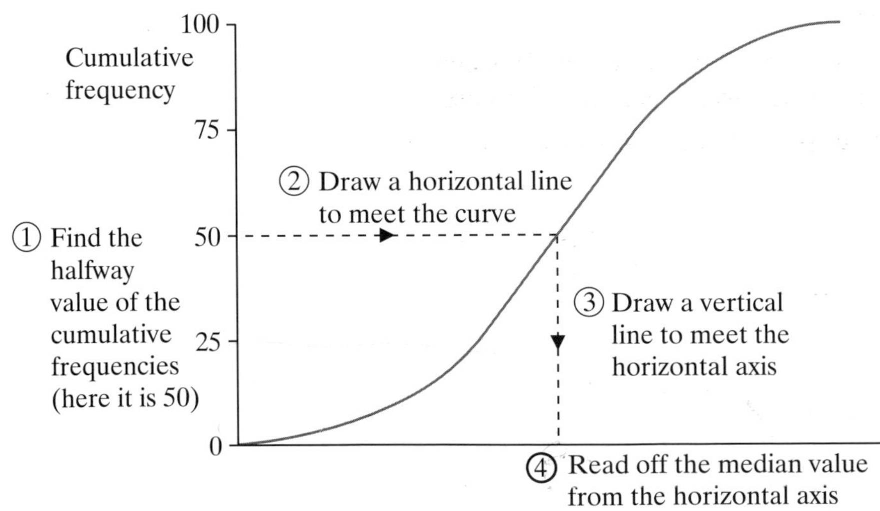
100
Cumulative frequency
75
② Draw a horizontal line to meet the curve
① Find the halfway value of the cumulative frequencies (here it is 50)
50
③ Draw a vertical line to meet the horizontal axis
25
0
④ Read off the median value from the horizontal axis

Strictly speaking the middle value of this distribution is the $\left(\frac{100+1}{2}\right) = 50\frac{1}{2}$th valuc

For an estimate from this graph it is accurate enough to read off the value when the cumulative frequency is 50.

For simplicity the cumulative frequency here is 100. Follow the same procedure for any cumulative frequency.

Page 205 shows you how to locate the positions of the median and quartiles when the cumulative frequency is not 100.

Estimating the quartiles

- **The lower quartile is the value one quarter of the way into the distribution.**

To estimate the lower quartile from a cumulative frequency graph:

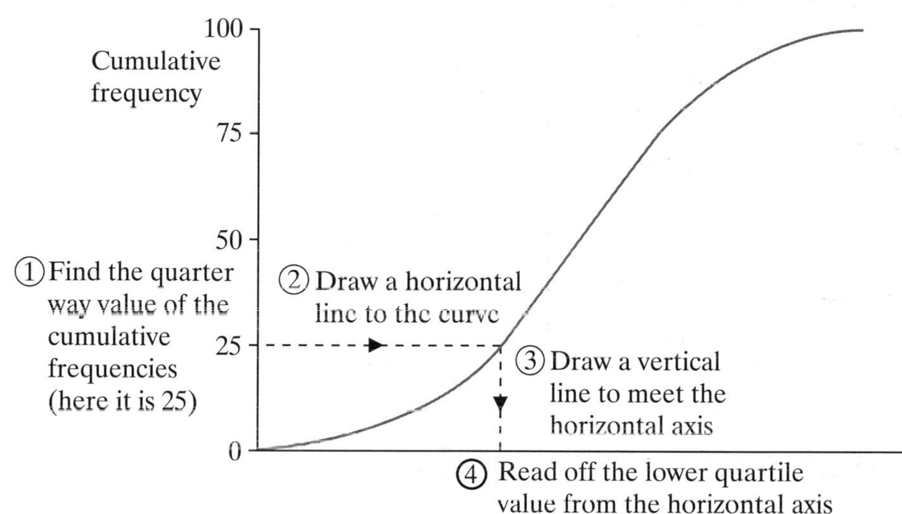
100
Cumulative frequency
75
50
25
0
① Find the quarter way value of the cumulative frequencies (here it is 25)
② Draw a horizontal line to the curve
③ Draw a vertical line to meet the horizontal axis
④ Read off the lower quartile value from the horizontal axis

- **The upper quartile is the value three quarters of the way into the distribution.**

To estimate the upper quartile use the same method as for the lower quartile but start at the three quarter way value of the cumulative frequencies. Here it would be the $75\frac{3}{4}$th value, but you could use the 75th value for an estimate.

The interquartile range

To estimate the interquartile range from a cumulative frequency diagram first estimate the upper and lower quartiles, then use:

interquartile range = upper quartile – lower quartile

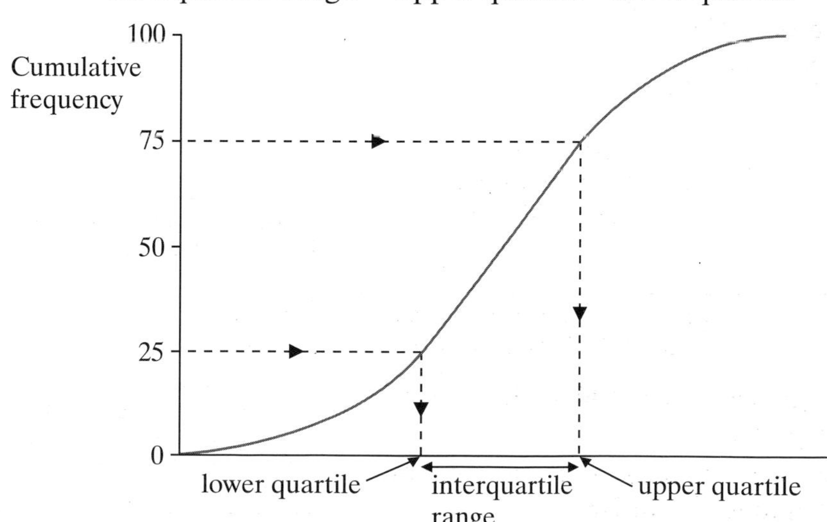
100
Cumulative frequency
75
50
25
0
lower quartile
interquartile range
upper quartile

Worked examination question

The grouped frequency table shows the distribution of the amounts of daily sunshine, in hours, in Mathstown in July 1994.

Amount (s) of daily sunshine in hours	Number of days in this class interval
$0 \le s < 2$	1
$2 \le s < 4$	2
$4 \le s < 6$	3
$6 \le s < 8$	7
$8 \le s < 10$	10
$10 \le s < 12$	6
$12 \le s < 14$	2

(a) Copy the cumulative frequency table below. Use the data on the right to complete your table.

Amount (s) of daily sunshine in hours	Cumulative frequency
$0 \le s < 2$	1
$0 \le s < 4$	3
$0 \le s < 6$	
$0 \le s < 8$	
$0 \le s < 10$	
$0 \le s < 12$	
$0 \le s < 14$	

Draw a grid using 1 cm for 1 hour to represent the amounts of daily sunshine (hours) on the horizontal axis and 2 cm for 5 on the vertical cumulative frequency axis.

(b) On your grid, construct the cumulative frequency graph for your table.

(c) Use your cumulative frequency graph to find an estimate for the median amount of daily sunshine, in hours, in July 1994. Make your method clear. [L]

(a) To find the cumulative frequencies add all the previous frequencies.

$1 + 2 = 3$
$1 + 2 + 3 = 6$
$1 + 2 + 3 + 7 = 13$
$1 + 2 + 3 + 7 + 10 = 23$
$1 + 2 + 3 + 7 + 10 + 6 = 29$
$1 + 2 + 3 + 7 + 10 + 6 + 2 = 31$

Amount (s) of daily sunshine in hours	Cumulative frequency
$0 \le s < 2$	1
$0 \le s < 4$	3
$0 \le s < 6$	6
$0 \le s < 8$	13
$0 \le s < 10$	23
$0 \le s < 12$	29
$0 \le s < 14$	31

(b) The points are plotted with crosses and joined with a smooth curve.

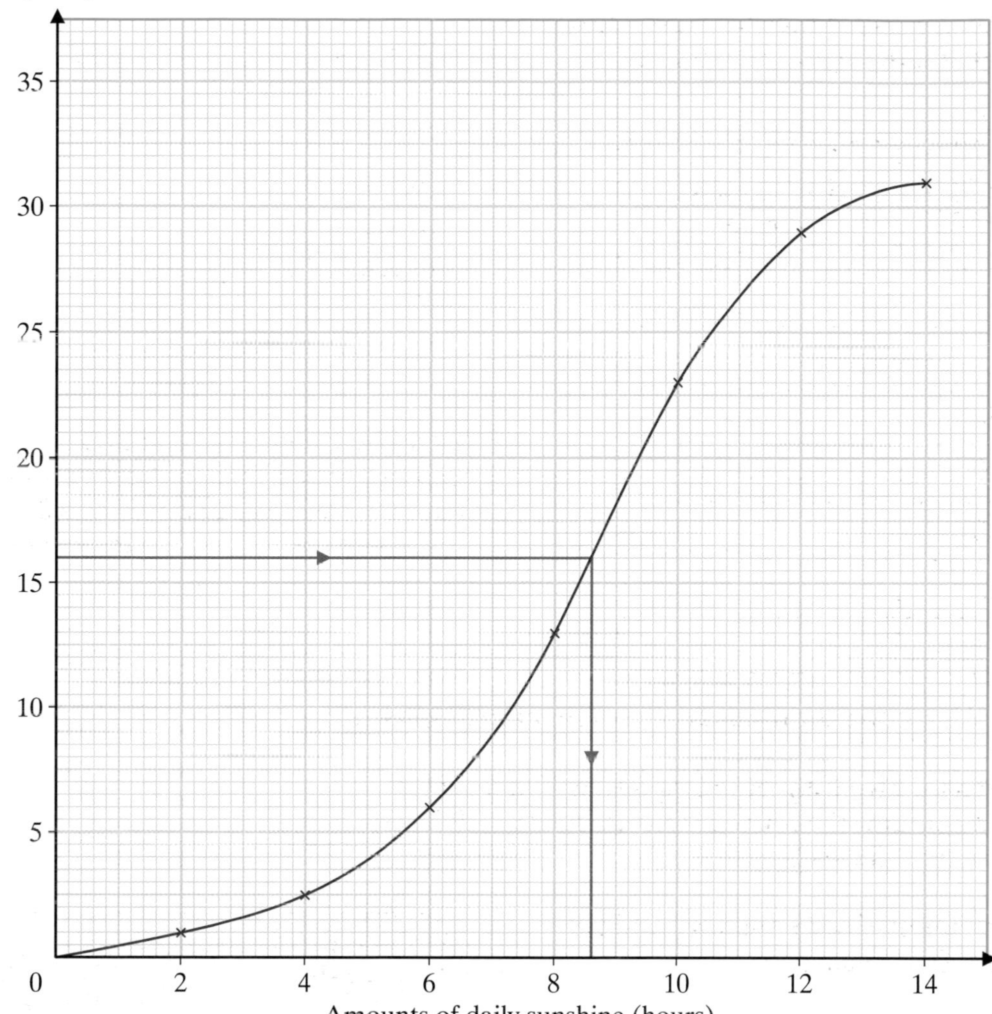

(c) The median is the $\left(\frac{n+1}{2}\right)$th $= \left(\frac{31+1}{2}\right)$th $=$ 16th value.

Draw a line horizontally where the cumulative frequency is 16.
From the point where this line meets the curve draw a line vertically.
The line meets the horizontal axis at 8.6.
So an estimate for the median amount of daily sunshine is 8.6 hours.

> If you read off the time when the cumulative frequency is
>
> $\frac{31}{2}$ $(= 15\frac{1}{2})$
>
> your answer would be accepted in an exam.

Example 12

Use your graph from the worked examination question to find
(a) an estimate for the interquartile range
(b) the number of days that have more than 11 hours of sunshine.

(a) The lower quartile is the

$$\left(\frac{n+1}{4}\right)\text{th} = \left(\frac{31+1}{4}\right)\text{th} = 8\text{th value}$$

Draw a horizontal line where the cumulative frequency is 8.
This line meets the curve where the amount of sunshine is 6.7 hours.

The upper quartile is the $\frac{3(31+1)}{4}$th value = 24th value.
Use the same method to find that the upper quartile is 10.2 hours.
The interquartile range = 10.2 – 6.7 hours
= 3.5 hours

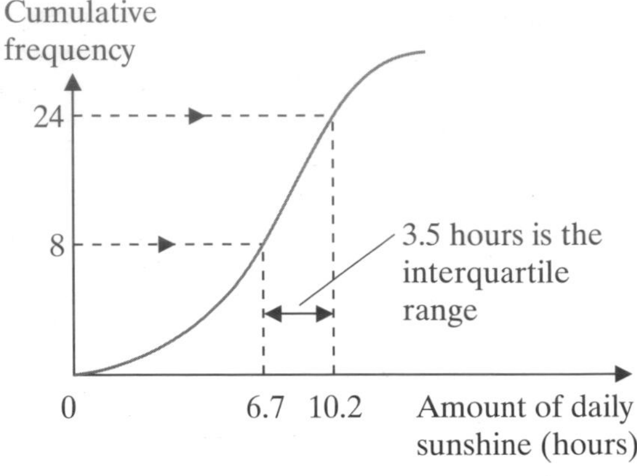

(b) Draw a vertical line where the amount of sunshine is 11 hours.
This line meets the curve where the cumulative frequency is 26.5
The days when the amount of sunshine is **more** than 11 hours are the 27th, 28th, 29th, 30th and 31st.
So 5 days have more than 11 hours of sunshine.

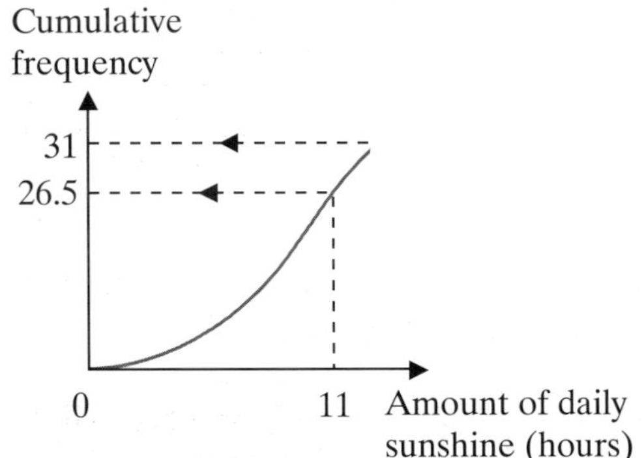

Exercise 16J

You will need 2 mm squared paper.

1 The speeds in miles per hour (mph) of 200 cars travelling on the A320 road were measured.
The results are in the table.

(a) Draw a cumulative frequency graph to show these figures. (Use a scale of 1 cm for 5 mph and 1 cm for 10 cars.)

(b) Use your graph to find an estimate for
(i) the median speed (in mph)
(ii) the interquartile range (in mph).
(iii) the percentage of cars travelling at less than 48 mph.

[L]

Speed (mph)	Cumulative frequency
not exceeding 20	1
not exceeding 25	5
not exceeding 30	14
not exceeding 35	28
not exceeding 40	66
not exceeding 45	113
not exceeding 50	164
not exceeding 55	196
not exceeding 60	200
Total	200

2 The cumulative frequency graph gives information on house prices in 1992. The cumulative frequency is given as a percentage of all houses in England.

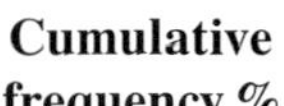

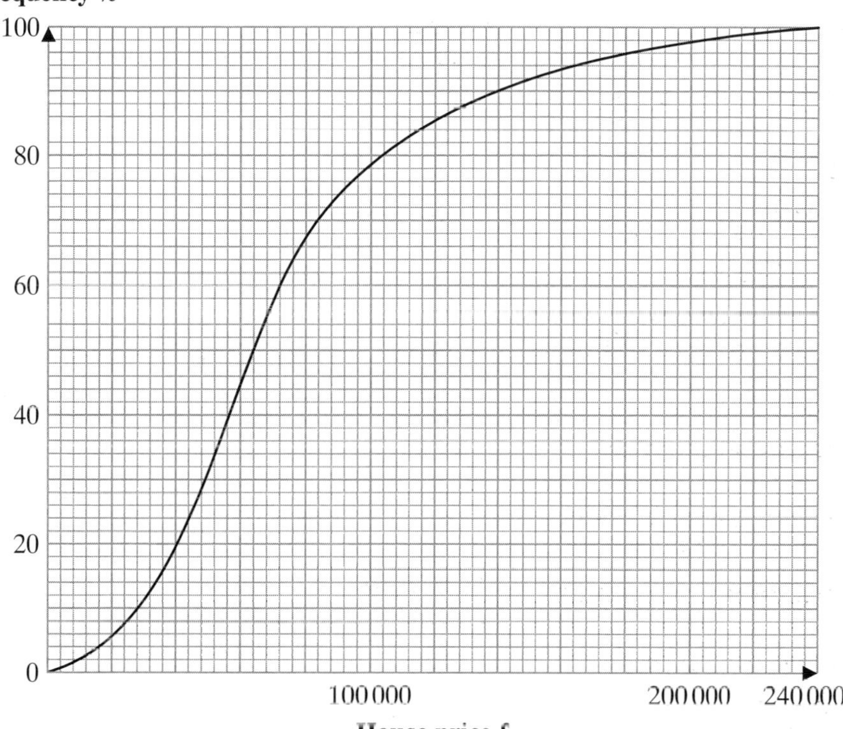

This grouped frequency table gives the percentage distribution of house prices (p) in England in 1993.

House prices (p) in pounds 1993	Percentage of houses in this class interval
$0 \leqslant p < 40\,000$	26
$40\,000 \leqslant p < 52\,000$	19
$52\,000 \leqslant p < 68\,000$	22
$68\,000 \leqslant p < 88\,000$	15
$88\,000 \leqslant p < 120\,000$	9
$120\,000 \leqslant p < 160\,000$	5
$160\,000 \leqslant p < 220\,000$	4

House prices (p) in pounds 1993	Cumulative frequency (%)
$0 \leqslant p < 40\,000$	
$0 \leqslant p < 52\,000$	
$0 \leqslant p < 68\,000$	
$0 \leqslant p < 88\,000$	
$0 \leqslant p < 120\,000$	
$0 \leqslant p < 160\,000$	
$0 \leqslant p < 220\,000$	

(a) Copy and complete the cumulative frequency table.

(b) Copy the cumulative frequency graph for 1992 and on it construct the cumulative frequency graph for your table.

(c) In 1992 the price of a house was £100 000. Use both cumulative frequency graphs to estimate the price of this house in 1993.
Make your method clear. [L]

3 The marks in a National Test are classified for each Local Education Authority. These are the results for a small LEA.

Marks	0–10	11–20	21–30	31–40	41–50	51–60	61–70	71–80	81–90	91–100
Number of students	54	118	286	580	714	830	324	74	18	2

(a) Draw and complete a suitable table to obtain the cumulative frequencies.
(b) Construct the cumulative frequency graph.
(c) From your graph find the median and the interquartile range.
(d) If the pass mark is set at 45, estimate how many students pass.
(e) If 70% of the students pass, estimate what the pass mark is.

Exercise 16K Mixed questions

You will need 2 mm squared paper.

1 Eleanor conducted a survey in which she recorded the shoe sizes of 40 girls. Her results are shown in the frequency table.

Shoe size	3	$3\frac{1}{2}$	4	$4\frac{1}{2}$	5	$5\frac{1}{2}$	6	$6\frac{1}{2}$	7	$7\frac{1}{2}$	8
Number of girls	1	2	2	5	5	6	7	5	4	1	2

(a) Write down the mode shoe size.
(b) Work out the median shoe size.
(c) Work out the range of the shoe sizes.
(d) Calculate the mean shoe size, giving your answer correct to 1 d.p.

2 Cole's sells furniture and will deliver up to a distance of 20 miles. The diagram shows the delivery charges made by Cole's. The table shows the information in the diagram and also the number of deliveries made in the first week of May 1994.

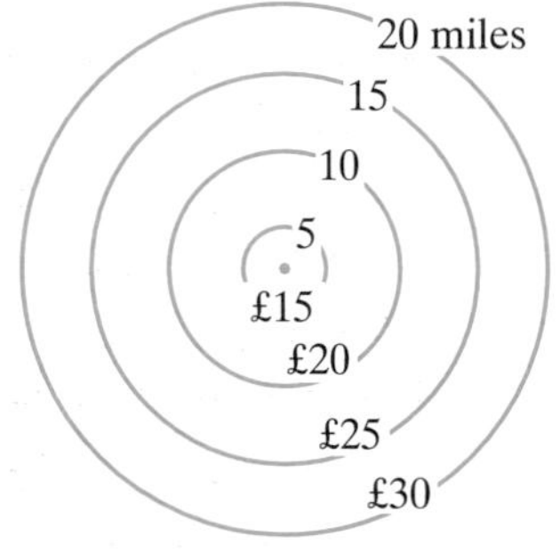

Distance (d) from Cole's in miles	Delivery charge in pounds	Number of deliveries			
$0 < d \leq 5$	15	27			
$5 < d \leq 10$	20	11			
$10 < d \leq 15$	25	8			
$15 < d \leq 20$	30	4			

(a) Copy the table and calculate the mean charge per delivery for these deliveries.
(b) Calculate an estimate for the mean distance of the customers' homes from Cole's. [L]

3 Records are kept each day for a year of the maximum temperature on the sea front of a holiday resort. Temperatures are measured to the nearest degree Celsius.

(a) Draw up a cumulative frequency table and construct the cumulative frequency graph.

(b) Use your graph to obtain estimates of the median and the interquartile range.

(c) Estimate the percentage of days when the temperature rises to 23°C or higher.

Temperature	Number of days
–5°C to 0°C	3
1°C to 5°C	22
6°C to 10°C	61
11°C to 13°C	59
14°C to 16°C	63
17°C to 20°C	74
21°C to 25°C	53
26°C to 30°C	27
31°C and over	3

Summary of key points

1 The mean of a set of data is the sum of the values divided by the number of values:

$$\text{mean} = \frac{\text{sum of values}}{\text{number of values}}$$

2 The mode of a set of data is the value which occurs most often.

3 When the data is arranged in ascending order of size:

- the median is the middle value
- the lower quartile is the value one quarter of the way into the data
- the upper quartile is the value three quarters of the way into the data

4 The range of a set of data is the difference between the highest and lowest values:

range = highest value – lowest value

5 The interquartile range is the difference between the upper and lower quartiles.

Interquartile range = upper quartile – lower quartile.

6 For a frequency distribution the mean can be written as:

$$\text{mean} = \frac{\Sigma fx}{\Sigma f}$$

Σfx ← the sum of all the $(f \times x)$ values in the distribution

Σf ← the sum of all the frequencies

7 For grouped data:

- You can state the class interval that contains the median.
- The class interval with the highest frequency is called the modal class.
- You can calculate an estimate of the mean using the middle value of each class interval.

8 The cumulative frequency is the running total of the frequency up to the end of each class interval.

17 The tangent ratio

This unit shows you how to calculate the lengths of sides and the sizes of angles in right angled triangles.

Tangents are part of the mathematical topic called trigonometry which always appears in questions in GCSE exams so it is very important that you understand it.

17.1 Discovering the tangent ratio

In the right angled triangle RST the angle RST (or angle S) is labelled θ. The Greek letter θ (pronounced theta) is often used in maths to label an angle.

The side TR is opposite θ so it is called the **opposite** side to θ.

T
opposite the angle θ
S R
adjacent (next to) the angle θ

The side RS is next to θ and the right angle. Another word for 'next to' is 'adjacent', so the side RS is called the side **adjacent** to θ.

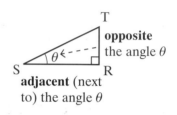

Here are two more triangles. Both have an angle of 35°.

In triangle ABC the ratio:

$$\frac{\text{length of opposite side}}{\text{length of adjacent side}} = \frac{1.4}{2} = 0.7$$

C
1.4 cm
35°
A 2 cm B

In triangle AXY the ratio:

$$\frac{\text{length of opposite side}}{\text{length of adjacent side}} = \frac{2.1}{3} = 0.7$$

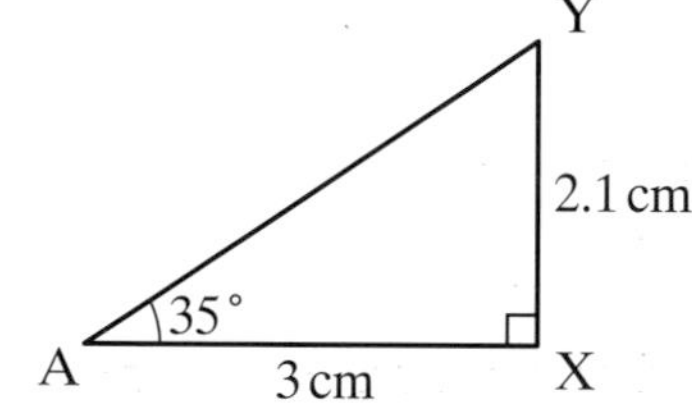

Is this ratio always the same for triangles with a 35° angle? To find out, try the next exercise.

Exercise 17A

You need a protractor and ruler.

Construct accurately triangle AEF with angle A = 35° and a right angle 90° at E. The sides can be any length.

(a) Measure the length of EF
(b) Measure the length of AE
(c) For the angle A (which is 35°) work out the value of

$$\frac{\text{length of opposite side}}{\text{length of adjacent side}}$$

(d) Write down anything you notice about your result.

The tangent ratio

For all right angled triangles with an angle of 35°, whatever the lengths of the sides, the ratio:

$$\frac{\text{length of opposite side to the angle of } 35°}{\text{length of adjacent side to the angle of } 35°}$$

is always the same. It is called the **tangent ratio**.

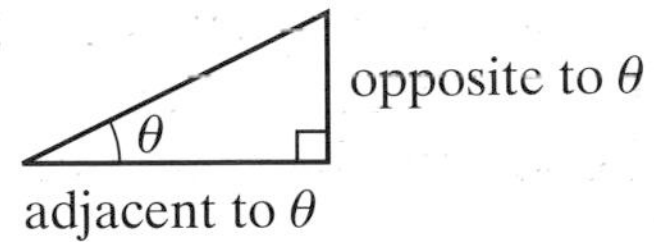

■ **The tangent ratio for any right angled triangle is:**

$$\textbf{tangent of } \theta = \frac{\textbf{opposite side to } \theta}{\textbf{adjacent side to } \theta}$$

or for short: $$\tan \theta = \frac{\text{opp}}{\text{adj}}$$

The tangent of 35° is approximately 0.7. This is usually written tan 35° = 0.7

17.2 The tangent ratio on a calculator

Each angle has a particular value for its tangent. These values have been worked out and stored in the memory of your calculator.

Use your calculator to check the result for tan 35°.

First make sure your calculator is in **degree mode**. (**DEG** will show at the top of your calculator display.)

Press these keys on your calculator:

You should see the value:

0.7002075 ...

on the calculator display. This is a more accurate result than you can get by drawing and measuring.

On a graphical calculator find tan 35° by pressing:

Example 1

Use a calculator to find tan 26.2°

Make sure your calculator is in degree mode. Pressing these keys:

gives 0.492061 ...

You will usually need to work with four figures only so use tan 26.2° = 0.4920

If you are going to use the result in a further calculation you could use 0.492061... as 0.4921 (correct to 4 s.f.). Using 0.4920 or 0.4921 usually gives the same final answer (correct to 3 s.f.). In an exam you would get full marks whichever value you used.

Exercise 17B

In this exercise write down the first four figures from your calculator display.

Use your calculator to find these tangents:

1	tan 2°	**2**	tan 8°	**3**	tan 13°
4	tan 24°	**5**	tan 36.5°	**6**	tan 45°
7	tan 57.3°	**8**	tan 69.1°	**9**	tan 75.8°
10	tan 84.6°	**11**	tan 87.2°	**12**	tan 89.9°

The inverse tangent function $\tan^{-1}$

Sometimes you may know the tangent of an angle but not the angle itself.

You can find the size of the angle by using the **inverse tangent function, $\tan^{-1}$**. This is like using an inverse function machine.

$\theta = 24.82° \rightarrow$ tan $\rightarrow 0.4625$

$24.82° \leftarrow$ $\tan^{-1}$ $\leftarrow \tan\theta = 0.4625$

$\tan^{-1} y$ is sometimes written arctan y. It is short for the inverse of the tangent function. $\tan^{-1} y$ means the angle whose tangent is y.

$\tan^{-1} y$ does NOT mean the reciprocal of tan y

$\left(\text{or } \frac{1}{\tan y}\right)$.

That would be written $(\tan y)^{-1}$.

Example 2

$\tan\theta = 0.85$

Work out the value of θ, writing down the first four figures from your calculator display.

You know the value of $\tan\theta$ so you need to use the inverse tan function, $\tan^{-1}$, to find θ.

Make sure your calculator is in degree mode. Press these keys:

The calculator display shows 40.364537 ...

so $\theta = 40.36°$

You may need different keystrokes to get the $\tan^{-1}$ function on your calculator, for example:

Check with your teacher if you are not sure.

Exercise 17C

In this exercise write down the first four figures from your calculator display.

Use your calculator to work out the values of θ if:

1	$\tan\theta = 0.32$	**2**	$\tan\theta = 0.63$	**3**	$\tan\theta = 0.9$
4	$\tan\theta = 1.1$	**5**	$\tan\theta = 1.8$	**6**	$\tan\theta = 5.34$

17.3 Using the tangent ratio to find an angle

When you know the lengths of the two shorter sides of a right angled triangle you can use the tangent ratio to find either of the acute angles.

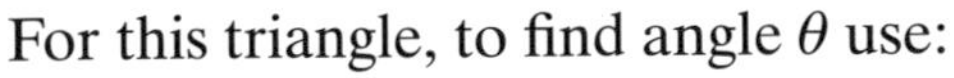
For this triangle, to find angle θ use:

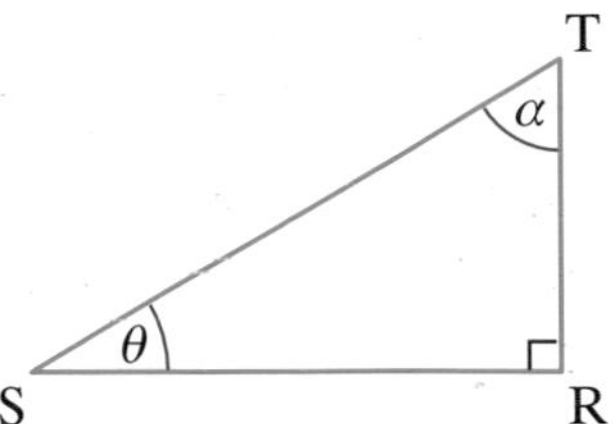

$$\tan\theta = \frac{\text{opposite side to }\theta}{\text{adjacent side to }\theta} = \frac{\text{TR}}{\text{SR}}$$

To find angle α use:

$$\tan\alpha = \frac{\text{opposite side to }\alpha}{\text{adjacent side to }\alpha} = \frac{\text{SR}}{\text{TR}}$$

Notice that:

$$\tan\theta = \frac{\text{TR}}{\text{SR}} \quad \text{and} \quad \tan\alpha = \frac{\text{SR}}{\text{TR}}$$

$$\text{so } \tan\theta = \frac{1}{\tan\alpha} \quad \text{and} \quad \tan\alpha = \frac{1}{\tan\theta}$$

Example 3

Calculate angle marked θ in the diagram. Give your answer correct to 1 decimal place.

(Hint: the side 5.4 cm is opposite to angle θ and the side 7.9 cm is adjacent to angle θ so you can use the tan ratio.)

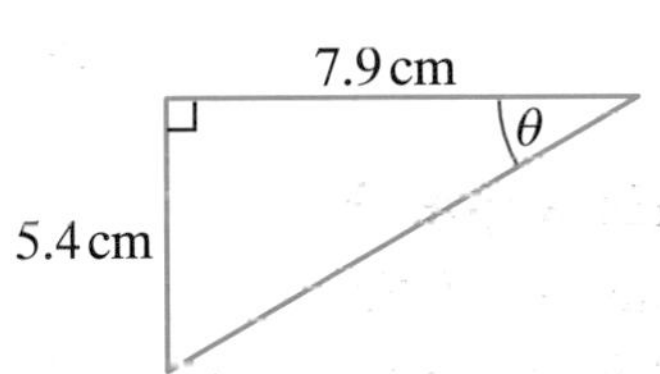

$$\tan\theta = \frac{\text{opp}}{\text{adj}}$$

$$= \frac{5.4}{7.9}$$

$$= 0.6835$$

To find θ use the inverse tan function, $\tan^{-1}$:

angle $\theta = 34.35° = 34.4°$ (to 1 d.p.)

Worked examination question

The diagram shows three places, which are on the same horizontal plane.

Windy Cragg is 5.2 km due north of Hill Top.
Walton Scree is 6.8 km due east of Hill Top.

(a) Calculate the distance from Walton Scree to Windy Cragg. Give your answer correct to 1 decimal place.

(b) Calculate the size of the angle marked θ in the diagram. Give your answer correct to 1 d.p.

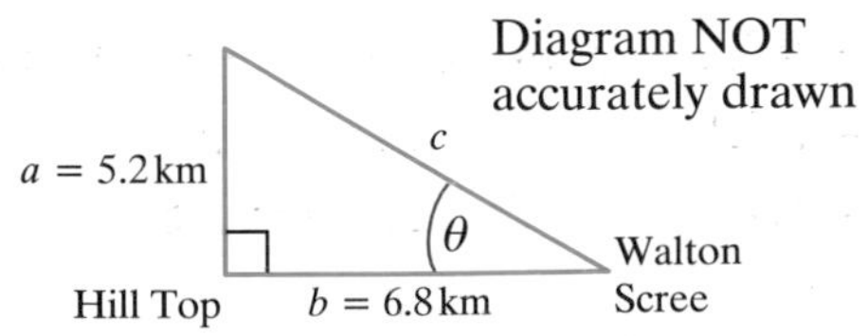

[L]

(a) To find the distance from Walton Scree to Windy Cragg use Pythagoras' theorem (page 193):

$$c^2 = a^2 + b^2$$
$$= 5.2^2 + 6.8^2$$
$$= 27.04 + 46.24$$
$$c^2 = 73.28$$

so $c = \sqrt{73.28} = 8.560$

Distance = 8.6 km (to 1 d.p.)

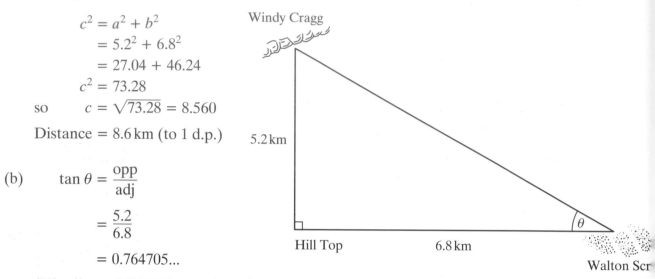

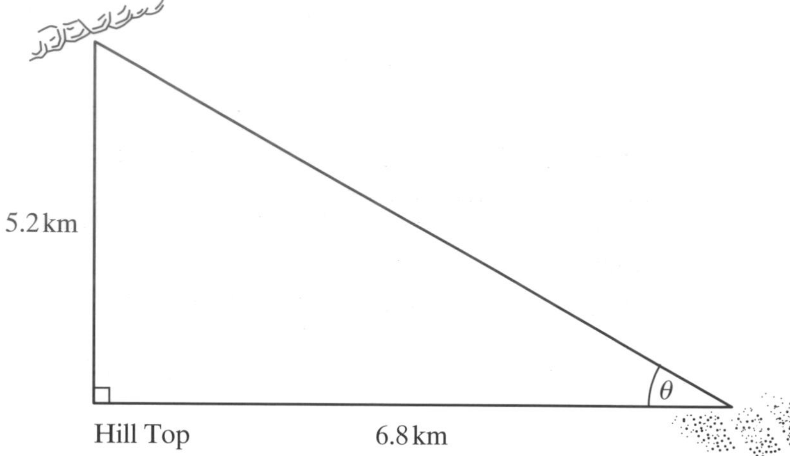

(b) $\tan\theta = \dfrac{\text{opp}}{\text{adj}}$

$$= \frac{5.2}{6.8}$$

$$= 0.764705...$$

(Hint: leave 0.764705... on the calculator display.)

$\theta = 37.40° = 37.4°$ (to 1 d.p.)

The question states 'calculate' so a calculation method must be used. Do not use a scale drawing.

Exercise 17D

In this exercise give your answers correct to 1 d.p.

1 Calculate the lettered angles in these triangles:

(a)

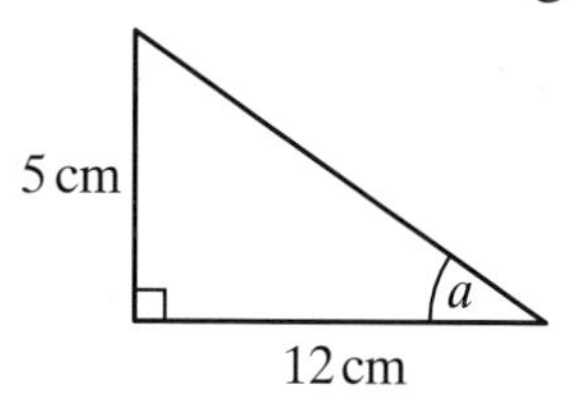

(b)

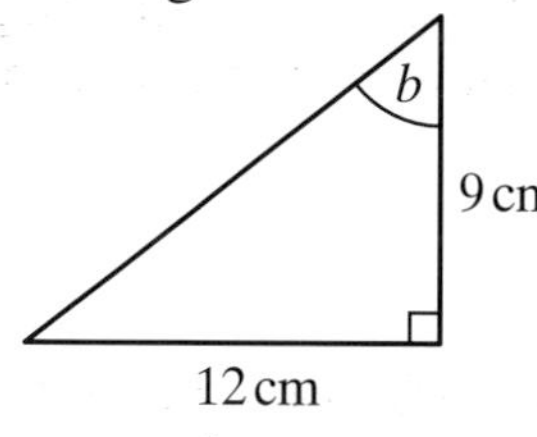

(c)

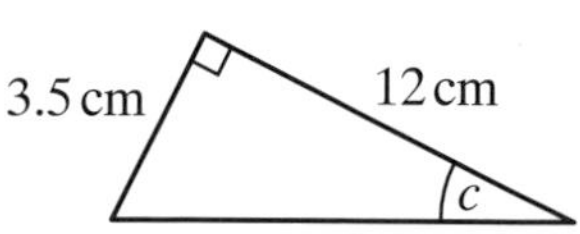

(d)

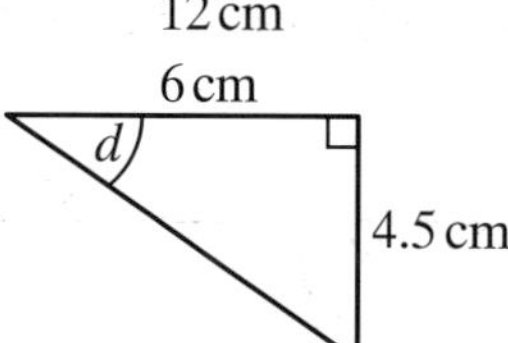

2 Calculate the named angles in these triangles:

(a) Find angle Y

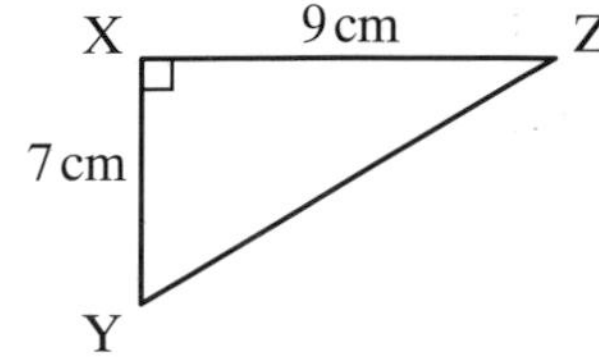

(b) Find angle S

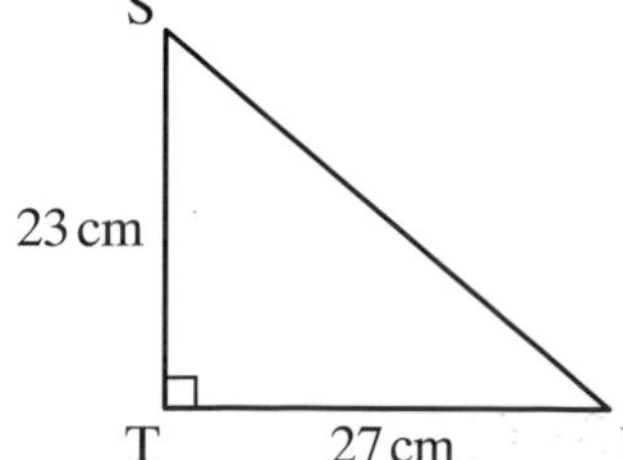

(c) Find angle J

J 5.3 m K

4.8 m

L

(d) Find angle C

B

13.6 m 15.7 m

A C

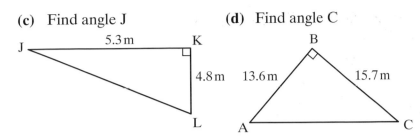

3 The diagram shows a sail on Ian's model boat.
The sail has a right angle at B.
The edge AB = 25 cm and the edge BC = 32 cm.
Calculate the angle at A.

4 The end of a bicycle shed has vertical edges 3 m and 2.5 m.
The end is 3.5 m wide.
Calculate the angle made by the roof with the horizontal.

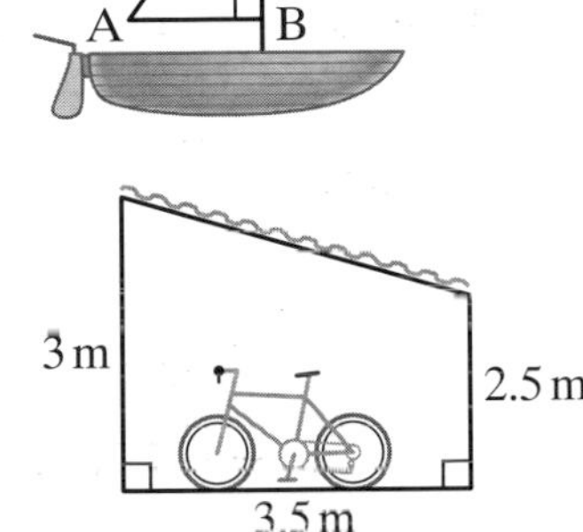

5

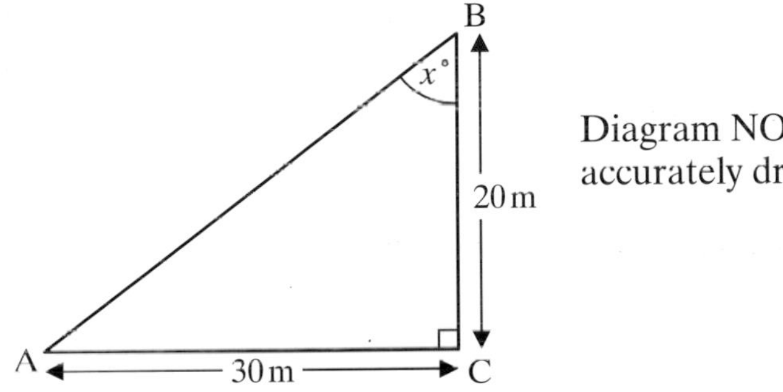

Diagram NOT accurately drawn

Work out the size of the angle marked $x°$. [L]

17.4 Using the tangent ratio to find a length

If you know one of the shorter sides and one acute angle of a right angled triangle you can use the tangent ratio to find the other short side.

Example 4

Calculate the length marked x in the diagram. Give your answer correct to 3 significant figures.

$$\tan\theta = \frac{\text{opp}}{\text{adj}}$$

$$\tan 39° = \frac{x}{18.6}$$

$$0.8097 = \frac{x}{18.6}$$

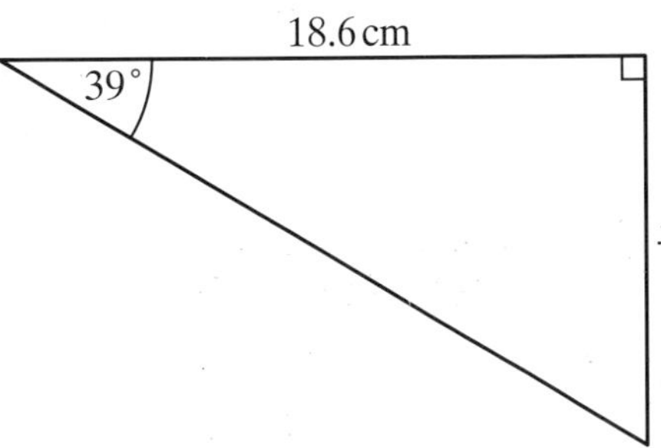

Multiply both sides by 18.6

$$0.8097 \times 18.6 = x$$

$$15.06 = x$$

$$x = 15.1\text{ cm (to 3 s.f.)}$$

When using the tangent ratio it is easier to calculate the opposite side than the adjacent side.

Example 5

Calculate the length PQ in the diagram.
Give your answer correct to 1 decimal place.

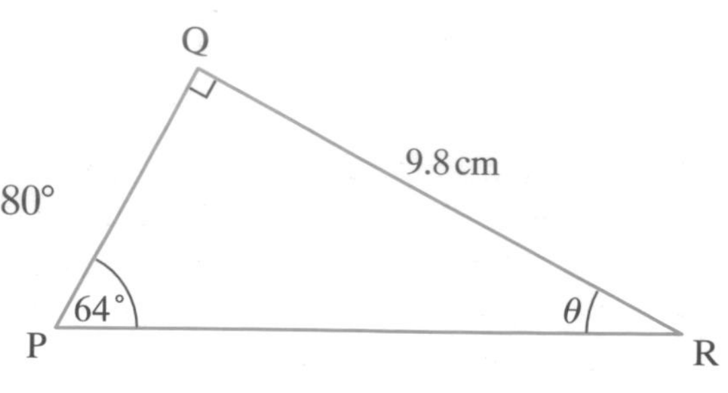

Label as θ the angle opposite the side PQ.

To find θ remember that the angles in a triangle add to 180° so $\theta = 180° - (64° + 90°) = 180° - 154° = 26°$.

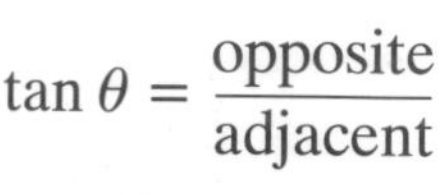

$$\tan\theta = \frac{\text{opposite}}{\text{adjacent}}$$

$$\tan 26° = \frac{PQ}{9.8}$$

$$0.4877 = \frac{PQ}{9.8}$$

Multiply both sides by 9.8

$$0.4877 \times 9.8 = PQ$$

$$4.779 = PQ$$

$$PQ = 4.8\,\text{cm (to 1 d.p.)}$$

Exercise 17E

In this exercise give your answers correct to 3 significant figures.

1 Calculate the lettered lengths in these triangles:

(a)

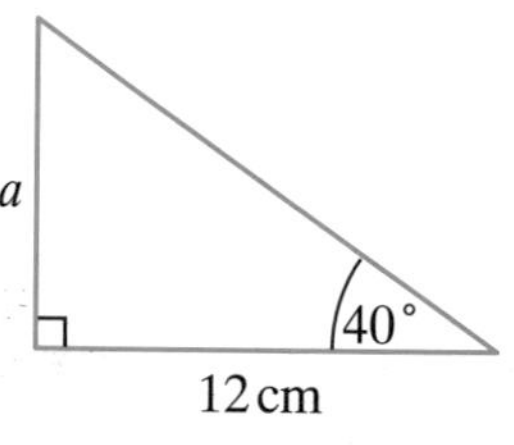

(b)

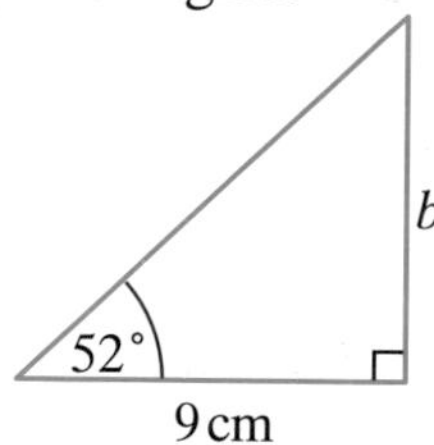

(c)

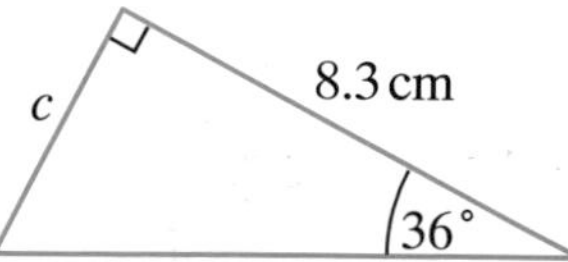

(d)

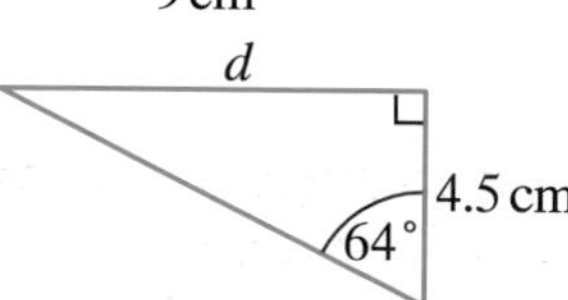

2 Calculate the named lengths in these triangles:

(a) Find YZ

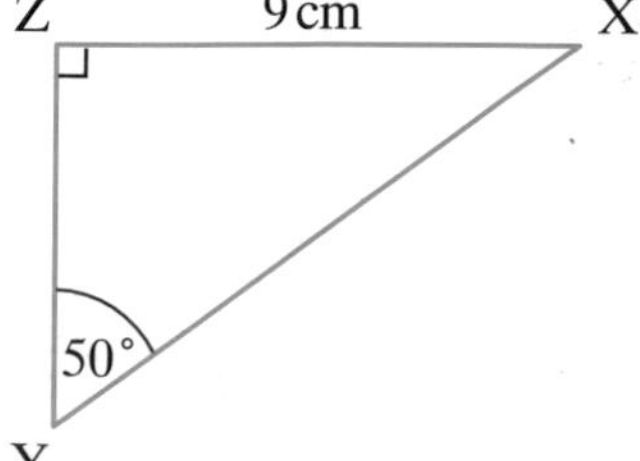

(b) Find SU

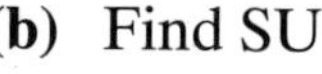

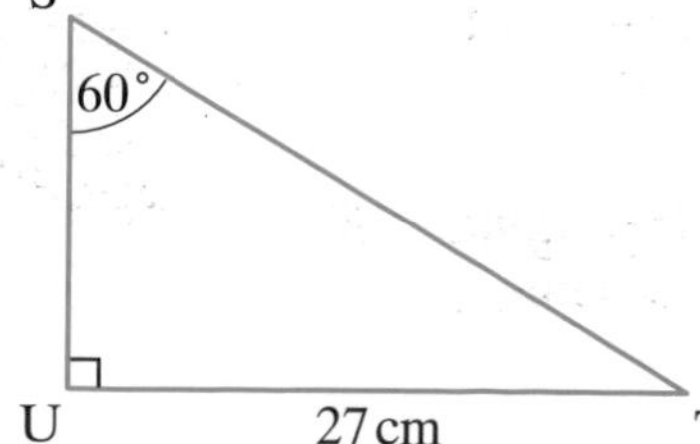

(c) Find JL

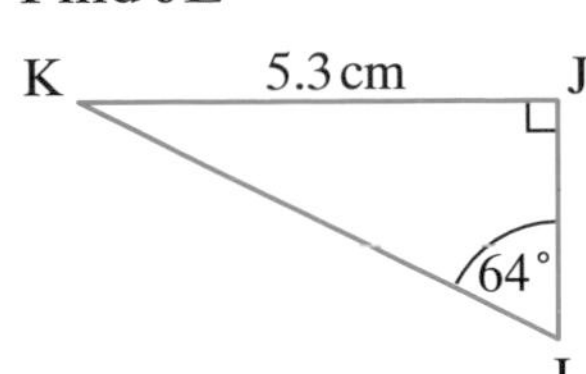

(d) Find AC

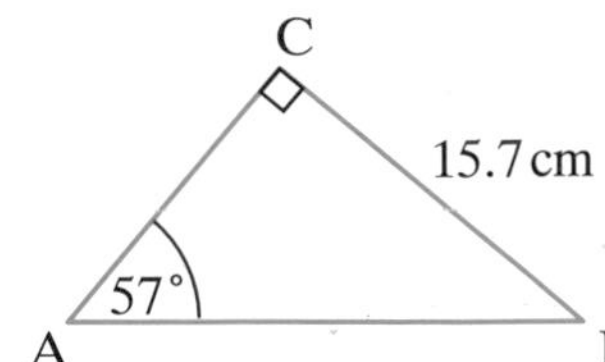

3 The length of a rectangle is 23 cm. The angle between a diagonal of the rectangle and the length is 35°.
Calculate the width of the rectangle.

4 Eleanor leans a stick against the top of the garden fence to support a climbing plant.
The bottom of the stick is 1.3 m from the bottom of the fence and the stick makes an angle of 57° with the ground.
Work out the height of the fence.

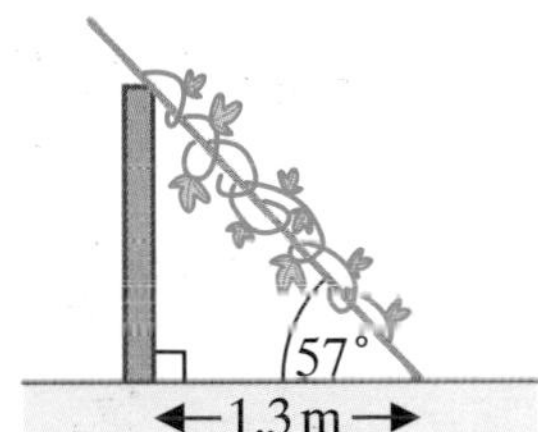

5 The flag pole has a guy rope which makes an angle of 61° with the ground.
The guy rope is pegged to the ground 1.8 m from the foot of the flag pole.
Calculate the height of the flag pole.

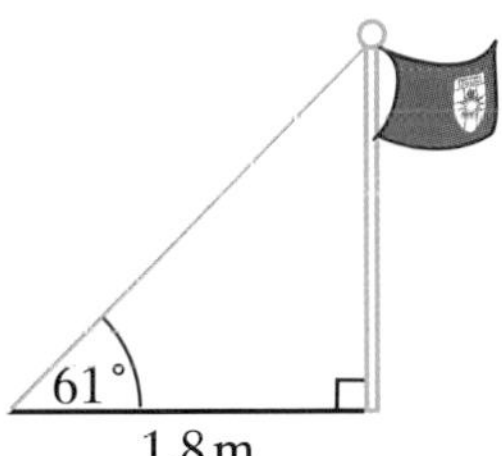

Exercise 17F Mixed questions

1 Calculate the size of angle AOB.

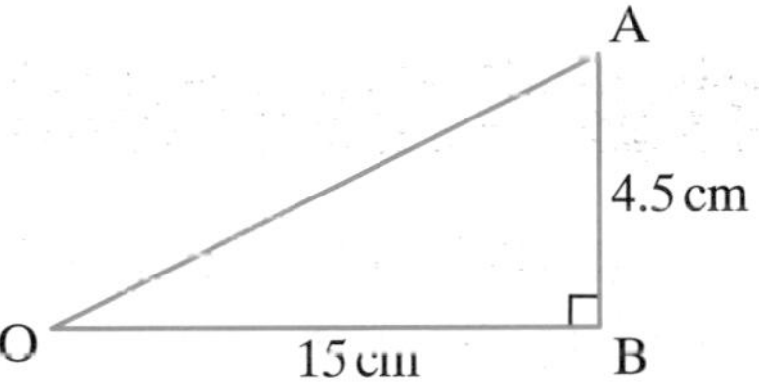

2 An aircraft is descending at an angle of 7°.
Its horizontal distance from the landing marks on the runway is 2000 m.
Calculate the height of the aircraft above the ground.

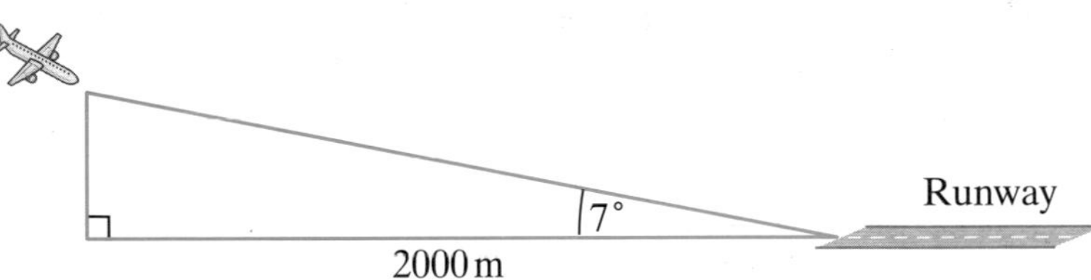

3 A flag pole is 8 m high. It is held in place by guy ropes pegged to the ground 2.7 m from the foot of the pole.
Work out the angle between a guy rope and the ground.

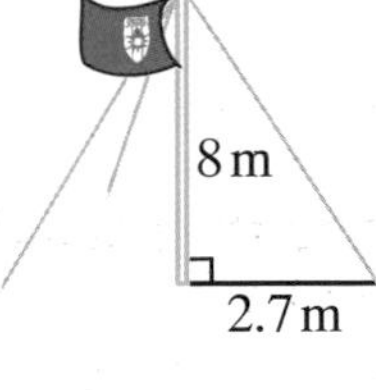

4 The length of the vertical part of the triangular metal shelf bracket is 15 cm and the length of the horizontal part is 21 cm.
Calculate the angle the sloping part of the bracket makes with the vertical.

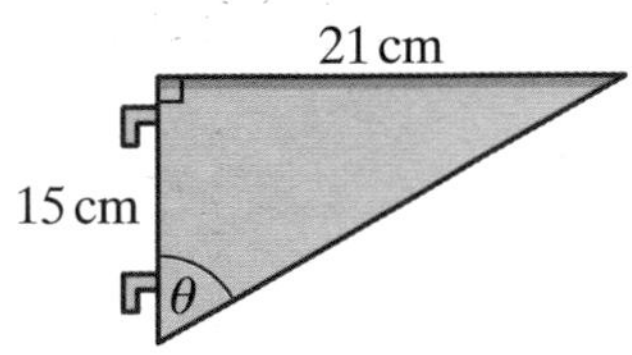

5

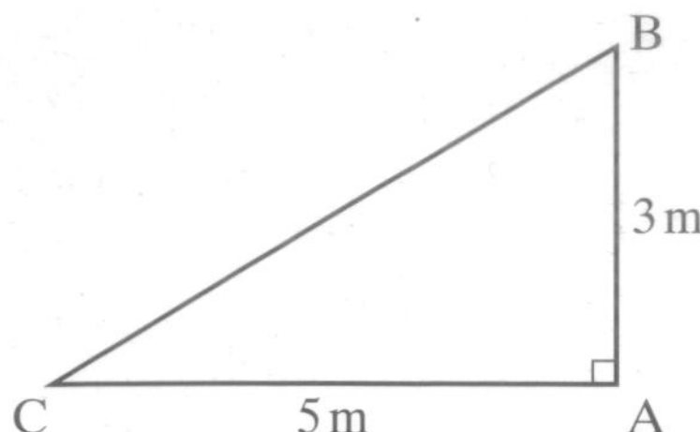

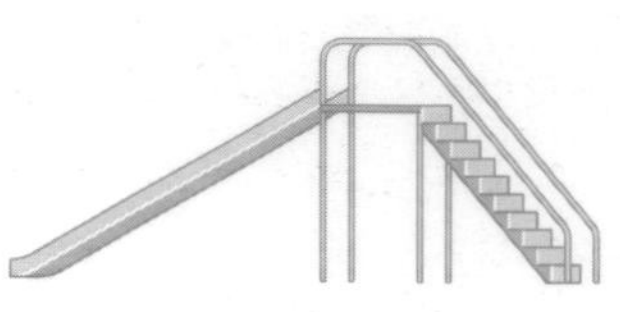

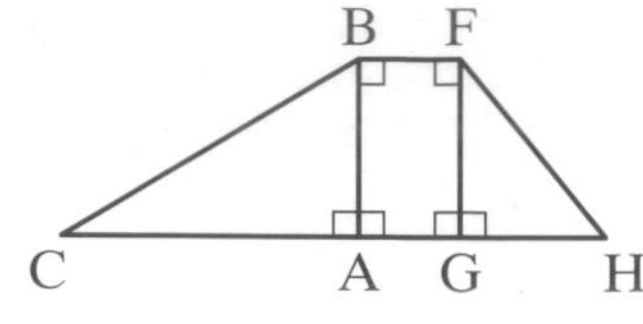

A designer is investigating children's playground slides.
She plans to build a slide in the shape of triangle ABC.
BC represents the slide itself.
The vertical height AB is 3 m.
The base length AC is 5 m.

(a) Calculate:
(i) the size of angle BCA
(ii) the length of the slide BC

The ladder, HF, starts from a point H, 1.6 m horizontally from G.
GH = 1.6 m.

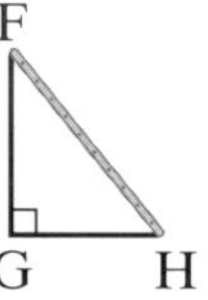

(b) Calculate angle GHF, the angle of inclination of the ladder. Give your answer in degrees correct to 1 decimal place.

6

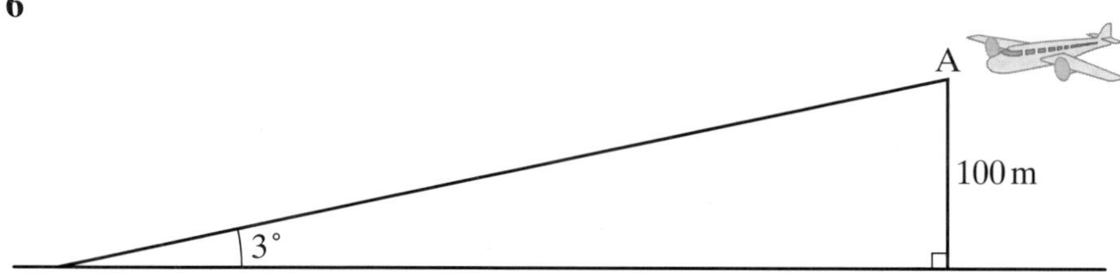

An aircraft approaching a runway descends on a flight path at an angle of 3° with the ground.

(a) Write down the size of angle TAL.
(b) Calculate the distance, to the nearest metre, of L from the landing point, T, of the aircraft. (Assume that TL is level ground.)
(c) Using Pythagoras' theorem in triangle ATL, or otherwise, calculate the length of AT. Give your answer to the nearest metre.

The aircraft is travelling at a constant speed of 91 metres per second.

(d) Calculate the time taken, in seconds, for the aircraft to reach T from A. Give your answer to the nearest second.

[L]

Summary of key points

The tangent ratio for a right angled triangle is:

$$\textbf{tangent of } \theta = \frac{\textbf{opposite side to } \theta}{\textbf{adjacent side to } \theta}$$

opposite to θ

θ

adjacent to θ

or for short:

$$\textbf{tan } \theta = \frac{\textbf{opp}}{\textbf{adj}}$$

18 Graphs of more complex functions

This unit extends the work on graph plotting in Unit 7 to graphs of more complex functions.

18.1 Drawing graphs of simple quadratic functions

A quadratic function is a function of the type $y = ax^2 + bx + c$ in which a is not zero. (Quadratic functions are introduced on page 171.)

Here is a table of values for the quadratic function $y = x^2$.

x	−3	−2	−1	0	1	2	3
y	9	4	1	0	1	4	9

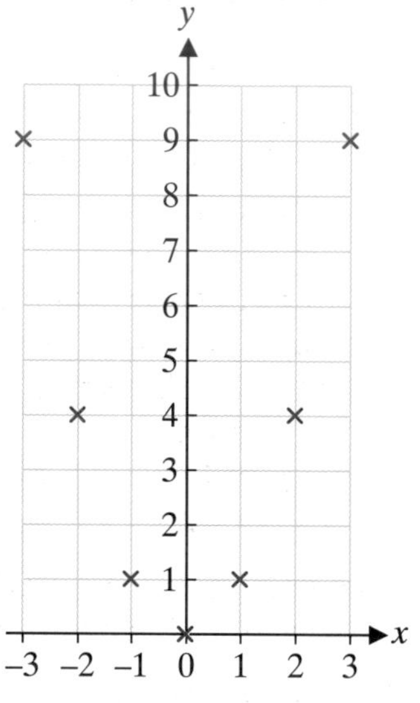

The points from the table of values are shown plotted on the graph. They do not lie on a straight line.

This exercise will give you a better idea of the shape of the graph:

Exercise 18A

You will need 2 mm squared graph paper and tracing paper.

1 **(a)** Make a full size copy of the graph above using 2 cm for 1 unit of x and y.

(b) Copy and complete this extended table of values for $y = x^2$.

x	−2.5	−1.5	−0.8	−0.6	−0.4	−0.2	−0.1	0	0.1	0.2	0.4	0.6	0.8	1.5	2.5
y															

(c) Plot these new points on your graph.

(d) The points should appear to lie on a ∪-shaped curve. Draw a smooth curve through the points you have plotted. The curve should not be pointed at (0, 0).

2 On the same axes as you used for question **1**, draw the graph of $y = x^2 + 1$.

Use the same values of x in your table of values as in question **1**.

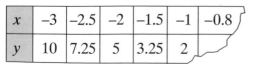

x	−3	−2.5	−2	−1.5	−1	−0.8
y	10	7.25	5	3.25	2	

3 **(a)** Use tracing paper to trace the axes and the graph of $y = x^2$.
(b) Slide the tracing paper up the y-axis of your graph of $y = x^2 + 1$.
You should find that the tracing of the graph for $y = x^2$ fits exactly on to the graph of $y = x^2 + 1$.
(c) Use the tracing paper to help you draw on the same axes the graphs of $y = x^2 + 2$, $y = x^2 + 3$, $y = x^2 - 1$.
(d) Do any of the graphs have a line of symmetry?
(e) Write down anything else that you notice.

Exercise 18B

1 It is best to use a graphical calculator or a graph drawing program on a computer for this question. However, you can draw your graphs on graph paper.
This question investigates the shapes of graphs of functions like $y = ax^2$, where a can take any value except 0.
(a) Put $a = 1$ and draw the graph of $y = x^2$ ($y = 1x^2$).
(b) Put $a = 2$ and draw the graph of $y = 2x^2$ and so on.
(c) Try three negative values for a and try two fractional values for a.
(d) What effect does the value of a have on the shapes of the graphs?

Use what you discovered in Exercise 18A and in question **1** in this exercise to help you answer the following questions.

2 The functions of each of these pairs of graphs are written beneath them.
Match each function to its graph.

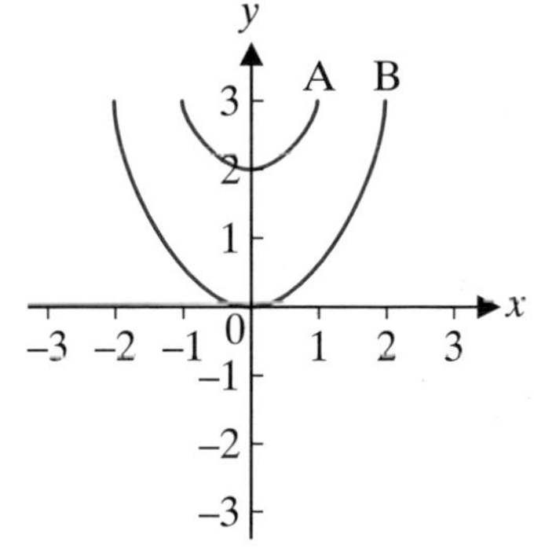

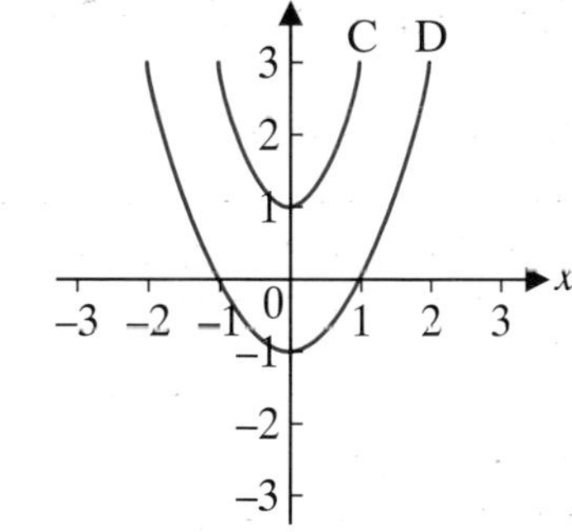

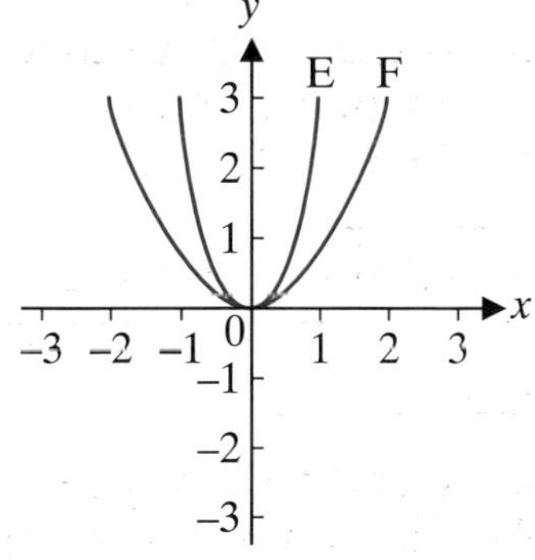

(a) $y = x^2$ $y = x^2 + 2$ **(b)** $y = x^2 + 1$ $y = x^2 - 1$ **(c)** $y = x^2$ $y = 2x^2$

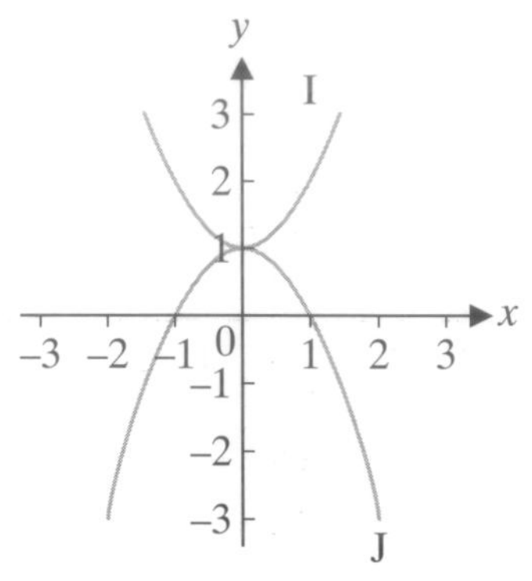

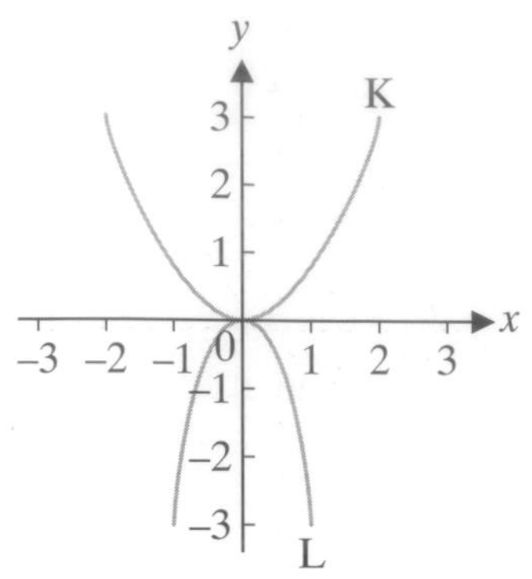

(d) $y = -x^2 \quad y = -x^2 + 1$ **(e)** $y = x^2 + 1 \quad y = -x^2 + 1$ **(f)** $y = 0.5x^2 \quad y = -2x^2$

This means $y = -1x^2$

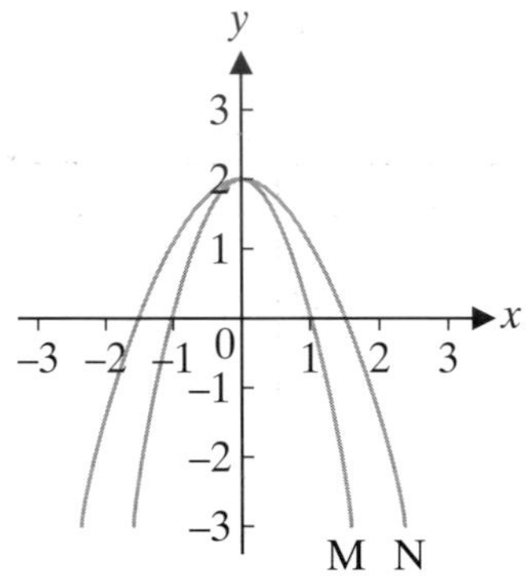

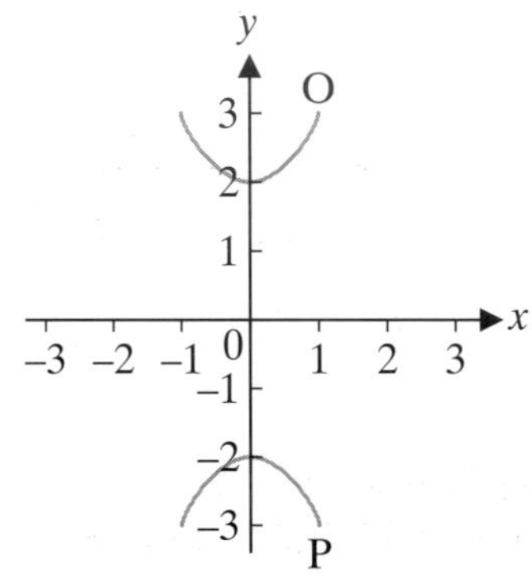

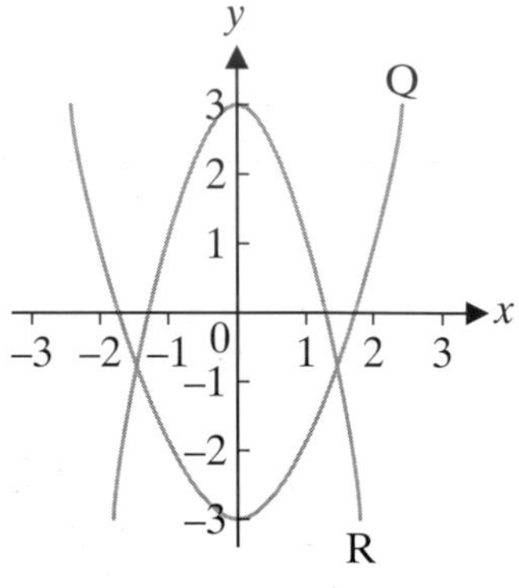

(g) $y = -2x^2 + 2$
$y = -x^2 + 2$ **(h)** $y = x^2 + 2 \quad y = -x^2 - 2$ **(i)** $y = -2x^2 + 3 \quad y = x^2 - 3$

3 Below are the graphs of these functions:

(a) $y = x^2$ **(b)** $y = 2x^2$ **(c)** $y = x^2 + 1$
(d) $y = -x^2$ **(e)** $y = x^2 - 3$ **(f)** $y = 0.5x^2 - 2$
(g) $y = 3x^2 + 1$ **(h)** $y = -2x^2$ **(i)** $y = 3 - x^2$

For each function write down the letter of its graph. Explain your answers.

A

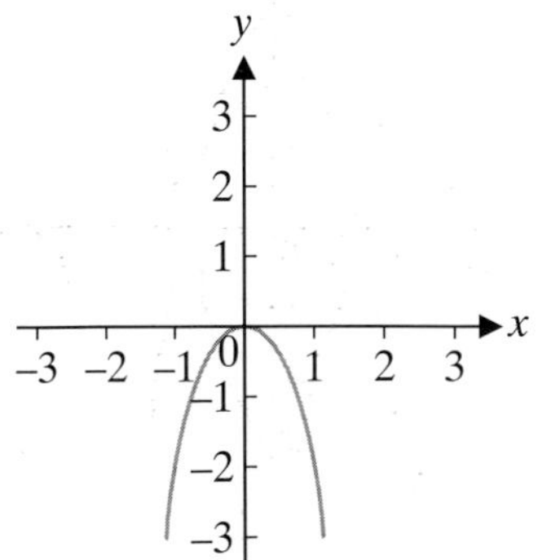

B

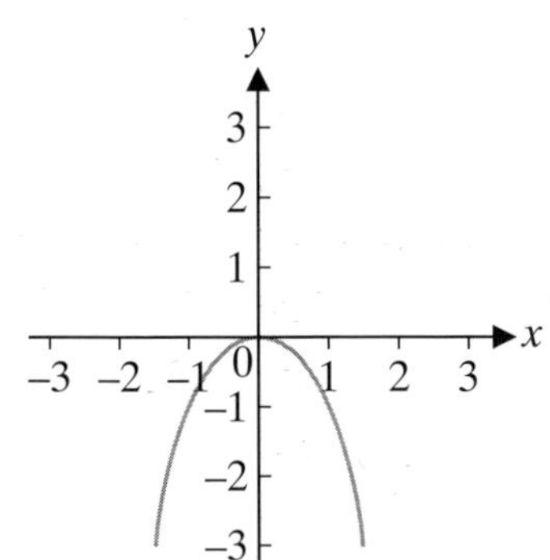

C

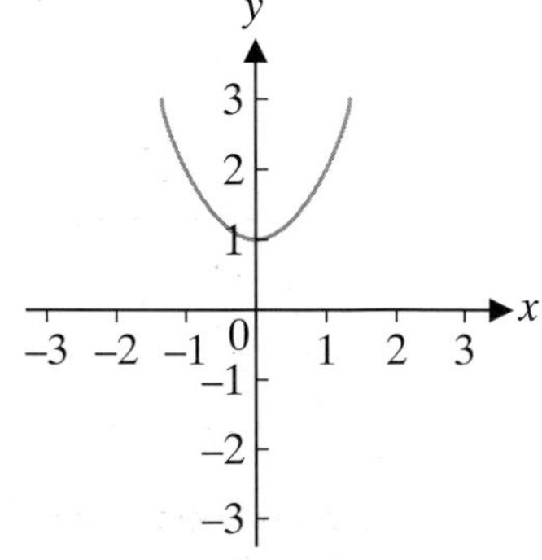

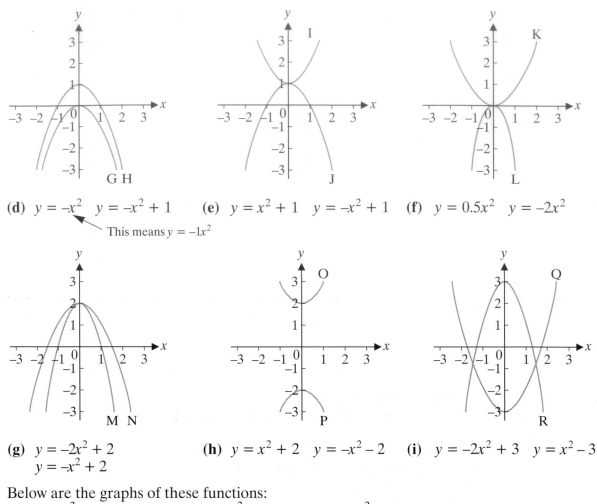

D

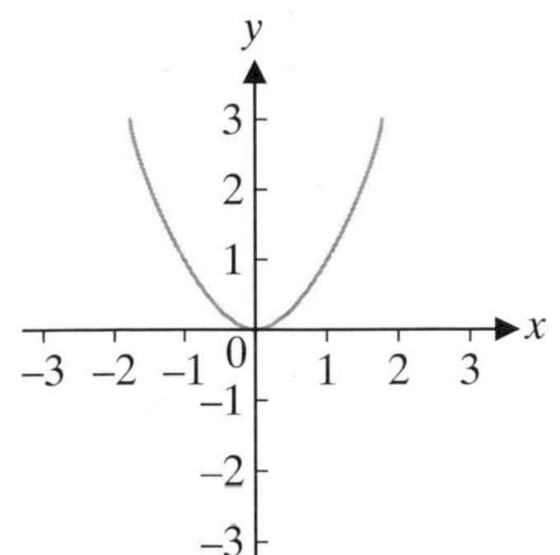

E

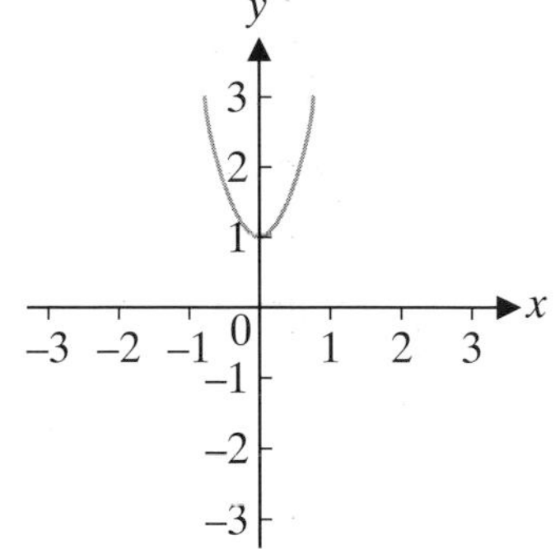

F

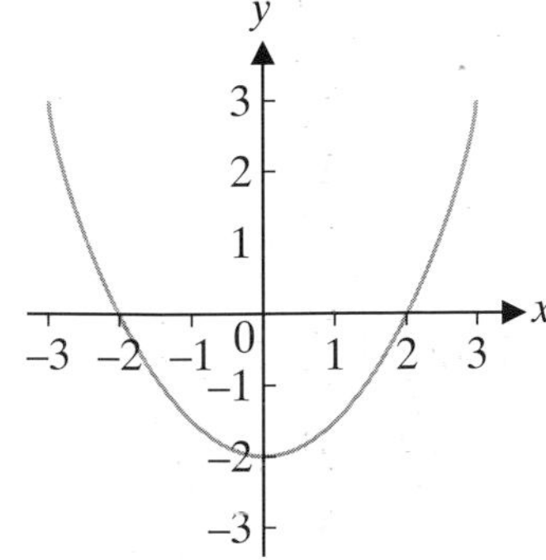

G

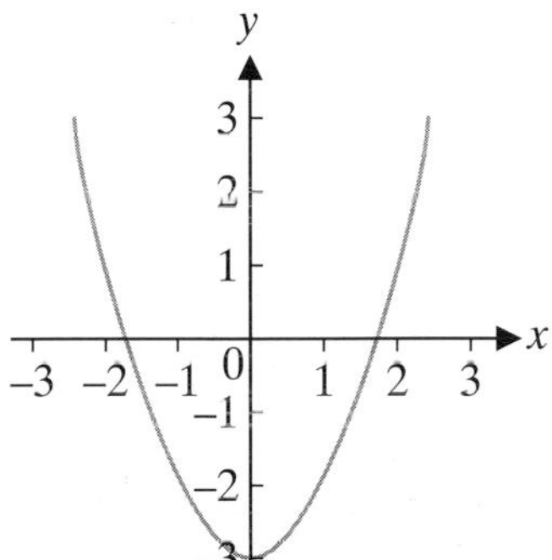

H

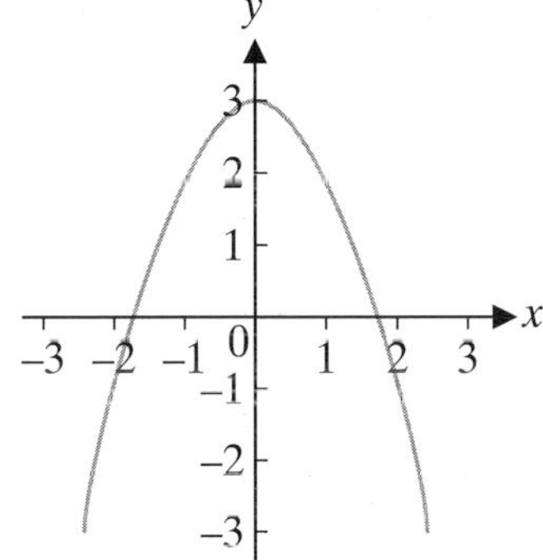

I

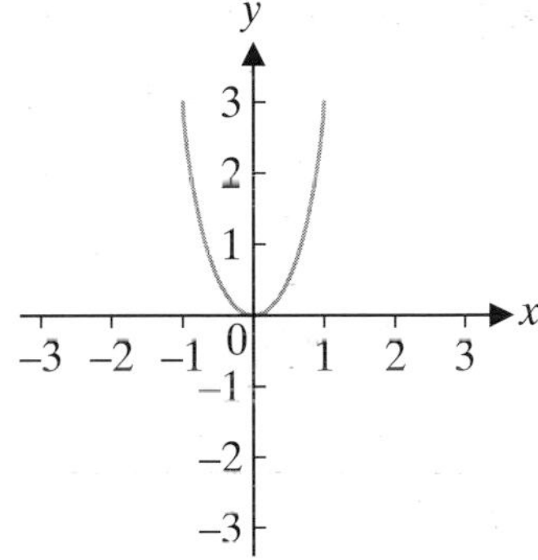

4 Sketch a set of axes like those in question **3**.
On the same set of axes sketch and label the graph of each of the functions below.
Do not work out tables of values for the functions. Use what you know about the shapes of graphs of functions like $y = x^2 + a$ and $y = ax^2$ to help you.
(a) $y = x^2$ **(b)** $y = 2x^2 + 2$ **(c)** $y = x^2 - 1$ **(d)** $y = 2x^2 - 2$

5 For each pair of graphs write down what functions you think they represent.
The first one has been done for you.

(a)

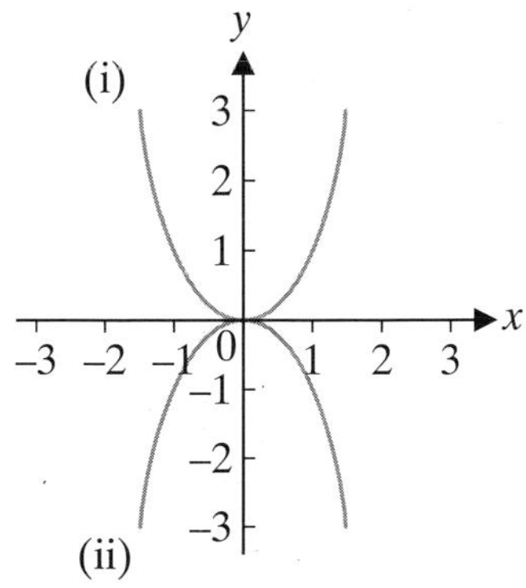

These functions could be:
(i) $y = x^2$ (ii) $y = -x^2$

(b)

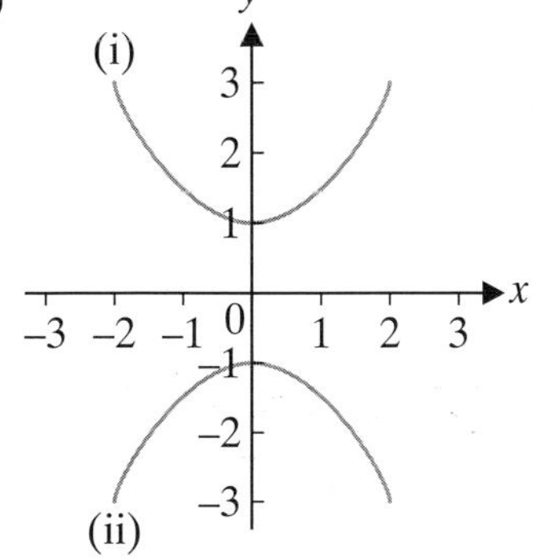

(c)

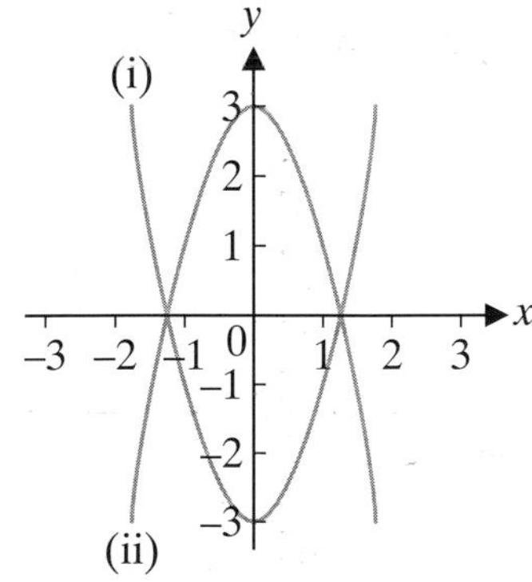

(d)

(e)

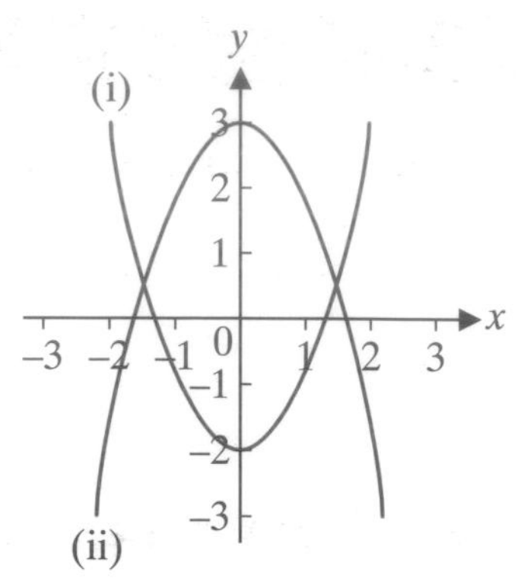

(f)

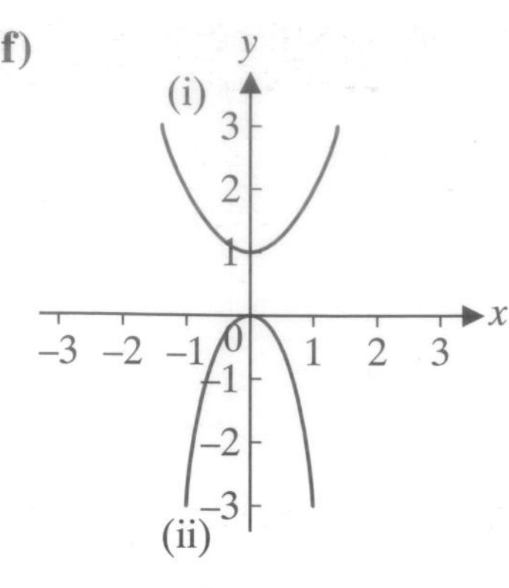

6 **Graphs challenge** You need either a graphical calculator or a graph drawing program on a computer. Work in pairs or small groups.
One of you sketches a pattern of graphs on paper using curves like those in questions **2**, **3** and **5**.
The others in the group try to reproduce the pattern on the calculator (or computer).
Take it in turns to sketch the pattern to be reproduced.

Graph shapes to remember

From your work in Exercise 18B you should have found:

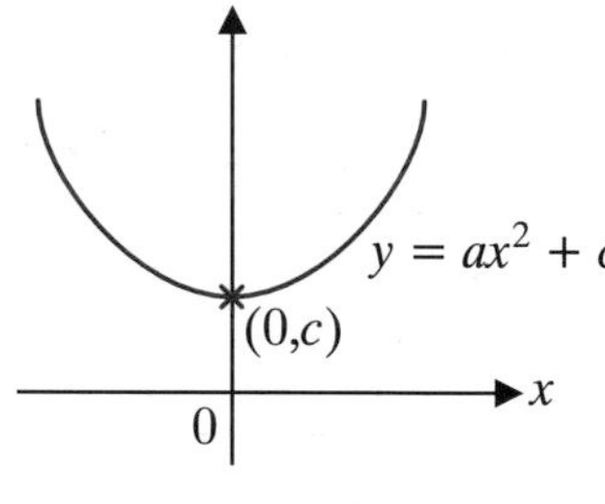

- **Graphs of functions of the form $y = x^2 + c$, where c can be positive, negative or 0, all have a ∪-shape.**
  The bottom of the ∪-shape cuts the y-axis at $(0, c)$.
  The y-axis is the line of symmetry.
- **Graphs of functions of the form $y = ax^2$, where a is positive, all have a ∪-shape.**
  The greater the value of a the narrower the ∪-shape.
  They all pass through (0, 0).
- **Graphs of functions of the form $y = -ax^2$ are the same as the graphs for $y = ax^2$ reflected in the x-axis.**

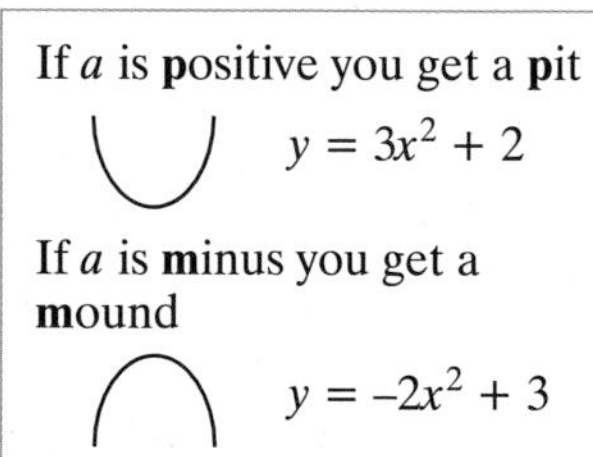

If a is **p**ositive you get a **pit**
$y = 3x^2 + 2$
If a is **m**inus you get a **m**ound
$y = -2x^2 + 3$

18.2 Solving simple quadratic equations

You need to be able to solve quadratic equations like $2x^2 + 3 = 21$.

This is the number machine for the equation $2x^2 + 3 = 21$, with the inverse number machine.

If you put 21 into the inverse number machine the output is +3 or –3.

So x could be +3 or –3.

You write the solution as $x = \pm 3$.

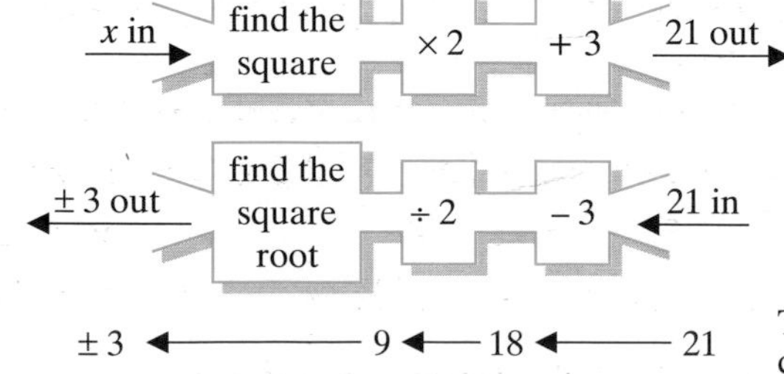

Finding the square root is the inverse function of finding the square.

The square root of 9 can be +3 or –3 because +3 × +3 = 9 and –3 × –3 = 9.

- **Quadratic equations of the type $ax^2 + c = d$, where a, c and d are numbers, can be solved by drawing the inverse number machine for $y = ax^2 + c$ and sending d through it.**

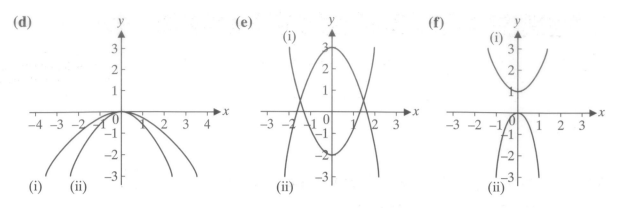

Exercise 18C

1 Solve each quadratic equation by drawing its number machine and its inverse number machine.

(a) $3x^2 - 4 = 8$ (b) $2x^2 + 5 = 37$ (c) $2x^2 - 6 = 12$

(d) $x^2 + 8 = 57$ (e) $4x^2 + 3 = 39$ (f) $\frac{x^2}{2} + 3 = 21$

For a reminder on inverse number machines see page 17.

18.3 Drawing graphs of more complex quadratic functions

To solve more complex quadratic equations you need to be able to draw graphs of quadratic functions accurately.

Example 1

(a) Draw the graph of $y = 2x^2 - 4x - 3$ using values of x from –2 to 4.
(b) Draw the axis of symmetry and write down its equation.
(c) What is the minimum value y can have for the function $y = 2x^2 - 4x - 3$?
(d) What value of x gives the minimum value of y?

(a) First make a table of values.

x	–2	–1	0	1	2	3	4
y	13	3	–3	–5	–3	3	13

If $x = -2$
$y = 2 \times (-2)^2 - 4 \times (-2) - 3$
$= 2 \times 4 + 8 - 3$
$= 8 + 8 - 3$
$y = 13$

You need to draw a grid with x going from –2 to 4 and y going from –5 to 13.
Plot the points then join them with a smooth curve.
The graph should not be pointed at (1, –5).

(b) The axis of symmetry of the curve is the line which has the equation $x = 1$.
(c) The minimum value of y is –5.
(d) When y is minimum the value of x is 1.

Graph of $y = 2x^2 - 4x - 3$

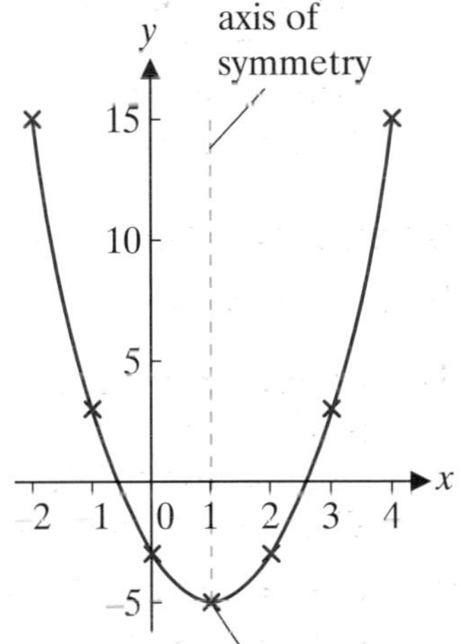

Exercise 18D

1 (a) Draw the graph of $y = 2x^2$ on graph paper. Use values of x from –4 to 4.
(b) Draw the axis of symmetry and write down its function.

Do the same as in question **1** for each of these functions:

2 $y = x^2 + 5$ **3** $y = x^2 - 2x$ **4** $y = -3x^2 + 9$

5 $y = x^2 + 2x - 1$ **6** $y = -x^2 + 3x + 5$ **7** $y = 2x^2 + 3x - 5$

■ **Graphs of functions of the form $y = ax^2 + bx + c$:**
have a ∪-shape if a is positive
have a ∩-shape if a is negative
cut the y-axis at $(0, c)$
The y-axis is only the line of symmetry when $b = 0$

18.4 Solving more complex quadratic equations

You can use a graph to solve quadratic equations like this:

$2x^2 + 3x + 4 = 18$

The number machine for the equation $y = 2x^2 + 3x + 4$ is difficult to draw and the inverse number machine cannot be drawn. Try it and see!

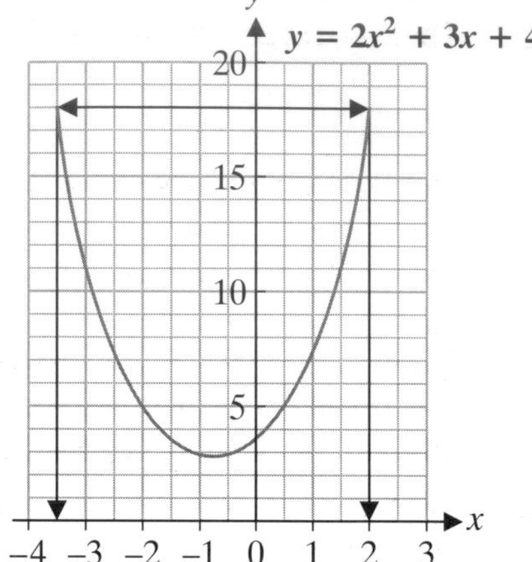

Instead you can find the points on the graph of $y = 2x^2 + 3x + 4$ where $y = 18$ like this:

step 1: draw the graph of $y = 2x^2 + 3x + 4$

step 2: find the value 18 on the y-axis. Draw a line through the point (0, 18) and parallel to the x-axis to meet the curve.

step 3: go down to the x-axis to find the two values of x which make $2x^2 + 3x + 4$ equal to 18.

The **two possible solutions** to the quadratic equation $2x^2 + 3x + 4 = 18$ are $x = 2$ and $x = -3.5$

You can check these answers using algebra.
When $x = 2$: $2x^2 + 3x + 4 = 8 + 6 + 4 = 18$
and when $x = -3.5$: $2x^2 + 3x + 4 = 24.5 - 10.5 + 4 = 18$
So the values $x = 2$ and $x = -3.5$ satisfy the equation.

To solve the equation $2x^2 + 3x + 4 = 1$ you draw the line $y = 1$. This line does not meet the curve so the equation has **no solutions**.

To solve the equation $2x^2 + 3x + 4 = 2.875$ you draw the line $y = 2.875$.
This curve just touches the curve at one point (where $x = -0.75$) so there is only **one solution**, $x = -0.75$.

- **More complex quadratic equations such as $ax^2 + bx + c = d$ can be solved by drawing the graph for $y = ax^2 + bx + c$ and the line $y = d$.**
- **Quadratic equations can have 0, 1 or 2 solutions.**

Exercise 18E

You need 2 mm squared graph paper.

1 Draw the graph of $y = 2x^2 - 3x + 2$. Make a table using values of x from −3 to +4.

(a) Use the graph to solve the quadratic equations:
(i) $2x^2 - 3x + 2 = 4$
(ii) $2x^2 - 3x + 2 = 11$
(iii) $2x^2 - 3x + 2 = 1$

(b) Write down the minimum value y can take in the equation $y = 2x^2 - 3x + 2$.

(c) What value of x gives the minimum value for y?

(d) Explain why the equation $2x^2 - 3x + 2 = 0.5$ does not have a solution.

2 Draw the graph of $y = -x^2 + 2x - 1$. Make a table using values of x from –3 to 5.

(a) Use the graph to solve the following quadratic equations:

(i) $-x^2 + 2x - 1 = -4$

(ii) $-x^2 + 2x - 1 = -1$

(iii) $-x^2 + 2x - 1 = -9$

(b) What is the maximum value y can take in the function $y = -x^2 + 2x - 1$?

(c) What value of x gives the maximum value for y?

(d) Give a value of y for which $y = -x^2 + 2x - 1$ does not have a solution.

Hint:
If $x = -3$
$-x^2 = -(-3 \times -3)$
$= -(+9)$
$-x^2 = -9$

If $x = 2$
$-x^2 = -(2 \times 2)$
$-x^2 = -4$

3 Draw the graph of $y = 2x^2 + 2x - 8$ using values of x from –4 to 3.

(a) Use the graph to solve the following quadratic equations:

(i) $2x^2 + 2x - 8 = 4$

(ii) $2x^2 + 2x - 8 = -4$

(iii) $2x^2 + 2x - 8 = -8$

(b) What is the minimum value y can take in the function $y = 2x^2 + 2x - 8$?

(c) What value of x gives the minimum value for y?

(d) Give a value of y for which $y = 2x^2 + 2x - 8$ does not have a solution.

18.5 Solving problems involving quadratic equations

Example 2

A scientific instrument has a rectangular detecting surface whose length is 2 cm more than its height. The area of the detecting surface must be 20 cm².

Find the dimensions of the detecting surface, by drawing a suitable graph.

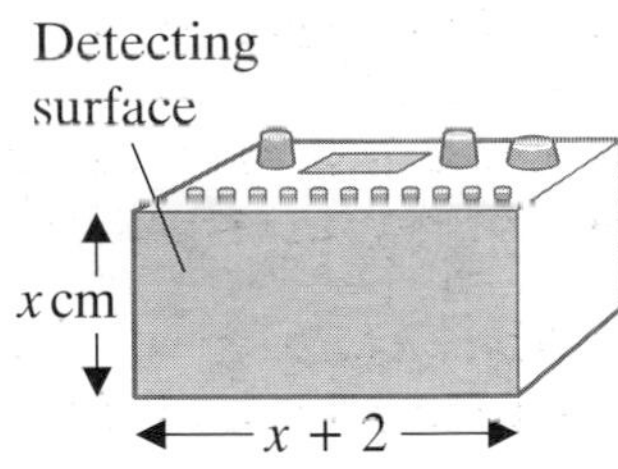

You can call the height of the detecting surface x cm so the length of the detecting surface is $x + 2$ cm.

The area of the detecting surface is $x(x + 2)$ cm².

Multiply to remove the brackets: area $= x^2 + 2x$ cm².

The area must be 20 cm² so you need to solve the equation $x^2 + 2x = 20$.

Draw the graph of $y = x^2 + 2x$. You need only take positive values for x as the detecting surface cannot have a negative length.

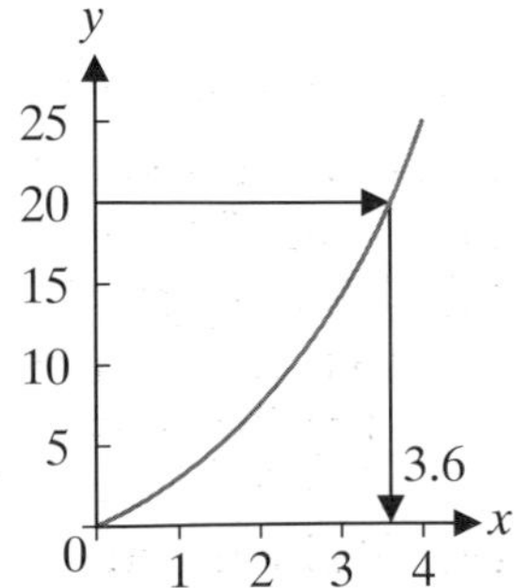

The required value of x is when $y = 20$ on the graph. Find 20 on the y-axis, go along to the curve and down to the x-axis to find the value of x for which y is 20.

This value is $x = 3.6$ so $x + 2 = 5.6$.

The dimensions of the detecting surface are 3.6 cm by 5.6 cm.

Exercise 18F

You need 2 mm squared graph paper.

1 A factory makes a series of picture frames. The lengths of the frames are 4 cm more than their widths.
Work out the dimensions of a picture frame which has an area of 150 cm^2 by drawing a suitable graph.

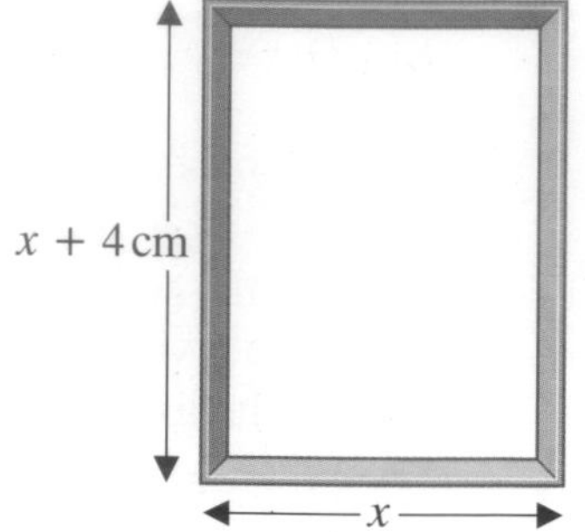

2 A farmer has 20 metres of chicken wire fencing.
She makes a rectangular enclosure for her chickens using a wall as one side of the rectangle. The area of the enclosure is 40 m^2.
Work out the dimensions of her enclosure by drawing a suitable graph.
Hint: call the length of the two opposite sides of fencing x metres so the length of the other side of the fencing is $20 - 2x$ metres.

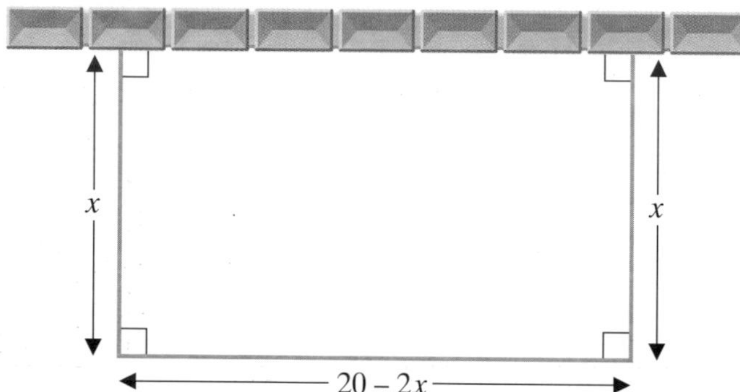

18.6 Graphs of functions involving x^3 and $\frac{1}{x}$

Exercise 18G

It is best to use a graphical calculator or a graph drawing program on a computer for questions **1** and **2**. However, you can draw your graphs on graph paper.

1 Investigate graphs of the form $y = ax^3$ and $y = x^3 + c$, where a and c take different values.
For example: put $a = 1$ and draw the graph of $y = x^3$ ($y = 1x^3$)
put $a = 2$ and draw the graph of $y = 2x^3$ and so on.
Try negative values for a; try fractional values for a.
Do the same for $y = x^3 + c$ using different values of c.

Reminder:
x^3 means $x \times x \times x$
$\frac{1}{x}$ means $1 \div x$

2 Investigate graphs of the form $\frac{a}{x}$ and $\frac{1}{x} + c$

where a and c take different values.

Use what you have discovered in questions **1** and **2** to help you to answer questions **3, 4** and **5**.

3 The functions of these pairs of graphs are written beneath them.
Match the functions to the graphs. Explain your answers.

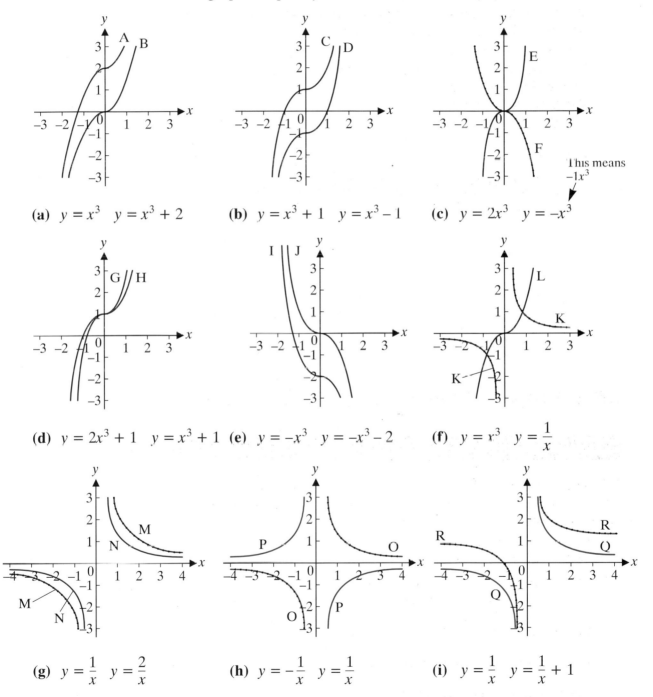

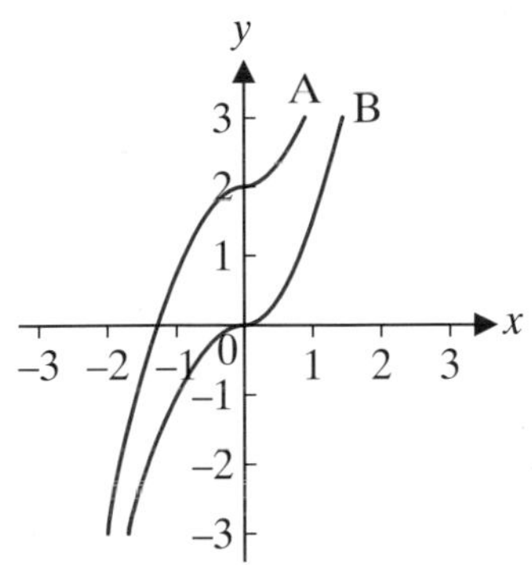

(a) $y = x^3 \quad y = x^3 + 2$

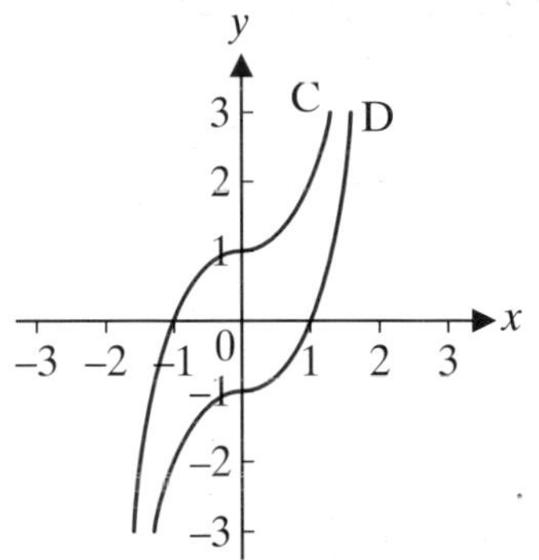

(b) $y = x^3 + 1 \quad y = x^3 - 1$

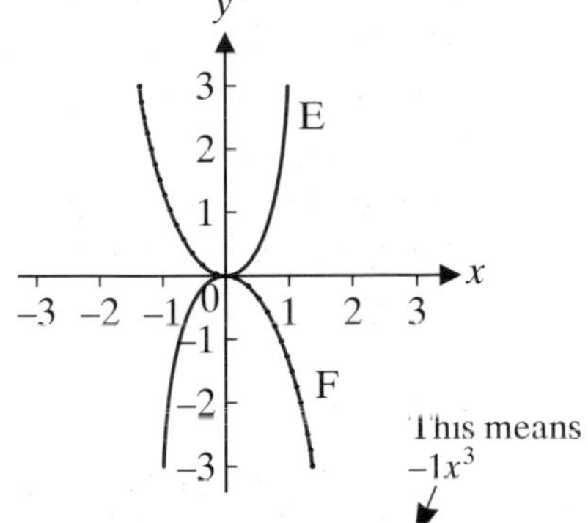

(c) $y = 2x^3 \quad y = -x^3$

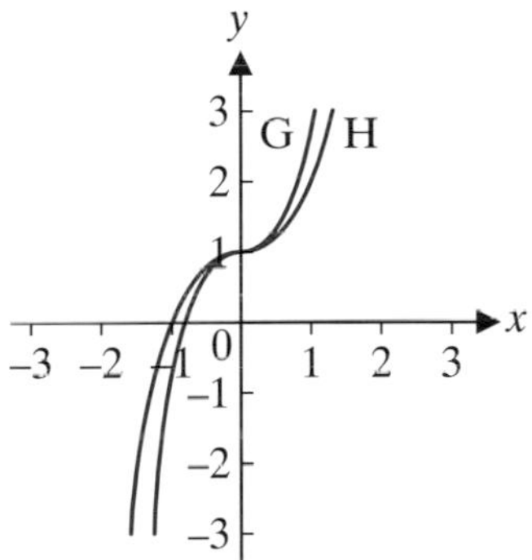

(d) $y = 2x^3 + 1 \quad y = x^3 + 1$

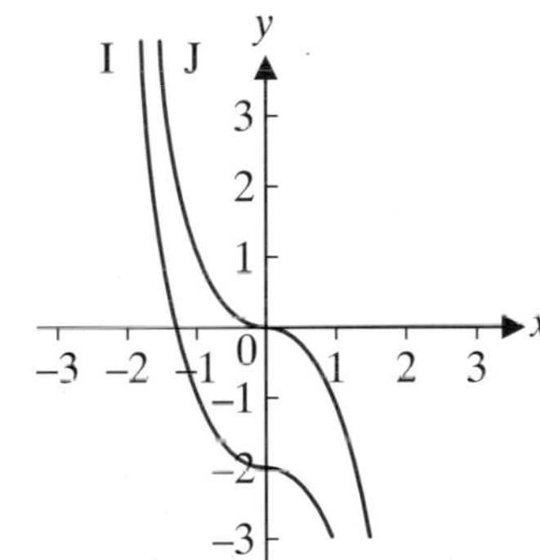

(e) $y = -x^3 \quad y = -x^3 - 2$

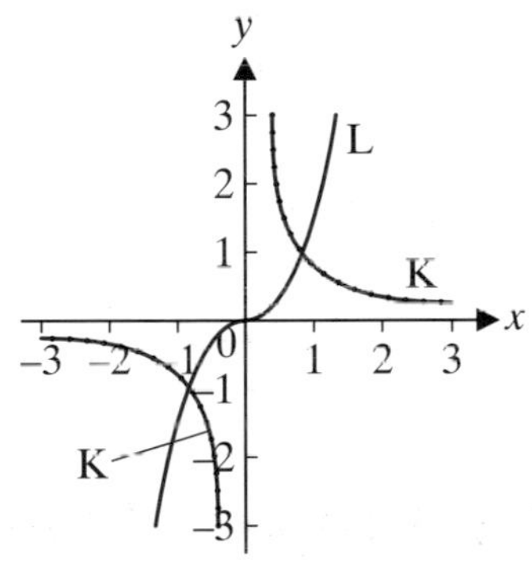

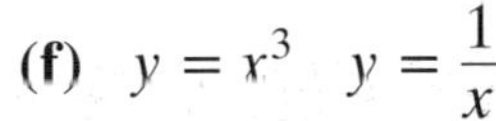

(f) $y = x^3 \quad y = \frac{1}{x}$

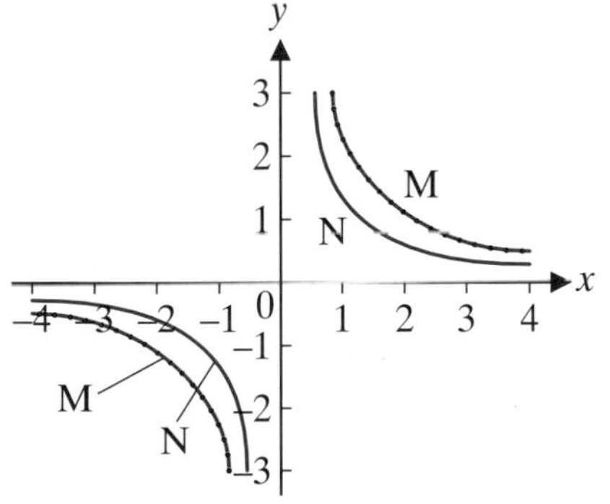

(g) $y = \frac{1}{x} \quad y = \frac{2}{x}$

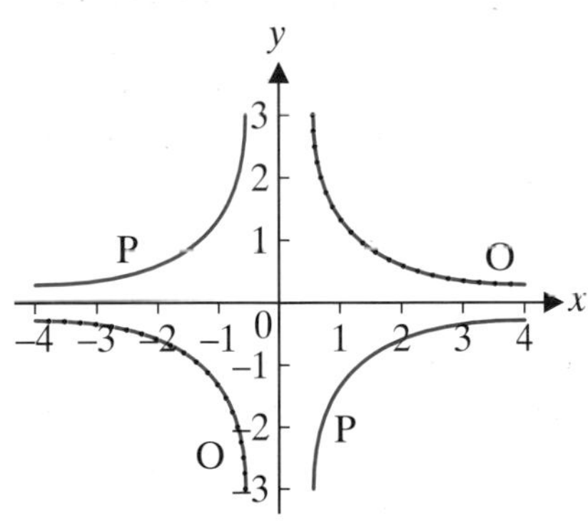

(h) $y = -\frac{1}{x} \quad y = \frac{1}{x}$

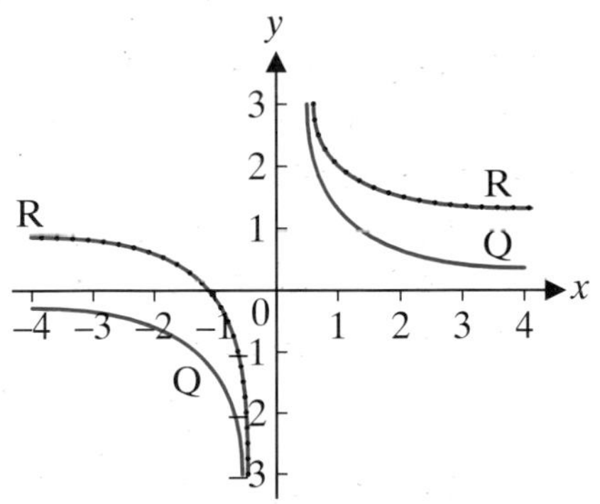

(i) $y = \frac{1}{x} \quad y = \frac{1}{x} + 1$

4 Below are the graphs of these functions:

(a) $y = \frac{1}{x}$ **(b)** $y = \frac{1}{x} + 2$ **(c)** $y = -\frac{1}{x}$

(d) $y = x^3$ **(e)** $y = x^3 + 2$ **(f)** $y = -x^3$

(g) $y = 3x^3$ **(h)** $y = -3x^3$ **(i)** $y = 3x^3 + 2$

For each function write down the letter of its graph.

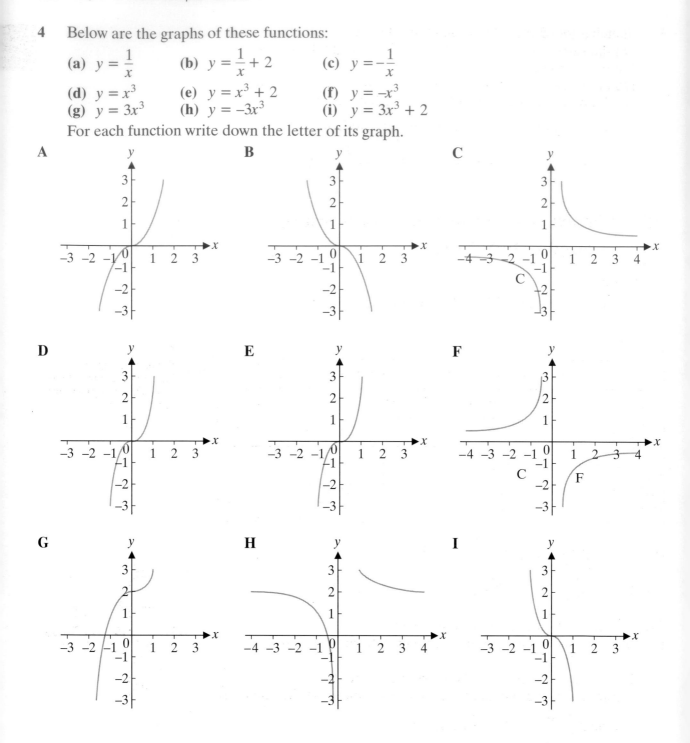

A

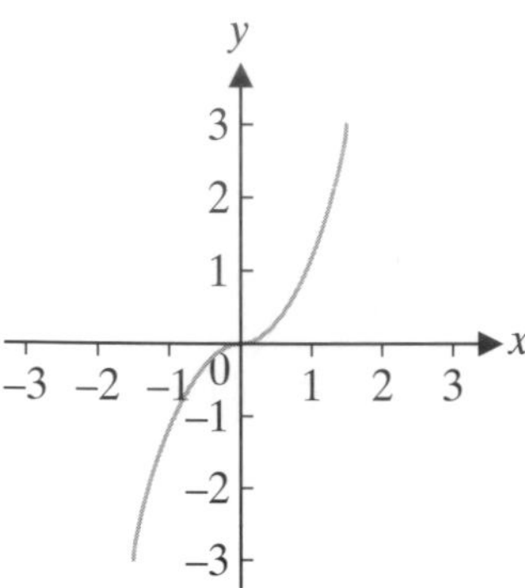

B

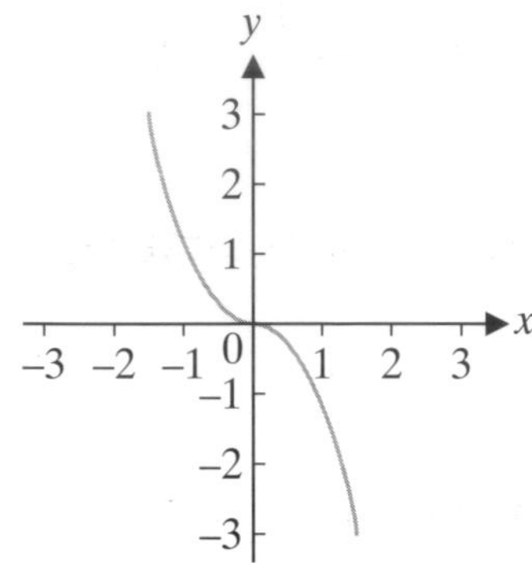

C

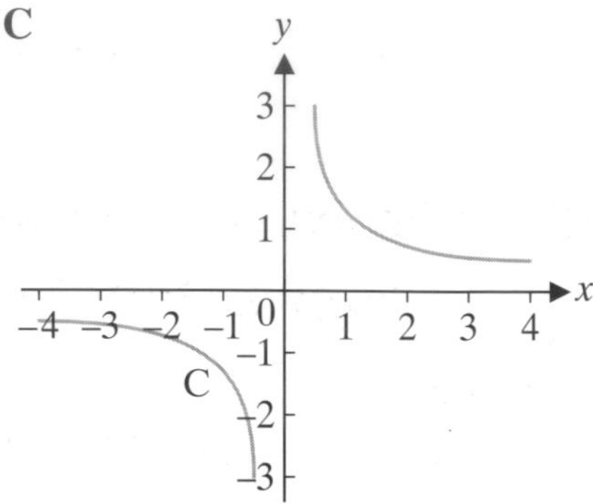

D

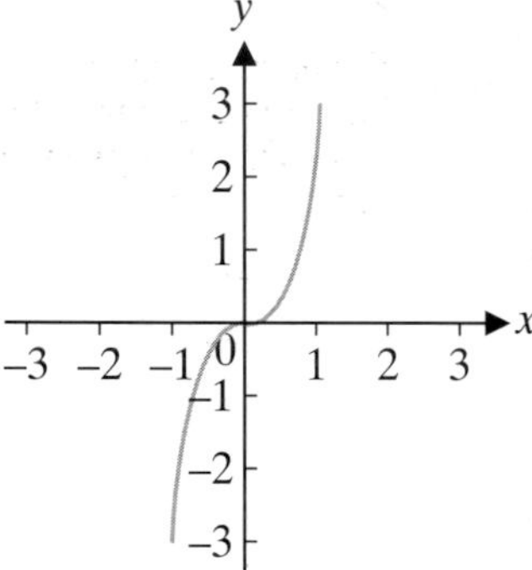

E

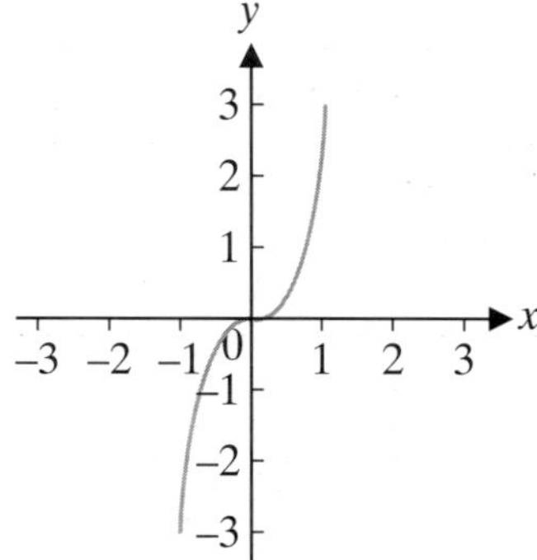

F

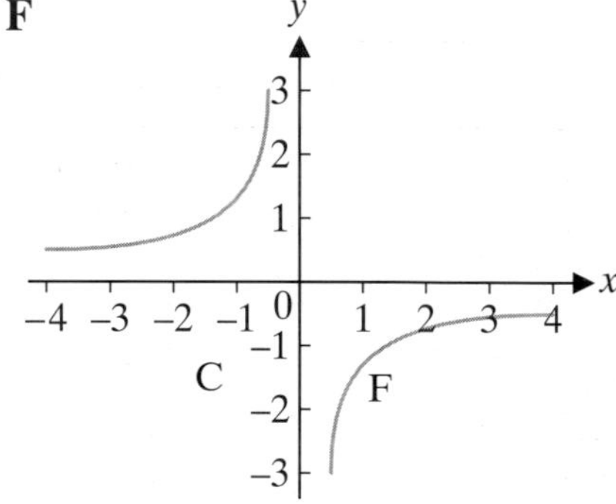

G

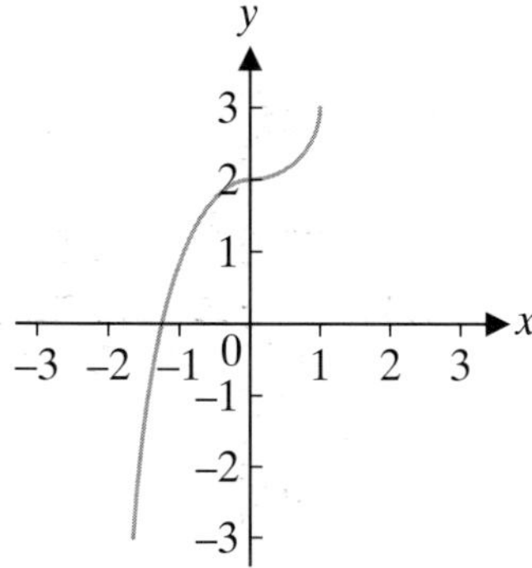

H

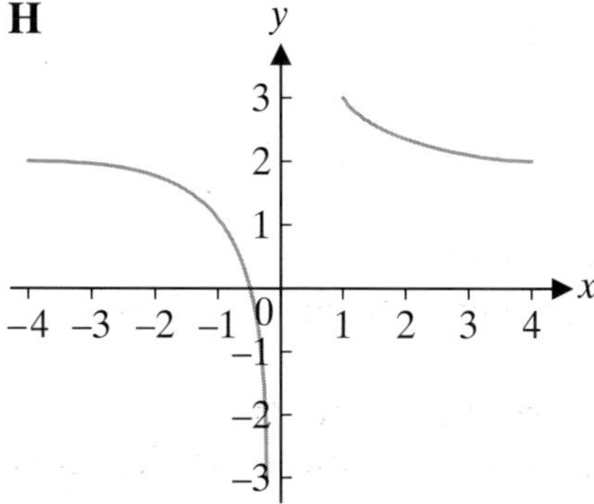

I

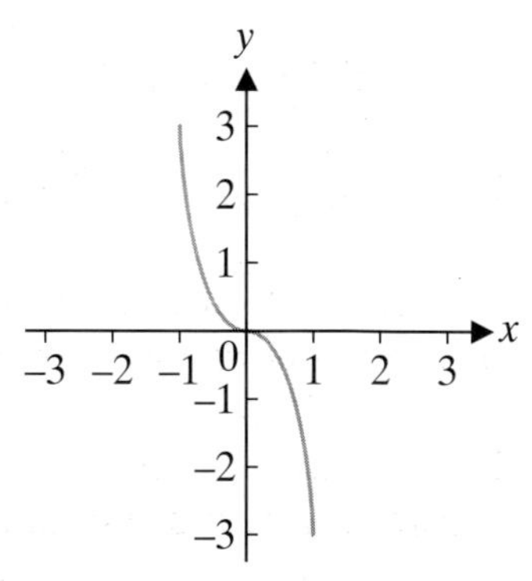

5 Sketch a set of axes like those in question **4**.
On the same set of axes sketch and label the graph of each of the functions below.
Do not work out tables of values for the functions. Use what you know about the shape of graphs of functions like
$y = x^3 + c$, $y = ax^3$, $y = \frac{a}{x}$ and $y = \frac{1}{x} + c$ to help you.

(a) $y = x^3$ **(b)** $y = x^3 + 2$ **(c)** $y = \frac{1}{x}$ **(d)** $y = x^3 - 2$

18.7 Drawing accurate graphs of more complex functions

Example 3

(a) Copy and complete this table of values for the function

$y - x^2 - x + \frac{2}{x}$

x	–3	–2	–1	–0.5	–0.2	0.2	0.5	1	2	3
x^2	9			0.25		0.04		1		9
$-x$	3			0.5		–0.2		–1		–3
$\frac{2}{x}$	–0.7			–4		10		2		0.7
y	11.3			–3.25		9.8		2		6.7

For more complex functions build up a table of values step by step like this.

(b) Draw the graph of $y = x^2 - x + \frac{2}{x}$

(c) Use your graph to solve the equation $x^2 - x + \frac{2}{x} = 5$

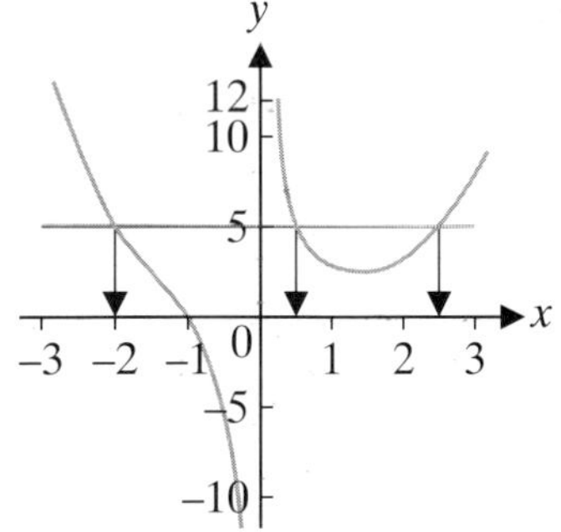

(a) You can copy and complete the table!
(b) You need to draw a graph with x values from –3 to 3 and y from –10 to 12.
Plot the points then join them up with a smooth curve.
There will be a break in the curve at $x = 0$ because the equation contains $\frac{2}{x}$

$\frac{2}{0}$ has no value

(c) Find the value 5 on the y-axis. Draw a line through the point (0, 5) parallel to the x-axis to meet the curve (it does so in three places). The three possible solutions to the equation

$$x^2 - x + \frac{2}{x} = 5$$

are $x = -2$, $x = 0.4$ and $x = 2.5$

Exercise 18H

You need 2 mm squared graph paper.

1 **(a)** Copy and complete this table of values for the function $y = x^3 + 2x^2$

x	–3	–2	–1.5	–1	–0.5	0	0.5	1	1.5	2
x^3	–27		–3.375					1		8
$2x^2$	18		4.5					2		8
y	–9		1.125					3		16

(b) Draw the graph of $y = x^3 + 2x^2$

(c) Use your graph to solve the equation $x^3 + 2x^2 = 2$

2 **(a)** Copy and complete this table of values for the function

$y = \frac{1}{x} + x^2$

There is no 0 column as you cannot calculate $\frac{1}{x}$ if $x = 0$

x	–2	–1.5	–1	–0.5	–0.1	0.1	0.5	1	1.5	2
$\frac{1}{x}$	–0.5			–2		10				
x^2	4			0.25		0.01				
y	3.5			–1.75		10.01				

(b) Draw the graph of $y = \frac{1}{x} + x^2$.

(Note: there is a break in the graph at $x = 0$.)

(c) Use your graph to solve the equation $\frac{1}{x} + x^2 = 3$.

(Hint: there are three possible solutions.)

Draw the graphs of the functions in questions **3** to **7** on graph paper.

3 $y = x^3 + 4$ from $x = -3$ to 3

4 $y = x^3 - 5x$ from $x = -3$ to 3

5 $y = x^3 - 2x^2 - 4x$ from $x = -2$ to 4

Use $x = -3, -2, -1, -0.5, -0.2, 0.2, 0.5, 1, 2$ and 3 for questions **6** and **7**

6 $y = 5 - \frac{4}{x}$ **7** $y = x^2 + 3 + \frac{2}{x}$

18.8 Solving equations by trial and improvement

If you did questions **1** and **2** of the last exercise you will have found that solving complex equations such as $x^3 + 2x^2 = 2$ by drawing a graph can take a long time.

Sometimes it is quicker to take a guess at the answer and improve upon it by a trial and improvement method until you have a good approximate answer.

Example 4

Solve the equation $x^3 + 2x^2 = 2$ giving your answer correct to 2 decimal places.

Draw a table like this one:

Put x equal to a number that you think might be the answer, for example 10.

When $x = 10$, $x^3 + 2x^2$ is bigger than 2 so put x equal to a smaller number, for example 1.

Repeat this process, trying values of x that bring $x^3 + 2x^2$ closer and closer to 2.

The solution is between 0.83 and 0.84. Try putting $x = 0.835$, half way between the two.

x	x^3	$2x^2$	$x^3 + 2x^2$	Bigger or smaller than 2
10	1000	200	1200	bigger
1	1	2	3	bigger
0	0	0	0	smaller
0.5	0.125	0.5	0.625	smaller
0.7	0.345	0.98	1.323	smaller
0.9	0.729	1.62	2.349	bigger
0.8	0.512	1.28	1.792	smaller
0.85	0.614 125	1.445	2.059 125	bigger
0.84	0.592 704	1.4112	2.003 904	bigger
0.83	0.571 787	1.3778	1.949 587	smaller
0.835	0.486122	1.39445	1.880573	smaller

The solution is between 0.835 and 0.84. Any number in this range rounds to 0.84 (to 2 d.p.). So the solution of the equation $x^3 + 2x^2 = 2$ is $x = 0.84$ (correct to 2 d.p.).

■ **You can find approximate solutions of complex equations by trial and improvement.**

Exercise 18I

1 Solve these equations by trial and improvement. Give your answers correct to 2 decimal places.

(a) $x^3 + 2x = 4$ **(b)** $2x^3 = 3$ **(c)** $x^3 - x^2 = 3$

(d) Find a solution bigger than 0 for $x^3 - 3x = 6$

(e) Find a solution bigger than 1 for $x^2 + \frac{1}{x} = 5$

(f) Find a solution bigger than 0 for $2x^2 - \frac{1}{x} = 9$

2 Use a trial and improvement method to find the length of a side of a cube which has a volume of 2 litres.
Give your answer correct to the nearest millimetre.
(Hint: call the length of a side of the cube x cm.)

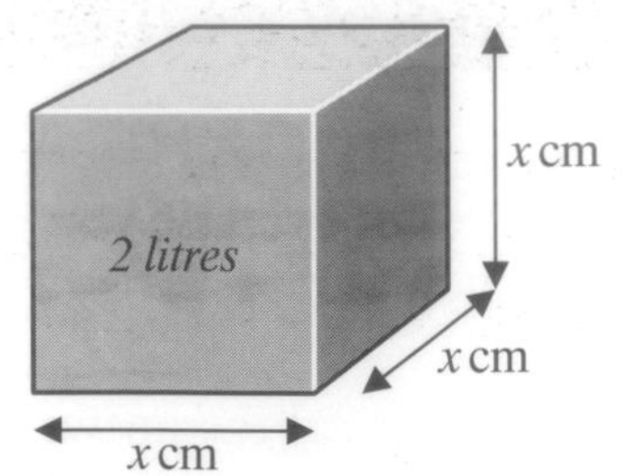

1 litre = 1000 cm^3
10 mm = 1 cm
1 mm = 0.1 cm

3 A cuboid has length $2x$ cm, width $3x$ cm and height x cm. The volume of the cuboid is 1100 cm^3.
Use a trial and improvement method to find the lengths of the sides, correct to the nearest millimetre.

18.9 Graphs that describe real life situations

You do not always need an accurately drawn graph to understand the situation that the graph represents.

In this section the axes are usually labelled, but they often have no values marked. Usually the axes meet at the point (0, 0).

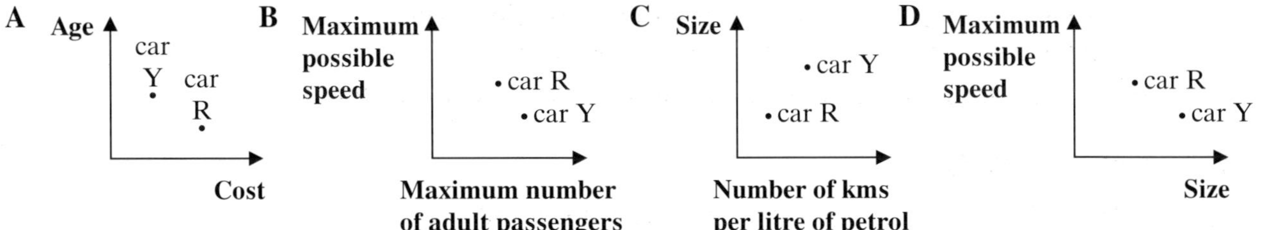

- Graph **A** shows that car Y is older than car R.
- Graph **B** shows that car R can travel faster than car Y.
- Graph **C** shows that car Y can travel further on one litre of petrol than car R.

You can use the information from graphs **A** and **B** to mark points that represent car R and car Y on this graph:

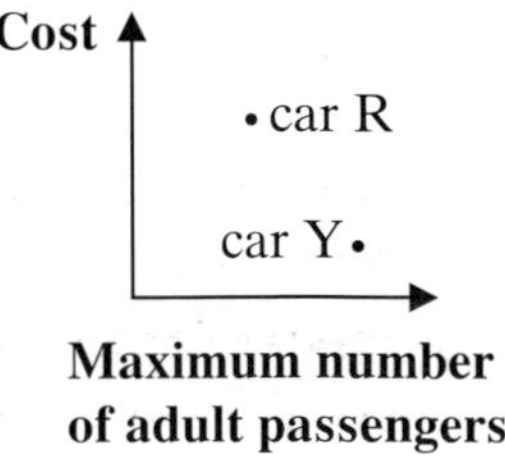

- Graph **A** shows that car R costs more than car Y so R is above Y.
- Graph **B** shows that car Y holds more adults than car R so Y is to the right of R.

■ **You can draw sketch graphs to represent given information from real life situations.**

Exercise 18J

1 From graph **C** write down another statement about the cars.

2 From graph **D** write down two statements about the cars.

3 Copy each graph and mark two points to represent car R and car Y.

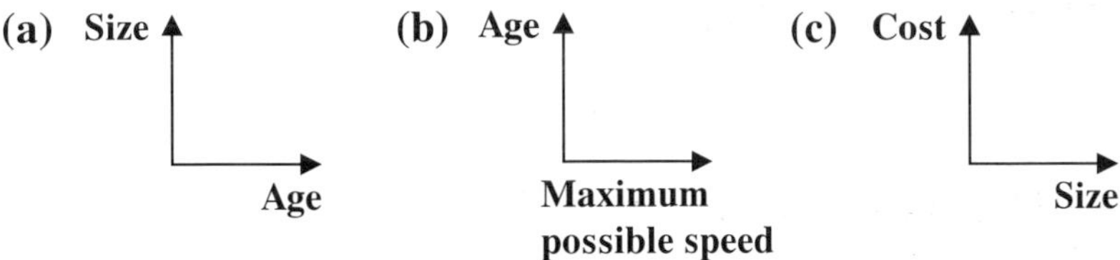

4

The point (f) on the scatter graph represents Tom.

(a) Write down the letter of each other point on the graph followed by the name of the person it represents.

(b) Use the graph to find who is the oldest person in the picture.

Practical activity

If possible try this experiment. Collect several transparent containers like these:

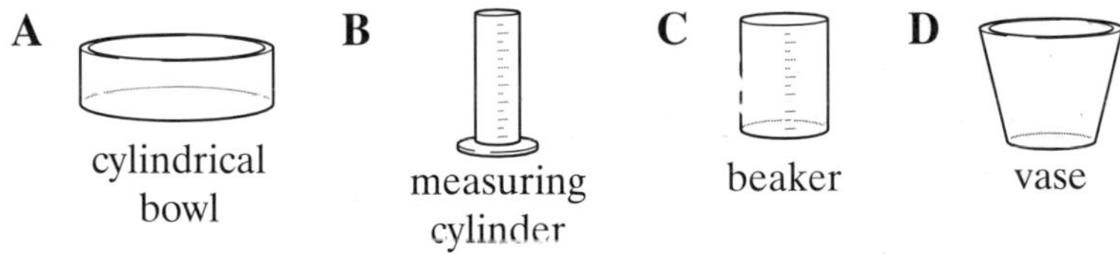

step 1: pour water at a steady rate into the first container and watch how quickly the water level rises

step 2: repeat for the other containers, making sure that the water pours in at the same steady rate

step 3: write down what you notice and discuss your results

You should find that:

- the water level rises at a steady rate in containers like **A**, **B** and **C**
- if the container is narrow the water level rises steadily but more quickly
- in a container like **D** the water level does not rise at a steady rate; the rate gradually gets slower.

Drawing graphs to show water levels

The tanks **P**, **Q**, **R** and **S** have circular cross-sections and they contain water.

They all start off with the same depth of water. The water is pumped out of the tanks at the same steady rate.

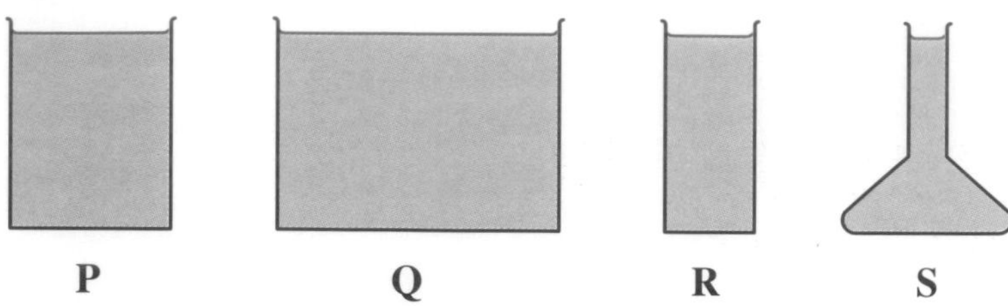

The graph shows the relationship between the water level in each tank and the volume of water pumped out of it.

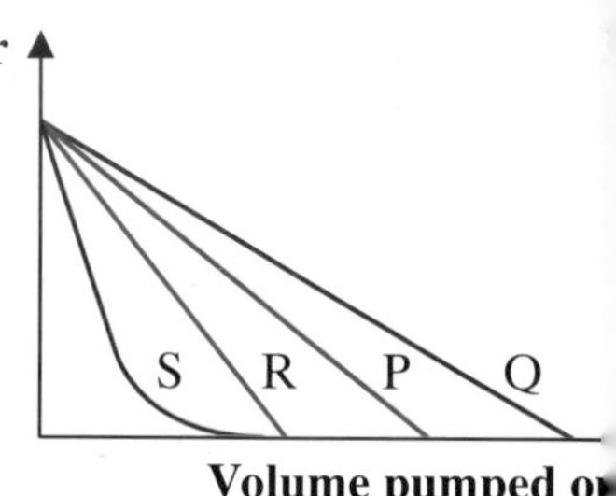

- Tank **Q** has a bigger area of cross-section than **P**. When the same volume has flowed out of each tank the water level in **Q** remains higher than in **P**. So the graph for **Q** is less steep than the graph for **P**.
- The water level in tank **R** drops more quickly than in **P**, so the graph for **R** is steeper.
- In tank **S** the level drops more quickly and steadily at first, then it gradually drops more slowly. The graph is straight to begin with (steeper than for **R**), but then it is curved to show the changing speed.

Exercise 18K

1 Here are some graphs:

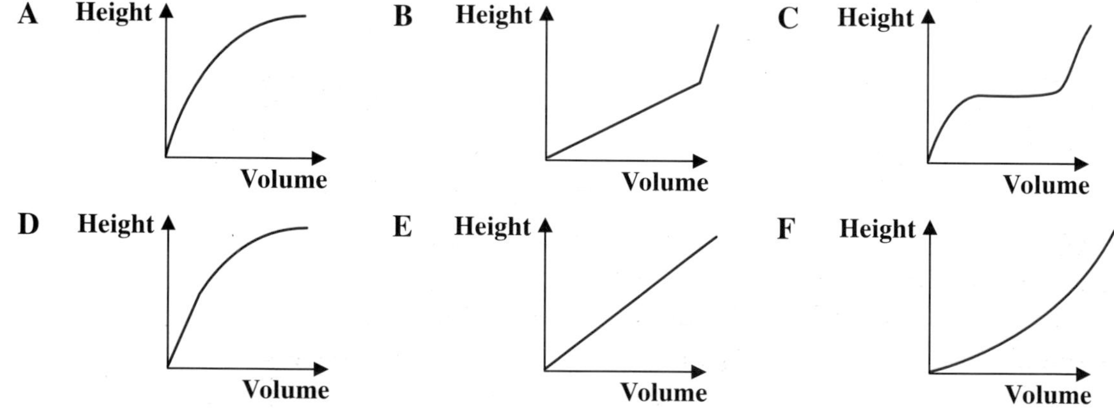

Coloured liquid is poured into these containers at a steady rate. For each one write down the letter of the graph which best illustrates the relationship between the height of the liquid and the volume in the container.

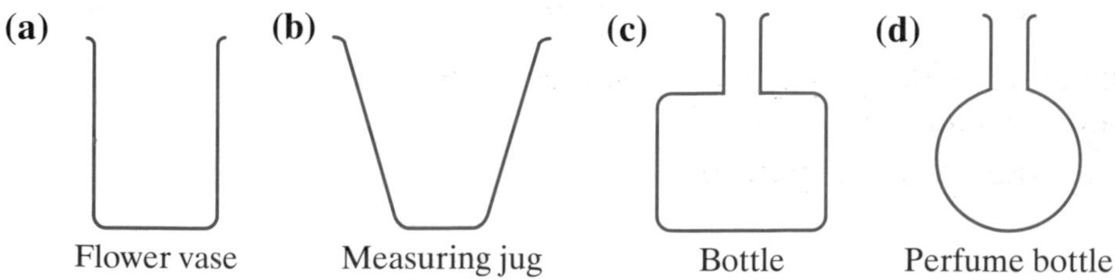

2 Water is poured into these containers at a steady rate. Sketch a graph to show the relationship between the water level height and the volume of water in each container:

(a) 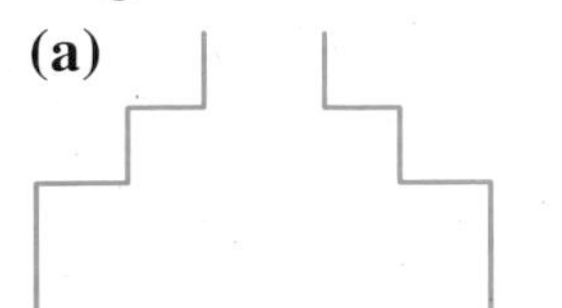
(b) 
(c) 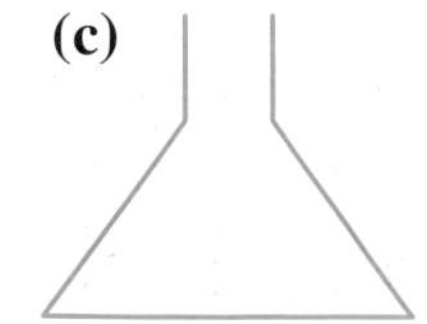
(d) 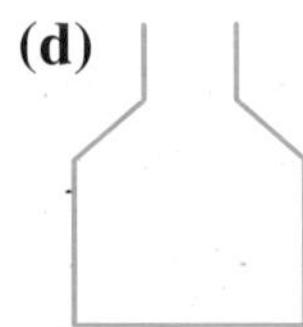

3 A DJ can control the sound level of the records he plays at a disco. The sketch graph below is a graph of the sound level against the time whilst one record was played.

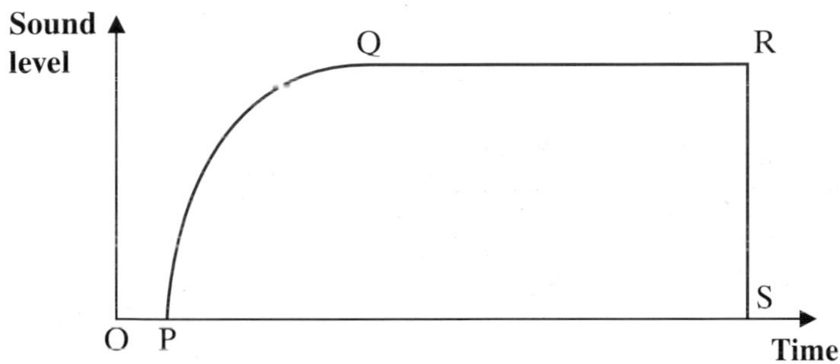

(a) Describe how the sound level changed between P and Q on the graph whilst the record was being played.

(b) Give one possible reason for the third part, RS, of the sketch graph. [L]

4

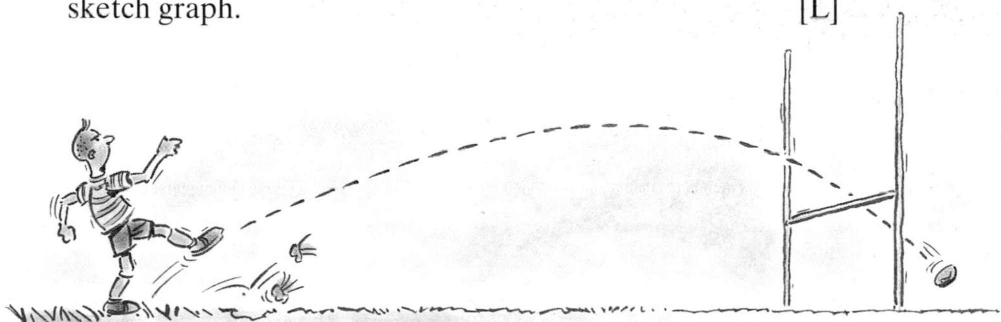

Cliff kicks a rugby ball over the goal posts. He thinks about the speed of the ball as it passes over the goal post and tries to imagine what the graph of speed against time would look like.

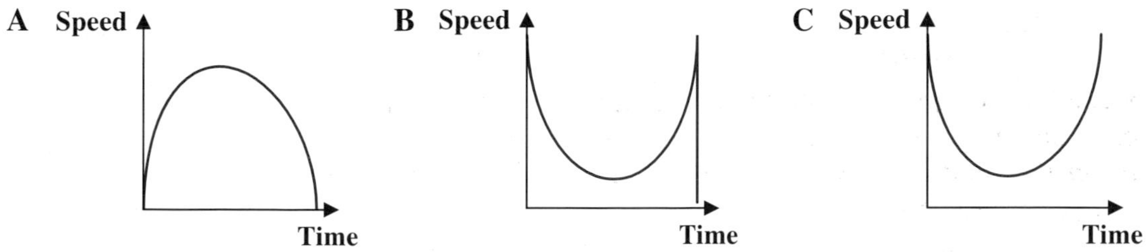

(a) Write down the letter of the graph which best illustrates the movement of the ball.

(b) Give reasons for your answer to part **(a)**.

5 A

0 80
Speed in miles per hour

B

0 80
Speed in miles per hour

C

0 80
Speed in miles per hour

D

0 80
Speed in miles per hour

E

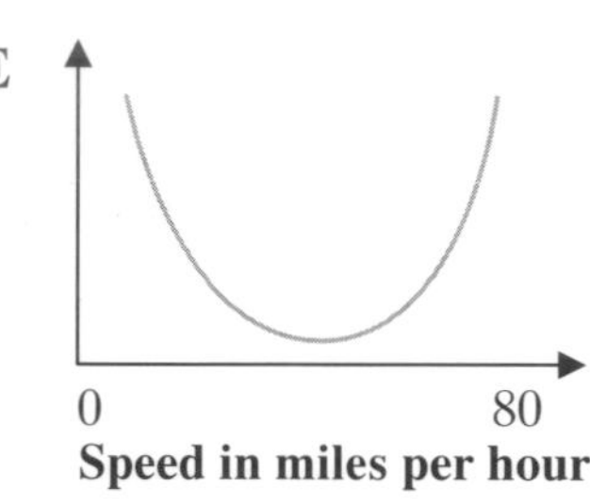

The diagrams show the shapes of five graphs **A**, **B**, **C**, **D** and **E**.
The vertical axes have not been labelled.
On one of the graphs, the missing label is
'Speed in km per hour'.

(a) Write down the letter of this graph.

On one of the graphs the missing label is 'Petrol consumption in miles per gallon'. It shows that the car travels furthest on 1 gallon of petrol when it is travelling at 56 miles per hour.

(b) Write down the letter of this graph. [L]

18.10 Summary of graph shapes

- Graphs of the form $y = x^3 + c$ all have the same shape. They cut the y-axis at the point $(0, c)$.

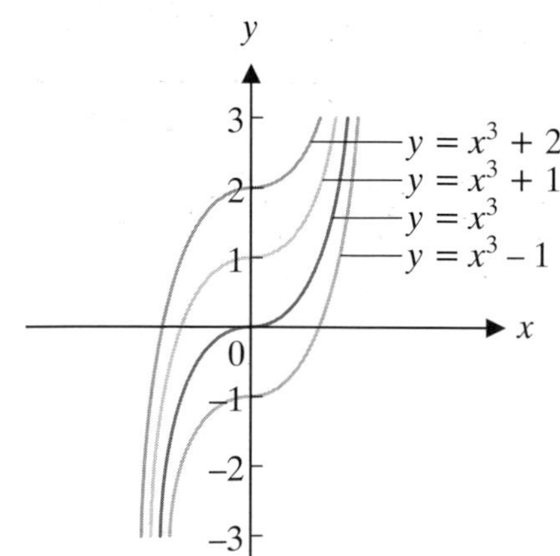

- Graphs of the form $y = ax^3$, where a is positive, have a similar shape. The greater the value of a the narrower the shape.

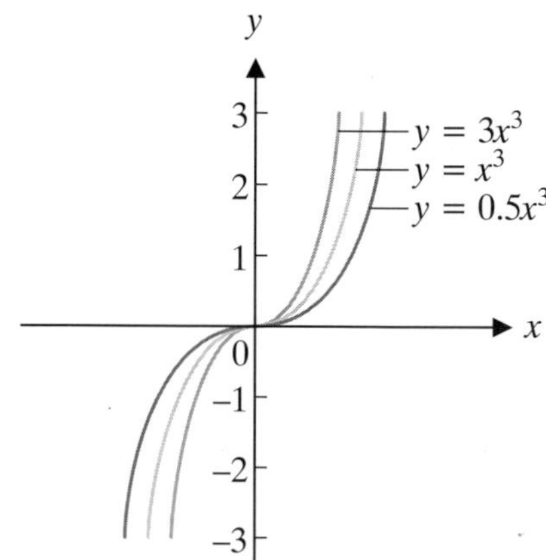

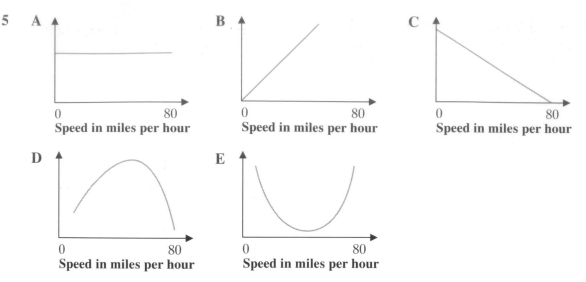

- Graphs of the form $y = ax^3$, where a is negative, have the same shape as when a is positive but reflected in the x-axis.

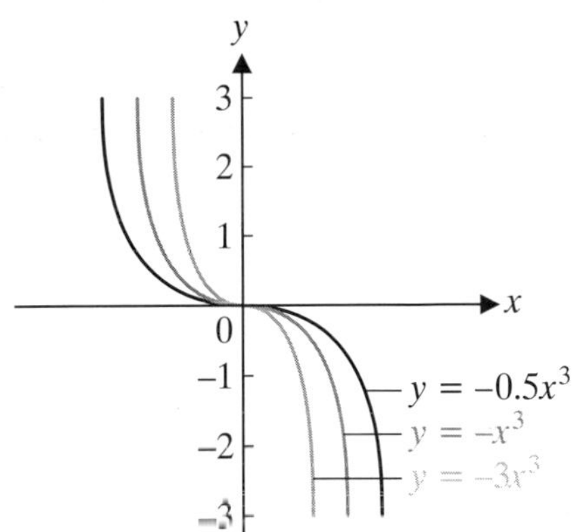

- The graph of $y = \frac{1}{x}$ has a break in it when $x = 0$.

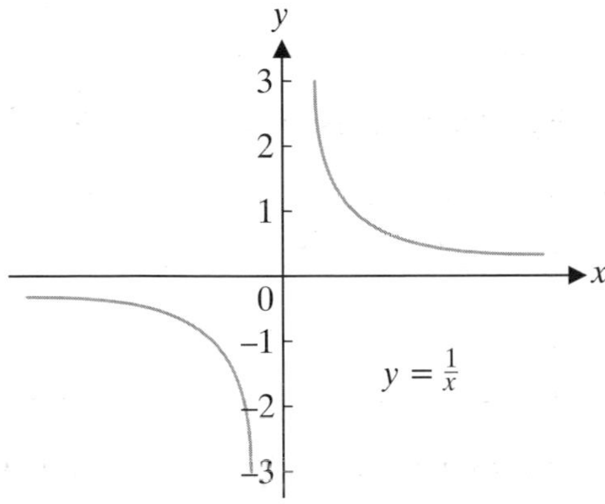

- Graphs of the form $y = \frac{1}{x} + c$ have the same shape as the graph of $y = \frac{1}{x}$ but move up the y-axis if c is positive and down the y-axis if c is negative.

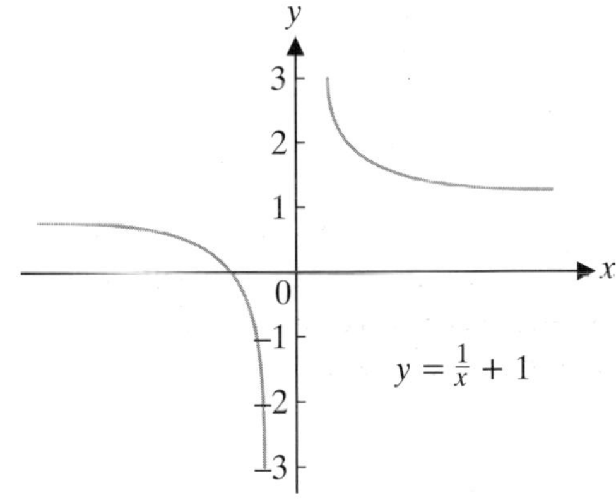

- Graphs of the form $y = \frac{a}{x}$, where a is positive, have a similar shape to the graph of $y = \frac{1}{x}$ but as a gets bigger they move further away from the axes. Graphs of the form $y = \frac{a}{x}$, where a is negative, have the same shape as for when a is positive but are reflected in the x-axis.

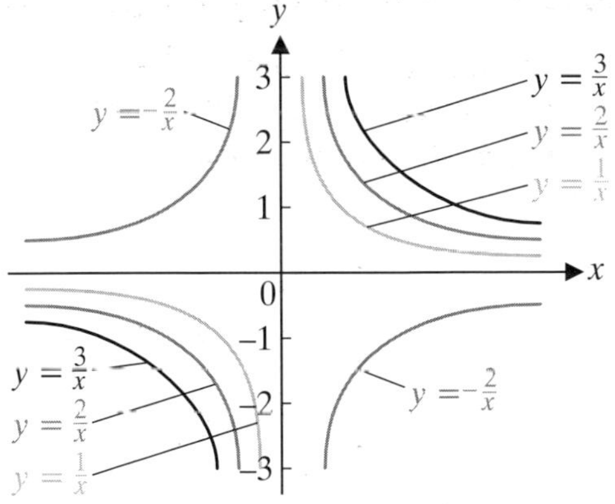

Summary of key points

1. Graphs of functions of the form $y = x^2 + c$, where c can be positive, negative or 0, all have a ∪-shape. The bottom of the ∪-shape cuts the y-axis at the point $(0, c)$. The y-axis is the line of symmetry.

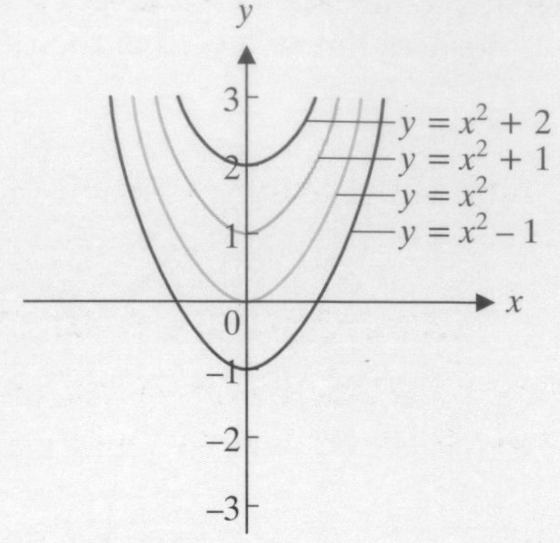

2. Graphs of functions of the form $y = ax^2$, where a is positive, all have a ∪-shape. The greater the value of a the narrower the ∪-shape. They all pass through the point (0, 0).
3. Graphs of functions of the form $y = -ax^2$ are the same as the graphs for $y = ax^2$ reflected in the x-axis.

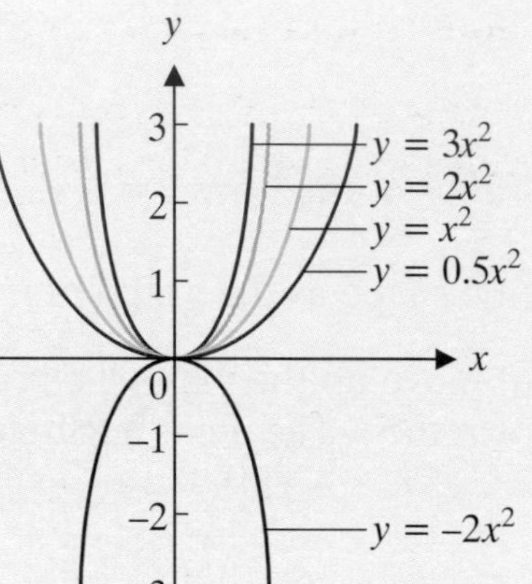

4. Quadratic equations of the type $ax^2 + c = d$, where a, c and d are numbers, can be solved by drawing the inverse number machine for $y = ax^2 + c$ and sending d through it.

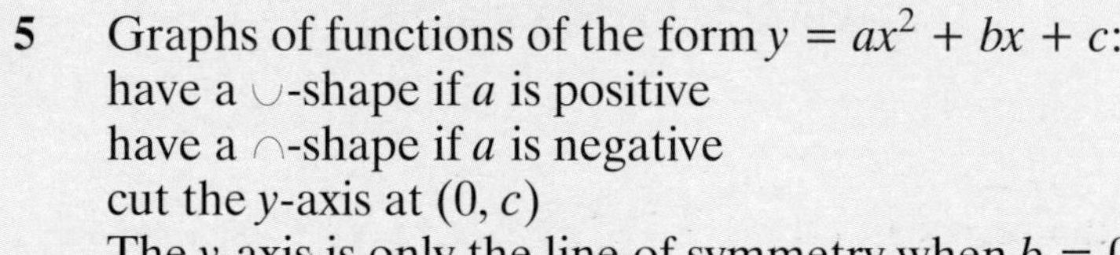

5. Graphs of functions of the form $y = ax^2 + bx + c$:
   have a ∪-shape if a is positive
   have a ∩-shape if a is negative
   cut the y-axis at $(0, c)$
   The y-axis is only the line of symmetry when $b = 0$
6. More complex quadratic equations such as $ax^2 + bx + c = d$ can be solved by drawing the graph for $y = ax^2 + bx + c$ and the line $y = d$.
7. Quadratic equations can have 0, 1 or 2 solutions.
8. You can find approximate solutions of complex equations by trial and improvement.
9. You can draw sketch graphs to represent given information from real life situations.

19 Probability 2

This unit is about finding probabilities when two events take place.

19.1 Independent events

When two coins are tossed the outcome of tossing the second coin does not depend on the outcome of tossing the first coin and vice versa.

- **When the outcome of one event does not affect the outcome of another event they are called independent events.**

All the possible combined outcomes of tossing two coins can be displayed and found using a space diagram like this:

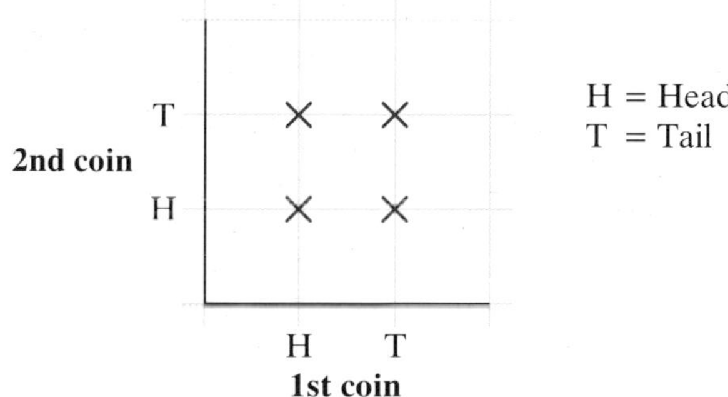

Each cross represents a different outcome. There are 4 different outcomes, all equally likely. These four outcomes are: HH, HT, TH, TT. You find these by reading off the 'coordinates' of each cross.

Another way of displaying and finding the possible combined outcomes of tossing two coins is by using a tree diagram.

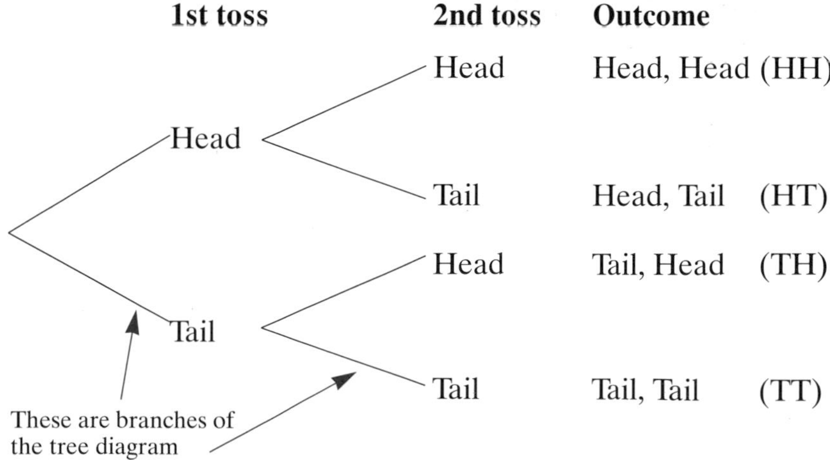

Example 1

A dice is rolled and a coin is tossed.

(a) Show all the possible combined outcomes in a space diagram.
(b) List all the possible outcomes.
(c) Show all the possible combined outcomes in a tree diagram.

(a) Space diagram

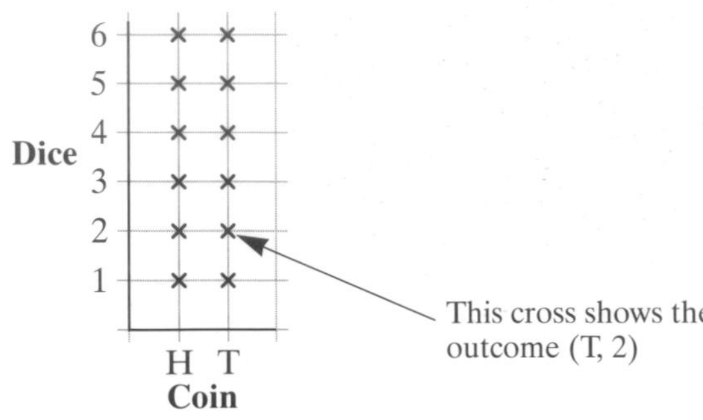

(b) There are 12 outcomes:
(H, 1), (H, 2), (H, 3), (H, 4), (H, 5), (H, 6),
(T, 1), (T, 2), (T, 3), (T, 4), (T, 5), (T, 6).

(c) Tree diagram

Toss of coin	Roll of dice	Outcome
H	1	(H, 1)
	2	(H, 2)
	3	(H, 3)
	4	(H, 4)
	5	(H, 5)
	6	(H, 6)
T	1	(T, 1)
	2	(T, 2)
	3	(T, 3)
	4	(T, 4)
	5	(T, 5)
	6	(T, 6)

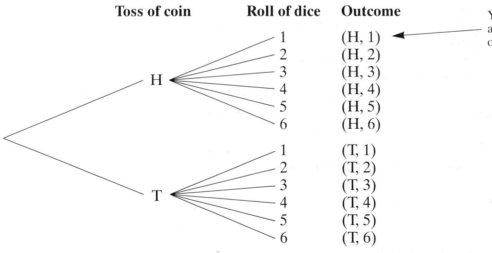

You go along one branch and then along a following one to get this outcome

Exercise 19A

1 A five-sided spinner is spun and a coin is tossed.
  (a) Show the combined outcomes in a space diagram and in a tree diagram.
  (b) List the combined outcomes and state the number of equally likely combined outcomes.

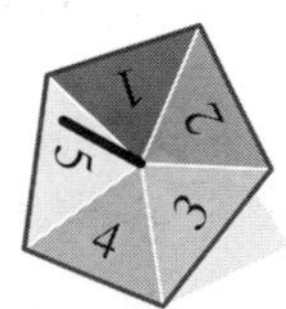

The score on the spinner is 4

2 In a bag there are three balls: one red, one blue and one yellow. A ball is selected, the colour is recorded and the ball is replaced. A second ball is then selected and the colour is recorded.
  (a) Show in a space diagram and in a tree diagram all the possible combined outcomes.
  (b) List these combined outcomes and state the number of equally likely combined outcomes.

For a reminder about equally likely outcomes see page 32.

3 Mary wants to buy a soft drink and a packet of crisps.

She has four choices of soft drink: cola, lemonade, orangeade and cherryade.
She has three choices of crisps: ready salted, salt and vinegar and cheese and onion.
Draw **(a)** a space diagram and
(b) a tree diagram
to show all the possible combined outcomes of the different choices she could make.

(c) List the different combined outcomes and state the number of different outcomes.

4 Peter and Christine are going on holiday to France. They can travel to the coast by car, coach or train, and then cross the channel by ferry, train, helicopter or hovercraft.

(a) In a space diagram and in a tree diagram show all the combined outcomes of the different ways they could travel to France.

(b) How many different ways could they travel?

19.2 Relative frequency

Unit 3 (page 29) shows that you can estimate the probability that an event will occur by carrying out an experiment or game and using the rule:

$$\text{estimated probability} = \frac{\text{number of successful trials}}{\text{total number of trials}}$$

This is also called the **relative frequency**.

■ $$\textbf{relative frequency} = \frac{\textbf{number of successful trials}}{\textbf{total number of trials}}$$

The relative frequency of an event occurring is used when you cannot calculate probabilities based on equally likely outcomes (page 32).

It can also be used to test whether a game of chance is fair, for example: to test whether a dice is fair.

Example 2

Show how you undertake an experiment and set out the results to test whether a coin is fair or not.

step 1: the number of trials (times the coin is tossed) must be large (about 500).

step 2: record in a table the number of heads after 50 throws, 100 throws, 150 throws and so on.

Number of trials	Number of successful trials	Relative frequency
50	20	$\frac{20}{50} = 0.40$
100	45	$\frac{45}{100} = 0.45$
150	71	$\frac{71}{150} = 0.47$
200	104	$\frac{104}{200} = 0.52$
250	119	$\frac{119}{250} = 0.48$
300	146	$\frac{146}{300} = 0.49$
350	172	$\frac{172}{350} = 0.49$
400	203	$\frac{203}{400} = 0.51$
450	222	$\frac{222}{450} = 0.49$
500	245	$\frac{245}{500} = 0.49$

step 3: work out the relative frequency (estimate of probability) correct to 2 d.p.

step 4: illustrate your results using a line graph.

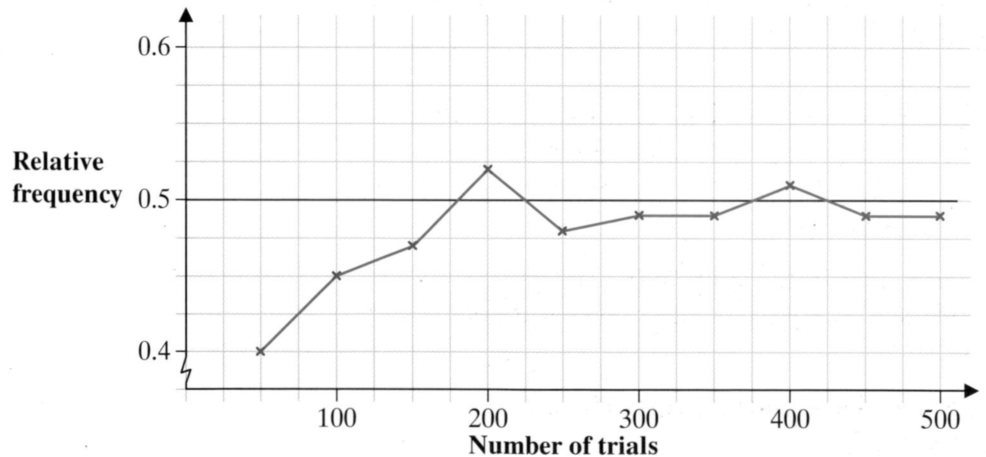

This line shows the probability of getting a head calculated by assuming that all outcomes are equally likely.

As the number of trials increases, the relative frequency of throwing a head (the estimated probability that you throw a head) settles down at about 0.49. This is very close to the calculated probability of 0.5, so it is reasonable to assume that the dice is fair.

Exercise 19B

You need a dice, blue beads, red beads, a bag, card and scissors.

1 Test a dice of your own to see whether or not it is fair.

2 Ask a friend to place some of the blue beads and red beads in the bag. You must not look in the bag or ask how many there are of each colour. You need to use relative frequency to estimate the proportion of red and blue beads.

(a) Carry out an experiment to work out the relative frequency of red beads.
Record your results in a table and work out the relative frequency after different numbers of trials.

(b) Record the relative frequencies on a line graph.

(c) Read off the relative frequency where the graph 'settles down'.

(d) Use the relative frequency to work out the ratio of red to blue beads in the bag.

3 Make a dice of your own out of card.
Test the dice to see whether it is fair or not.

4 A dice is thrown and the score is recorded. After many trials the relative frequency of throwing a 5 is found to be 0.09.
Compare this with the calculated probability based on equally likely outcomes for a fair dice. Do you think the dice is fair?

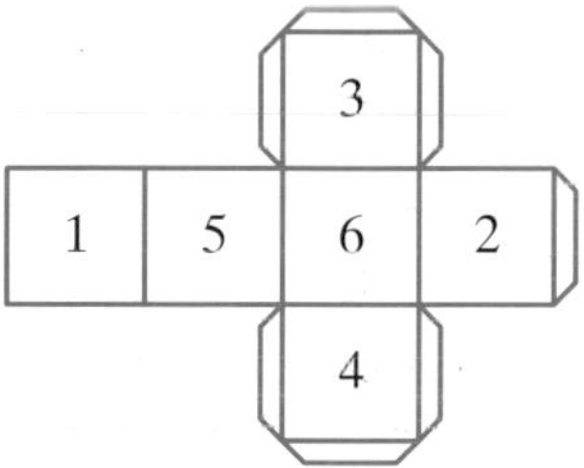

Net of dice

19.3 The probability of combined events

You need to be able to calculate the probability of combined events like those at the start of this unit.

Remember:

- when the outcome of the first event does not affect the outcome of the second event, the two events are independent.
- when one outcome prevents another outcome from happening the events are mutually exclusive.

The OR rule for calculating the probability of mutually exclusive events A and B is introduced on page 34. This is the probability that either A OR B will happen:

■ **When two events A and B are mutually exclusive:**
P(A or B) = P (A) + P (B)

This can be extended to any number of mutually exclusive events.

You also need to know the AND rule for independent events:

When two events A and B are independent the probability that both A AND B happen is the probability of A × the probability of B

■ **P (A and B) = P (A) × P (B)**

This is known as the **AND rule**.
Similarly when three events A, B and C are independent the probability that A and B and C will happen is:

P (A and B and C) = P (A) × P (B) × P (C)

and so on for any number of independent events.

Example 3

A coin is tossed and a dice is rolled.
Find the probability that a Tail and a 3 will be obtained.

As these events are independent we use the AND rule.

$$\text{P(Tail and 3)} = \text{P(Tail)} \times \text{P(3)}$$

Now $\quad \text{P(Tail)} = \frac{1}{2}$ and $\text{P(3)} = \frac{1}{6}$

so $\quad \text{P(Tail and 3)} = \frac{1}{2} \times \frac{1}{6} = \frac{1}{12}$

Example 4

These two dice are rolled.
What is the probability that two sixes will be obtained?

As the events are independent use the AND rule.

$$\text{P(six and six)} = \text{P(six)} \times \text{P(six)}$$

Now $\quad \text{P(six)} = \frac{1}{6}$

So $\quad \text{P(six and six)} = \frac{1}{6} \times \frac{1}{6} = \frac{1}{36}$

Exercise 19C

1 A coin is tossed and a dice is rolled.
Work out the probability that a head and a 2 will be obtained.

2 Two dice are thrown.
What is the probability that two fives will be obtained?

3 A coin is tossed and a card is drawn at random from a normal pack of playing cards.
What is the probability of getting:
(a) a Head and the Ace of spades
(b) a Tail and a club
(c) a Tail and a red card
(d) a Tail and a picture card
(e) a Head and a ten
(f) a Head and a red two?

4 In a bunch of roses 3 are red, 2 are white and 1 is pink. In a bunch of carnations 3 are white and 2 are mauve. One rose and one carnation are both selected at random.
Work out the probability of getting:
(a) a red rose and a white carnation
(b) a red rose and a mauve carnation
(c) a white rose and a white carnation
(d) a pink rose and a white carnation
(e) a pink rose and a mauve carnation.

19.4 Tree diagrams

■ **You can use tree diagrams to help solve probability problems involving combined events.**

Example 5

A dice is rolled twice.
Draw a tree diagram to help you find the probability of throwing:
(a) two sixes (b) one six (c) no sixes

If you draw a tree diagram for every possible outcome, 1, 2, 3, 4, 5 or 6 it will be very large. Here you are only interested in the outcomes 6 and not 6, so use these two outcomes in the tree diagram branches.

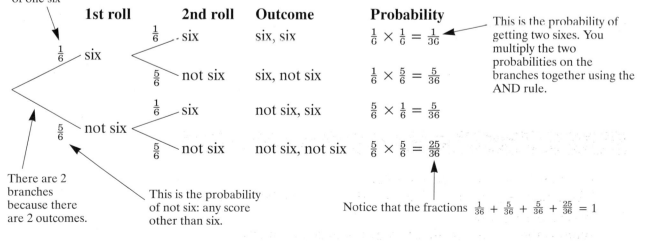

1st roll	2nd roll	Outcome	Probability
$\frac{1}{6}$ six	$\frac{1}{6}$ six	six, six	$\frac{1}{6} \times \frac{1}{6} = \frac{1}{36}$
	$\frac{5}{6}$ not six	six, not six	$\frac{1}{6} \times \frac{5}{6} = \frac{5}{36}$
$\frac{5}{6}$ not six	$\frac{1}{6}$ six	not six, six	$\frac{5}{6} \times \frac{1}{6} = \frac{5}{36}$
	$\frac{5}{6}$ not six	not six, not six	$\frac{5}{6} \times \frac{5}{6} = \frac{25}{36}$

This is the probability of one six

This is the probability of getting two sixes. You multiply the two probabilities on the branches together using the AND rule.

There are 2 branches because there are 2 outcomes.

This is the probability of not six: any score other than six.

Notice that the fractions $\frac{1}{36} + \frac{5}{36} + \frac{5}{36} + \frac{25}{36} = 1$

(a) Probability of throwing two sixes:
There is only one successful outcome for this event.
Either: use the AND rule

$$P(\text{two sixes}) = P(\text{six}) \times P(\text{six})$$
$$= \frac{1}{6} \times \frac{1}{6} = \frac{1}{36}$$

Or: you could read the answer directly from the tree diagram.

(b) Probability of throwing one six:
This involves two branches of the tree diagram which have outcomes (six, not six) and (not six, six). As these outcomes are mutually exclusive (both cannot happen at the same time) use the OR rule.

$$P(\text{A or B}) = P(\text{A}) + P(\text{B})$$

$$P(\text{one six}) = P(\text{six, not six}) + P(\text{not six, six})$$
$$= \frac{5}{36} + \frac{5}{36} = \frac{10}{36}$$

(c) Probability of throwing no sixes:
There is only one outcome for this event, taken directly from the tree diagram.

$$P\ (\text{no sixes}) = \frac{5}{6} \times \frac{5}{6} = \frac{25}{36}$$

The outcome must be two sixes, one six or no sixes so it is certain that one of these outcomes will happen.

Notice that the sum of all these outcomes is 1

$$\frac{1}{36} + \frac{10}{36} + \frac{25}{36} = \frac{36}{36}$$

The tree diagram could be extended with further branches on the right if the dice were rolled for a third time.

Example 6

A bag contains 5 red balls, 3 green balls and 2 white balls. A ball is selected at random and then replaced in the bag. A second ball is then selected at random.

(a) Draw a tree diagram for these events.
(b) What is the probability that:
  (i) both balls will be green
  (ii) both balls will be the same colour
  (iii) at least one red ball will be drawn?

(a) Let R, G and W represent red, green and white balls.

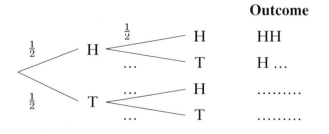

1st ball		2nd ball	Outcome	Probability
R ($\frac{5}{10}$)	$\frac{5}{10}$	R	RR	$\frac{5}{10} \times \frac{5}{10} = \frac{25}{100}$
	$\frac{3}{10}$	G	RG	$\frac{5}{10} \times \frac{3}{10} = \frac{15}{100}$
	$\frac{2}{10}$	W	RW	$\frac{5}{10} \times \frac{2}{10} = \frac{10}{100}$
G ($\frac{3}{10}$)	$\frac{5}{10}$	R	GR	$\frac{3}{10} \times \frac{5}{10} = \frac{15}{100}$
	$\frac{3}{10}$	G	GG	$\frac{3}{10} \times \frac{3}{10} = \frac{9}{100}$
	$\frac{2}{10}$	W	GW	$\frac{3}{10} \times \frac{2}{10} = \frac{6}{100}$
W ($\frac{2}{10}$)	$\frac{5}{10}$	R	WR	$\frac{2}{10} \times \frac{5}{10} = \frac{10}{100}$
	$\frac{3}{10}$	G	WG	$\frac{2}{10} \times \frac{3}{10} = \frac{6}{100}$
	$\frac{2}{10}$	W	WW	$\frac{2}{10} \times \frac{2}{10} = \frac{4}{100}$

Notice there are three branches, as on each turn a red, green or white ball could be selected.

(b) (i) P (GG) $= \frac{3}{10} \times \frac{3}{10} = \frac{9}{100}$ (from the tree diagram)

(ii) P (both balls same colour)

$= \text{P (RR)} + \text{P (GG)} + \text{P (WW)}$

$= \frac{25}{100} + \frac{9}{100} + \frac{4}{100} = \frac{38}{100}$

These are mutually exclusive events so use the **OR rule** and add the probabilities.

(iii) P (at least one red ball)

$= \text{P (RR)} + \text{P (RG)} + \text{P (RW)} + \text{P (GR)} + \text{P (WR)}$

$= \frac{25}{100} + \frac{15}{100} + \frac{10}{100} + \frac{15}{100} + \frac{10}{100}$

$= \frac{75}{100} = \frac{3}{4}$

Again these are mutually exclusive, so use the **OR rule** and add.

Exercise 19D

1 Keith tosses a fair coin twice.

(a) Copy and complete the tree diagram:

1st toss		2nd toss	Outcome	Probability
H ($\frac{1}{2}$)	$\frac{1}{2}$	H	HH	$\frac{1}{2} \times \frac{1}{2} = \frac{1}{4}$
	...	T	H ...	$\frac{1}{2} \times$ ... ...
T ($\frac{1}{2}$)	...	H	....	....
	...	T	....	....

(b) What is the probability that he will obtain:

(i) two heads

(ii) at least one head

(iii) no heads?

(Hint: 'at least one head' also includes the outcome of two heads.)

2 Wendy spins the spinner three times.

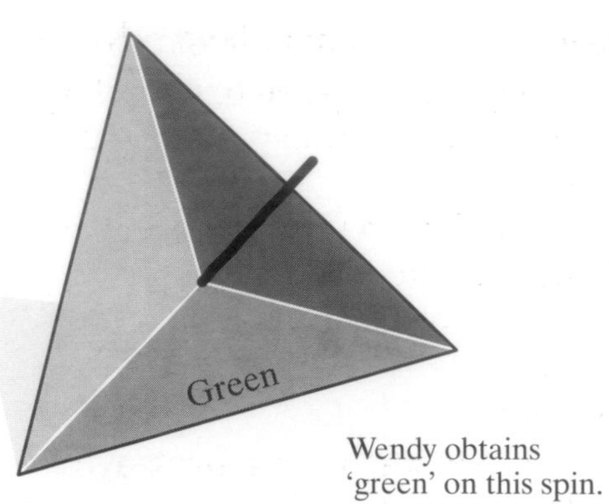

Wendy obtains 'green' on this spin.

(a) Copy and complete the tree diagram:

1st spin	2nd spin	3rd spin	Outcome	Probability
$\frac{1}{3}$ R	$\frac{1}{3}$ R	$\frac{1}{3}$ R	RRR	$\frac{1}{3} \times \frac{1}{3} \times \frac{1}{3} = \frac{1}{27}$
		G	RRG	
		B		
	$\frac{1}{3}$ G	R		
		G		
		B		
	$\frac{1}{3}$ B	R		
		G		
		B		
$\frac{1}{3}$ G	R			
	G			
	B			
$\frac{1}{3}$ B	R			
	G			
	B	R		
		G		
		B	BBB	$\frac{1}{3} \times \frac{1}{3} \times \frac{1}{3} = \frac{1}{27}$

Complete **all** the possible outcomes

Mark **every** branch with its probability

Find the probability of **each** outcome

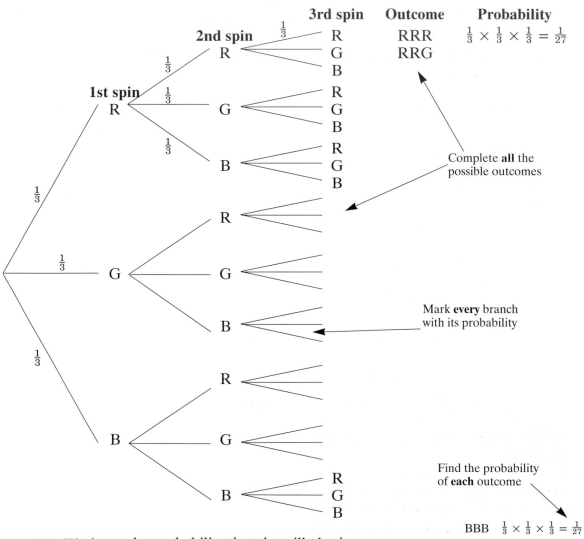

(b) Work out the probability that she will obtain:
(i) three blues
(ii) at least two greens
(iii) two reds and a blue
(iv) no blues.

For question **3** draw a tree diagram to help solve the problem.

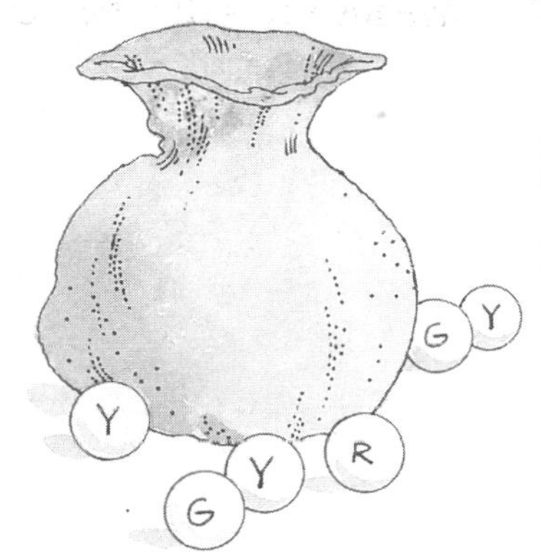

3 A bag contains 1 red ball, 2 green balls and 3 yellow balls. Winford chooses a ball at random and replaces it. He repeats this two more times.
Work out the probability that Winford will obtain:
(a) all 3 balls of the same colour
(b) all 3 balls of different colours
(c) 2 yellow balls
(d) no yellow balls.

4 You draw a card at random from a pack of 52 normal playing cards. You replace the card and draw another one.
What is the probability that you will obtain:
(a) 2 Aces **(b)** at least one Ace **(c)** no Aces?

5 Two dice are rolled. The numbers obtained are added together to get the score for the throw.
(a) Copy and complete the space diagram to show all the possible outcomes.

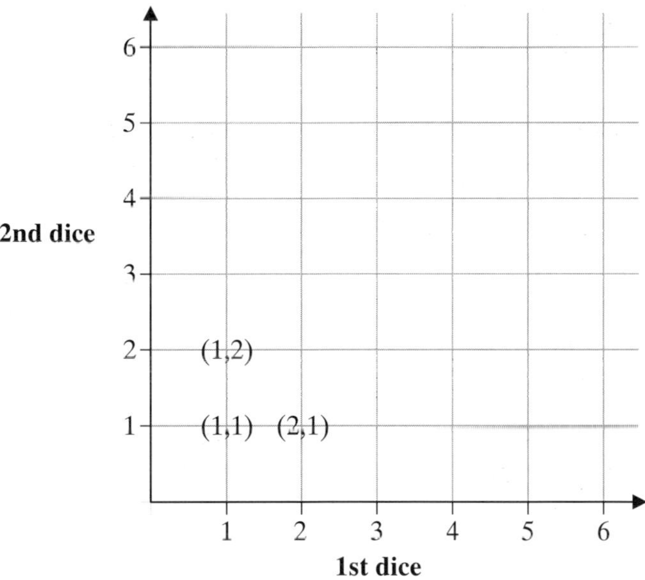

(b) What is the probability that a score of seven will be obtained?
(c) What is the probability that a score of seven will not be obtained?

The dice are both rolled again.
(d) Draw a tree diagram to show the probabilities of scoring a seven or not a seven in the two throws.
(e) Use the tree diagram to answer these questions.
What is the probability that you will obtain:
(i) a score of seven followed by a score of seven
(ii) at least one score of seven?

Exercise 19E Mixed questions

1 A game is played with two spinners. They are spun at the same time. The result shown in the diagram is Blue 3.

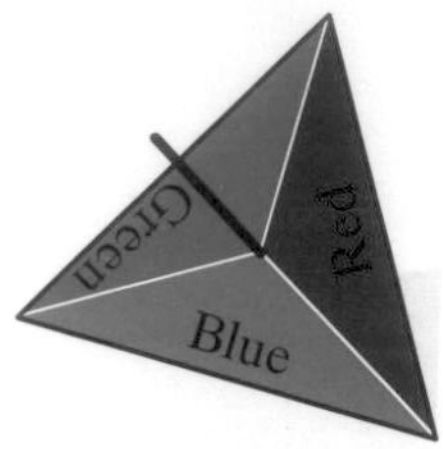

Spinner A

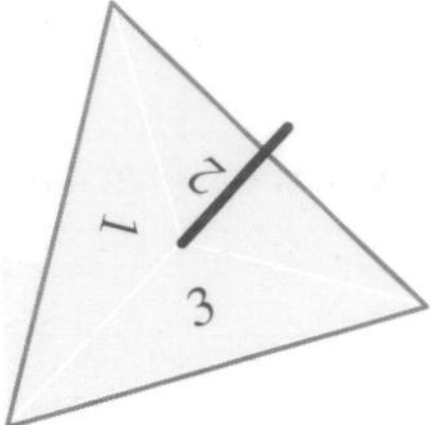

Spinner B

(a) List all the possible results when the spinners are spun.

Spinner A is a fair spinner.
(b) What is the probability of not getting green with spinner A?

Spinner B is weighted (biased).
The probability of getting a 3 is 0.2 and the probability of getting a 1 is 0.
(c) What is the probability of getting a 2 with spinner B?

Spinner B is going to be spun 100 times.
(d) Approximately how many times will it show
(i) a 3
(ii) a 1 or a 3? [L]

2 A box contains only blue pencils and red pencils.
6 of the pencils are blue and 5 are red.
A pencil is to be taken at random from the box.
Write down the probability that:
(i) a blue pencil will be taken
(ii) a blue pencil will **not** be taken. [L]

3 Some pupils have thought of a game to use at a school fair.

A tennis ball is rolled down a slope into one of eight holes. It can score a number from 1 to 8.

The pupils try out their game **200 times**.
The frequencies of the scores are shown on the diagram.

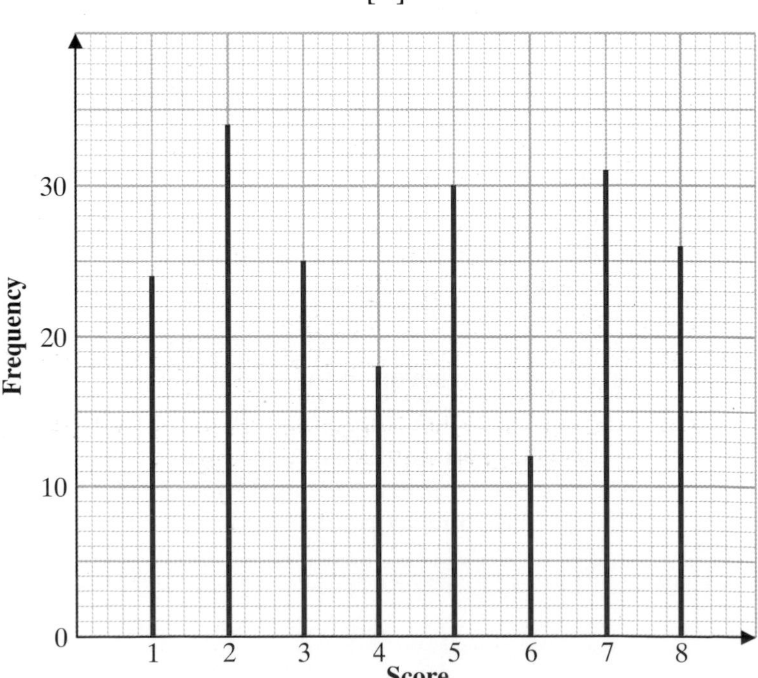

According to the diagram, which number is:
(a) (i) the hardest to score
(ii) the easiest to score?
(b) Estimate the probability that the next ball rolled will score 3. [L]

4 A bag contains a red bead, a black bead, a yellow bead and a white bead.
One single bead is to be picked out at random.
What is the probability that the bead picked will be:
(a) red
(b) pink
(c) not white? [L]

5 A six-faced dice and a coin are thrown at the same time.
One possible outcome is a Head and a 1 (H, 1).
List all the other possible outcomes.
(H, 1), ... [L]

6 Anil is conducting a series of tests on a biased coin.
He does 5 tests.
In each test he throws the coin 10 times and counts the number of Heads.
The table shows the result of the 5 tests.

1st 10 throws	2nd 10 throws	3rd 10 throws	4th 10 throws	5th 10 throws
7 Heads	6 Heads	8 Heads	6 Heads	9 Heads

Anil then calculates the proportion of Heads throughout his tests.
He sets out his calculations as shown below.

	Number of Heads	Proportion of Heads
1st 10 throws	7	$\frac{7}{10} = 0.7$
1st 20 throws	$7 + 6 = 13$	$\frac{13}{20} = 0.65$
1st 30 throws	$7 + 6 + 8 = 21$	
1st 40 throws		
1st 50 throws		

(a) Copy and complete the table.
(b) Explain what happens to the proportion of Heads as the number of throws increases. [L]

7 A bag contains counters which are green, blue or white.
When one counter is picked at random
the probability that it will be green is $\frac{1}{2}$
the probability that it will be blue is $\frac{1}{8}$
(a) What is the probability that a counter picked out at random will be either green or blue?
(b) What is the probability that a counter picked out at random will be either white or green? [L]

8 Ahmed and Kate play a game of tennis.
The probability that Ahmed will win is $\frac{5}{8}$.

Ahmed and Kate play a game of snooker.
The probability that Kate will win is $\frac{4}{7}$.

(a) Copy and complete the probability tree diagram below.

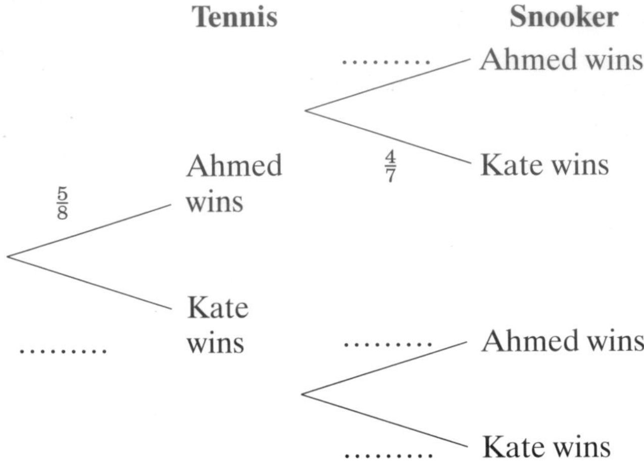

(b) Calculate the probability that Kate will win both games. [L]

9 A letter has a first-class stamp on it.
The probability that it will be delivered on the next working day is 0.86.

(a) What is the probability that the letter will **not** be delivered on the next working day?

Sam posts 2 letters with first-class stamps.

(b) Copy and complete the tree diagram.
Write all the missing probabilities on the appropriate branches.

First letter | **Second letter**

0.86 / …… — Delivered next working day
- …… — Delivered next working day
- …… — Not delivered next working day

…… — Not delivered next working day
- …… — Delivered next working day
- …… — Not delivered next working day

[L]

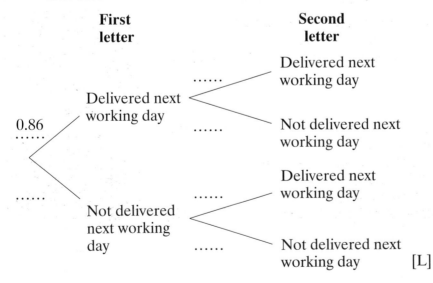

(c) Calculate the probability that both letters will be delivered on the next working day.

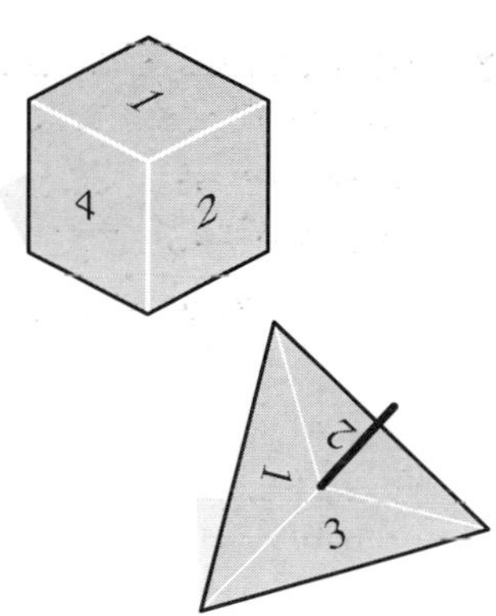

10 A fair dice has the numbers 1 to 6 on it.

(a) When the dice is rolled, what is the probability that a 4 will be scored?

A fair spinner has the numbers 1, 2 and 3 on it.

(b) When the spinner is spun, what is the probability that a 3 will be scored?

In a game, the dice is rolled and the spinner is spun. The two scores are added.

(c) Copy and complete the table to show all the possible **totals**.

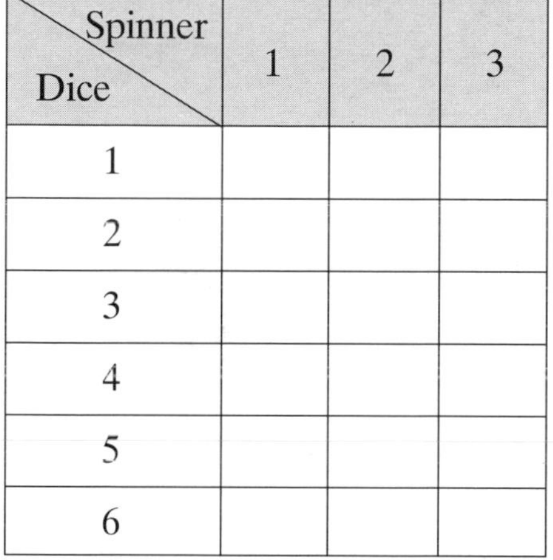

Dice \ Spinner	1	2	3
1			
2			
3			
4			
5			
6			

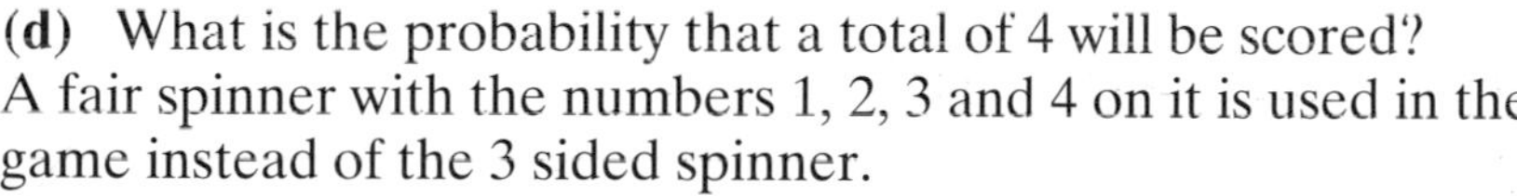

(d) What is the probability that a total of 4 will be scored?

A fair spinner with the numbers 1, 2, 3 and 4 on it is used in the game instead of the 3 sided spinner.

(e) Will there be an increase or decrease in the probability that a total of 4 will be scored? Explain your answer. [L]

11 There are two fish tanks in a pet shop.
In tank A there are four white fish and one black fish.
In tank B there are three white fish and four black fish.
One fish is taken out of each tank at random.

(a) Write down the probability that the fish taken from tank A will be:

(i) black

(ii) white.

(b) Draw a tree diagram to show all the probabilities when one fish is taken out of each tank.

One fish is to be taken out of each tank at random.

(c) Work out the probability that:

(i) the two fish will both be white

(ii) the two fish will be of different colours. [L]

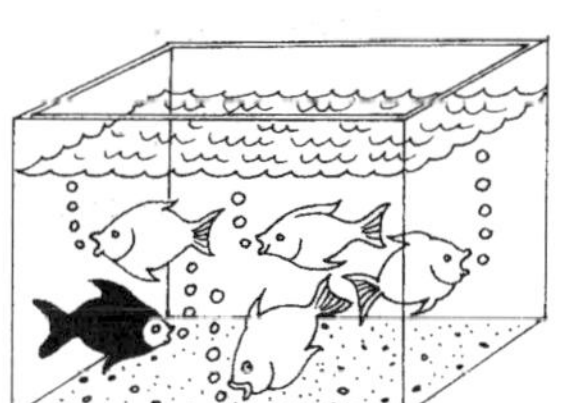

Tank A

Tank B

Summary of key points

1 When the outcome of one event does not affect the outcome of another, they are independent events.

2 You can estimate the probability that an event will occur by carrying out an experiment or game and using the rule:

$$\text{estimated probability} = \frac{\text{number of successful trials}}{\text{total number of trials}}$$

This is also called the relative frequency.

3 When one outcome prevents another outcome from happening the events are mutually exclusive.

4 When two events A and B are mutually exclusive the probability that either A or B will happen is:

$$P\,(A \text{ or } B) = P\,(A) + P\,(B)$$

This is known as the OR rule. It can be extended to any number of mutually exclusive events.

5 When two events A and B are independent the probability that both A and B will happen is:

$$P(A \text{ and } B) = P\,(A) \times P\,(B)$$

This is known as the AND rule. It can be extended to any number of independent events.

6 You can use tree diagrams like this to solve probability problems involving combined events.

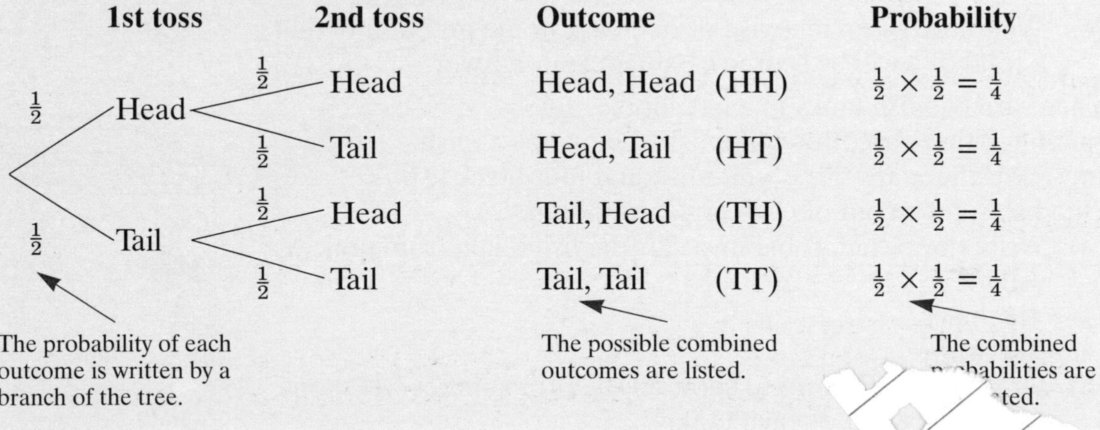

20 Lengths, areas and volumes

This unit shows you how to find perimeters, areas and volumes for a variety of 2-D and 3-D shapes.

20.1 Lengths and areas of rectangles, triangles and composite shapes

■ **The perimeter of a shape is the total length of its boundary.**

You can find the perimeter of a shape by adding the lengths of its sides.

length l

width w w

l

Perimeter of rectangle $= l + l + w + w$
$= 2(l+w)$

■ **The area of a shape is a measure of the amount of space it covers.**

Typical units of area are square centimetres (cm^2) and square kilometres (km^2).

l

w

Area of rectangle $= l \times w$

You can find the area of a rectangle using the formula:

■ **area of a rectangle = length × width**
$= l \times w$

Area of a parallelogram

You can use the rectangle formula to find the area of a parallelogram:

Any side of a parallelogram can be called its base. The perpendicular distance between the base and its opposite side is called the perpendicular height (or height) of the parallelogram.

D 5 cm C
4 cm
A B
2 cm E 3 cm

The base of parallelogram ABCD is 5 cm long and the perpendicular height is 4 cm.
AE is 2 cm.

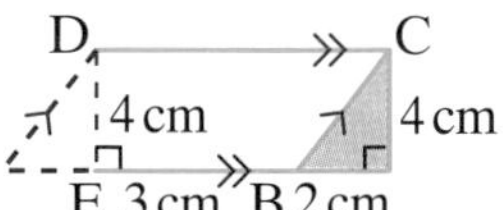

You can cut off the triangle ADE from one end of the parallelogram and place it at the other end. AD is equal and parallel to BC so they fit exactly together.

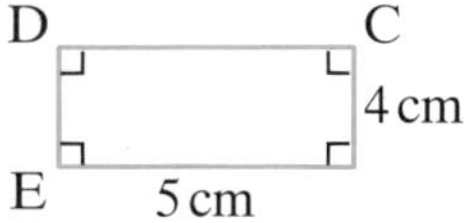

The new shape is a rectangle. The area of the original parallelogram is the same as the area of this rectangle, $5 \times 4\,\text{cm}^2$, which is the base multiplied by the height.

■ **area of a parallelogram = base × height**
$= b \times h$

Area of a triangle

You can use the parallelogram formula to help find the area of a triangle:

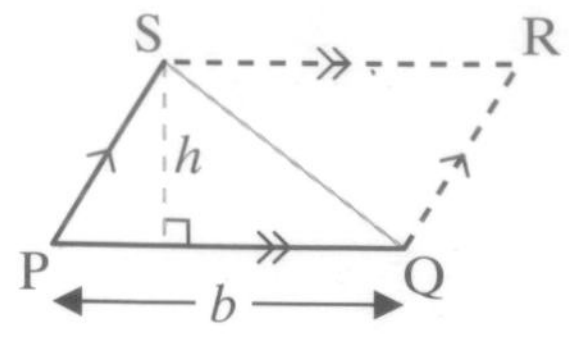

PQRS is a parallelogram with base b and height h. Triangle PQS and triangle QRS are congruent (exactly the same size and shape) so they have equal areas.

The area of triangle PQS is half the area of parallelogram PQRS. This can be written: $\frac{1}{2} \times (b \times h)$

So for any triangle:

■ **area of a triangle** $= \frac{1}{2} \times \textbf{base} \times \textbf{height}$
$= \frac{1}{2} \times \boldsymbol{b} \times \boldsymbol{h}$

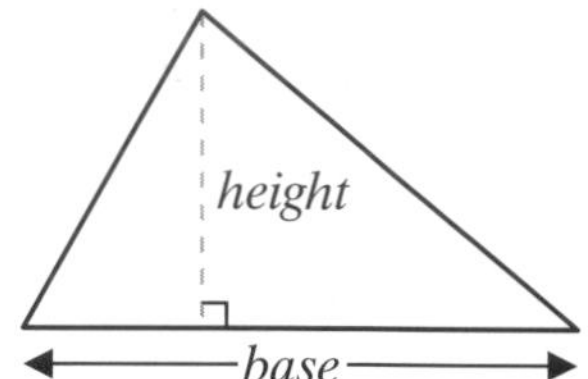

Any side can be used as the base of a triangle. Once the base has been chosen the height is the line drawn from the opposite vertex (corner) to the base.

Example 1

Work out the area of triangle XYZ.

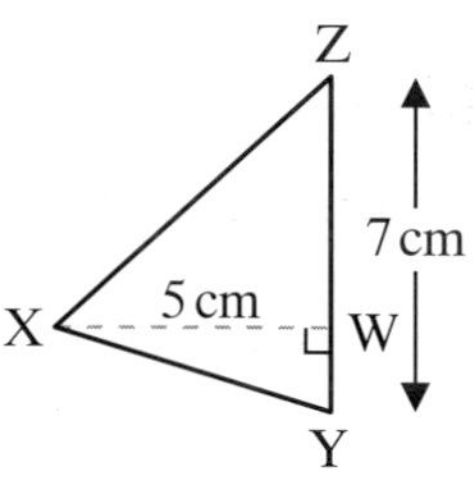

If you take YZ as the base the height is XW.

The area of triangle XYZ is $\frac{1}{2} \times \text{base} \times \text{height} = \frac{1}{2} \times 7 \times 5 = \frac{35}{2}$

The area of triangle XYZ is 17.5 cm^2.

Example 2

Calculate the area of the trapezium ABCD.

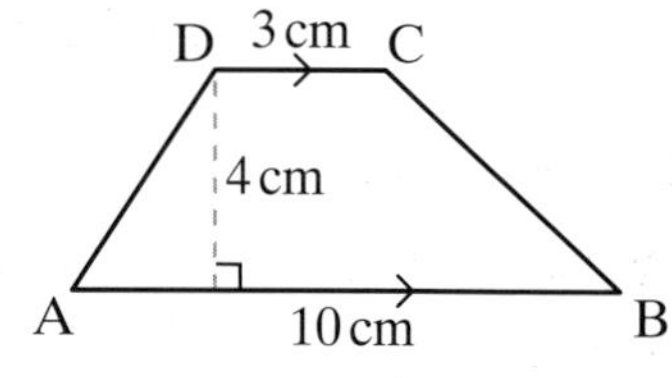

The trapezium can be split into two parts: a triangle and a parallelogram.

Area of triangle ADE $= \frac{1}{2} \times \text{base} \times \text{height} = \frac{1}{2} \times 7 \times 4 = 14\,\text{cm}^2$

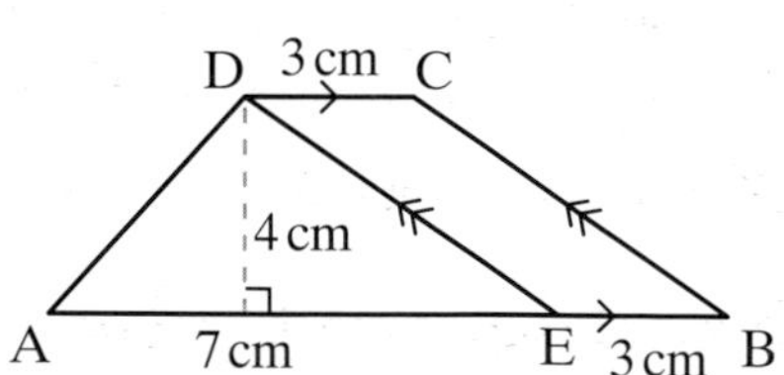

Area of CDEB = base × height = 3 × 4 = 12 cm^2

So the area of ABCD is 14 + 12 cm^2 = 26 cm^2
The area of the trapezium ABCD is 26 cm^2

Area of a trapezium

You can replace the lengths of the sides of trapezium ABCD in Example **2** with letters. Then you can find a formula for the area of a trapezium.

Area of triangle ADE $= \frac{1}{2} \times \text{base} \times \text{height} = \frac{1}{2} \times c \times h$

Area of CDEB = base × height = $a \times h$

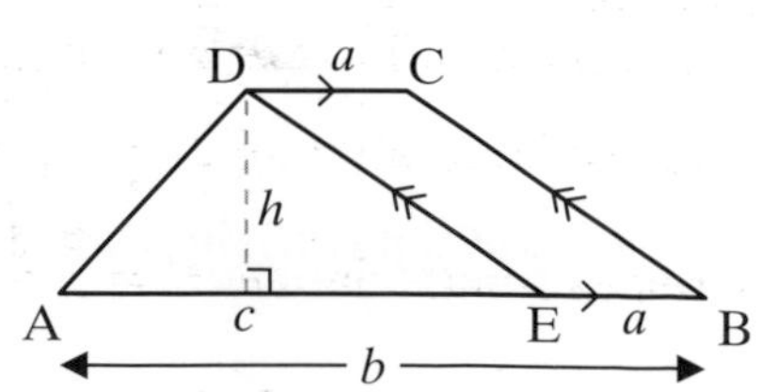

So area of ABCD is:

$$\frac{1}{2} \times c \times h \qquad + a \times h$$

$$= \frac{1}{2} \times c \times h + \frac{1}{2} \times a \times h + \frac{1}{2} \times a \times h$$

All terms have the common factor $\frac{1}{2} \times h$ or $\frac{h}{2}$.

$$= \frac{h}{2}(c + a + a)$$

$$= \frac{h}{2}(a + [a + c])$$

Notice that $a + c = b$, the length of the long side of the trapezium.
So:

$$\text{area} = \frac{h}{2}(a + b)$$

■ **area of a trapezium** $= \frac{1}{2}(a + b)h$

$\frac{1}{2}(a + b)h$ is $\frac{1}{2}$ the sum of the parallel sides × the perpendicular distance between them.

Example 3

Use the formula to calculate the area of the trapezium in Example **2**.

$$\text{Area of trapezium} = \frac{1}{2}(a + b)h = \frac{1}{2}(3 + 10) \times 4$$

$$= \frac{1}{2} \times 13 \times 4 = \frac{1}{2} \times 52$$

$$= 26\,\text{cm}^2 \text{ (as before)}$$

Example 4

Work out the area of this shape.

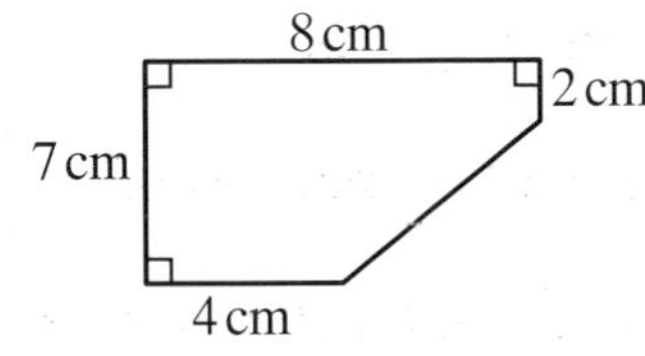

First method
Divide the shape into parts whose areas you can find.
This can be done in several ways. One way is:

Area of rectangle **A** $= l \times w = 7 \times 4 = 28\,\text{cm}^2$

Area of trapezium **B** $= \frac{1}{2}(a + b)h = \frac{1}{2}(7 + 2) \times 4 = \frac{1}{2} \times 9 \times 4$

$= 18\,\text{cm}^2$

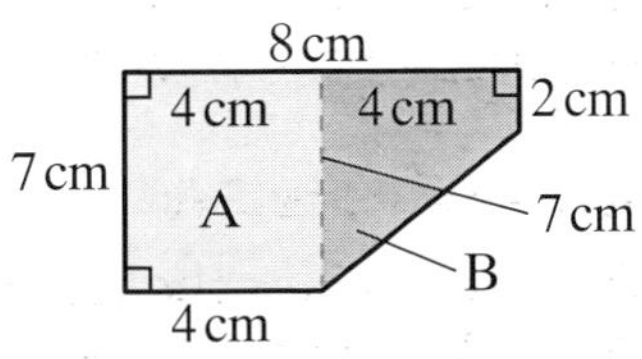

So the shaded area is $28 + 18 = 46\,\text{cm}^2$

Second method
Add on a small triangle to make a larger rectangle.

Area of large rectangle $= l \times w = 7 \times 8 = 56\,\text{cm}^2$

Area of small triangle **C** $= \frac{1}{2} \times \text{base} \times \text{height} = \frac{1}{2} \times 5 \times 4 = 10\,\text{cm}^2$

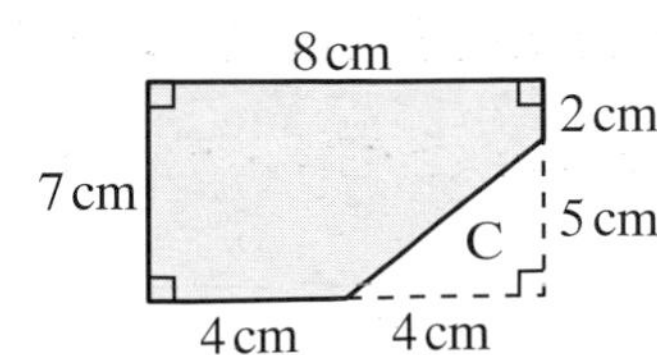

So the shaded area is $56 - 10 = 46\,\text{cm}^2$

Example 5

The area of triangle PQR is $30\,\text{cm}^2$ and its height RS is 8 cm.
Calculate the length of PQ.

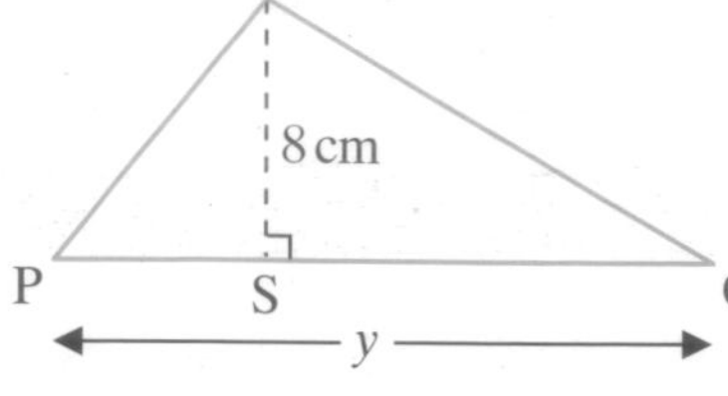

Let the length of PQ be y.

Area of triangle PQR is $\frac{1}{2} \times \text{base} \times \text{height}$

so

$$30 = \frac{1}{2} \times y \times 8$$

$$30 = y \times 4$$

$$30 \div 4 = y$$

The length of PQ is 7.5 cm.

Exercise 20A

1 For these shapes calculate (i) the perimeter (ii) the area.

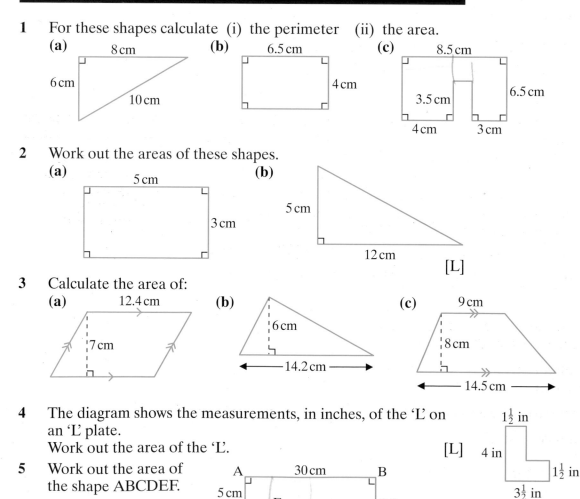

(a)

8 cm
6 cm
10 cm

(b)

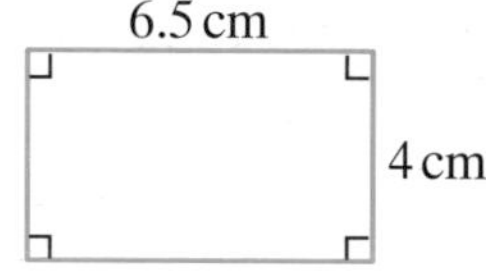

(c)

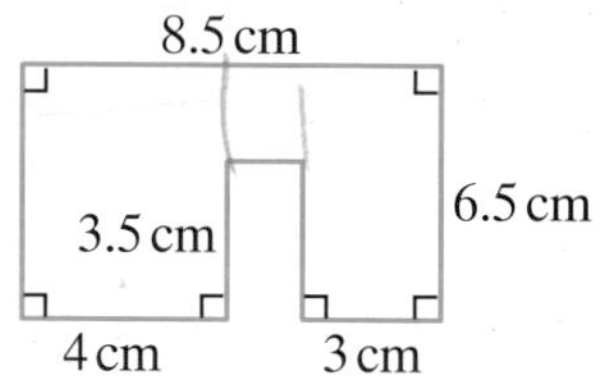

2 Work out the areas of these shapes.

(a)

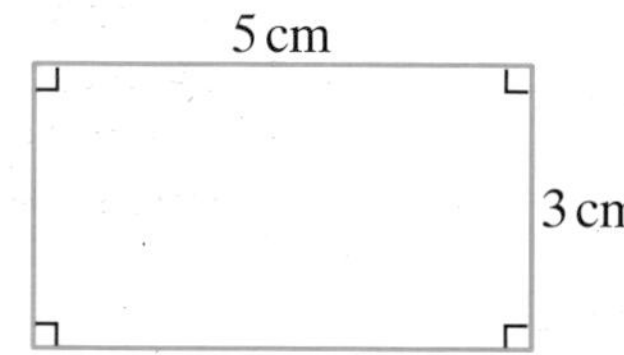

(b)

5 cm
12 cm

[L]

3 Calculate the area of:

(a)

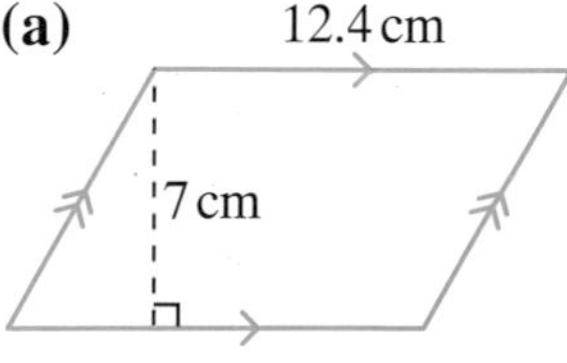

(b)

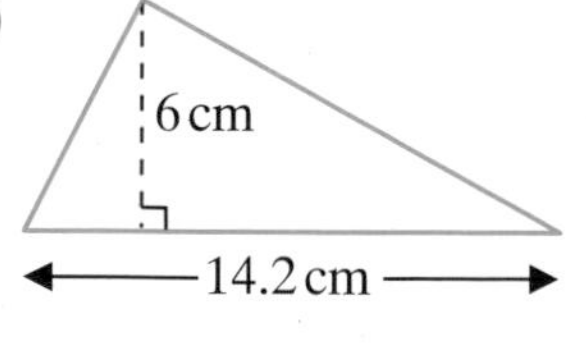

(c)

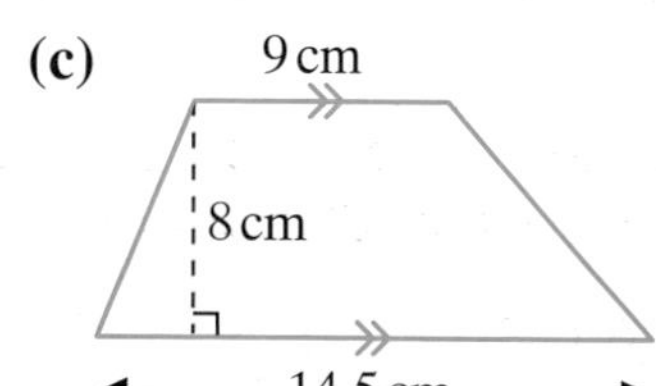

4 The diagram shows the measurements, in inches, of the 'L' on an 'L' plate.
Work out the area of the 'L'. [L]

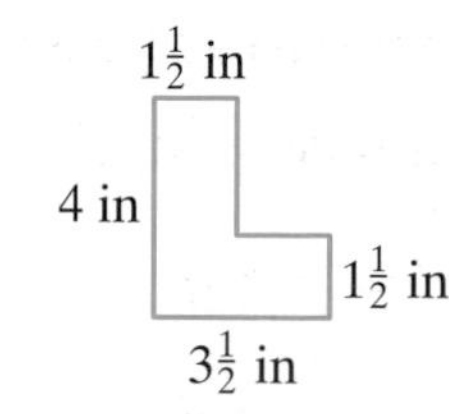

5 Work out the area of the shape ABCDEF.

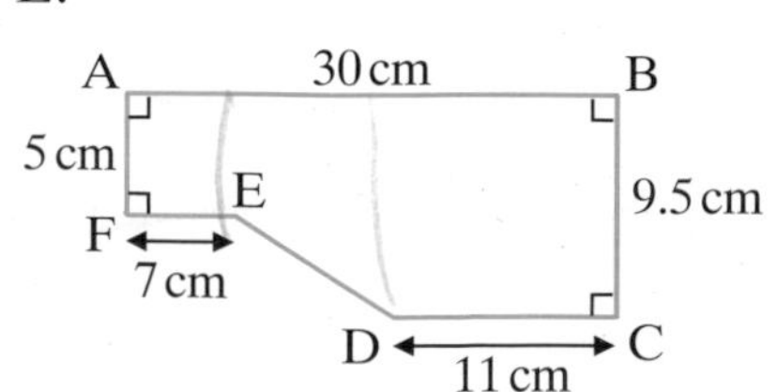

20.2 Circumference of a circle

The perimeter of a circle is called its **circumference**. The circumference of a circle is related to its diameter; this exercise will help you see how.

Exercise 20B

You will need a ruler, compasses and some string or thread.

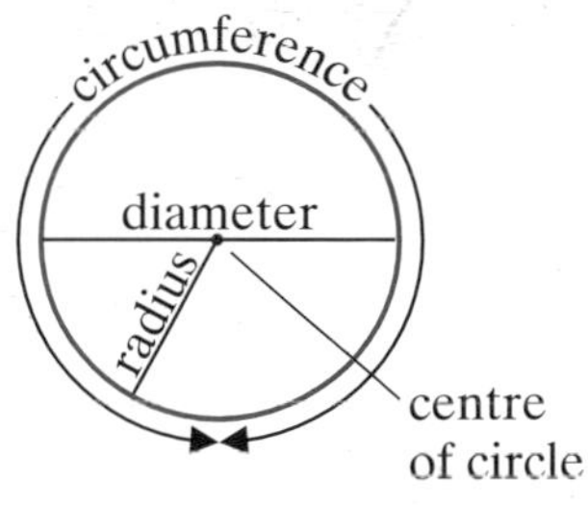

1 **(a)** Mark a point on your paper. Use compasses to draw a circle with the marked point as its centre.

(b) Use a piece of string or thread and place it round your circle. Cut the string to fit exactly round the circumference once and measure its length. The length of the string is the same as the circumference of the circle.

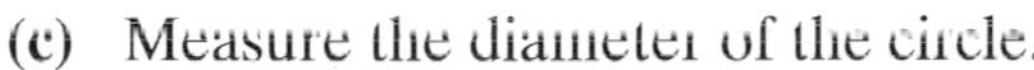

(c) Measure the diameter of the circle.

(d) Work out: $\dfrac{\text{circumference of circle}}{\text{diameter of circle}}$

2 Repeat question **1** for two more circles with a different radius each time.

3 What do you notice about the ratio $\dfrac{\text{circumference of circle}}{\text{diameter of circle}}$ for each of your circles?

Introducing π (pi)

If you compare answers to Exercise 20B with your friends you should find that the circumference of a circle divided by its diameter is approximately equal to 3 each time. The actual value is a special number called π.

3.141 592 3.141 593

π = **3.141 592 65...** is somewhere here but you cannot pinpoint its position exactly

You cannot write down the value of π exactly. The number π is an **irrational number** (a *non-recurring*, *non-terminating* decimal) somewhere between 3.141 592 and 3.141 593.

If you press the π key on a calculator the value 3.141592654... appears.

In calculations you often use the value correct to 2 d.p. (3.14) or correct to 3 d.p. (3.142).

Finding a formula for the circumference

You can rearrange the relationship:

$$\frac{\text{circumference}}{\text{diameter}} = \pi$$

to give a formula to find the circumference of a circle from its diameter.

Multiply both sides by d

$$\frac{C}{\not{d}} \times \not{d} = \pi \times d$$

so $C = \pi \times d$

or $C = \pi d$

The diameter is twice the radius

$d = 2r$

so $C = \pi \times 2r$

or $C = 2\pi r$

■ **The perimeter of a circle is called the circumference.**
$C = \pi \times d$ where C is the circumference,
or d is the diameter and
$C = 2 \times \pi \times r$ r is the radius.

Example 6

The diameter of a circular fish pond is 3 m.
Work out the circumference of the pond correct to 2 decimal places.

Use circumference $C = \pi \times \text{diameter} = \pi \times 3 = 9.424...$
The circumference of the pond is 9.42 m (correct to 2 d.p.)

Example 7

Calculate the diameter of a circle which has a circumference of 45 cm.

Use $C = \pi \times d$

Divide both sides by π to get $\frac{C}{\pi} = d$

So $d = \frac{45}{\pi} = 14.32...$ cm

The diameter is 14.3 cm (correct to 3 s.f.)

Exercise 20C

1 Calculate the circumference of a circle with:
(a) diameter 5 cm **(b)** diameter 6.7 m
(c) radius 7 cm **(d)** radius 12.8 m

2 Calculate the diameter of a circle with:
(a) circumference 28 cm **(b)** circumference 14.5 m

3 Calculate the radius of a circle with:
(a) circumference 43 cm **(b)** circumference 5.7 m

4 Calculate the perimeter of a semicircle with diameter 8 cm.

5 The diagram represents the plan of a window frame.
The arc PR is a quarter of a circle. The centre of the circle is at O and the radius of the circle is 67 cm.
Calculate the length of the perimeter of the window frame.

6 A window is in the shape of a rectangle with a semicircular top.
The window frame is made of strips of metal along the straight and curved lines shown in the diagram.
Calculate the total length of metal needed to make the frame.

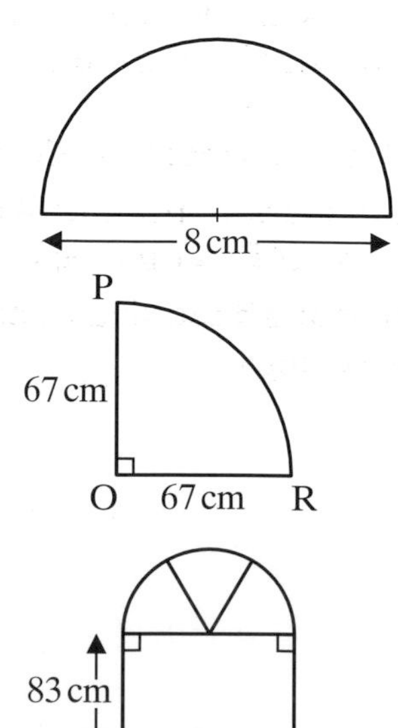

20.3 Area of a circle

Example 8

Here is a circle with radius 4 units drawn on a square grid.
Estimate the area of the circle.

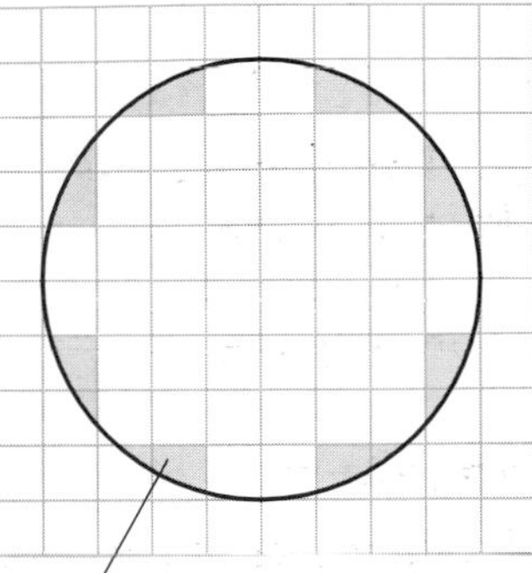
Each of these shapes is about $\frac{1}{4}$ square + $\frac{3}{4}$ square.

There are 44 nearly whole squares. The area of these is 44 square units.

The shaded shapes are each about $\frac{3}{4}$ square plus $\frac{1}{4}$ square which makes about a whole square.

So the 8 shaded shapes make about 8 whole squares, with area 8 square units.

The total area of the circle is about $44 + 8 = 52$ square units.

Exercise 20D

You will need a ruler, compasses, a protractor, squared paper and glue.

1 **(a)** Draw a circle with a radius of 9 units on squared paper.
(b) Estimate the area of the circle in square units, by counting the squares.
(c) Divide your answer to **(b)** by 81 (which is 9×9, the square of the radius).

2 **(a)** Draw a circle with radius 3 cm.
(b) Draw diameters at angles of 20° to each other to divide the circle into 18 parts. Carefully cut out the 18 parts.

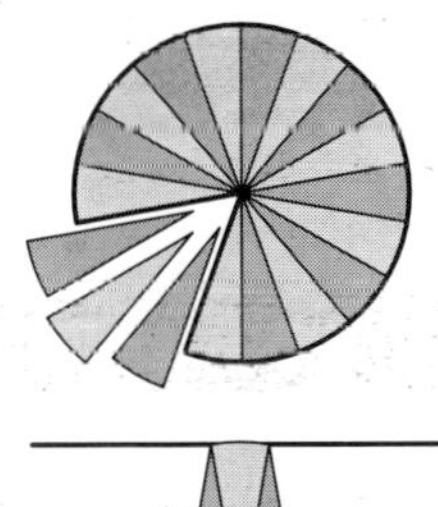

(c) Draw a straight line. Place the cut out pieces alternately corner and curved edge against the line.
Stick them close together.

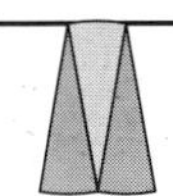

3 Repeat question **2**, but draw diameters at 10° to each other to divide the circle into 36 equal parts.

Finding a formula for the area of a circle

The shape you made with the 18 pieces in question **2** of Exercise 20D should be approximately a rectangle.

In question **3** the shape should be closer to a rectangle.

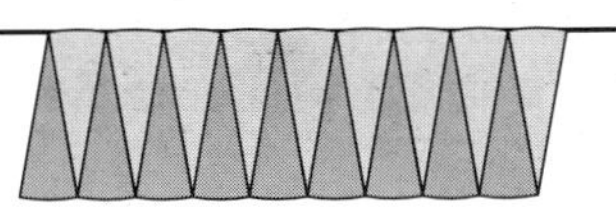

It would be very difficult to cut out the parts of the circle if you used 1° between the diameters, but the final shape would be almost an exact rectangle.

The two longer sides of the rectangle make up the whole circumference πd or $2\pi r$, so one length is πr. The width is the same as the radius of the circle, r.

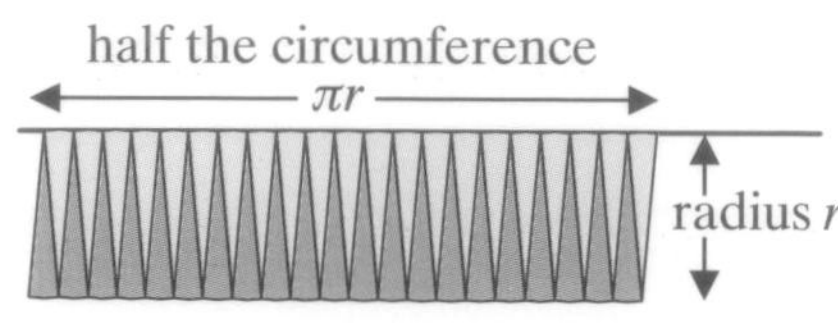

The more parts the circle is divided into, the closer to a rectangle the shape becomes.

So the area of the rectangle is length × width = $\pi r \times r = \pi r^2$
This is the same as the area of the circle, so

■ **area of a circle = π × (radius)^2**
$A = \pi r^2$

Example 9

Calculate the area of a circle with diameter 15 cm.

First work out the radius, 15 cm ÷ 2, which is 7.5 cm.

Use $A = \pi r^2 = \pi \times 7.5 \times 7.5 = 176.7...$

So the area of the circle is 177 cm^2 (correct to 3 s.f.)

Exercise 20E

1 Calculate the area of a circle with:
(a) radius 6 m **(b)** radius 29.5 cm **(c)** radius 4.7 m
(d) diameter 24 cm **(e)** diameter 3.8 cm

2 Calculate the area of a semicircular rug with diameter 90 cm.

3 An ice cream wafer is in the shape of a quadrant of a circle with radius 7 cm.
Work out the area of the wafer.

4 A lawn is in the shape of a rectangle with a semicircular end.
Calculate the area of the lawn.

5 A circular pond has diameter 3.22 m. The pond is surrounded by a path 28 cm wide. Calculate:
(a) the area of the pond
(b) the area of the path.
Give your answers in m^2, correct to 2 decimal places.

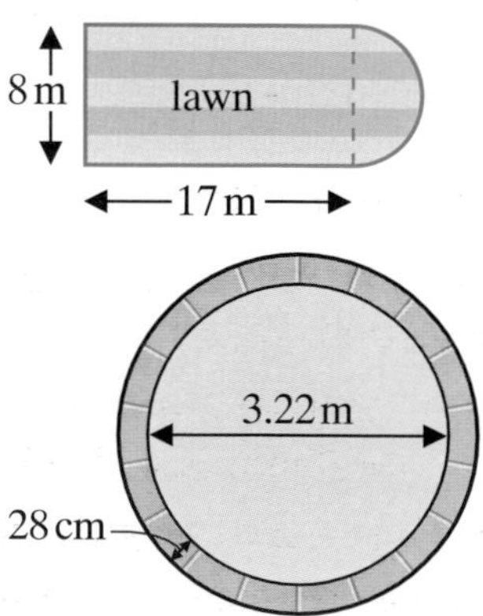

6 A circle has an area of 39 cm^2.
Calculate the radius. (Hint: work out the square of the radius first, then find the square root to calculate the radius.)

7 Calculate the radius of a circle whose area is 48 cm^2.

20.4 Areas and volumes of 3-D shapes

Volume of a cuboid

■ **The volume of a 3-D shape is a measure of the amount of space it occupies.**

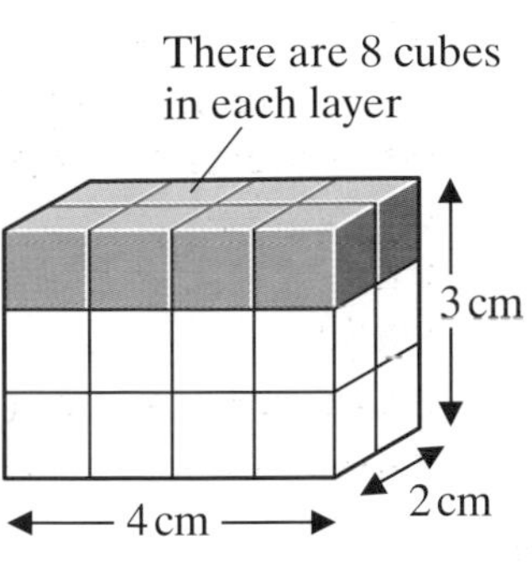

Typical units of volume are cubic centimetres (cm^3) and cubic metres (m^3).

This cuboid is made from cubes with sides all 1 cm long. The cuboid measures 4 cm by 2 cm by 3 cm.

There are 8 (= 4 × 2) cubes in the top layer. There are 3 layers of cubes so the total number of cubes is 8 × 3 = 24.

This can be worked out from 4 × 2 × 3 which is length × width × height for the cuboid.

The volume of the cuboid is 24 cm^3.

■ **volume of a cuboid = length × width × height**
$= l \times w \times h$

You can think of this as **(length × width)** × **height** or
area of cross-section × **height**

Volume of a prism

■ **A prism is a 3-D shape with the same cross-section all along its length.**

A cuboid can be cut in half to make this triangular prism.

The volume of the prism is half the volume of the cuboid so it is:

$24 \div 2 = 12\,cm^3$

This can be thought of as:

$$\frac{4 \times 2}{2} \times 3 = 12\,cm^3$$

or **area of cross-section** × **height**.

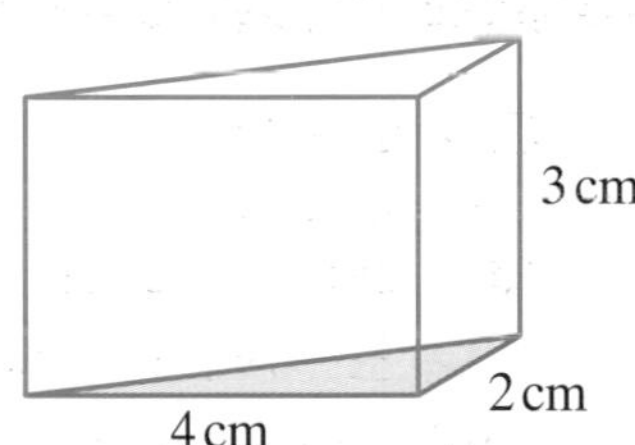

This is half the cuboid from the top of the page.

Does this work for any prism? Try an octagonal prism:

To make an octagonal prism you can first make the shape of the octagonal base.

You need five whole cubes and 4 half cubes.

The total number of cubes in the base is 5 + 2 = 7.

For a prism of height 3 cm you need 21 cubes (7 × 3).

So the volume of the prism is 21 cm^3.

This is the **area of cross-section** × **height**.

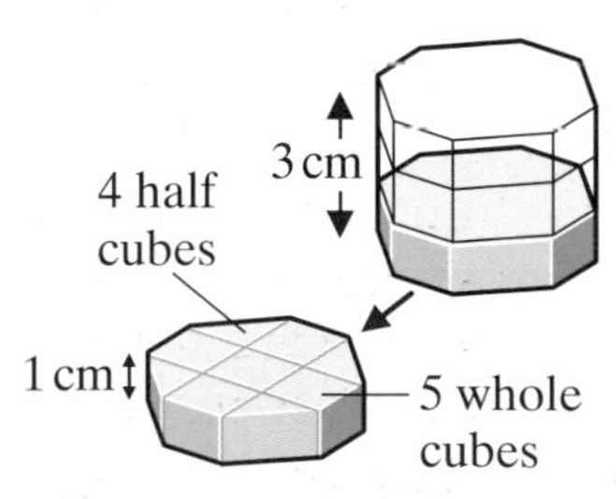

If the prism is lying on its side the height is called length.

■ **volume of a prism = area of cross-section × length**

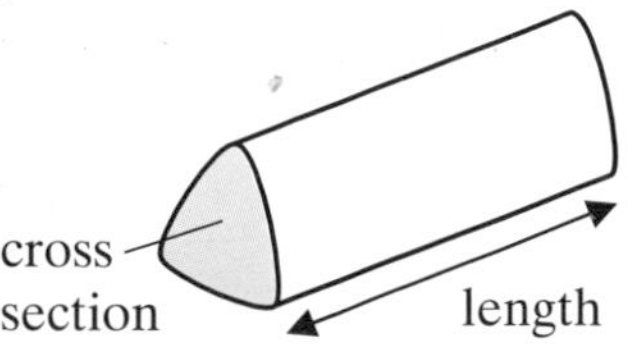

Volume of a cylinder

A **cylinder** is a prism where the cross-section is a circle.

The area of cross-section is πr^2, so:

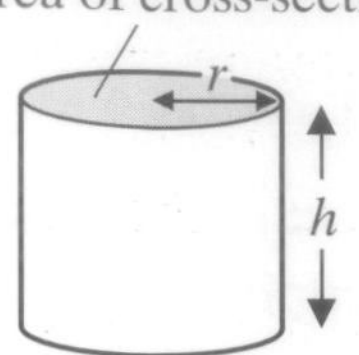

$$\text{area of cross-section} \times \text{height} = \pi r^2 \times h$$

■ **volume of a cylinder = $\pi r^2 h$**

Area of the surface of a cylinder

You can work out the area of the curved surface of a cylindrical can of soup by removing the label.

Cut the label parallel to the height of the cylinder. Remove the label and open it out flat. The label should be a rectangle.

The length of the rectangle is the same as the circumference of an end of the cylinder.

The width is the same as the perpendicular height of the cylinder.

The area is the circumference of an end multiplied by the height.

Unroll the label...

... to give a rectangle:

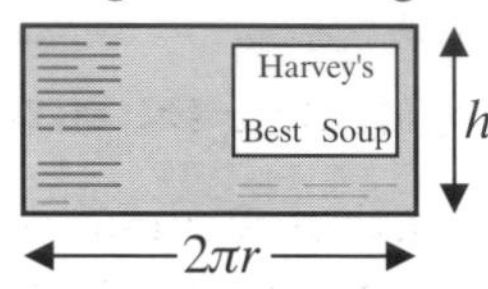

area of curved surface $= 2\pi r \times h$

■ **area of the curved surface of a cylinder = $2\pi rh$**

To find the total surface area of a closed cylinder you need to add the areas of the two circular ends to the curved surface area to get $2\pi rh + 2\pi r^2$.

To find the surface area of a cylinder open at one end you add the area of one circular end to the curved surface area to get $2\pi rh + \pi r^2$.

Example 10

The base of a cylindrical can containing 1 litre of orange juice has a diameter of 9 cm.
Work out the height of the can.

Remember:
1 litre = 1000 cm^3

The volume of the cylinder is 1 litre = 1000 cm^3.
The radius of the base is $9 \div 2 = 4.5$ cm.
The area of the base is $\pi r^2 = \pi \times 4.5 \times 4.5 = 63.617 = 63.62$ (4 s.f.)

$$\text{Volume} = \text{area of cross-section} \times \text{height}$$

so $$1000 = 63.62 \times h$$

Divide both sides by 63.62

$$\frac{1000}{63.62} = h \text{ giving } h = 15.71$$

so the height of the can is 15.7 cm (correct to 3 s.f.)

Worked examination question

The diagram represents a concrete post. The base of the post is a circle with a radius of 30 cm.

(a) Calculate the circumference of the base of the post.

The top of the post is a circle with a radius of 20 cm.

(b) Calculate the area of the top of the post.

The weight, W kg, of dry concrete needed to make the post is given by the formula $W = \frac{13\pi r^2 h}{15\,000}$ where r cm is the radius of the top of the post and h cm is the vertical height of the post.

(c) Calculate the weight of dry concrete needed to make the post.

The mould used to make the post is built from the lower part of an upright cone.

(d) Calculate the height, H cm, of the cone.

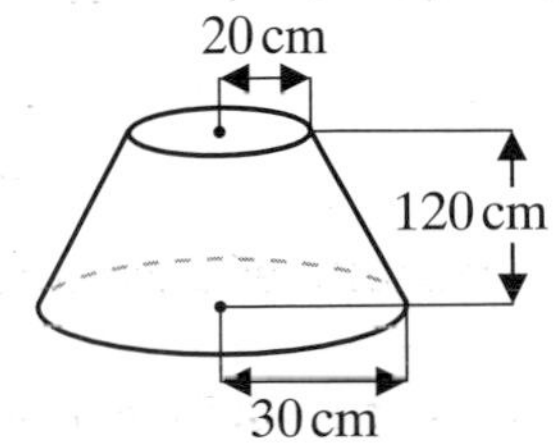

Diagram NOT accurately drawn

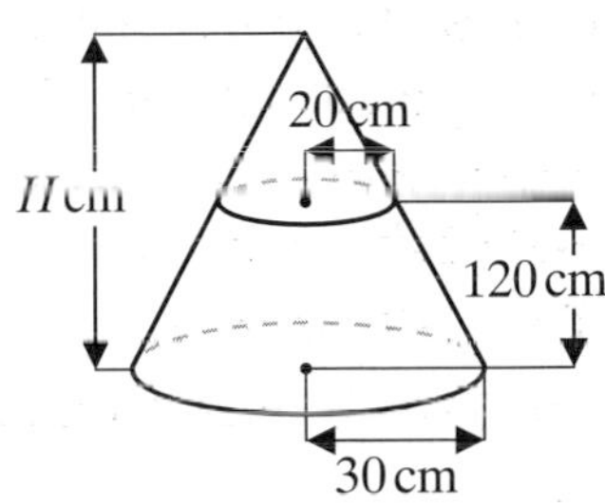

(a) Circumference $= 2\pi r = 2 \times \pi \times 30 = 188.49...$ cm
so the circumference of the base of the post is 188.5 cm.

(b) Area $= \pi r^2 = \pi \times 20 \times 20 = 1256.6...$ cm^2
so the area of the top of the post is 1257 cm^2.

(c)
$$W = \frac{13\pi r^2 h}{15\,000}$$
$$= \frac{13 \times \pi \times 20 \times 20 \times 120}{15\,000}$$
$$= 130.69...$$

so the weight of dry concrete needed is 130.7 kg.

(d) Triangle ABC and triangle ADE are similar. The ratios of pairs of corresponding sides are equal.

so $$\frac{AB}{AD} = \frac{BC}{DE}$$
$$\frac{H - 120}{H} = \frac{20}{30}$$

Multiply both sides by $30H$

$$30(H - 120) = 20H$$
$$30H - 3600 = 20H$$
$$10H = 3600$$

Divide both sides by 10 to get $H = 360$.
So the height of the cone is 360 cm.

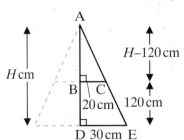

A
H–120 cm
H cm
B C
20 cm 120 cm
D 30 cm E

There is more about similarity on page 43 and pages 392 to 394.

Exercise 20F

1 Calculate the volume of this wedge which is a triangular prism.

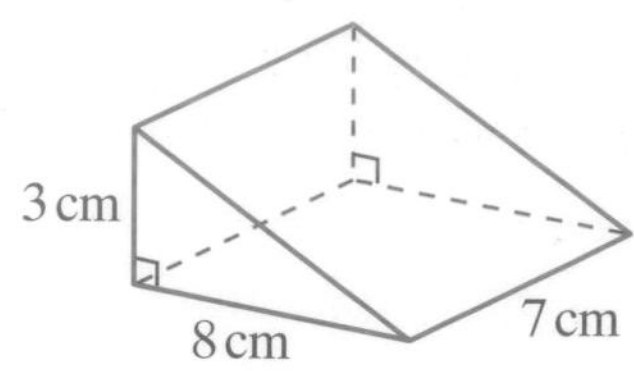

2 A closed box is a cuboid made of wood 1 cm thick. Its external measurements are 80 cm by 50 cm by 42 cm.
Calculate:
(a) the internal measurements of the box
(b) the inside volume of the box
(c) the total surface area of the outside of the box.

3 The diagram shows a tank which is a prism with a trapezium cross-section.
Calculate the volume of the tank.

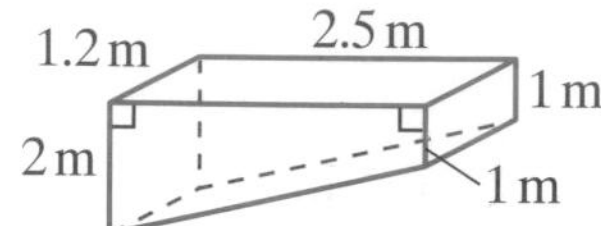

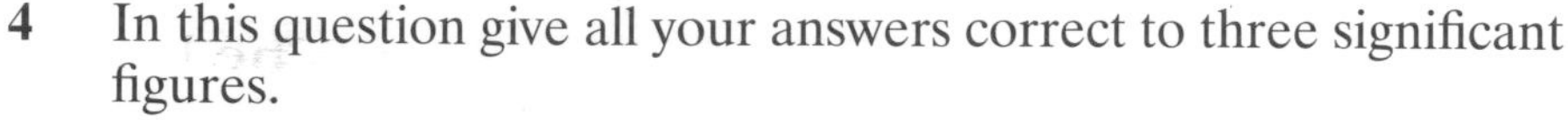

4 In this question give all your answers correct to three significant figures.
A gold bar is in the shape of a cylinder. It has a diameter of 18 cm and a length of 105 cm.
The gold is to be recast into cuboids. Each cuboid is to be 30 cm long, 14 cm wide and 8 cm high.
(a) Calculate the volume of the cylinder.
(b) Calculate the volume of the cuboid.
(c) Calculate the maximum number of cuboids that can be made from the gold bar.
(d) What volume of gold is left over after the cuboids have been made? [L]

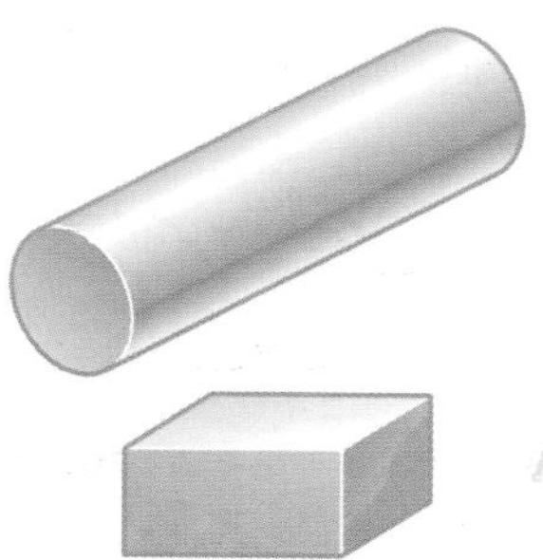

Diagram NOT accurately drawn

5 A closed cardboard box is a cuboid with a base 63 cm by 25 cm. The box is 30 cm high.
Calculate:
(a) the volume of the box
(b) the total surface area of the box.

6 The cross-section of a house is shown.
The house is 9 m wide.
Calculate the volume of the house.

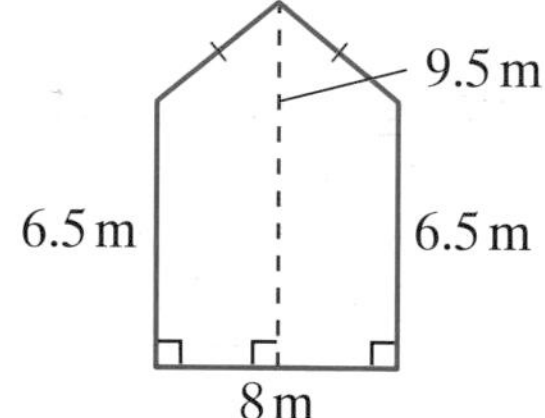

7 A flat rectangular roof measures 15 m by 20 m. Rainwater from the roof drains into a tank which is 1.3 m deep and has a square base of side 1.4 m.
Calculate the depth of rainfall that would just fill the tank.

8 A cuboid with a square base is 18 cm high. The volume of the cuboid is 882 cm^3.
Calculate the length of a side of the base.

9 An open waste paper bin is a cylinder. The diameter of the base is 22 cm and the height is 28 cm.
Calculate:
(a) the volume of the bin
(b) the total surface area of the bin.

20.5 Considering dimensions

You can check whether a formula represents a length, area or volume by looking at its **dimensions**. Here are the expressions for the perimeters of some shapes:

Shape	Diagram	Expressions for the perimeter
A square with side p	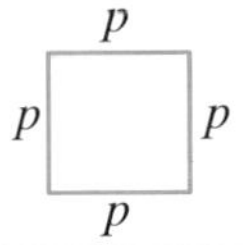	$4p$
A rectangle with length l and width w		$2l + 2w$ or $2(l + w)$
A circle with diameter d	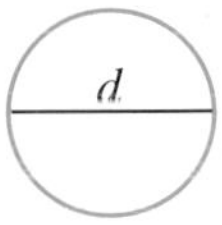	πd or $2\pi r$

p is a length

$l + w$ is a length

d and r are both lengths

All the expressions for perimeters represent a length.

■ **All formulae for *length* or *distance* have the dimension: length**

numbers like 4, 2, $\frac{4}{3}$ or π are **dimensionless** (they have *no dimensions*)

The areas of squares, rectangles and circles are:

Shape	Expressions for the area
A square with side p	$p \times p$ or p^2
A rectangle with length l and width w	$l \times w$ or lw
A circle with radius r	πr^2

p^2 (or $p \times p$) is a length times a length

lw (or $l \times w$) is a length times a length

The expressions p^2, lw and r^2 are a **length multiplied by a length.**

■ **All formulae for *area* have the dimensions: length × length**

The volumes of cubes, cuboids and cylinders are:

Shape	Expressions for the volume
A cube with side p	$p \times p \times p$ or p^3
A cuboid with length l, width w and height h	$l \times w \times h$ or lwh
A cylinder with height h and a circular base with radius r	$\pi r^2 h$

p^3 (or $p \times p \times p$) is a length times a length times a length

$r^2 h$ or ($r \times r \times h$) is a length times a length times a length

The expressions p^3, lwh and r^2h are **a length multiplied by a length multiplied by a length**.

■ **All formulae for *volume* have the dimensions:**
length × length × length.

Worked examination question

The dimensions of four cuboids are shown:

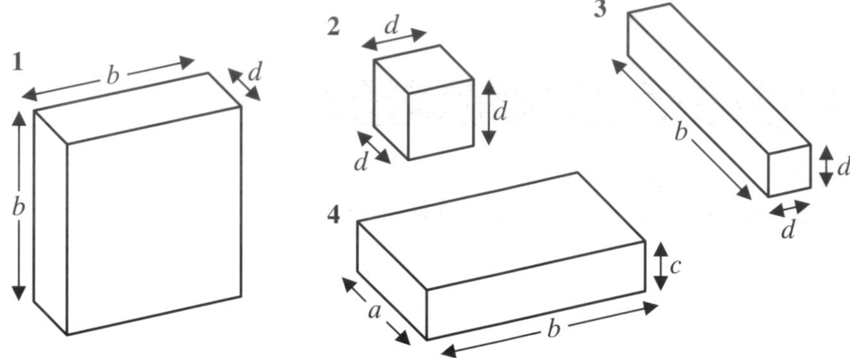

These expressions

$abc,\quad 4d,\quad d^2,\quad 2(a + b),\quad bd,\quad d^3$

give the perimeter of a face of one of the cuboids, or the area of a face of one of the cuboids, or the volume of one of the cuboids.

Complete the statements below by writing Perimeter, or Area, or Volume.

abc gives a ....

$2(a + b)$ gives a ....

bd gives a .... [L]

abc is a length times a length times a length so it gives a **volume**. (It is the volume of this cuboid.)

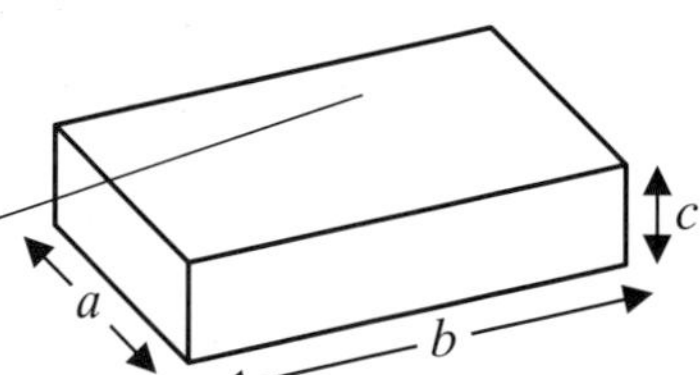

$a + b$ is the sum of two lengths so $2(a + b)$ is a length. It is a length times a number so it gives a **length**. (It is the perimeter of this face of the cuboid.)

bd is a length times a length so it gives an **area**. (It is the area of each long face of cuboids **1** and **3**.)

Example 11

Jon knows that one of these expressions represents the volume of a sphere with radius r, but he cannot remember which one:

$4\pi r^2 \qquad \frac{4}{3}\pi r^3 \qquad \frac{4}{3}\pi r^2$

How can you work out which expression gives the volume of a sphere?

The expressions $4\pi r^2$ and $\frac{4}{3}\pi r^2$ are both a length times a length times a number. This means they each represent an area, not a volume.

The expression $\frac{4}{3}\pi r^3$ is a length times a length times a length times a number so it gives a volume.
It is the one which represents the volume of a sphere.

Exercise 20G

1 The letters b, h, l and r represent lengths.
For each expression write down whether it represents a length, an area or a volume:

(a) $2\pi r$ **(b)** $\frac{1}{3}\pi r^2 h$ **(c)** πrl

(d) $2(l + b)$ **(e)** πr^2 **(f)** $2\pi rh$

2 Some of the expressions in the table can be used to calculate lengths, areas or volumes of some shapes.
The letters b, h, l and r represent lengths.
π, 2 and 4 are numbers with no dimension.
Copy the table. Put a tick in the box underneath those expressions that can be used to represent
(a) a length **(b)** an area
(c) a volume **(d)** none of these.

	$\pi r^2 h$	$\frac{1}{2}bh$	$2(l + b)$	$r^2 + h$	$\frac{4}{3}\pi r^3$	lbh	$4\pi r^2$	
(a)								represent lengths
(b)								represent areas
(c)								represent volumes
(d)								none of these

3 The letters b and h represent lengths.
Explain why the expression $b + h^2 + bh$ cannot represent an area.

Exercise 20H Mixed questions

1 Calculate the number of *complete* revolutions made by a cycle wheel of diameter 70 cm in travelling a distance of $\frac{1}{2}$km. [L]

2 (a) Find the area of a circle of diameter 5.6 cm, giving your answer in cm^2 correct to two significant figures.
(b) A fence which surrounds a rectangular field of length 300 metres and width 184 metres is taken down and is just long enough to fence in a circular paddock.
Calculate the radius of the paddock. [L]

3 The expressions shown in the table below can be used to calculate lengths, areas or volumes of various shapes.
π, 2, 4 and $\frac{1}{2}$ are numbers which have no dimensions.
The letters r, l, b and h represent lengths.
Copy the table and put a tick in the box underneath those expressions that can be used to calculate a volume.

$2\pi r$	$4\pi r^2$	$\pi r^2 h$	πr^2	lbh	$\frac{1}{2}bh$

[L]

4 The diagram represents a swimming pool.
The pool has vertical sides.
The pool is 8 m wide.

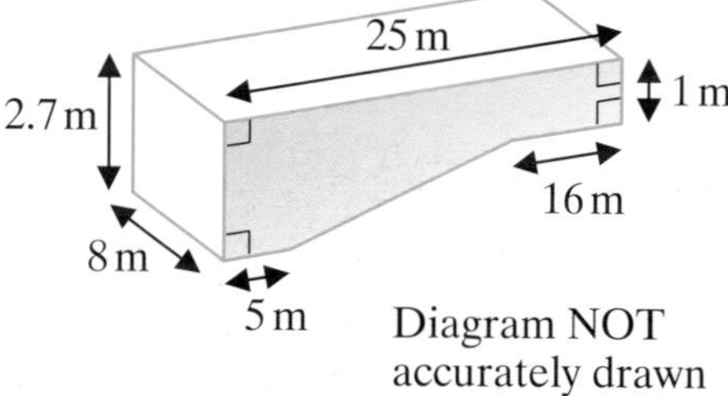

Diagram NOT accurately drawn

(a) Calculate the area of the shaded cross-section.
The swimming pool is completely filled with water.
(b) Calculate the volume of water in the pool.
64 m^3 of water leaks out of the pool.
(c) Calculate the distance by which the water level falls. [L]

5 The diagram represents a chocolate box in the shape of a pyramid. The box has a square base and four triangular faces.
The net of the chocolate box is shown.

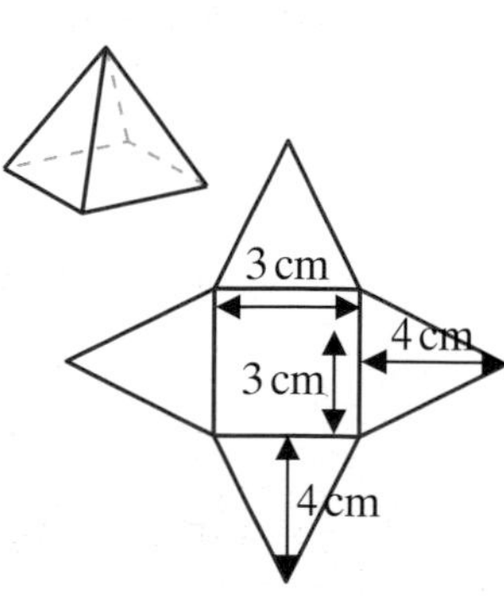

(a) Work out (i) the area of the base
(ii) the area of a triangular face
(iii) the total surface area of the box.

Each net is cut from a square card of area 121 cm^2. Any card not used for the box is thrown away.
n boxes are made.
(b) Write down a formula for the total area, A cm^2, of card which is thrown away.
(c) Draw an accurate net for the box. [L]

6 The diagram represents a tea packet in the shape of a cuboid.

(a) Calculate the volume of the packet.

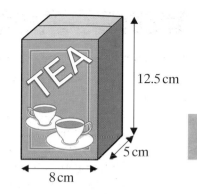

There are 125 grams of tea in a full packet. Jason has to design a new packet that will contain 100 grams of tea when full.

(b) (i) Work out the volume of the new packet.

(ii) Express the weight of the new tea packet as a percentage of the weight of the packet shown.

The new packet of tea is in the shape of a cuboid.
The base of the new packet measures 7 cm by 6 cm.

(c) (i) Work out the area of the base of the new packet.

(ii) Calculate the height of the new packet. [L]

7 A cylindrical can has a radius of 6 centimetres.

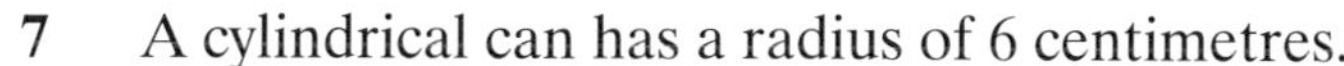

(a) Calculate the area of the circular end of the can.
(Use the π button on your calculator or $\pi = 3.14$.)

The capacity of the can is $2000\,\text{cm}^3$.

(b) Calculate the height of the can.
Give your answer correct to 1 decimal place. [L]

8 A cylindrical garden roller has a diameter of 40 cm and is 70 cm wide.
Calculate the area, in m^2, rolled during 100 revolutions of the roller. [L]

Summary of key points

1 The perimeter of a shape is the total length of its boundary.

2 The area of a shape is a measure of the amount of space it covers. Typical units of area are square centimetres (cm^2) and square kilometres (km^2).

3 Area formulae for 2-D shapes:

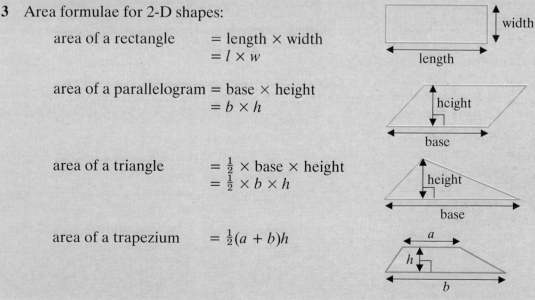

area of a rectangle $= \text{length} \times \text{width}$
$= l \times w$

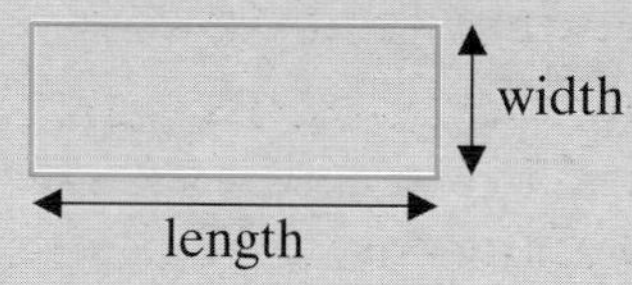

area of a parallelogram $= \text{base} \times \text{height}$
$= b \times h$

area of a triangle $= \frac{1}{2} \times \text{base} \times \text{height}$
$= \frac{1}{2} \times b \times h$

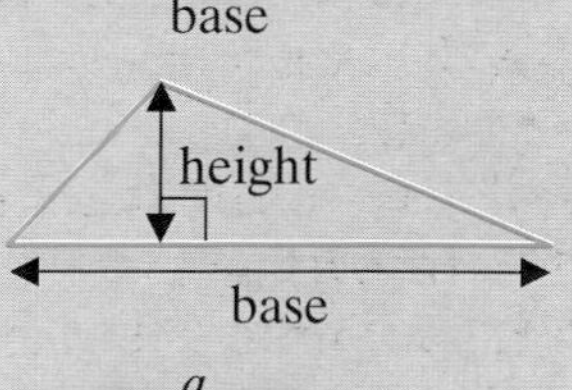

area of a trapezium $= \frac{1}{2}(a + b)h$

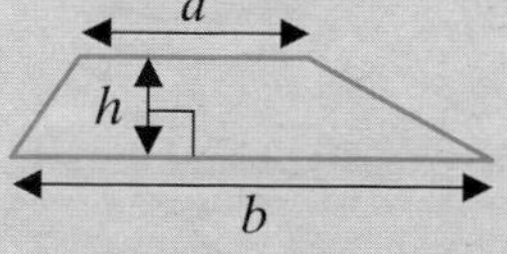

4 The perimeter of a circle is called the circumference.
$C = \pi \times d$ where C is the circumference,
or d is the diameter and
$C = 2 \times \pi \times r$ r is the radius.

5 The area of a circle $= \pi \times (\text{radius})^2$
$$A = \pi r^2$$

6 The volume of a 3-D shape is a measure of the amount of space it occupies.

7 Volume formulae for 3-D shapes:

volume of a cuboid $= \text{length} \times \text{width} \times \text{height}$
$= l \times w \times h$

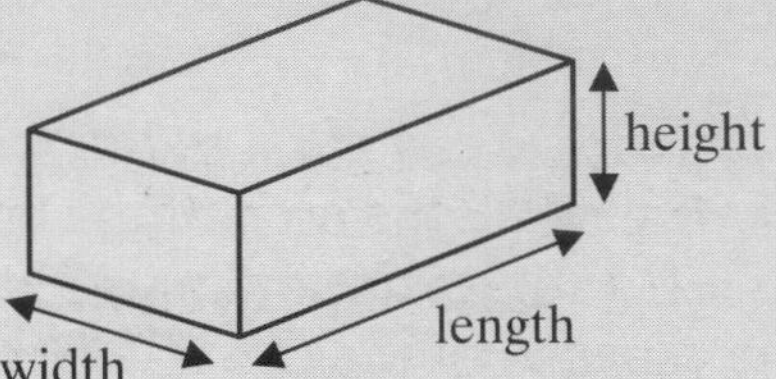

volume of a prism = area of cross-section × length

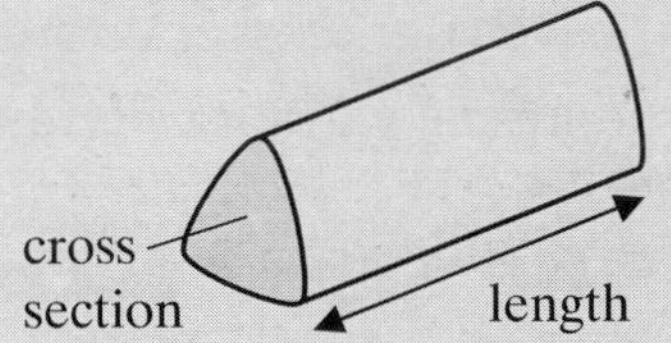

volume of a cylinder $= \pi r^2 h$

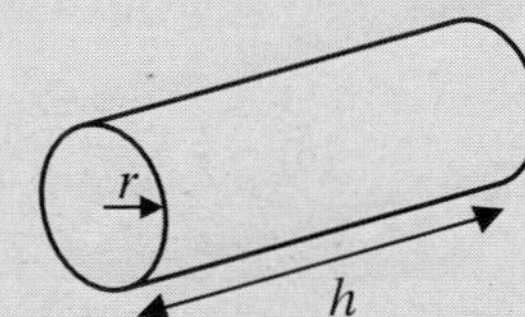

8 The area of the curved surface of a cylinder $= 2\pi rh$

9 All formulae for length or distance have the dimension:
length

10 All formulae for area have the dimensions:
length × length

11 All formulae for volume have the dimensions:
length × length × length

21 Algebraic expressions and formulae

This unit shows you how to manipulate algebraic expressions and formulae and use them to solve problems.

21.1 Evaluating algebraic expressions

Units 2 and 13 introduce functions like these:

$n \rightarrow 2n + 3 \quad n \rightarrow 3(n - 2) \quad n \rightarrow 3n^2 + 1$

These are called **algebraic expressions.**

An algebraic expression can have letters other than n. It can also have more than one letter.

Remember:

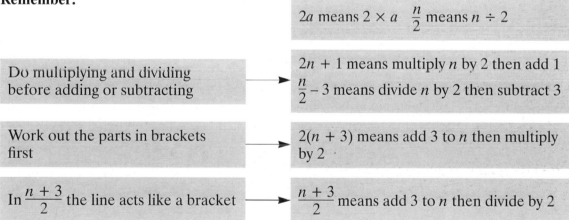

$2a$ means $2 \times a$ $\quad \frac{n}{2}$ means $n \div 2$

Do multiplying and dividing before adding or subtracting → $2n + 1$ means multiply n by 2 then add 1; $\frac{n}{2} - 3$ means divide n by 2 then subtract 3

Work out the parts in brackets first → $2(n + 3)$ means add 3 to n then multiply by 2

In $\frac{n+3}{2}$ the line acts like a bracket → $\frac{n+3}{2}$ means add 3 to n then divide by 2

Example 1

Evaluate the expression $\frac{2a + b}{c}$ when $a = 3$, $b = 4$ and $c = 2$.

$2a = 2 \times 3 = 6$

so $\quad 2a + b = 6 + 4 = 10$

and $\quad \frac{2a + b}{c} = \frac{10}{2} = 5$

Exercise 21A

Work out the value of these algebraic expressions using the values given:

1 **(a)** $4a + 1$ if $a = 3$ **(b)** $3b + c$ if $b = 5, c = 2$
(c) $2f - g$ if $f = 1.5, g = 4$ **(d)** $hg - 2$ if $h = 1.5, g = 3$
(e) $10 + 3x$ if $x = -2$ **(f)** $2x - 3y$ if $x = 4, y = -2$
(g) $2x + 3$ if $x = \frac{1}{5}$ **(h)** $3ab$ if $a = \frac{1}{4}, b = 2$

2 **(a)** $2(a + 3)$ if $a = 5$ **(b)** $3(s - 2)$ if $s = 7$
(c) $4(p + q)$ if $p = 5, q = 3$ **(d)** $r(8 - s)$ if $r = 3, s = 5$
(e) $3(b + 7)$ if $b = -2$ **(f)** $2(3 - c)$ if $c = -4$

3 **(a)** $5(a + b)$ if $a = 3, b = 4$ **(b)** $4(x + y)$ if $x = 5, y = -3$
(c) $\frac{a}{4} + 3$ if $a = 12$ **(d)** $\frac{a}{b} + 5$ if $a = 20, b = 4$
(e) $\frac{m - 4}{2}$ if $m = 12$ **(f)** $\frac{7 - x}{y}$ if $x = -3, y = -2$

4 **(a)** $\frac{m + n}{r}$ if $m = 8, n = 7, r = 5$
(b) $\frac{4q + r}{6}$ if $q = 5, r = 4$ **(c)** $\frac{3s - r}{t}$ if $s = 8, r = 6, t = 3$
(d) $\frac{3s}{4} - r$ if $s = 8, r = 3$ **(e)** $x - \frac{3y}{6}$ if $x = 3, y = -4$

5 **Activity**
(a) (i) Copy and complete this table by putting values for r and t into the algebraic expression $2r + t$.
(ii) Look for number patterns in the table.
(iii) Try to explain the number patterns.
(iv) Do the number patterns still hold for negative values of r and t?

$2r + t$	t = 0	1	2	3	4
r = 0	0	1	2	3	4
1	2	3	4	5	6
2	4	5	6		
3	6	7			
4					

(b) Repeat part **(a)** for other algebraic expressions involving 2 letters.
For example, use $r + 2t$, $2r + 3t$, $r + t$, $2(r + t)$, $rt + 1$.
(c) Find the algebraic expression used to make this table.
(d) Set some problems like part **(c)** for your friends.

?	t = 0	1	2	3	4
r = 0	0	1	2	3	4
1	4	5	6	7	8
2	8	9	10	11	12
3	12	13	14	15	16
4					

21.2 Evaluating algebraic expressions involving squares

Remember:

n^2 is called n squared or n to the power of 2	→	n^2 means n is multiplied by itself: $n \times n$
Squaring is done before multiplying	→	$2n^2 + 1$ means work out n^2, multiply by 2, then add 1

A good way to remember the order in which to evaluate an algebraic expression is to use the nonsense word BODMAS.

■ **Use BODMAS to help you remember the order of mathematical operations.**

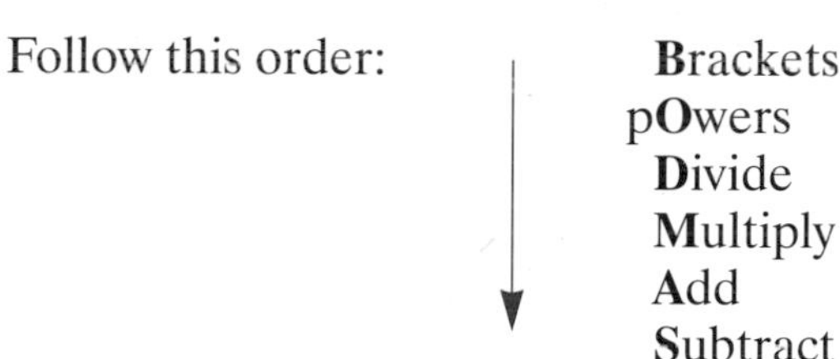

Follow this order:

Brackets
pOwers
Divide
Multiply
Add
Subtract

> **Remember:**
> Another way of saying x^2 (x squared) is 'x to the power 2'

Example 2

Work out the value of $\frac{4r^2 - t}{5}$ when $r = 3, t = 1$

Brackets (the line acts as a bracket so work out the 'top' first)

$r^2 = 3 \times 3 = 9$ ← pOwers

so $4r^2 = 4 \times 9 = 36$ ← Multiply

so $4r^2 - t = 36 - 1 = 35$ ← Subtract

so $\frac{4r^2 - t}{5} = 35 \div 5 = 7$ Now divide the top by 5

Exercise 21B

Work out the value of each of these algebraic expressions using the values given:

1 **(a)** $4m^2 + 1$ if $m = 5$ **(b)** $3m^2 - 1$ if $m = 4$
(c) $2p^2 - c$ if $p = 3, c = 4$ **(d)** $4x^2 + d$ if $x = 6, d = 3$
(e) $2p^2 + 5$ if $p = -3$ **(f)** $10 - q^2$ if $q = -2$

2 **(a)** $ar^2 + t$ if $r = 3, a = 2, t = 1$ **(b)** $3m^2 + 2m$ if $m = 3$
(c) $p^2q - r$ if $p = 4, q = 2, r = 5$ **(d)** $2p^2 - 3p$ if $p = 4$
(e) $x^2 - y^2$ if $x = -5, y = 3$ **(f)** $a^2 - b^2$ if $a = 4, b = -3$

3 (a) $4p^2 + ar$ if $p = 3, a = 2, r = 4$ (b) $\frac{p^2 + 4}{2}$ if $p = 4$

(c) $\frac{p^2}{3} + 4$ if $p = 6$ (d) $\frac{p^2}{2} + \frac{q^2}{3}$ if $p = 4, q = 6$

(e) $2a(b^2 + c^2)$ if $a = 3, b = -2, c = 1$ (f) $\frac{2r^2 - t}{8}$ if $r = -3, t = -6$

4 **Activity**
Repeat question **5** from Exercise 21A using expressions which contain squares, such as $2r^2 + t$ and $r^2 + t^2$.

5 **Activity**
This is a good activity to do on a spreadsheet but you can also do it quite easily with pen and paper.

(a) (i) Investigate the difference between $2a$ and $2 + a$ for different values of a. Be systematic in your approach, let $a = 0, 1, 2, 3$, and so on.
(ii) What number patterns can you spot?
(iii) Try to explain the number patterns.

(b) Repeat part (a) for other pairs of similar expressions such as: a^2 and $2a$, $2a + 1$ and $2(a + 1)$, $\frac{a+2}{2}$ and $\frac{a}{2} + 2$

a	$2a$	$2 + a$	Difference between $2a$ and $2 + a$
0	0	2	−2
1	2	3	−1
2	4	4	0
3	6	5	1
4			

21.3 Using indices

Unit 14 (page 184) shows how to calculate with powers of numbers. You can use similar ideas in algebra.

Notice that:
$a^4 \times a^3 = a^{4+3} = a^7$

$$a^4 \times a^3 = (a \times a \times a \times a) \times (a \times a \times a) = a^7$$

■ $x^a \times x^b = x^{a+b}$

To multiply powers of the same letter add the indices.

$$b^6 \div b^2 = \frac{b \times b \times b \times b \times b \times b}{b \times b} = b \times b \times b \times b = b^4$$

Notice that:
$b^6 \div b^2 = b^{6-2} = b^4$

■ $x^a \div x^b = x^{a-b}$

To divide powers of the same letter subtract the indices.

$$(c^2)^3 = c^2 \times c^2 \times c^2 = (c \times c) \times (c \times c) \times (c \times c) = c^6$$

Notice that:
$(c^2)^3 = c^{2\times3} = c^6$

■ $(x^a)^b = x^{ab}$

To raise a power of a letter to a further power multiply the indices.

Notice that:

$$\frac{d^3}{d^2} = \frac{d \times d \times d}{d \times d} = d \quad \text{and} \quad \frac{d^3}{d^2} = d^{3-2} = d^1$$

So $d^1 = d$

- $x^1 = x$

  Any letter raised to the power 1 is equal to the letter itself.

Also:

$$\frac{e^2}{e^2} = 1 \qquad \text{and} \qquad \frac{e^2}{e^2} = e^{2-2} = e^0$$

So $e^0 = 1$

- $x^0 = 1$ **if x is not zero**

  Any letter raised to the power 0 is equal to 1.

Sometimes you will be asked to simplify an expression containing different powers of the same letter multiplied or divided.

- **To simplify an expression containing different powers of the same letter multiplied or divided, write the expression as a single power of the letter.**

Example 3

Simplify:

(a) $x^8 \times x^3$ (b) $x^{10} \times x$ (c) $x^{16} \div x^2$ (d) $x^5 \div x$

(e) $x^4 \times x^3 \times x^5$ (f) $(x^4)^5$ (g) $\dfrac{x^5 \times x^2}{x^7}$

(a) $x^8 \times x^3 = x^{8+3} = x^{11}$ (b) $x^{10} \times x = x^{10} \times x^1 = x^{10+1} = x^{11}$

(c) $x^{16} \div x^2 = x^{16-2} = x^{14}$ (d) $x^5 \div x = x^5 \div x^1 = x^{5-1} = x^4$

(e) $x^4 \times x^3 \times x^5 = x^{4+3+5} = x^{12}$ (f) $(x^4)^5 = x^{4\times5} = x^{20}$

(g) $\dfrac{x^5 \times x^2}{x^7} = x^{5+2} \div x^7 = x^7 \div x^7 = x^{7-7} = x^0 = 1$

Example 4

Simplify:

(a) $3y^2 \times 4y^3$ (b) $12y^8 \div 4y^3$ (c) $(3y^5)^3$

(a) $3y^2 \times 4y^3 = 3 \times 4 \times y^2 \times y^3 = 3 \times 4 \times y^{2+3} = 12y^5$

(b) $12y^8 \div 4y^3 = \dfrac{12y^8}{4y^3} = \dfrac{12}{4} \times \dfrac{y^8}{y^3} = 3 \times y^{8-3} = 3y^5$

(c) $(3y^5)^3 = 3^3 \times (y^5)^3 = 27y^{5\times3} = 27y^{15}$

Exercise 21C

Simplify

	(a)	(b)	(c)	(d)
1	$x^8 \times x^2$	$y^3 \times y^8$	$z^7 \times z$	$w^9 \times w^5$
2	$a^5 \times a^3$	$b^3 \times b^3$	$c \times c^9$	$d^7 \times d^4$
3	$p^5 \div p^2$	$q^{12} \div q^2$	$r^9 \div r$	$t^8 \div t^4$
4	$j^9 \div j^3$	$k^5 \div k^4$	$m^2 \div m$	$n^{25} \div n^{23}$
5	$(d^3)^4$	$(e^5)^2$	$(f^3)^3$	$(g^7)^9$
6	$(g^6)^4$	$(h^2)^2$	$(k^4)^0$	$(m^0)^{56}$

	(a)	(b)	(c)
7	$3x^2 \times 2x^3$	$5y^9 \times 3y^{20}$	$6z^8 \times 4z$
8	$12p^8 \div 4p^3$	$15q^5 \div 3q^3$	$6r^5 \div 3r$
9	$(3d^2)^7$	$(4e)^3$	$(3f^{129})^0$
10	$x^5 \times x^2 \times x$	$y^2 \times y^4 \times y^3$	$z^3 \times z^5 \times z$
11	$\dfrac{a^4 \times a^5}{a^3}$	$\dfrac{b^7 \times b}{b^4}$	$\dfrac{c^3 \times c^4}{c^2 \times c^5}$
12	$4d^9 \times 2d$	$8e^8 \div 4e^4$	$(4f^2)^2$
13	$3p^6 \times p^3 \times p^4$	$5q^5 \times 3q^3 \times 2q^2$	
14	$\dfrac{3x^3 \times 4x^7}{2x^5}$	$\dfrac{(6x^5)^2}{9x^8}$	

21.4 Removing brackets from algebraic expressions

Unit 2 (page 20) shows that some functions are equivalent to each other. For example, $n \to 2(n + 1)$ is equivalent to $n \to 2n + 2$.

So the expression $2(n + 1)$ is equivalent to $2n + 2$

Notice that $2(n + 1)$ is the same as:

$$2 \times n \quad + \quad 2 \times 1 \quad = \quad 2n + 2$$

The 2 has been multiplied by each term inside the brackets.

■ **To remove brackets from an algebraic expression multiply each term inside the brackets by the term outside.**
This is sometimes called 'expanding the brackets'.

You can also use the areas of rectangles like these to show the same results:

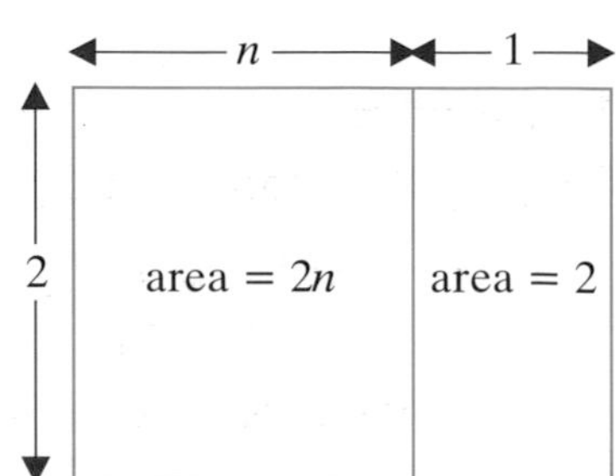

total area $= 2(n + 1)$

sum of separate areas $= 2n + 2$

so $2(n + 1) = 2n + 2$

Example 5

Remove the brackets from the expression $4(2n - 3)$.

Multiply each term inside the brackets by 4:

$$4(2n - 3) = 4 \times 2n + 4 \times -3$$
$$= 8n - 12$$

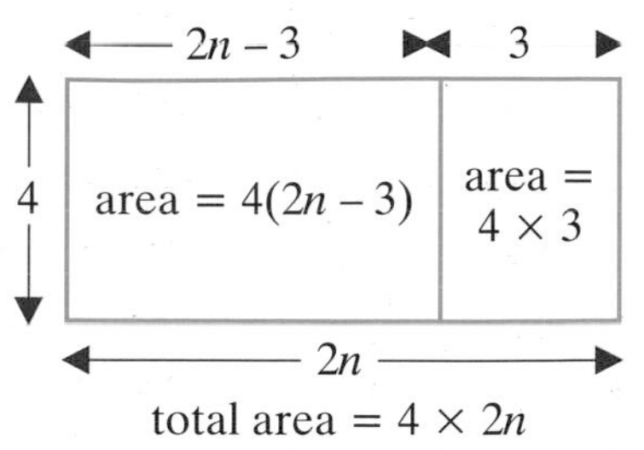

Or, using rectangles:

area of left rectangle = whole area – area of right rectangle

$$4(2n - 3) = 4 \times 2n - 4 \times 3$$
$$= 8n - 12$$

Exercise 21D

1 Draw rectangles to find expressions without brackets, equivalent to these expressions:
(a) $2(n + 3)$ (b) $4(3p + 2)$ (c) $y(2y + 3)$
(d) $2x(x + 5)$ (e) $3(n - 2)$ (f) $1(2p - 3)$

2 Write these expressions without brackets:
(a) $4(n + 3)$ (b) $2(p - 4)$ (c) $5(a + 1)$
(d) $2(3x - 1)$ (e) $4(5q - 3)$ (f) $3(2r + s)$
(g) $a(b + 2)$ (h) $p(p + q)$ (i) $p(2p - 1)$

3 Write these expressions without brackets:
(a) $3(x + 6)$ (b) $4(y - 2)$ (c) $7(t + 1)$
(d) $4(3x + 2)$ (e) $5(3y - 4)$ (f) $2(3p + q)$
(g) $x(x + 3)$ (h) $x(x + y)$ (i) $y(3y - 2)$

4 Expand the brackets:
(a) $2(m + 5)$ (b) $9(n - 4)$ (c) $8(u - 1)$
(d) $5(7x + 3)$ (e) $4y(y - 6)$ (f) $3x^2(2x^2 + 5)$
(g) $4t^3(5t^2 - 3)$ (h) $4x^2(3x^3 + 7y)$ (i) $5y(3y^3 - 4x^2)$

21.5 Simplifying algebraic expressions

Sometimes you can simplify an algebraic expression by removing the brackets and collecting like terms together. Here are some examples:

Example 6

Simplify the expression: $3(3a + 2b) + 2(a - b)$

$3(3a + 2b) + 2(a - b)$

$= 9a + 6b + 2a - 2b$ First remove the brackets.

$= 9a + 2a + 6b - 2b$ Change the order for adding and subtracting to put the a terms and the b terms together.

$= 11a + 4b$

This is called collecting **like terms**.

Example 7

Simplify the expression: $\frac{4n + 2}{2}$

$\frac{4n + 2}{2}$

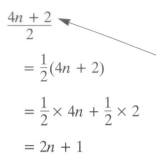

$= \frac{1}{2}(4n + 2)$ Remember: the line acts like a bracket.

$= \frac{1}{2} \times 4n + \frac{1}{2} \times 2$ Remove the brackets.

$= 2n + 1$

Example 8

Simplify the expressions: $x(x + 3y) + 2x(x + y)$

$x(x + 3y) + 2x(x + y)$

$= x^2 + 3xy + 2x^2 + 2xy$ Remove the brackets

$= x^2 + 2x^2 + 3xy + 2xy$ Collect like terms

$= 3x^2 + 5xy$

Exercise 21E

Simplify these expressions:

1 **(a)** $2(3r + 1) + 2r$ **(b)** $3(4p - 2) - 10p$
(c) $4(2x + y) + 2x - 3y$ **(d)** $2m - 3n + 3(m + n)$

2 **(a)** $4(2a + b) + 2(3a - b)$ **(b)** $3(p + q) + 2(p - q)$
(c) $2(3r + s) + 4(r - s)$ **(d)** $3(2p - q) + 3(p + q)$

3 **(a)** $3(x + y) + 4(x - y)$ **(b)** $4(m - n) + 3(2m - n)$
(c) $2(p - q) + 2(q - p)$ **(d)** $3(p - q) + 3(p + q)$

4 **(a)** $3(b - a) + 1(6a - 6b)$ **(b)** $r(r + 2) - r$
(c) $m(n + m) + m(n - m)$ **(d)** $m(3 + n) + n(1 - m)$

5 **(a)** $r(r^2 + 2) - r$ **(b)** $3t(t^2 + t) - t^2$
(c) $x^2(x^3 + 4x) - 3x^3$ **(d)** $y^2(2y^2 + 3y) + y^3(1 - 4y)$

6 Write these expressions in a simpler form:

(a) $\frac{6n + 4}{2}$ **(b)** $\frac{9n - 6}{3}$ **(c)** $\frac{10n - 20}{5}$

(d) $\frac{6p + 10r}{2}$ **(e)** $\frac{4r - 8q}{4}$ **(f)** $\frac{6r - 3s}{3}$

7 **Activity**
When an algebraic expression was simplified it became: $2a + b$
(a) Write down as many different expressions as you can which simplify to $2a + b$
(b) What is the most complex expression you can think of that simplifies to $2a + b$?

(c) What is the simplest expression you can think of that simplifies to $2a + b$?

(d) Repeat this activity for some other simple expressions such as: $a, \frac{a}{2}, 2a$

Dealing with negative numbers

The expression $-2\,(3a - 2)$ has a negative number before the brackets. You remove the brackets like this:

Multiply -2 by each term inside the brackets:

$$-2(3a - 2) \quad \text{with } -2 \times 3a \text{ and } -2 \times -2$$

$= -2 \times 3a \qquad -2 \times -2$

$= \quad -6a \qquad\quad + 4$

$= -6a + 4$

Example 9

Simplify the expression: $4(2a + b) - 2(a - b)$

$4(2a + b) - 2(a - b)$

$= 8a + 4b - 2a + 2b$ Remove the brackets.

$= 8a - 2a + 4b + 2b$ Collect like terms.

$= 6a + 6b$

Exercise 21F

Simplify these expressions:

1 **(a)** $4a - 3(a - b)$ **(b)** $2(2p + q) - 3(p - q)$
(c) $3(2n - 3) - 4(n - 2)$ **(d)** $2(s - r) - 2(r - s)$
(e) $3(x + y) - 3(x - y)$ **(f)** $r(s - t) - r(3 - t)$

2 **(a)** $3x - 2(x + y)$ **(b)** $2(6x - y) - (x + y)$
(c) $x(4x + 5) - 2x(x + 3)$ **(d)** $5y(4y - 3) - 2(4y - 3)$
(e) $x(2x - 5) - 2(2x - 5)$ **(f)** $2y^3(2y - 3) + 3y^2(4y^2 + 5y)$

Multiplying bracketed expressions

Sometimes you will need to multiply bracketed expressions by each other. For example: $(e + f)\,(g + h)$

This means $(e + f)$ multiplied by $(g + h)$ or $(e + f) \times (g + h)$

Look at these rectangles:

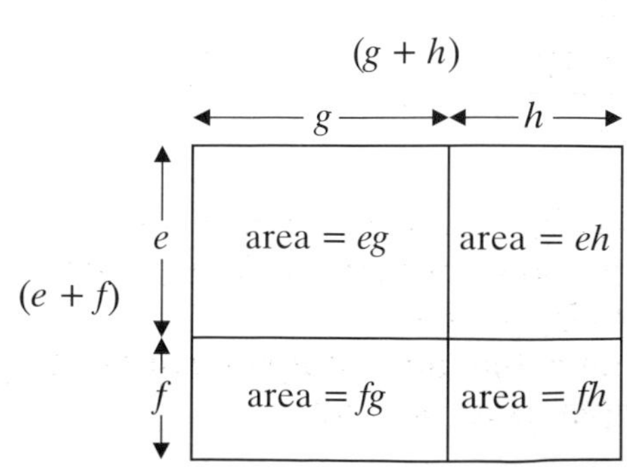

The area of the whole rectangle is $(e + f)\,(g + h)$.

It is the same as the sum of the **four** separate areas so:

■ $(e + f)(g + h) = eg + eh + fg + fh$

Notice that each term in the first bracket is multiplied by each term in the second bracket:

$e \times h$

$e \times g$

$(e + f)\ (g + h)$

$f \times g$

$f \times h$

You can also think of the area of the rectangle as the sum of **two** separate parts:

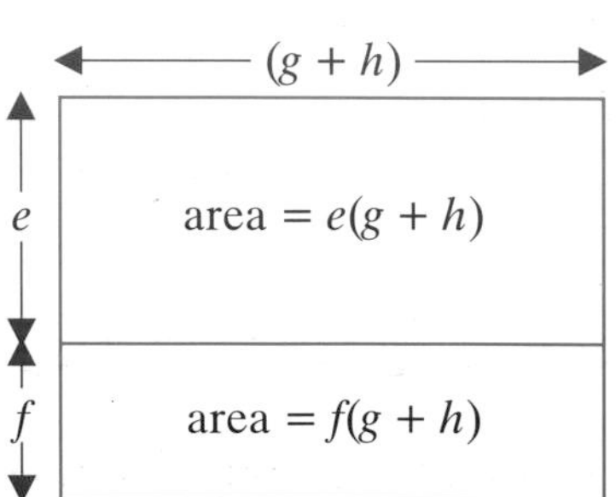

■ $(e + f)(g + h) = e(g + h) + f(g + h)$

Think of multiplying each term in the first bracket by the whole of the second bracket.

These are two ways of thinking about the same process. The end result is the same.

This is called **multiplying out** the brackets.

Example 10

Multiply out the brackets in the expression:

$(2a + 2)(3a - 4)$

$$\begin{aligned}(2a + 2)(3a - 4) &= 2a(3a - 4) + 2(3a - 4)\\ &= 6a^2 - 8a + 6a - 8\\ &= 6a^2 - 2a - 8\end{aligned}$$

$2a \times 3a$
$= 2 \times a \times 3 \times a$
$= 2 \times 3 \times a \times a$
$= 6a^2$

Exercise 21G

1 Use rectangles to show these results:
(a) $(a + b)(c + d) = a(c + d) + b(c + d)$
(b) $(a - b)(c - d) = a(c - d) - b(c - d)$

Hint for question 1 (b):

c

$c - d$ $\quad d$

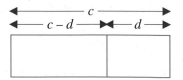

In questions **2** to **8** multiply out the brackets then simplify your expressions where possible.

2 **(a)** $(a + 4)(b + 3)$ **(b)** $(c + 5)(d + 4)$ **(c)** $(x + 3)(y + 6)$
(d) $(a + 3)(a + 8)$ **(e)** $(b + 7)(b + 4)$ **(f)** $(x + 6)(x + 2)$

3 **(a)** $(2a + 3)(b + 4)$ **(b)** $(3b + 2)(c + 3)$ **(c)** $(4c + 3)(d + 6)$
(d) $(2a + 5)(a + 3)$ **(e)** $(3b + 4)(b + 2)$ **(f)** $(4c + 5)(c + 2)$

4 **(a)** $(a - 4)(b - 3)$ **(b)** $(c - 5)(d - 4)$ **(c)** $(x - 3)(y - 6)$
(d) $(a - 3)(a - 8)$ **(e)** $(b - 7)(b - 4)$ **(f)** $(x - 6)(x - 2)$

5 **(a)** $(a-4)(b+3)$ **(b)** $(c+5)(d-4)$ **(c)** $(x-3)(y+6)$
(d) $(a-3)(a+8)$ **(e)** $(b-7)(b+4)$ **(f)** $(x+6)(x-2)$

6 **(a)** $(2a-5)(b+5)$ **(b)** $(3b+4)(b-6)$ **(c)** $(3c-2)(c-3)$
(d) $(3a-4)(a-5)$ **(e)** $(3x-4)(x+5)$ **(f)** $(2a+3)(a-6)$

7 **(a)** $(x+y)(2x+3y)$ **(b)** $(x+y)(3x-4y)$
(c) $(x-y)(5x-3y)$ **(d)** $(2x+5y)(3x+4y)$
(e) $(3x+5y)(2x-5y)$ **(f)** $(6x-5y)(2x-3y)$

8 **(a)** $(x+3)^2$ **(b)** $(y-5)^2$ **(c)** $(2x+1)^2$
(d) $(3y-4)^2$ **(e)** $(3x+5y)^2$ **(f)** $(6x-7y)^2$

9 **(a)** $(3a+1)(a-2)$ **(b)** $(3p+2)(4p-1)$
(c) $(3a+2)(a+1)$ **(d)** $(4p+2)(3p+2)$
(e) $(2b-3)(b-1)$ **(f)** $(4b-1)(2b+1)$

10 **(a)** $(a+1)(b+2)-ab$ **(b)** $(2p+1)(q-2)+3p-pq$
(c) $(3r-s)(r-1)+s-2r$ **(d)** $(2p+3a)(2p-3a)+9a^2$

21.6 Using formulae

A formula (plural: formulae) is a way of describing a rule or a relationship using algebraic expressions.

A formula must contain an equals (=) sign.

Example 11

The formula to change temperatures measured in degrees Celsius (°C) into degrees Fahrenheit (°F) is: $F = 1.8C + 32$

What is the temperature in Fahrenheit when the temperature is 16 degrees Celsius?

Put $C = 16$ in the formula:

$$F = 1.8 \times 16 + 32$$
$$= 28.8 + 32$$
$$F = 60.8$$

The temperature is 60.8 °F.

Worked examination question

$$E = \frac{1}{2}m\,(v^2 - u^2)$$

Calculate the value of E when $m = 15$, $v = -3$ and $u = 4$. [L]

$$E = \frac{1}{2} \times 15([-3]^2 - 4^2)$$
$$= 7.5\,(9 - 16)$$
$$= 7.5 \times -7$$
$$E = -52.5$$

Exercise 21H

1 As you go up a mountain the temperature always drops. The amount by which the temperature drops is given by the formula $t = \frac{h}{200}$

t is the drop in temperature in degrees Celsius and h metres is the height you have gone up the mountain.

Mount Snowdon is about 1000 metres high.

(a) Work out the drop in temperature from the bottom to the top of Snowdon.

(b) If the temperature at the bottom is 17 °C, what is the temperature at the top?

(c) Change your answer to part (b) to degrees Fahrenheit. (Hint: use the formula in Example 8.)

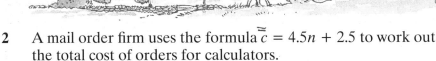

2 A mail order firm uses the formula $c = 4.5n + 2.5$ to work out the total cost of orders for calculators.

c is the cost in pounds of the order and n is the number of calculators ordered.

The cost of one calculator is £4.50

(a) Write down the charge made by the firm for packing and posting an order.

(b) Use the formula to work out the total cost of an order for 10 calculators.

3 This is the charge for hiring a car from a car-hire firm.

£20 per day plus 5 pence per mile travelled

The formula the firm uses to work out the cost of hiring a car is

$c = 0.05m + 20$

where c is the cost, in pounds, of hiring and m is the number of miles travelled.

(a) Explain why 0.05 is in the formula and not 5.

A customer hires a car and travels 250 miles in it.

(b) Use the formula to work out how much the firm will charge.

4 The cost of printing worksheets on a school's duplicating machine is 25 pence to make the master copy and 1.5 pence for every sheet printed. The cost, c pence, to print n copies can be written as a formula: $c = 1.5n + 25$

(a) Work out the cost of printing 30 copies of a worksheet.

(b) Work out the total cost of printing 20 copies of one worksheet and 28 copies of another worksheet.

5 A washing machine repair firm uses this formula to work out the cost of their engineer's time: $c = 40h + 30$
where c is the cost, in pounds, of the engineer's time and h is the number of hours the repair takes. The cost of any parts used in a repair is added on to the final bill.
The firm makes a charge just for the engineer to come to your house.

(a) How much is that charge?
(b) How much does the firm charge for each hour the engineer spends at your house?
(c) Calculate the cost of the engineer's time for a repair that takes 2 hours.
(d) The engineer fits new parts that cost £75 and the repair takes 1 hour.
Calculate the total cost of the repair.

6 A foreign currency exchange bureau makes a standard charge of £2.50 per transaction.

(a) Explain why the number of French francs, F, you can buy with £P is given by the formula: $F = n(P - 2.5)$ where n stands for the number of francs equivalent to £1.
(b) Calculate how many French francs you would get for £50 on a day when £1 was equivalent to 7.43 French francs.

7 A printing firm uses this formula to work out the cost of printing postcards: $c = \dfrac{10\,000}{n} + 2$
where c is the cost in pence per postcard and n is the number of postcards ordered.

(a) The firm gets an order to print 5000 postcards.
Work out the printing cost per postcard.
(b) What happens to the cost per postcard as the number of postcards ordered increases?
(c) (i) Can the cost per postcard ever be 2 pence?
(ii) Explain your answer to part (i).

8 A thermometer in a potter's kiln works out the temperature by measuring the amount of electricity flowing through a wire.
The flow of electricity is measured in amps.

The formula for the temperature in the kiln is: $C = \dfrac{50}{A}$

where C is the temperature in degrees Celsius and A is the flow of electricity in amps.
Describe what happens to the flow of electricity as the temperature in the kiln increases.

21.7 Rearranging formulae

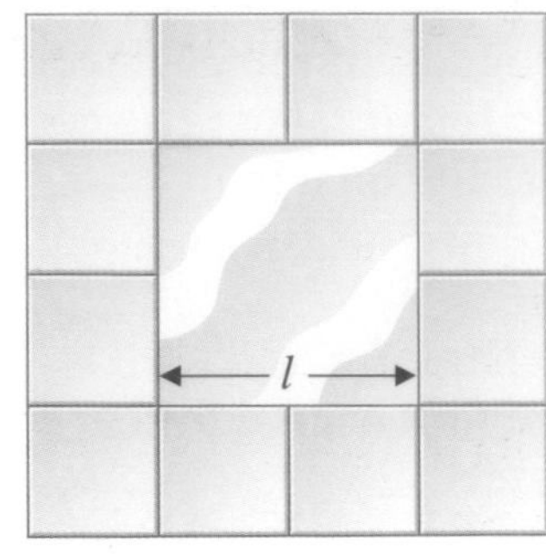

You can build a square picture frame using small square tiles. Call the internal length of the picture frame l tiles long. Call the total number of tiles used t.
t and l are connected by the formula:

$$t = 4l + 4$$

Here is how the formula can be rearranged to find l for any given value of t:

This is the flowchart for the formula:

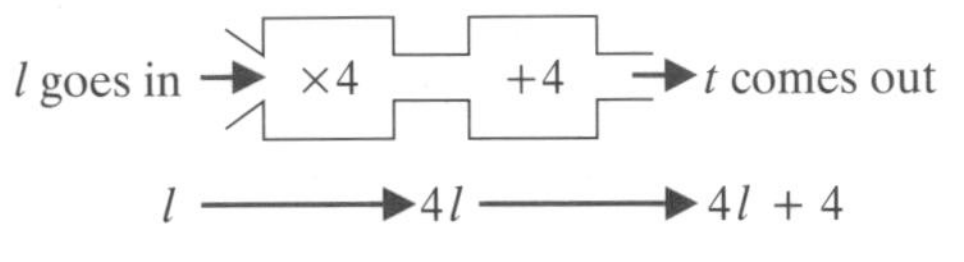

When a number machine is used to input and output letters and not numbers it is called a **flowchart**.

This is the reverse flowchart: l comes out ← ÷4 ← −4 ← t goes in

$\frac{t-4}{4}$ ← $t - 4$ ← t

So $l = \frac{t-4}{4}$

Changing the formula $t = 4l + 4$ so that it becomes $l = \frac{t-4}{4}$ is called rearranging the formula to make l the subject.

■ **The subject of a formula appears on its own on one side of the formula and does not appear on the other side.**

Example 12

Martin uses square tiles to make square picture frames like the ones above.
Work out the internal length l, as a number of tiles, of the largest square picture frame that Martin can make using 37 tiles.

Put $t = 37$ in $l = \frac{t-4}{4}$

to get $l = \frac{37-4}{4}$

$= 8.25$

But l can only take whole number values so $l = 8$ tiles. The number of tiles used is $t = 4 \times 8 + 4 = 36$ and there is 1 tile left over.

Example 13

Rearrange the formula $a = \frac{b}{4} - 5$ to make b the subject.

First method

$a = \frac{b}{4} - 5$ This is the flow chart for the formula:

$b \rightarrow \boxed{\div 4} \rightarrow \boxed{-5} \rightarrow a$

This is the reverse flow chart:

$b \leftarrow \boxed{\times 4} \leftarrow \boxed{+5} \leftarrow a$

$4(a + 5) \leftarrow a + 5 \leftarrow a$

so $b = 4(a + 5)$

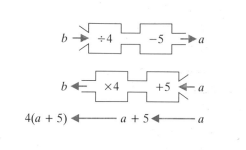

(or $b = 4a + 20$ with the brackets removed)

Second method

$$a = \frac{b}{4} - 5$$

add 5 to both sides:

$$a + 5 = \frac{b}{4}$$

multiply both sides by 4:

$$4(a + 5) = b$$

so $b = 4(a + 5)$

Third method

$$a = \frac{b}{4} - 5$$

multiply both sides by 4:

$$4a = b - 20$$

add 20 to both sides:

$$4a + 20 = b$$

so $b = 4a + 20$

Exercise 21I

1 The formula for the number of dominoes, d, in a domino bridge of length l dominoes is:

$$d = 2l + 1$$

(a) Draw the flowchart for the formula $d = 2l + 1$

(b) Draw the reverse flowchart.

(c) Use the reverse flowchart to rearrange the formula to make l the subject.

(d) Use your formula from part **(c)** to work out the length of the longest bridge that can be made with 40 dominoes.

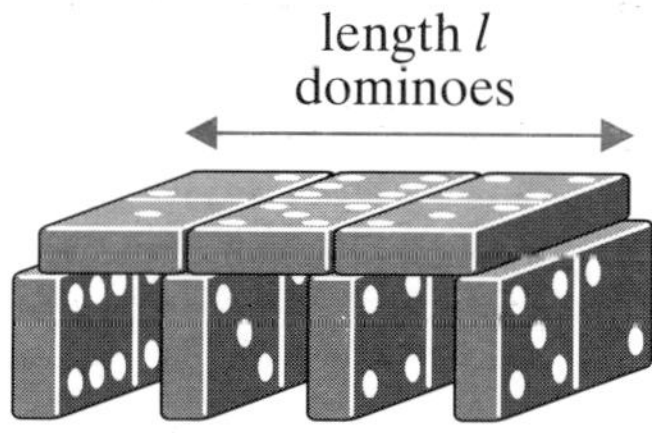

This bridge is 3 dominoes long so $l = 3$

2 The formula to change degrees Celsius, °C, into degrees Fahrenheit, °F, is:

$$F = 1.8C + 32$$

(a) Rearrange the formula to make C the subject.

(b) What is 76 °F in degrees Celsius?

3 Rearrange each of these formulae to make d the subject:

(a) $c = 3d + 2$ (b) $c = 4d + 5$ (c) $c = 5d - 6$

(d) $c = 7d + 8$ (e) $c = \frac{1}{2}d + 3$ (f) $c = \frac{1}{3}d - 4$

4 Make x the subject of the formula:

(a) $y = 3x + 5$ (b) $y = 4x - 7$ (c) $y = 2(x + 3)$

(d) $y = 3(x - 5)$ (e) $y = \frac{x-4}{3}$ (f) $y = \frac{x+5}{9}$

(g) $y = \frac{x}{3} + 4$ (h) $y = \frac{x}{2} - 7$ (i) $y = \frac{2x-3}{6}$

5 Rearrange each of these formulae to make b the subject:

(a) $a = 4b - 3$ (b) $a = 3(b + 2)$ (c) $a = 2(b - 3)$

(d) $a = \frac{b-3}{4}$ (e) $a = \frac{b+4}{2}$ (f) $a = \frac{b+3}{22}$

(g) $a = \frac{b}{2} - 3$ (h) $a = 2(b + 4) + 3(b - 2)$

Hint: in parts (b) and (c) remove the brackets first.

In part (h) simplify the right hand side first.

6 **Activity**

You need squared dotty paper.

(a) Draw some polygons which do not have dots inside them.
Draw some with area 1 cm^2, 2 cm^2, 3 cm^2.
Try some with areas 0.5 cm^2, 1.5 cm^2, etc.

(b) Count the number of dots on the perimeter of each shape and work out the area of the shape.

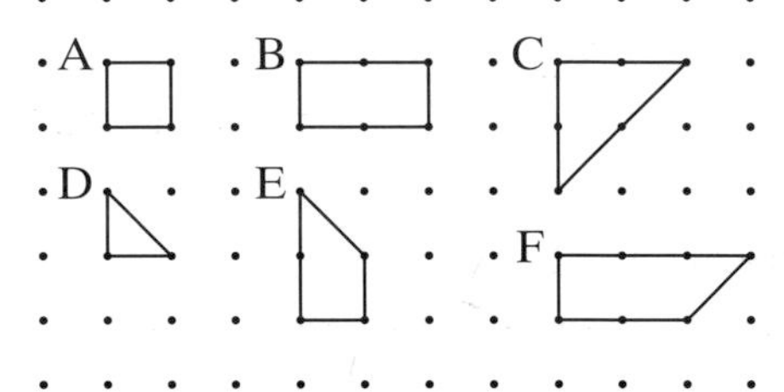

(c) Put your results into a table.

Shape	Area in cm^2 (a)	Dots on perimeter (p)
D	0.5	3
A	1	4
E	1.5	5
B	2	6
C	2	6
F	2.5	7

(d) Try to spot the rule connecting the area, a, to the number of dots on the perimeter p. Write the rule as a formula with p as the subject and as a formula with a as the subject.

(e) Repeat parts **(a)**, **(b)**, **(c)** and **(d)** for shapes with exactly 1 dot inside them.

(f) Repeat parts **(a)**, **(b)**, **(c)** and **(d)** for shapes with exactly 2 dots inside them, and so on.

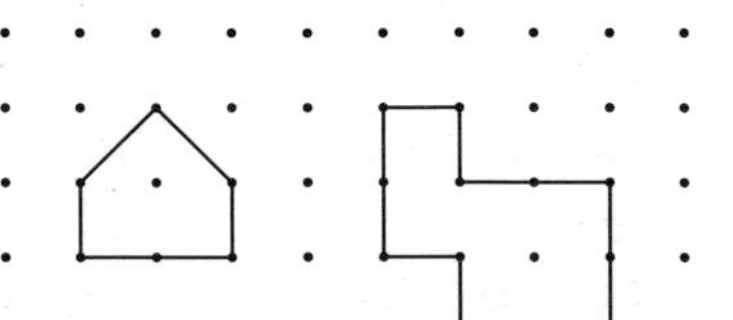

These shapes have only one dot inside them.

(g) Try to find a formula connecting a, p and d, the number of dots inside the shape.
(h) Make each letter in turn the subject of your formula in part **(g)**.
(i) Try looking at shapes which contain windows.

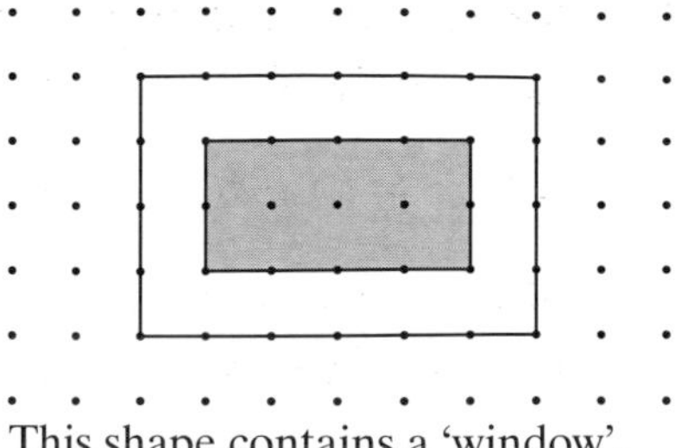
This shape contains a 'window'.

21.8 Factorizing

■ **Factorizing is the reverse process to removing brackets.**

Factorizing lets you write algebraic expressions in a different form using brackets.

Example 14

Factorize the expression $3x + 6$

$3x + 6$	Look for common factors of the terms $3x$ and 6.
$= 3(x + 2)$	3 is a common factor so it can be taken outside a bracket.

Example 15

Factorize the expression $5x^2 + 15x$

$5x^2 + 15x$	Look for common factors of the terms $5x^2$ and $15x$.
$= 5(x^2 + 3x)$	5 is a common factor so it can be taken outside a bracket.
$= 5x(x + 3)$	x is a common factor of x^2 and $3x$ so it too can be taken outside the bracket.

Exercise 21J

Factorize each of these expressions:

1	**(a)** $2x + 6$	**(b)** $6y + 2$	**(c)** $15b - 5$
	(d) $4r - 2$	**(e)** $3x + 5xy$	**(f)** $12x + 8y$
	(g) $12x - 16$	**(h)** $9 - 3x$	**(i)** $9 + 15g$
2	**(a)** $3x^2 + 4x$	**(b)** $5y^2 - 3y$	**(c)** $2a^2 + a$
	(d) $5b^2 - 2b$	**(e)** $7c - 3c^2$	**(f)** $d^2 + 3d$
	(g) $6m^2 - m$	**(h)** $4xy + 3x$	**(i)** $n^3 - 8n^2$
3	**(a)** $8x^2 + 4x$	**(b)** $6p^2 + 3p$	**(c)** $6x^2 - 3x$
	(d) $3b^2 - 9b$	**(e)** $12a + 3a^2$	**(f)** $15c - 10c^2$
	(g) $21x^4 + 14x^3$	**(h)** $16y^3 - 12y^2$	**(i)** $6d^4 - 4d^2$
4	**(a)** $ax^2 + ax$	**(b)** $pr^2 - pr$	**(c)** $ab^2 - ab$
	(d) $qr^2 - q^2$	**(e)** $a^2x + ax^2$	**(f)** $b^2y - by^2$
	(g) $6a^3 - 9a^2$	**(h)** $8x^3 - 4x^4$	**(i)** $18x^3 + 12x^5$

5 **(a)** $12a^2b + 18ab^2$ **(b)** $4x^2y - 2xy^2$
(c) $4a^2b + 8ab^2 + 12ab$ **(d)** $4x^2y + 6xy^2 - 2xy$
(e) $12ax^2 + 6a^2x - 3ax$ **(f)** $a^2bc + ab^2c + abc^2$

6 **(a)** $5x + 20$ **(b)** $12y - 10$ **(c)** $3x^2 + 5x$
(d) $4y - 3y^2$ **(e)** $8a + 6a^2$ **(f)** $12b^2 - 8b$
(g) $cy^2 + cy$ **(h)** $3dx^2 - 6dx$ **(i)** $9c^2d + 15cd^2$

Factorizing quadratics

Sometimes you will need to factorize quadratic expressions of the type $x^2 + bx + c$, where b and c are numbers.

For example, $x^2 + 6x + 5$ factorizes to give the expression:

$$(x + 5)(x + 1)$$

Notice that these two numbers:
- multiply together to give 5
- add together to give the 6 in $6x$

Check this yourself by multiplying out $(x + 5)(x + 1)$.

Here factorizing is the reverse process of removing brackets by multiplying out.

Example 16

Factorize $x^2 - 7x + 12$

Find two numbers that:
- multiply together to give 12
- add together to give –7

The two numbers are –4 and –3, so:

$x^2 - 7x + 12$ factorizes to $(x - 4)(x - 3)$

Example 17

Factorize $x^2 + x - 6$

Find two numbers that:
- multiply together to give –6
- add together to give 1

The two numbers are –2 and 3, so:

$x^2 + x - 6$ factorizes to $(x - 2)(x + 3)$

Example 18

Factorize $x^2 - 25$

Find two numbers that:
- multiply together to give –25
- add together to give 0
  (Think of $x^2 - 25$ as $x^2 + 0x - 25$)

The two numbers are –5 and 5, so:

$x^2 - 25$ factorizes to $(x - 5)(x + 5)$

Example 19

Factorize $5x^2 - 80x$

Both terms have a common factor 5, so first take 5 outside a bracket:

$$5(x^2 - 16)$$

Now $x^2 - 16$ factorizes to $(x - 4)(x + 4)$, so:

$5x^2 - 80x$ factorizes to $5(x - 4)(x + 4)$

Remember: always check your factorizing by multiplying out the brackets.

Some quadratic expressions cannot be factorized. It is very unlikely that you would be given one like that in an examination.

Exercise 21K

Factorize:

1 **(a)** $x^2 + 4x + 3$ **(b)** $x^2 + 3x + 2$ **(c)** $x^2 + 12x + 11$
(d) $x^2 + 5x + 6$ **(e)** $x^2 + 5x + 4$ **(f)** $x^2 + 4x + 4$

2 **(a)** $x^2 - 3x + 2$ **(b)** $x^2 - 14x + 13$ **(c)** $x^2 - 6x + 5$
(d) $x^2 - 6x + 8$ **(e)** $x^2 - 6x + 9$ **(f)** $x^2 - 8x + 12$

3 **(a)** $x^2 + 2x - 3$ **(b)** $x^2 + 4x - 5$ **(c)** $x^2 + 6x - 7$
(d) $x^2 + 5x - 6$ **(e)** $x^2 + x - 6$ **(f)** $x^2 + 2x - 15$

4 **(a)** $x^2 - 6x - 7$ **(b)** $x^2 - 5x - 6$ **(c)** $x^2 - 2x - 15$
(d) $x^2 - 7x - 8$ **(e)** $x^2 - 2x - 8$ **(f)** $x^2 - x - 20$

5 **(a)** $x^2 - 9$ **(b)** $x^2 - 36$ **(c)** $3x^2 - 12$
(d) $x^2 - 25$ **(e)** $2x^2 - 32$ **(f)** $3x^2 - 27$

Hint: look for a common factor first.

6 **(a)** $p^2 + 8p + 7$ **(b)** $q^2 - 14q + 13$ **(c)** $r^2 + 4r - 12$
(d) $a^2 - a - 12$ **(e)** $b^2 - 49$ **(f)** $c^2 + 2c - 24$

7 **(a)** $d^2 - 5d - 24$ **(b)** $2t^2 - 50$ **(c)** $u^2 + 15u + 36$
(d) $v^2 - 13v + 36$ **(e)** $w^2 + w - 30$ **(f)** $x^2 - 8x - 20$

Exercise 21L Mixed questions

1 **(a)** Write in symbols the rule 'To find y, double x and add 1'.
(b) Use your rule from part **(a)** to calculate the value of x when $y = 9$. [L]

2 Here is the formula for working out the perimeter of a rectangle:

$$P = 2(l + w).$$

Use the formula to work out the value of P when $l = 6$ and $w = 4$. [L]

3 A quarterly gas bill is given by the formula:

$$C = S + nx$$

where C is the total cost of the bill in pence
S is the standing charge in pence
n is the number of units used
x pence is the cost per unit.

(a) Calculate the value of C when $S = 860$, $n = 152$ and $x = 7$.
(b) Rewrite the formula so that it is written in the form $n = \ldots\ldots$ [L]

4 Find the value of $x(x + y)$ when $x = -2$ and $y = 1$. [L]

5 If $a = 1$, $b = 2$ and $c = -3$, find the value of $\dfrac{c - ab}{c + ab}$ [L]

6 Simplify:

(a) $x^3 \times x^5$ **(b)** $y^7 \div y^3$ **(c)** $(z^3)^8$

(d) $3a^2 \times 5a^3$ **(e)** $14y^8 \div 2y^2$ **(f)** $(4z^2)^3$

(g) $4(3p + 5q) - 3(2p - q)$ **(h)** $x(2x^2 + y) + x(x^2 - 3y)$

7 A formula is $v = \frac{x}{ut}$

Make t the subject of the formula. [L]

8 Here is a formula: $p = kq^2 - qr$.
Rearrange the formula so that k is the subject.

9 Write down an expression in terms of n and g for the total cost, in pence, of n buns at 18 pence each and 5 bread rolls at g pence each. [L]

10 **(a)** Expand $(2x + 1)(x + 4)$.
(b) Factorize completely $4x^2 - 6x$.

11 Choc bars cost 27 pence each.
Write down a formula for the cost, C pence, of n choc bars. [L]

12 The air temperature, T°C, outside an aircraft flying at a height of h feet is given by the formula: $T = 26 - \frac{h}{500}$

An aircraft is flying at a height of 27 000 feet.

(a) Use the formula to calculate the air temperature outside the aircraft.

The temperature outside an aircraft is –52 °C.

(b) Calculate the height of the aircraft. [L]

13 **(a)** Expand and simplify $(2x + 3)(x - 4)$.
(b) Factorize completely $10x^2 - 5x$. [L]

14 Factorize completely:

(a) $x^2 + 8x + 7$ **(b)** $x^2 - 10x + 24$ **(c)** $x^2 - 4x - 12$

(d) $y^2 + 3y - 10$ **(e)** $y^2 - 13y - 14$ **(f)** $y^2 + 11y + 24$

(g) $x^2 - 16$ **(h)** $2x^2 + 8x + 6$ **(i)** $4x^3 - 36x$

Summary of key points

1 Use BODMAS to help you remember the order of mathematical operations when evaluating an algebraic expression.

Follow this order: ↓

Brackets
p**O**wers
Divide
Multiply
Add
Subtract

2 $x^a \times x^b = x^{a+b}$

To multiply powers of the same letter add the indices.

$x^a \div x^b = x^{a-b}$

To divide powers of the same letter subtract the indices.

$(x^a)^b = x^{ab}$

To raise a power of a letter to a further power multiply the indices.

$x^1 = x$

Any letter raised to the power 1 is equal to the letter itself.

$x^0 = 1$ if x is not zero.

Any letter raised to the power 0 is equal to 1.

3 To simplify an expression containing different powers of the same letter multiplied or divided, write the expression as a single power of the letter.

4 To remove brackets from an algebraic expression multiply each term inside the brackets by the term outside. For example:

$2(n + 1) = 2n + 2$

This is sometimes called 'expanding the brackets'.

5 To multiply out bracketed expressions, multiply each term in the first bracket by each term in the second bracket:

$(e + f)(g + h) = eg + eh + fg + fh$

You can also think of this as multiplying each term in the first bracket by the whole of the second bracket:

$(e + f)(g + h) = e(g + h) + f(g + h)$

6 The subject of a formula appears on its own on one side of the formula and does not appear on the other side. For example:

$t = 4l + 4$ can be rearranged to give $l = \frac{t - 4}{4}$

t is the subject $\quad$ l is the subject

7 Factorizing is the reverse process to removing brackets. For example:

$3x + 6$ factorizes to $3(x + 2)$
$x^2 + x - 6$ factorizes to $(x - 2)(x + 3)$

22 Percentages

Increases in wages, reductions in prices during 'sales', and discounts are often shown as percentages.

The symbol % and the letters pc mean 'per cent'. The numbers in the newspaper are all percentages.

The words 'per cent' mean 'in every hundred'. So 20 per cent means '20 in every hundred', written 20% for short.

22.1 Percentages, fractions and decimals

Percentages, fractions and decimals are linked. You can write '20 in every hundred' as the fraction $\frac{20}{100}$ or as the decimal 0.2, so:

$$20\% = \frac{20}{100} = 0.2$$

■ **To change a percentage to a fraction write as a fraction with a denominator (bottom) of 100.**

40% is the same as $\frac{40}{100}$ and this simplifies to $\frac{2}{5}$

There is more about cancelling fractions on page 139 and about changing fractions to decimals on page 142 of Unit 11

■ **To change a percentage to a decimal, first change it to a fraction and then to a decimal.**

$35\% = \frac{35}{100} = 35 \div 100 = 0.35$

$225\% = \frac{225}{100} = 225 \div 100 = 2.25$

Example 1

Write these percentages as: (i) decimals (ii) fractions.

(a) 65% (b) $17\frac{1}{2}\%$

(a) (i) $65\% = \frac{65}{100} = 65 \div 100 = 0.65$

(ii) $65\% = \frac{65}{100} = \frac{13}{20}$

(b) (i) $17\frac{1}{2}\% = \frac{17\frac{1}{2}}{100} = 17.5 \div 100 = 0.175$

(ii) $17\frac{1}{2}\% = \frac{17\frac{1}{2}}{100} = \frac{35}{100} = \frac{7}{40}$

Exercise 22A

Write these percentages as: **(a)** decimals **(b)** fractions.

1 45%	**2** 60%	**3** 85%	**4** 56%	**5** 69%
6 6%	**7** 82%	**8** $12\frac{1}{2}\%$	**9** 44%	**10** $67\frac{1}{2}\%$
11 $2\frac{1}{2}\%$	**12** $62\frac{1}{4}\%$	**13** $33\frac{1}{3}\%$	**14** $42\frac{1}{2}\%$	**15** $55\frac{2}{3}\%$

Changing fractions and decimals to percentages

- **To change a decimal to a percentage multiply the decimal by 100%.**
- **To change a fraction to a percentage, first change the fraction to a decimal then multiply by 100%.**

Example 2

Write these numbers as percentages:

(a) 0.42 (b) $\frac{7}{20}$ (c) 0.335 (d) $\frac{37}{40}$

(a) $0.42 \times 100\% = 42\%$

(b) $\frac{7}{20} = 7 \div 20 = 0.35 \qquad 0.35 \times 100\% = 35\%$

(c) $0.335 = 0.335 \times 100\% = 33.5\% = 33\frac{1}{2}\%$

(d) $\frac{37}{40} = 0.925 \qquad 0.925 \times 100\% = 92.5\% = 92\frac{1}{2}\%$

Exercise 22B

Write these numbers as percentages:

1 $\frac{3}{4}$	**2** 0.9	**3** $\frac{37}{25}$	**4** $\frac{2}{5}$	**5** $\frac{9}{20}$
6 0.83	**7** 0.49	**8** $\frac{21}{40}$	**9** 0.36	**10** 0.075
11 $\frac{7}{8}$	**12** 0.375	**13** $\frac{17}{60}$	**14** 0.1875	**15** $\frac{5}{12}$
16 $\frac{1}{3}$	**17** $\frac{1}{8}$	**18** 0.4	**19** 0.03	**20** 1.4
21 $\frac{7}{40}$	**22** 0.176	**23** $\frac{23}{80}$	**24** $\frac{2}{3}$	**25** 0.008
26 2.36	**27** $\frac{4}{9}$	**28** $\frac{3}{5}$	**29** 1.07	**30** $\frac{3}{20}$

Comparing percentages, fractions and decimals

Sometimes you will be asked to arrange percentages, fractions and decimals in order of size.

Example 3

Write in order of size, smallest first:

63%, $\frac{3}{5}$, 0.65, $\frac{7}{10}$

Write each as a decimal for easy comparison.

	63%	$\frac{3}{5}$	0.65	$\frac{7}{10}$
decimals:	0.63	0.6	0.65	0.7

Then rearrange the decimals in order of size:

0.6	0.63	0.65	0.7
$\frac{3}{5}$	63%	0.65	$\frac{7}{10}$

The new order is: $\frac{3}{5}$, 63%, 0.65, $\frac{7}{10}$

Adding and subtracting percentages

Notice that:

$$\underset{\text{percentage}}{100\%} = \underset{\text{fraction}}{\frac{100}{100}} = \underset{\text{decimal}}{1}$$

A score of 100% in a test is full marks.
100% of a class is the whole class.

Example 4

Within a Humanities option 45% of a year group study History, and 32% study Geography. The remainder study RE.
What percentage study RE?

The percentage studying History or Geography is 45% + 32% = 77%
The whole year group is 100% of the students.
So the percentage studying RE is 100% – 77% = 23%
So 23% study RE.

Exercise 22C

1 Write these in order of size, smallest first:
(a) 49%, $\frac{9}{20}$, 0.44 **(b)** 60%, 0.64, $\frac{5}{8}$ **(c)** 0.41, $\frac{2}{5}$, 38%
(d) 65%, $\frac{11}{16}$, 0.64 **(e)** 66%, $\frac{2}{3}$, 0.6 **(f)** 76%, $\frac{3}{4}$, 0.7

2 If 53% of the pupils in a class are girls, what percentage are boys?

3 If 92% of households have at least one television set, what percentage of households have no television set?

4 A school team drew 13% of their matches, and lost 42% of them. What percentage of matches did the teams win?

5 On a particular day 73% of the passengers arriving at Luton airport are UK citizens.
What percentage of them are not UK citizens?

22.2 Finding a percentage of a quantity

Here are two ways of finding a percentage of a quantity:

Example 5

Find 15% of £70.

Method 1
Change the percentage to a fraction:

$$15\% = \frac{15}{100}$$

$$\text{So } 15\% \text{ of } £70 = \frac{15}{100} \times £70$$

$$= \frac{1050}{100} = £10.50$$

Method 2
Change the percentage to a decimal:

$$15\% = \frac{15}{100} = 0.15$$

$$\text{So } 15\% \text{ of } £70 = 0.15 \times £70$$

$$= £10.50$$

Remember: *of* means *multiply*.

■ **To find a percentage of a quantity change the percentage to a fraction or a decimal and multiply it by the quantity.**

Worked examination question

Work out 20% of £25. [L]

$$20\% \text{ of } £25 = \frac{20}{100} \times £25 = \frac{500}{100} = £5.00$$

Example 6

Find: (a) 10% of £4.25 (b) $12\frac{1}{2}\%$ of 40 kg

(a) $10\% \text{ of } £4.25 = \frac{10}{100} \times £4.25 = \frac{42.5}{100} = £0.425 = £0.43$ (or 43p)

So 10% of £4.25 is 43p (rounded to the nearest penny).

(b) $12\frac{1}{2}\% \text{ of } 45\,\text{kg} = \frac{12.5}{100} \times 45\,\text{kg} = 5.625\,\text{kg}$

Exercise 22D

In questions **1** to **9** work out:

1	10% of £90	**2**	15% of £6.40	**3**	30% of 20 g
4	30% of £3.20	**5**	75% of 400 kg	**6**	5% of 370 m
7	23% of 550 g	**8**	$37\frac{1}{2}\%$ of 42 m*l*	**9**	$10\frac{1}{4}\%$ of £80

10 In a village 48% of the population is male. The total population is 3500.
Find the number of: **(a)** males **(b)** females.

11 Of 120 shops in a survey, 30% sold food.
How many shops sold food?

12 Denise earns £34 500 a year. She pays 25% income tax.
How much tax does she pay on these earnings?

13 There are 220 seats on a plane and 85% of the seats have been taken.
How many seats are vacant?

14 A saleswoman makes a car journey of 240 miles and 58% of the journey is on non-motorway roads.

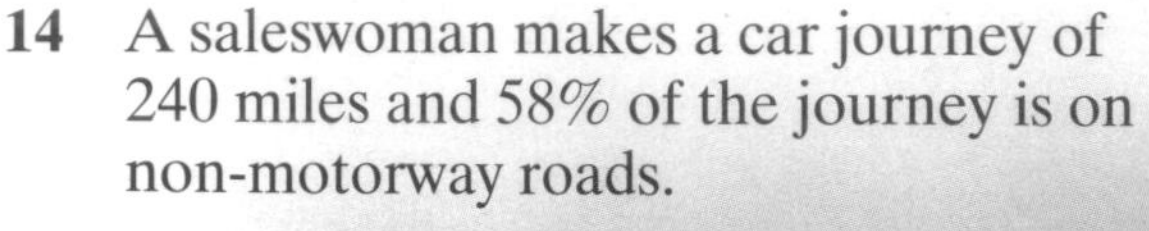

What is her mileage on motorways?

15 A school raises £2800 during a summer fete. The school gives 38% of the money to charity.
How much money is left?

Percentage increase and decrease

Example 7

A factory employs 320 workers. The number of workers increases by 10%.
How many are now employed?

$$10\% \text{ of } 320 = \frac{10}{100} \times 320 = \frac{3200}{100} = 32$$

This is an increase. So you need to add 32 to the original amount.
The number of workers now employed is 320 + 32 = 352

Example 8

A suit would normally cost £120. In a sale there is a reduction of $12\frac{1}{2}\%$.
What is the sale price?

$$12\tfrac{1}{2}\% \text{ of } 120 = \frac{12.5}{100} \times 120 = \frac{1500}{100} = 15$$

This is a decrease. So you need to subtract £15 from the original amount.
The sale price is £120 – £15 = £105

- **To increase a quantity by a percentage find the percentage of the quantity and add it to the original quantity.**
- **To decrease a quantity by a percentage find the percentage of the quantity and subtract it from the original quantity.**

Exercise 22E

1 Increase 340 tonnes by 45%

2 Increase 1250 g by 85%

3 Decrease £250 by 30%

4 Increase £32 by $10\frac{1}{2}$%

5 Decrease 400 g by 77%

6 Decrease 93 m*l* by $33\frac{1}{3}$%

7 Increase £90 by $6\frac{1}{2}$%

8 Decrease £208 by $87\frac{1}{2}$%

9 Last year Remi's water rates were £200. The rates have risen by $7\frac{1}{2}$%.
What are they now?

10 Senga is an office worker. Her annual salary of £12 800 is increased by $5\frac{1}{2}$%.
What is her new salary?

11 What is the sale price of a coat normally priced at £45?

12 Bill has reduced his weight by 6% from 115 kg.
What is his new weight?

13 A motorcycle originally cost £2800. Its value has depreciated by 35%.
What is its value now?

14 Last week a shop sold 320 CDs. This week it has already sold 15% more.
How many CDs have been sold this week?

15 A school employs 80 teachers. Next year it must reduce its teaching staff by 5%.
How many teachers will there be next year?

22.3 Finding one quantity as a percentage of another

Sometimes you need to write one quantity as a percentage of another.

Example 9

Tina has gained a mark of 45 out of 60 in a test.
Write this as a percentage.
To find 45 as a percentage of 60 follow these steps:

Step 1: Write the two quantities as a fraction: $\frac{45}{60}$

Step 2: Convert the fraction to a decimal: $\frac{45}{60} = 45 \div 60 = 0.75$

Step 3: Multiply the decimal by 100%: $0.75 \times 100\% = 75\%$

Tina's mark was 75%

- **To write one quantity as a percentage of another:**
  1 Write one quantity as a fraction of the other
  2 Change the fraction to a decimal
  3 Multiply the decimal by 100%

Sometimes you need to work out the percentage by which a quantity has changed. You work out the change as a percentage of the original amount.

- **When a quantity changes (increases or decreases) find the percentage change using:**

$$\textbf{percentage change} = \frac{\textbf{actual change}}{\textbf{original quantity}} \times \textbf{100\%}$$

Example 10

A 32 metre path is extended to 36 metres.

By what percentage has the length of the path increased?

The increase in length is 4 metres.

To find the percentage increase, find 4 metres as a percentage of the original length of 32 metres.

Write the quantities as a fraction: $\frac{4}{32}$

Convert to a decimal: $\frac{4}{32} = 4 \div 32 = 0.125$

Multiply by 100%: $0.125 \times 100\% = 12.5\%$

The path has increased in length by 12.5% (or $12\frac{1}{2}\%$).

Exercise 22F

1 Sean scored 27 out of 45 in a test. Write this as a percentage.

2 In a class of 30 pupils, 21 are girls.
What percentage of the class is **(a)** girls **(b)** boys?

3 A car park contains 120 cars. There are 45 cars that were made in Japan and the rest were made in Europe.
What percentage of the cars were
(a) made in Japan **(b)** made in Europe?

4 Express the first quantity as a percentage of the second:
(a) 20 mg, 50 mg **(b)** 54 mm, 20 cm **(c)** £1.53, £4.50 **(d)** 54 cm, 2 m

5 The cost of a CD player has fallen from £250 to £175.
What is the percentage decrease in price?

> Hint: in question 4 parts (b) and (d) convert both quantities to the same units first.

6 The price of a meal in a restaurant has risen from £9.00 to £9.45.
Work out the percentage increase in the price.

7 Leroy delivers 80 reams of paper to a school. Of these, 12 reams are coloured.
What percentage of the paper was coloured?

8 The cost of a holiday has risen from £650.00 to £731.25.
Work out the increase as a percentage of the original cost.

9 In a shop 14 out of 16 clocks keep good time.
What percentage of the clocks do not keep good time?

10 There were 4205 people at a pop concert and 2015 of these were female.
What percentage were male?

22.4 Finding the original amount before a percentage change

You may be told an amount which is the result of a percentage increase or decrease. This section shows how to work out the original amount before the percentage change.

Example 11

The cost of a train ticket from Manchester to London has risen by 25% to £109.
What was the original price of the ticket?

Think of the original price as 100%.
£109 is the original price plus 25% of the original price, or
100% + 25% = 125% of the original price.

So £109 is 125% of the original price.

Divide both numbers by 125:

$$\frac{£109}{125} \text{ is } 1\% \text{ of the original price}$$

Multiply both numbers by 100:

$$\frac{£109}{125} \times 100 = £87.20 \text{ is } 100\% \text{ of the original price}$$

The original price was £87.20

> Another way of thinking about this is:
>
> original price = $\frac{100}{125} \times$ new price

Example 12

The price of a shirt has been reduced by $12\frac{1}{2}\%$ to £21 in a sale.
What was the original price?

Think of the original price (before the $12\frac{1}{2}\%$ reduction) as 100%
The £21 (after the reduction) is $100\% - 12\frac{1}{2}\%$ or $87\frac{1}{2}\%$ of the original price.
So £21 is $87\frac{1}{2}\%$ (or 87.5%) of the original price.

Divide both numbers by 87.5:

$$\frac{£21}{87.5} \text{ is } 1\% \text{ of the original price.}$$

Multiply both numbers by 100:

$$\frac{£21}{87.5} \times 100 = £24 \text{ is } 100\% \text{ of the original price.}$$

The original price was £24.

> original price = $\frac{100}{87.5} \times$ new price

■ **If an original amount is increased by *R*% to become a new amount**

$$\text{original amount} = \frac{100}{100 + R} \times \text{new amount}$$

If an original amount is decreased by *R*% to become a new amount

$$\text{original amount} = \frac{100}{100 - R} \times \text{new amount}$$

Exercise 22G

1 A piece of elastic was stretched by 24% to a length of 31 cm. Work out its unstretched original length.

2 A gas fire costs £135 to buy, after a price increase of 8%. What did the gas fire cost before the increase?

3 Saleem received £112 after a 30% deduction from his wages. Calculate his wages *before* deductions.

4 A suit has been reduced by $12\frac{1}{2}$% to £56 in a sale. What was its original price?

5 Karen sells her motorbike for £2112, making a loss of 12% on its original price. Work out its original price.

6 A man's wage has increased by $6\frac{1}{4}$% to £127.50 What wage did he receive before the increase?

7 A man weighs 209 kg, having lost 5% of his original weight. Calculate his original weight.

8 The price of a freezer is increased by 15% to £299. What was its price before the increase?

22.5 Dealing with profit and loss

When you buy something then sell it for a higher price you make a **profit**. If you sell it for a lower price you make a **loss**.
The cost price is the amount you originally paid for it.
The selling price is the amount you sold it for.

■ **Profit (or loss) is the difference between the cost price and the selling price.**

You can write the profit or loss as a percentage of the original price.

■ $$\textbf{Percentage profit} = \frac{\text{profit}}{\text{cost price}} \times 100\%$$

$$\textbf{Percentage loss} = \frac{\text{loss}}{\text{cost price}} \times 100\%$$

Example 13

Ali bought a CD for £8.50 and sold it on his market stall for £11.20
What was his percentage profit?

Profit = £11.20 – £8.50 = £2.70

$$\text{Percentage profit} = \frac{\text{profit}}{\text{cost price}} \times 100\%$$

$$= \frac{£2.70}{£8.50} \times 100\% = 31.8\% \text{ (rounded to 1 d.p.)}$$

Example 14

In a closing down sale a dining room suite bought for £625 is sold for £585.
Calculate the percentage loss.

Loss = £625 – £585 = £40

$$\text{Percentage loss} = \frac{\text{loss}}{\text{cost price}} \times 100\%$$

$$= \frac{£40}{£625} \times 100\% = 6.4\%$$

Exercise 22H

1 For each of these find the percentage profit:
- **(a)** cost price = £20, selling price = £33
- **(b)** cost price = £40, selling price = £54
- **(c)** cost price = £60, selling price = £63

2 For each of these find the percentage loss:
- **(a)** cost price = £125, selling price = £120
- **(b)** cost price = £30, selling price = £27
- **(c)** cost price = £80, selling price = £61

3 A shop buys a radio cassette player for £28, and sells it for £35. Find the percentage profit.

4 Chantelle buys a coffee-maker for £64, but decides later to sell it. She sells it for £44.
Find her percentage loss.

5 A toaster is bought for resale by a shop for £38.40 In a sale it is sold for £35.52
Find the percentage loss.

6 Charlotte bought a second-hand knitting machine for £560.
A new one costs £770.
Find the saving Charlotte made as a percentage of the cost of a new machine.

7 Adam bought a used car for £1500. He later sold it for £1200. Find the percentage loss he made.

8 A shop buys a carpet for £375. A customer then buys it for £500. Find the percentage profit made by the shop.

22.6 Calculating VAT

Value Added Tax (VAT) is the amount that is added to bills for services and purchases. In 1996 the rate for VAT in the UK was $17\frac{1}{2}\%$.

The VAT rate can be set at any percentage by the government. Different countries have different VAT rates from each other.

Example 15

Two shops advertise the same camcorder. Find the cheaper buy.

You need to add the VAT to the price of the Whittaker's camcorder.

VAT $= 17\frac{1}{2}\%$ of £515 $= \frac{17.5}{100} \times 515 = 90.125 =$ £90.13 (rounded to the nearest penny)

Total cost = £515 + £90.13 = £605.13
The Discount camcorder is the cheaper one, at £599.

Example 16

A computer costs £846, inclusive of VAT. A school does not have to pay the VAT.
What price does a school pay for the computer?

To remove the VAT you need to calculate the original price.

Think of the original price (without the $17\frac{1}{2}\%$ VAT) as 100%
£846 (with the VAT) is the original price plus $17\frac{1}{2}\%$ of the original price, or $100\% + 17\frac{1}{2}\% = 117\frac{1}{2}\%$ of the original price.

So £846 is $117\frac{1}{2}\%$ or 117.5% of the original price.

Divide both numbers by 117.5:

$$\frac{£846}{117.5} = 1\% \text{ of the original price.}$$

Multiply both numbers by 100:

$$\frac{£846}{117.5} \times 100 = £720 \text{ is } 100\% \text{ of the original price.}$$

The school pays £720 for the computer.

Exercise 22I

In this exercise take the VAT rate to be $17\frac{1}{2}\%$.

1 Work out the VAT on these prices:
(a) £200 **(b)** £50 **(c)** £46 **(d)** £268
(e) £19.80 **(f)** £73.50 **(g)** £28.43 **(h)** £6.15

2 Add VAT to the price of:
(a) a £399 TV **(b)** a £110 rowing machine
(c) a golf set costing £74.99

3 These prices include VAT.
Calculate the price exclusive of VAT:
(a) a £135 mountain bike **(b)** a £209 hammer drill
(c) a £49 snack grill

4 A deep fat fryer is advertised as:
£27.50 + VAT
Find the total cost, including VAT.

5 Find the VAT on an £85.90 bill for a meal for four people.

6 VAT is added to a telephone bill of £75.90
Find the total bill.

7 VAT is added to the price of £12 for a video tape.
Find the total cost.

8 A lawnmower costs £125, inclusive of VAT.
How much VAT has been added?

9 A typewriter costs £65, inclusive of VAT.
What is the cost of the typewriter without the VAT?

22.7 Buying on credit

If you want to buy items without paying the full cost immediately you can buy them **on credit**. You pay a deposit and then make a number of regular payments.

Example 17

Jasper buys a video recorder on credit. Here are the credit costs: 20% deposit, and 36 monthly payments of £10.70

Calculate:
(a) the total cost of buying the video recorder on credit.
(b) the amount Jasper would save if he bought the video recorder for cash.

(a) 20% of £340 = £68.00 (deposit)
36 × £10.70 = £385.20 (total of monthly payments)
Total credit cost = £453.20

(b) Difference in cost = £453.20 – £340 = £113.20 Jasper would save £113.20 if he bought the video recorder for cash.

Exercise 22J

For questions **1** – **6** find:
(a) the total cost of buying on credit.
(b) the difference between the cash price and the cost of buying on credit.

1 A bicycle costs £132. It can also be bought with a deposit of 15%, followed by six monthly payments of £21.50

2 Double glazing would cost £1485. The credit terms are 36 monthly payments of £43.65, and a deposit of 18%.

3 A trailer for a car costs £254, but can also be bought by making 15 payments of £17.46, plus an initial deposit of £24.90

4 Photographic equipment costs £350. The credit agreement requires a 20% deposit and 15 monthly payments of £24.90

5 A £225 electric typewriter can be bought on credit with a deposit of 20%, and 12 monthly payments of £20.99

6 An armchair normally costs £360. It can be bought on credit with 24 monthly payments of £15.50, and a deposit of 25%.

22.8 Calculating with simple and compound interest

If you invest money in a building society or a bank savings account the building society or bank pays you **interest**.

If you borrow money you pay interest to the building society or bank.

The interest is worked out as a percentage of the amount you lend or borrow.

Simple interest

■ **Simple interest over several years is calculated by assuming that the sum of money invested (or borrowed) remains the same over those years and that the percentage rate of interest remains the same over those years.**

Example 18

per annum (or p.a.) means each year

£300 is invested for 4 years at an interest rate of 5% per annum. Calculate the simple interest earned.

$$\text{Interest for 1 year} = 5\% \text{ of } £300 = \frac{5}{100} \times £300$$

$$\text{Simple interest for 4 years} = \frac{5}{100} \times £300 \times 4$$

$$= \frac{(£300 \times 5 \times 4)}{100}$$

$$= £60$$

Formula for simple interest

You can write a formula for simple interest using these letters:

R Rate of interest (% p.a.)
T Time (years)
P Principal (sum of money) lent or borrowed
I simple interest

In Example 17 $P = 300$, $R = 5$ and $T = 4$.

So the equation:

$$\text{Simple interest} = \frac{£300 \times 5 \times 4}{100}$$

becomes the formula: $I = \dfrac{P \times R \times T}{100}$ or $I = \dfrac{PRT}{100}$

Example 19

£400 is invested for $1\frac{1}{2}$ years at an interest rate of $6\frac{1}{2}\%$ p.a. Find the simple interest earned.

$$I = \frac{P \times R \times T}{100} = \frac{£400 \times 6.5 \times 1.5}{100} = £39 \text{ interest}$$

Example 20

Work out how long it would take for an invested sum of £850 to produce £200 simple interest at 11% p.a.

$$I = \frac{P \times R \times T}{100} \quad \text{so} \quad £200 = \frac{£850 \times 11 \times T}{100}$$

$$200 = 93.5T$$

$$\text{so} \quad T = \frac{200}{93.5} = 2.139 \text{ years}$$

It would take 2.14 years (to 2 d.p.) to produce £200 simple interest.

Exercise 22K

In this exercise the interest is 'simple interest'.

Remember: p.a. (or per annum) means 'each year'.

1 Find the simple interest when:
   (a) £726 is invested for 3 years at 9% p.a.
   (b) £615 is invested for 6 years at 8% p.a.
   (c) £2140 is invested for 6 months at 11% p.a.
   (d) £725 is invested for $2\frac{1}{2}$ years at 7% p.a.
   (e) £8134 is invested for $7\frac{1}{2}$ years at $5\frac{1}{2}$% p.a.

2 Find the time it takes for a sum of £600 to produce £80 interest at 6% p.a.

3 Find the sum of money which should be invested to earn £250 interest over 4 years at 7% p.a.

4 Find the rate of interest needed to produce interest of £123 on an investment of £500 over $3\frac{1}{2}$ years.

5 Find the time it takes for a sum of £300 to produce £40 interest at $8\frac{1}{4}$% p.a.

6 Find the sum of money which should be invested to earn £45 interest over 1 year at 9% p.a.

Compound interest

Usually when you invest or borrow money you earn or pay **compound interest**.

■ **The compound interest for any year is interest paid on the total of the sum of money invested and the interest earned in previous years. The compound interest over several years is the total of the compound interest earned for each year.**

Example 21

Find the compound interest when £300 is invested for $1\frac{1}{2}$ years at an interest rate of $8\frac{1}{2}$% p.a. The interest is paid every six months.

Use $I = \dfrac{PRT}{100}$ with $T = 0.5$ year

Interest for the first six months:

$$\frac{£300 \times 8.5 \times 0.5}{100} = £12.75$$

New principal = £300 + £12.75 = £312.35

Remember: the **principal** is the sum of money on which interest is paid.

Interest for the second six months:

$$\frac{£312.75 \times 8.5 \times 0.5}{100} = £13.29 \text{ (to the nearest penny)}$$

New principal = £312.75 + £13.29 = £326.04

Interest for the third six months:

$$\frac{£326.04 \times 8.5 \times 0.5}{100} = £13.86 \text{ (to the nearest penny)}$$

Total now = £326.04 + £13.86 = £339.90

Compound interest earned over $1\frac{1}{2}$ years
= £339.90 – £300 = £39.90

Exercise 22L

1 £650 is invested for 2 years at 7% compound interest which is paid annually.
What is the total interest earned?

2 £400 is invested for 3 years at 8% compound interest which is paid annually.
What is the total interest earned?

3 £200 is invested for 3 years at $9\frac{1}{2}$% compound interest which is paid annually.
What is the total interest earned?

4 The price of a new Taurus car is £15 000 now. Each year the price decreases by 6% of the price at the beginning of the year.
Calculate the price of a Taurus car in three years' time.

5 A clarinet can be bought for £184 now. The price is expected to increase each year by 15% of its price at the beginning of the year.
What will its price be in two years' time?

6 A new chainsaw costs £240. With depreciation, its value is expected to fall each year by 15% of its value at the beginning of the year.
What will be the value of the chainsaw in three years' time?

7 £180 is invested for $1\frac{1}{2}$ years at $9\frac{1}{2}$% p.a. compound interest which is paid every six months.
What is the total interest earned?

8 £240 is invested for two years at $7\frac{1}{2}$% p.a. compound interest which is paid every six months.
What is the total interest earned?

Formula for calculating compound interest

Often a sum of money is invested (or borrowed) for several years. Calculating the compound interest earned (or paid) using the method shown in Example 21 would be tedious and take a long time. Instead you can use this formula:

■ $A = P\left(1 + \frac{R}{100}\right)^n$

P is the principal: (sum of money lent or borrowed)
R is the rate of interest (% p.a.)
n is the number of years of the investment or loan
A is the amount (principal + compound interest after n years).

You can use this formula when the compound interest is paid at the end of each year (annually).

Example 22

Sophie dances the lead role in a show for a month when the star of the show is ill. Sophie then invests her extra £2500 earnings for five years at a rate of 7.6% p.a.
Calculate the compound interest that her investment will earn.

$$A = P\left(1 + \frac{R}{100}\right)^n = £2500\left(1 + \frac{7.6}{100}\right)^5$$

$1 + \frac{7.6}{100} = 1 + 0.076 = 1.076$

$$= £2500\,(1.076)^5$$
$$= £2500 \times 1.4423...$$
$$A = £3605.797$$

Compound interest $= A - P =$ £3605.80 – £2500
= £1105.80

Exercise 22M

Repeat questions **1** to **6** of Exercise 22L using the formula

$$A = P\left(1 + \frac{R}{100}\right)^n.$$

22.9 Solving problems involving percentages

This section introduces you to some of the many everyday situations in which you may use percentage calculations.

Example 23

Sylvia is paid £90 a week plus commission of 8% on £600 sales. Find the total amount she receives.

Commission = 8% of £600 = $\frac{8}{100} \times$ £600 = £48

Total amount Sylvia receives = £90 + £48 = £138

Example 24

A car tyre normally costs £58 + $17\frac{1}{2}$% VAT. A garage offers a discount of 15% before the VAT is added. Find the price of four new car tyres.

Discount = 15% of £58 = $\frac{15}{100} \times$ £58 = £8.70

Cost (excluding VAT) of one tyre = £58 – £8.70 = £49.30

VAT = $17\frac{1}{2}$% of £49.30 = $\frac{17.5}{100} \times$ £49.30 = £8.63 (to the nearest penny)

Total cost of one tyre is £49.30 + £8.63 = £57.93

Total cost of four tyres is £57.93 × 4 = £231.72

Exercise 22N

1 William is paid a basic rate of £2.30 per hour, and a $14\frac{1}{2}$% commission on sales.
How much is he paid if he works 25 hours and makes sales of £180 during a particular week?

2 At a company the basic rate paid per hour is £2.80 The hourly rate for overtime is 25% more.
Find the amount paid to an employee who works a basic 35 hours, plus four hours overtime.

3 Interest of 11% per annum is charged on a mortgage of £87 000. How much interest is paid per month, if there are twelve equal monthly payments during the year?

4 Sandra sells cosmetics in people's homes. She is paid £1.80 per hour, and 20% commission on sales.
How much is she paid for five hours work if she makes sales of £95?

5 A rose tree is priced at £28 + $17\frac{1}{2}$% VAT, with discount of 15% of the total price if more than four are bought.
How much would it cost you to buy five rose trees?

6 Serafim is paid a basic rate of £2.60 per hour. The hourly rate for overtime is 40% more.
During a week Serafim works a basic 40 hours and then five hours overtime.
(a) Calculate the amount he has earned in the week.
(b) Deductions of 30% of his earnings are made for tax and national insurance contributions.
Calculate Serafim's 'take home' pay.

Exercise 22 O Mixed questions

1 The price of a car stereo is increased by $7\frac{1}{2}\%$ to £172.
What was the original price?

2 Find the cost of this exhaust system.

3 A salesman receives a wage of £1.60 per hour, plus 15% commission on sales.
What will be his wage for 35 hours work if he makes sales of £1900?

4 Find the percentage reduction on the Mega Ace Games System. [L]

Mega Ace Games System
Normal price £320
Sale price £272

5 Use your calculator to find $12\frac{1}{2}\%$ of £118. [L]

6 Nesta invests £508 in a bank account at an interest rate of 8.5% per annum.
(a) Calculate the interest on £508 after one year.
At the end of the first year the interest is added to her bank account. The interest rate remains at 8.5%.
(b) Calculate the total amount of money in Nesta's bank account at the end of the second year. [L]

7 Janet invests £50 in a building society for one year. The interest rate is 6% per year.
(a) How much interest, in pounds, does Janet get?
Nisha invests £60 in a different building society. She gets £3 interest after one year.
(b) Work out the percentage interest rate that Nisha gets. [L]

8 In 1990 a charity sold $2\frac{1}{4}$ million lottery tickets at 25p each. 80% of the money obtained was kept by the charity.
(a) Calculate the amount of money kept by the charity.
In 1991 the price of a lottery ticket fell by 20%. Sales of lottery tickets increased by 20%.
80% of the money obtained was kept by the charity.
(b) Calculate the percentage change in the amount of money kept by the charity. [L]

9 A new electronic typewriter costs £86.53 At the end of every year its value falls by 15% of its value at the start of that year. Calculate the value of the typewriter at the end of three years. [L]

10 Jake buys a television. He pays £125 deposit and 12 monthly instalments of £29.62

(a) Work out the total amount that Jake pays.

In Cooper's Store BRITE colour televisions are priced at £390 each in 1996. Lyn pays cash and is given a discount of 12%

(b) Calculate the amount that Lyn pays.

The price of a BRITE colour television has risen by 4% since 1995 to £390.

(c) Calculate the price of the television in 1995. [L]

11 **(a)** (i) Change $\frac{3}{8}$ to a decimal.

(ii) Write down your answer to part (i) correct to two decimal places.

(b) Change 67% to a decimal.

Here is a list of fractions, decimals and percentages.

67%, $\frac{1}{2}$, 0.6, 25%, 0.3, $\frac{3}{8}$

(c) Rewrite the list in order of size, starting with the smallest first. [L]

Summary of key points

1 To change a percentage to a fraction, write it as a fraction with a denominator (bottom) of 100. For example:

$$40\% = \frac{40}{100} \text{ which simplifies to } \frac{2}{5}$$

2 To change a percentage to a decimal, first change it to a fraction and then to a decimal:

$$35\% = \frac{35}{100} = (35 \div 100) = 0.35$$

3 To change a decimal to a percentage multiply the decimal by 100%:

$$0.35 \times 100\% = 35\%$$

4 To change a fraction to a percentage, first change the fraction to a decimal then multiply by 100%:

$$\frac{37}{40} = 0.925 \qquad 0.925 \times 100\% = 92.5\% \text{ (or } 92\tfrac{1}{2}\%)$$

5 To find a percentage of a quantity change the percentage to a fraction or a decimal and multiply it by the quantity. For example, to find 15% of £70 either:

change 15% to a fraction or change 15% to a decimal

$$\frac{15}{100} \times £70 = \frac{1050}{100} = £10.50 \qquad 15\% = \frac{15}{100} = 0.15 \qquad 0.15 \times £70 = £10.50$$

6 To increase a quantity by a percentage find the percentage of the quantity and add it to the original quantity.

7 To decrease a quantity by a percentage find the percentage of the quantity and subtract it from the original quantity.

8 To write one quantity as a percentage of another (for example 45 as a percentage of 60)

1 write one quantity as a fraction of the other: $\frac{45}{60}$

2 change the fraction to a decimal: $\frac{45}{60} = 45 \div 60 = 0.75$

3 multiply the decimal by 100%: $0.75 \times 100\% = 75\%$

9 When a quantity changes (increases or decreases) find the percentage change using:

$$\text{percentage change} = \frac{\text{actual change}}{\text{original quantity}} \times 100\%$$

10 If an original amount is increased by $R\%$ to become a new amount:

$$\text{original amount} = \frac{100}{100 + R} \times \text{new amount}$$

If an original amount is decreased by $R\%$ to become a new amount:

$$\text{original amount} = \frac{100}{100 - R} \times \text{new amount}$$

11 Profit (or loss) is the difference between the cost price and the selling price.

12 $\text{percentage profit} = \dfrac{\text{profit}}{\text{cost price}} \times 100\%$

$\text{percentage loss} = \dfrac{\text{loss}}{\text{cost price}} \times 100\%$

13 Simple interest over several years is calculated by assuming that the sum of money invested remains the same over those years and that the percentage rate of interest remains the same over those years. The formula for simple interest I is:

$I = \dfrac{PRT}{100}$ where R is the rate of interest (% per annum)
T is the time (in years)
P is the principal (sum of money lent or borrowed)

14 The compound interest for any year is interest paid on the total of the sum of money invested and the interest earned in previous years. The compound interest over several years is the total of the compound interest earned for each of the years.

The formula for the amount (principal plus compound interest) when interest is paid annually is:

$A = P\left(\dfrac{1 + R}{100}\right)^n$ where R is the rate of interest (% per annum)
n is the number of years of investment or loan
P is the principal
A is the amount (principal + compound interest after n years.)

23 Transformations

■ **Changes in the position or size of a shape are called transformations.**

For your GCSE exam you need to know about four types of transformations: translations, reflections, rotations and enlargements.

23.1 Translations

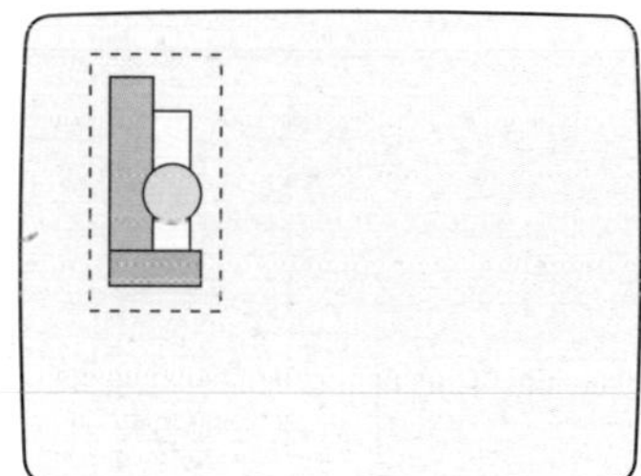

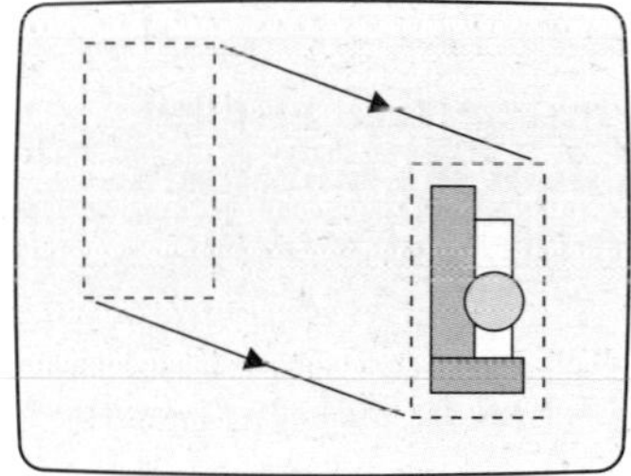

You can use computer drawing software to draw shapes and move them about like this. Each point on this shape has moved the same distance in the same direction.

This type of movement is called a **translation**.

■ **A translation moves every point on a shape the same distance in the same direction.**

In mathematics the transform shape is called the **image** of the shape.

Notice that after a translation the image is the same shape and size and the same way up.

How to translate a shape on paper

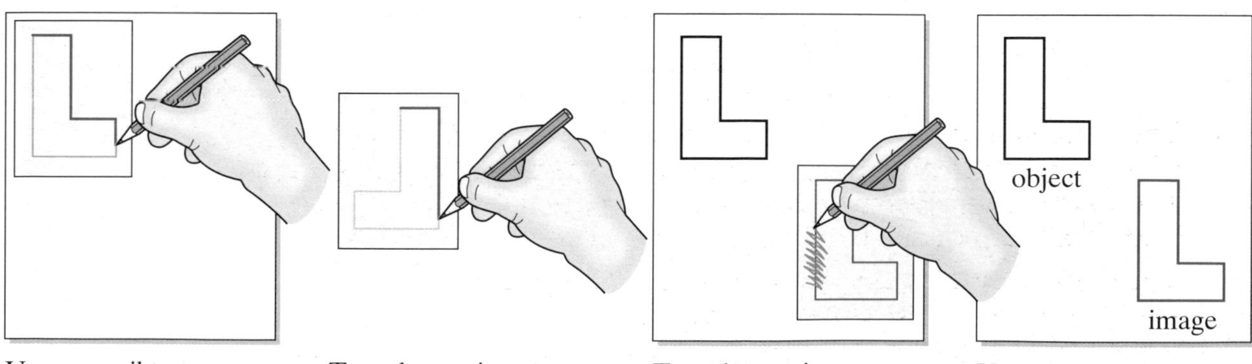

Use a pencil to trace the shape on to tracing paper.

Turn the tracing paper over and place it on a piece of scrap paper. Draw over the revised shape.

Turn the tracing paper over again. Put it in the required place and scribble over the traced shape.

You may need to draw over the image to make it clear.

Patterns can be made by repeated translations of a shape.
For example:

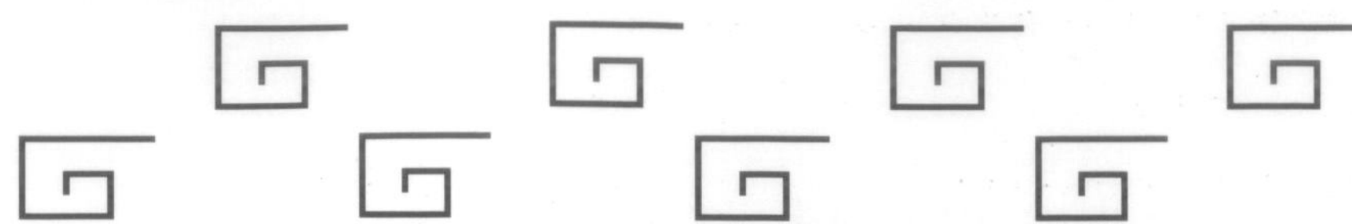

This pattern of floor tiles is made by translating two shapes. When the tiles completely cover the floor it is called a **tessellation**.

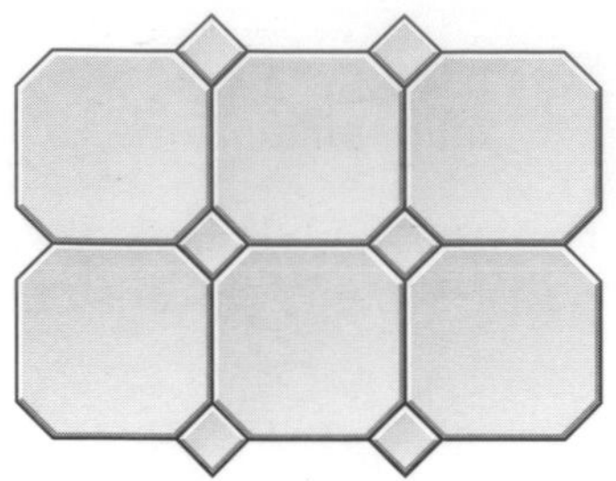

- **A tessellation is an arrangement of a shape or set of shapes on a flat surface so that all the space is filled, with no gaps and no overlaps.**

Describing translations

- **To describe a translation fully you need to give the distance moved and the direction of the movement. You can do this by writing down the vector of the translation.**

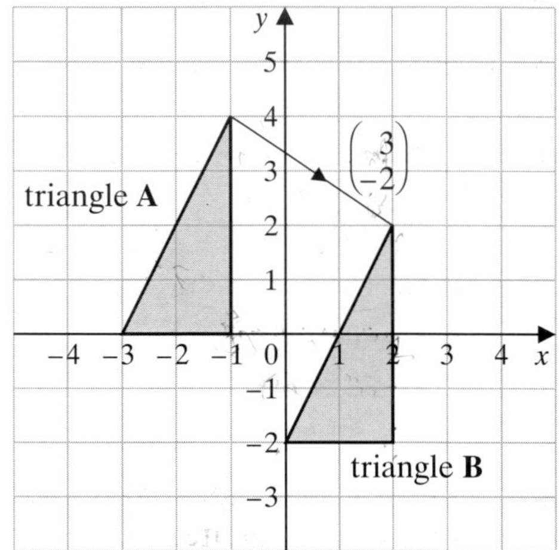

We say that triangle **A** 'maps on to' triangle **B**.

In this diagram triangle **A** is translated to **B**. All the points on **A** are moved +3 units parallel to the x-axis followed by –2 units parallel to the y-axis.

This translation is described by the **vector** $\begin{pmatrix} 3 \\ -2 \end{pmatrix}$

Coordinates are often used in questions involving transformations. The grid shows a set of coordinate axes with positive and negative values of x and y. At P, $x = 3$ and $y = 1$ so the coordinates of P are (3, 1).
Note: Write the x value before the y value.

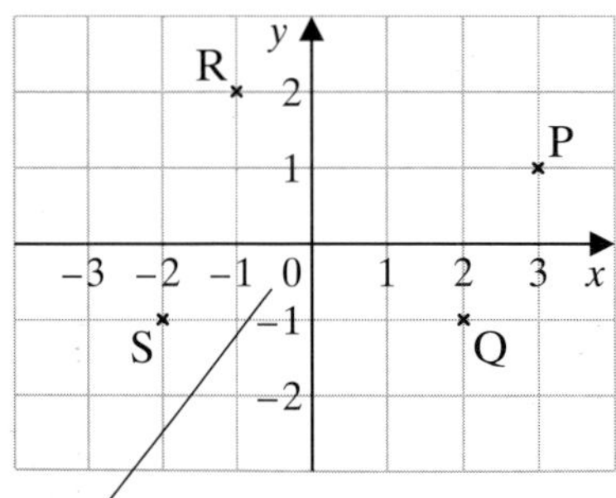

The point (0, 0) is called the Origin.

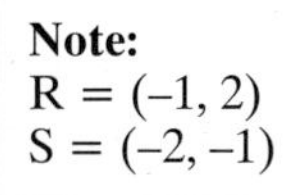
Note:
R = (–1, 2)
S = (–2, –1)

Example 1

The shape ABCD is shown on the grid.

(a) Write down the coordinates of A, B, C and D.

ABCD is translated to PQRS so that P(2, –1) is the image of A.

(b) Plot P and draw the image of ABCD

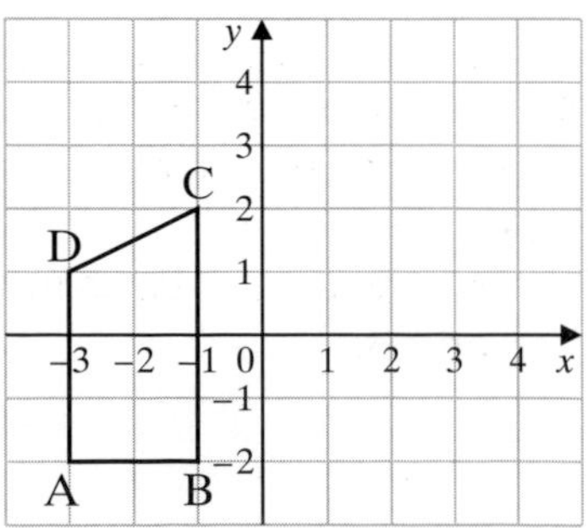

(a) A = (–3, –2), B = (–1, –2), C = (–1, 2) and D = (–3, 1).

(b) The point A (–3, –2) is translated to P (2, –1) so the x-coordinate is increased by 5 and the y-coordinate is increased by 1. It is a translation by the vector $\begin{pmatrix} 5 \\ 1 \end{pmatrix}$.

Q is the image of B, so the coordinates of Q are (–1+5, –2+1) = (4, –1). In the same way R = (–1+5, 2+1) = (4, 3) and S = (–3+5, 1+1) = (2, 2).
PQRS is shown on the grid:

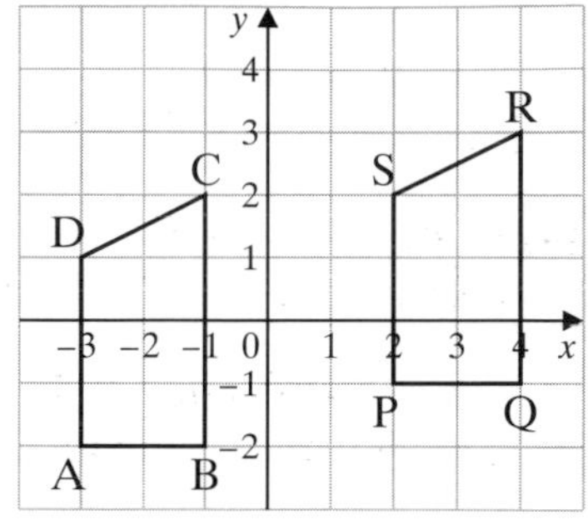

Exercise 23A

You will need isometric and squared paper and a ruler. Tracing paper could be useful.

1 Copy this shape onto squared paper. A translation of the shape makes the point N the image of the point M. Draw the whole shape.

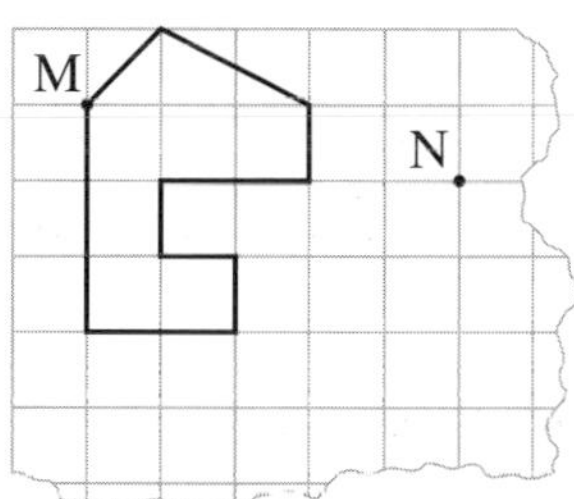

2 On isometric paper show how regular hexagons tessellate.

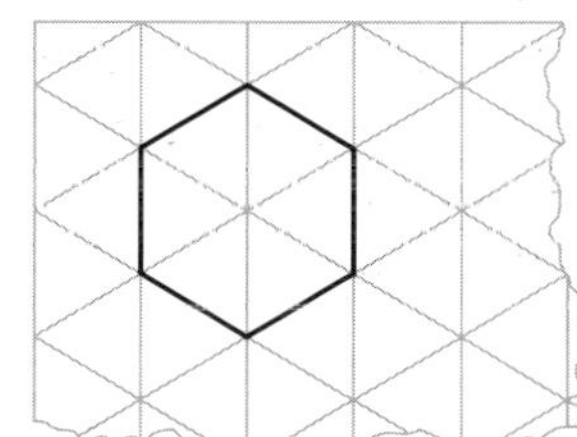

3 Shape **A** is shown on the grid.
A is translated using this rule:

Move all points +4 units parallel to the x-axis followed by +2 units parallel to the y-axis. This means move them by the vector $\begin{pmatrix} 4 \\ 2 \end{pmatrix}$.

On squared paper draw a set of coordinate axes with x and y both going from –5 to 5.

(a) Draw the image of **A** after the translation and label it **B**.

(b) Write down the coordinates of the corners of shape **B**.

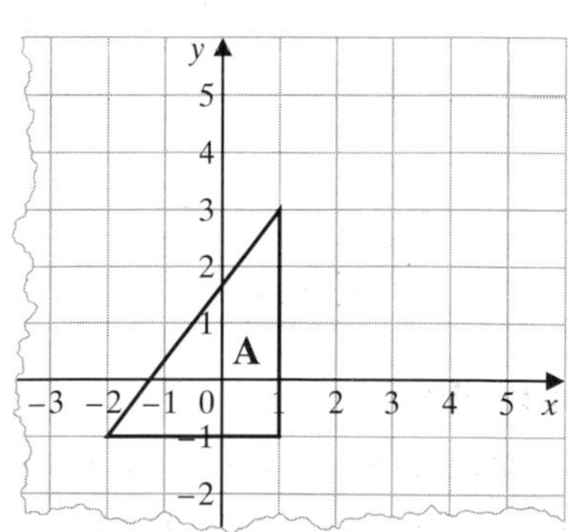

4 On squared paper draw a set of coordinate axes with x and y both going from –5 to 5.
The corners of triangle ABC are A(–1, 1), B(–1, 4) and C(1, 3).
(a) Draw triangle ABC on your grid.
Triangle ABC is translated to triangle A′B′C′ using this rule: Add 3 to the x-coordinate and subtract 4 from the y-coordinate.
(b) Work out the coordinates of A′, B′ and C′.
(c) Draw triangle A′B′C′ on your grid.

5 Describe fully the transformation which maps shape **P** on to shape **Q**.

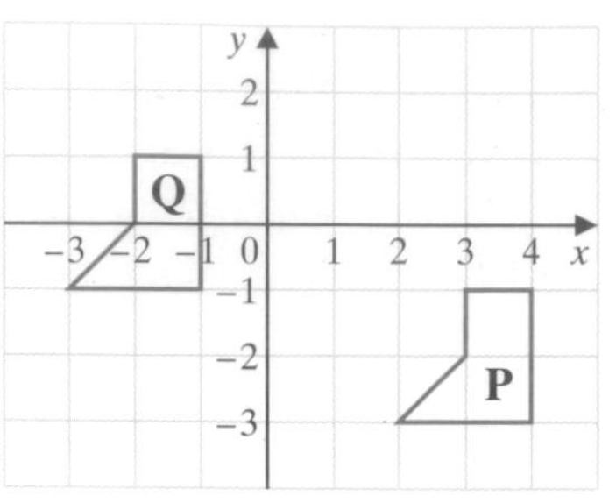

6 Make a pattern using repeated translations. You may use one, two or more shapes.

7 Make a tessellation by translating a suitable shape or shapes.

23.2 Reflections

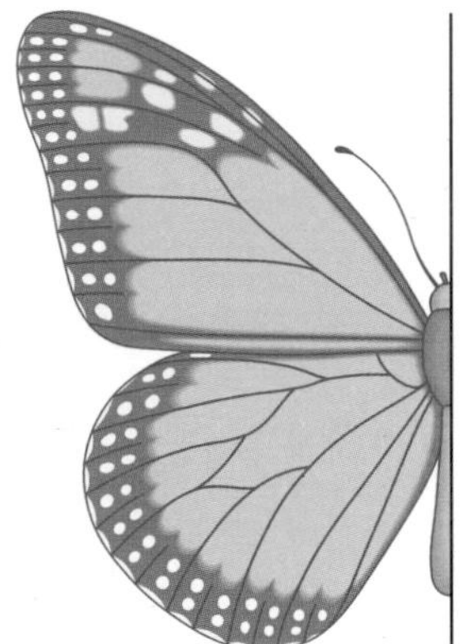

This picture was made by reflecting a shape in the mirror. Each point on the shape has a mirror image. The mirror line is a reflection line or **line of reflection**.

A **reflection** is another type of transformation.

Here is a point A reflected in a line.

The original shape A and the image A′ are the same distance from the line, but on opposite sides.

If you draw a line from A to A′ to cross the line of reflection at M:

AM = A′M and AA′ is at right angles to the line of reflection

You can draw the reflection of a shape by using these facts to find the images of different points on the shape.

(Hint: if the line of reflection is at an angle it is easier to draw a reflection if you turn the paper until the line is vertical.)

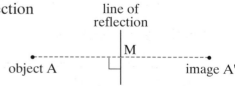

line of reflection

M

object A

image A'

Notice that A' is a reflection of A and A is a reflection of A'.

■ **A reflection in a line produces a mirror image.**

The image is the same size but it is a reflection of the original shape.

Example 2

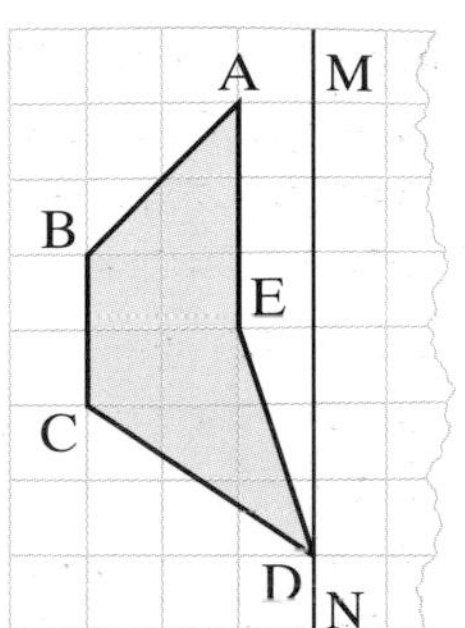

The shape ABCDE is reflected in the line MN.
Draw the image of the shape and label it A′B′C′D′E′.

Draw a line from A at right angles to MN. Continue the line to a point the same distance the other side and label the point A′. Repeat this for the points B, C, D and E. Join the points to make the reflected shape.
(Note: a point on the line MN is its own image.)

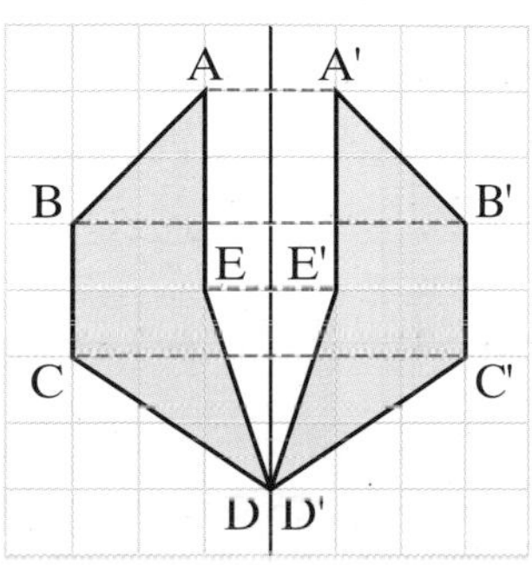

We say that shape ABCDE maps on to shape A′B′C′D′E′ after the reflection. The corners of shape ABCDE are labelled anticlockwise. The corners of shape A′B′C′D′E′ are labelled clockwise. If ABCDE were cut out, it would have to turn over to fit exactly over A′B′C′D′E′.

How to reflect a shape on paper
Tracing paper can be used to draw a reflection.

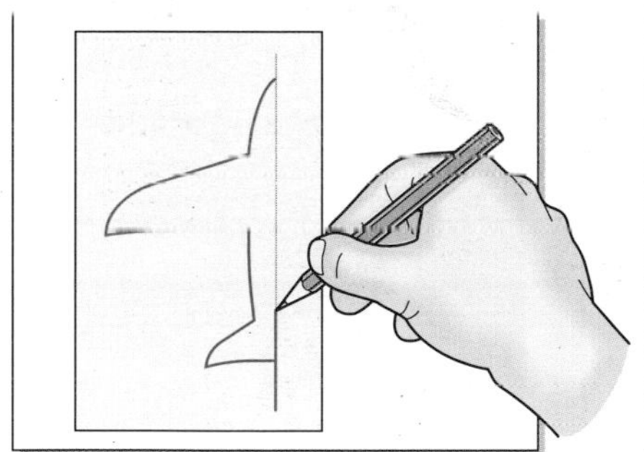
Trace the shape and the reflection line.

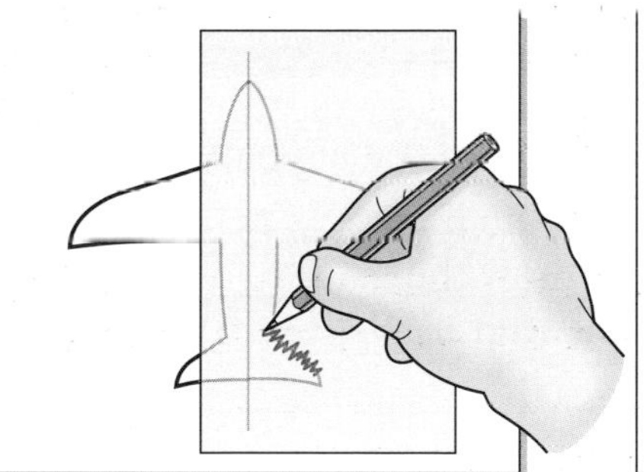
Turn the tracing paper over, lining up the reflection lines. Scribble over the traced shape.

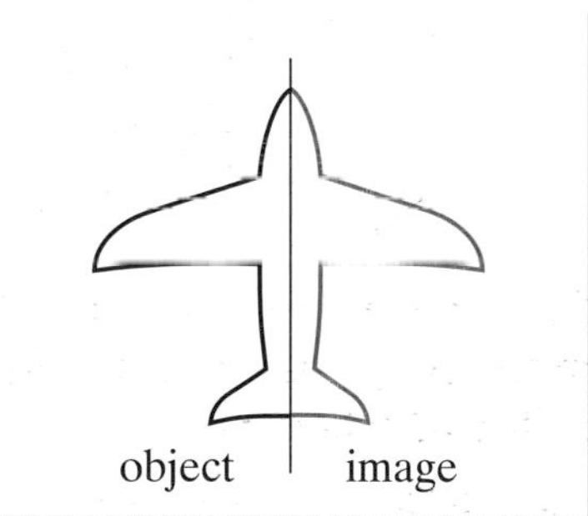

You may need to draw over the image to make it clear.

This pattern is made by repeated reflections of a shape. **A** is reflected to **B** and **B** is reflected to **C**.

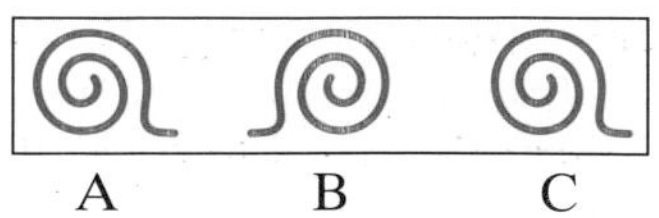

Describing reflections

■ **To describe a reflection fully you need to give the equation of the line of reflection.**

Example 3

Describe fully the transformation that maps shape **A** on to **B**.

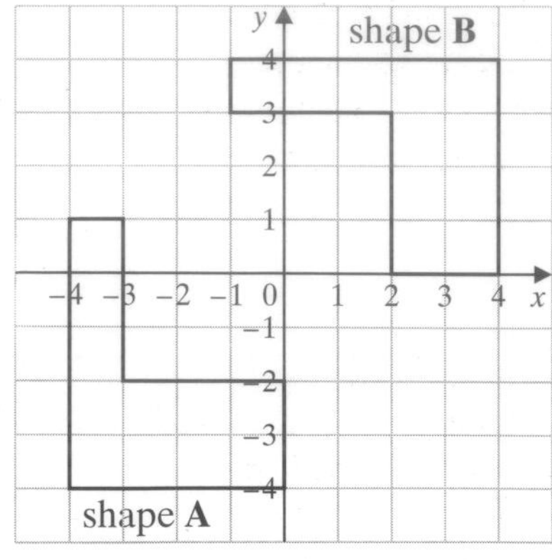

The image **B** is the same shape and size as the original shape **A**, but it is 'turned over'. So the transformation is a reflection.

We say these shapes are **congruent** (the same size and shape) even though one is a reflection of the other.

First draw the line of reflection.
Draw a line from a point on A to its corresponding point on B (shown by a broken line on the diagram).
Find the middle point of the line. Repeat for another point on A. The line joining the two middle points is the line of reflection.

The equation of the line is $y = -x$. A maps on to B after a reflection in the line $y = -x$.

The transformation is a reflection in the line $y = -x$.

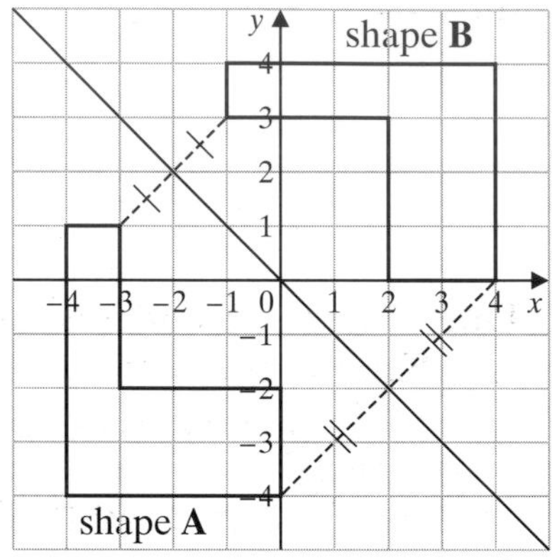

Exercise 23B

You need squared or graph paper and tracing paper.

1 Copy the shaded shape and the line MN. Use tracing paper to draw the image of the shaded shape after a reflection in the line MN.

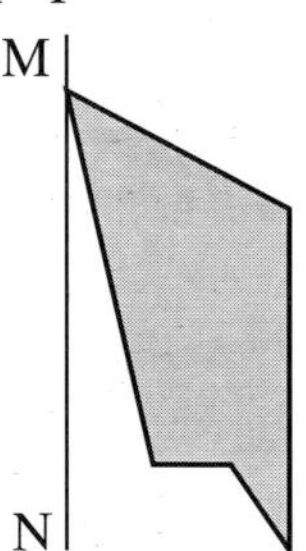

2 Copy the shape and the line MN on squared paper. Draw the image of this shape after a reflection in the line MN.

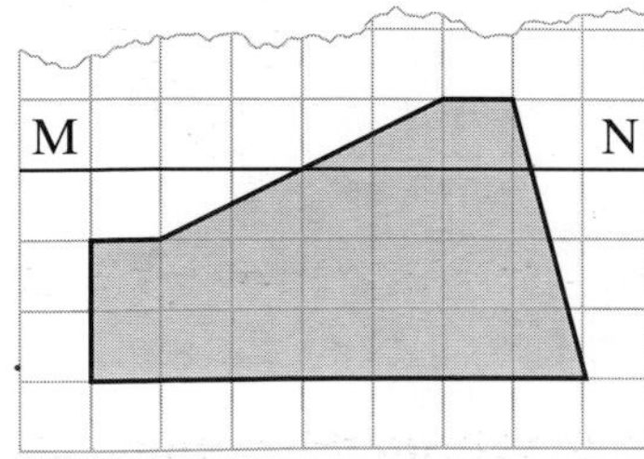

3 Copy the grid and the shaded shape. Draw the image of the shape after a reflection in the line $y = 1$. (Hint: first draw the line whose equation is $y = 1$.)

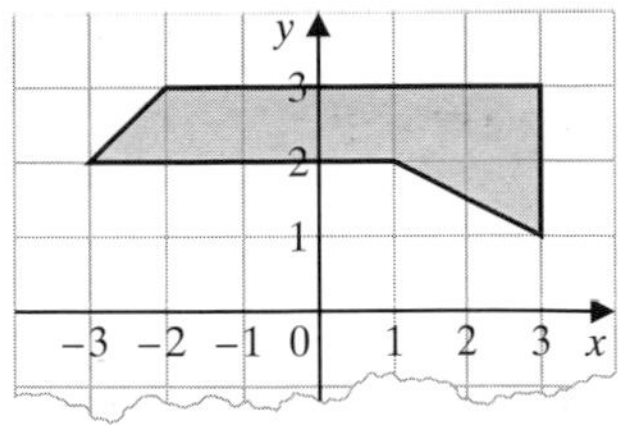

4 Copy triangle ABC and the line TU on squared paper. Draw the image of triangle ABC after it is reflected in the line TU. The image of the point A has been found for you. (Hint: turn the page so that TU is vertical.)

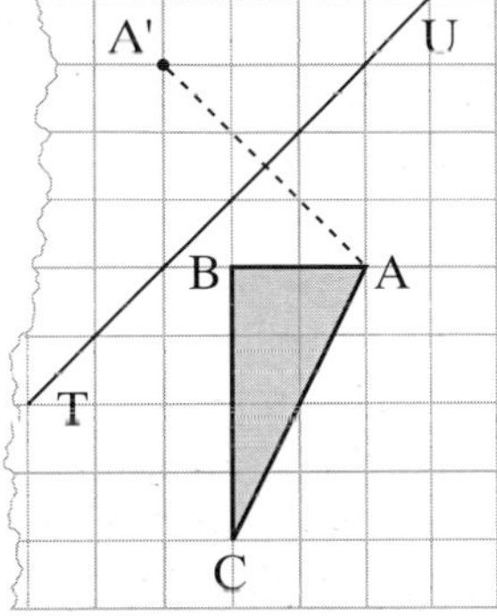

5 Draw a grid with both x and y coordinate axes going from −6 to 6.
 (a) Plot the points P(−2, 1), Q(0, 1), R(1, 0), S(3, 4) and T(−2, 4) and join them in order to form the closed shape PQRST.
 (b) Draw the image of PQRST after a reflection in the x-axis.

6 Describe fully the tranformation that maps shape **A** on to **B**.

7 Use tracing paper to draw a pattern by making repeated reflections of a shape.

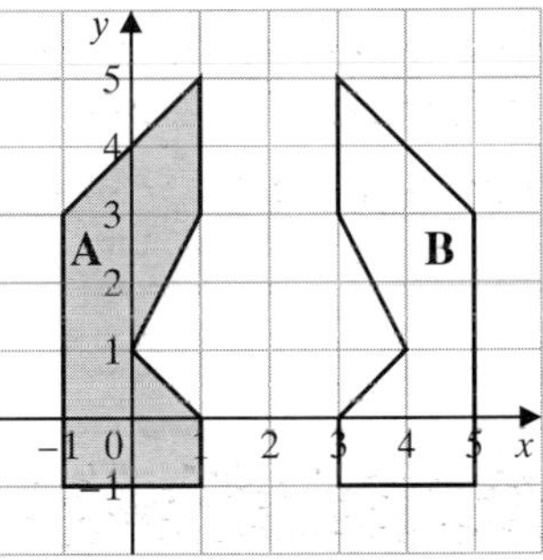

23.3 Rotations

The minute hand of a clock **rotates** (turns) about a point near one of its ends. A blade of a pair of scissors rotates about a point part way along its length.

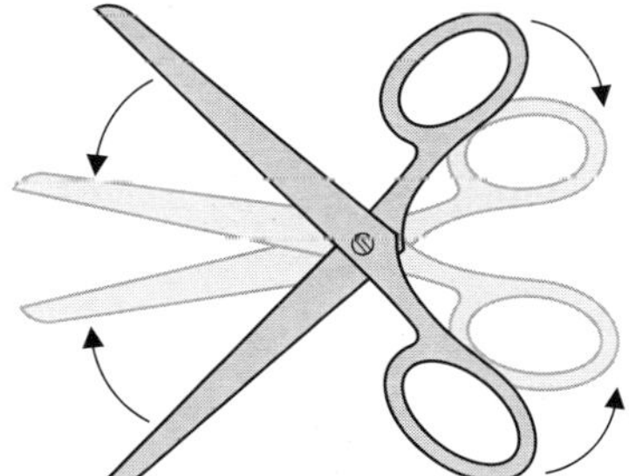

The clock hand and the scissor blade **turn through an angle** about a fixed point.

■ **A rotation turns a shape through an angle about a fixed point.**

Notice that the image is the same shape and size as the original shape.

How to rotate a shape on paper

To rotate this shape half a turn about the point marked with a dot:

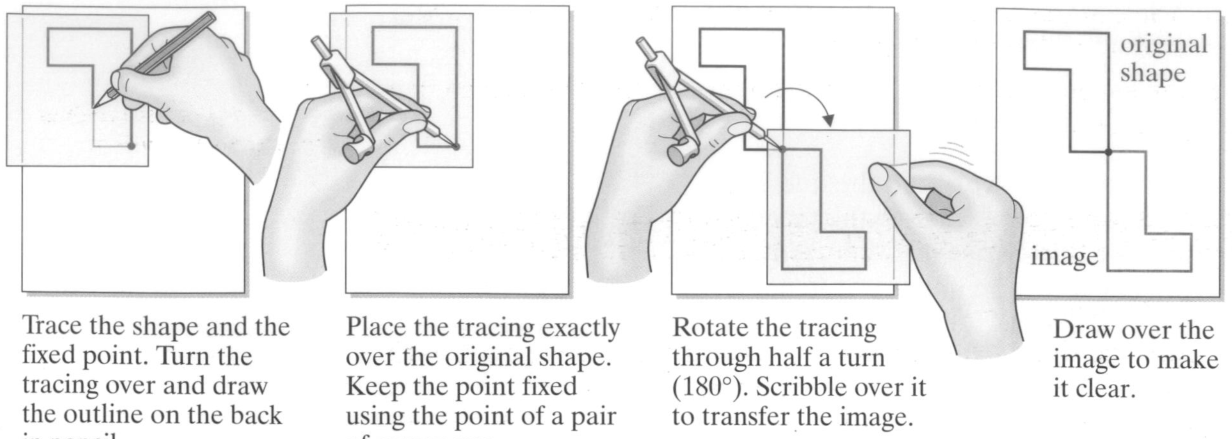

Trace the shape and the fixed point. Turn the tracing over and draw the outline on the back in pencil.

Place the tracing exactly over the original shape. Keep the point fixed using the point of a pair of compasses.

Rotate the tracing through half a turn (180°). Scribble over it to transfer the image.

Draw over the image to make it clear.

You could also do this using a card cut-out of the shape.

This pattern has been made by repeated rotations.

A is rotated to **B**, **B** is rotated to **C**, **C** is rotated to **D**.

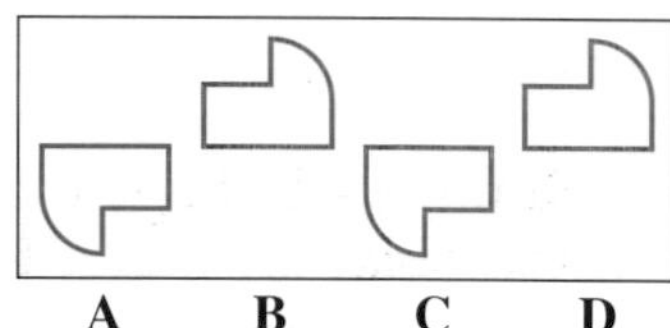

Exercise 23C

You need tracing paper, a ruler and a protractor.

1. Copy the shapes. Use tracing paper to rotate each shape half a turn about the point marked with a dot.

   (a) **(b)** 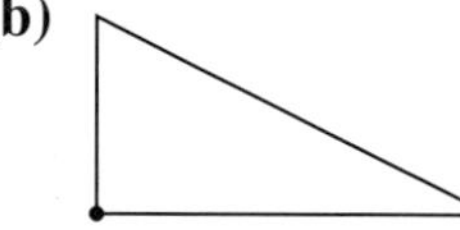 **(c)** 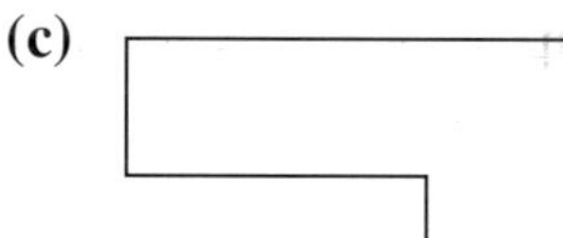

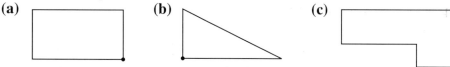

2. Rotate each of the shapes in question **1** a quarter of a turn anticlockwise about the point marked with a dot.

3. Copy the flag shape. Draw the image after a rotation about the point R of:
   - **(a)** a quarter of a turn anticlockwise
   - **(b)** a half turn
   - **(c)** a quarter of a turn clockwise.

R

4. Copy the shape. Draw the image after a rotation about the point of:
   - **(a)** 120° anticlockwise
   - **(b)** 240° anticlockwise
   - **(c)** 120° clockwise

   (Hint: use a protractor to make sure the turn is exactly 120°.)

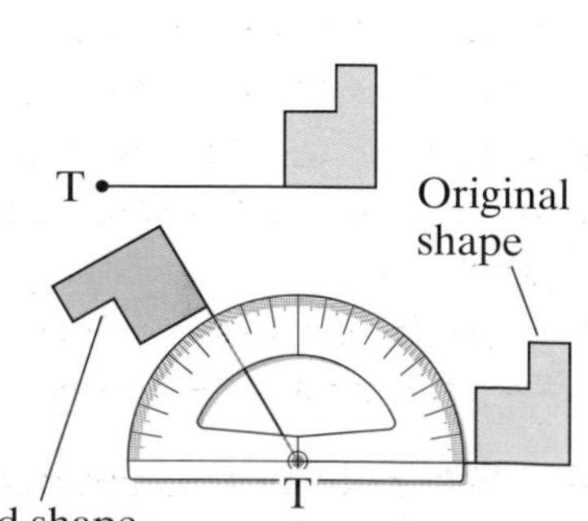

When the fixed point is not on the object

Sometimes you need to rotate a shape about a point that is outside itself. You can think of this as though it was a flag in question **3** of Exercise 23C without the flagpole.

Trace the shape and the dot. Then keep the dot fixed and rotate the tracing paper as before.

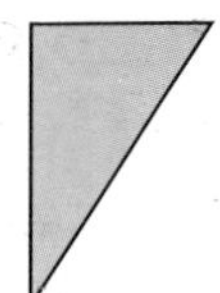

The fixed point R is called the **centre of rotation.**

Exercise 23D

You need tracing paper.

1 Copy the shapes and the dots. Use tracing paper to rotate each shape half a turn about the point marked with a dot.

(a) 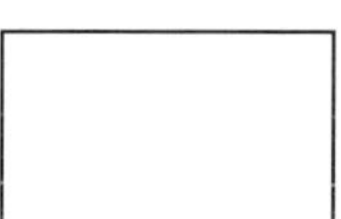 **(b)** 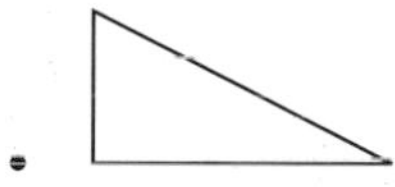 **(c)** 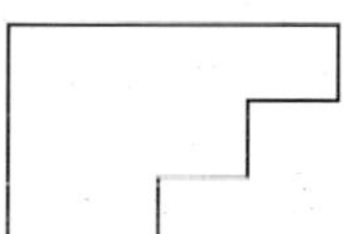

2 Rotate each shape in question **1** a quarter of a turn anticlockwise about the point marked with a dot.

3 Copy this shape and the dot.

Make a pattern by rotating the shape about the dot through these angles:

(a) clockwise: 60°, 120° and 180°

(b) anticlockwise: 60° and 120°.

Rotating shapes on a grid

You can use squared paper to help you rotate shapes.

Example 4

On squared paper draw coordinate axes with x going from 0 to 7 and y going from –3 to 7. Copy the shape and draw its image after a quarter of a turn anticlockwise about the point P(1, –1).

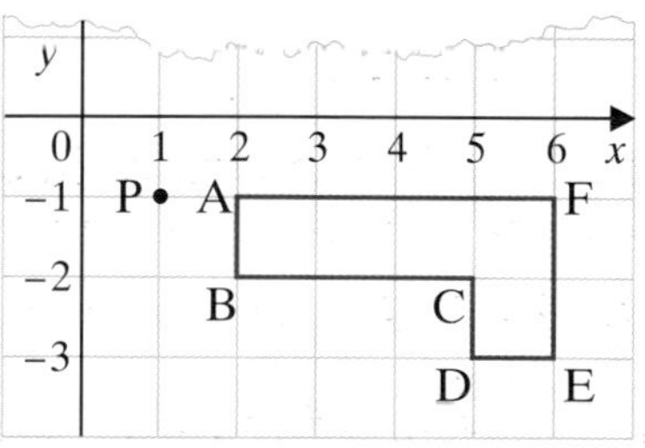

You can use tracing paper as before or you can use the lines on the grid to help you. Work out the image of each point on the shape and then join them to form the image.

Rotate A about P through a quarter of a turn (90°) anticlockwise and it ends up at (1, 0).

Rotate B about P through a quarter of a turn (90°) anticlockwise and it ends up at (2, 0).

F goes to (1, 4).

You could continue with the other points, but these image points are probably enough for you to complete the shape.

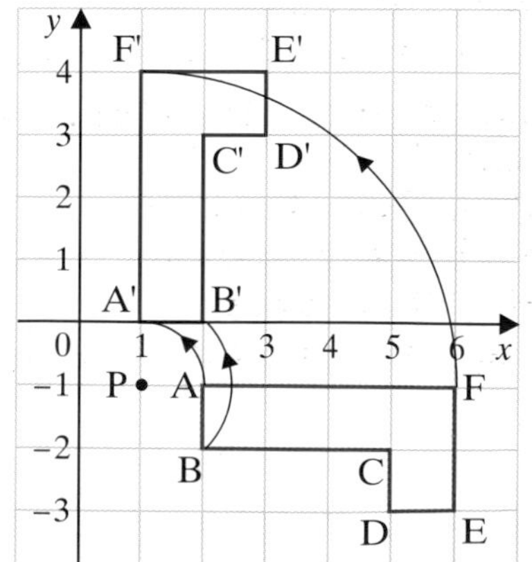

■ **When a shape is rotated all lines in the shape rotate through the same angle. The distance of an image point from the centre of rotation is the same as the distance of the original point from the centre.**

Describing rotations

■ **To describe a rotation fully you need to give the:**
- **centre of rotation**
- **angle of turn**
- **direction of turn (clockwise or anticlockwise)**

Example 5

Describe fully the transformation which maps shape **P** on to **Q**.

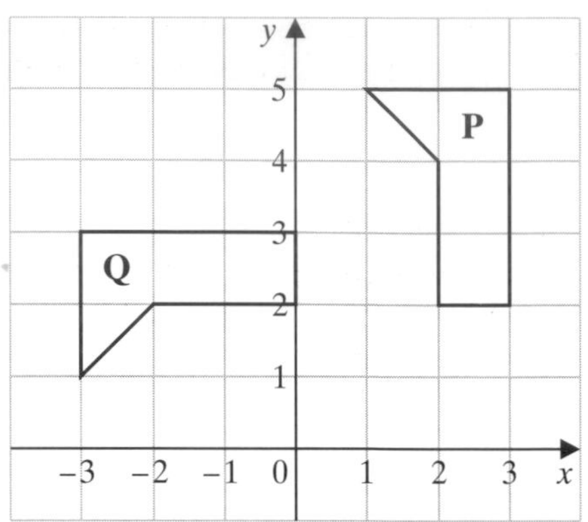

Each side of **Q** is at right angles to the corresponding side of **P** so **P** has made a quarter turn anticlockwise to get to **Q**.

To describe the rotation fully you need to say which point is the centre of rotation.

Each point on the original shape is the same distance from the centre of rotation as its image point. You might be able to see that the centre is (1, 1). So the transformation is a rotation of a quarter of a turn (90°) anticlockwise about the point (1, 1).

You can also find the centre of rotation geometrically. The centre is the same distance from each point and its image. So if you draw a line from any point to its image, the centre of rotation will be *somewhere* on the perpendicular bisector of the line.

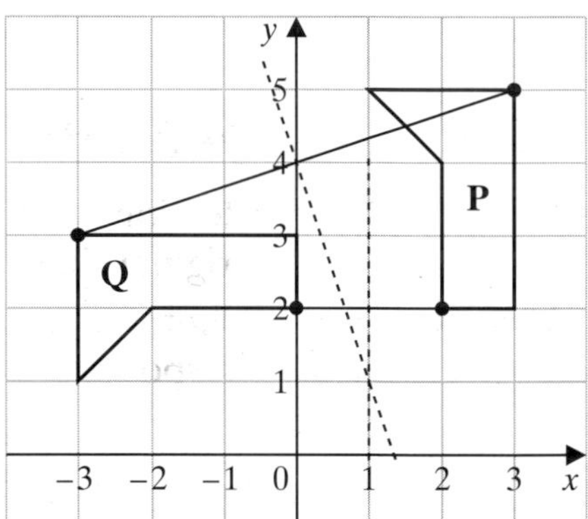

To find the centre of rotation, draw lines connecting *two* points to their images. Draw the perpendicular bisectors of both lines. The bisectors are dotted lines in the diagram.

As the centre of rotation is somewhere on *both* bisectors it must be at the point (1, 1) where they cross.

There is more about perpendicular bisectors on page 390.

Exercise 23E

You will need squared or graph paper.

1 Draw coordinate axes on graph paper with x and y going from –6 to 6. Copy the shaded shape.
Draw the image of the shaded shape after:
(a) a half turn about the origin (0, 0) (label the image **A**)
(b) a quarter turn clockwise about the origin (label it **B**)
(c) a quarter turn anticlockwise about the origin (label it **C**).

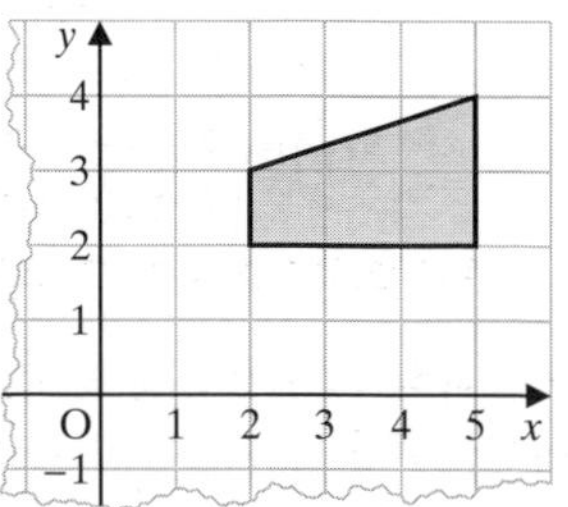

2 Draw coordinate axes on graph paper with x going from –6 to 6 and y going from –4 to 8. Copy the shaded shape.
Draw the image of the shaded shape after:
(a) a half turn about the pont P(0, 2) (label the image **A**)
(b) a quarter turn clockwise about the point P(0, 2) (label the image **B**)
(c) a quarter turn anticlockwise about the point P(0, 2) (label the image **C**).

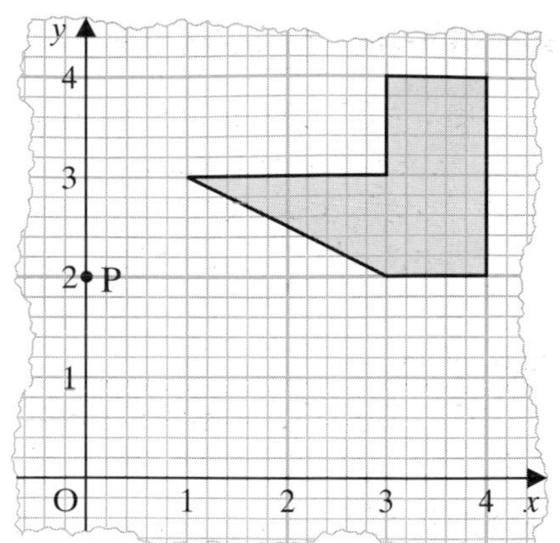

3 Describe fully the transformation which maps shape **A** on to shape **B**.

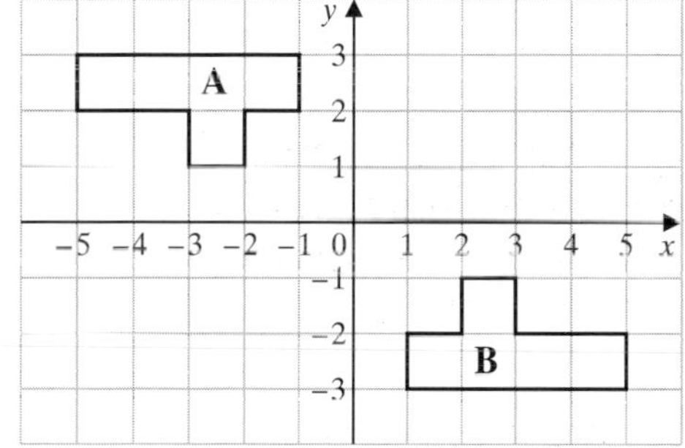

23.4 Enlargements

In translations, reflections and rotations the image is the same size and shape as the original shape (they are congruent).

When you have a photograph enlarged all the shapes remain the same but their corresponding lengths are enlarged by a **scale factor**.

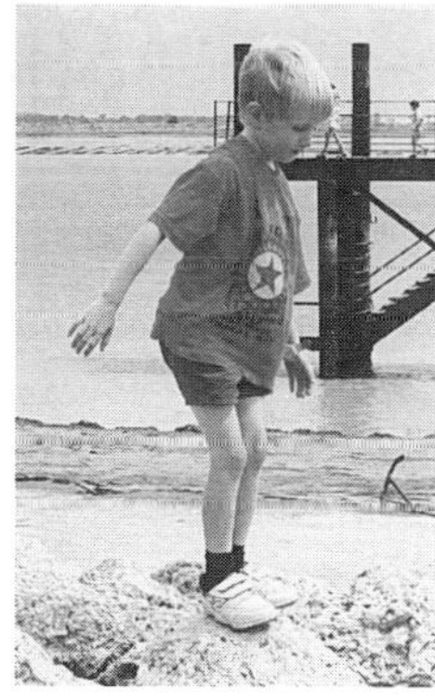

This photograph has been enlarged with scale factor 2. All the dimensions of the boy in the enlargement are twice as long as they are in the original.

■ **An enlargement changes the size but not the shape of an object. The scale factor of the enlargement is the number of times the lengths of the original object have been enlarged.**

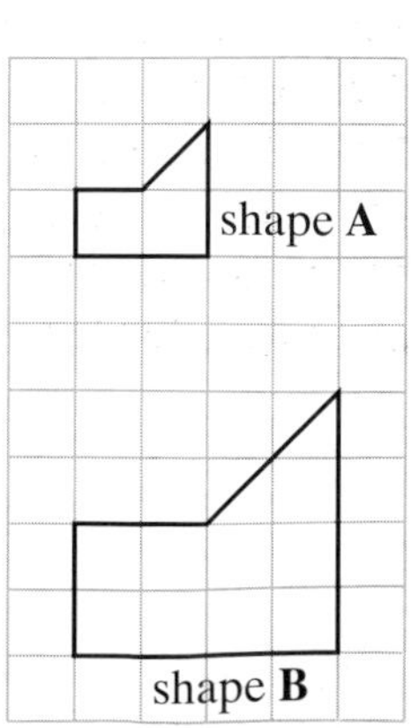

The sides of shape **B** are all 2 times the lengths of corresponding sides of shape **A**. You can say that **B** is an enlargement of **A** with scale factor 2.

All the corresponding angles are equal so **A** and **B** are **similar** (they are the same shape).
A and **B** are the same way up.
Each line of **B** is parallel to the corresponding line of **A**.

Worked examination question

On the grid, enlarge the shaded shape by a scale factor of 3. Start your enlargement at point B. [L]

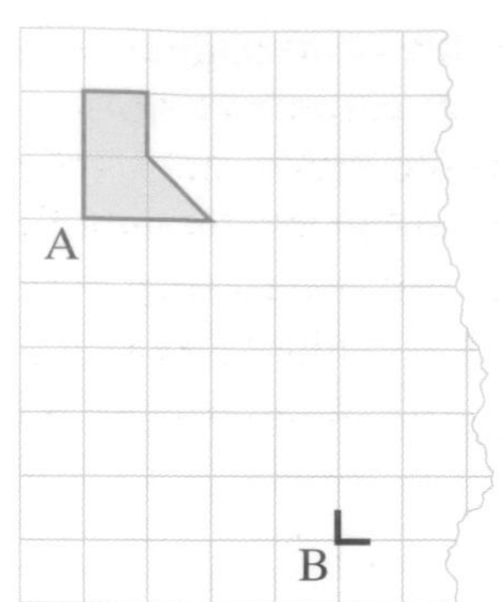

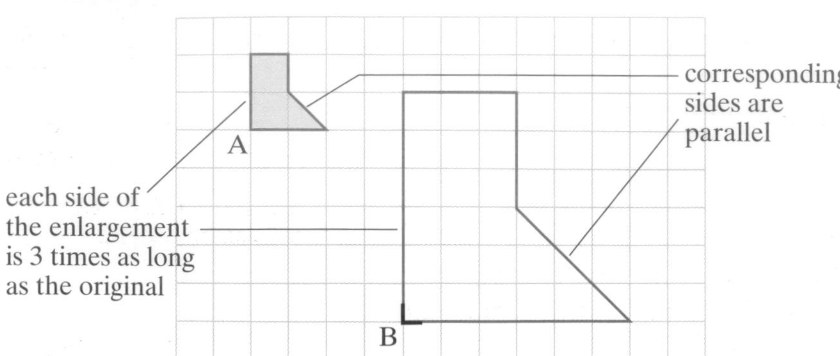

The sides in the image must be parallel to the corresponding sides in the original shape and three times as long. The vertical line at A is 2 units long so the vertical line at B is $2 \times 3 = 6$ units long. Draw in that line at B.
The horizontal line at A is 2 units long so the horizontal line at B is $2 \times 3 = 6$ units long. Draw that line at B.
The diagonal line goes 1 unit across and 1 unit down. In the enlargement this must be 3 units across and 3 units down.
All the other sides of the image are 3 times the corresponding original sides so you can complete the enlarged shape.

Exercise 23F

You need squared paper and a ruler.

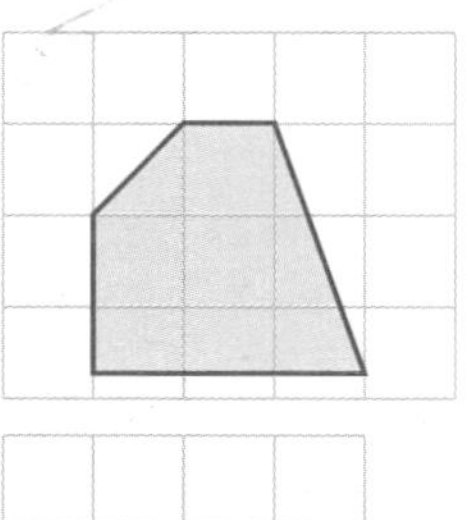

1 Copy the shaded shape on to squared paper.
On the same paper draw enlargements of the shaded shape with scale factor: **(a)** 2 **(b)** 3 **(c)** 4.

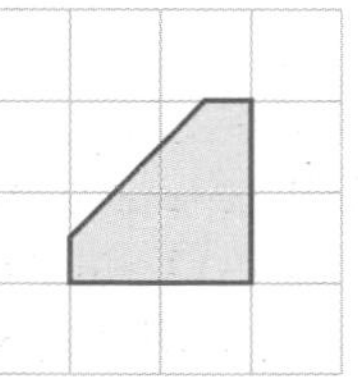

2 On grid **B** draw an enlargement, scale factor 3, of the shaded shape. [L]
(Note: copy the shaded shape on squared paper. Then draw grid **B** on the same paper with 11 squares across and 10 squares down.)

3 What is the scale factor of the enlargement that maps shape **P** on to shape **Q**?

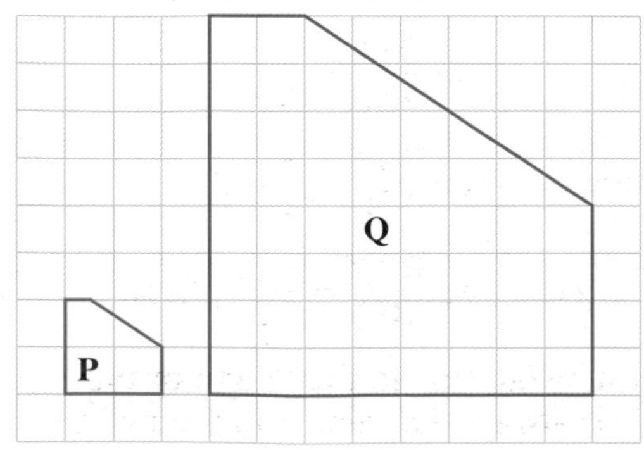

Centre of enlargement

When you make a photographic enlargement the original negative and the image are fixed in special positions relative to each other and to the source of light at C.

When the scale factor is 2 the enlarged shape is twice as far from C as the original negative.

C is called the **centre of enlargement**.

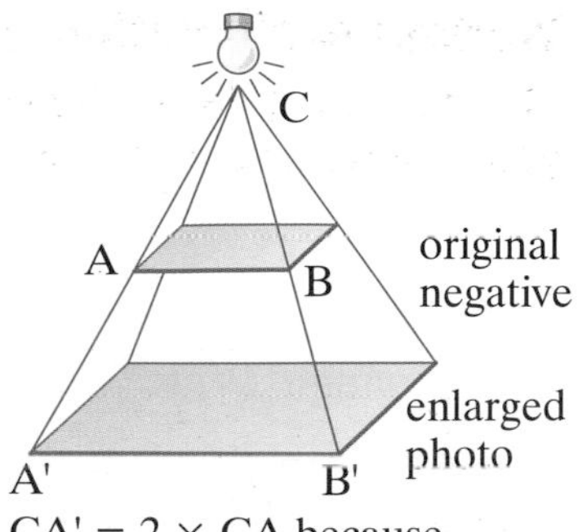

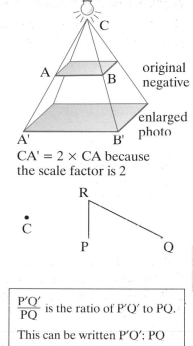

CA' = 2 × CA because the scale factor is 2

Example 6

Copy triangle PQR and the point C.

(a) Construct accurately the image of triangle PQR after an enlargement by a scale factor of 3, using C as the centre of enlargement. Label the image P′Q′R′.

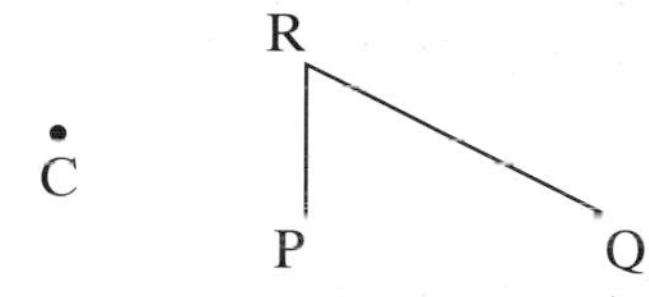

(b) (i) Measure the lengths P′Q′ and PQ and work out $\frac{P'Q'}{PQ}$.

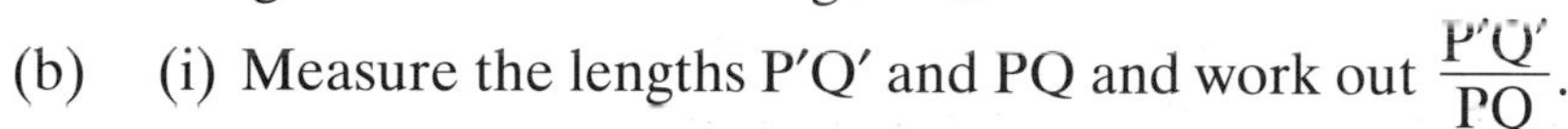

(ii) Measure the lengths P′R′ and PR and work out $\frac{P'R'}{PR}$.

(iii) Measure the lengths R′Q′ and RQ and work out $\frac{R'Q'}{RQ}$.

(c) What do you notice about your answers to part (b)?

> $\frac{P'Q'}{PQ}$ is the ratio of P′Q′ to PQ.
>
> This can be written P′Q′: PQ

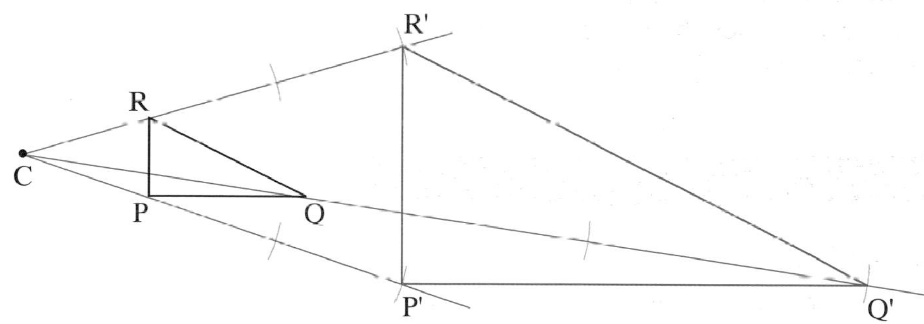

(a) Draw a line from C to P and continue it to P′ so that CP′ is 3 times CP.
(Hint: use compasses to mark off three lengths equal to CP.)
Join CR and continue it to R′ so that CR′ is 3 times CR.
Join CQ and continue it to Q′ so that CP′ is 3 times CQ.
Join the points P′, Q′ and R′ to form the image triangle P′Q′R′.

(b) (i) P′Q′ = 6 cm, PQ = 2 cm so $\frac{P'Q'}{PQ} = \frac{6}{2} = 3$

(ii) P′R′ = 3 cm, PR = 1 cm so $\frac{P'R'}{PR} = \frac{3}{1} = 3$

(iii) R′Q′ = 6.7 cm, RQ = 2.2 cm so $\frac{R'Q'}{RQ} = \frac{6.7}{2.2} = 3.04 \approx 3$

(c) The ratio of the length of an image side to the length of the corresponding original side is always the same and is equal to the scale factor of the enlargement.

■ **The original shape and its image after an enlargement are similar to each other.**

There is more about similarity on page 43.

Example 7

Copy triangle PQR and the point C inside the triangle.

Construct the image of triangle PQR after an enlargement by the scale factor of 3, using C as the centre of enlargement.

Repeat the method as described in part (a) of Example 6.
The enlargement should look like this:

This is called a **spider enlargement**.

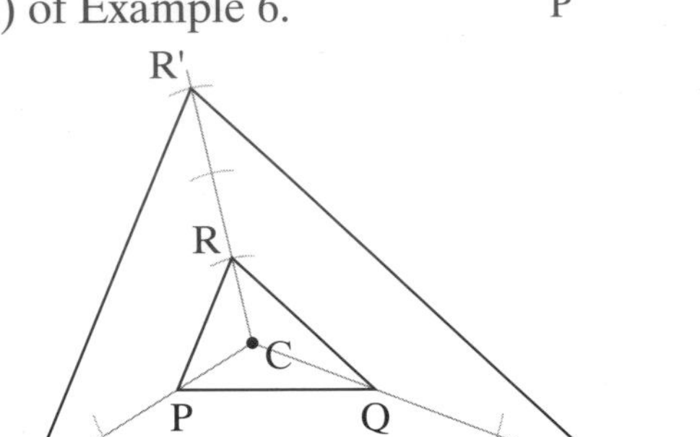

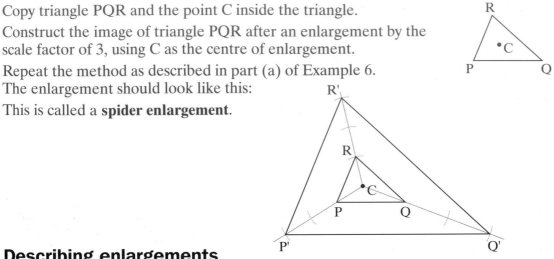

Describing enlargements

■ **To describe an enlargement fully you need to give the scale factor and the centre of enlargement.**

The centre of enlargement can be given by the letter of the point or by the coordinates of the point.

Example 8

Describe fully the transformation that maps ABCD on to PQRS.

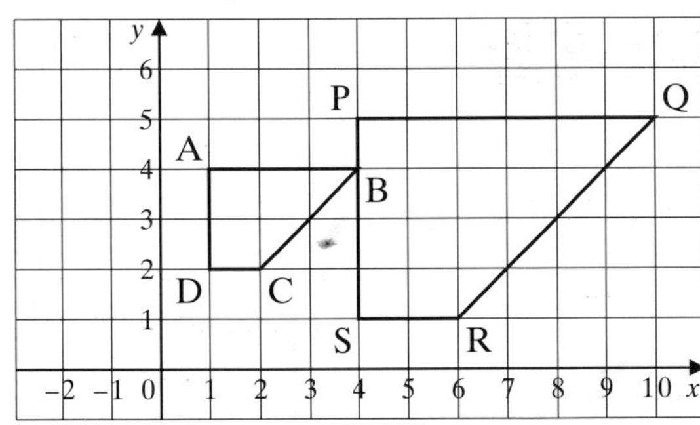

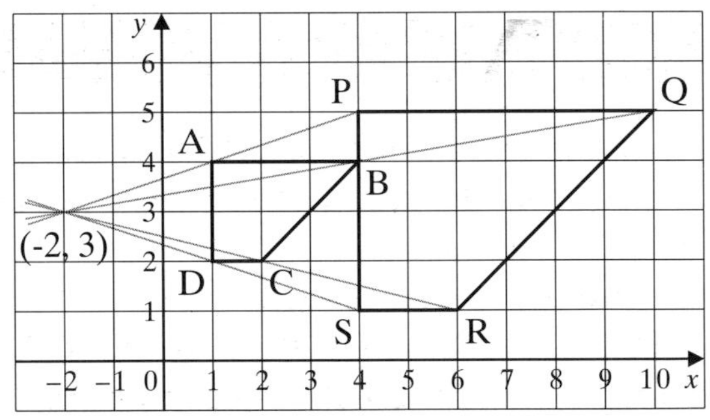

PQRS is the same shape as ABCD. The sides of PQRS are all 2 times the lengths of the corresponding sides of ABCD. So the transformation is an enlargement by a scale factor 2.

To describe the transformation fully you need to give the centre of enlargement.
To find the centre of enlargement, reverse the method used in Example 7.
Join P to A and continue the line.
Join Q to B and continue the line.
In the same way join R to C and S to D and continue the lines. The lines all pass through the same point (–2, 3) so this is the centre of enlargement.

The transformation is an enlargement by scale factor 2 with centre of enlargement (–2, 3).

Enlargement with scale factors less than 1

If you start with shape PQRS from Example 9 and transform it to ABCD the shape remains the same, but the size is changed, so the transformation is an enlargement.

The sides of ABCD are all $\frac{1}{2}$ the lengths of the corresponding sides of PQRS so the transformation that maps PQRS on to ABCD is an enlargement by the scale factor $\frac{1}{2}$ with centre (–2, 3).

Example 9

Draw the image of the shape KLMN after an enlargement by scale factor $\frac{1}{2}$ with centre C. Label the image K′L′M′N′.

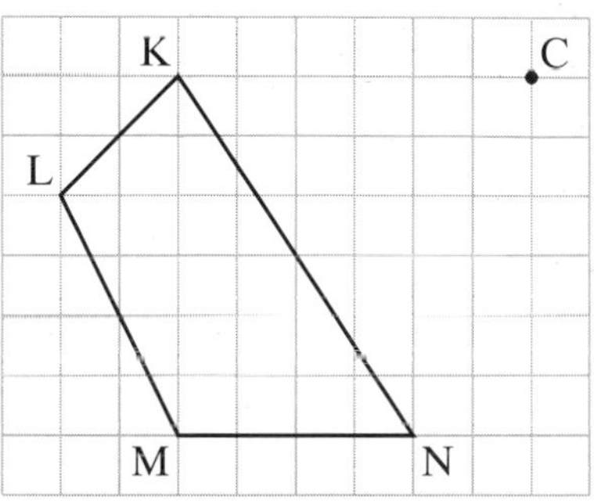

Join CK. CK = 6 units. The scale factor is $\frac{1}{2}$ so CK′ = $\frac{1}{2} \times 6$ = 3 units.

Mark the point K′ 3 units from C along CK.

In the same way mark L′ where CL′ = $\frac{1}{2}$ CL, M′ where CM′ = $\frac{1}{2}$ CM and N′ where CN′ = $\frac{1}{2}$ CN.

(Hint: use the squares and their diagonals so you can do this without a ruler.)

Join K′L′M′N′ to form the image.

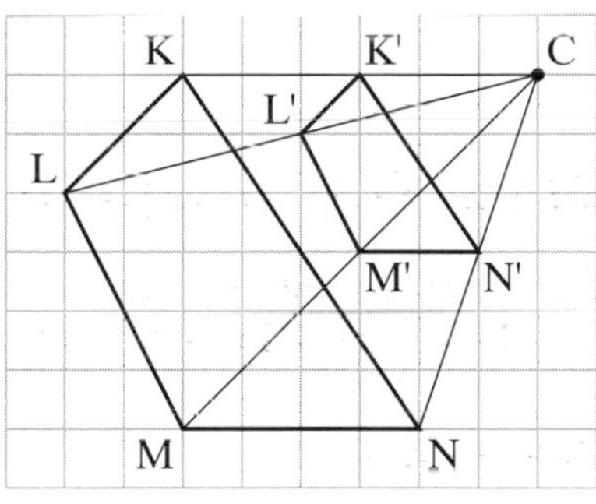

Exercise 23G

You will need squared or graph paper and a ruler.

1 Copy the shape and the dot marked C in the bottom left-hand corner of some squared paper.
Construct accurately the enlargement of the shape by scale factor 4, using the point C as the centre of enlargement.

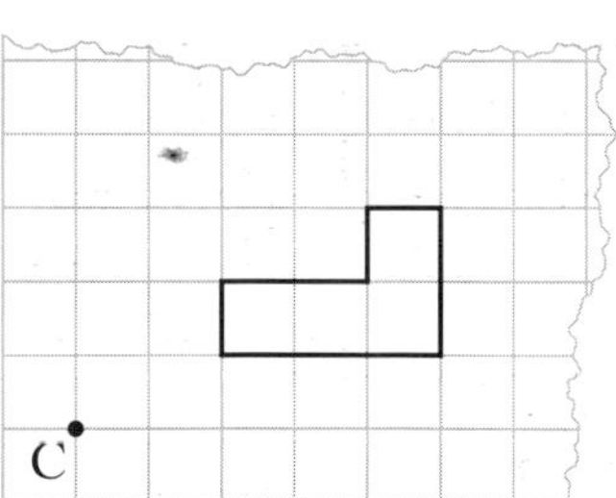

2 Describe fully the transformation that maps the shape **A** on to the shape **B**.

3 Describe fully the transformation that maps the shape **B** on to the shape **A**.

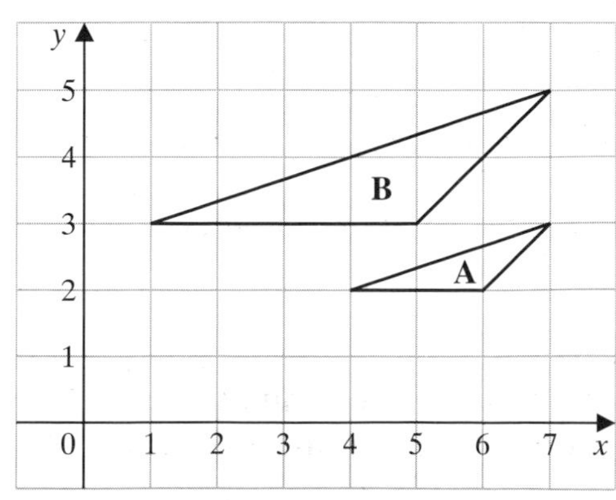

4 Draw the image of the shaded shape after an enlargement by the scale factor $\frac{1}{4}$ with C as the centre of enlargement. Label the image **L**.

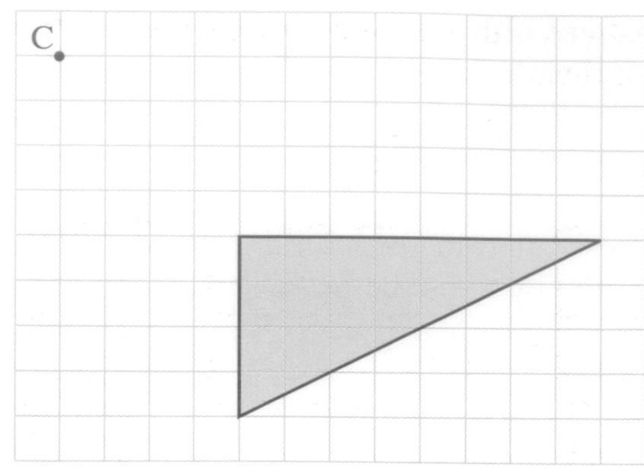

23.5 Combining transformations

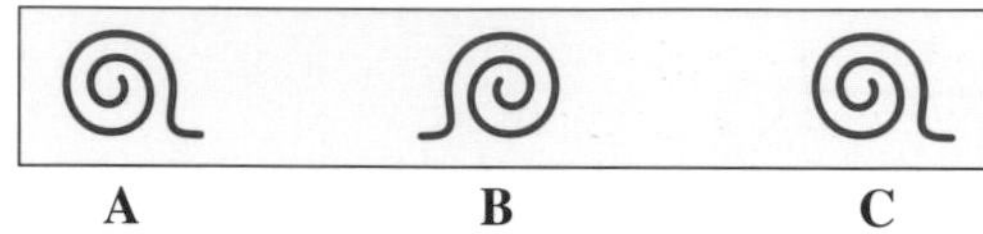

This pattern is made by repeated reflections of a shape.
A is reflected to the image **B** and **B** is reflected to the image **C**.
C is the image of **A** after two reflections.
C is also the image of **A** after a single translation. So the combination of the two reflections is equivalent to a single translation.

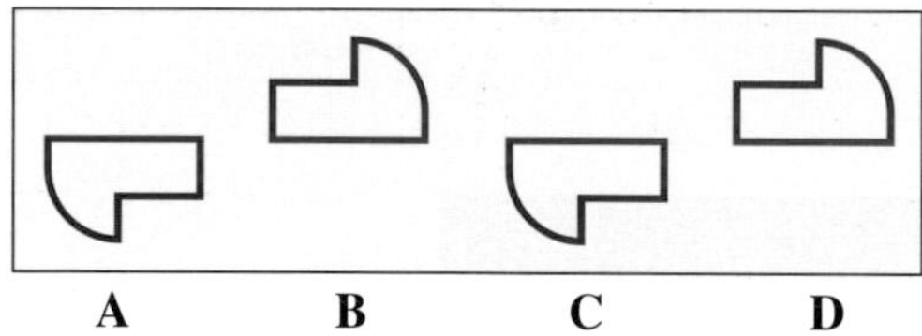

This pattern has been made by repeated rotations.
A has been rotated to the image **B**.
B has been rotated to the image **C**.
C is the image of **A** after two rotations.
C is also the image of **A** after a single translation. So the combination of the two rotations is equivalent to a single translation.

These examples show that:

- **One transformation followed by another can be equivalent to a single transformation.**

This pattern is made using tiles that are all transformations of the original tile:

The original tile

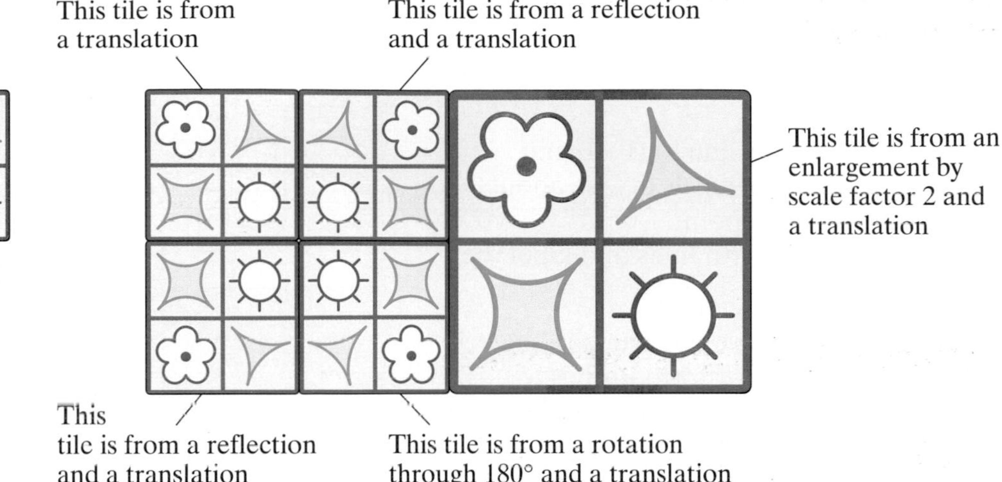
This tile is from a translation
This tile is from a reflection and a translation
This tile is from an enlargement by scale factor 2 and a translation
This tile is from a reflection and a translation
This tile is from a rotation through 180° and a translation

Worked examination question

(a) On the grid below draw the image of the shaded shape after a reflection in the y-axis. Label the image **A**.

(b) On the same grid draw the image of the shaded shape after a quarter turn clockwise about the origin (0, 0). Label this image **B**.

(c) Describe fully the *single* transformation which maps **A** on to **B**.

[L]

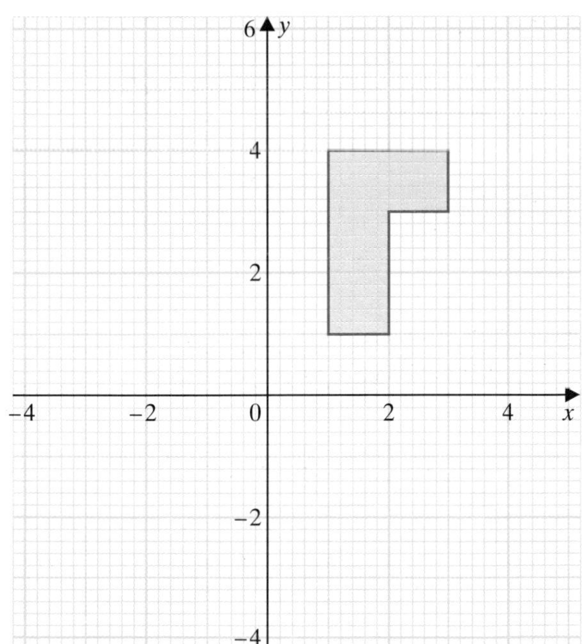
6
y
4
2
0
−2
−4
−4
−2
2
4
x

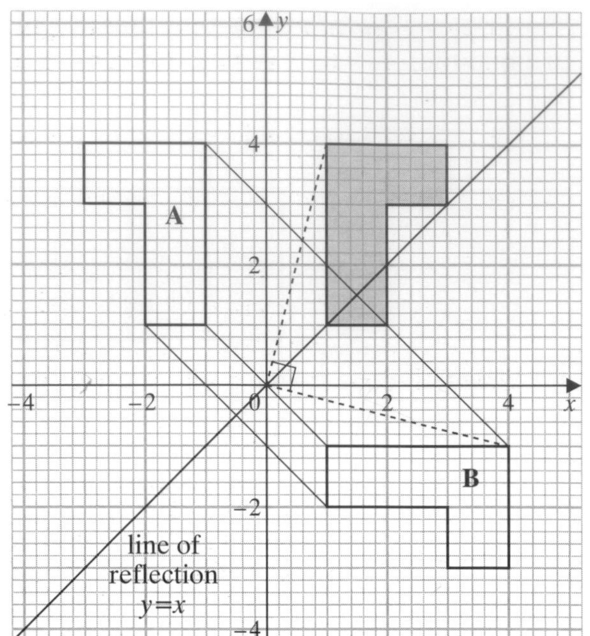

(a) From each corner of the shaded shape draw a line at right angles to the y-axis. Continue the line the same distance the other side to find the image point.
Join the image points with lines and label the image **A**.

(b) Join each corner with a line to (0, 0) and rotate the line through 90° clockwise about (0, 0) to find the image point.
Join the image points with lines and label the image **B**.

(c) **A** and **B** are the same size but one has been 'turned over'. So the transformation is a reflection. To describe it fully you need to state the equation of the line of reflection.
First draw the line of reflection. Join a pair of corresponding points with a line. Mark the middle point of the line because the line of reflection must pass through it. Do this for another pair of corresponding points.
The line joining the two middle points is the line of reflection. The equation of this line is $y = x$. So the single transformation that maps **A** on to **B** is a reflection in the line $y = x$.

Exercise 23H

You need squared paper and a ruler.

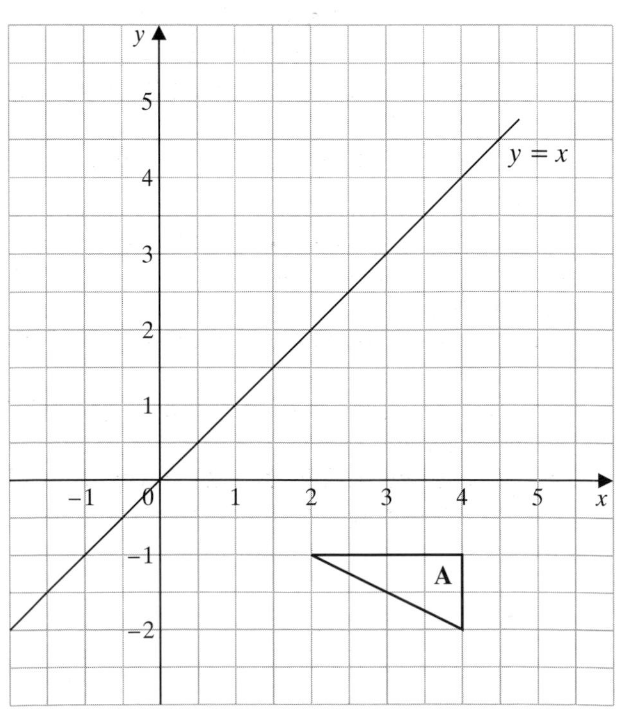

1 **(a)** Reflect the triangle **A** in the x-axis. Label the reflection **B**.
(b) Reflect the triangle **B** in the line $y = x$. Label the reflection **C**.
(c) Describe fully the single transformation which maps the triangle **A** on to the triangle **C**. [L]

2 Copy and complete the coordinate grid so that x goes from –9 to 9 and y goes from –5 to 5. Copy the triangle **L**.

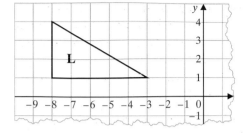

(a) Reflect the triangle **L** in the y-axis. Label the reflection **M**.

(b) Reflect the triangle **M** in the x-axis. Label the image **N**.

(c) Describe fully the *single* transformation which maps the triangle **L** on to the triangle **M**.

3 Write down the transformations which are applied to the original tile to make each lettered part of this pattern:

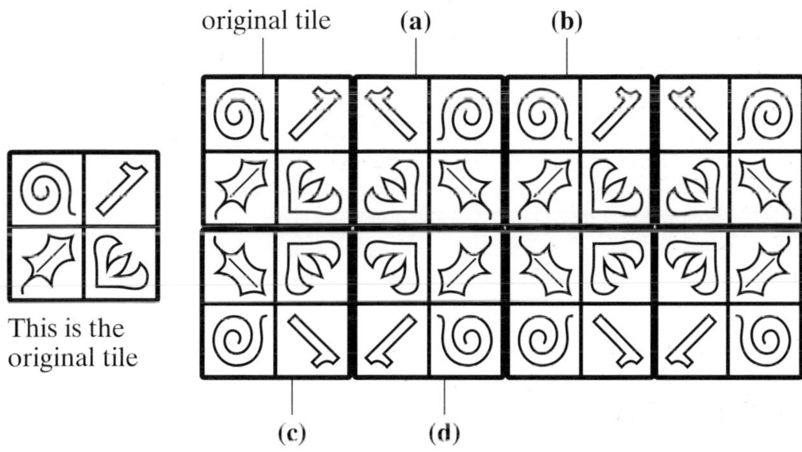

4 On squared paper draw coordinate axes so that x and y both go from –6 to 6.

(a) Plot the points (2, 2), (4, 1), (6, 2) and (4, 5). Join them in order and label the shape **P**.

(b) Reflect **P** in the x-axis. Label the reflection **Q**.

(c) Rotate **P** through 180° about the origin (0, 0). Label this image **R**.

(d) Describe fully the single transformation which maps **Q** on to **R**.

5 Copy and complete this coordinate grid for x from –7 to 10 and y from –6 to 6.
Copy shape **F**.

(a) Rotate **F** through 180° about (0, 0). Label the image **G**.

(b) Rotate **G** through 180° about (5, –3). Label the image **H**.

(c) Describe in full the single transformation which makes **H** the image of **F**.

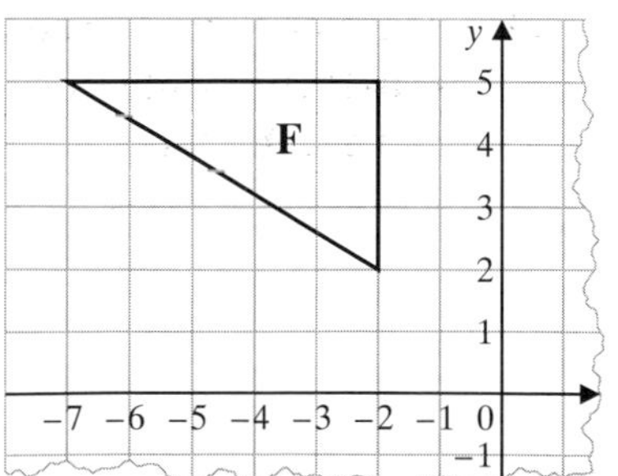

6 (a) Rotate triangle **A** clockwise through 90° about (0, 0).
Label the image **B**.
(b) Draw the image of **B** after a reflection in the line $y = -x$.
Label the reflection **C**.
(c) Describe fully the single transformation which maps triangle **A** on to triangle **C**.

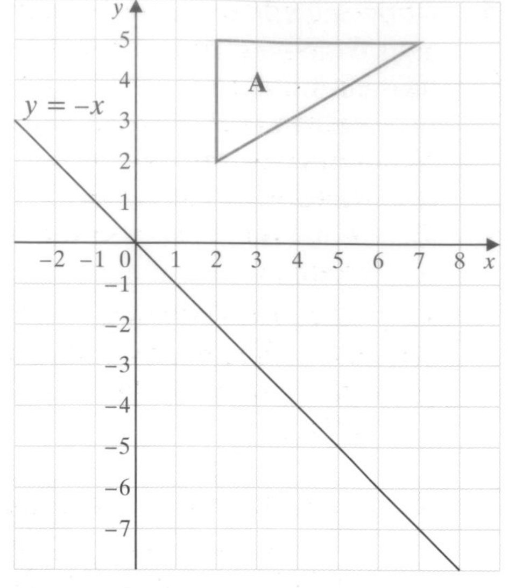

Exercise 23 I Mixed questions

You will need squared or graph paper and a ruler.

1 The triangle **Q** is an enlargement of the triangle **P**.
(a) Write down the scale factor of the enlargement.
(b) Work out the coordinates of the centre of enlargement.

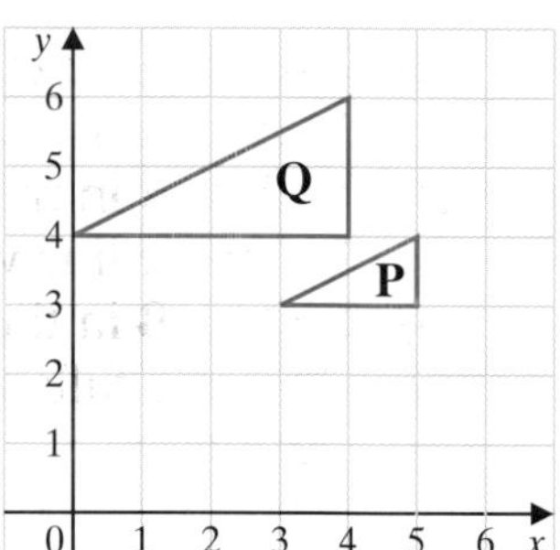

2 Draw a set of coordinate axes with x from –4 to 10 and y from 0 to 7.
(a) Plot the points (–2, 1), (1, 3) and (0, 5).
Join them and label the triangle **A**.

The triangle **A** is reflected in a line **M**. Two of the image points have coordinates (5, 3) and (6, 5).
(b) Write down the coordinates of the third corner of the image.
(c) Work out the equation of **M**, the line of reflection.

3 Rotate the triangle through 180° about centre A. On a copy of the grid draw the new position of the triangle.
[L]

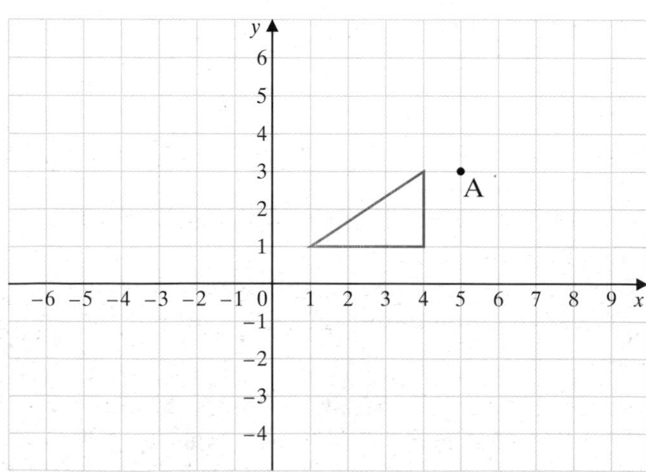

4 Draw a grid on squared paper with the x-axis from –10 to 10 and the y-axis from –14 to 4.

(a) Plot the points A (3, 1), B (2, –4) and C (–3, 1) and join them to form triangle ABC.

(b) Draw the enlargement of triangle ABC by the scale factor 3, using the origin (0, 0) as centre of enlargement.

(c) Write down the coordinates of the vertices of the image triangle.

5 Copy the grid and the shaded triangle.

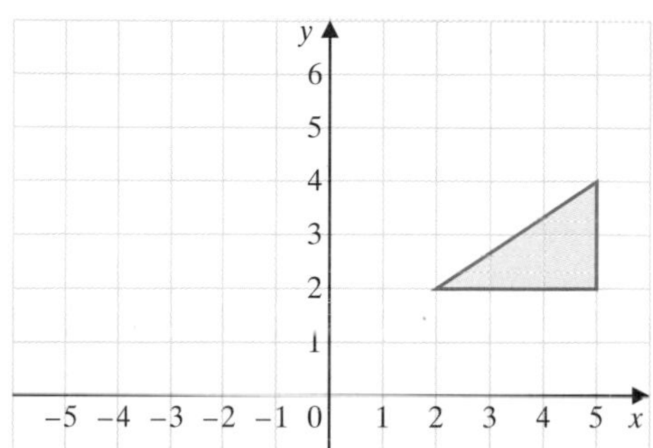

(a) Draw the image of the shaded triangle after a rotation through an angle of 90° anticlockwise about the origin (0, 0). Label the image **S**.

(b) Draw the image of the shaded triangle after a rotation through an angle of 90° anticlockwise about the point (2, 1). Label the image **T**.

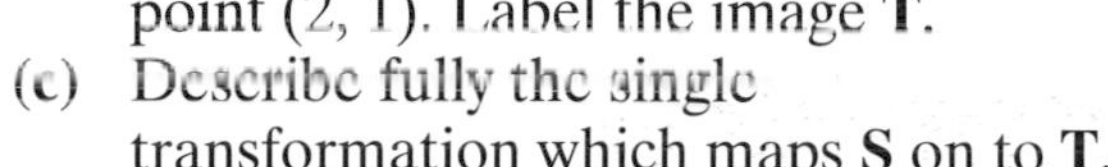

(c) Describe fully the single transformation which maps **S** on to **T**.

6 Draw a set of coordinate axes with x from –8 to 8 and y from –7 to 7.

(a) Plot the points (2, 1), (6, 1) and (6, 4). Join them up and label the triangle **A**.

(b) Reflect **A** in the y-axis. Label the reflection **B**.

(c) Draw the line $y = x$.

(d) Reflect **B** in the line $y = x$. Label the reflection **C**.

(e) Describe fully the single transformation which maps **A** on to **C**.

Summary of key points

1 Changes in the position or size of a shape are called transformations. Reflections, rotations, enlargements and translations are all types of transformations.

2 In mathematics the transformed shape is called the image of the shape.

3 A translation moves every point on a shape the same distance in the same direction.
The image is the same shape and size as the original shape and it is the same way up.

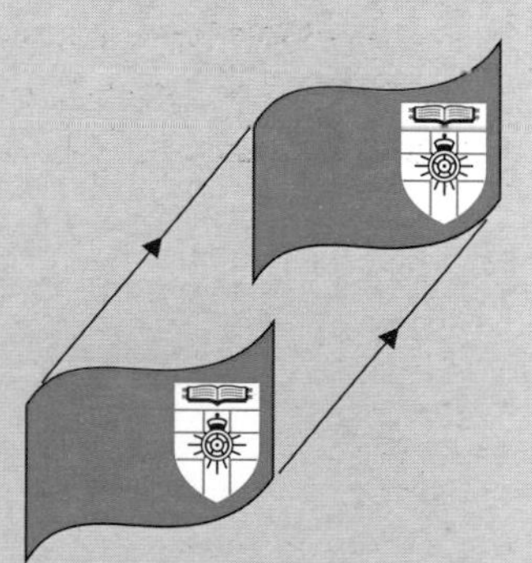

4 A tessellation is an arrangement of a shape or set of shapes on a flat surface so that all the space is filled, with no gaps and no overlaps.

5 To describe a translation fully you need to give the distance moved and the direction of the movement. This can be done by writing down the vector of the translation.

6 A reflection in a line produces a mirror image. The image is the same size as the original shape, but it is 'turned over'.

7 To describe a reflection fully you need to give the equation of the line of symmetry.

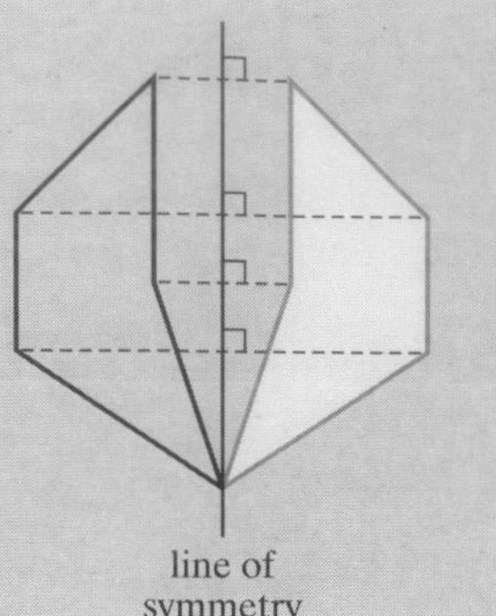

8 A rotation turns a shape through an angle about a fixed point. The image is the same shape and size as the original shape.

9 When a shape is rotated all lines in the shape rotate through the same angle. The distance of an image point from the centre of rotation is the same as the distance of the original point from the centre.

10 To describe a rotation fully you need to give the:
- centre of rotation
- angle of turn
- direction of turn (clockwise or anticlockwise)

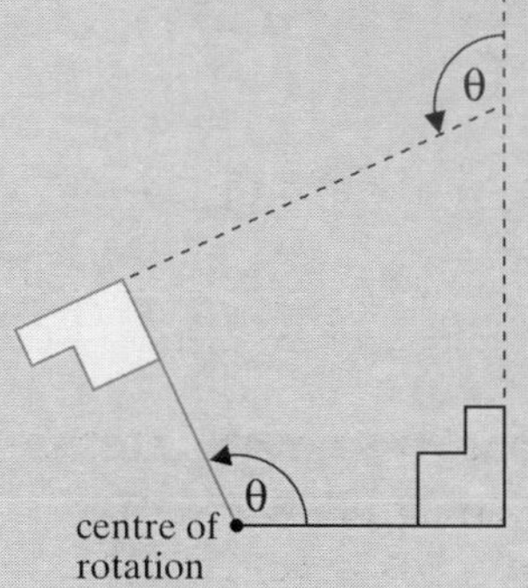

11 An enlargement changes the size but not the shape of an object. The scale factor of the enlargement is the number of times the lengths of the original object have been enlarged.

12 The original shape and its image after an enlargement are similar to each other.

13 To describe an enlargement fully you need to give the scale factor and the centre of enlargement.

14 One transformation followed by another can be equivalent to a single transformation.

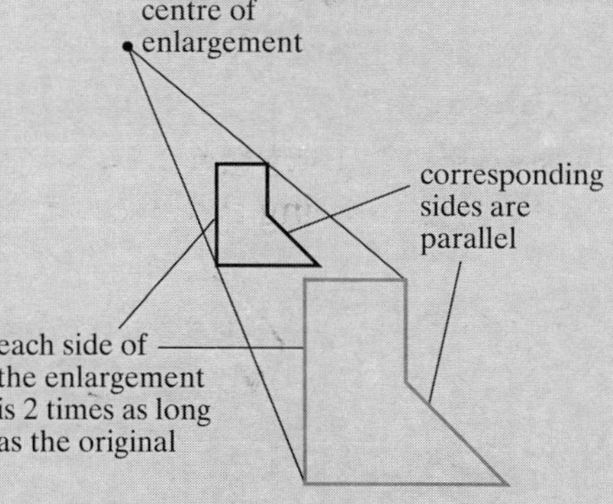

24 Presenting data

Unit 8 (page 98) shows you how to collect data and organize it in a table.

This unit shows you how to present data visually in diagrams and charts. This can make it easier to see patterns and trends in the data.

Diagrams are more interesting to look at than the original data, but they are often less precise.

24.1 Pictograms

■ **In a pictogram a picture or symbol is used to represent a number of items.**

When you draw a pictogram you must decide how many items each symbol represents. You may have to use part symbols for some quantities. People looking at your pictogram will have to decide for themselves how many items the part symbol represents.

Example 1

This pictogram shows how much money was made from ice cream sales at a kiosk during the summer.

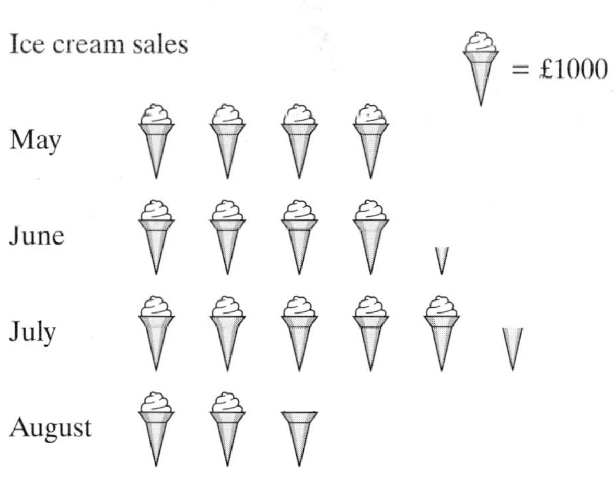

How much money was made from ice cream sales in August?

The two complete symbols represent £1000 each.
This comes to £2000.
You have to estimate the part symbol as a fraction of the whole symbol. It looks as if it represents about £700.
So the total sales in August are about £2700.

24.2 Bar charts

■ **Bar charts can be used to show up patterns in data. The bars may be horizontal or vertical.**

Example 2

This bar chart shows the numbers of people visiting some popular tourist attractions in 1993.

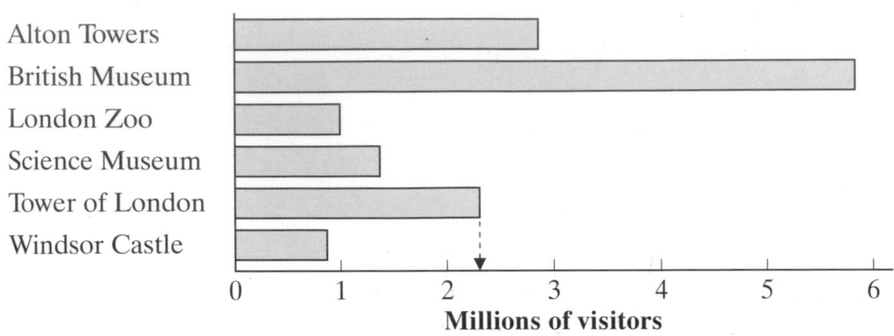

Attendance at selected tourist attractions 1993

(i) Which tourist attraction had the fewest visitors in 1993?
(ii) How many visitors went to the Tower of London in 1993?

(i) London Zoo and Windsor Castle had fewer visitors than the other attractions. Using a ruler to compare the lengths of these bars shows that Windsor Castle had the fewest visitors.
(ii) The arrow on the chart shows that about 2.3 million visitors went to the Tower of London.

This bar chart gives you a rough idea of the numbers of visitors but it would be much easier to answer the questions if the bar chart were drawn on a grid.

Example 3

The average contents of a box of matches is claimed to be 43. The actual number of matches in each box is counted for a sample of boxes. The results are shown in the bar chart:

(i) How many boxes of matches are in the sample?
(ii) Is the claim of average contents 43 reasonable?

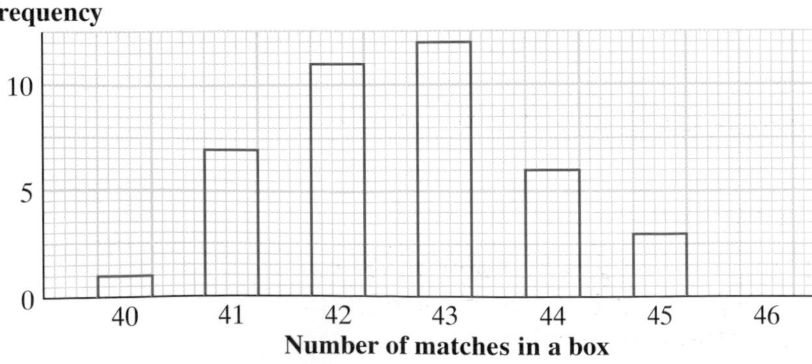

In this example the data is **discrete**. There can be 40 matches per box, or 41, but not 40.7. (There is more about discrete data on page 000.)

(i) The number of boxes is 1 + 7 + 11 + 12 + 6 + 3 = 40
(ii) The Mode is 43 matches, the value with the highest frequency. The Median is the number of matches in the $20\frac{1}{2}$th box, so the Median is 43 matches per box. The Mean is between 42 and 43. So the claim is reasonable.

Calculating the mean:

40 × 1 = 40
41 × 7 = 287
42 × 11 = 462
43 × 12 = 516
44 × 6 = 264
45 × 3 = 135
46 × 0 = 0

Total = 1704

$$\text{Mean} = \frac{1704}{40} = 42.6$$

24.3 Line graphs

So far all the data displayed has been discrete.

This table shows the temperature in degrees Centigrade in Leeds at midday during the first week in May:

May	1	2	3	4	5	6	7
Temperature (°C)	12	16	14	11	12	15	13

This data is **continuous**. The temperatures have been recorded to the nearest 1°C but the actual value recorded as 12 °C could be, for example, 11.6 °C or 12.142 °C depending on the accuracy of the measurement made.

You could show this data on a **line graph**. Here are two ways of doing so:

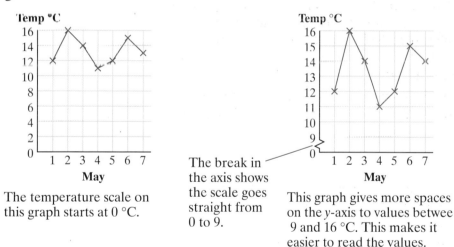

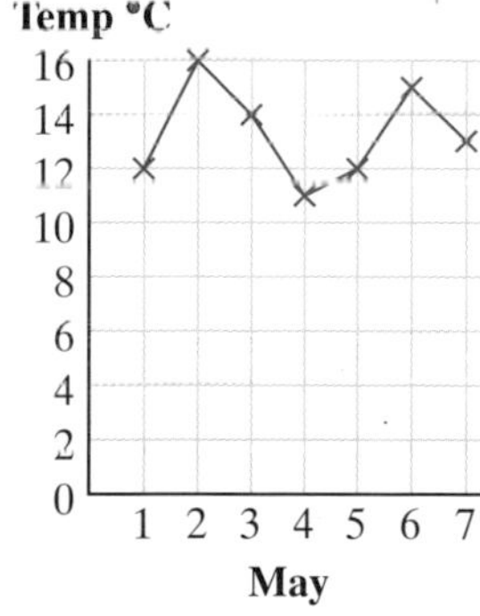

The temperature scale on this graph starts at 0 °C.

The break in the axis shows the scale goes straight from 0 to 9.

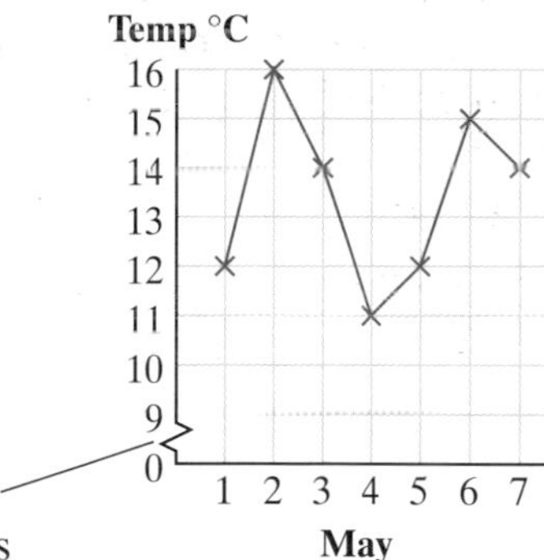

This graph gives more spaces on the y-axis to values betwee 9 and 16 °C. This makes it easier to read the values.

■ **Line graphs can be used to display continuous data.**

24.4 Histograms

■ **Histograms are usually used to display data that is grouped and continuous.**

A histogram *looks* like a bar chart but:

- the data is continuous so there can be no gaps between the bars
- the data must be grouped into equal class intervals if you want to use the lengths of the bars to represent data values

(There is more about class intervals on page 105.)

Exercise 24A

1 The diagram shows how many ships were in Mathsland's navy in 1992 and 1993.

1992	🚢 🚢 🚢 🚢 🚢
1993	🚢 🚢 🚢 half 🚢

🚢 = 10 ships

Use the diagram to answer these questions.
(a) How many ships were there in Mathsland's navy in 1992?
(b) How many ships were there in Mathsland's navy in 1993? [L]

2 The number of different animals on a farm are given by the data in the table.

Type of animal	Horse	Cow	Sheep	Dog	Cat	Goat	Pig
Number	6	15	11	3	2	1	8

(a) Draw a pictogram to display this information.
(b) Draw a bar chart to display this information.

3 A survey was taken to find the favourite flavour of crisps. The results of the survey are given in this table.

Flavour of crisp	Number of people
Plain	5
Salt & Vinegar	18
Cheese & Onion	11
Smokey Bacon	7
Prawn Cocktail	14
Beef	3
Other	2

(a) Draw a bar chart to display this information.
(b) How many people were in the survey?

4 The table shows the monthly rainfall in inches in Hong Kong.

Rainfall (inches)	1.3	2	3	5.5	11.5	15.5	15	14	10	4.5	2	1
Month	J	F	M	A	M	J	J	A	S	O	N	D

(a) Draw a line graph to display this information.
(b) Work out the mean monthly rainfall for Hong Kong.

5 The share value of Edgers Oil on the last day of each month is shown in the table.

(a) Draw a line graph to display this data.

(b) Use your line graph to estimate the share value on the last day of September.

Month	Value (pence)
Jan	52
Feb	57
Mar	60
Apr	66
May	69
Jun	73
Jul	77
Aug	85

Example 4

In this example the data is grouped and continuous.
Construct a histogram for this data on the heights of students in a class:

Height (cm)	Frequency
$130 \leqslant h < 135$	4
$135 \leqslant h < 140$	7
$140 \leqslant h < 145$	8
$145 \leqslant h < 150$	5
$150 \leqslant h < 155$	2
$155 \leqslant h < 160$	1

For grouped continuous data:

- the length of the bar will only make sense if the class intervals are the same. In this example they are.
- the data is continuous so the bars must be drawn next to each other with no gaps.

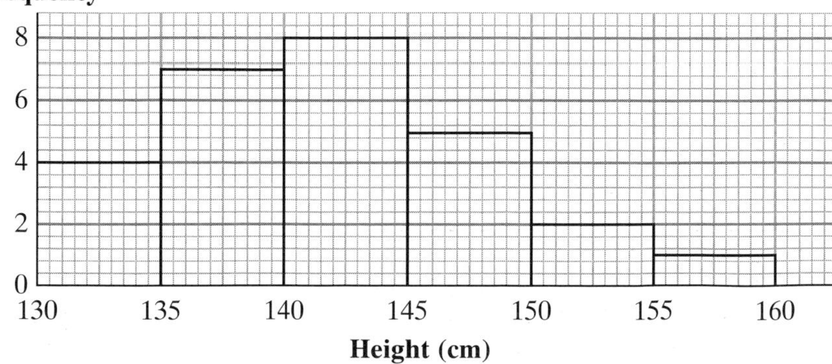

24.5 Frequency polygons

Another useful way of displaying grouped data is a **frequency polygon** in which the mid-points (or middle values) of the class intervals are joined by straight lines.

This table shows the frequency distribution of the ages of members of a swimming club in 1990 and 1991.

Age	0–9	10–19	20–29	30–39	40–50	over 50
1991	5	15	21	30	17	15
1992	10	24	28	22	10	6

You can draw histograms and join the midpoints to get frequency polygons.

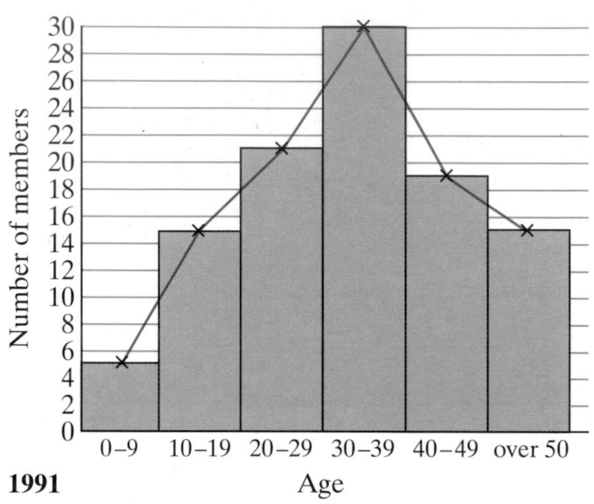

1991

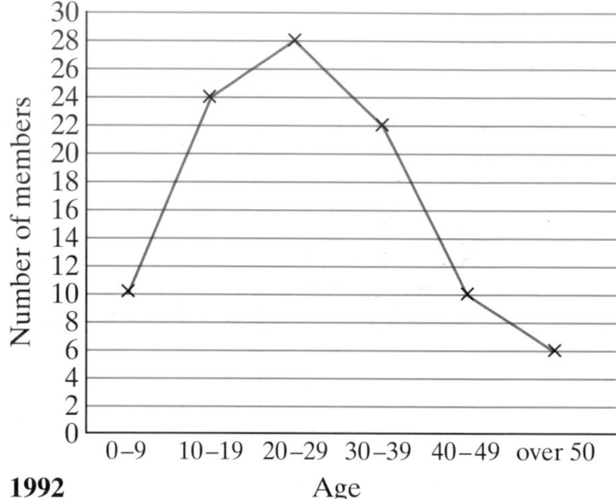

1992

■ **Frequency polygons can show the general pattern of data represented by bar charts or histograms.**

It is often easier to compare data like this by placing one polygon on top of the other.

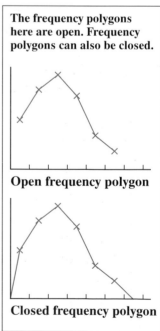

The frequency polygons here are open. Frequency polygons can also be closed.

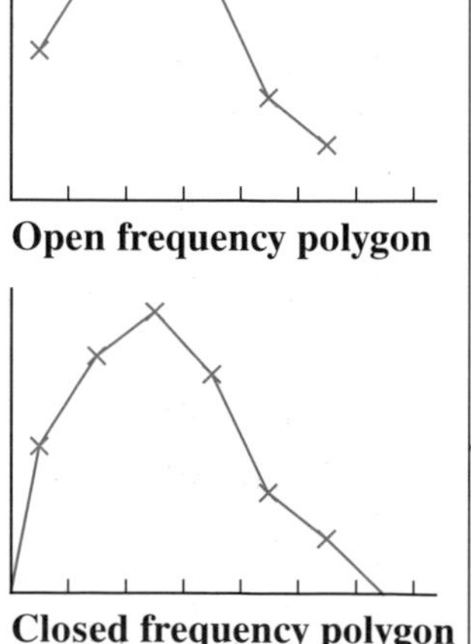

Example 5

Study these frequency polygons and comment on trends in sales in the music industry.

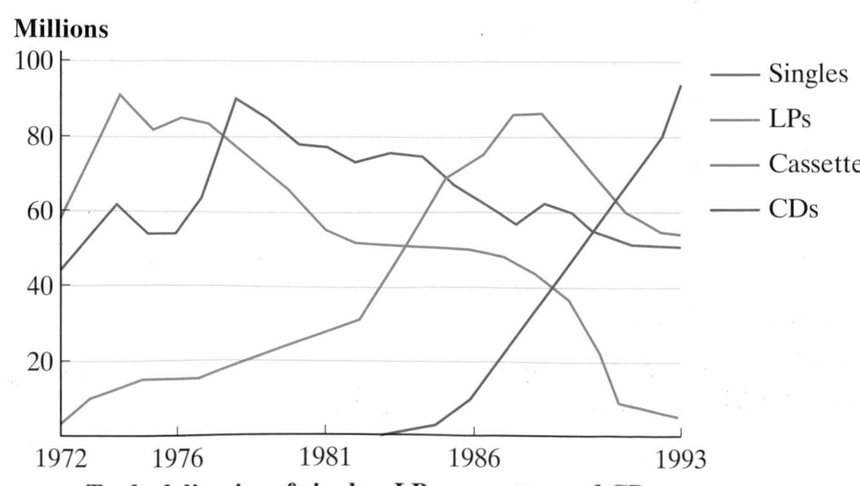

Trade deliveries of singles, LPs, cassettes and CDs

In the late 1970s and early 1980s cassettes were taking the place of records.
The introduction of CDs in the mid 1980s accelerated the decline in popularity of LPs and singles.
By 1992 CDs held the largest share of the market.

Exercise 24B

1 As part of his Geography fieldwork, Tony took measurements of the steepness of slopes. The steepness was measured as the angle the slope made with the horizontal.
Tony's results are:

15°, 16°, 9°, 21°, 32°, 37°, 25°, 36°, 40°
13°, 21°, 32°, 29°, 32°, 7°, 4°, 18°, 17°

(i) Complete the observation sheet below, using 4 equal class intervals.

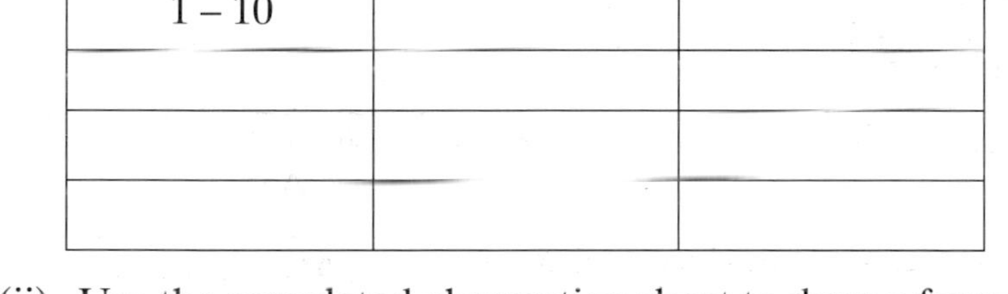

Class interval (steepness °)	Tally	Frequency
1 – 10		

(ii) Use the completed observation sheet to draw a frequency diagram of the data. [L]

2 The table shows the frequency distribution of marks scored by 100 candidates in a Science examination.

Marks	Mid-point	Frequency
0 – 9		3
10 – 19		5
20 – 29		12
30 – 39		20
40 – 49		24
50 – 59		18
60 – 69		12
70 – 79		6

(i) Use the mid-points to draw the frequency polygon.
(ii) Calculate an estimate of the Mean mark. [L]

3 Each morning in September, Liz picked mushrooms from her field.
The bar chart below shows the number of mushrooms that she picked in the 30 days of September.

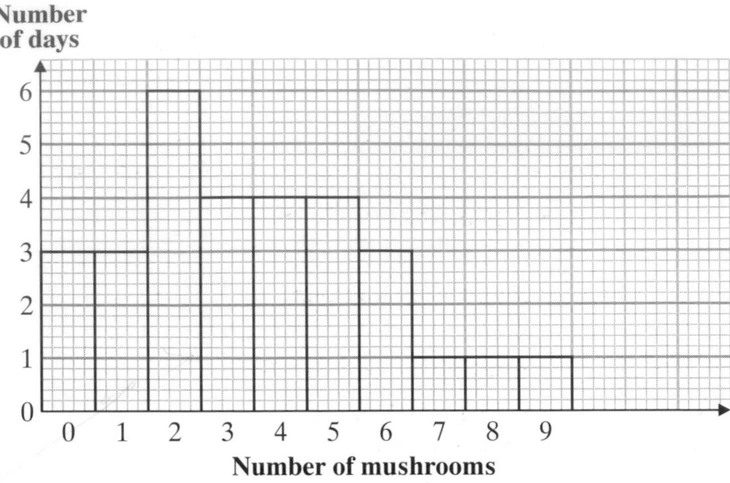

(a) Write down the number of days on which Liz picked two mushrooms.
(b) Find the total number of mushrooms Liz picked in the month.
(c) Find the modal number of mushrooms Liz picked in the month.
(d) Calculate the mean number of mushrooms per day that Liz picked.

24.6 Pie charts

■ **A pie chart is a way of displaying data that shows how something is shared or divided.**

These pie charts show:

... how Wayne spent the last 24 hours:

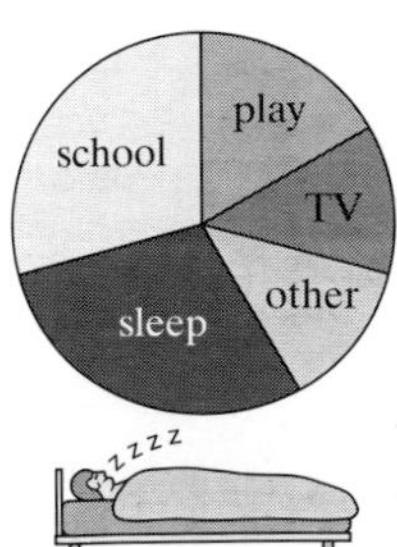

... how the land is used in the UK:

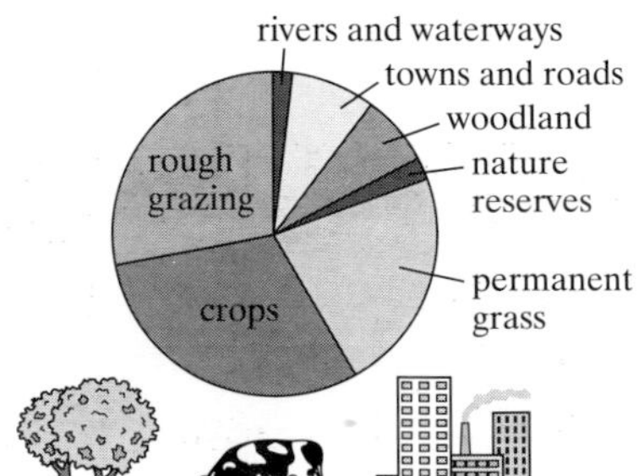

... how much market share different cat food brands have:

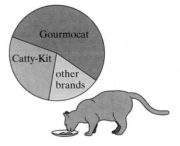

You need to develop two skills:

- reading information from a pie chart that is already drawn
- drawing a pie chart from information you are given.

To help with both these you need to understand the connection between fractions, decimals, percentages and angles.

Here are four copies of the same pie chart:

The sectors are shown as:

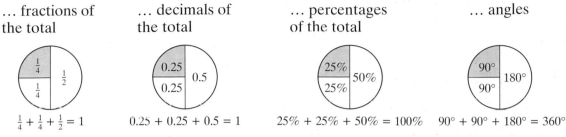

... fractions of the total

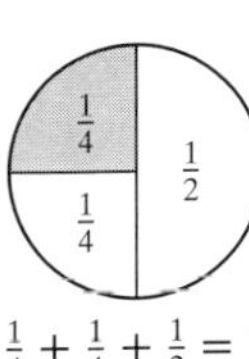

$\frac{1}{4} + \frac{1}{4} + \frac{1}{2} = 1$

... decimals of the total

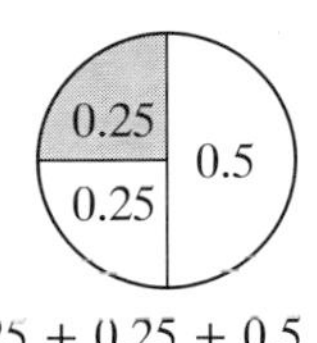

$0.25 + 0.25 + 0.5 = 1$

... percentages of the total

25%
50%
25%

$25\% + 25\% + 50\% = 100\%$

... angles

90°
180°
90°

$90° + 90° + 180° = 360°$

However many sectors you divide it into, the angles at the centre of a pie chart will total 360°.

The angle of the shaded sector is 90°. Notice that whether you use fractions, decimals or percentages:

$\frac{1}{4} \times 360° = 90°$ $\quad 0.25 \times 360° = 90°$ $\quad 25\%$ of $360° = \frac{25}{100} \times 360° = 90°$

So when you know what fraction, decimal or percentage of the pie chart should represent a quantity you can find the angle of the sector by multiplying by 360°.

Example 6

The information is about the constituents of a human body:

Muscle	30 kg
Fat	14 kg
Bone	16 kg
Other things	20 kg
Total weight	80 kg

(a) Write each weight as a:
(i) fraction (ii) decimal (iii) percentage
of the total weight.

(b) Display the weights in a pie chart.

(a) Write your answers in a table:

Item	Amount	Fraction	Decimal	Percentage	Angle
Muscle	30 kg	$\frac{30}{80}$	0.375	$37\frac{1}{2}\%$	
Fat	14 kg	$\frac{14}{80}$	0.175	$17\frac{1}{2}\%$	
Bone	16 kg	$\frac{16}{80}$	0.2	20%	
Other	20 kg	$\frac{20}{80}$	0.25	25%	
Total	80 kg	1	1	100%	360°

(b) Use either the fractions, decimals or percentages to find the angles for the pie chart. For example, using fractions: 30 kg is represented by an angle of:

$$\frac{30}{80} \times 360° = 135°$$

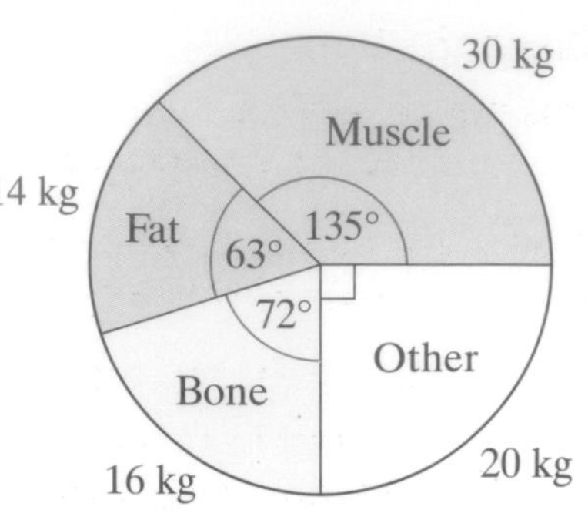

The other angles are Fat 63°; Bone 72°; Other 90°. You can now draw a pie chart with these angles at the centre.

Sometimes the information to be displayed in a pie chart is given as percentages of the total.

Example 7

In a survey pupils who watch TV are asked which is their favourite type of TV programme.
The results are: drama (including 'soaps') 35%, sport 30%, news (including current affairs) 25%, 'other' 10%.
Draw a pie chart to show the results.

You can enter the information in a table:

Item	Percentage	Fraction	Angle
Drama	35%	$\frac{7}{20}$	126°
Sport	30%	$\frac{3}{10}$	
News	25%	$\frac{1}{4}$	
Other	10%	$\frac{1}{10}$	
Total	100%	1	360°

Here the first angle has been calculated by changing 35% to a fraction:

$$35\% = \tfrac{35}{100} \text{ which simplifies to } \tfrac{7}{20}$$

To change this fraction to an angle:

$$\tfrac{7}{20} \times 360° = 126°$$

The other angles are 108°, 90° and 36°
Now you can draw a pie chart with these angles at the centre.

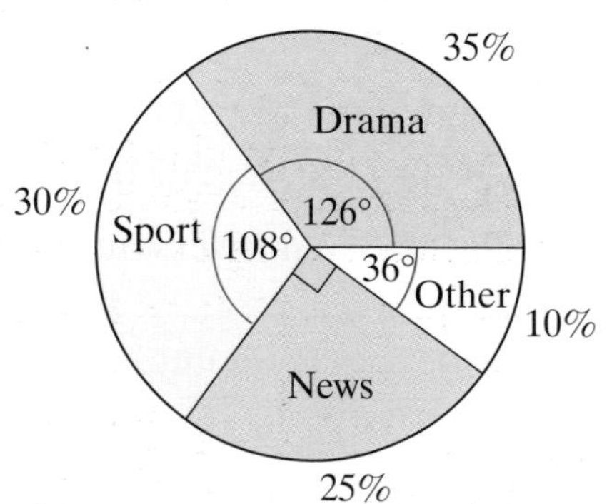

Interpreting pie charts

Sometimes you will be given the angle of a sector of a pie chart and asked what quantity it represents.

Example 8

This pie chart shows how a family spends its money in a year. The amount the family spends on housing is £3038.

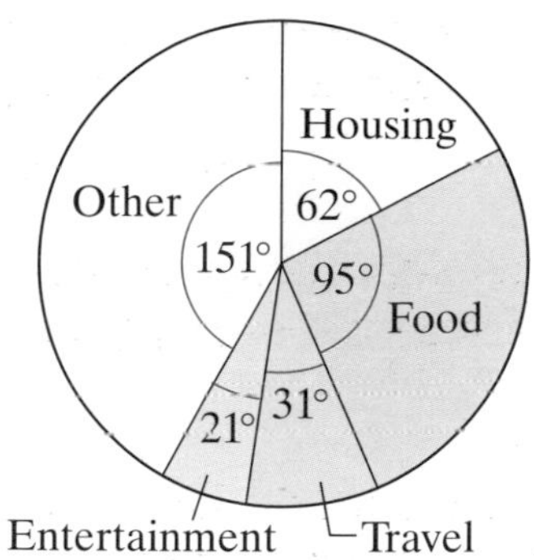

How much do they spend on:
(a) food (b) travel (c) entertainment?

(a) Housing costs are represented by 62° and are £3038.

62° represents expenditure of £3038

So 1° represents expenditure of £3038 ÷ 62 = £49

So the amount spent on food is 95 × £49 = £4655

(b) Amount spent on travel is 31 × £49 = £1519

(c) Amount spent on entertainment is 21 × £49 = £1029

Exercise 24C

You will need a protractor.

1 In a general election three candidates stood for election in Tonville. The percentages of the total vote in Tonville were:

Conservative 44% Labour 30% Liberal Democrat 26%

Construct a pie chart to show this information.

2 The amounts of the ingredients in a recipe are:

flour 300 g
butter 375 g
water 145 g
sugar 75 g
salt 5 g

(a) Calculate the angle in a pie chart which would represent water.

(b) Construct a pie chart to show the ingredients.

3 The percentages of different metals in a silver solder are silver 50%, copper 35% and the rest is zinc.
Calculate the angles of a pie chart to represent this.

4 Sita spent £90. The table shows what she spent it on.

Items	Amount spent	Angle of sector
bus fares	£12	
going out	£25	
clothes	£30	
records	£15	
other	£ 8	
Total spending	£90	360°

Sita is asked to construct a pie chart to show her spending.
(a) Work out the angle of each sector of the pie chart.
(b) Construct the pie chart.
(c) What fraction of Sita's spending was on clothes? [L]

5 The BBC estimated that the money collected from licences was spent in this way:

Capital expense and transmission	25%
BBC1	35%
BBC2	20%
Radio	20%

Draw a fully labelled pie chart to show this information. [L]

6 300 young people were asked what they did after completing year 11 at school. The pie chart shows the results of the survey.
(a) How many of the young people were working?

Gwen made an accurate drawing of the pie chart. She first drew the sector representing the young people out of work.
(b) Calculate the size of the angle of this sector. Give your answer correct to the nearest degree.
(c) Change to a decimal the percentage going to college.
(d) What fraction of young people stayed at school? Change your answer to its simplest form. [L]

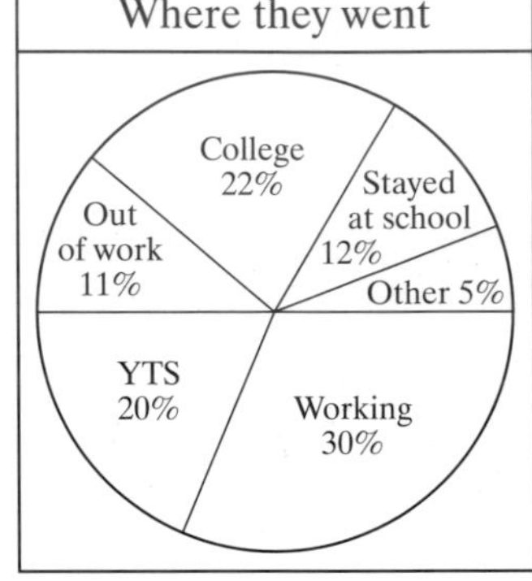

Diagram NOT accurately drawn

7 720 students were asked how they travelled to school. The pie chart shows the results of this survey.

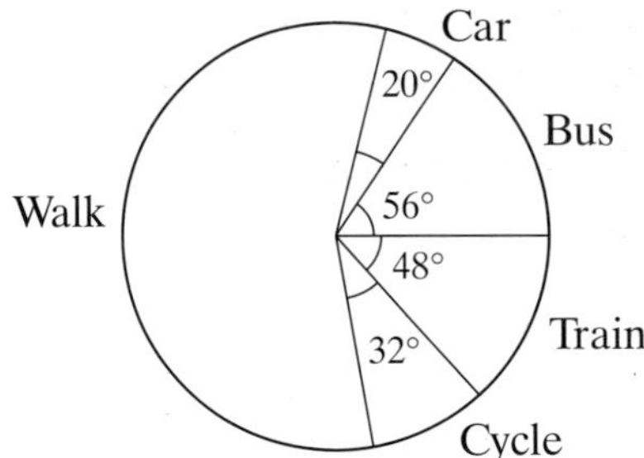

Work out:
(a) how many of the students travelled to school by bus
(b) how many of the students walked to school. [L]

24.7 Scatter graphs

■ **Scatter graphs can be used to show whether two sets of data are related.** For example:

In a small survey the heights of eight boys were measured and their shoe sizes were recorded.

Height in cm	172	182	164	190	167	169	175	185
Shoe size	$8\frac{1}{2}$	$10\frac{1}{2}$	7	13	$8\frac{1}{2}$	8	10	12

You can use a scatter graph to find out whether there is a relationship between these two sets of data: the heights and the shoe sizes.

This scatter graph shows height on the horizontal axis and shoe size on the vertical axis. Each pair of height and shoe size values in the table is used as coordinates to plot a point on the graph.

The points are approximately along a straight line, suggesting that the shoe size of a boy **is** related to his height.

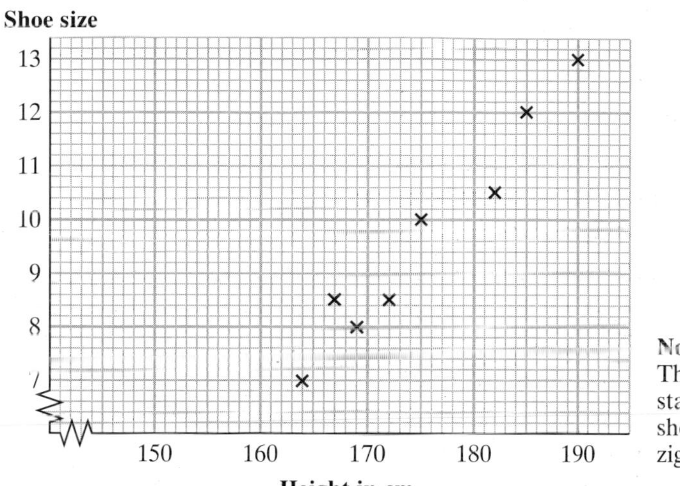

Note:
The axes do not start at 0. You show this by zigzag lines.

Looking for a correlation

If you think two sets of data may be related you can plot them on a scatter graph and examine the points without joining them up.

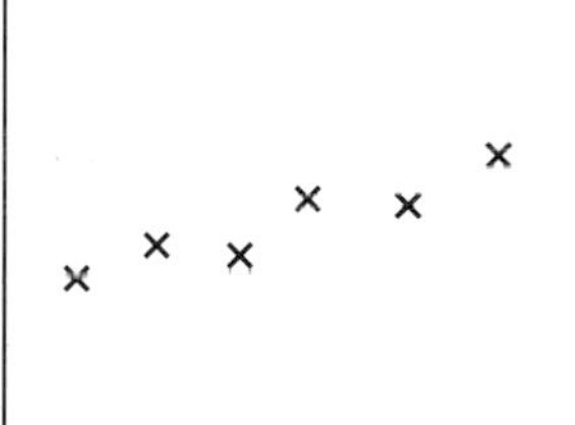

- **If the points on a scatter graph are very nearly along a straight line there is a high correlation between the variables.**

Here **high correlation** means that there is strong evidence of a relationship.

In the height–shoe size survey the shoe size increases as height increases. This is described as **positive correlation**.

Think of the relationship between the number of people helping with a task and the time it takes to complete the task. As the number of people increases the time taken decreases. This is a negative correlation.

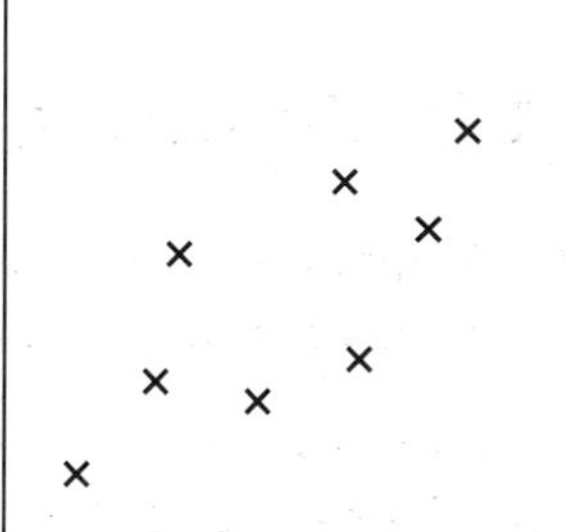

- **Positive correlation: as one quantity increases the other one increases; as one quantity decreases the other one decreases.**

  Examples:
  Height and weight of people.
  Distance travelled and petrol used.
  Number of passengers and fares collected.

- **Negative correlation: as one quantity increases the other quantity decreases.**

  Examples:
  Number of people helping with a task and the time taken to complete the task.
  Distance a person runs and average speed at which they run.
  Median weight of the potatoes in a 5 kg bag and number of potatoes in the bag.

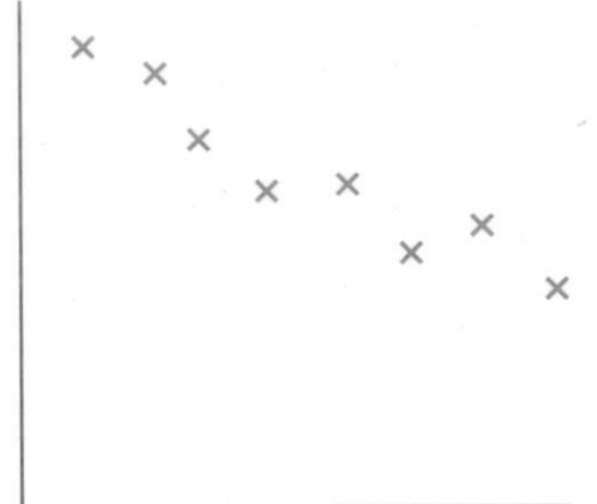

Finding the line of best fit

Sometimes there is not a straight line which passes through all the points but you can still draw the straight line which comes closest to fitting all the points. At GCSE level you need to estimate the position of the line by eye.

- **A line which is drawn to pass as close as possible to all the plotted points on a scatter graph is called the line of best fit.**

The closer the points are to this line of best fit the higher the correlation. The gradient of the line is not important except that a vertical or horizontal line of best fit means that the variables are not connected. Here are some typical examples and their interpretation:

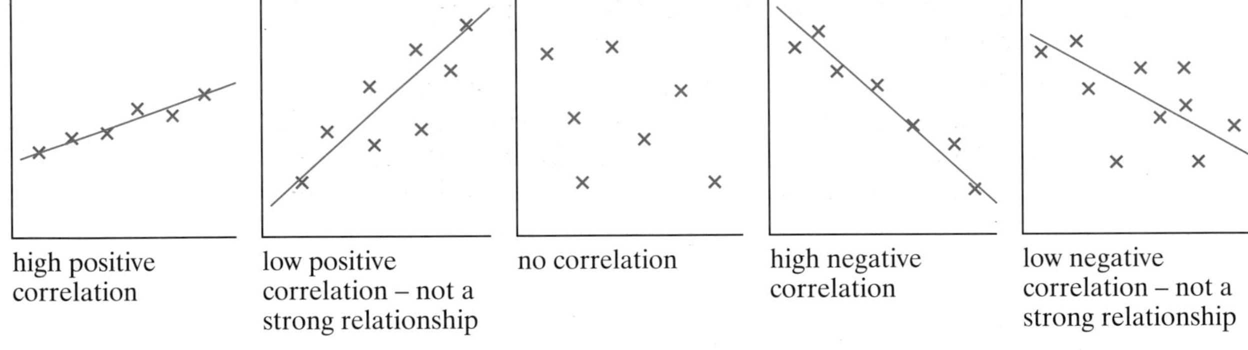

high positive correlation | low positive correlation – not a strong relationship | no correlation | high negative correlation | low negative correlation – not a strong relationship

Worked examination question

This table gives the marks scored by pupils in a French test and in a German test.

French	15	35	34	23	35	27	36	34	23	24	30	40	25	35	20
German	20	37	35	25	33	30	39	36	27	20	33	35	27	32	28

(a) Draw a scatter graph of the marks scored in the French and German tests.

(b) Describe the correlation between the marks scored in the two tests. [L]

(a) Plot the points using (French mark, German mark) as coordinates.

(b) You could draw a line of best fit but it is not essential. In general, as the French marks get higher the German marks get higher. The points are also close to fitting a straight line. There is high positive correlation between the marks in the two tests.

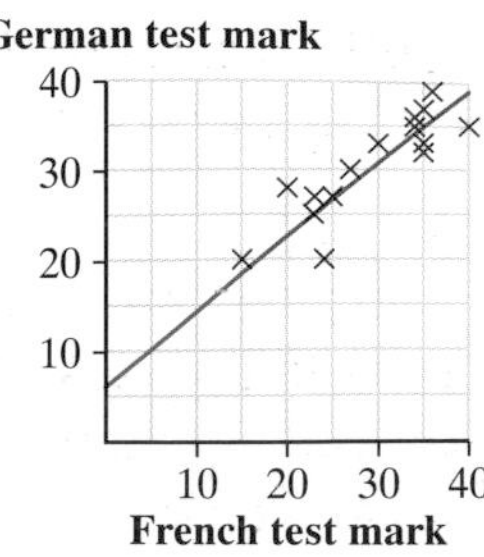

Exercise 24D

You will need graph paper.

1 The table contains information about the returns of postal surveys conducted by a market research organization.

Issued	2000	2500	3000	2800	1400	2100	2000	1800	2400	2600
Returned	480	605	712	683	308	515	492	421	592	624

(a) Construct a scatter graph of the postal surveys issued and returned.

(b) Draw in a line of best fit.

(c) Describe the correlation between the postal surveys issued and returned.

2 The ages of 12 cross-channel swimmers and their swimming times are recorded as:

17 yrs in 15 hrs 26 min	23 yrs in 14 hrs 32 min	36 yrs in 18 hrs 5 min
25 yrs in 11 hrs 12 min	18 yrs in 21 hrs 21 min	28 yrs in 13 hrs 43 min
26 yrs in 17 hrs 50 min	31 yrs in 12 hrs 7 min	21 yrs in 15 hrs 12 min
30 yrs in 16 hrs 10 min	42 yrs in 14 hrs 28 min	21 yrs in 11 hrs 42 min

(a) Draw a scatter graph of the ages and swimming times of the swimmers.

(b) Comment on the correlation between the ages of the swimmers and their swimming times.

3 A physicist is experimenting with the resistance in a circuit she is using. She measures and records the resulting current:

Resistance (ohms)	5	10	15	20	25	30	50
Current (amps)	10	4.9	3.2	2.4	1.9	1.7	1.0

(a) Draw a scatter graph of her results.

(b) Estimate the current for a resistance of 40 ohms.

(c) Estimate the resistance for a current of 7.5 amps.

4 The points on this scattergraph show the miles per gallon (mpg) and the size of engine (in cm^3) of thirteen cars.

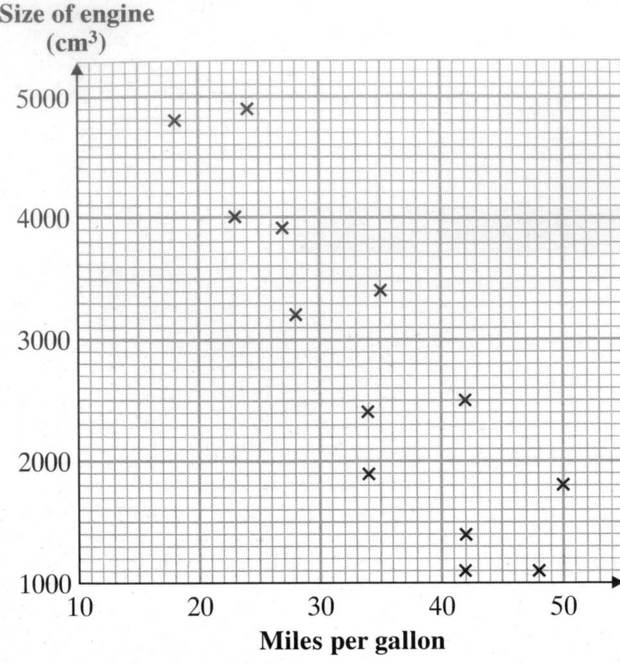

(a) How does the miles per gallon change as the size of engine increases?

(b) What type of correlation does the graph have?

(c) Draw a line of best fit on the scatter graph.

(d) A new car is made with an engine size of 3500 cm^3. Use your line of best fit to estimate the miles per gallon for this car.

[L]

Summary of key points

1 In a pictogram a picture or symbol is used to represent a number of items.

Ice cream sales

= £1000

May  

June

July  

August 

2 Bar charts can be used to show up patterns in data. The bars may be horizontal or vertical.

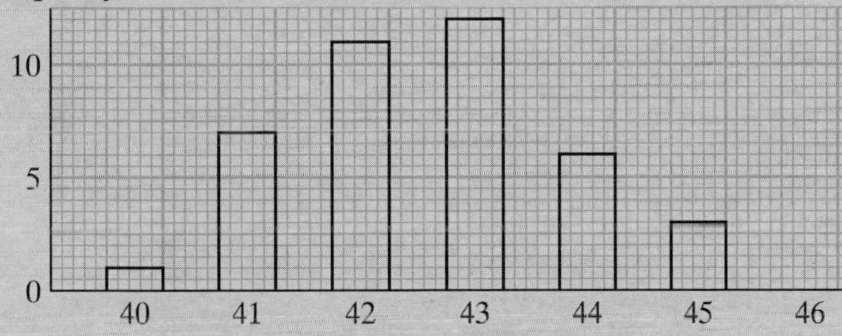

3 Line graphs can be used to show continuous data.

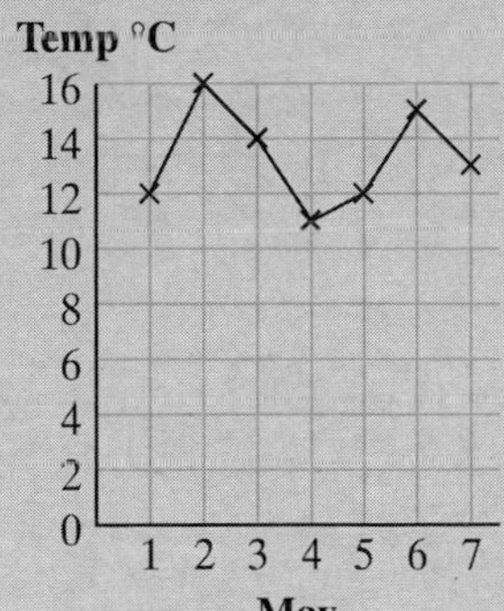

4 Histograms are used to display data that is grouped and continuous.

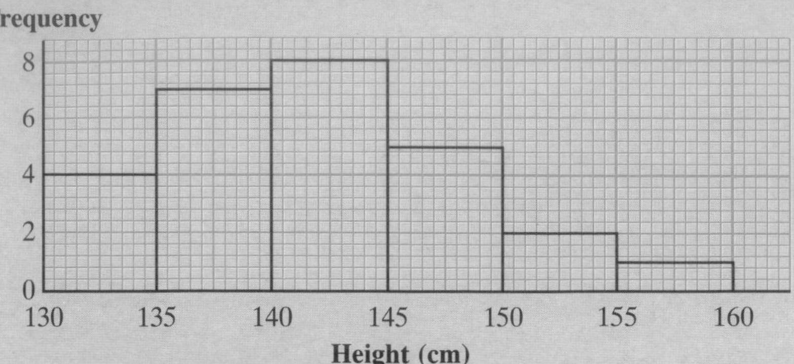

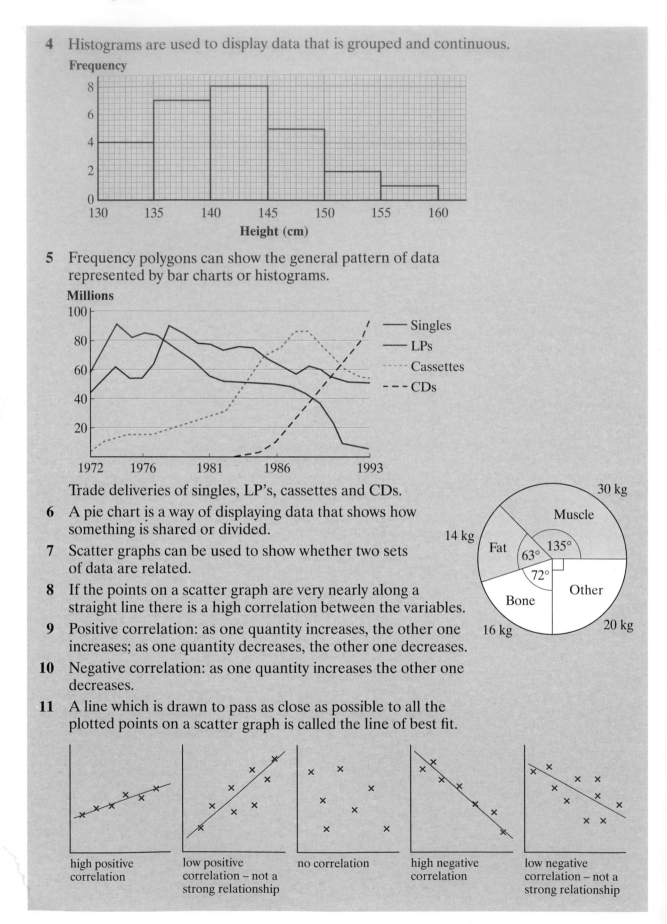

5 Frequency polygons can show the general pattern of data represented by bar charts or histograms.

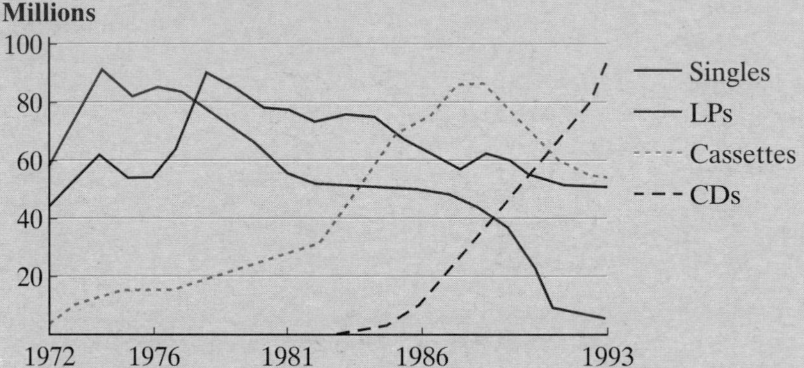

Trade deliveries of singles, LP's, cassettes and CDs.

6 A pie chart is a way of displaying data that shows how something is shared or divided.

30 kg
Muscle
14 kg
Fat
63°
135°
72°
Bone
Other
16 kg
20 kg

7 Scatter graphs can be used to show whether two sets of data are related.

8 If the points on a scatter graph are very nearly along a straight line there is a high correlation between the variables.

9 Positive correlation: as one quantity increases, the other one increases; as one quantity decreases, the other one decreases.

10 Negative correlation: as one quantity increases the other one decreases.

11 A line which is drawn to pass as close as possible to all the plotted points on a scatter graph is called the line of best fit.

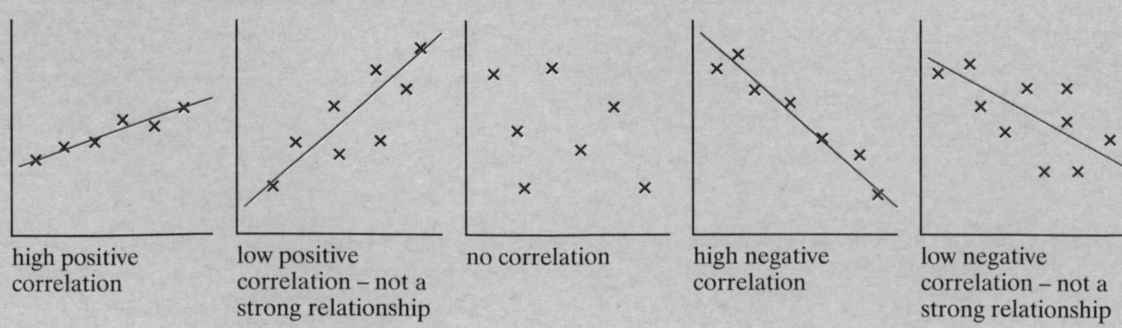

25 Ratio and proportion

Before starting this unit make sure you understand the ideas in Unit 11 Fractions (page 137).

25.1 What is a ratio?

■ **A ratio is a way of comparing two or more quantities.**

Ratios can be used to compare costs, weights, sizes and other quantities

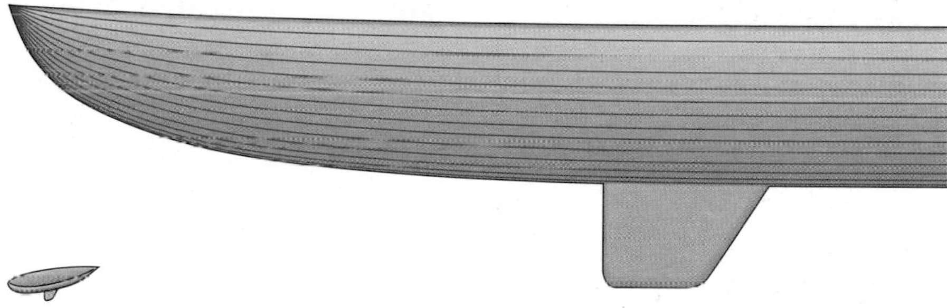

If a model of a boat is 1 metre long, but the actual boat is 25 metres long, then the ratio of the length of the model to the length of the actual boat is 1 to 25. This is written 1:25

Ratios are also used to describe the quantities of different ingredients in mixtures. Pharmacists making up medicines, manufacturers making biscuits and builders mixing cement all need to make mixtures using ingredients in the correct ratio.

Example 1

Frank is making pastry for 5 apple pies. How much of each ingredient does he need?

I always use
4oz flour and
2oz fat to make
pastry for my
apple pies

Amount of flour needed is 4 ounces × 5 = 20 ounces

Amount of fat needed is 2 ounces × 5 = 10 ounces

In Example 1 Frank's quantities for making one apple pie can be written as a ratio.

The ratio of flour to fat is 4:2

Simplifying ratios

Two ratios can be equivalent in the same way that two fractions can be equivalent.

In Example 1 the ratio of flour to fat is the same however many pies are made. It can be written as:

20 : 10 or
10 : 5 or
4 : 2 or
2 : 1 This ratio is the **simplest form** of the ratio 20:10

All these ratios are **equivalent** – the relationship between each pair of numbers is the same.

■ **A ratio is normally written using whole numbers only, in its simplest form.**

Example 2

Express these ratios in their simplest form:

(a) 12 : 18 (b) 260 m : 1.4 km
(c) $\frac{1}{4}:\frac{2}{3}$ (d) 4.2 : 3.58 : 5

(a) 12 : 18
To simplify the ratio divide both numbers by the highest common factor (in this case 6).

12 : 18 is equivalent to 2 : 3

(b) 260 m : 1.4 km
First convert the quantities to the same units (metres). Then simplify.

260 m : 1400 m
260 : 1400
26 : 140
13 : 70

(c) $\frac{1}{4}:\frac{2}{3}$
Multiply both fractions by the lowest common multiple of the denominators to change the fractions to whole numbers. The lowest common multiple of 4 and 3 is 12 so $\frac{1}{4}:\frac{2}{3}$ is equivalent to:
$(\frac{1}{4} \times 12) : (\frac{2}{3} \times 12)$
or 3 : 8

(d) 4.2 : 3.58 : 5
Convert to whole numbers by multiplying all three numbers by 100:
420 : 358 : 500

Simplify by dividing all three numbers by 2:
210 : 179 : 250

Exercise 25A

Write these ratios in their simplest form.

1 **(a)** 20 : 16 **(b)** 3 : 15 **(c)** 12 : 48
(d) 8 : 4 **(e)** 18 : 12 **(f)** 36 : 6
(g) 24 : 72 : 12 **(h)** 3 : 6 : 9

2 **(a)** 2 cm : 1 m **(b)** 350 mg : 1 g **(c)** 10 m*l* : 2 *l*
(d) 64 g : 4 kg **(e)** £3 : 40p : £1.20 **(f)** 150 mm : 40 cm

3 **(a)** 340 m : 1.2 km **(b)** 40 mins : 2h : $\frac{1}{2}$h **(c)** 45 g : 1 kg
(d) 42p : £1.05 **(e)** 45 cm : 0.1 m **(f)** 2.4 tonne : 132 kg

4 **(a)** $2 : \frac{1}{3}$ **(b)** $4 : \frac{1}{4}$ **(c)** $\frac{1}{2} : \frac{1}{4}$
(d) $\frac{1}{2} : \frac{1}{3}$ **(e)** $\frac{3}{4} : \frac{1}{4} : \frac{1}{2}$ **(f)** $\frac{1}{3} : \frac{3}{4}$
(g) $\frac{3}{4} : 1 : 2\frac{1}{2}$ **(h)** $\frac{5}{9} : \frac{4}{5}$

5 **(a)** 1.2 : 3.4 **(b)** 5.5 : 1.15 **(c)** 3 : 1.4
(d) 5.9 : 0.04 **(e)** 4 : 3.5 : 5.5 **(f)** 0.08 : 0.2 : 1

25.2 Writing ratios in unitary form

■ **Ratios can be written in the form 1:*n* or *n*:1**
The number *n* is written as a decimal (unless it is a whole number).

When one of the numbers in a ratio is 1 the ratio is in **unitary form**.

Example 3

(a) Write these ratios in the form 1:*n*
(i) 8 : 10 (ii) 5 cm : 1 km (iii) 20 : 1
(b) Write these ratios in the form *n*:1
(i) 21 : 5 (ii) 1 kg : 4 g

(a) (i) 8 : 10
Divide both numbers by 8:
$1 : \frac{10}{8}$
1 : 1.25

(ii) 5 cm : 1 km
Write both numbers in cm:
5 : 100 000
Divide by 5:
1 : 20 000

(iii) 20 : 1
Divide by 20:
$1 : \frac{1}{20}$
1 : 0.05

(b) (i) 21 : 5
Divide by 5:
4.2 : 1

(ii) 1 kg : 4 g
Write both quantities in g:
1000 g : 4 g
Divide by 4:
250 : 1

Exercise 25B

Write these ratios in the form 1 : n

1 **(a)** 2 : 5 **(b)** 32 g : 8 g **(c)** 10 cm : 10 m **(d)** 4 : 10
(e) 32p : £2 **(f)** 2 : 15 **(g)** 5 : 11 **(h)** 25 g : 1 kg

Write these ratios in the form n : 1

2 **(a)** 6 : 8 **(b)** 1 km : 2 cm **(c)** 3 h : $\frac{1}{2}$h **(d)** £3 : 40p
(e) 5 l : 10 ml **(f)** 2 m : 2 mm **(g)** 1000 : 30 **(h)** 5p : 25p

25.3 Writing ratios as fractions

■ **A ratio can be written as a fraction.**

You can write ratios as fractions and fractions as ratios. This can help you solve some mathematical problems more easily.

The ratio 10 : 12 can be written as the fraction $\frac{10}{12}$

The ratio x : 6 can be written as the fraction $\frac{x}{6}$

This can help you solve problems in which you need to find equivalent ratios. For example, if the ratios x : 6 and 10 : 12 are equivalent you can write:

$$\frac{x}{6} = \frac{10}{12}$$

In the same way if 16 : 12 is equivalent to x : 3 you can write:

$$\frac{16}{12} = \frac{x}{3}$$

Example 4

(a) Given that 6 : 8 is equivalent to 9 : x, find x.
(b) In a garden tulips and daffodils are in the ratio 4 : 5. There are 45 daffodils.
How many tulips are there?

(a) $6:8$ is equivalent to $9:x$
Changing the order of the numbers in each ratio, $8:6$ is equivalent to $x:9$ so:

$$\frac{8}{6} = \frac{x}{9}$$

Write each fraction as an equivalent fraction with the same denominator (in this case 18).

$$\frac{24}{18} = \frac{2 \times x}{18}$$

The numerators must be equal, so $2 \times x = 24$.
$x = 12$

(b) The ratio of tulips to daffodils is 4:5
Use x to represent the number of tulips when there are 45 daffodils. The flowers are in the ratio $x:45$ and $4:5$ is equivalent to $x:45$.

Writing these ratios as fractions gives:

$$\frac{4}{5} = \frac{x}{45}$$

Write each fraction with the same denominator of 45.

$$\frac{36}{45} = \frac{x}{45}$$

So $x = 36$
There are 36 tulips.

Exercise 25C

1 Find x for each of these pairs of equivalent ratios:

(a)	$x:3$	$16:24$	**(b)**	$5:11$	$30:x$	**(c)**	$12:4$	$3:x$
(d)	$16:8$	$x:1$	**(e)**	$24:64$	$3:x$	**(f)**	$1:6$	$x:42$
(g)	$36:9$	$x:1$	**(h)**	$7:x$	$35:40$			

2 An alloy contains iron and tungsten in the ratio 5 : 1 If there is 15 kg of iron in a quantity of the alloy, how much tungsten is there?

3 A concrete mix is made by adding sand and cement in the ratio 4 : 1 Five buckets of cement are put in a mixer. How much sand is needed?

4 The ratio of girls to boys in a class is 5 : 4 There are 12 boys in the class.
How many girls are there?

5 The ratio of the lengths of two rectangles is 5 : 6 The length of the first rectangle is 12.5 cm.
What is the length of the second rectangle?

25.4 Dividing quantities in a given ratio

■ **Ratios can be used to share or divide quantities.**

Example 5

Shreena and Sue between them complete a shop window design, for which they are paid £84. Shreena has worked for seven hours, Sue for five hours. They decide to divide the earnings in the ratio of the hours they have each worked.
How much does each receive?

£84 is to be divided in the ratio 7 : 5

Think of the money being divided into 7 + 5 = 12 parts altogether. Then Shreena will get 7 parts and Sue will get 5 parts.

12 parts is £84.

So 1 part is £84 ÷ 12 = £7

then 7 parts is £7 × 7 = £49

5 parts is £7 × 5 = £35

Shreena receives £49 and Sue receives £35.

(Check by adding: £49 + £35 = £84)

Exercise 25D

In questions 1, 2 and 3 divide the quantities in the ratios given.

1 **(a)** £14.91 in the ratio 2 : 5 **(b)** £45 in the ratio 4 : 5
(c) £51.92 in the ratio 2 : 9 **(d)** £170.52 in the ratio 1 : 4 : 7

2 **(a)** 600 g in the ratio 3 : 2 **(b)** 32 cm in the ratio 3 : 5
(c) 23.4 *l* in the ratio 1 : 5 **(d)** 34.65 m in the ratio 2 : 4 : 5

3 **(a)** 30.78 m in the ratio 4 : 5 **(b)** 75 cm in the ratio 3 : 2
(c) 48 kg in the ratio 3 : 5 **(d)** £357 in the ratio 1 : 2 : 4

4 The ratio of girls to boys in a class is 4 : 3 There are 28 pupils in the class.
Find how many are **(a)** girls **(b)** boys.

5 The angles of a triangle are in the ratio 6 : 5 : 7.
Find the sizes of the three angles. Remember: the angles of a triangle add to 180°.

6 Shortcrust pastry is made from flour and fat in the ratio 2 : 1.
How much flour do you need to make 600 g of pastry.

7 A business makes a profit of £660. The directors divide it in the ratio 3 : 4 : 8.
How much do they each receive?

8 An alloy is made from iron, copper, nickel and phosphorous in the ratio 6 : 4 : 3 : 1.
Find the weight of **(a)** copper **(b)** nickel in 714 g of the alloy.

25.5 Direct proportion

■ **Two quantities are in direct proportion if their ratio stays the same as the quantities increase or decrease.**

Example 6

A car uses eight litres of petrol to travel 124 km. If the amount of petrol used is in direct proportion to the distance travelled, how far can the car travel on one litre?

I told you we wouldn't do the 20 km on one litre of petrol !
Services
4 km

8 litres is used for 124 km, a ratio of 8 : 124

Dividing both numbers by 8 gives:

$$1 : \frac{124}{8}$$

So 1 litre is used for $\frac{124}{8} = 15.5$ km

Example 7

Seven pencils cost 63p. The cost is directly proportional to the number of pencils. How much will 12 pencils cost?

First method:

The ratio of the number of pencils to the cost is 7 : 63

If the cost of 12 pencils is x, the ratio of the number of pencils to the cost is $12 : x$

To get from 7 to 12 you multiply 7 by $\frac{12}{7}$.

To get from the cost of 7 pencils to the cost x of 12 pencils you multiply 63p by $\frac{12}{7}$.

So the cost of 12 pencils $x = 63 \times \frac{12}{7}$ pence
$= 108$ pence $= £1.08$

7 : 63 is equivalent to 12 : 108

Second method:

It is easier to first find out what one pencil costs. This is called the unitary method.

7 pencils cost 63p

So 1 pencil costs $\frac{63\text{p}}{7} = 9\text{p}$

and 12 pencils cost $9\text{p} \times 12 = £1.08$

Worked examination question

Here is a list of ingredients for making some Greek food. These amounts make enough for six people.

2 cloves of garlic
4 ounces of chick peas
4 tablespoons of olive oil
5 fluid ounces of Tahina paste

Change the amounts so that there will be enough for nine people. [L]

Nine people is half as much again as six (six has been multiplied by 1.5 to give nine).

The 2 cloves of garlic become 3.
The 4 ounces of chick peas become 6.
The 4 tablespoons of olive oil become 6.
The 5 fluid ounces of Tahina paste become $7\frac{1}{2}$.

2 : 4 : 4 : 5 is equivalent to 3 : 6 : 6 : $7\frac{1}{2}$

Exercise 25E

1 Dress material costs £23.40 for 4 metres.
How much does 1 metre cost?

2 14 cm^3 of copper weighs 126 g.
What is the weight of 1 cm^3?

3 Betty is paid £34.30 for seven hours' work at a nursing home.
How much should she receive for five hours' work?

4 Six razor blades cost 42p.
How much will ten razor blades cost?

5 A machine makes 490 engine parts in 35 minutes.
How many engine parts will the machine make in one hour?

6 Four packets of tea cost £1.28.
How much will three packets cost?

7 A 6 kg bag of sprouts cost £1.98.
How much does an 8 kg bag of sprouts cost if the cost per kg is the same?

8 Seven tubes of toothpaste have a total weight of 854 g.
Work out the weight of eight tubes of toothpaste.

9 Anisha buys 12 rubbers for £1.80.
How much would it cost her to buy 15 rubbers?

10 Five bottles of detergent have a capacity of 1560 cm^3.
Work out the total capacity of nine similar bottles.

11 The recipe for eight small cakes includes the following:
480 g flour, 720 g fat, 2 eggs.

Change the amounts so there will be enough to make 12 small cakes.

25.5 Inverse proportion

If one man takes 4 days to dig a trench how long will it take 2 men working at the same rate to dig it?

Here the time taken to dig the trench is in **inverse proportion** to the number of men. As the number of men *increases* the time taken *decreases.*

The rate of increase and decrease are inversely proportional: if the number of men is multiplied by 2 the time taken will be divided by 2.

Example 8

3 men dig a trench in 4 days.

How long would it take 6 men working at the same rate?

3 men take 4 days

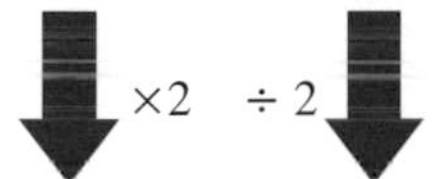

6 men take 2 days

■ **Two quantities are in inverse proportion when one increases at the same rate as the other decreases.**

If you are told that two quantities are in proportion, or proportional to each other, without using the words 'direct' or 'inverse', it usually means that the quantities are in direct proportion.

Example 9

Four identical machines take 30 hours to complete enough parts for an order. One machine breaks down.
How long will it now take to complete a similar order?

Using the unitary method to work out how long one machine would take:

4 machines take 30 hours
1 machine takes $30 \times 4 = 120$ hours
3 machines take $120 \div 3 = 40$ hours.

So it will now take 40 hours to complete the order.

Exercise 25F

1 Six people can harvest a field of strawberries in four days. How long would it take eight people to harvest the same field?

2 Five pumps can empty a tank of water in four hours. If one pump has broken down, how long would the remaining four pumps take?

3 A field of grass provides enough food for 25 cows for eight days. For how long would the same field feed 10 cows?

4 In a school 33 classrooms are required for classes of 32 pupils each.
How many classrooms would be needed if the class size were reduced to 22 pupils?

5 Four bricklayers can build a wall 10 feet high in 10 days.
How long would it take five bricklayers to build a similar wall?

6 Two secretaries can type a large document between them in nine hours.
How long would it take three secretaries to type the document?

7 Bags of sugar are packed in seven boxes, each holding 12 bags.
If the same quantity of sugar is packed into larger boxes and only six boxes are used, how many bags are there in each box?

8 A quantity of food will last six pigs for 10 days.
For how long would the same quantity last four pigs?

9 It takes nine men 30 days to complete a contracted job.
How long would it take 20 men?

10 A circular flower bed has space for 160 plants, placed 18 cm apart around the outside edge.
How many plants could you fit in round the edge if the plants were 24 cm apart?

Exercise 25G Mixed questions

1 Express these ratios in their simplest form:
(a) 35 : 10 **(b)** 6 : 18 **(c)** $\frac{1}{4}$: 5
(d) $\frac{7}{8}$: $\frac{3}{4}$ **(e)** 3.5 : 4.25 **(f)** 75p : £6
(g) 600 g : 1.8 kg **(h)** 5min : $1\frac{1}{2}$hrs **(i)** 5 mm : 4 cm

2 Express these ratios in the form 1 : n
(a) 3: 15 **(b)** 8 : 6 **(c)** $\frac{1}{2}$ sec : 1 min
(d) 1.25 km : 150 m

3 Express these ratios in the form n : 1
(a) 15 : 10 **(b)** 3h : $\frac{1}{2}$h **(c)** 100 g : 1 kg

4 Find x for each of these pairs of equivalent ratios
(a) 2 : 10 x : 35 **(b)** 4 : x 20 : 45

5 Divide:
(a) 30.78 metres in the ratio 4 : 5
(b) £18.40 in the ratio 2 : 3 : 5

6 One bottle of wine holds 0.75 litres. Another holds 1.2 litres. Work out the ratio (in its simplest form) of the capacities of the bottles.

7 The ratio of boys to girls in a youth club is 4 : 5 There are 28 boys.
How many girls are there in the youth club?

8 In the past year a garage sold 468 cars. They were either estate cars or saloon cars. The ratio of estate cars to saloon cars sold was 2 : 7.
Find how many estate cars the garage sold.

9 In 24 hours the earth turns about its axis through an angle of 360°. What angle has it turned through in 15 hours?

10 A florist has a delivery of the same number of single roses every week day. When he has nine single roses to a bunch he can make exactly 60 bunches. One day he decides to put 12 single roses in each bunch.
How many bunches will there be?

11 12 bags of oats will be enough for three donkeys for eight days. How long will 10 bags last four donkeys if they are given the same amount each per day?

12 Here are the ingredients for making 18 rock cakes.
9 ounces of flour
6 ounces of sugar
6 ounces of margarine
8 ounces of mixed dried fruit
2 large eggs
Mark wants to make 12 rock cakes.
(a) (i) How much sugar does he need?
(ii) How much dried fruit does he need? Give your answer correct to the nearest ounce.
Mark only has 9 ounces of margarine. He has plenty of all the other ingredients.
(b) What is the greatest number of rock cakes he can make?
[L]

13 Mortar is made by mixing five parts by weight of sand with one part by weight of cement.
How much sand is needed to make 8400 kg of mortar?

[L]

14 The heights of two buildings are in the ratio 5:8. The bigger building is 56 feet high.
Calculate the height of the lower building.

[L]

Summary of key points

1 A ratio is a way of comparing two or more quantities.

2 A ratio is normally written using whole numbers only, in its simplest form.

10 : 15 simplifies to 2 : 3 $\frac{2}{5} : \frac{1}{4}$ simplifies to 8 : 5

1.2 : 5 simplifies to 6 : 25

3 Ratios can be written in the form, 1 : n or n : 1 The number n is written as a decimal (unless it is a whole number).

2 : 3 can be written as 1 : 1.5 in unitary form

4 A ratio can be written as a fraction. For example, the ratio of 3 to 7 can be written 3 : 7 or as the fraction $\frac{3}{7}$.

5 Ratios can be used to share or divide quantities.

6 Two quantities are in direct proportion when their ratio stays the same as the quantities increase or decrease.

7 Two quantities are in inverse proportion when one increases at the same rate as the other decreases.

26 Accurate drawings, scales and loci

26.1 Making accurate drawings

Sometimes you will be asked to make an accurate drawing from given measurements.

Example 1

Make an accurate drawing of triangle ABC with AB = 6 cm, BC = 5 cm and CA = 4 cm.

Make a rough sketch to get an idea of what your finished drawing should be like.

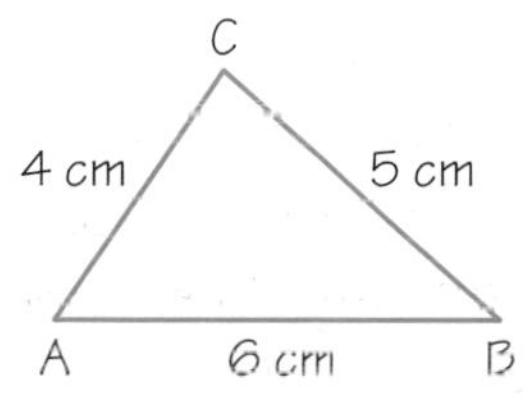

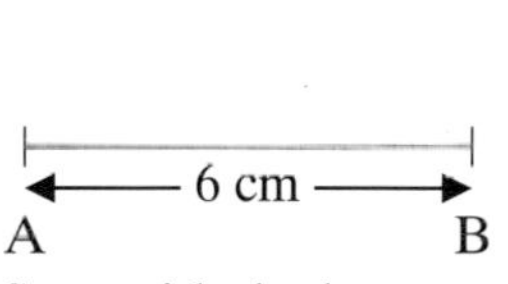

Start with the longest side. Draw a line 6 cm long and label its ends A and B.

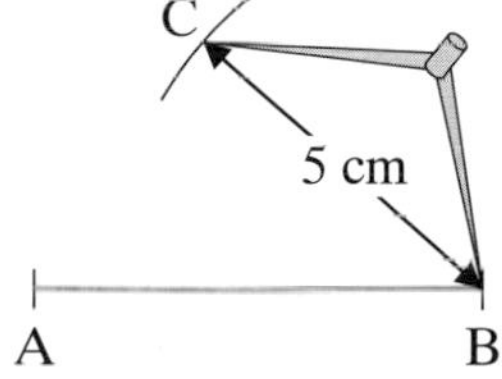

Set your compasses to a radius of 5 cm. Put the point at B and draw an arc near where you think C will be.

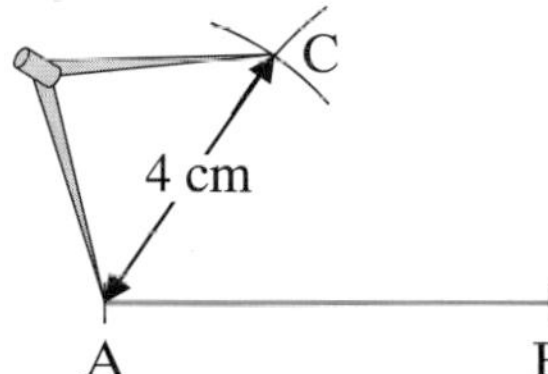

Set your compasses to 4 cm. Put the point at B and draw a second arc. Point C is where the two arcs cross.

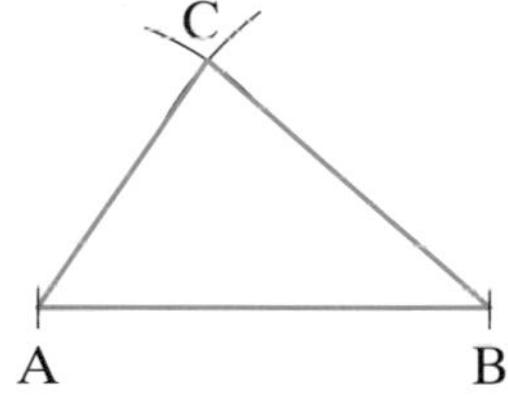

Join C to A and B to complete the triangle.

Example 2

Make an accurate drawing of triangle PQR with PQ = 5 cm, angle P = 40° and angle Q = 60°

Make a rough sketch first.

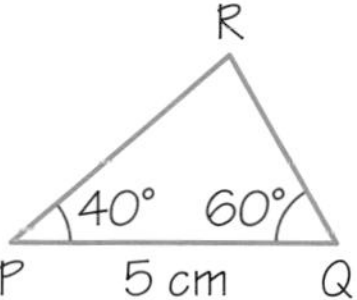

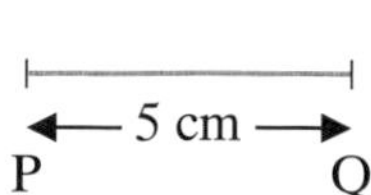

Draw a line 5 cm long and label its ends P and Q.

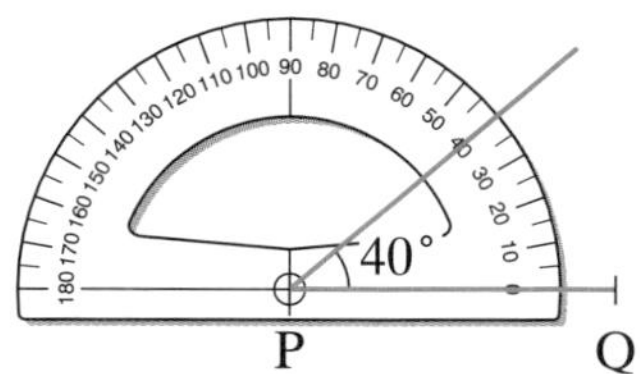

Place your protractor over point P. Mark a point at 40° (anticlockwise) and join it to P with a line.

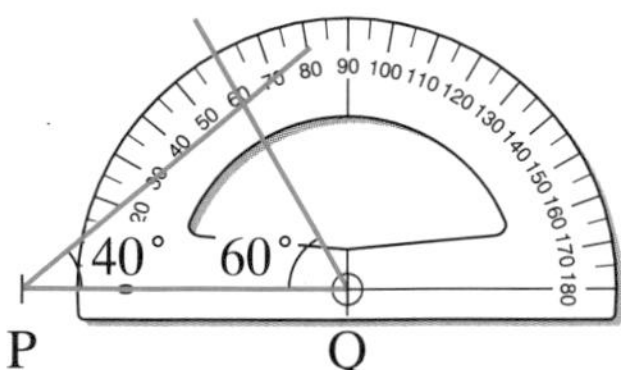

Place your protractor over point Q. Mark a point at 60° (clockwise) and join it to Q with a line.

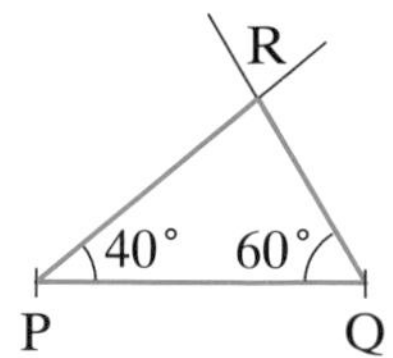

The new lines cross at R. Join R to P and Q to complete the triangle PQR.

Example 3

(a) Make an accurate drawing of quadrilateral PQRS with PQ = 6.4 cm, PS = 3.5 cm, SR = 4.7 cm, QR = 5.3 cm and angle P = 112°

(b) Measure angle QRS.

Make a rough sketch with the longest side at the bottom. The vertices P, Q, R and S should be in that order around the quadrilateral.

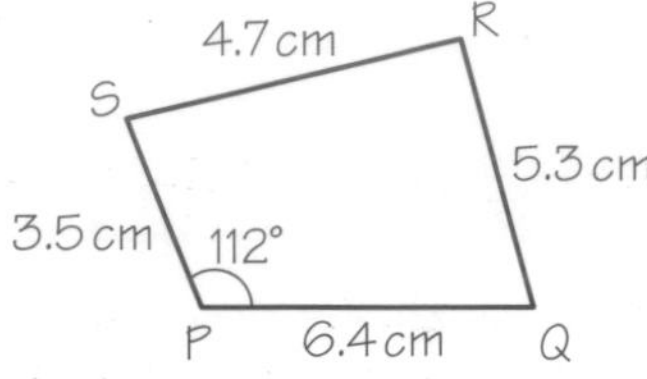

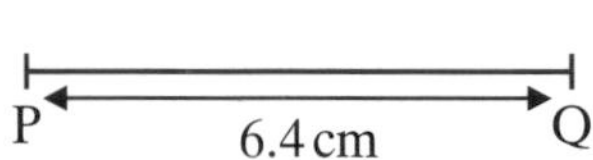

Draw a line 6.4 cm long and label the ends P and Q.

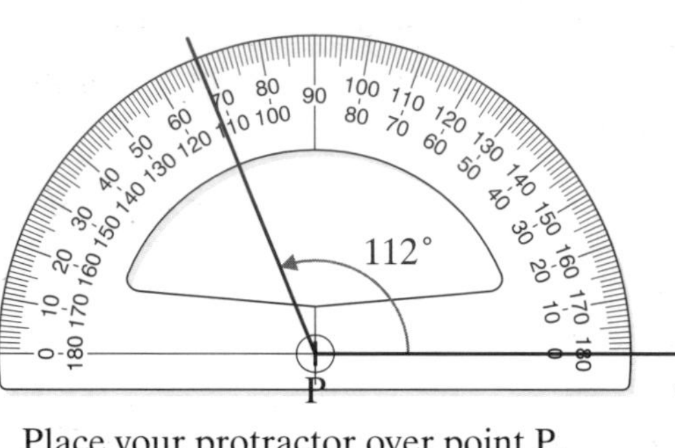

Place your protractor over point P. Mark a point at 112° (anticlockwise) and join it to P with a line.

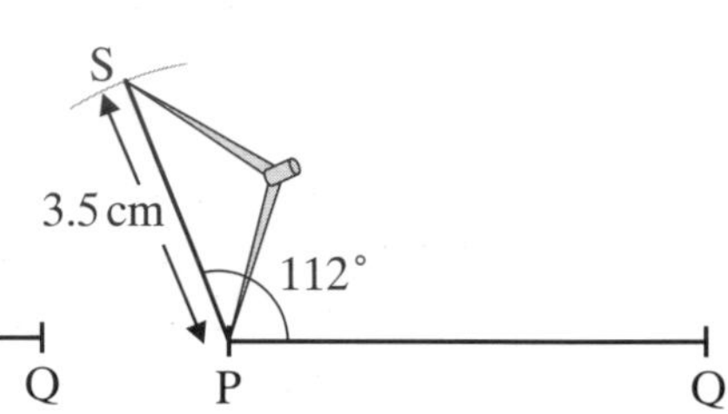

Use compasses to mark point S 3.5 cm along the line from P.

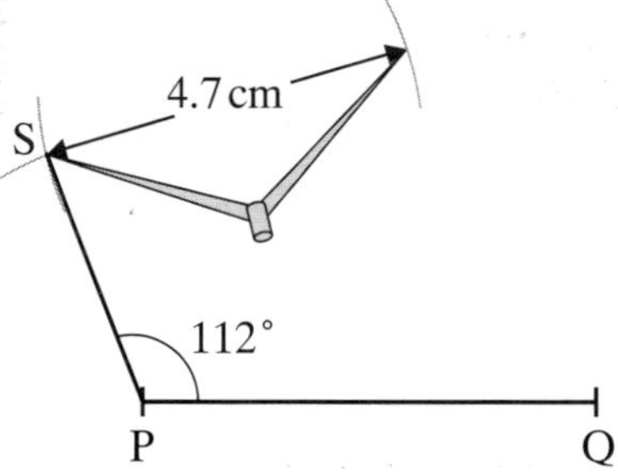

Set your compasses to 4.7 cm. With the point at S draw an arc near where you expect R to be.

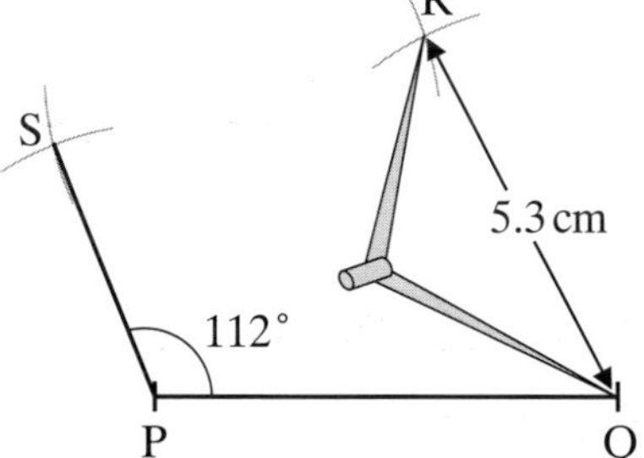

Set your compasses to 5.3 cm. With the point at Q draw another arc near where you expect R to be. The two arcs cross at R.

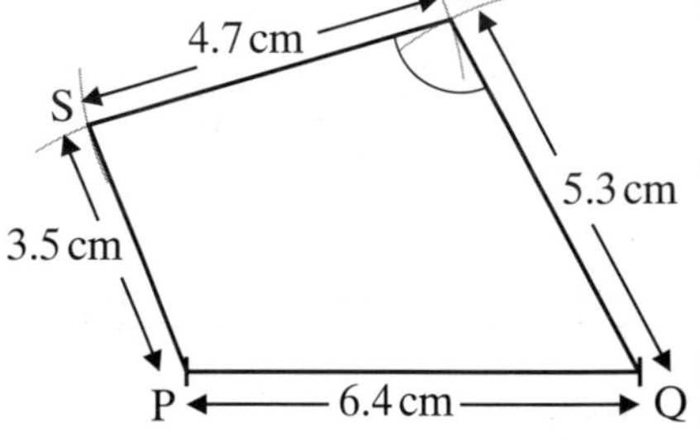

Join R to S and Q to complete the quadrilateral PQRS. Use a protractor to measure angle QRS.

If you have made an accurate drawing angle QRS should be about 115°

Exercise 26A

You need a ruler, compasses and a protractor.

1 Make accurate full size drawings of these triangles:

(a)

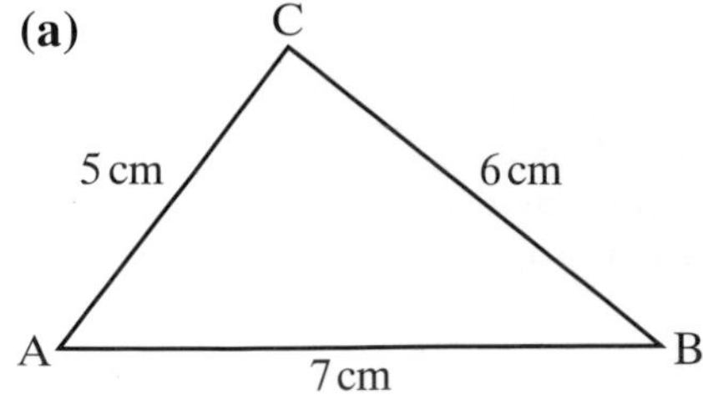

(b)

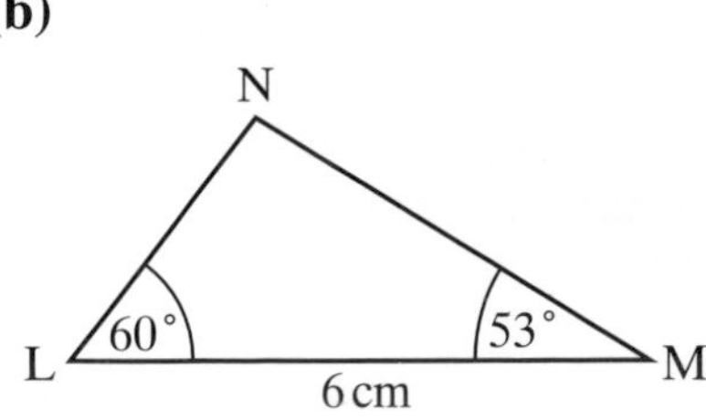

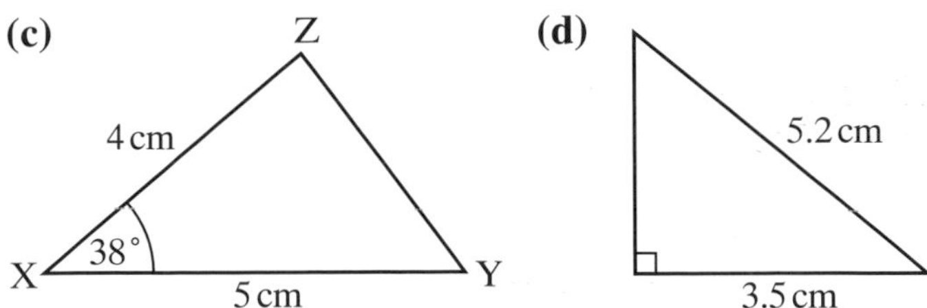

2 Try to make accurate drawings of triangles with these measurements:
(a) ABC with AB = 9 cm, angle A = 30° and BC = 3 cm
(b) LMN with LM = 9 cm, angle L = 30° and MN = 5 cm
(c) XYZ with XY = 9 cm, angle X = 30° and YZ = 4.5 cm
(Hint: it may be possible to draw more than one triangle, or no triangle at all for some measurements.)

3 (a) Make an accurate drawing of the quadrilateral ABCD.
(b) Measure and write down the size of angle BAD.

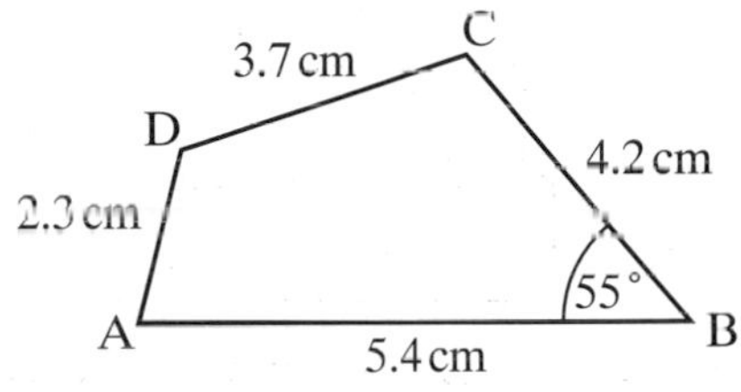

4 (a) Make an accurate drawing of the quadrilateral PQRS with PQ = 6.2 cm, QR = 3.5 cm, PS = 4.7 cm, angle P = 53° and angle Q = 42°
(b) Measure and write down the length of RS.

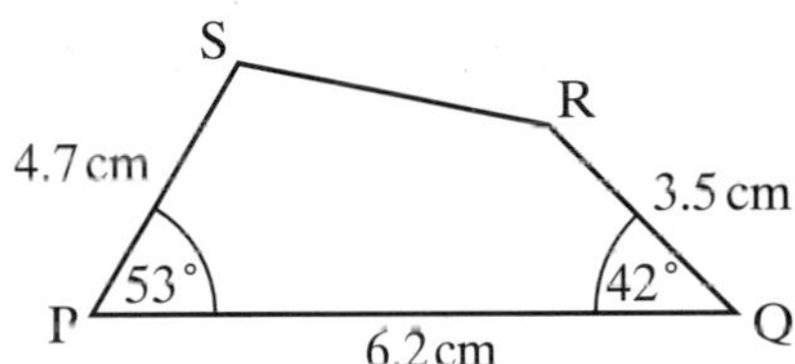

26.2 Using scales in accurate drawings

Maps and plans are accurate drawings from which measurements can be made.

- **A scale is a ratio which shows the relationship between a length on a drawing and the actual length in real life.**

(There is more about ratios on page 373.)

Ordnance Survey Pathfinder maps used by hill walkers are on a scale of 1 to 25 000, written 1:25 000.

1 cm on the map represents 25 000 cm in real life, which is 250 m or a quarter of a kilometre.

Only another 16 km to go.
1:25000
But you said it was only 64 cm!

Example 4

The scale on a road map is 1 : 200 000.
Preston and Blackburn are 8 cm apart on the map.

(a) Work out the real distance, in km, between Preston and Blackburn.

York is 37 km in a straight line from Leeds.

(b) Work out the distance of York from Leeds on the map.

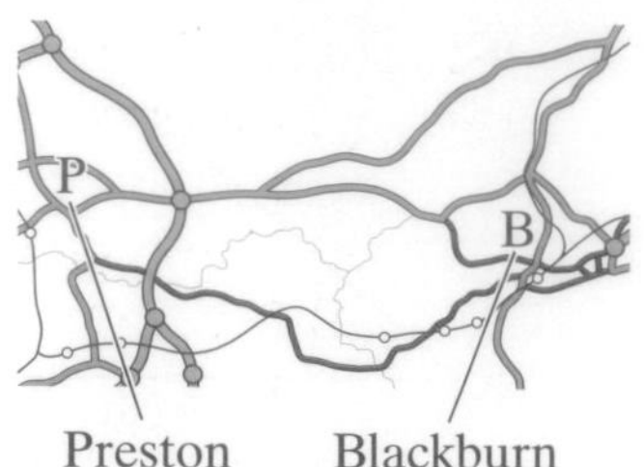

A scale of 1 : 200 000 is commonly used in road atlases.

(a) The distance on the map is 8 cm.
The real distance is 8 cm × 200 000
= 1 600 000 cm

Divide by 100 to change cm to m:
real distance = 16 000 m.

Divide by 1000 to change m to km:

The distance between Preston and Blackburn is 16 km.

(b) The real distance is 37 km.

Multiply by 1000 to change km to m:
real distance = 37 × 1000 = 37 000 m

Multiply by 100 to change m to cm:
real distance = 37 000 × 100 = 3 700 000 cm

Divide by 200 000 to find the distance on the map:

$$\text{Distance on the map} = \frac{3\,700\,000}{200\,000} = 18.5\text{ cm}$$

Exercise 26B

You will need a ruler and protractor.

1 A model of a van is made to a scale of 1 : 20. The height of the model is 10 cm.
Work out the height, in metres, of the full size van.

2 A map is drawn on a scale of 3 cm to 1 km.

(a) Work out the real length of a lake which is 4.2 cm long on the map.

(b) The distance between the church in Canwick and the town hall in Barnton is 5.8 km. Work out the distance between them on the map.

Scale: 3 cm to 1 km
This means that a real length of 1 km is represented on the map by a length of 3 cm.

3 A plan of a rectangular playing field is drawn using a scale of 1 : 2500.
The width of the field on the plan is 5 cm.

(a) (i) Work out the real width of the field in centimetres.
(ii) Change your answer to metres.

The area of the field on the plan is $31.5\,\text{cm}^2$.

(b) (i) Work out the length, in centimetres, of the playing field on the plan.

(ii) Work out the real length, in metres, of the playing field.

(iii) Work out the real area, in square metres, of the playing field. [L]

4 On the map the scale is 1 : 50 000.
Use the map to work out:

(a) the distance of the church with a tower at Rampton from the church with a tower at Cottenham.

(b) the bearing of the church at Rampton from the church with a tower at Cottenham.

Remember: a bearing is a three-figure angle measured from the North.

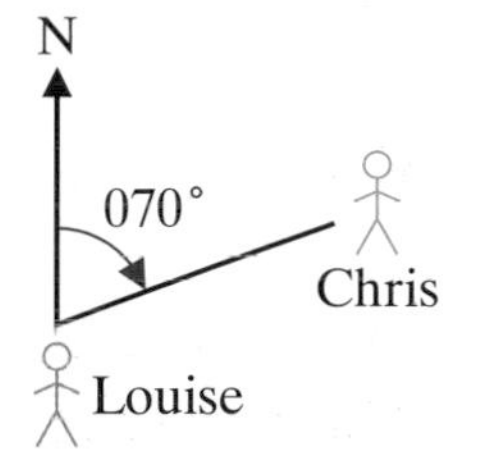

The bearing of Chris from Louise is 070°

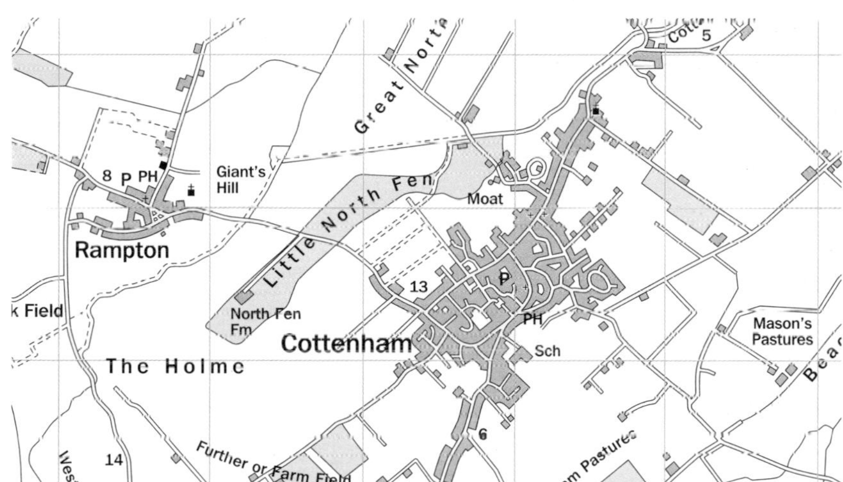

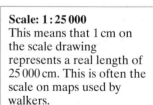

The sign on this map represents a church with a tower.

5 Witley is 2 km due south of Milford. The bearing of Hydestile from Milford is 125° and the distance from Milford to Hydestile is 2.8 km.

(a) Make a scale drawing to show the three villages.
Use a scale of 1 : 25 000.

(b) Use your drawing to find:

(i) the distance of Hydestile from Witley

(ii) the bearing of Hydestile from Witley.

Scale: 1 : 25 000
This means that 1 cm on the scale drawing represents a real length of 25 000 cm. This is often the scale on maps used by walkers.

26.3 Finding the locus of an object

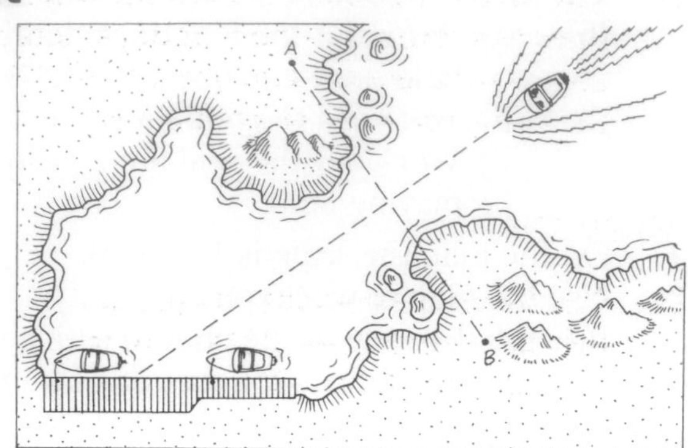

To enter the harbour safely this boat must follow the path shown with a dotted line.

All the points on the path obey a rule:

Each point is always equidistant (the same distance) from A and B.

This path is called the **locus** of the points.

■ **A locus is a set of points that obey a given rule.**

Notice that the locus is at right angles to the line AB, and divides it exactly in half. It is the **perpendicular bisector** of AB.

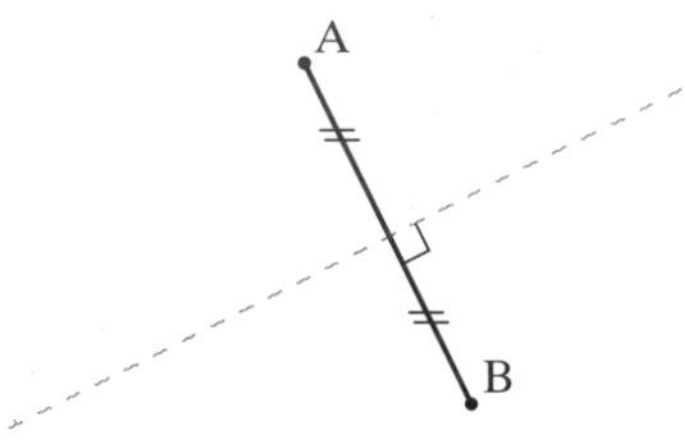

■ **The locus of the points equidistant from two points A and B is the perpendicular bisector of the line AB.**

Example 5

Draw a line AB of length 5 cm.
Construct accurately the perpendicular bisector of AB.

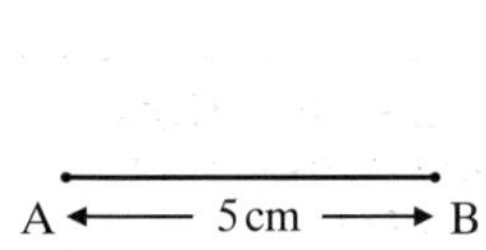

Draw a line 5 cm long and label its ends A and B.

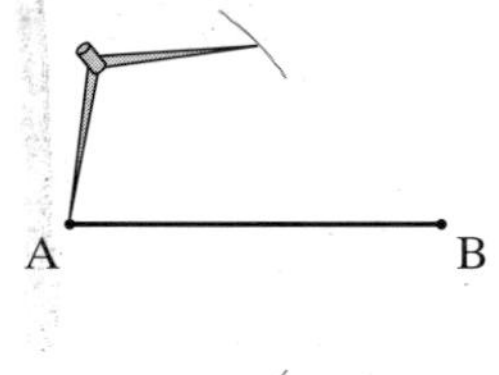

Set your compasses to any radius greater than 2.5 cm (5 cm ÷ 2). With the point at A draw arcs on each side of the line where you expect the bisector to be.

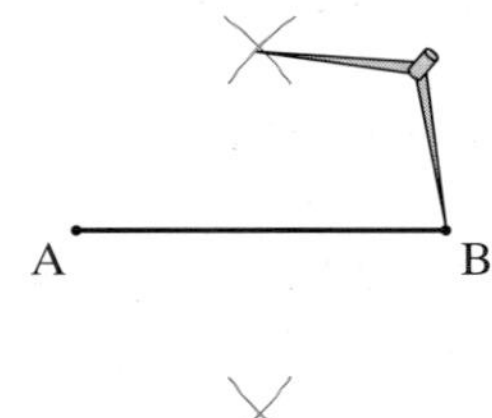

Keep the compasses at the same radius but move the point to B and draw two new arcs.

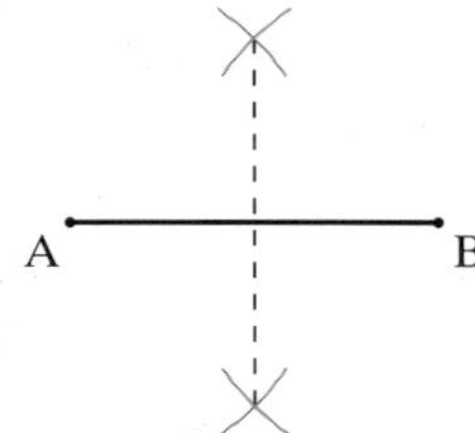

Draw a line joining the points where the arcs cross. This is the perpendicular bisector of AB.

Example 6

Draw any two lines XYZ and AYB to cross at Y.
Construct accurately the line that bisects angles XYA and BYZ.

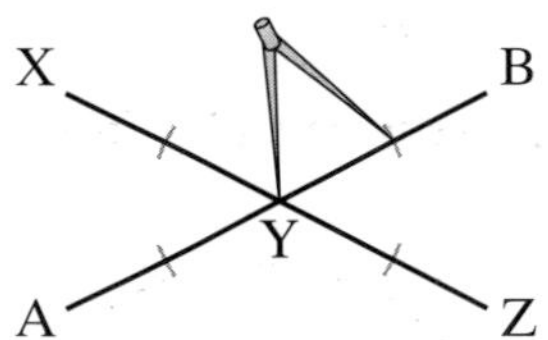

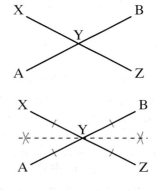

Keep your compasses at a set radius. With the point at Y draw an arc on each line.

Move the compass point to an arc and draw a new arc where you expect the bisector to be.

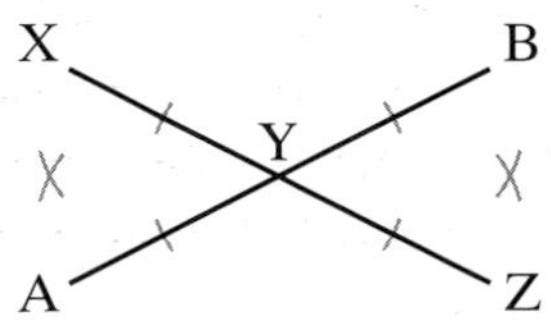

Repeat the process for each line in turn until you have arcs that cross like these.

Draw a line from the points where the arcs cross. This is the bisector of angles XYA and BYZ.

Notice that you could use the same method to find the line that bisects angles XYB and AYZ.

- **The locus of points equidistant from two given lines that cross is a pair of lines that bisect the angles between the two given lines. The lines of the locus are lines of symmetry.**

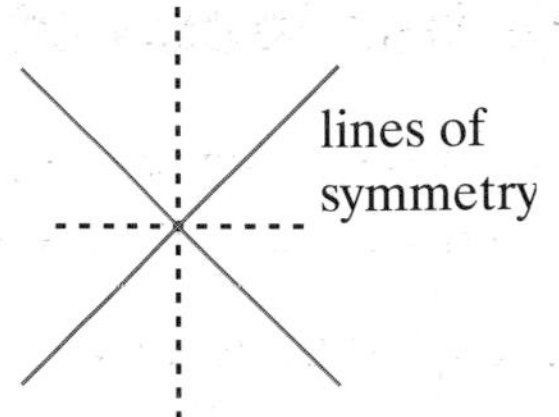

More loci

- **The locus of the points a constant distance from a line AB is a pair of lines parallel to AB.**

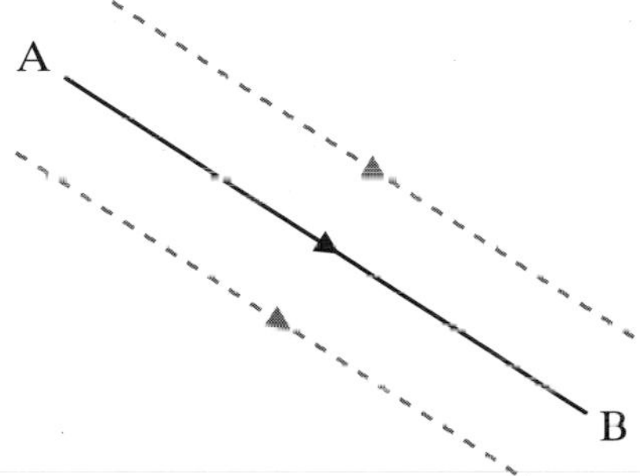

- **The locus of the points a constant distance from a fixed point is a circle.**

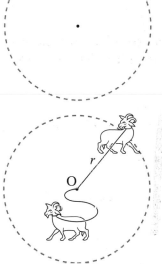

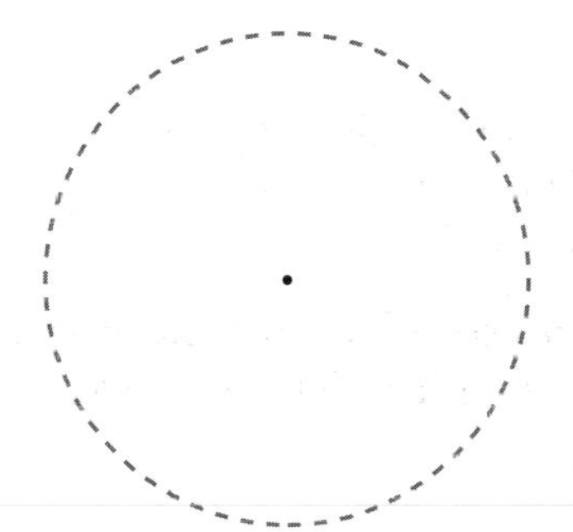

Sometimes the locus of a set of points is a **region** of space. Imagine a goat tethered to a peg by a lead.
The goat can move anywhere inside a circle of radius r and centre O, where r is the length of the lead. The points the goat can reach are described by the rule:

> The distance of each point from O is always less than or equal to d.

Remember these signs:
≤ less than or equal to
< less than
≥ greater than or equal to
> greater than

- **When points obey a rule that includes an inequality their locus is a region.**

(There is more about inequalities on page 427).

Worked examination question

A, B and C represent three radio masts on a plan. Signals from mast A can be received 300 km away, from mast B 350 km away and from mast C 200 km away. Show, by shading, the region in which signals can be received from all three masts. [L]

Scale: 1 cm represents 100 km

Signals from A can be heard inside a circle with centre A and radius 300 km.
1 cm represents 100 km so 3 cm represents 300 km. Draw a circle with centre A and radius 3 cm.
In the same way draw circles with centre B and radius 3.5 cm and with centre C and radius 2 cm.
The region in which all signals can be received must be inside all the circles, so it is the region shaded in the diagram.

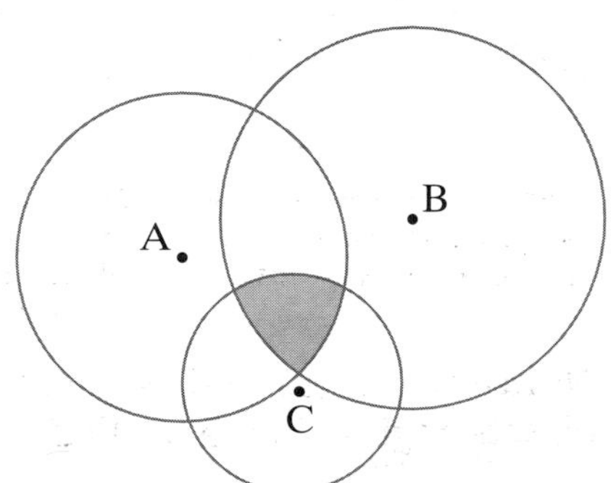

This is a scaled down sketch.

Exercise 26C

You will need compasses, a ruler and a protractor.

1 Two marker buoys A and B are in the sea near the town of Barry. B is 250 m due East of A.
  (a) Using a scale of 1 cm to 50 m make an accurate drawing to show the positions of A and B.
  Juliet sails her boat so that she is the same distance from A as from B.
  (b) Construct accurately the course along which Juliet sails.

2 In triangle DEF, DE = 7 cm, angle D = 42° and angle E = 57°.
  (a) Make an accurate drawing of triangle DEF.
  (b) Draw accurately the locus of all points that are the same distance from D as from E.
  (c) Draw the locus of all points that are 4 cm from D.
  (d) Mark the points P and Q which are on both loci.

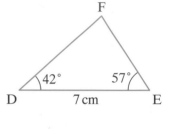

3 The map shows part of a coastline and a coastguard station. 1 cm on the map represents 2 km.
  A ship is 12 km from the coastguard station on a bearing of 160°.
  (a) Plot the position of the ship from the coastguard station, using a scale of 1 cm to represent 2 km.
  It is not safe for ships to come within 6 km of the coastguard station.
  (b) Shade the area on the map which is less than 6 km from the coastguard station.
  The distance of a buoy from the coastguard station is 14 km to the nearest km.
  (c) (i) Write down the maximum distance it could be.
  (ii) Write down the minimum distance it could be. [L]

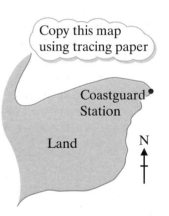

26.4 Using mathematical similarity

Page 43 introduces the idea of similar shapes. It shows you that if two shapes are similar:

- similar shapes have the same shape
- all the corresponding angles are equal
- all the corresponding lengths are in the same ratio.

The shapes in maps and scale drawings are similar to the larger shapes in real life that they represent.

■ **A scale drawing of a shape is similar to the original shape.**

Example 7

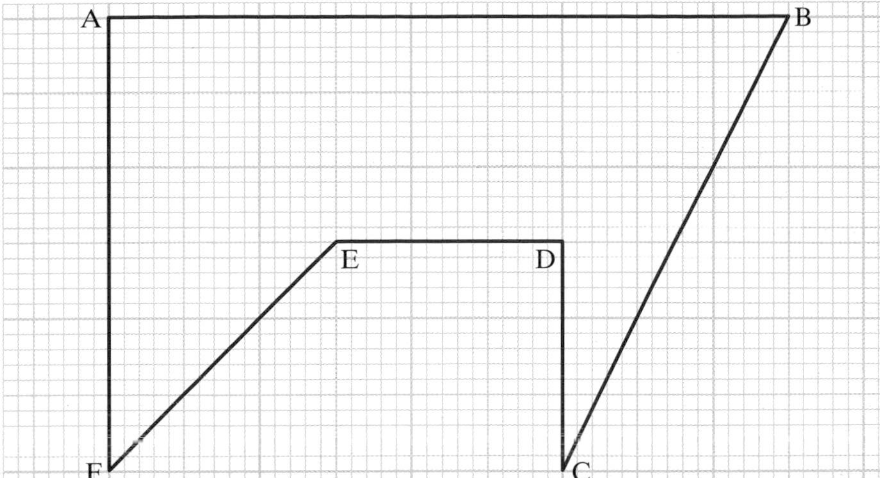

(a) On graph paper make a scale drawing of the shape ABCDEF and call it PQRSTU.
Use a scale of 1 cm represents 3 cm.
(b) Measure all the angles of the shape ABCDEF.
(c) Measure all the corresponding angles of PQRSTU.
(d) What do you notice about your answers to (b) and (c)?
(e) What can you say about the edges of ABCDEF and the edges of the scale drawing PQRSTU?

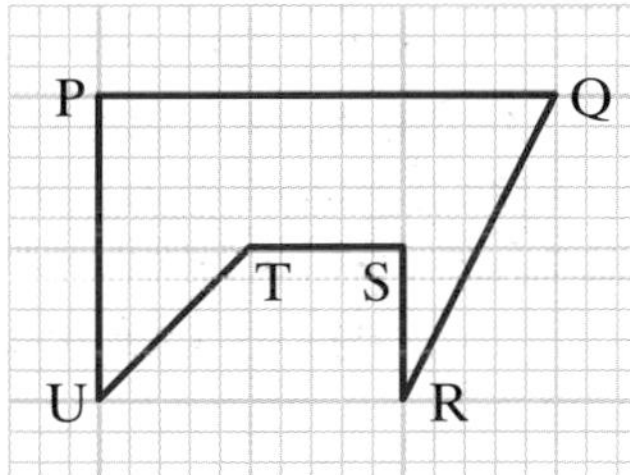

(a) Use the 1 cm squares of the graph paper to help you.
AB = 9 cm so PQ = 9 cm ÷ 3 = 3 cm.
AF = 6 cm so PU = 2 cm.
FE is the result of going along 3 cm and up 3 cm so UT is the result of going along 1 cm and up 1 cm, and so on.

(b) A = 90°, B = 64°, C = 26°, D = 270° (3 right angles), E = 225° (2 right angles plus 45°) and F = 45°.

(c) P = 90°, Q = 64°, R = 26°, S = 270° (3 right angles), T = 225° (2 right angles plus 45°) and U = 45°.

(d) A = P, B = Q, C = R, D = S, E = T and F = U.

(e) All the edges of ABCDEF are 3 times the corresponding edges of PQRSTU.

You could say that ABCDEF is an enlargement of PQRSTU with scale factor 3, because all the sides of ABCDEF are 3 times the corresponding sides of PQRSTU.

There is more about enlargements and scale factors on page 343.

All the sides of PQRSTU are $\frac{1}{3}$ the length of the corresponding sides of ABCDEF so you could say that PQRSTU is an enlargement of ABCDEF with scale factor $\frac{1}{3}$.

PQRSTU is smaller than ABCDEF, but you still use the mathematical term **enlargement**. Using a scale factor that is a fraction (less than 1) tells you the image is *smaller*.

■ **A scale drawing is an enlargement of the original shape with a scale factor less than 1.**

Worked examination question

Calculate the length of OY.

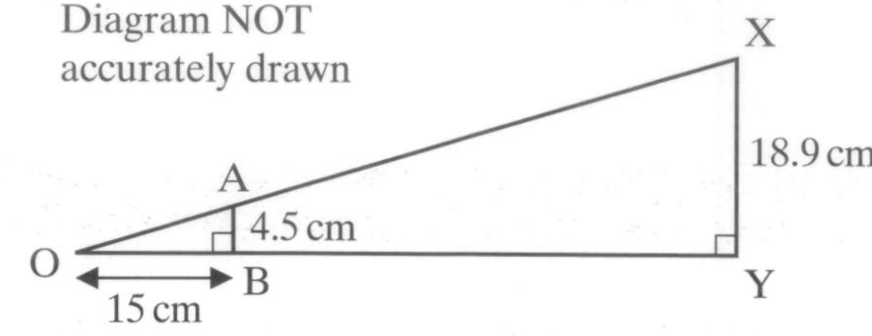

Triangles OXY and OAB are similar so their corresponding sides are in the same ratio. OY corresponds to OB and XY corresponds to AB

so $\dfrac{OY}{OB} = \dfrac{XY}{AB}$

or $\dfrac{OY}{15} = \dfrac{18.9}{4.5}$

Multiply both sides by 15

$$OY = \frac{18.9}{4.5} \times 15$$

$$OY = 63\,\text{cm}$$

Or you could say that triangle OXY is an enlargement of triangle OAB with scale factor $\dfrac{18.9}{4.3} = 4.2$
So OY is 15 cm × 4.2 which is 63 cm.

Exercise 26D

1 Triangle PQR is similar to triangle XYZ. PR = 8 cm, PQ = 16 cm, XZ = 4 cm and angle QPR = 60°.
(a) Write down the size of angle XYZ.
(b) Work out the length of XY.

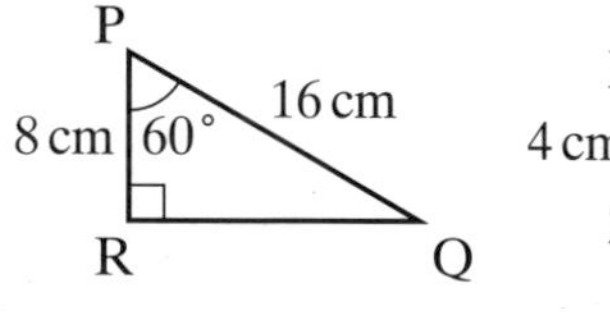

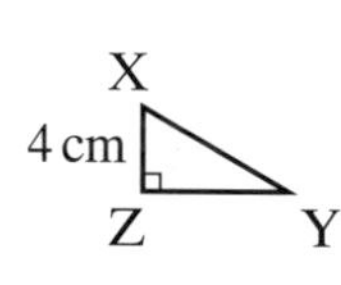

2 In each pair of similar figures calculate the marked lengths:

(a)

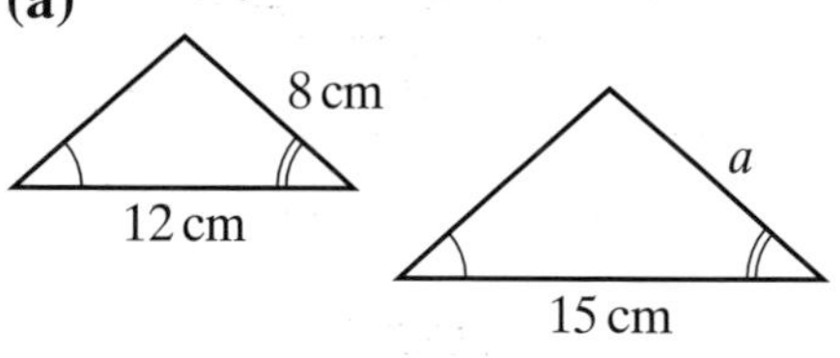

(b)

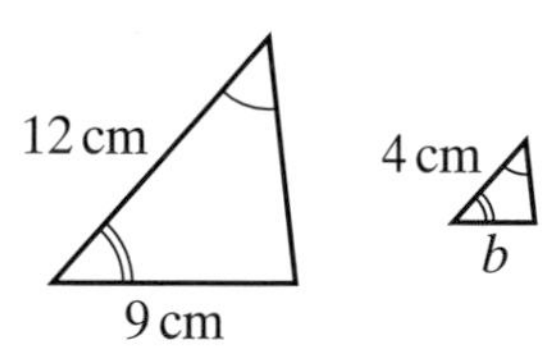

The same sign in the angles shows that they are equal.

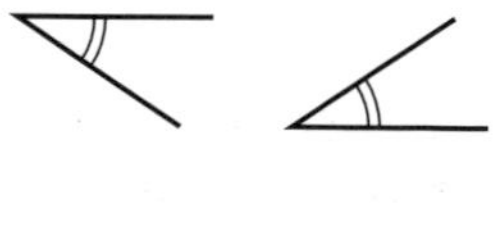

(c)

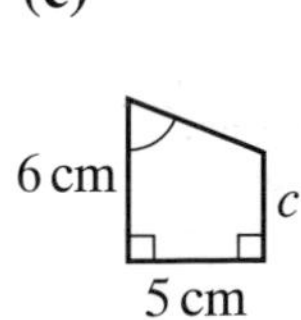

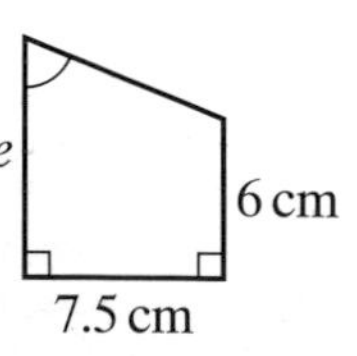

(d)

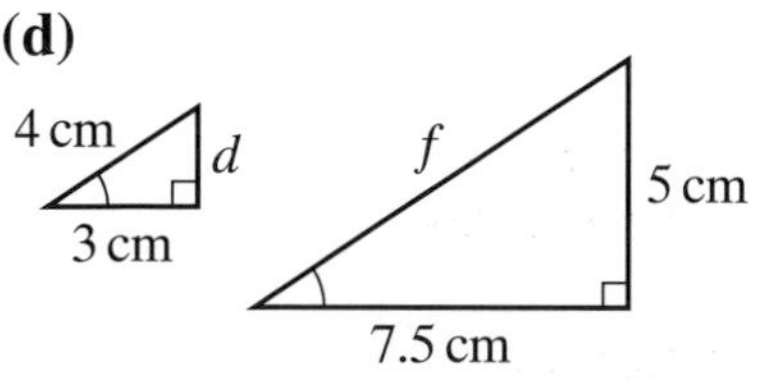

3 In the diagram EB is parallel to DC.
(a) Write down the size of angle AEB.
(b) Work out the length of AB.

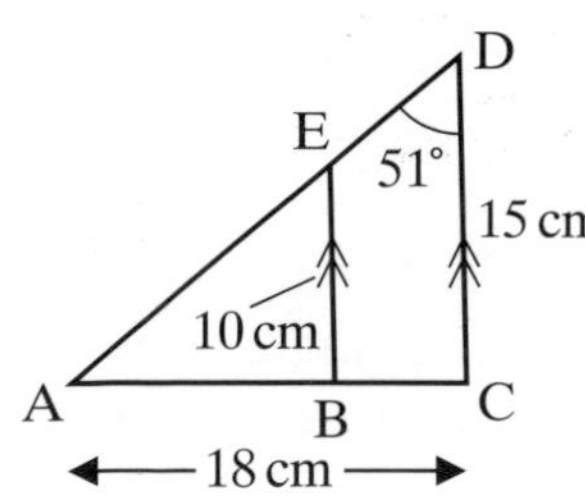

4 The height of a cone is 16 cm and the diameter of the base is 9.2 cm.
The cone is cut parallel to its base to make a smaller cone.
The height of the smaller cone is 12 cm.
Calculate the diameter of the smaller cone.

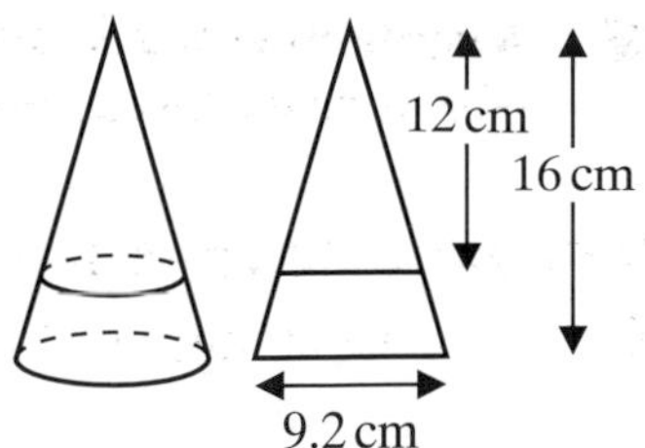

Exercise 26E Mixed questions

1 In triangle ABC, BC = 8 cm, CA = 6 cm and AB = 5 cm.

(a) Make an accurate drawing of triangle ABC.

(b) The point X is equidistant from B and C. Draw the locus of X.

(c) The point Y is equidistant from BC and CA. Draw the locus of Y.

(d) The locus of X and the locus of Y meet inside triangle ABC at P.
Label P and measure the length of PA.

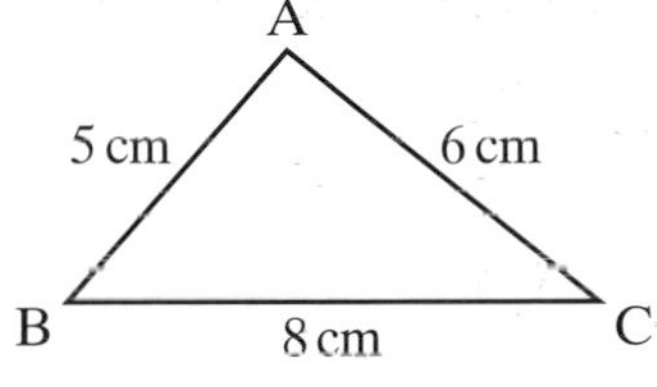

2 Wendy wants her friend Paula to walk along a particular route on the school playing field. The diagram shows the route and part of a list of instructions for Paula to follow. Three instructions have been omitted from the list of instructions.
Copy the boxes onto your paper and fill in the missing instructions.

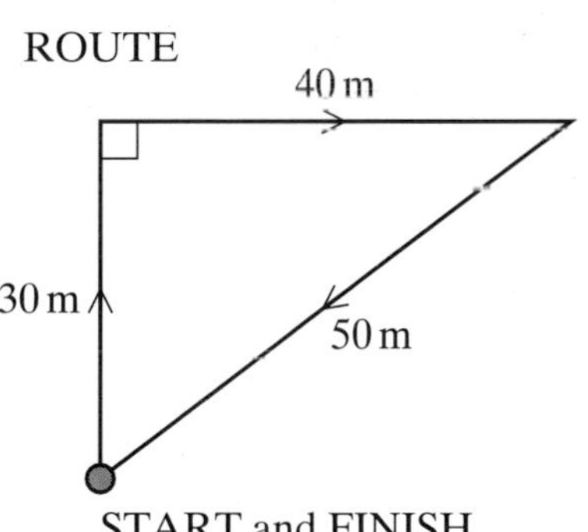

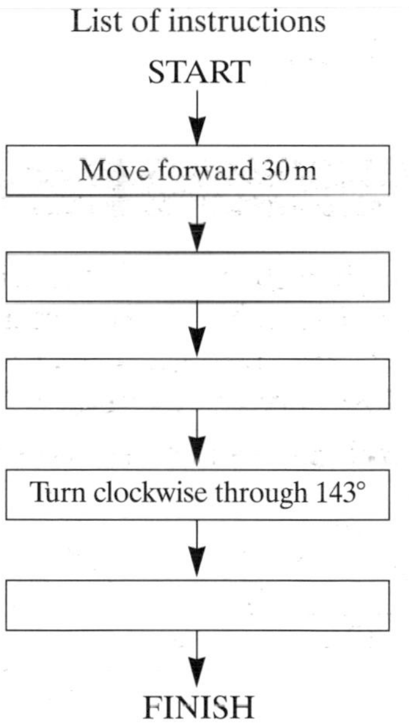

[L]

3 In the diagram CD = 4 metres, CE = 3 metres and BC = 5 metres
AB is parallel to DE.
ACE and BCD are straight lines.

(a) Explain why triangle ABC is similar to triangle EDC.

(b) Calculate the length of AC.

[L]

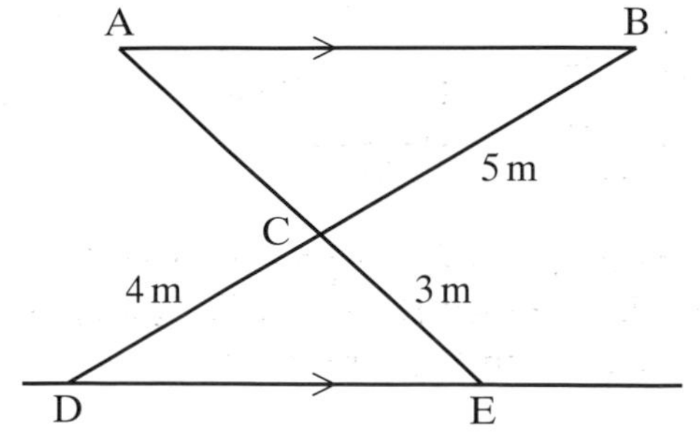

In question **4** copy the diagram for part **(a)** making AY a straight line 10 cm long.

4 The diagram represents a box which is to be moved across a floor XY, AD = 30 cm and AB = 20 cm.

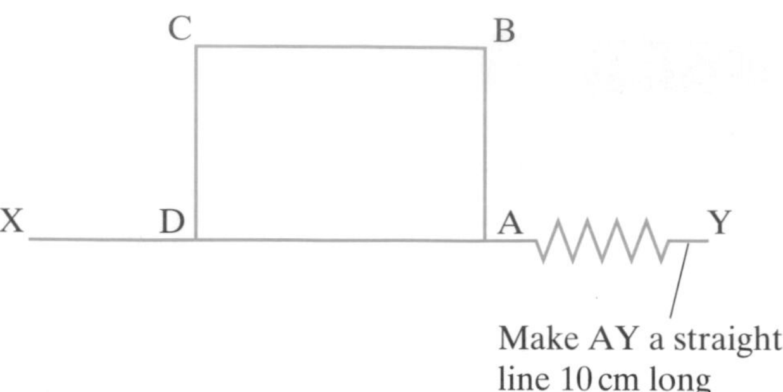

First the box is rotated about the point A so that BC becomes vertical.
Then the box is rotated about the new position of the point B so that CD becomes vertical.

> There is more about rotations on page 339. Pythagoras' theorem (page 193) will also be useful.

(a) Make a scale drawing on the diagram above of the locus of the point C.

(b) Calculate the maximum height of C above the floor. Give your answers correct to one decimal place. (A measurement from the scale drawing is unacceptable.) [L]

Summary of key points

1 A scale is a ratio which shows the relationship between a length on a drawing and the actual length in real life.
For example, a scale of 1:25 000 means that 1 cm on a map represents 25 000 cm or 250 m in real life.

2 A locus is a set of points that obey a given rule.

3 The locus of the points equidistant from two points A and B is the perpendicular bisector of the line AB.

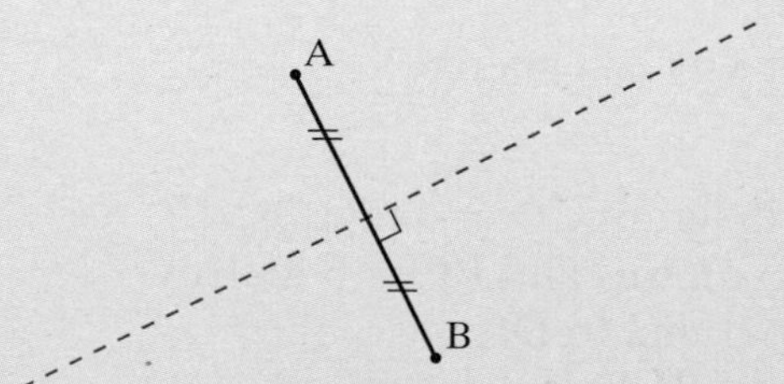

4 The locus of points equidistant from two given lines that cross is a pair of lines that bisect the angles between the two given lines. The lines of the locus are lines of symmetry.

lines of symmetry

5 The locus of the points a constant distance from a line AB is a pair of lines parallel to AB.

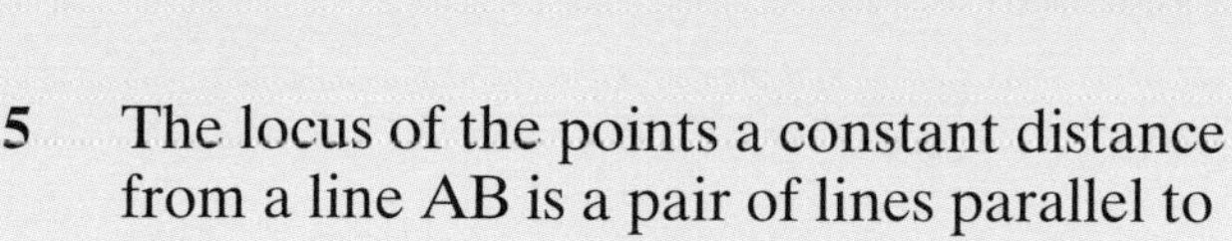

A

B

6 The locus of the points a constant distance from a fixed point is a circle.

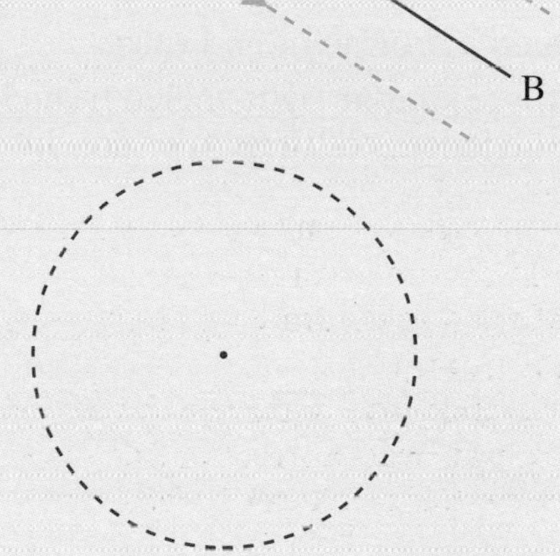

7 When points obey a rule that includes an inequality their locus is a region. For example, the locus of the points defined by the rule:

Distance from C is less than r, where r is constant

is the region *inside* the circle with centre C and radius r

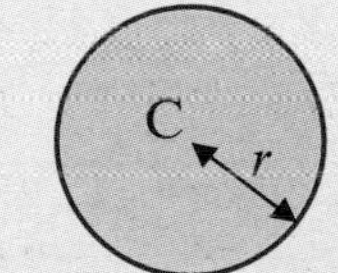

The locus of these points is a region. Notice that points on the circumference are not in the region because the distance from the centre must be less than r.

8 A scale drawing of a shape is similar to the original shape.

9 A scale drawing is an enlargement of the original shape with scale factor less than 1.

27 The sine and cosine ratios

Unit 17 shows you how to use the tangent ratio to solve problems involving right angled triangles. This unit shows you how to use more ratios: the sine and cosine ratios.

27.1 Discovering the sine ratio

Exercise 27A

You will need a protractor and ruler.

Here are three **similar** right angled triangles – their angles are the same but the lengths of their sides are different.

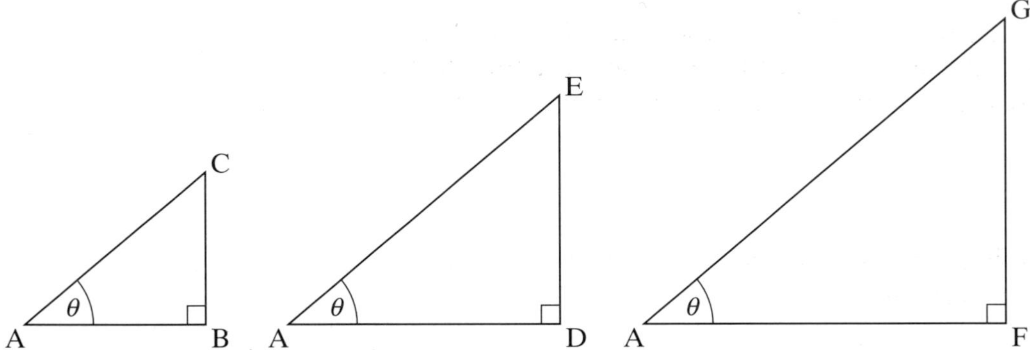

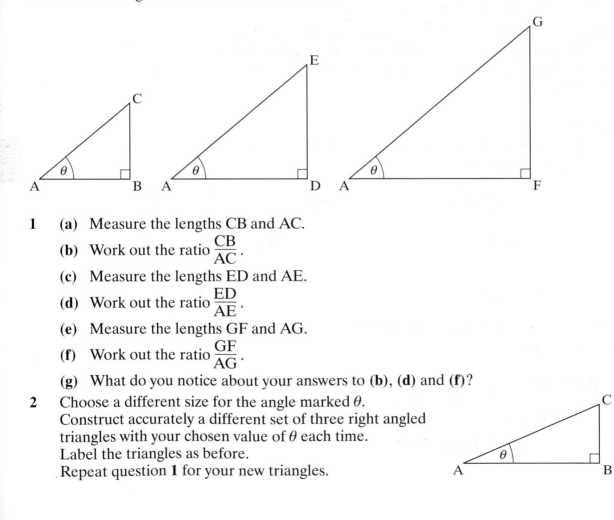

1 **(a)** Measure the lengths CB and AC.

(b) Work out the ratio $\frac{CB}{AC}$.

(c) Measure the lengths ED and AE.

(d) Work out the ratio $\frac{ED}{AE}$.

(e) Measure the lengths GF and AG.

(f) Work out the ratio $\frac{GF}{AG}$.

(g) What do you notice about your answers to **(b)**, **(d)** and **(f)**?

2 Choose a different size for the angle marked θ.
Construct accurately a different set of three right angled triangles with your chosen value of θ each time.
Label the triangles as before.
Repeat question **1** for your new triangles.

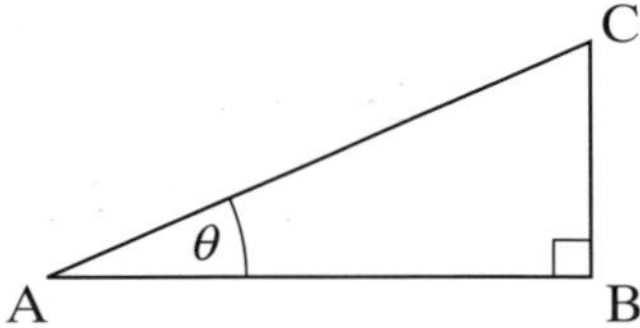

The sine ratio

In Exercise 27A you should have found that for all right angled triangles that have the same value of θ the ratio:

$$\frac{\text{length of opposite side to angle } \theta}{\text{length of hypotenuse}}$$

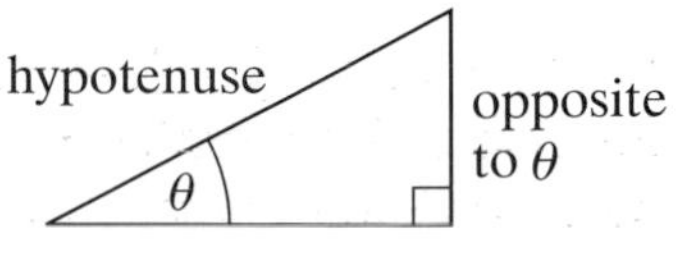

is the same. This is called the **sine ratio**. The word sine is often written as **sin** but is pronounced like the word sign.

■ **The sine ratio for a right angled triangle is:**

the sine of θ $= \dfrac{\textbf{opposite side to } \theta}{\textbf{hypotenuse}}$

or for short **sin** $\theta = \dfrac{\textbf{opp}}{\textbf{hyp}}$

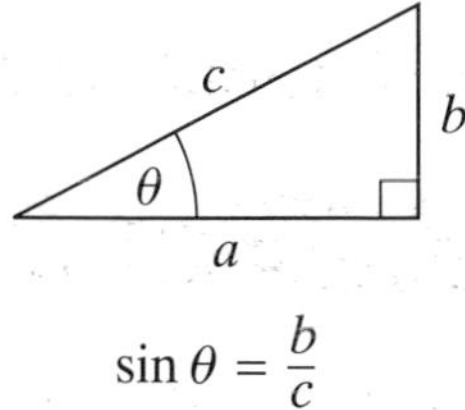

$\sin\theta = \dfrac{b}{c}$

27.2 Using the sine ratio

You can use the sine ratio and the inverse sine function ($\sin^{-1}$) on your calculator in the same way as the tan ratio and the inverse tan function ($\tan^{-1}$). If you need to remind yourself about these see pages 227 and 228.

Example 1

Calculate the length marked x in the diagram. Give your answer correct to 3 significant figures.

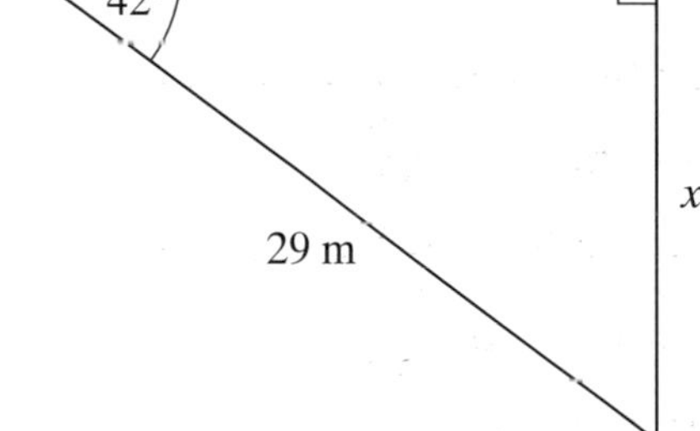

Use $\sin\theta = \dfrac{\text{opposite}}{\text{hypotenuse}}$

$$\sin 42° = \frac{x}{29}$$

$$0.6691 = \frac{x}{29}$$

(Hint: leave 0.6691... on the calculator display.)

Multiply both sides by 29

$$0.6691 \times 29 = \frac{x}{29} \times 29$$

$$19.40 = x$$

So $x = 19.4\,\text{m}$ (to 3 s.f.)

Example 2

A ladder 5 metres long is leaning against a wall. The bottom of the ladder is 1 metre from the wall.
Calculate the angle between the ladder and wall. Give your answer correct to 1 decimal place.

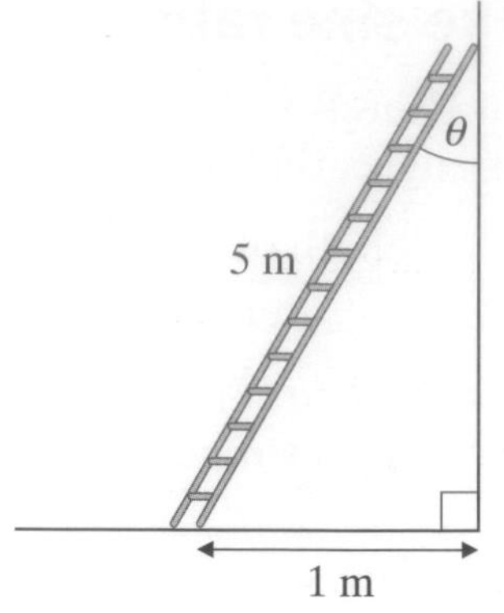

Use $\sin\theta = \dfrac{\text{opposite}}{\text{hypotenuse}}$

$$\sin\theta = \frac{1}{5}$$

$$\sin\theta = 0.2$$

To find θ use the inverse sin function, $\sin^{-1}$.

$\sin^{-1}$

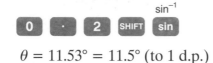

$$\theta = 11.53° = 11.5° \text{ (to 1 d.p.)}$$

The angle between the ladder and the wall is 11.5°.

You may need to use a combination of keys to get $\sin^{-1}$ on your calculator. Ask your teacher if you need help.

Exercise 27B

In this exercise give your answers correct to 3 significant figures.

Make sure your calculator is in degree (DEG) mode.

1 Use your calculator to find the values of the following:
(a) sin 12° **(b)** sin 28° **(c)** sin 40° **(d)** sin 82°

2 Use your calculator to work out the value of θ if:
(a) $\sin\theta = 0.2$ **(b)** $\sin\theta = 0.658$ **(c)** $\sin\theta = 0.9564$

3 Calculate the named lengths in these triangles:

(a)

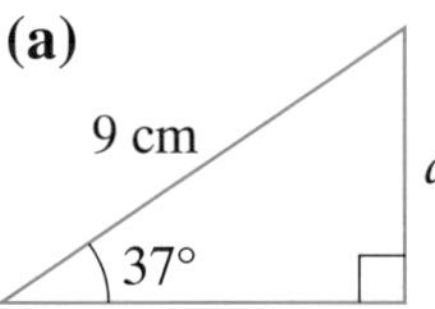

(b)

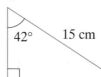

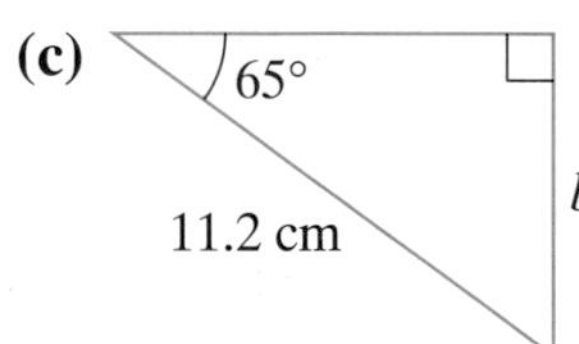

(c)

(d)

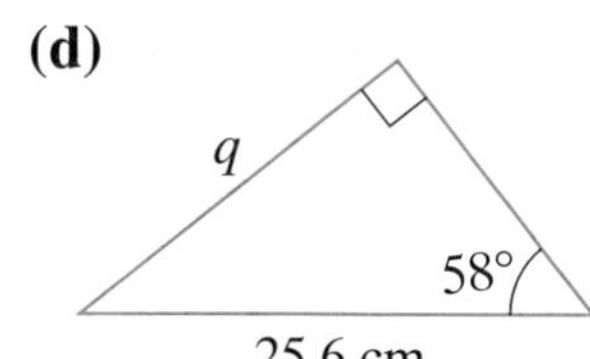

4 In these triangles:

(a) Find angle D

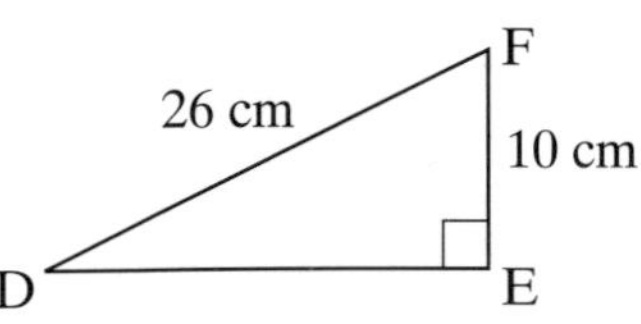

(b) Find angle S

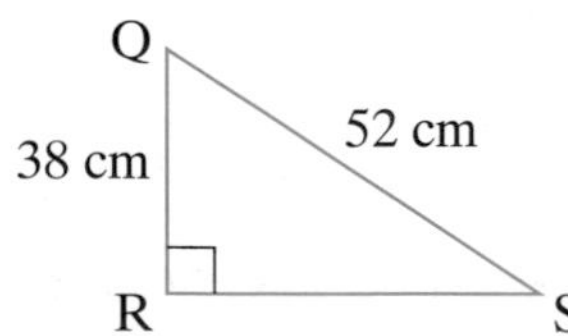

(c) Find angle G

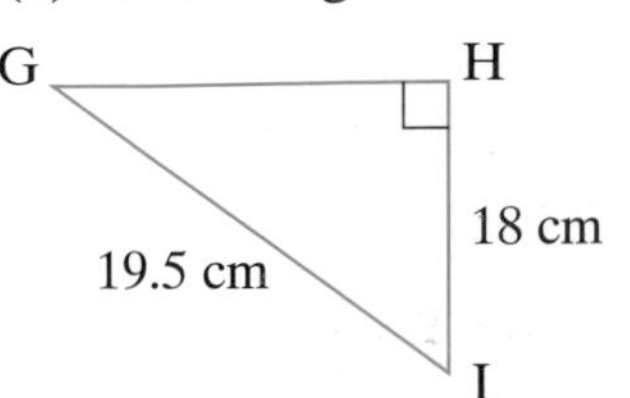

(d) Find angle L

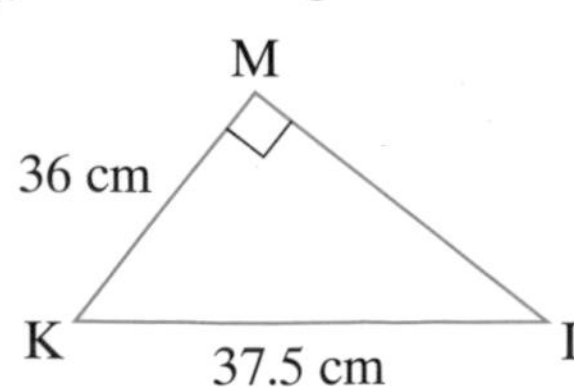

5 Johanna walks 50 m up a straight road. The road makes an angle of 10° with the horizontal.
Calculate how much higher Johanna is than when she started.

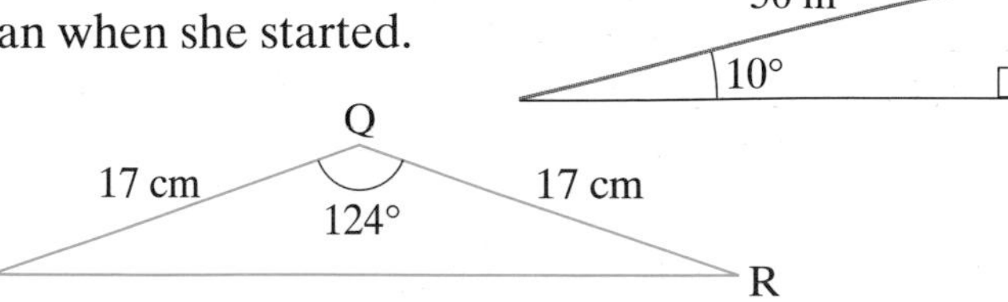

6 An isosceles triangle PQR has equal sides PQ and QR each 17 cm long. The angle between the equal sides is 124°
Calculate the length of the side PR.

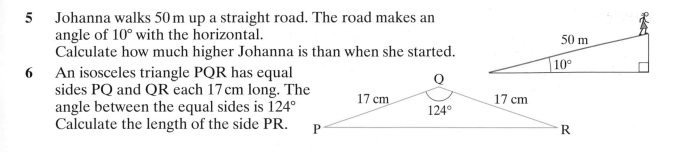

27.3 Discovering the cosine ratio

Exercise 27C

You will need a protractor and ruler.

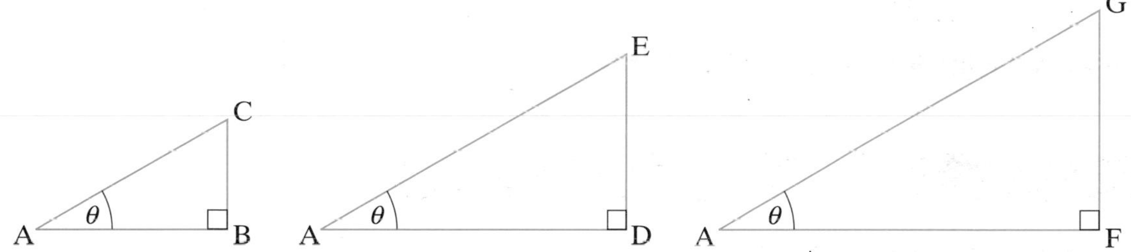

1 (a) Measure the lengths AB and AC.
(b) Work out the ratio $\frac{AB}{AC}$.
(c) Measure the lengths AD and AE.
(d) Work out the ratio $\frac{AD}{AE}$.
(e) Measure the lengths AF and AG.
(f) Work out the ratio $\frac{AF}{AG}$.
(g) What do you notice about your answers to **(b)**, **(d)** and **(f)**?

The cosine ratio

In Exercise 27C you should have found that for all right angled triangles that have the same value of θ the ratio:

$$\frac{\text{length of adjacent side to the angle marked } \theta}{\text{length of hypotenuse}}$$

is the same. This is called the **cosine ratio** and is usually written **cos**.

■ **The cosine ratio for a right angled triangle is:**

the cosine of θ $= \dfrac{\textbf{adjacent side to } \theta}{\textbf{hypotenuse}}$

or for short $\cos\theta = \dfrac{\textbf{adj}}{\textbf{hyp}}$

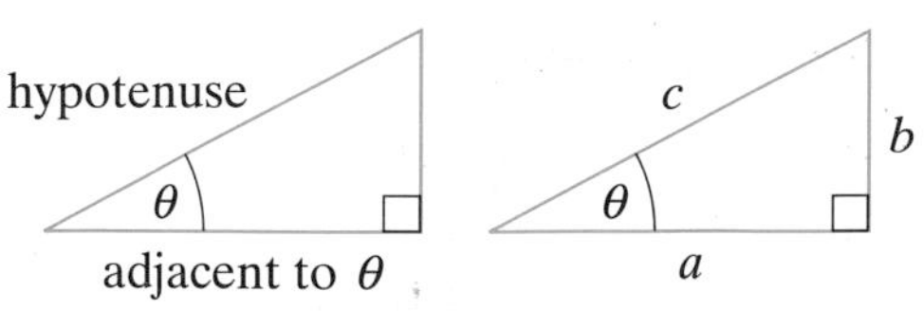

$\cos\theta = \frac{a}{c}$

27.4 Connecting the sine and cosine ratios

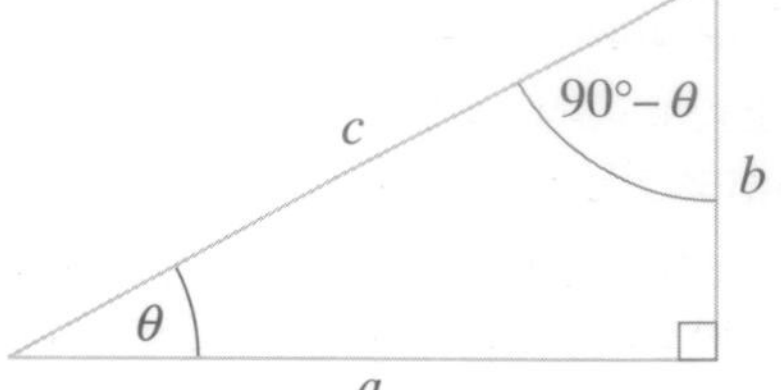

In this triangle, $\sin \theta = \dfrac{\text{opposite side to } \theta}{\text{hypotenuse}} = \dfrac{b}{c}$

and $\cos (90° - \theta) = \dfrac{\text{adjacent side to } (90° - \theta)}{\text{hypotenuse}} = \dfrac{b}{c}$

■ **So** $\mathbf{\sin \theta = \cos (90° - \theta)}$

Also $\cos \theta = \dfrac{\text{adjacent side to } \theta}{\text{hypotenuse}} = \dfrac{a}{c}$

and $\sin (90° - \theta) = \dfrac{\text{opposite side to } (90° - \theta)}{\text{hypotenuse}} = \dfrac{a}{c}$

■ **So** $\mathbf{\cos \theta = \sin (90° - \theta)}$

Exercise 27D

In this exercise use a calculator and write your answers correct to 4 decimal places.

Copy and complete the table:

θ	$\sin \theta$	$(90° - \theta)$	$\cos (90° - \theta)$
42°	0.6691	48°	0.6691
26°			
30°			
53°			
60°			

27.5 Using the cosine ratio

You can use the cosine ratio and the inverse cos function ($\cos^{-1}$) on your calculator in the same way as the tan ratio and the inverse tan function ($\tan^{-1}$) described on pages 227 and 228.

Example 3

Triangle ABC is an isosceles triangle with AC = 15 cm, BC = 15 cm and AB = 14 cm. Calculate angle BAC, giving your answer correct to 1 decimal place.

(Notice: there is no right angle in triangle ABC. If you draw in the height CD it divides AB into two equal parts. Angle ADC is a right angle.)

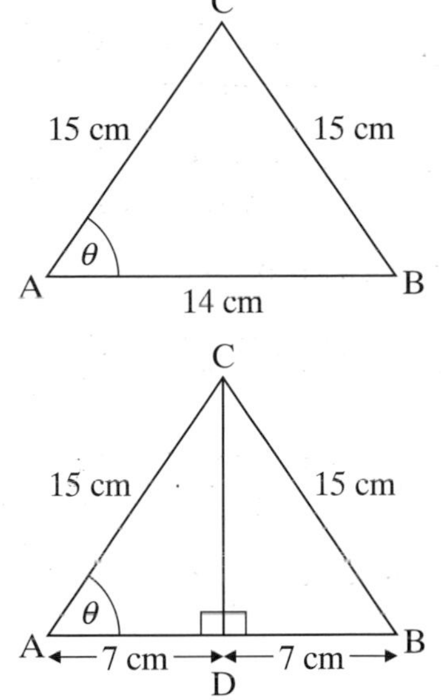

Using triangle ADC:

$$\cos\theta = \frac{\text{adjacent}}{\text{hypotenuse}}$$

$$= \frac{7}{15}$$

$$\cos\theta = 0.4666...$$

To find θ use the inverse cos function, $\cos^{-1}$.

$$\theta = 62.18°$$

So angle BAC is 62.2° (to 1 d.p.)

Example 4

Ranjit has a radio mast in his garden. An iron rod supports the mast and is fixed to the ground 2 metres from the mast. The rod makes an angle of 28° with the ground.
Calculate the length of the rod.

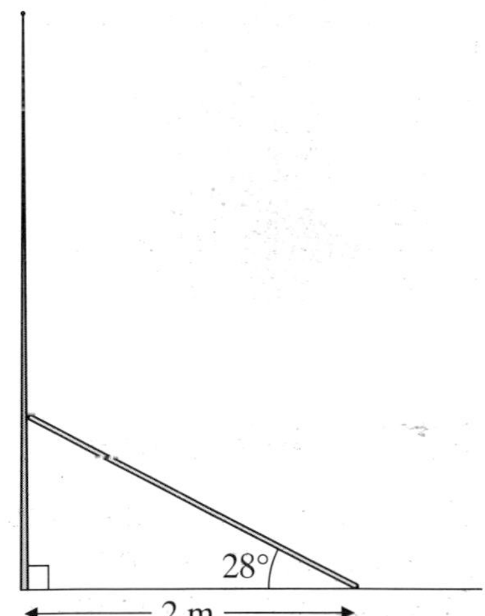

Use $\quad \cos\theta = \frac{\text{adjacent}}{\text{hypotenuse}}$

$$\cos 28° = \frac{2}{h}$$

$$0.8829 = \frac{2}{h}$$

Multiply both sides by h

$$0.8829 \times h = 2$$

Divide both sides by 0.8829

$$h = \frac{2}{0.8829}$$

So $\quad h = 2.265$

and the length of the rod is 2.27 m (to 3 s.f.)

Exercise 27E

In this exercise give your answers correct to 3 significant figures.

1 Use your calculator to find the values of the following:
(a) cos 12° (b) cos 28° (c) cos 40° (d) cos 82°

2 Use your calculator to find the value of θ if:
(a) $\cos\theta = 0.2$ (b) $\cos\theta = 0.658$ (c) $\cos\theta = 0.9564$

3 Calculate the named lengths in these triangles:

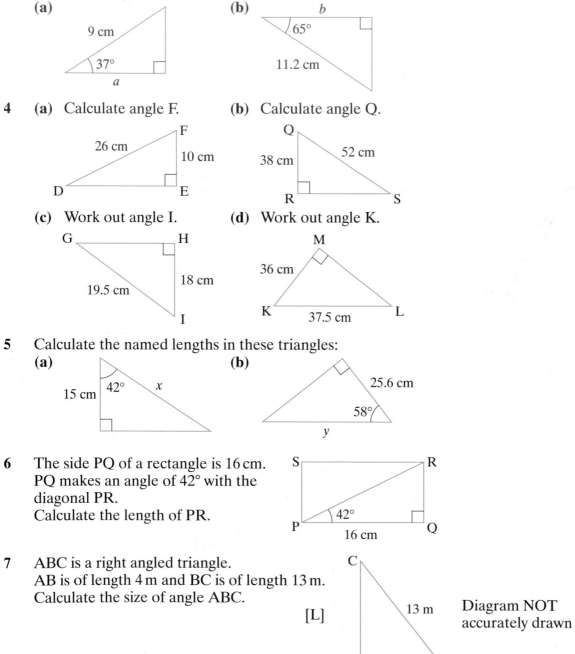

(a)

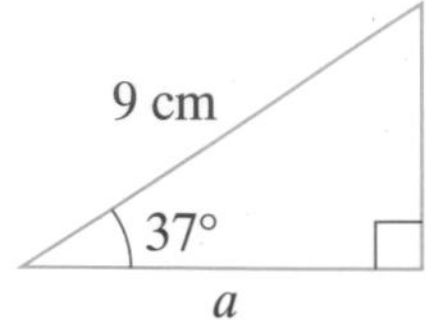

(b)

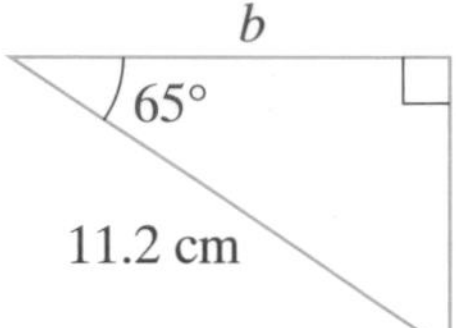

4 (a) Calculate angle F.

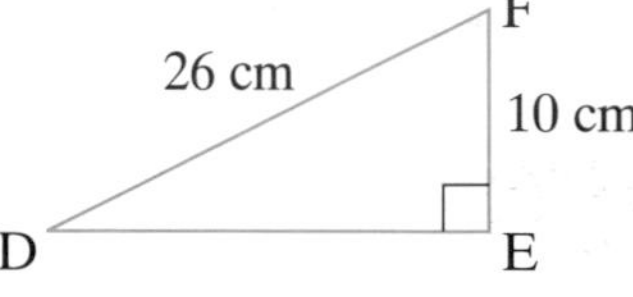

(b) Calculate angle Q.

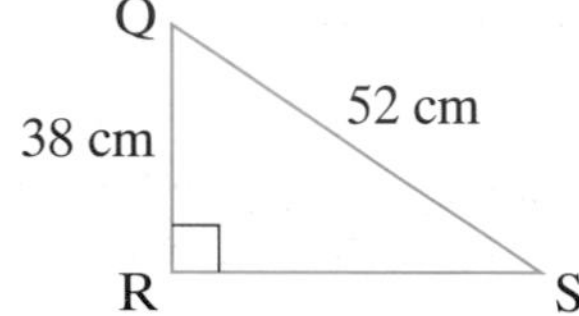

(c) Work out angle I.

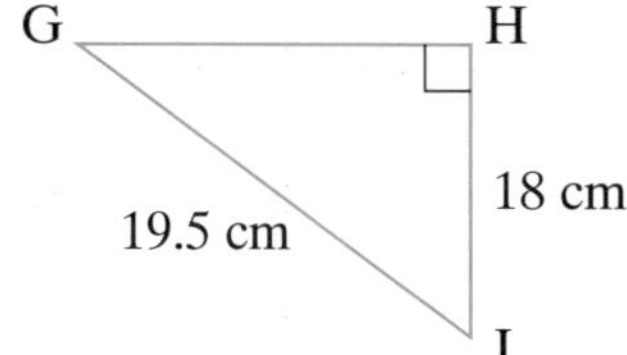

(d) Work out angle K.

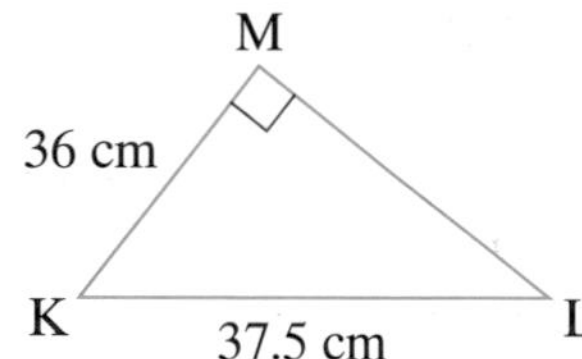

5 Calculate the named lengths in these triangles:

(a)

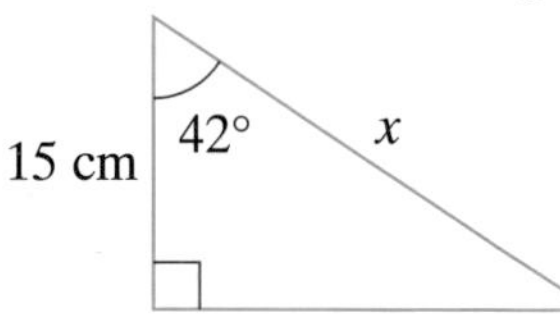

(b)

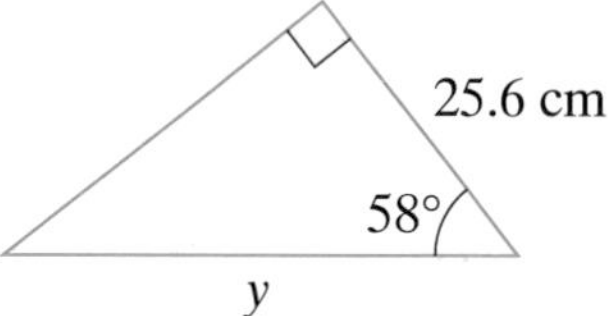

6 The side PQ of a rectangle is 16 cm.
PQ makes an angle of 42° with the diagonal PR.
Calculate the length of PR.

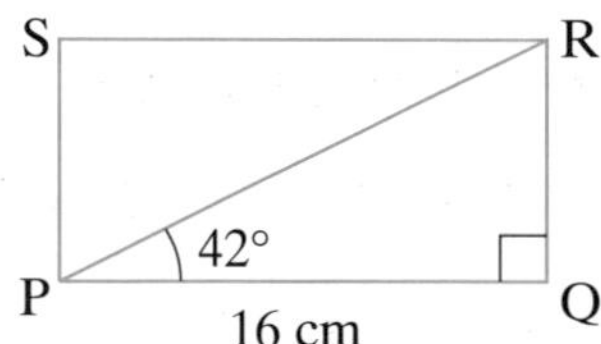

7 ABC is a right angled triangle.
AB is of length 4 m and BC is of length 13 m.
Calculate the size of angle ABC.

[L]

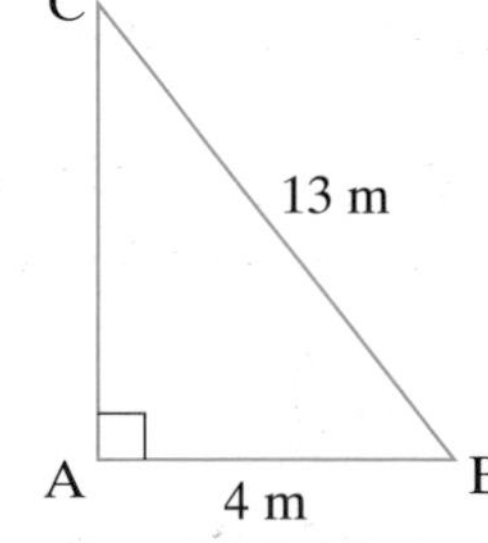

Diagram NOT accurately drawn

27.6 Angles of elevation and depression

Questions involving angles will sometimes use the terms **angle of elevation** and **angle of depression**.

- **If you look up from the ground to the top of a tower the angle of elevation is measured from the horizontal upwards.**

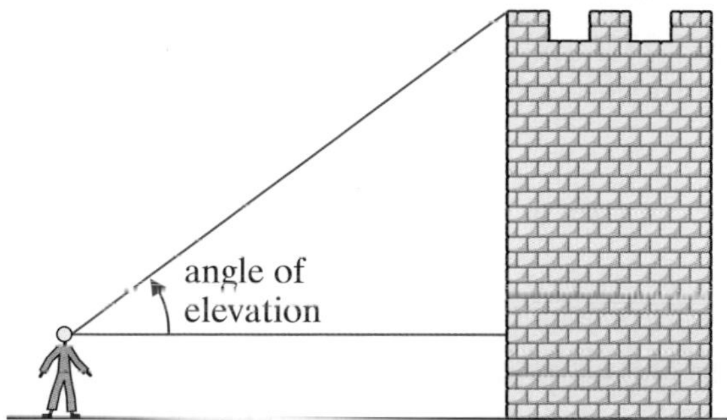

- **If you look down from the top of a cliff to a marker buoy in the sea the angle of depression is measured from the horizontal downwards.**

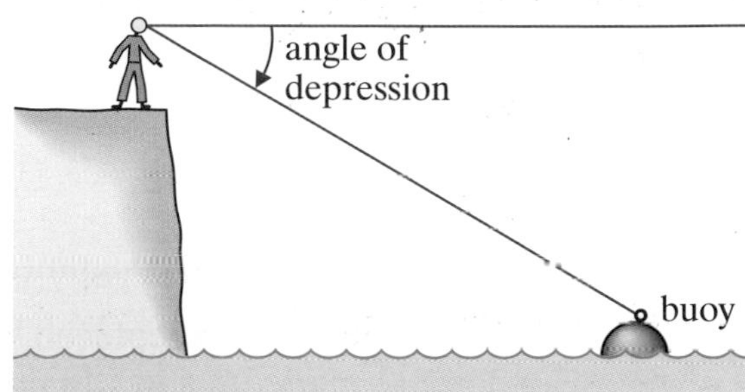

Exercise 27F

1 Lloyd stands 40 m from the base of a tower. He measures the angle of elevation from ground level to the top of the tower as 53°. Calculate the height of the tower.

2 TP is a flag pole 6 metres high. Q is a point on the ground 8 metres from the base, P, of the flag pole.
Calculate the angle of elevation of the top of the flag pole from Q.

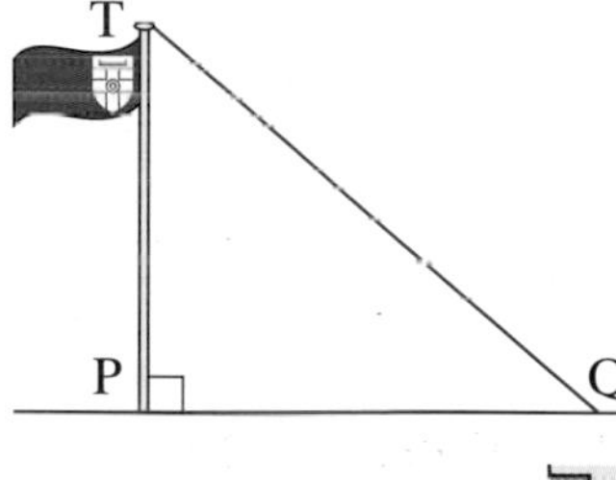

3 Yasmina is looking at a stone on the ground from an upstairs window. The level of Yasmina's eyes above the ground is 5.2 metres. The stone is 2.5 metres horizontally from the wall of the house.
Calculate the angle of depression of the stone from Yasmina.

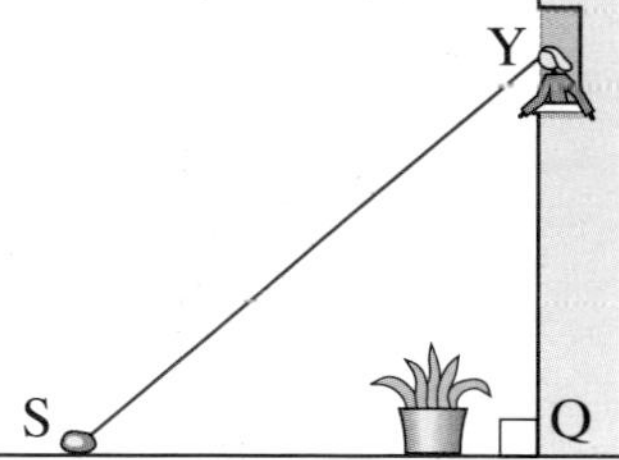

27.7 Using trigonometrical ratios

Make sure you know these ratios for a right angled triangle:

- $\sin\theta = \dfrac{\textbf{opposite}}{\textbf{hypotenuse}}$ $\quad\cos\theta = \dfrac{\textbf{adjacent}}{\textbf{hypotenuse}}$ $\quad\tan\theta = \dfrac{\textbf{opposite}}{\textbf{adjacent}}$

One easy way to remember them is to use this sentence, called a mnemonic:

Some **O**fficers **H**ave **C**urly **A**uburn **H**air **T**ill **O**ld **A**ge

The initial letters of the words stand for the ratios:

$S = \dfrac{O}{H}$ $\qquad C = \dfrac{A}{H}$ $\qquad T = \dfrac{O}{A}$

The letters of the nonsense word **sohcahtoa** also stand for the ratios. You could make up your own mnemonic.

> Remember: **always write down at least four figures** of your answer from your calculator display **before rounding the answer** to the required degree of accuracy. You could lose marks in an exam if you don't do this.

Worked examination question

The diagram represents the plan of a window frame. The arc AB is a quarter of a circle. The centre of the circle is at C and the radius of the circle is 68 cm.

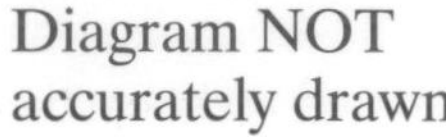

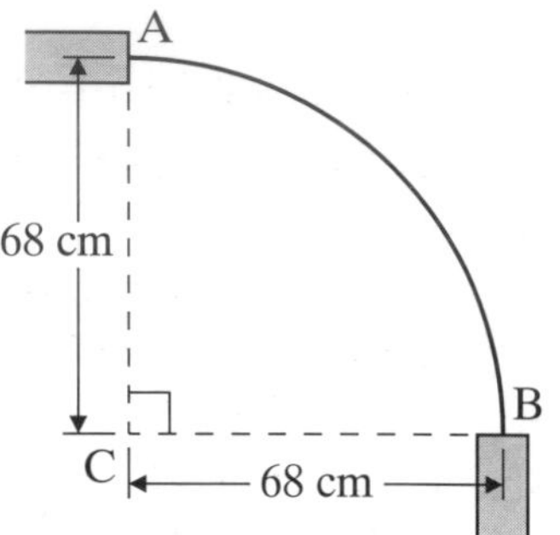

(a) Calculate the length of the arc AB. (Use $\pi = 3.14$ or use the π button on your calculator.)
Give your answer correct to 3 significant figures.

The window frame in (a) is replaced by double glazed panels. These panels are made only in straight lengths. The arc AB is replaced by three identical panels AX, XY and YB.

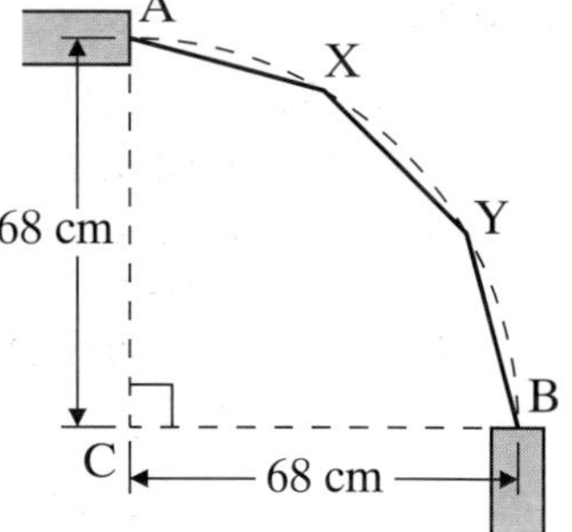

(b) Calculate the length of AX. Give your answer correct to 2 significant figures. [L]

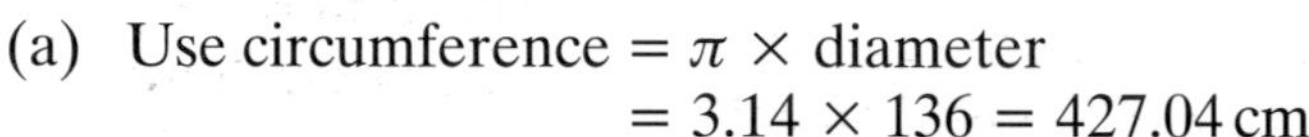

(a) Use circumference = $\pi \times$ diameter
$= 3.14 \times 136 = 427.04$ cm

The arc AB is a quarter of the circumference so:

arc AB = $427.04 \div 4 = 106.76$ cm

So the length of the arc AB is 107 cm (to 3 s.f.)

(b) (Hint: draw a diagram of triangle AXC on its own. There is no right angle in triangle AXC, but CA and CX are both 68 cm (the radius) so triangle ACX is isosceles. You can make a right angle by drawing the height CD. D is the mid-point of the line AX and CD divides angle ACX exactly in half.)

Angle ACX = $90° \div 3 = 30°$ (by symmetry).

So angle ACD = $30° \div 2 = 15°$

In triangle ACD $\sin\theta = \dfrac{\text{opposite}}{\text{hypotenuse}}$

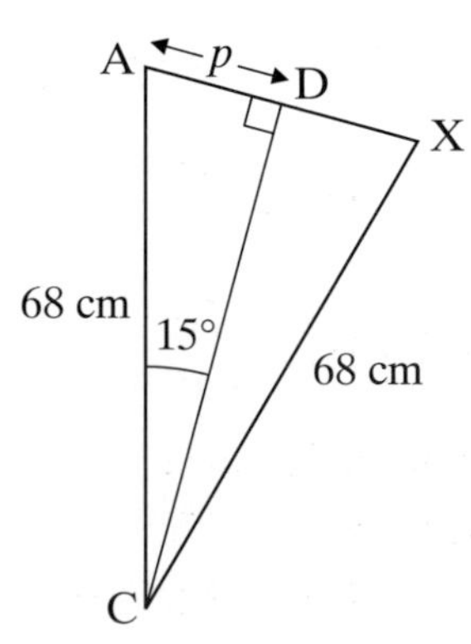

So $\qquad \sin 15° = \dfrac{p}{68}$

$$0.2588... = \frac{p}{68}$$

(Hint: leave 0.2588... on the calculator display.)

Multiply both sides by 68

$$0.2588... \times 68 = p$$
$$17.59... = p$$
$$AX = p \times 2$$
$$= 17.59... \times 2$$
$$= 35.19... \text{ cm}$$

The length of AX is 35 cm (correct to 2 s.f.).

Worked examination question

In this question give at least 3 figures in each of your answers.

In the diagram, AB represents a ladder leaning against a wall of a house. The ladder is 4 m long. The angle between the ladder and the horizontal ground is 50°. There is a garage near the house. It is 5 m from the house.

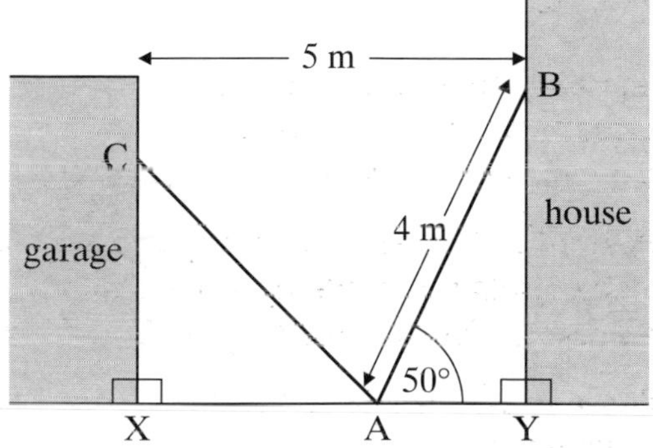

Diagram NOT accurately drawn

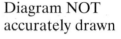

(a) Calculate, in metres:
  (i) the height, BY, of the top of the ladder above the ground
  (ii) the distance, AY, of the foot of the ladder from the wall of the house
  (iii) the distance, AX, of the foot of the ladder from the wall of the garage.

The top of the ladder is moved from the house wall at B to the garage wall at C. The bottom of the ladder, A, stays in the same place.

(b) Calculate:
  (i) the new height, CX, in metres, of the top of the ladder above the ground
  (ii) the angle, CAB, through which the ladder has been turned.

[L]

(a) (i) In triangle BAY $\sin\theta = \dfrac{\text{opposite}}{\text{hypotenuse}}$

So $\quad \sin 50° = \dfrac{BY}{4}$

$$0.7660... = \frac{BY}{4}$$

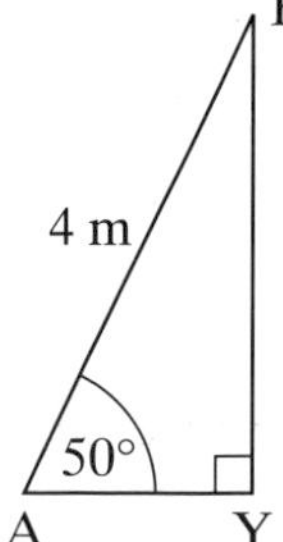

Multiply both sides by 4:

$$0.7660... \times 4 = BY$$

So $\quad BY = 3.064 \text{ m}$

(ii) In triangle BAY $\cos\theta = \dfrac{\text{adjacent}}{\text{hypotenuse}}$

So $\cos 50° = \dfrac{AY}{4}$

$0.6427... = \dfrac{AY}{4}$

Multiply both sides by 4:

$0.6427... \times 4 = AY$

So $AY = 2.571\,\text{m}$

(iii) The distance XY is 5 m

So $AX = 5 - AY$

$= 5 - 2.571$

$AX = 2.429\,\text{m}$

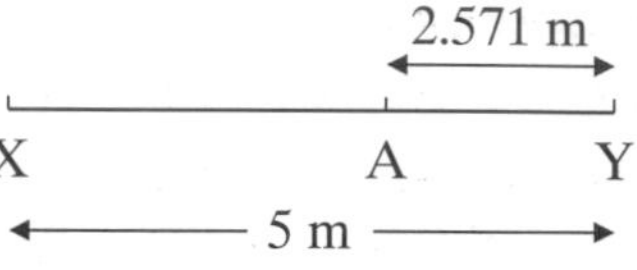

(b) (i) The ladder, CA, is 4 m long.
Use Pythagoras' theorem in triangle CAX.

$(a^2 + b^2 = c^2)$

So $a^2 = c^2 - b^2$

$CX^2 = 4^2 - 2.429^2$

$= 16 - 5.900$

$= 10.10$

So $CX = \sqrt{10.10}$

$CX = 3.178\,\text{m}$

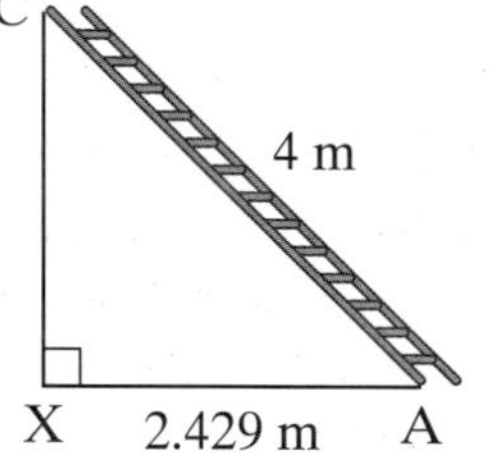

(ii) In triangle CAX $\cos\theta = \dfrac{\text{adjacent}}{\text{hypotenuse}}$

$\cos\theta = \dfrac{2.429}{4}$

$= 0.6072...$

So $\theta = \cos^{-1} 0.6072...$

angle CAX = 52.6°

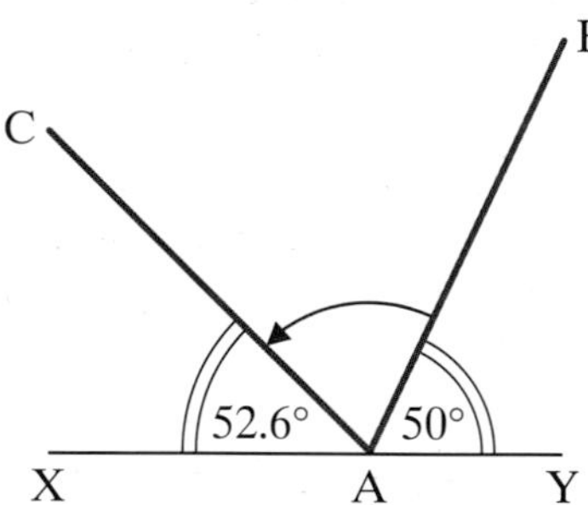

The angles on a straight line add to 180°

So angle CAB = 180° – (52.6° + 50°)

angle CAB = 77.4°

Exercise 27G Mixed questions

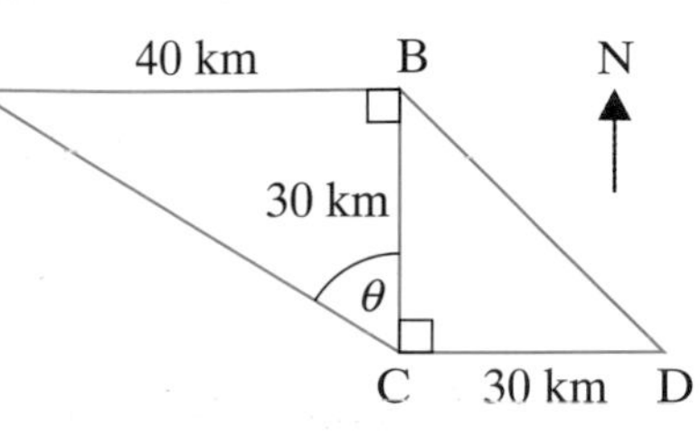

1 A, B, C and D are four sign posts joined by straight roads.
(a) Calculate the lengths of:
(i) AC
(ii) BD
(b) (i) In triangle ABC calculate the marked angle θ, giving your answer correct to the nearest degree.
(ii) Write down the three figure bearing of A from C.

For a reminder on bearings see page 134.

2 A ladder 7 m long is leaning against a vertical wall. It just reaches an upstairs window. The ladder makes an angle of 52° with the horizontal ground.
Calculate the height of the window above the ground.

3 Tom stands at the top of a vertical cliff 63 m high. The angle of depression of a boat in the sea is 38°.
Calculate the distance of the boat from the base of the cliff.

4 Graeme walks 5 km due east from Amblewick to Borderton. He then walks 7 km due south from Borderton to Cornerville.
Calculate:
(a) the distance from Cornerville direct to Amblewick
(b) the bearing of Cornerville from Amblewick.

5 Kitty stands at the top of a tower. Her friend Bronwen is on the ground 30 m from the bottom of the tower. The angle of depression of Bronwen from Kitty is 56°
Calculate the height of the tower.

6 A stick is 4 m long. When the sun is vertically overhead the shadow of the stick is 3 m long.
Calculate the angle between the stick and the horizontal ground.

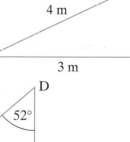

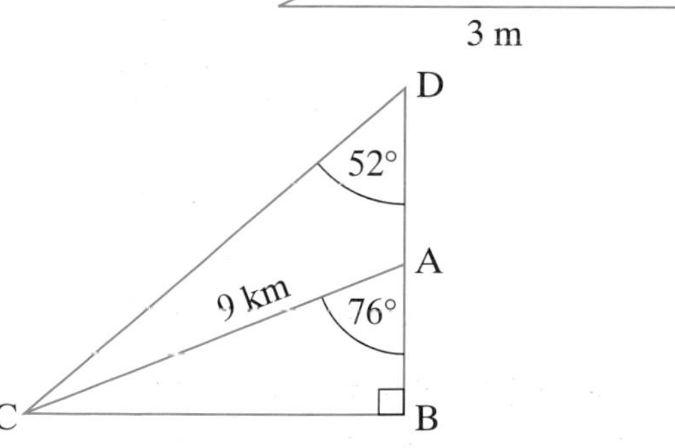

7 In the diagram DAB is a straight line. C is 9 km from A on a bearing of 256°. B is due south of A and due east of C. Angle ADC = 52°.
Work out:
(a) the bearing of C from D
(b) the size of angle ACB
(c) the distance AB
(d) the distance that C is west of B.

8 A kite is flying at a height of 72 m. The string to the kite makes an angle of 63° with the horizontal.
Calculate the length of the string.

9 The diagram represents the Bridgnorth Castle Hill Railway, which is the steepest in Great Britain. It has 201 feet of straight track. The inclination to the horizontal is 33.5°.
Calculate the value of x. [L]

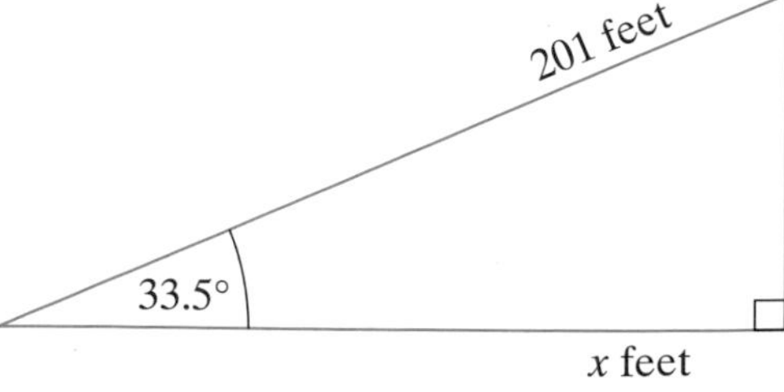

10 The diagram represents the landing area for a shot put competition. OACB is a sector of a circle, centre O, radius 10 m. Angle AOB equals 80°.

Calculate the length of the straight line AB.

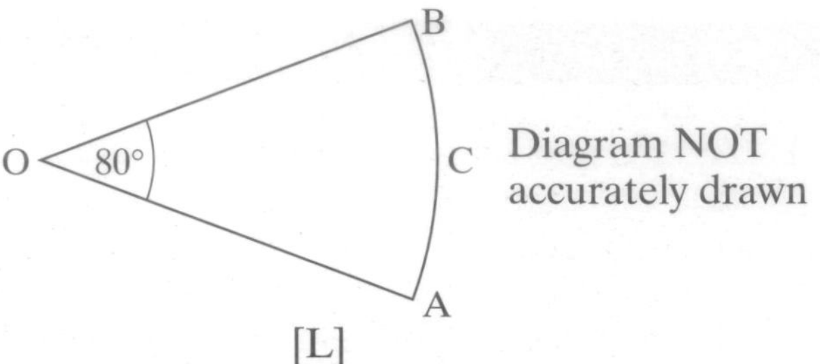

[L]

(Hint: draw a diagram with AB joined by a straight line.)

11 Katharine has made a clinometer. With it she measures the angle of elevation of the top of a flag pole as 52°

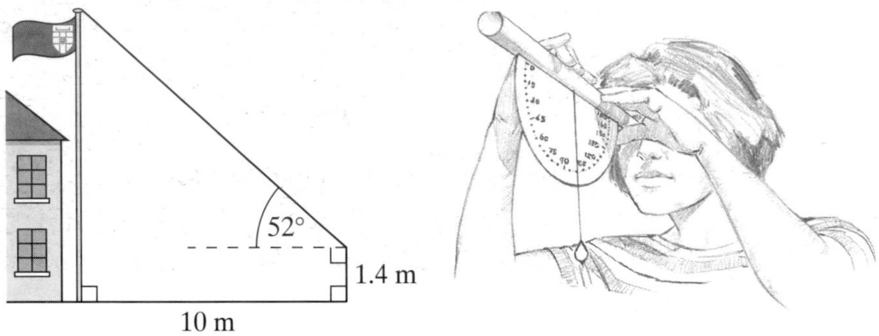

Katharine's eyes are 1.4 m above the ground. The bottom of the flag pole is 10 m horizontally away from her.
Calculate the height of the flag pole.

12 Diagram not accurately drawn.

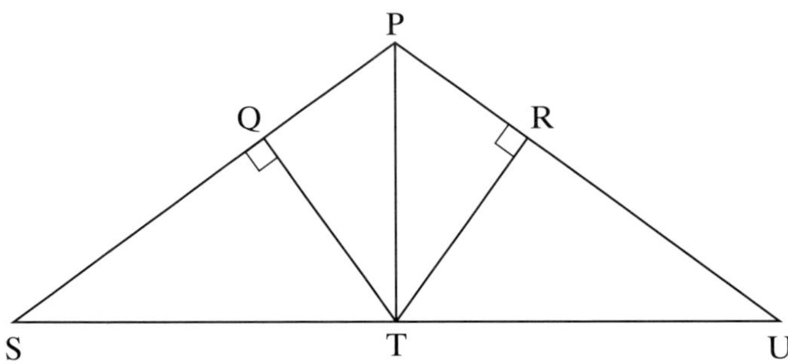

The diagram represents the framework of the roof of a building.
The framework is symmetrical about the line PT.
The angles at Q and R are right-angles.
The length of SU is 10 metres.
The angle PST is 30°.

(a) (i) Calculate the length of PT. Write down **all** the figures in the answer on your calculator display.

(ii) Write this answer correct to three significant figures.

(b) Calculate the length of QT. [L]

Summary of key points

1 In a right angled triangle you can use:

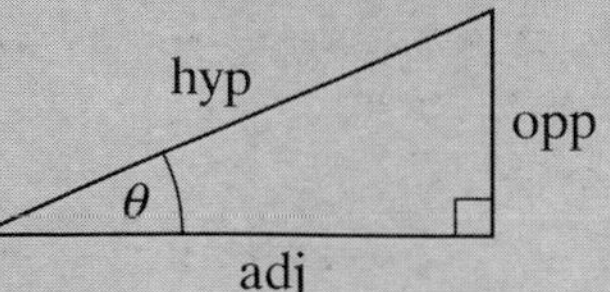

$$\sin\theta = \frac{\text{opp}}{\text{hyp}} \qquad \cos\theta = \frac{\text{adj}}{\text{hyp}} \qquad \tan\theta = \frac{\text{opp}}{\text{adj}}$$

2 $\sin\theta = \cos(90^\circ - \theta) \quad \left(= \frac{b}{c}\right)$

3 $\cos\theta = \sin(90^\circ - \theta) \quad \left(= \frac{a}{c}\right)$

4 Angles of elevation are measured from the horizontal upwards.

5 Angles of depression are measured from the horizontal downwards.

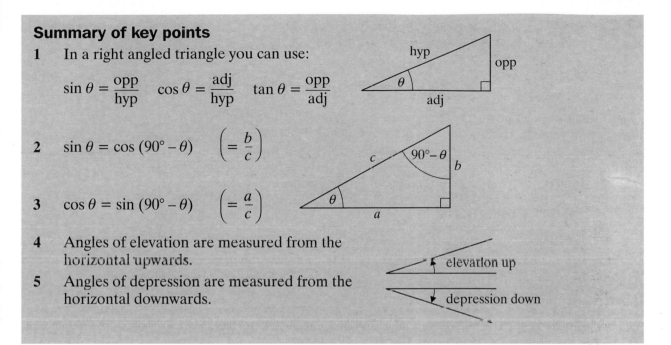

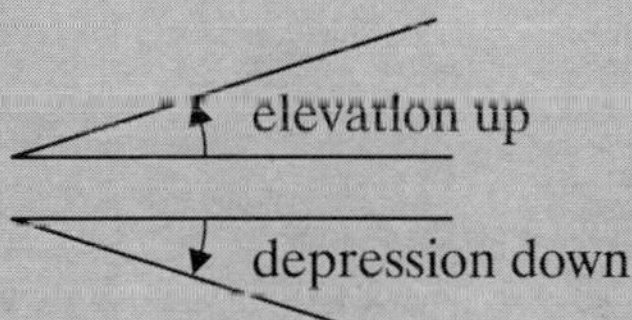

28 Equations and inequalities

This unit shows you how to solve a variety of problems that involve linear equations.

28.1 Using inverse number machines to solve problems

This is the rule a plumber uses to work out how much to charge for labour when doing a repair job:

Charge = £36 per hour worked + a call out fee of £30

It can be written as a formula:

$$c = 36h + 30$$

where c is the charge in pounds for labour and h is the number of hours worked.

The plumber charges a customer £120 for labour.
How can the customer calculate the number of hours the plumber worked?

Draw the number machine for $h \rightarrow 36h + 30$

input h → ×36 → +30 → output c

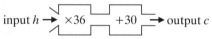

When the number of hours worked h is put into this machine the charge c pounds comes out.

Draw the inverse number machine:

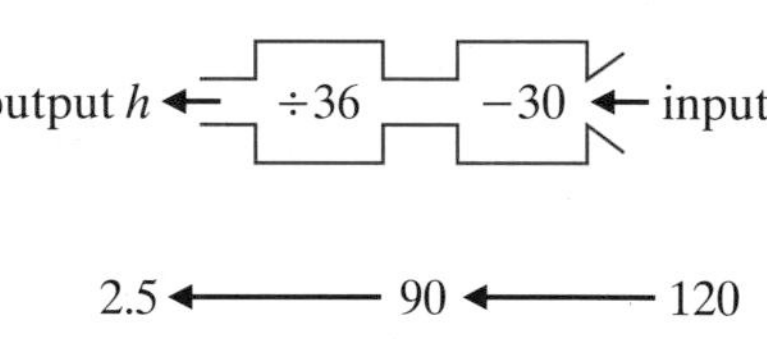

When the charge c pounds is put into the machine the number of hours worked h comes out.

Put 120 into the inverse number machine:
The plumber worked for 2.5 hours.

Exercise 28A

1 How many hours did the plumber work for each of these charges?

(a) £84 **(b)** £138 **(c)** £48
(d) £102 **(e)** £39 **(f)** £129

2 A washing machine repair engineer uses this rule to work out how much to charge for labour when doing a repair job:

Charge = £24 per hour worked + a call out fee of £40

(a) Write this as a formula, using c for the charge in pounds and h for the number of hours worked.
(b) Draw the number machine for your formula.
(c) Draw the inverse number machine for your formula.
(d) Use the inverse number machine you have drawn to work out how many hours the engineer worked for each of these charges:

(i) £100	(ii) £136	(iii) £112
(iv) £76	(v) £94	(vi) £82

What did you say you put in it ...?

3 A tool-hire company uses this rule to work out the charge for hiring a power tool:

Charge = £18 per day hired + £5 insurance fee

(a) Write this as a formula using c for the charge in pounds and d for the number of days hired.
(b) Draw the number machine for your formula.
(c) Draw the inverse number machine.
(d) Use the inverse number machine to work out how many days the power tool was hired out for each of these charges:

(i) £59	(ii) £95	(iii) £32
(iv) £86	(v) £41	(vi) £131

4 A skip-hire firm charges £5 for each day the customer has the skip plus a single charge of £38 for delivery and collection of the skip.
(a) Write this as a formula and state what the letters in your formula represent.
(b) Use the inverse number machine for your formula to work out how many days the skip was hired out for each of these charges:

(i) £53	(ii) £73	(iii) £58
(iv) £108	(v) £93	(vi) £83

28.2 Solving linear equations using inverse number machines

In the plumber problem on page 412 this formula was used:

$$c = 36h + 30$$

The plumber charged £120. Put $c = 120$ in the formula to get:

$$120 = 36h + 30$$

This is called an **equation**. A **formula** and an **equation** are similar but there is one important difference.

A formula like $c = 36h + 30$ is a rule for finding the value of c for *any* value of h.

An equation like $120 = 36h + 30$ is only true for a certain number of values of h. In this case it is only true when $h = 2.5$

Section 28.1 shows you how to find the value of h in the equation $120 = 36h + 30$ by drawing the inverse number machine for $h \rightarrow 36h + 30$ and sending 120 through it.

This is called **solving the equation.**

$c = 36h + 30$

$120 = 36h + 30$

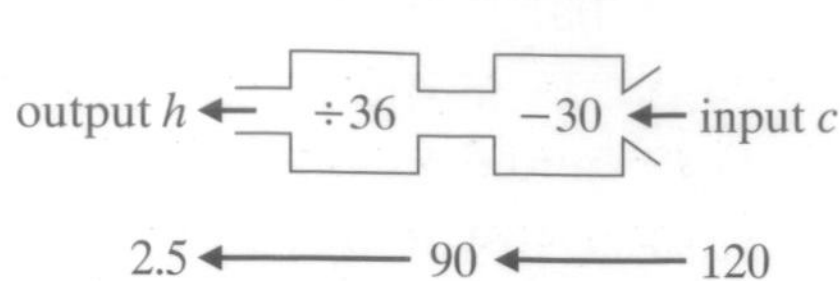

- **Some linear equations can be solved using inverse number machines.**

Example 1

Solve the equation:

$99 = 12h + 15$

Draw the number machine for $h \rightarrow 12h + 15$

Draw the inverse number machine for $h \rightarrow 12h + 15$

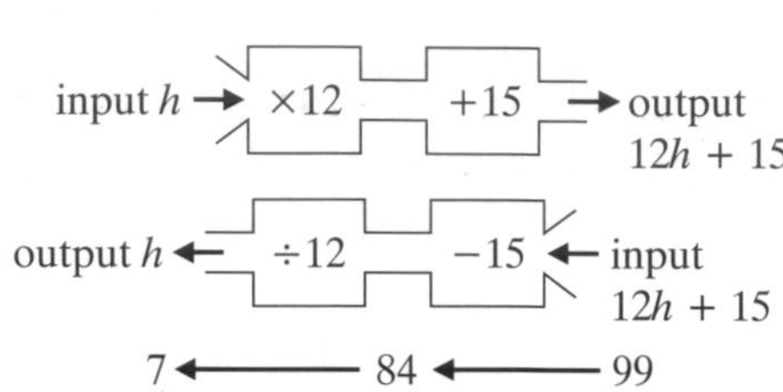

Send 99 through the inverse number machine.

The solution is: $h = 7$

Exercise 28B

1 Solve these equations:

(a) $38 = 5h + 3$ **(b)** $61 = 13d + 9$ **(c)** $36 = 4(d + 8)$ — add 8 to d then multiply by 4

(d) $29 = 9h - 7$ **(e)** $24 = 4(h - 3)$ **(f)** $24 = \frac{d}{2} + 5$ — divide d by 2 then add 5

2 Solve the equation $5h + 8 = 68$

(Hint: $5h + 8 = 68$ is the same as $68 = 5h + 8$)

3 Solve these equations:

(a) $8h + 7 = 31$ **(b)** $11b - 9 = 79$ **(c)** $\frac{b + 8}{4} = 9$ — add 8 to b then divide by 4

(d) $\frac{h - 12}{7} = 5$ **(e)** $\frac{b}{8} - 3 = 5$ **(f)** $\frac{2h - 4}{3} = 6$ — multiply h by 2, subtract 4 then divide by 3

28.3 Solving linear equations by the balance method

Some linear equations cannot be solved by inverse number machines. A more powerful way is to use the **balance method**.

This section shows you how to use the balance method to solve linear equations which could be solved using inverse number machines. Then the method is used to solve more complex linear equations.

This equation appears in question 2 of Exercise 28B:

$$5h + 8 = 68$$

You can think of the equals sign = as the pivot of an old fashioned kitchen balance or a see saw. One side of the equation balances the other.

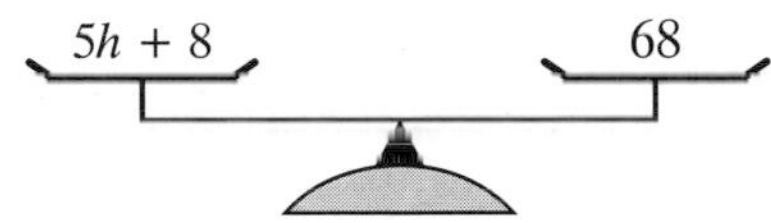

Here is the inverse number machine for $5h + 8 = 68$

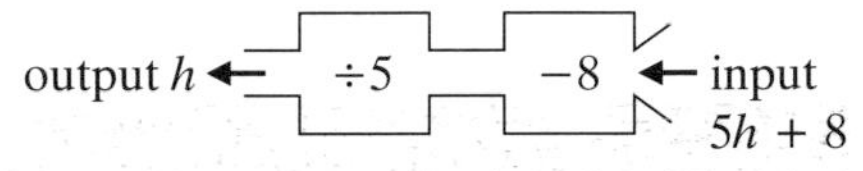

The inverse number machine carries out two operations:
subtract 8 then divide by 5

To solve the equation $5h + 8 = 68$ by the balance method you carry out the same operations in the same order.

To keep the equation balanced you must do the same to both sides of the equation.

Subtract 8 from both sides of the equation:

Divide both sides of the equation by 5:

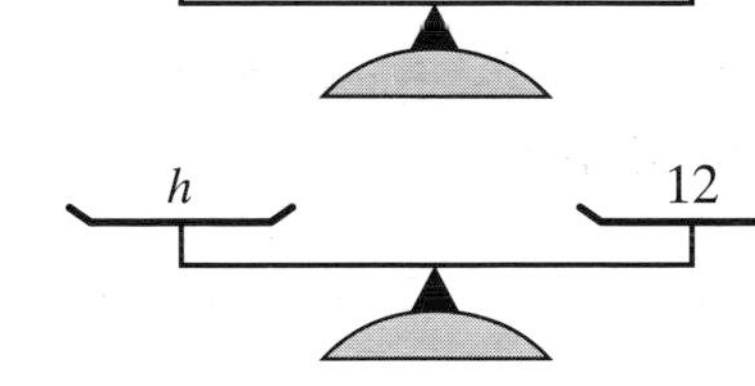

h balances 12 so the solution to the equation $5h + 8 = 68$ is: $h = 12$

Of course when you use the balance method you do not draw the kitchen balances!
Set out the working like this:

$$\begin{aligned} 5h + 8 &= 68 \\ 5h &= 60 \quad (-8) \\ h &= 12 \quad (\div 5) \end{aligned}$$

This tells other people what you are doing and helps you check your work

■ **Most linear equations can be solved by the balance method.**

Exercise 28C

1 Solve the equations in Exercise 28B question 3 using the balance method.

2 Solve these equations using the balance method:

(a) $6d + 9 = 45$ **(b)** $5h - 7 = 23$ **(c)** $\frac{h}{5} + 4 = 16$

(d) $\frac{p-4}{8} = 7$ **(e)** $7(q - 8) = 63$ **(f)** $2(3r + 7) = 38$

(g) $\frac{m+7}{5} = 7$ **(h)** $4(5r - 7) = 152$ **(i)** $5\left(\frac{r}{3} - 3\right) = 40$

multiply r by 3, add 7 then multiply the result by 2

Equations with the 'unknown' on both sides

In this equation the unknown quantity h appears on both sides:

$$7h + 5 = 3h + 15$$

To solve it eliminate (remove) the unknown from one side of the equation. Here you can do this by subtracting $3h$ from both sides:

$$7h + 5 = 3h + 15$$
$$4h + 5 = 15 \qquad (-3h)$$

Now continue using the balance method to solve the equation.

$$4h = 10 \qquad (-5)$$
$$h = 2.5 \qquad (\div 4)$$

Example 2

Solve the equation

$$9m + 4 = 3m - 8$$
$$6m + 4 = -8 \qquad (-3m)$$
$$6m = -12 \qquad (-4)$$
$$m = -2 \qquad (\div 6)$$

$3m - 8 - 3m$
$= 3m - 3m - 8$
$= 0 - 8$
$= -8$

Exercise 28D

1 Solve these equations using the balance method:

(a) $8r + 3 = 5r + 12$ **(b)** $9p - 14 = 4p + 11$

(c) $5s + 6 = 2s - 9$ **(d)** $3m + 7 = 5m - 11$

(e) $5d + 7 = 7d - 5$ **(f)** $3g - 11 = 8g + 4$

You could rewrite this as $5m - 11 = 3m + 7$

2 Two pupils go on a school journey. They like the same sort of chewing gum. One pupil brings two full packets and four loose sticks of gum, the other pupil brings one full packet and nine loose sticks of gum. They are amazed to find that they have each brought the same number of sticks of gum.

(a) Write an equation to describe the situation. Use p to stand for the number of sticks of gum in a packet.
(b) Solve your equation to find the number of sticks of gum in a packet.
(c) How many sticks of gum did each pupil take?

3 A man and a woman took their two children to the school pantomime. At the pantomime they met a friend who had taken his five children. Whilst talking together they discovered that each family had paid the same total amount for their tickets. Write down an equation and solve it to find the cost of an adult ticket.

4 Two children were each given the same amount of money by their grandmother. One of them bought three cans of drink and had £1.26 left. The other bought five cans of drink and had 10p left. The cans of drink each had the same price.
Write down an equation and solve it to find the cost of one can of drink.
(Hint: think of £1.26 as 126p.)

5 This rectangle and triangle each have the same perimeter. Write down an equation and solve it to find the value of x.

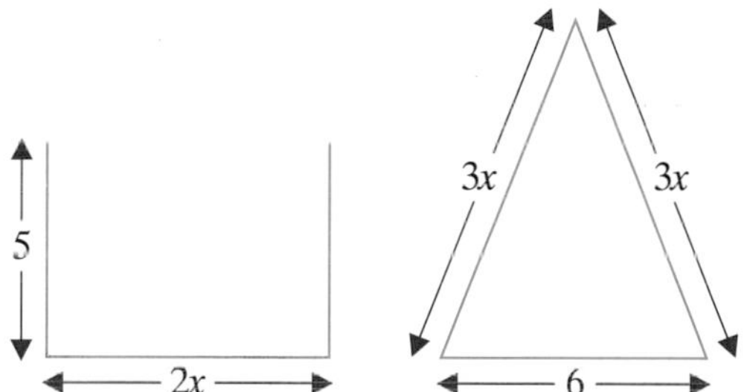

6 A waiter worked for four hours one night and got £3 in tips. The next night he worked for six hours, he got no tips and was fined £5 by the manager for being rude to a customer. Both nights he received the same amount of money.
How much was the waiter paid per hour?

Example 3

Solve the equation $4g + 2 = 8 - 2g$

Eliminate g from one side of the equation by adding $2g$ to both sides:

$$4g + 2 = 8 - 2g$$
$$6g + 2 = 8 \qquad (+2g)$$
$$6g = 6 \qquad (-2)$$
$$g = 1 \qquad (\div 6)$$

It is best to eliminate the term in g that has the smallest value. $-2g$ is smaller than $4g$

Example 4

Solve the equation $2 - 2p = 7 - 5p$

Eliminate p from one side of the equation by adding $5p$ to both sides:

$$2 - 2p = 7 - 5p$$
$$2 + 3p = 7 \qquad (+5p)$$
$$3p = 5 \qquad (-2)$$
$$p = \frac{5}{3} = 1\frac{2}{3} \qquad (\div 3)$$

$-5p$ is smaller than $-2p$ so eliminate it by adding $5p$ to each side

Exercise 28E

1 Solve these equations using the balance method:

(a) $3p + 6 = 21 - 2p$ **(b)** $5x - 2 = 14 - 3x$
(c) $6t + 3 = 18 - 4t$ **(d)** $42 - h = 4h + 7$
(e) $25 - 4m = 7 + 2m$ **(f)** $x + 1 = 3 - x$

You could write this as $4h + 7 = 42 - h$

2 Solve these equations using the balance method:

(a) $2 - 3p = 11 - 6p$ **(b)** $5 - q = 17 - 3q$
(c) $6 - 3s = 16 - 7s$ **(d)** $16 - 5n = 10 - 8n$
(e) $7 - 5k = 1 - 3k$ **(f)** $4 - y = 9 - 3y$

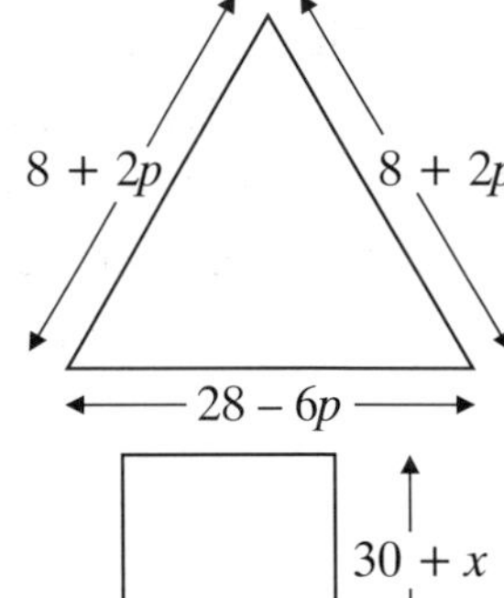

3 **(a)** The diagram shows an equilateral triangle. Write down an equation in p that must be true.
(b) Solve your equation to find the value of p.
(c) What is the length of a side of the triangle?

4 **(a)** The diagram shows a square. Write down an equation in x that must be true.
(b) Solve your equation to find the value of x.
(c) What is the length of a side of the square?

5 Priya has £15 at the start of half-term holiday. During the holiday she goes to the cinema three times. Her friend starts with £12 and goes to the cinema twice. Neither of them spends any other money. At the end of the week they have equal amounts of money left.
Let c stand for the cost of going to the cinema.
(a) Write down an equation in c which must be true.
(b) Solve your equation to find the cost of going to the cinema.

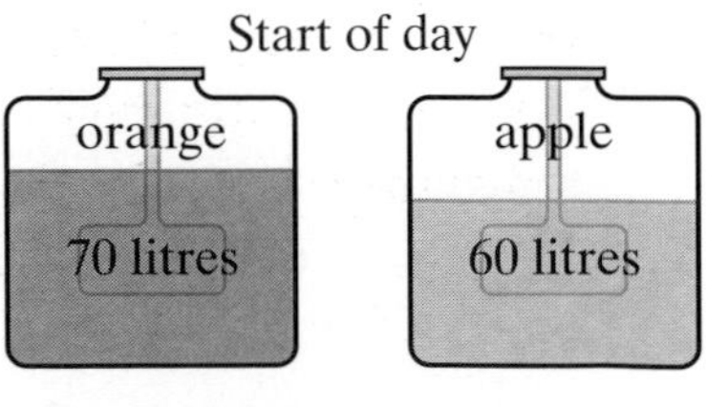

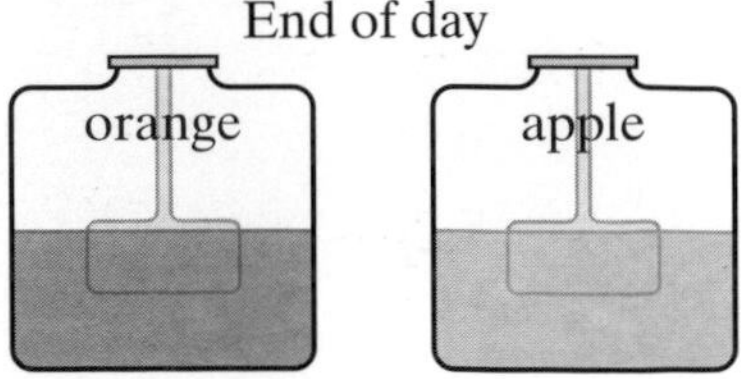

6 A cafe sells orange juice and apple juice. At the start of one day there are 70 litres of orange juice and 60 litres of apple juice.
During the day the cafe sells 60 glasses of orange juice and 20 glasses of apple juice. At the end of the day there are equal amounts of orange and apple juice left.
Let g stand for the volume of juice in a glass.
(a) Write down an equation in g which must be true.
(b) Solve your equation to find the volume of juice in a glass.

Equations involving brackets and fractions

Sometimes you will need to solve equations involving brackets.

Example 5

Solve the equation $5(2g - 1) = 7(9 - g)$

First remove the brackets by expanding each bracketed expression. (There is more about this on page 296.)

Then solve by the balance method.

$$\begin{aligned} 5(2g - 1) &= 7(9 - g) & \\ 10g - 5 &= 63 - 7g & \text{(remove brackets)} \\ 17g - 5 &= 63 & (+ 7g) \\ 17g &= 68 & (+ 5) \\ g &= 4 & (\div 17) \end{aligned}$$

Example 6

Solve the equation $\frac{p}{4} - 2 = \frac{p + 4}{6}$

This equation involves algebraic fractions.

First clear the denominators by multiplying both sides of the equation by the lowest common multiple of the denominators.

The lowest common multiple of 4 and 6 is 12. (There is more about lowest common multiples on page 186.)

$$\begin{aligned} 12\left(\frac{p}{4} - 2\right) &= 12 \times \frac{p + 4}{6} & (\times 12) \\ 3p - 24 &= 2p + 8 & \text{(remove brackets)} \\ p - 24 &= 8 & (- 2p) \\ p &= 32 & (+ 24) \end{aligned}$$

$$\begin{aligned} & 12 \times \frac{p + 4}{6} \\ &= 12 \times \frac{1}{6} \times (p + 4) \\ &= 2 \times (p + 4) \\ &= 2p + 8 \end{aligned}$$

Exercise 28F

1 Solve these equations:

(a) $3(2h + 1) = h - 2$ **(b)** $2(3p - 3) = 5(p - 1)$

(c) $2(2q + 3) = 3(4q - 2)$ **(d)** $4(9 - 3r) = 3(r + 2)$

(e) $4 - 2t = 2(8 + t)$ **(f)** $2(13 - 2x) = 9(9 + 2x)$

2 Solve these equations:

(a) $\frac{m}{3} + 2 = \frac{m}{4} + 3$ **(b)** $\frac{g}{2} - 1 = \frac{g}{4} + 1$

(c) $\frac{n + 3}{3} = \frac{n}{5} + 3$ **(d)** $\frac{x}{6} + 1 = \frac{x - 4}{4}$

(e) $3(2p - 10) = \frac{4p - 7}{2}$

28.4 Using graphs to solve simultaneous linear equations

A school office has two machines for making copies of letters: a photocopier and a stencil machine. The photocopier costs 3p per copy. The stencil machine costs 1p per copy plus 30p for the stencil. Which is the cheapest machine to use?

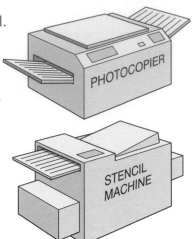

It depends on how many copies are required.

- If only 1 copy is required it costs 3p on the photocopier and 31p on the stencil machine. It is cheaper to use the photocopier.
- If 100 copies are required it costs £3 on the photocopier and £1.30 on the stencil machine. It is cheaper to use the stencil machine.

If c is the cost in pence of making n copies of a letter, the cost of using each machine can be written as an equation.

equation for photocopier	equation for stencil machine
$c = 3n$	$c = n + 30$

For what number of copies will the cost of using the photocopier and using the stencil machine be the same?

You can find out by plotting graphs of the two equations, with n on the horizontal axis and c on the vertical axis:

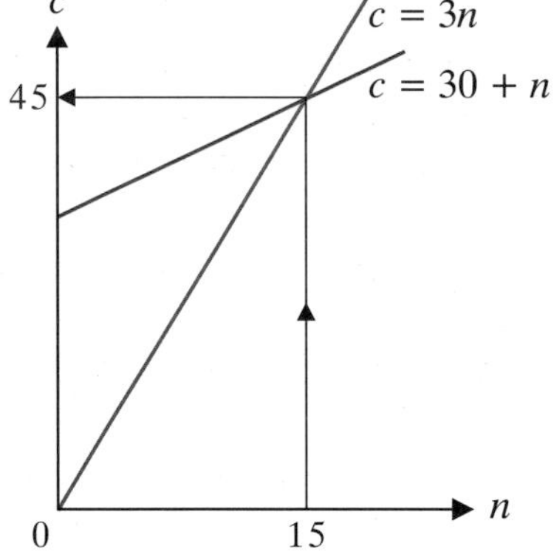

The straight line graphs of the two equations intersect when $n = 15$. This means that the cost of printing 15 copies is the same on either machine at 45p.

- If fewer than 15 copies are required the photocopier is cheaper.
- If more than 15 copies are required the stencil machine is cheaper.

The values $n = 15$ and $c = 45$ satisfy the equations $c = 3n$ and $c = 30 + n$ simultaneously (at the same time).
So these equations are called **simultaneous equations**.

- **Two equations for which you need a common solution are called simultaneous equations.**
- **Simultaneous equations can be solved using graphs.**

Exercise 28G

You will need graph paper.

1 **(a)** $y = 2x + 1$
$y = 4 - x$

(i) For each equation make a table of values to find y when x is –2, 0, 2 and 4. (This has been started for you.)

x	–2	0	2	4
$y = 2x + 1$	–3			9

x	–2	0	2	4
$y = 4 - x$	6		2	

(ii) On graph paper draw a set of axes with x and y going from –6 to 6.
On the axes draw the graphs of both equations.

(iii) Write down the values of x and y which satisfy both equations.

Repeat part **(a)** for the equations in parts **(b)** and **(c)**

(b) $y = 2x - 5$
$y = 3 - 2x$

(c) $y = x - 2$
$y = 3x + 4$

2 The advertisements show the charges made by two car-hire companies. Let c pounds be the cost of hiring a car for d days.

(a) Write an equation to show the cost of hiring a car from Safedrive Motors.

(b) Write an equation to show the cost of hiring a car from Welldrive Cars.

(c) On one set of axes draw the graphs of the two equations in parts **(a)** and **(b)**.

(d) Use your graph to find the number of days for which the cost of hiring a car is the same for both companies.

3 An electrical goods shop offers a customer these two schemes to pay for an audio system.

(a) Write an equation for Scheme 1 to show the total amount paid, t pounds, after m months.

(b) Write an equation for Scheme 2 to show the total amount paid, t pounds, after m months.

(c) On one set of axes draw the graphs of the two equations you have written for values of m up to 3 years.

(d) Use your graphs to find the cost of the system and the number of months the customer will take to pay for it.

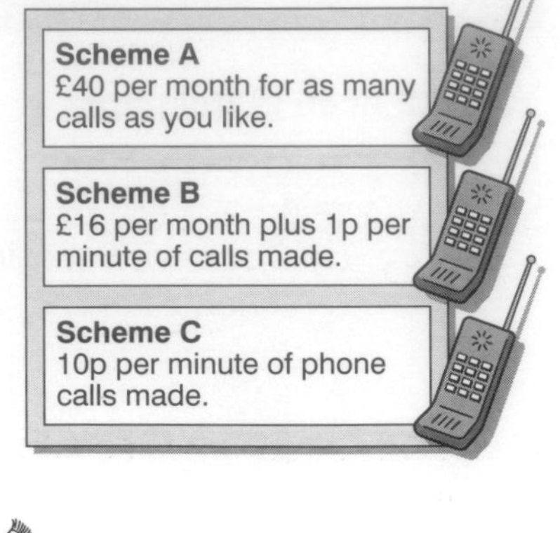

Scheme A
£40 per month for as many calls as you like.
Scheme B
£16 per month plus 1p per minute of calls made.
Scheme C
10p per minute of phone calls made.

4 A mobile phone company offers its customers these three schemes of charging:

(a) Write an equation for Scheme A to show the total cost, g pounds, of making m minutes of telephone calls in a month.

(b) Write equations for Scheme B and Scheme C to show the total cost of, g pounds, of making m minutes of telephone calls in a month.

(c) On one set of axes draw the graphs of the three equations you have drawn for values of m up to 50 hours.

(d) Use your graph to advise someone which scheme they should choose.

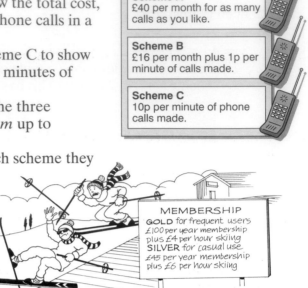

5 A dry-ski club offers two types of membership:

(a) On one set of axes draw graphs to show the cost of the two types of membership.

(b) Use your graphs to give advice to someone about the type of membership they should have.

MEMBERSHIP
GOLD for frequent users
£100 per year membership
plus £4 per hour skiing
SILVER for casual use
£45 per year membership
plus £6 per hour skiing

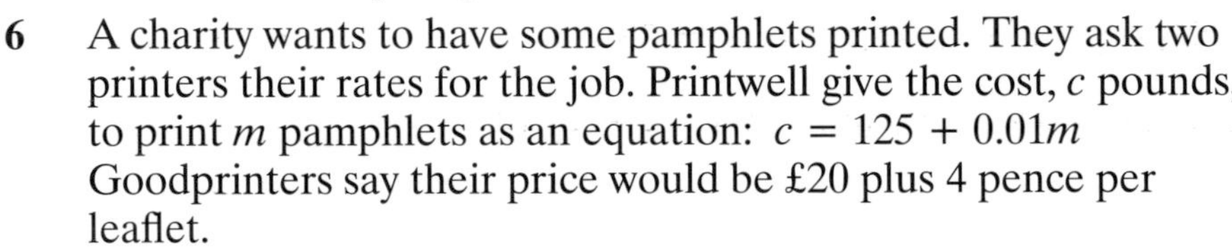

6 A charity wants to have some pamphlets printed. They ask two printers their rates for the job. Printwell give the cost, c pounds, to print m pamphlets as an equation: $c = 125 + 0.01m$
Goodprinters say their price would be £20 plus 4 pence per leaflet.
Use a graph to find:

(a) the number of pamphlets for which both printers would charge the same.

(b) the cost of printing that number of pamphlets.

28.5 Solving simultaneous linear equations by substitution

Look again at the problem of the photocopier and the stencil machine in section 28.4.

The problem involves solving the two simultaneous equations:
$c = n + 30$ and $c = 3n$

A graph was used to find the value of n which gave the same value for c in each equation: $n = 15$ and $c = 45$

You can also solve the simultaneous equations using an algebraic method:

One of the equations is $c = n + 30$

Replace the c in this equation with $3n$ (as you know from the other equation that $c = 3n$). This is called **substitution** because you substitute (or replace) c with an equivalent expression or value, ...ing:

$$3n = n + 30$$

Now you can solve this equation using the balance method:

$$3n = n + 30$$
$$2n = 30 \qquad (-n)$$
$$n = 15 \qquad (\div 2)$$

You can find the value of c by substituting $n = 15$ in the first equation $c = n + 30$:

$$c = 15 + 30$$
$$= 45$$

Check the solution by substituting $n = 15$ in the second equation $c = 3n$

$$c = 3 \times 15$$
$$= 45$$

The two values of c are the same when $n = 15$ so the solution is $n = 15$ and $c = 45$.

■ **Simultaneous linear equations can be solved by the method of substitution.**

Example 7

Solve the simultaneous equations: $y - 1 = 2x$ and $3y - 4x = 13$.

Use the balance method to rearrange the first equation $y - 1 = 2x$ to make y the subject :

$$y - 1 = 2x$$
$$y = 2x + 1 \qquad (+1)$$

Substitute this expression for y into the second equation $3y - 4x = 13$:

$$3(2x + 1) - 4x = 13$$

remove brackets $\quad 6x + 3 - 4x = 13$

collect like terms $\quad 2x + 3 = 13$

subtract 3 from both sides $\quad 2x = 10 \qquad (-3)$

divide by 2 $\quad x = 5 \qquad (\div 2)$

Find the solution for y by substituting $x = 5$ into $y = 2x + 1$ (the rearranged first equation) and solving for y.

$$y = 2 \times 5 + 1$$
$$y = 10 + 1 = 11$$

Check the solution by substituting $x = 5$ and $y = 11$ in the left hand side of the second equation.

$$3y - 4x = 3 \times 11 - 4 \times 5$$
$$= 33 - 20$$
$$= 13 \text{ (true)}$$

Exercise 28H

1 Solve by substitution these pairs of simultaneous equations:

(a) $y = 27 + 2x$, $y = 5x$ (b) $y = 40 + 3x$, $y = 8x$ (c) $y = 25 + 9x$, $y = 80 + 4x$

(d) $y = 3x + 4$, $y = 7x - 4$ (e) $y = 18 - 3x$, $y = 3x + 6$ (f) $y = 4 - 2x$, $y = 12 - 3x$

2 Solve these pairs of simultaneous equations by rearranging the first equation to make y the subject and then using the method of substitution:

(a) $y + 2 = 2x$, $3x + 2y = 10$ (b) $y - 6 = 2x$, $5x = 3 + 2y$ (c) $y - 2 = 3x$, $2y = 8x - 3$

(d) $y + 3x = 4$, $x + 2y = 2$ (e) $y - 3x = 3$, $2y - 5x = 9$ (f) $2y - 2x = 6$, $6x - 5y = 9$

28.6 Solving simultaneous linear equations by elimination

Solving some simultaneous linear equations by substitution involves awkward fractions. Here is another way of solving simultaneous equations.

Eliminating unknowns by adding the equations

Here are two simultaneous equations, labelled **A** and **B** for convenience:

$y + 2x = 19$ **A**
$3y - 2x = 17$ **B**

The left hand side of each equation is equal to the right hand side of that equation. So the two left hand sides of the equations added together must equal the two right hand sides added together.

A + B $y + 2x + 3y - 2x = 19 + 17$

Notice that on the left hand side $+2x - 2x = 0$, so x terms can be **eliminated** from the equation, giving:

$4y = 36$

Divide by 4 $y = 9$

Now the value of x can be found by substituting $y = 9$ in equation **A.**

$9 + 2x = 19$

Subtract 9 from both sides $2x = 10$

Divide by 2 $x = 5$

So the solution is $x = 5$, $y = 9$. (This can be checked by substituting these values back into equation **B.**)

This is called solving by **elimination**. The original equations were combined to eliminate one of the unknowns, x, making an equation that was easier to solve.

Simultaneous linear equations can be solved by the method of elimination.

Example 8

Solve these simultaneous equations by elimination:

$4d - 3c = 10$ **A**

$2d + 3c = 23$ **B**

c can be eliminated by adding equations **A** and **B**.

$$4d - 3c + 2d + 3c = 10 + 23 \qquad \textbf{(A + B)}$$

$$6d = 33$$

Divide by 6 $\quad d = \frac{33}{6} = 5\frac{3}{6} = 5\frac{1}{2} \quad (\div 6)$

Now you can find c by substituting $d = 5\frac{1}{2}$ in equation **A**, giving:

$$22 - 3c = 10$$

Add $3c$ to both sides $\quad 22 = 10 + 3c \quad (+3c)$

Subtract 10 from both sides $\quad 22 - 10 = 3c \quad (-10)$

$$12 = 3c$$

Divide by 3 $\quad 4 = c \quad (\div 3)$

The solution is $c = 4$, $d = 5\frac{1}{2}$. (Check this by substituting these values back into equation **B**.)

Exercise 28I

Solve these simultaneous equations by elimination:

1 **(a)** $3p + q = 7$, $2p - q = 3$ **(b)** $2x + 3y = 8$, $2x - 3y = 2$

2 **(a)** $3x + y = 8$, $3x - y = 2$ **(b)** $4p + 3q = 6$, $2p - 3q = 12$

Eliminating unknowns by subtracting the equations

Example 9

Solve these simultaneous equations by elimination:

$3x - 2y = 19$ **A**

$x - 2y = 9$ **B**

You cannot eliminate the y terms by adding because $-2y + -2y = -4y$.

However, you can eliminate them by subtracting because $-2y - -2y = -2y + 2y = 0$.

Subtract equation **B** from equation **A**:

$$3x - 2y - (x - 2y) = 19 - 9 \qquad \textbf{(A – B)}$$

Remove brackets $3x - 2y - x + 2y = 10$

$2x = 10$

Divide by 2 $x = 5$ $(\div 2)$

Now you can find y by substituting $x = 5$ in equation **A** giving:

$15 - 2y = 19$

Add $2y$ to both sides $15 = 19 + 2y$ $(+2y)$

Subtract 19 $15 - 19 = 2y$ (-19)

$-4 = 2y$

Divide by 2 $-2 = y$ $(\div 2)$

So the solution is $x = 5, y = -2$

(Check your solution by substituting these values in equation **B**.)

When to add and when to subtract

Hint: look at the terms which are the same. If the signs are the **S**ame you **S**ubtract. If the signs are **D**ifferent you ad**D**

Worked examination question

Mrs Rogers bought 3 blouses and 2 scarves. She paid £26.
Miss Summers bought 4 blouses and 1 scarf. She paid £28.
The cost of a blouse was x pounds.
The cost of a scarf was y pounds.

(a) Use the information to write down two equations in x and y.
(b) Solve these equations to find the cost of one blouse. [L]

(a) For Mrs Rogers: $3x + 2y = 26$

For Miss Summers: $4x + y = 28$

(b) Label the equations **A** and **B**

$3x + 2y = 26$ **A**

$4x + y = 28$ **B**

Multiply **B** by 2 $8x + 2y = 56$ $(2 \times$ **B**$)$

$2 \times$ **B** $-$ **A** $8x + 2y - (3x + 2y) = 56 - 26$

$8x + 2y - 3x - 2y = 30$

Remove brackets $5x = 30$

Divide by 5 $x = 6$ $(\div 5)$

You need to find the cost of one blouse, which is x pounds. The cost of one blouse is £6.

There is no need to find y in this question.

None of the terms are the same, but if you multiply **B** by 2 you will get $2y$ in each equation.

It is $+2y$ in both equations. Signs **S**ame so **S**ubtract

Exercise 28J

Solve these simultaneous equations by elimination:

1 (a) $5x + 2y = 16$
$3x + 2y = 8$
(b) $7x - 3y = 13$
$4x - 3y = 7$
(c) $3x + 4y = 9$
$3x + y = 18$

2 (a) $3x + 2y = 2$
$x + y = 2$
(b) $4x - y = 9$
$2x + 3y = 1$
(c) $4d - 3e = 26$
$d - 3e = 11$

3 (a) $4x + 3y = 11$
$3x - 2y = 21$
(b) $5p + 4q = 22$
$3p + 5q = 21$
(c) $5m - 4n = 17$
$2m - 3n = 18$

28.7 Solving inequalities

In the expression $5x - 4 > 3x + 2$ the left hand side is **not** equal to the right hand side.

An expression like this is called an **inequality**.

You solve an inequality in a similar way to a linear equation, but you must be careful **not to multiply or divide by a negative number**.

> $>$ means 'greater than'
> $<$ means 'less than'
> $\geqslant$ means 'greater than or equal to'
> $\leqslant$ means 'less than or equal to'

For example, 5 is greater than 2 can be written:

$$5 > 2$$

If you multiply by the negative number -3 you get:

$$-15 \ ? \ -6$$

As -15 is less than -6 the $>$ sign is replaced by a $<$ sign:

$$-15 < -6$$

■ **An expression in which the right and left hand sides are not equal is called an inequality.**

$x>3$ can be represented by a region shaded on a graph

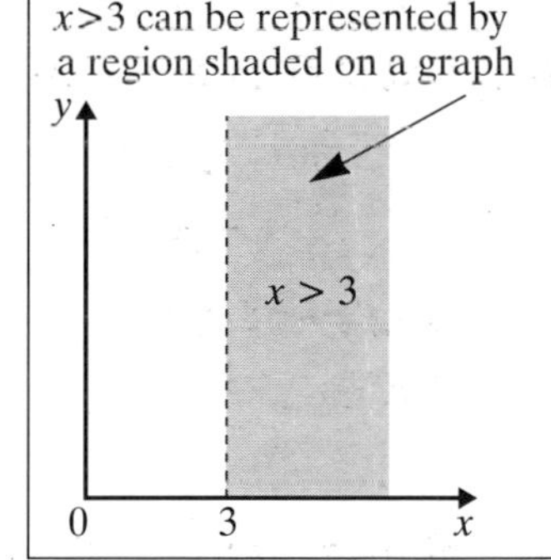

Example 10

Solve the inequality $5x - 4 > 3x + 2$

Subtract $3x$ from both sides $\quad 5x - 4 - 3x > 2$

Simplify $\quad 2x - 4 > 2$

Add 4 to both sides $\quad 2x > 6$

Divide by 2 $\quad x > 3$ is the solution.

Worked examination question

List all the possible integer values of n such that $-3 \leqslant n < 2$. [L]

The $\leqslant$ sign means that n can equal -3 or be bigger than -3.
The $<$ sign means that n is smaller than 2.

So the integers are $-3, -2, -1, 0, 1$

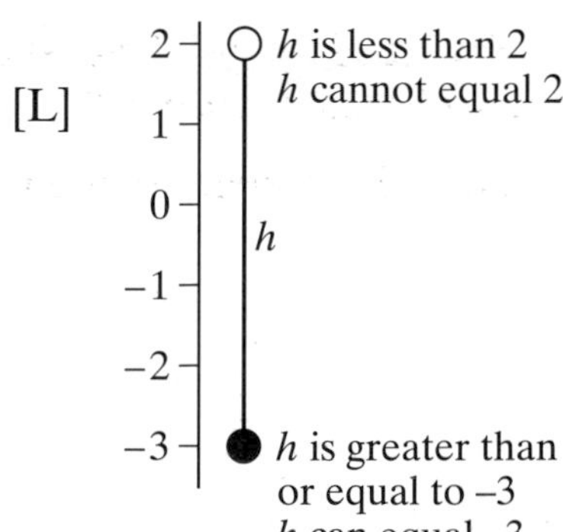

Exercise 28K

1 Write down all the integers which satisfy each inequality:
(a) $3 < n < 8$ (b) $-4 < n < 5$ (c) $3 < n \leqslant 7$
(d) $-3 < n \leqslant 4$ (e) $-6 \leqslant n \leqslant -2$ (f) $-68 < n < -64$

2 Solve these inequalities:
(a) $3n < 6$ (b) $2n \leqslant 12$ (c) $2n < -6$
(d) $4n > 12$ (e) $5n > -15$ (f) $3n \geqslant 15$
(g) $6n < 2$ (h) $8n < -4$ (i) $6n \leqslant -3$

3 Solve these inequalities:
(a) $3n + 2 < 14$ (b) $x - 5 > 3$
(c) $2x - 7 \geqslant 4$ (d) $3y - 5 < y + 3$
(e) $4x + 7 < 2x + 1$ (f) $3y + 8 < 5y - 2$

Remember:
If $9 < x$ then you can write $x > 9$

28.8 Solving quadratic equations by factorizing

Unit **18** shows how to solve quadratic equations by drawing accurate graphs. This section shows how you can solve some quadratic equations by factorizing.

Example 11

Solve the equation $x^2 - x - 12 = 0$

First factorize the quadratic expression into two brackets.

$$(x - 4)(x + 3) = 0$$

So either $x - 4 = 0$ or $x + 3 = 0$

Now solve the two linear equations and you get

$$x = 4 \quad \text{or} \quad x = -3$$

Note: you can check your answers by putting $x = 4$ into the given equation or putting $x = -3$ into the equation.

If $x = 4$, $x^2 - x - 12 = 4^2 - 4 - 12 = 16 - 4 - 12 = 0$

so $x = 4$ satisfies the equation $x^2 - x - 12 = 0$.

Read about factorizing quadratic expressions on page 308 of Unit **21**.

$0 \times 5 = 0$, $7 \times 0 = 0$ and $0 \times 0 = 0$.

If you multiply two numbers or two expressions the result can only equal 0 if either one of the numbers is 0 or both are 0.

■ **Some quadratic equations can be solved by factorizing.**

Exercise 28L

Solve these equations:

1 (a) $x^2 - 5x + 4 = 0$ (b) $x^2 - 4x + 3 = 0$ (c) $x^2 - 5x + 6 = 0$
2 (a) $x^2 + 3x + 2 = 0$ (b) $x^2 + 6x + 8 = 0$ (c) $x^2 + 8x + 12 = 0$
3 (a) $x^2 + 10x - 11 = 0$ (b) $x^2 - 2x - 8 = 0$ (c) $x^2 + 8x - 20 = 0$
4 (a) $x^2 - 16 = 0$ (b) $x^2 - 49 = 0$ (c) $x^2 - 81 = 0$
5 (a) $p^2 - 9p + 14 = 0$ (b) $q^2 + 6q + 9 = 0$ (c) $y^2 - 2y - 15 = 0$
6 (a) $c^2 + 9c + 18 = 0$ (b) $d^2 + 4d - 21 = 0$ (c) $g^2 - 10g + 16 = 0$

Exercise 28M Mixed questions

1 Solve the equations:
(a) $4x + 2 = 26$ **(b)** $19 + 4y = 9 - y$ [L]

2 **(a)** Find an expression, in terms of x, for the perimeter of the polygon shown. Give your answer in its simplest form.

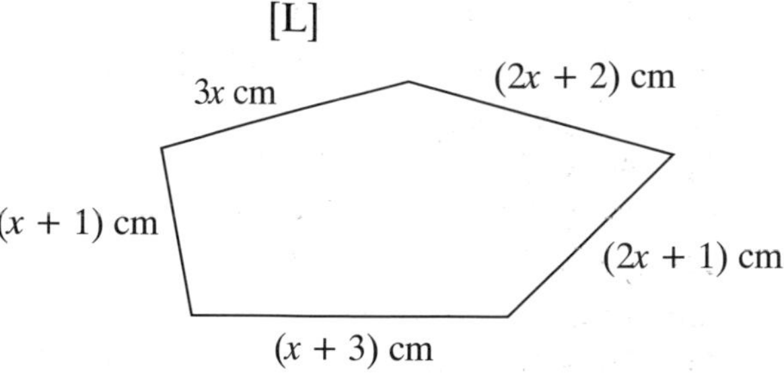

The perimeter of this polygon is 43 cm.
(b) Calculate the value of x. [L]

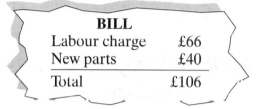

3 Rebecca is a washing machine engineer. She uses this rule to work out her labour charge for a repair lasting h hours:

Labour charge in pounds $= 30 + 12h$

She then adds on the cost of any new parts she has fitted.

This is the bill Rebecca gave to a man for a repair:

BILL

Labour charge	£66
New parts	£40
Total	£106

For how many hours of labour has she charged?

4 This picture shows some packets of rice in the pans of a weighing machine. Each packet of rice weighs x kg. In Pan A there are 9 packets of rice and a weight of 5 kg. An expression for the total weight in kg in Pan A is $9x + 5$. In Pan B there are 4 packets of rice and a weight of 20 kg.

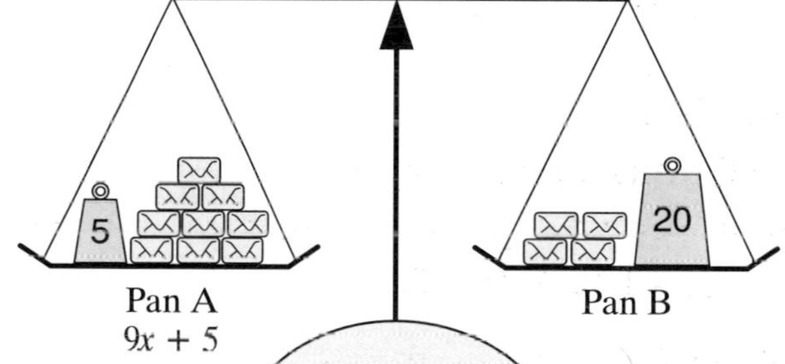

(a) Write down in terms of x an expression for the total weight in Pan B.

The total weight in each pan is the same.
(b) Write down an equation in terms of x to represent this information.
(c) Use your equation to calculate the weight, x kg, of one packet of rice. [L]

5 Ruchi is $\frac{1}{3}$ the age of her father.
Ruchi is x years old.
(a) Write down, in terms of x,
(i) her father's age
(ii) Ruchi's age 9 years ago
(iii) her father's age 9 years ago.

Nine years ago, her father was 6 times as old as Ruchi.
(b) (i) Using some of your answers to **(a)**, write down an equation in x which represents the above statement.
(ii) Solve your equation to find the value of x. [L]

6 Solve the equation: $11x + 5 = x + 25$. [L]

7 Solve the simultaneous equations:
$$5p - 2q = 16$$
$$3p - q = 9$$
[L]

8 **(a)** Solve these equations:
(i) $2x + 3 = 17$ (ii) $4 - 3y = 10$ (iii) $2t + 1 = 3(t - 4)$

(b) The perimeter, P centimetres, of a rectangle is given by the formula $P = 2(x + y)$.
Where the lengths of the sides of the rectangle are x centimetres and y centimetres.
(i) Find the value of P when $x = 2.4$ and $y = 4.8$.
(ii) Rearrange the formula so that y is the subject. [L]

9 **(a)** Solve the equation: $9x + 6 = 36 - x$.
(b) Solve the simultaneous equations: $4p - q = 15$
$2p - q = 9$ [L]

10 **(a)** Solve the inequality: $4n + 3 < 18$
Given that n is an integer,
(b) write down the greatest value of n for which $4n + 3 < 18$. [L]

11 Solve these equations
(a) $x^2 + 9x + 14 = 0$ **(b)** $x^2 + 3x - 10 = 0$

12 Marc is baking loaves and buns for La Boulangerie.
He bakes x loaves and y buns.
Write down the inequalities that x and y must satisfy if:
(a) the number of buns must be less than 500
(b) the number of loaves and buns must be less than 600
(c) there must be at least twice as many buns as loaves.
By drawing straight lines on a graph and shading:
(d) indicate the region within which x and y must lie to satisfy all the inequalities

Summary of key points

1. Some linear equations can be solved using inverse number machines.
2. Most linear equations can be solved by the balance method.
3. Two equations for which you need a common solution are called simultaneous equations.
4. Simultaneous equations can be solved using graphs.
5. Simultaneous equations can be solved using algebra by the method of substitution and by the method of elimination.
6. An expression in which the right and left hand sides are not equal is called an inequality, for example: $5x - 4 > 3x + 2$.
7. You need to know these symbols:

$>$ greater than	$<$ less than
$\geqslant$ greater than or equal to	$\leqslant$ less than or equal to

8. Some quadratic equations can be solved by factorizing.

29 Interpreting data

Earlier units in this book show you how to collect, record and present data (Units 8 and 24), and how to calculate averages and measures of spread (Unit 16).

Sometimes you will be asked to **interpret** data – to explain what it shows – or to comment on an interpretation you are given.

If you are asked for an explanation a description of the information is not enough.

■ **When interpreting data, 'explain' does not mean 'describe'.**

Here are two typical situations that show the type of thinking required:

Situation 1

A group of boys and a group of girls have taken a mathematics test. The average mark for the girls is more than the average mark for the boys.

Can you say that on the whole the girls have done better in this test than the boys?

At first, it might seem reasonable to agree with the interpretation that the girls have done better in the test than the boys. In fact, it might not be reasonable to agree with this interpretation.

Imagine that five boys and five girls took the test.

The marks for the girls:

48, 49, 50, 50, 53

The three measures of average for these marks are:

mean = 50 mode = 50 median = 50

and the range of the marks is 5.

The marks for the boys could be:

20, 20, 59, 60, 61

The three measure of average for these marks are:

mean = 44 mode = 20 median = 59

and the range of the marks is 41.

Notice that:

the mean mark for girls is greater than the mean mark for boys

the mode mark for girls is greater than the mode mark for boys

Either of these statements might suggest that overall the girls have done better than the boys. But 3 out of the 5 boys (that is 60% of the boys) scored a mark in the test higher than any of the girls. It would be unreasonable to say that the girls have done better than the boys when the majority of the boys outscored all of the girls.

Notice too that:

the median mark for girls is less than the median mark for boys

So, if you took the median as your measure of average you could not even say that on average the girls have done better than the boys.

The range of the marks for the girls is quite low (range = 5) whilst the range of the marks for the boys is relatively high (range = 21). Two of the boys' marks are much lower than the rest. This increases the range and lowers the mean.

In any situation such as this one you always need to know:

- which measure of average is being used
- what is the range, or other measure of spread

Unless you have both of these statistics then any interpretation or comment will be unreliable or unreasonable.

Situation 2

A research agency reported that:

> The average weekly wage in the UK is higher than the average weekly wage in Germany.

Would it be reasonable to interpret this as meaning that people in the UK are generally better off financially than people in Germany?

The answer to this is that it might not be reasonable. To be able to make any reasonable interpretation you would need to know:

- which measure of average (mean, median or mode) was being quoted
- what was the range of weekly wages in the UK and in Germany

You could have a situation like the one shown below. The lowest, highest and mean weekly wages are shown on two number lines:

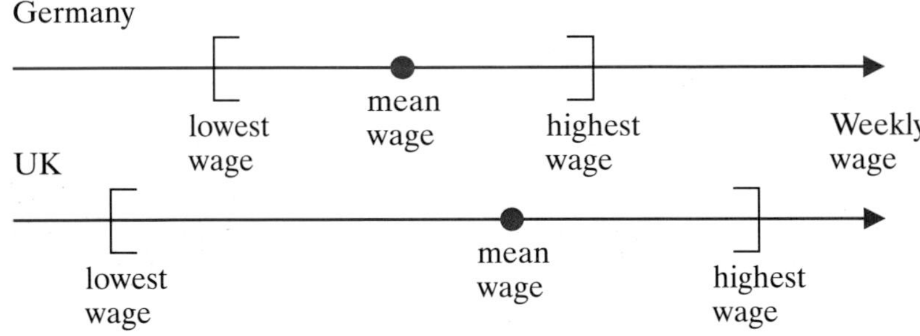

In this diagram the mean UK wage is greater than the mean German wage

But the spread of wages in the UK is much greater than the spread of the wages in Germany.

There might be only a few people in the UK who are better off financially than most people in Germany, but there could be very many people in the UK whose wages are much lower than the wages of anyone in Germany.

Without having the full information about the relevant statistics any interpretation or comments are inconclusive. In a fuller analysis you would also need to know about relative prices in the UK and Germany.

The statistics will be more reliable if the number of people in the sample questioned by the research agency is large.

■ **When interpreting data you must clearly state the statistics you are using to support your interpretation.**

Example 1

A group of people took a fitness test. They exercised hard. Then they were timed to see how long their pulses took to return to normal.

The time taken for a pulse to return to normal is called the recovery time. The recovery times for the group are shown in the table below.

Recovery time (seconds)	Frequency
0 up to but not including 20	0
20 up to but not including 40	7
40 up to but not including 60	9
60 up to but not including 80	18
80 up to but not including 90	13
90 up to but not including 100	12
100 up to but not including 120	9
120 up to but not including 140	6

Recovery time (seconds)	Cumulative frequency
$0 \leqslant x < 20$	0
$0 \leqslant x < 40$	7
$0 \leqslant x < 60$	16
$0 \leqslant x < 80$	34
$0 \leqslant x < 90$	47
$0 \leqslant x < 100$	59
$0 \leqslant x < 120$	68
$0 \leqslant x < 140$	74

(a) Use the figures in the table to draw a cumulative frequency curve.

(b) Use your cumulative frequency curve to estimate the value of:
  (i) the median
  (ii) the interquartile range.

A second group of people took the fitness test. The recovery times of people in this group had a median of 61 seconds and an interquartile range of 22 seconds.

(c) Compare the fitness results of the two groups. [L]

(a) Here is the cumulative frequency curve:

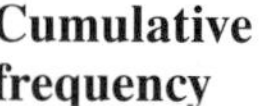

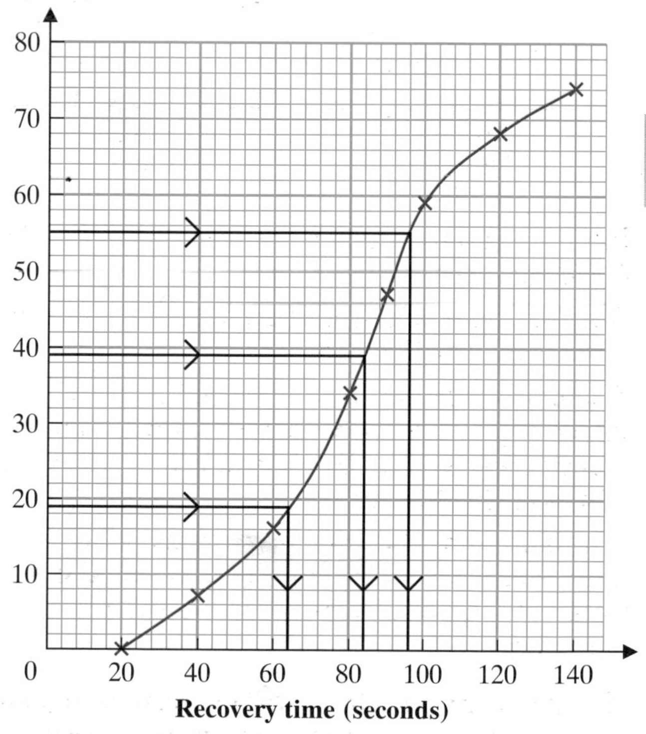

(b) (i) Median time (when the cumulative frequency is 37)
= 82 seconds

(ii) Lower quartile (cumulative frequency is 18.5)
= 64 seconds
upper quartile (cumulative frequency is 55.5)
= 96 seconds
Interquartile range = 96 – 64
= 32 seconds

(c) Members of the first group have a median recovery time of 82 s. Those in the second group have a median recovery time of only 61 s. So it might appear that those in the second group are fitter than those in the first. However the interquartile range of times for the first group is greater than the interquartile range of times for the second group so the recovery times for the middle 50% of the first group are more spread out than for the second group. This means there may be many people in the first group who are fitter than those in the second group.

Example 2

Martina and Tessa are taking part in a javelin competition.

Before the competition both women have the following statistics related to their throws for the season.

	Mean throw (metres)	Range of throws (metres)
Martina	53.7	7.8
Tessa	54.6	4.2

What interpretation can be made of these statistics?

The statistics tell us that Tessa's mean throw is greater than Martina's.

Tessa's range is less than Martina's range, so we can say that Tessa's throws are more consistent than Martina's.

We can also interpret these statistics to say that Martina may well have the longest throw but without more evidence this is inconclusive.

On the evidence we have we could not make any judgements about which of the two women is more likely to do best in the competition.

Example 3

Used cars in a sample all had about the same price when they were new. This scatter diagram shows the prices of the sample of used cars plotted against their ages:

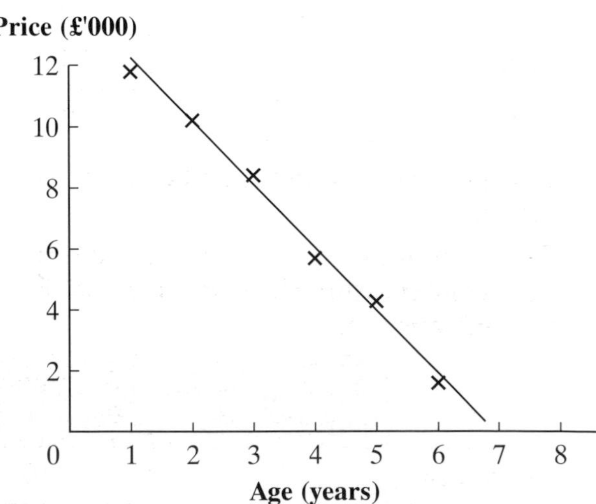

The line of best fit has been drawn on the scatter diagram.

(a) Describe the correlation shown in this diagram.

(b) What conclusions can you draw about the relationship between the price of a used car and its age?

(a) The diagram shows high negative correlation. (The points almost lie on a straight line.)

(b) This means that in general the price of a used car decreases as it gets older. A larger sample of cars would lead to a more reliable conclusion.

Exercise 29A

1 Year 11 at Budhil High School is split into three forms: A, B, and C, of 30 pupils each.

This table provides information about the number of absentees from each form during a week:

	Mon	Tues	Weds	Thurs	Fri
A	0	0	0	0	5
B	1	1	1	1	1
C	0	2	0	3	0

Interpret these statistics and use them to make comments about the number of absentees from each form during that week.

2 In a game of golf the score is the number of strokes a golfer makes to get the ball into all 18 holes of the course.

Here is a table of information about the scores of two groups of golfers called the Hawks and the Buzzards:

	Mean score	Range
Hawks	79	18
Buzzards	75	6

Interpret these statistics and comment on the scores of the two groups.

3 The town of Lucea has two sports clubs: the Tavistock club and the President club. Here are some statistics about the ages of the club members.

	Median age of members	Interquartile range of ages
Tavistock	35	10
President	30	17

Do the statistics give an indication that the members of one club are in general older than the members of the other club? Interpret these statistics and comment on them to explain your answer.

4 Passengers travelling by air for their holiday were asked how much they paid for their holiday and how far from the UK their holiday destination was. Their answers were plotted on the scatter diagram.

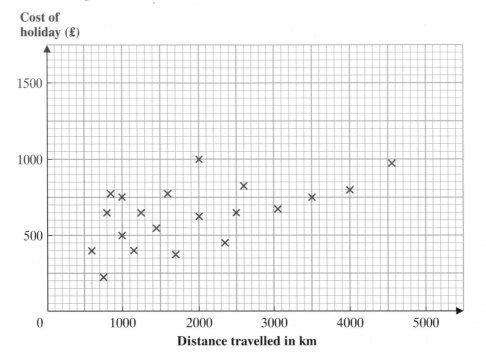

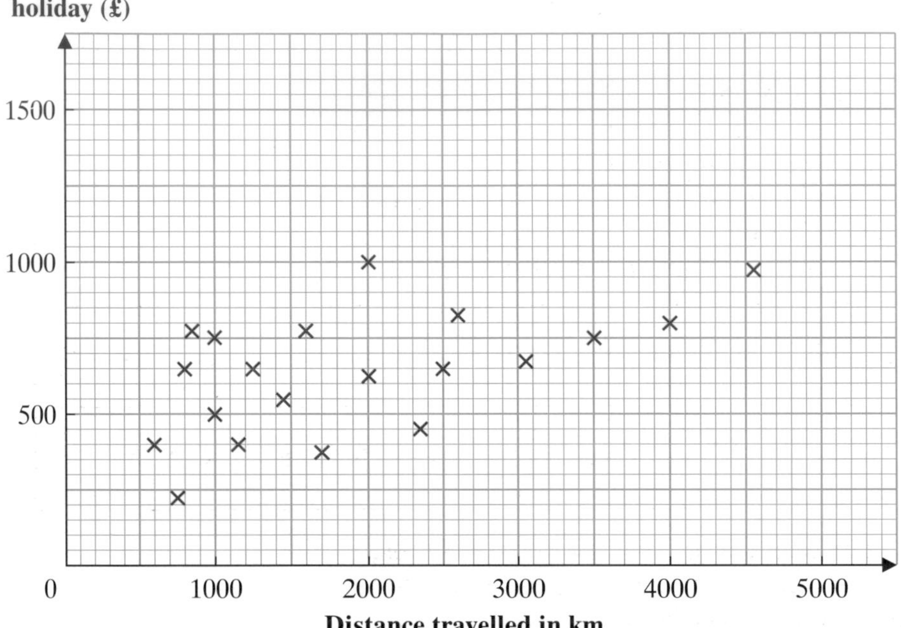

Comment on the relationship between the cost of the holiday and the distance of the destination from the UK. [L]

5 In a motor race there were 16 competitors.
The number of laps each competitor completed was recorded. The average lap time was also recorded.
These two pieces of data were recorded on the scatter diagram.
Comment on the relationship between the average lap time and the number of completed laps. [L]

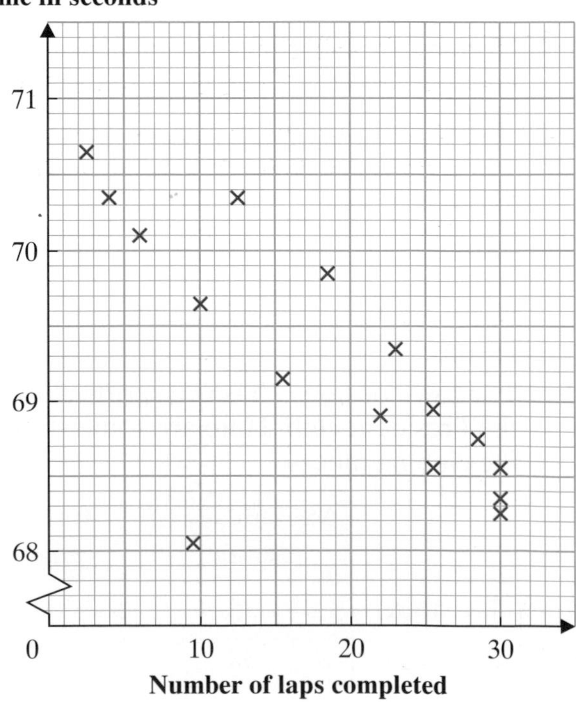

6 Tejinder wonders if there is any connection between a person's shoe size and their height. She collects information from others in the class. These are the results:

Shoe size	$5\frac{1}{2}$	7	11	$8\frac{1}{2}$	8	$8\frac{1}{2}$	$7\frac{1}{2}$	9	$9\frac{1}{2}$	$10\frac{1}{2}$	$7\frac{1}{2}$
Height in cm	152	161	190	183	176	177	180	176	163	178	160

Shoe size	10	$7\frac{1}{2}$	6	$6\frac{1}{2}$	7	$8\frac{1}{2}$	7	$7\frac{1}{2}$	8
Height in cm	180	173	156	170	170	172	165	170	180

(i) Construct a scatter diagram.

(ii) Comment on any possible connection between the shoe sizes and heights of different people.

7 The postwoman delivers letters to houses in Vale Close and Wheeler Gardens. Here is a record of the number of letters delivered to the houses in each place during one day:

Vale Close	1	0	2	4	2	30	3	4	2	2	0	0
Wheeler Gardens	4	6	7	3	2	5	5	6	8	4	5	5

Make at least four statistical comments, with explanations, about the numbers of letters delivered to the houses in Vale Close and the number of letters delivered to the houses in Wheeler Gardens on that day.

Summary of key points

1 When interpreting data 'explain' does not mean 'describe'.

2 When interpreting data you must clearly state the statistics you are using to support your interpretation.

30 Calculators and computers

This unit shows you some ways of using scientific calculators, graphical calculators and computers to help you solve mathematical problems.

The examples will work on Casio calculators and most computers. You teacher will tell you if you need to change any of the instructions.

30.1 How well do you know your scientific calculator?

You can use your calculator to help with fractions, decimals, percentages and money problems.

Try the following examples:

Example 1: fractions and decimals

Work out $\frac{2}{5} + 1\frac{1}{4}$

Press the keys 2 a b/c 5 + 1 a b/c 1 a b/c 4 =

The calculator display is 1⌟13⌟20 so the answer is $1\frac{13}{20}$

d/c

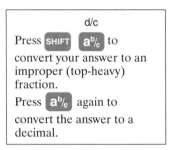

Press SHIFT a b/c to convert your answer to an improper (top-heavy) fraction.

Press a b/c again to convert the answer to a decimal.

Example 2: fractions and money

Work out $\frac{3}{8}$ of £6

Press the keys 3 a b/c 8 × 6 =

The calculator display is 2⌟1⌟4

Press a b/c again to get £2.25

Example 3: percentages

Work out 20% of 6 metres

Press 6 × 2 0 SHIFT = (%)

The answer is 1.2 metres

Example 4: percentage increase or decrease

Reduce £18 by 10%

Press 1 8 × 1 0 SHIFT % = −

The calculator display is 16.2

The answer is £16.20

You can make your calculator show pounds and pence correctly by using Fix 2. This will always display two decimal places. Don't forget to return your calculator to normal mode after doing this.

> Find out how to use FIX mode (decimal places) on your calculator.

Example 5: constant calculations

Work out £2.80 × 1.2

£8.90 × 1.2

£7.65 × 1.2

		Answers
Press	1 · 2 × × 2 · 8 0 =	£3.36
then	8 · 9 0 =	£10.68
then	7 · 6 5 =	£9.18

> Find out what happens when you press any of the keys 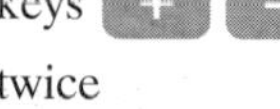 twice

Example 6: compound interest

A student borrows £600 to buy a computer. Interest is added to the loan each year at the rate of 5% per annum.
How much does the student owe after 3 years if no repayments are made?

Press 1 · 0 5 × × 6 0 0 =

Now press = =

Answer £694.58

> Each year the loan is increased by 5%
> 105% is 1.05
> Pressing = multiplies the last answer by 1.05 each time

Example 7: brackets

Work out $\frac{7 + 12 + 5}{3}$

Press (7 + 1 2 + 5) ÷ 3 =

Answer 8

Example 8: memory calculations

Find the total cost of the following items, and calculate the change from £10.

2 at £1.15, 3 at 98p and 1 at £1.79

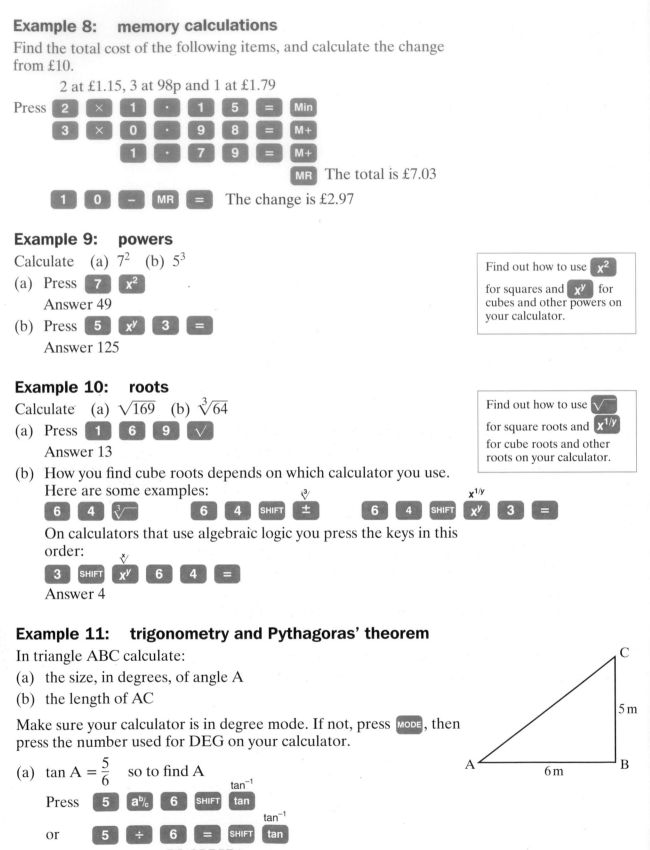

Press [2] [×] [1] [·] [1] [5] [=] [Min]
[3] [×] [0] [·] [9] [8] [=] [M+]
[1] [·] [7] [9] [=] [M+]
[MR] The total is £7.03

[1] [0] [−] [MR] [=] The change is £2.97

Example 9: powers

Calculate (a) 7^2 (b) 5^3

(a) Press [7] [x^2]
Answer 49

(b) Press [5] [x^y] [3] [=]
Answer 125

Find out how to use [x^2] for squares and [x^y] for cubes and other powers on your calculator.

Example 10: roots

Calculate (a) $\sqrt{169}$ (b) $\sqrt[3]{64}$

(a) Press [1] [6] [9] [√]
Answer 13

(b) How you find cube roots depends on which calculator you use.
Here are some examples:

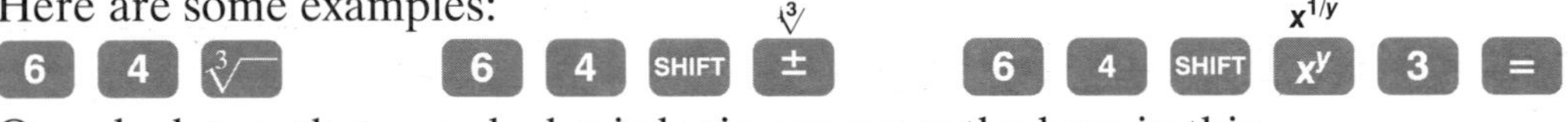

On calculators that use algebraic logic you press the keys in this order:

[3] [SHIFT] [x^y] [6] [4] [=]
Answer 4

Find out how to use [√] for square roots and [$x^{1/y}$] for cube roots and other roots on your calculator.

Example 11: trigonometry and Pythagoras' theorem

In triangle ABC calculate:

(a) the size, in degrees, of angle A

(b) the length of AC

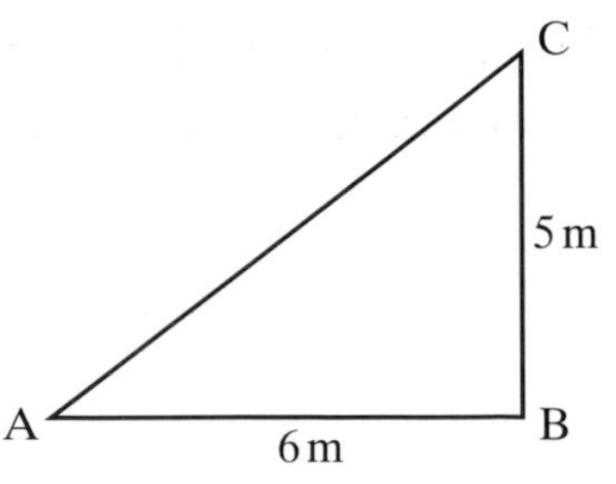

Make sure your calculator is in degree mode. If not, press [MODE], then press the number used for DEG on your calculator.

(a) $\tan A = \frac{5}{6}$ so to find A

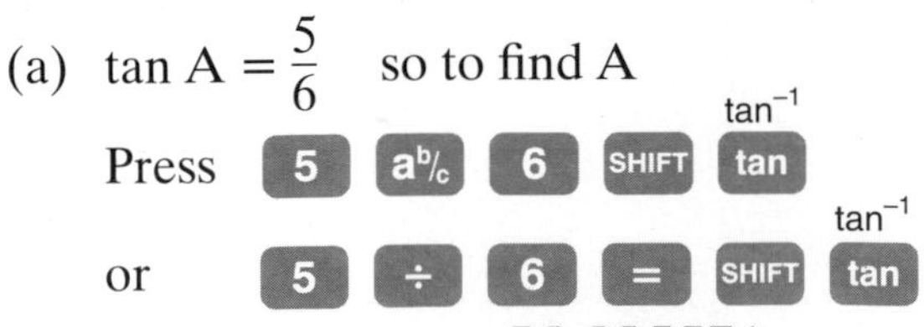

The display shows 39.805571 so the answer is 39.8°

(b) $AC^2 = 5^2 + 6^2$ so $AC = \sqrt{5^2 + 6^2}$

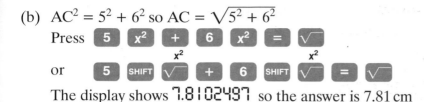

Press 5 x^2 + 6 x^2 = $\sqrt{\ }$

or 5 SHIFT $\sqrt{\ }$ (x^2) + 6 SHIFT $\sqrt{\ }$ (x^2) = $\sqrt{\ }$

The display shows 7.8102497 so the answer is 7.81 cm

Example 12: entering numbers in standard form

(a) The distance from the Earth to the Sun is 9.3×10^7 miles. Write 9.3×10^7 as an ordinary number.

(b) A nanometre is 10^{-9} metres.

Write 60 nanometres in standard form.

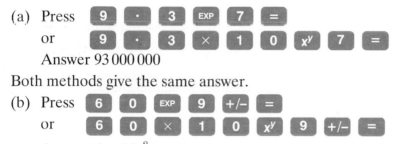

(a) Press 9 · 3 EXP 7 =

or 9 · 3 × 1 0 x^y 7 =

Answer 93 000 000

Both methods give the same answer.

(b) Press 6 0 EXP 9 +/– =

or 6 0 × 1 0 x^y 9 +/– =

Answer 6×10^{-8}

Use the EXP key for powers of 10.

Example 13: converting numbers into standard form

The distance from the Earth to the Moon is 384 400 km. Write the total distance from the Earth to the Moon and back again in standard form.

Find out how to use SCI mode (standard form) on your calculator.

Press 3 8 4 4 0 0 × 2 =

Answer 768 800

You can make your calculator show this answer in standard form by using SCI 0. On a calculator for which SCI is mode 8 you press

MODE 8 0

The calculator will now display the maximum number of digits.

It will show 7.6880000^{05}

You can write this in standard form as 7.688×10^5 km.

Don't forget to return your calculator to normal mode after doing this.

30.2 Using memories to represent formulae on a graphical calculator

Look at this problem:

Find the area and perimeter of a rectangle 9.83 cm by 5.21 cm using the graphical calculator memories.

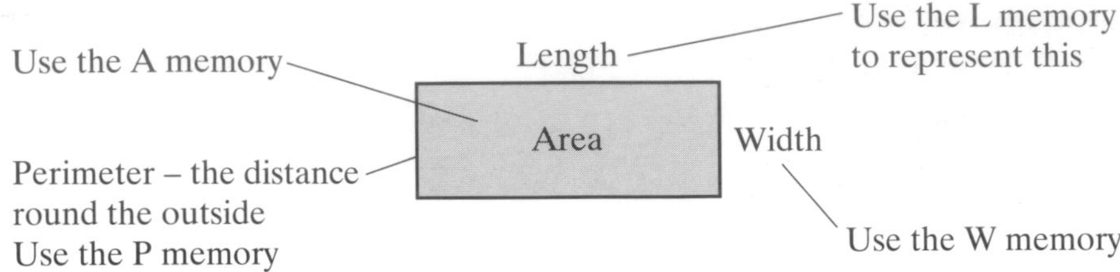

Example 14

Use memories L, W, A and P to calculate the area and perimeter of a rectangle 9.83 cm by 5.21 cm.

(a) store the number 9.83 in memory L.
(b) store the number 5.21 in memory W.
(c) multiply memories L and W and store the answer in memory A.
(d) calculate the perimeter and store it in memory P.

Find out how to clear the memories.

Remember to press the ALPHA key before each letter key:

(a) press the keys 9 · 8 3 → L EXE

(b) press the keys 5 · 2 1 → W EXE

(c) press the keys L W → A EXE

The area of the rectangle is 51.2143 cm^2

(d) press the keys 2 L + 2 W → P EXE

The perimeter of the rectangle is 30.08 cm

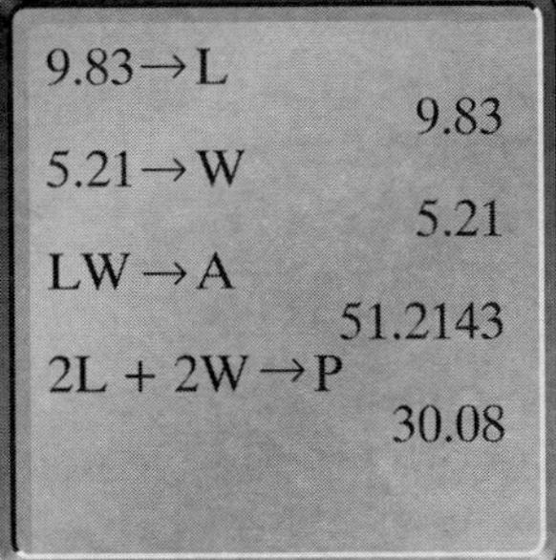

It is useful *but not essential* to store each answer in a memory for future use as shown above.

Now try pressing the keys L W EXE

This produces the same result for the area but the answer is not stored in a memory.

Example 15

Use the memories set up in Example 14 to find:

(a) the area of the rectangle again.
(b) the perimeter of the rectangle.

(a) Type:

(i) [L] [W] [EXE] (ii) [W] [L] [EXE]

(iii) [L] [×] [W] [EXE] (iv) [W] [×] [L] [EXE]

All four answers are the same: 5.2143

(b) Type:

(i) [2] [L] [+] [2] [W] [EXE]

(ii) [2] [×] [L] [+] [2] [×] [W] [EXE]

(iii) [2] [(] [L] [+] [W] [)] [EXE]

(iv) [2] [×] [(] [L] [+] [W] [)] [EXE]

All four answers are the same: 30.08

Notice that formulae are typed exactly as you would write them. Multiplication signs are not needed between letters or before brackets.

Exercise 30A

1 Calculate the area and perimeter of a rectangle 73 cm by 49 cm using any of the methods described above.
Write down the sequence of keys as you press them.

2 Calculate the area A and circumference C of a circle whose radius is 12 cm. You should store the value 12 in memory R, then use the formulae:

$$\pi R^2 \rightarrow A$$

$$\text{and } 2\pi R \rightarrow C$$

Write down the sequence of keys as you press them.

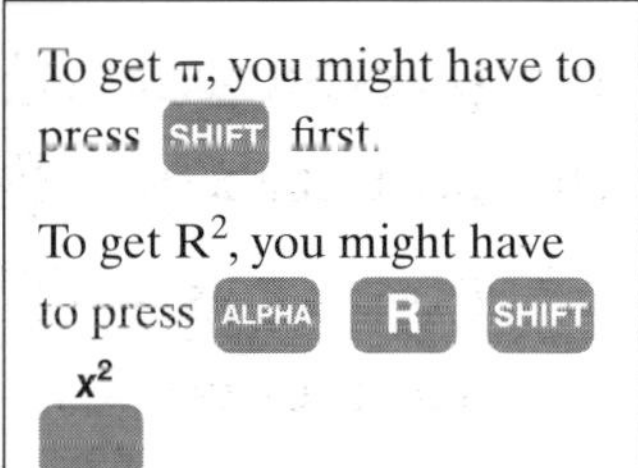

To get π, you might have to press SHIFT first.
To get R^2, you might have to press ALPHA R SHIFT x^2

3 Calculate the area A of a triangle whose base B is 15 cm and whose height H is 9 cm, using the formula:

$$(BH) \div 2 \rightarrow A$$

Write down the sequence of keys as you press them.

4 Calculate the volume V of a rectangular box whose length L is 120 cm, width W is 60 cm and height H is 20 cm using the formula:

$$LWH \rightarrow V$$

Write down the sequence of keys as you press them.

5 Calculate the volume V of a cylinder whose base radius R is 5 cm and whose height H is 12 cm using the formula:

$$\pi R^2 H \rightarrow V$$

Write down the sequence of keys as you press them.

30.3 Saving formulae so you can use them again

If you want to use the same formula several times you should save it as a program. Then you can use it again with different numbers.

Find out how to *write*, *run* and *clear* programs on your graphical calculator.

Select the 'WRT' mode on the calculator, and choose a program number, say Prog 3.

Now type $\pi R^2 \rightarrow A$

Select the 'RUN' mode on the calculator and then press

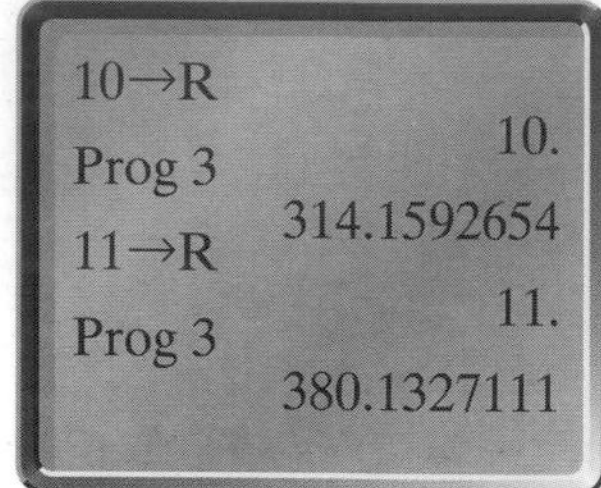

You can improve this program by adding more lines which tell you what to do:

"RADIUS"

$? \rightarrow R$

$\pi R^2 \rightarrow A$

? is used to input a number which is then stored in memory R

To run this new program, press Prog 3 EXE

When the ? appears press:

1 0 EXE EXE
1 1 EXE EXE
1 2 EXE

Notice that EXE is pressed twice.

The first EXE enters the radius and Prog 3 produces the area.

The second EXE runs the program again.

You can do the same thing by writing a computer program in BASIC:

```
10 PRINT "RADIUS"
20 INPUT R
30 LET A = PI * R ^ 2
40 PRINT A
50 END
```

```
RUN
RADIUS
?
10
314.1592654
RUN
```

Exercise 30B

1 Write a program for your graphical calculator or computer which will calculate the volume V of a cube whose sides are of length L.
Use it to find the volumes of cubes whose sides are 5 cm, 6 cm and 7 cm.

2 Write a program for your graphical calculator or computer which will convert a temperature in degrees Fahrenheit (°F) to degrees Celsius (°C) using the formula:

$$C = (F - 32) \times \frac{5}{9}$$

Use it to convert 86°F, 50°F, 68°F to Celsius.

3 Write a program for your graphical calculator or computer which will calculate the area A of a triangle using the formula:

$$A = (B \times H) \div 2$$

Use it to find the area of a triangle whose base B is 15 cm and whose perpendicular height H is 7 cm.

30.4 Solving problems and equations by trial and improvement

Look at this problem:

Find the radius of a circle whose area is 100 cm^2.

Sometimes you can solve problems like this by guessing a solution and trying it out.

You can find the radius by guessing it and trying it in the formula $A = \pi r^2$

You can improve your guess and try again until you get a good enough answer.

This method of solving problems is called trial and improvement. You can use your calculator or computer to help you do this.

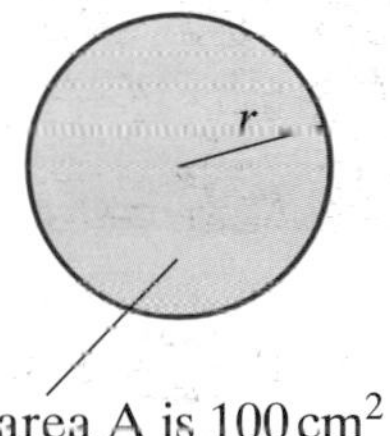

area A is 100 cm^2

What is the radius r?

There is more about trial and improvement methods on pages 182 and 249.

Example 16

Use a trial and improvement method to find the radius R of a circle whose area A is 100 cm^2.

Your answer should be accurate to 2 d.p.

Method

Guess a value for R.
Calculate πR^2.
Compare your answer with 100.
If your answer was too small, choose a bigger value for R.

If your answer is too big, choose a smaller value for R.

Keep repeating this process until you find a value of R correct to 2 d.p. which makes πR^2 as close as possible to 100.

Solution

On a graphical calculator type $? \rightarrow R : \pi R^2$ EXE

When the ? appears, enter your first guess. Suppose this is $R = 10$ cm.

Type 1 0 EXE EXE

Notice that EXE is pressed twice.

The first EXE enters the radius and the area is calculated.

The second EXE repeats the process and another ? appears.

The answer 314.159 265 4 is too big so try a smaller value for R.

> You must include the colon : as shown or else replace it by SHIFT EXE

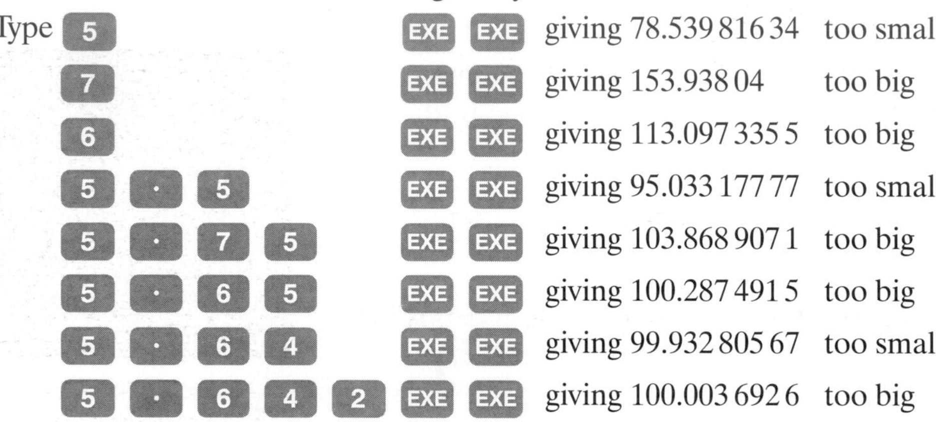

Type 5 EXE EXE giving 78.539 816 34 too small
7 EXE EXE giving 153.938 04 too big
6 EXE EXE giving 113.097 335 5 too big
5 · 5 EXE EXE giving 95.033 177 77 too small
5 · 7 5 EXE EXE giving 103.868 907 1 too big
5 · 6 5 EXE EXE giving 100.287 491 5 too big
5 · 6 4 EXE EXE giving 99.932 805 67 too small
5 · 6 4 2 EXE EXE giving 100.003 692 6 too big

You can now see that the radius R lies between 5.64 cm and 5.642 cm. So $R = 5.64$ cm correct to 2 d.p.

You can do the same thing by writing a computer program in BASIC:

```
10 INPUT R
20 PRINT PI * R ^ 2
30 GOTO 10
40 END
```

Try it using the numbers 5, 7, 6, 5.5, 5.75 and so on until you decide when to stop.

Exercise 30C

1 Use a trial and improvement method to find the length L of the side of a cube whose volume V is 100 cm^3.
The formula is $V = L^3$.
Your answer should be accurate to 2 d.p.

> Find out how to enter L^3 (L raised to the power 3) on your graphical calculator.

2 Use a trial and improvement method to find the length L of the side of a cube whose total surface area A is $50\,\text{cm}^2$.
The formula is $A = 6L^2$.
Your answer should be correct to 2 d.p.

3 Use ? → F : (F – 32) × 5 ÷ 9 → C to convert a temperature of 22°C to Fahrenheit (°F) by trial and improvement. Stop when you have an answer correct to 1 d.p.

4 Use a trial and improvement method to solve the equation $x^3 + x = 19$, giving your answer correct to 1 d.p.

? → X : X³ + X

30.5 Using the Ans and EXE keys to produce number sequences

You can use these keys together on a graphical calculator to generate number sequences.
For example:

Press  1 EXE

then  Ans + 1 EXE EXE EXE ... keep pressing EXE

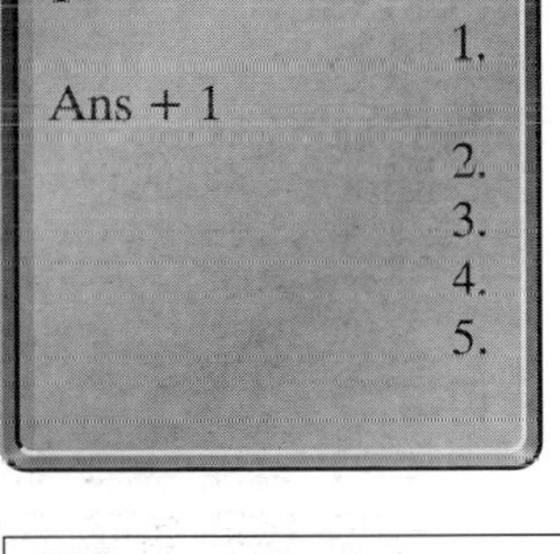

The calculator appears to be 'counting'.
Each time EXE is pressed, 'Ans + 1' is calculated, where Ans is the *last displayed answer*.

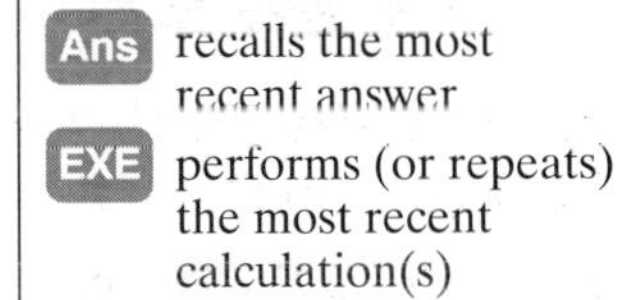

Ans recalls the most recent answer
EXE performs (or repeats) the most recent calculation(s)

Example 17

(a) Use the Ans and EXE keys to produce the even numbers, starting with 2.
(b) Show how the Ans and EXE keys can be used to produce the sequence 2, 6, 18, 54, and so on.

(a) 2 EXE Ans + 2 EXE EXE EXE ...
(b) 2 EXE Ans × 3 EXE EXE EXE ...

Exercise 30D

Write down the key presses, including Ans and EXE to generate the following sequences:

1 5, 10, 15, 20, 25, ...
2 2, 4, 8, 16, 32, ...
3 10, 9, 8, 7, 6, ...
4 200, 20, 2, 0.2, 0.02, ...
5 –5, –7, –9, –11, –13, ...
6 3, 9, 81, 6561, ...
7 3, 7, 3, 7, 3, ...

Example 18: compound interest (see also Example 6)

A student borrows £600 to buy a computer. Interest is added to the loan each year at the rate of 5% per annum.
How much does the student owe after 3 years if no repayments are made?

Press 6 0 0 EXE

then Ans + Ans × 5 ÷ 1 0 0 EXE EXE EXE

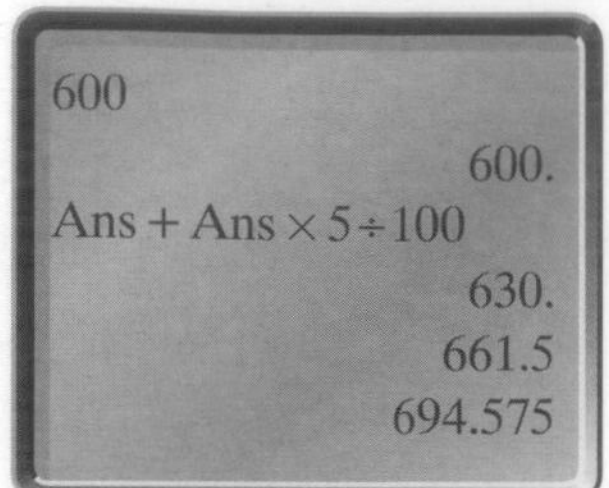

30.6 Drawing graphs on your calculator

Choose the *default ranges* for x and y by pressing Range INIT Range Range
On some calculators you may need to press

Range SHIFT Mcl DEL Range

to choose the default ranges for x and y
Clear the graphics screen by pressing SHIFT Cls EXE
Have a look at the graphics screen by pressing G↔T
Both axes are marked off in intervals of 1.

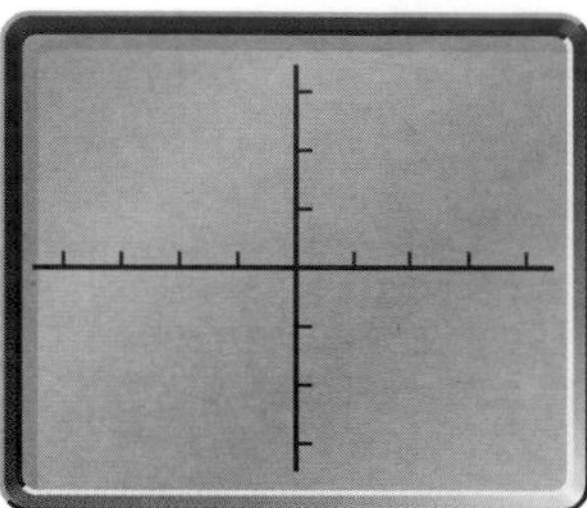

Example 19

Draw the graphs of $y = x + 1$ and $y = x - 1$
Press the Graph key, then X + 1 EXE
The first graph is drawn.
To see the second graph, press the Graph key again then
X − 1 EXE
Notice that the second graph is *superimposed*. It is drawn on the same axes as the first without erasing the first. This will continue to happen with further graphs until you *clear the Graphics Screen*. Clear the screen by pressing SHIFT Cls EXE

If your calculator has a key marked x, θ, T press it to get X.

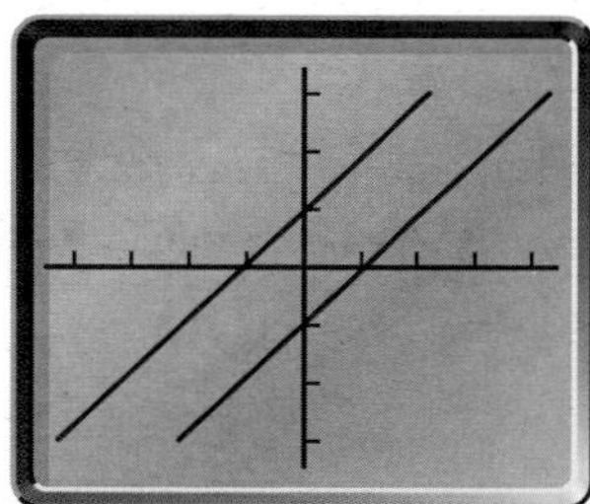

Example 20

Draw the graphs of $y = mx + c$ for several different values of m and c.
Take $m = 2$ and values of c between −4 and 4.
Type "M" ? → M : "C" ? → C : Graph MX + C EXE
When the first ? appears, enter your value for M, then press EXE
When the second ? appears, enter your value for C, then EXE.
Wait until the graph is drawn.
Now press EXE again to draw more graphs on the same axes.

Find out how to set the ranges of x and y to your own chosen values.

Press:

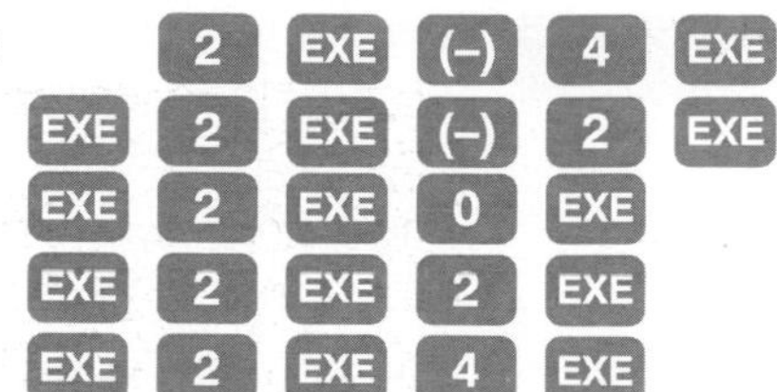

Each time wait until the graph is drawn before continuing.

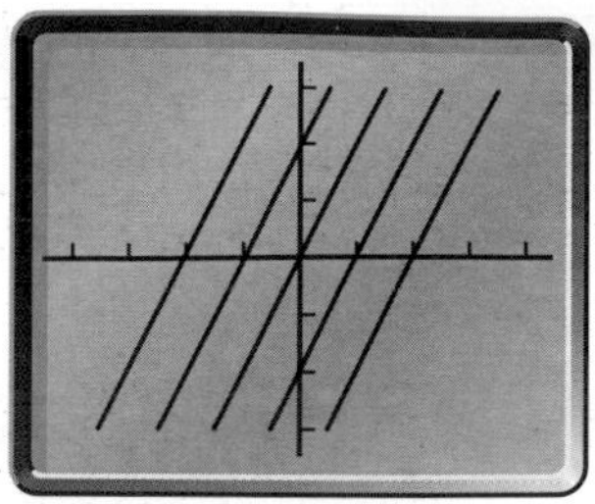

Clear the screen to finish.
Try other values for m and c.

Exercise 30E

In each question draw all the graphs on the same axes and write down what you see.
Clear the screen before starting the next question.

1 $y = ax^2 + c$ for different values of a and c

2 $y = ax^3 + c$ for different values of a and c

3 $y = ax^3 + bx$ for different values of a and b

4 $y = x + a \div x$ for different values of a

30.7 Solving equations by drawing graphs on your calculator

Example 21

You can solve the equation $x^2 - 4 = 2x - 3$ by drawing the graphs of $y = x^2 - 4$ and $y = 2x - 3$ on suitable axes and finding their point(s) of intersection.

Choose the *default ranges* for x and y and clear the graphics screen.

Press:            

Both graphs will be drawn. If they do not quite fit on the screen, zoom out by a factor of 2.

Now press 

A flashing cross or dot is placed on the last line drawn and its x and y coordinates are displayed on the screen.

Press the right arrow (and left arrow) keys several times to make this dot move along the line. Stop when you reach a point where the two graphs cross and write down the x coordinate of the point of intersection.

The answers are 2.4 and −0.4 (correct to 1 d.p.).

Find out how to *zoom* and *trace* on your graphical calculator.

On some you zoom by changing the x and y ranges.

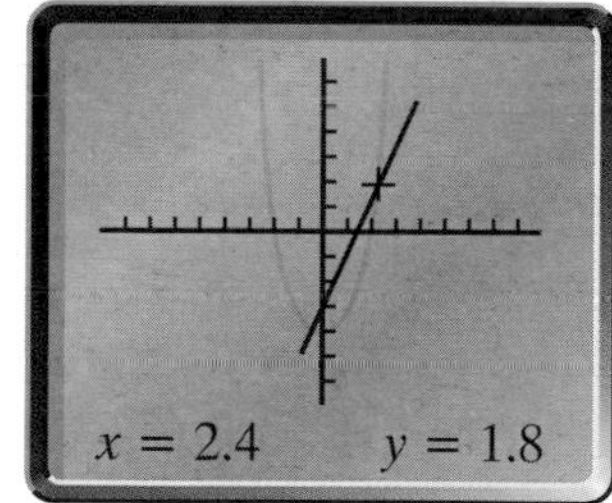

Exercise 30F

Draw suitable graphs on a graphical calculator to solve these equations:

1 $x^2 - 2x = 2 - x$ **2** $2x^2 + 1 = 7x - 2$

3 $x^3 - 2x + 1 = 1 - x$ **4** $2x^3 - 3x^2 = 5x - 6$

Change the range so that y min = 0 and y max = 20.

You will need to change the range for y to find two of the answers.

30.8 Investigating number sequences with a spreadsheet

You can generate many number sequences on the same spreadsheet and compare them.

Find out how to enter numbers and formulae in the cells of your spreadsheet.

Find out how to copy a formula from one cell to other cells.

Example 22

Generate the whole numbers up to 10 in column A.

Put the number 1 in cell A1.
Put the formula A1 + 1 in cell A2.
Copy the formula in A2 down column A as far as A10.

Formula A2 = A1 + 1

Formula B2 = B1 + 2

Formula C2 = C1 + A2

Formula D2 = B1 + B2

Formula E2 = C1 + C2

	A	B	C	D	E	F
1	1	1	1			
2	2	3	3	4	4	
3	3	5	6	8	9	
4	4	7	10	12	16	
5	5	9	15	16	25	
6	6	11	21	20	36	
7	7	13	28	24	49	
8	8	15	36	28	64	
9	9	17	45	32	81	
10	10	19	55	36	100	
11						

Example 23

Generate the odd numbers in column B.

Put the number 1 in cell B1.
Put the formula B1 + 2 in cell B2.
Copy the formula in B2 down column B as far as B10.

Example 24

Generate the triangular numbers in column C.

Put the number 1 in cell C1.
Put the formula C1 + A2 in cell C2.
Copy the formula in C2 down column C as far as C10.

Example 25

(a) Add consecutive odd numbers and put the answers in column D.
(b) Describe the numbers in column D.

(a) Put the formula B1 + B2 in cell D2.
Copy the formula in D2 down column D as far as D10.
(b) The numbers in column D are multiples of 4.

Example 26

(a) Add consecutive triangular numbers and put the answers in column E.

(b) Describe the number sequence in column E.

(a) Put the formula C1 + C2 in cell E2.
Copy the formula in E2 down column E as far as E10.

(b) The numbers in column E are square numbers.

Exercise 30G

1 **(a)** Enter the letter n in cell A1 of a spreadsheet.
Generate the whole numbers from 1 to 10 in column A, starting with 1 in cell A2.

(b) Put the formula $3 \times$ A2 + 2 in cell B2.

(c) Copy the formula in B2 down column B as far as B11.

2 Work in pairs for this game.
In question **1**, an expression for the nth term of the sequence in column B is $3n + 2$. (The formula entered in cell B2 was $3 \times$ A2 + 2.)

(a) One person, **X**, enters a different formula in terms of A2 into cell C2, without showing **Y**. **X** then copies the formula in C2 down column C as far as C11.

(b) **Y** writes down an expression for the nth term of the sequence generated in column C and shows it to **X**. If the expression is correct **Y** scores a point.

(c) Repeat parts **(a)**, **(b)** and **(c)** using other columns, with **X** and **Y** taking it in turn to enter a formula.

The person with the highest score wins the game.

30.9 Problem solving with a spreadsheet

Look at this problem:

> A farmer has 200 metres of fencing. He wants to use all the fencing to enclose a rectangular area of his field for his animals to graze.
> Find the length and width of the rectangle which gives his animals the maximum grazing area.

You can solve problems like this on a computer by using a spreadsheet.

Example 27

Think of all the rectangles you can draw whose perimeters are 200 metres. For example, some could be long and thin and others short and wide.
Use a spreadsheet to find the length L and width W of the rectangle which has the maximum area.

The perimeter of each rectangle is 200 metres, so:

$$2L + 2W = 200$$

You can divide by 2 to make this equation simpler:

$$L + W = 100$$

Subtracting L from both sides gives:

$$W = 100 - L$$

Make sure your spreadsheet has at least 12 rows and 3 columns. Use column A for the length, column B for the width and column C for the area of each rectangle.

Use your spreadsheet to try lots of values for L from $L = 0$ to $L = 100$ metres.

Increase L by 10 metres each time.

For each value of L calculate a value for W using:

$$W = 100 - L$$

Multiply each value of L by the corresponding value of W to find the area of each rectangle. You can now find the maximum value for the area in column C quite easily.

Formula A3 = A2 + 10

(W = 100 – L) Formula B2 = 100 – A2

(A = L × W) Formula C2 = A2 × B2

	A	B	C	D
1	L	W	LW	
2	0	100	0	
3	10	90	900	
4	20	80	1600	
5	30	70	2100	
6	40	60	2400	
7	50	50	2500	
8	60	40	2400	
9	70	30	2100	
10	80	20	1600	
11	90	10	900	
12	100	0	0	

The maximum area is $2500\,m^2$ when L = 50 m and W = 50 m.

Here is a graph of the data in each column of the spreadsheet. It gives you a better understanding of how the area changes as the lengths and widths of the rectangle changes.

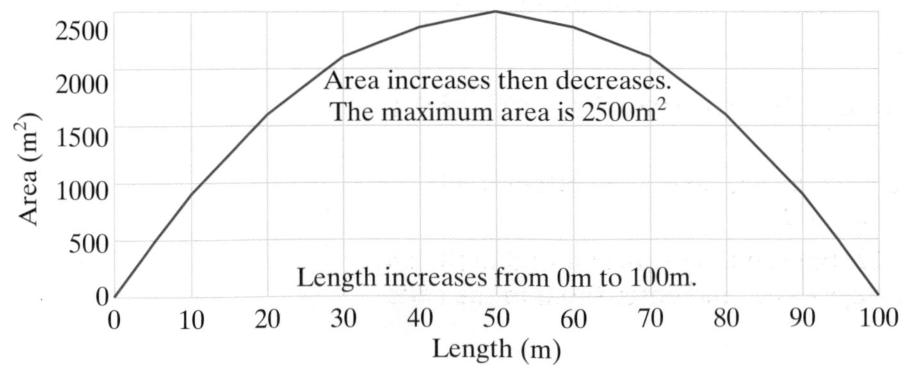

Find out how your spreadsheet produces graphs.

Rectangles can be long and thin or short and wide, but the rectangle with the biggest area is SQUARE!

Exercise 30H

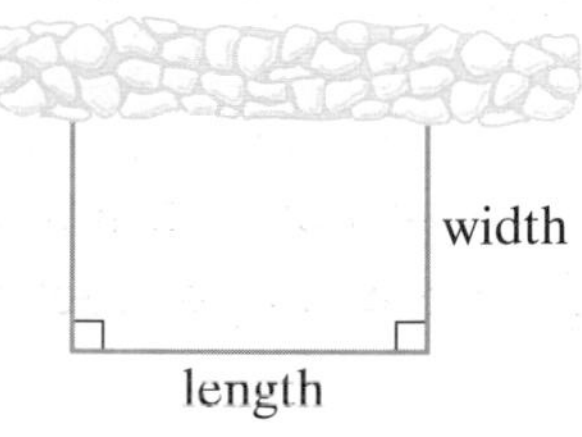

1 A farmer has 120 metres of fencing. She uses the fencing to make three sides of a rectangular enclosure for her sheep. The fourth side of the rectangle is part of a stone wall.
Use a spreadsheet to find the length and width of the rectangle which gives the biggest area for the enclosure.

2 Zehra has 31 stamps. She has twice as many green stamps as red ones, and three more brown stamps than red ones.
Use a spreadsheet to find out how many stamps Zehra has of each colour.
(Hint: Use r for the number of red stamps. Enter values of r in steps of 1 in column A. Use column B for the number of green stamps and column C for the number of brown stamps.)

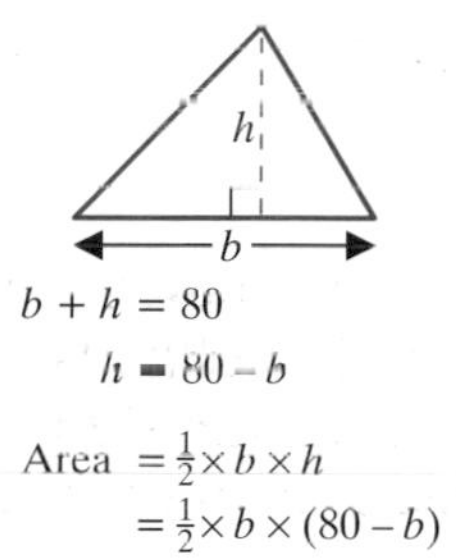

3 The base b cm of a triangle plus the height h cm equals 80 cm.
Use a spreadsheet to find the base and height of the triangle which has the maximum area.
(Hint: Start by entering the values of b in steps of 10 in column A. Use column B for the height and column C for the area of the triangle.)

30.10 Trial and improvement on a spreadsheet

Example 28

area = 30 cm^2 width W
$W = L - 2$
length L

The width of a rectangle is 2 cm less than the length.
Use a trial and improvement method to find the length when the area of the rectangle is 30 cm^2. Give your answer correct to 2 d.p.

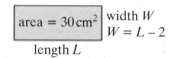

Use L for the length and W for the width of the rectangle. Put the length in column A, the width in column B and the area of the rectangle in column C.

Make sure your spreadsheet has at least 12 rows and 3 columns.

Step 1: Use your spreadsheet to try values for L from 0 to 10 in steps of 1.

Step 2: For each value of L calculate a value for W using:

$$W = L - 2$$

Step 3: Multiply each value of L by the corresponding value of W to find the area of each rectangle.

Step 4: Look for the two areas which are nearest to 30 cm^2 and record the corresponding values of L.

Step 5: Choose new values of L between the values found in Step 4. Use values of L going up in steps of 0.1 and enter them in the cells of column A.

(Notice that the values in all the other cells change automatically. You don't need to enter the formulae again.)

Step 6: Repeat Steps 4 and 5 with values of L going up in steps of 0.01 and 0.001 to get an answer correct to the accuracy you need.

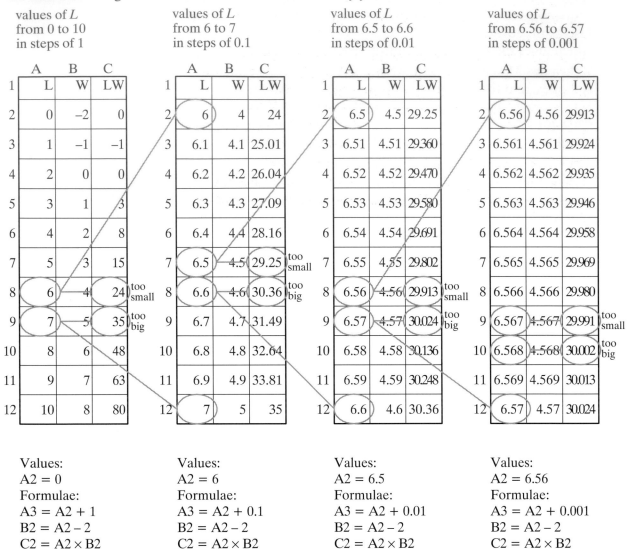

values of L from 0 to 10 in steps of 1

	A	B	C	
1	L	W	LW	
2	0	−2	0	
3	1	−1	−1	
4	2	0	0	
5	3	1	3	
6	4	2	8	
7	5	3	15	
8	6	4	24	too small
9	7	5	35	too big
10	8	6	48	
11	9	7	63	
12	10	8	80	

Values:
A2 = 0
Formulae:
A3 = A2 + 1
B2 = A2 − 2
C2 = A2 × B2

values of L from 6 to 7 in steps of 0.1

	A	B	C	
1	L	W	LW	
2	6	4	24	
3	6.1	4.1	25.01	
4	6.2	4.2	26.04	
5	6.3	4.3	27.09	
6	6.4	4.4	28.16	
7	6.5	4.5	29.25	too small
8	6.6	4.6	30.36	too big
9	6.7	4.7	31.49	
10	6.8	4.8	32.64	
11	6.9	4.9	33.81	
12	7	5	35	

Values:
A2 = 6
Formulae:
A3 = A2 + 0.1
B2 = A2 − 2
C2 = A2 × B2

values of L from 6.5 to 6.6 in steps of 0.01

	A	B	C	
1	L	W	LW	
2	6.5	4.5	29.25	
3	6.51	4.51	29.360	
4	6.52	4.52	29.470	
5	6.53	4.53	29.580	
6	6.54	4.54	29.691	
7	6.55	4.55	29.802	
8	6.56	4.56	29.913	too small
9	6.57	4.57	30.024	too big
10	6.58	4.58	30.136	
11	6.59	4.59	30.248	
12	6.6	4.6	30.36	

Values:
A2 = 6.5
Formulae:
A3 = A2 + 0.01
B2 = A2 − 2
C2 = A2 × B2

values of L from 6.56 to 6.57 in steps of 0.001

	A	B	C	
1	L	W	LW	
2	6.56	4.56	29.913	
3	6.561	4.561	29.924	
4	6.562	4.562	29.935	
5	6.563	4.563	29.946	
6	6.564	4.564	29.958	
7	6.565	4.565	29.969	
8	6.566	4.566	29.980	
9	6.567	4.567	29.991	too small
10	6.568	4.568	30.002	too big
11	6.569	4.569	30.013	
12	6.57	4.57	30.024	

Values:
A2 = 6.56
Formulae:
A3 = A2 + 0.001
B2 = A2 − 2
C2 = A2 × B2

You can now see that the length L lies between 6.567 cm and 6.568 cm.

So $L = 6.57$ cm correct to 2 d.p.

This is much easier than it looks!

Remember that the computer is doing all the really hard work.

Exercise 30I

1 The length of a rectangle is 3 cm more than the width. Use a trial and improvement method on a spreadsheet to find the width when the area of the rectangle is $38\,cm^2$. Give your answer correct to 2 d.p.

2 Winford, Barry and Syreeta count how much cash they each have. Barry has 45p less than Winford and Syreeta has £1.06 more than Winford. Altogether they have £4.54
Use a spreadsheet to find how much each person has.
(Hint: Let the amount that Winford has be W pence. Begin by entering values of W in steps of 10 in column A.)

3 The height of a triangle is 2 cm less than the base. Use a trial and improvement method to find the base of a triangle with an area of $37\,cm^2$. Give your answer correct to 2 d.p.

Examination practice paper

Answer ALL NINETEEN questions. 1 hour 45 minutes

You must write down all stages in your working.

1 Work out the area of this shape.

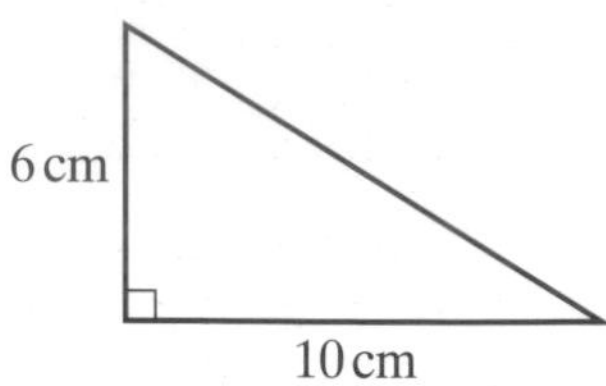

2 Use the formula $v = \frac{s}{t}$

to work out the value of v when $s = 24$ and $t = 3$.

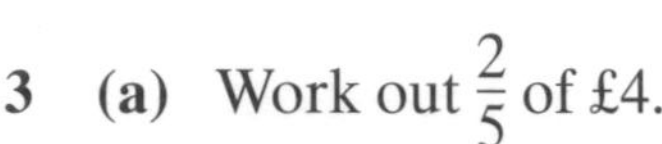

3 **(a)** Work out $\frac{2}{5}$ of £4.

(b) Change 40% to a fraction in its lowest terms.

(c) Work out 12% of 325 km.

(d) £2700 is divided between Ahmed, Dilys and Siobhan in the ratio 4:3:2.
Work out how much each person receives.

4 Solve the equations:

(a) $5x + 3 = 18$

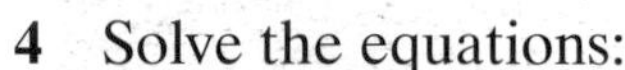

(b) $6y + 15 = 3 - 2y$

5 **(a)** Write down two numbers you could use to get an approximate answer to: 312×59

(b) Write down your approximate answer.

(c) Without using a calculator work out the exact value of 312×59. YOU MUST SHOW ALL YOUR WORKING.

6 The diagram shows part of a sequence of shapes. The shapes are made from hexagons with a dot at each corner and a dot in the centre.

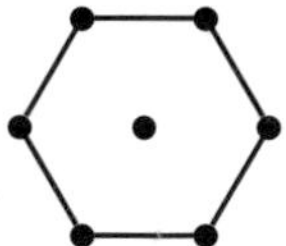

Shape 1

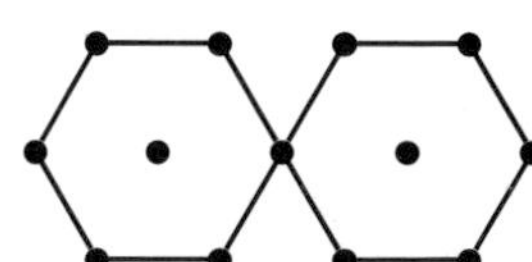

Shape 2

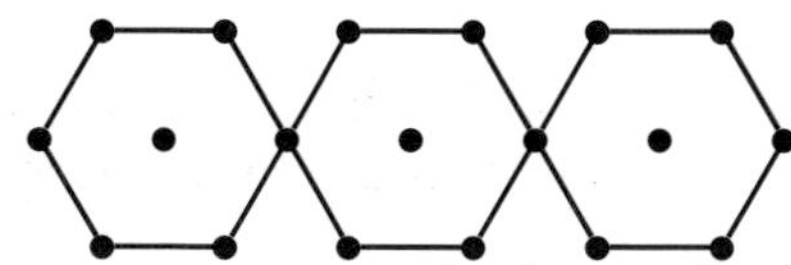

Shape 3

The table shows the number of dots in each of the first 4 shapes in the sequence.

Shape number (n)	1	2	3	4
Number of dots (d)	7	13	19	25

(a) Write down the number of dots for shape number 8.

(b) Write down a formula which can be used to calculate the number of dots, d, in terms of the shape number, n.

7 The distance by road from Newry to Coleraine is 80 miles.
(a) Work out this distance approximately in kilometres.
Davitt drives from Newry to Coleraine in $1\frac{1}{2}$ hours.
(b) Work out Davitt's average speed in miles per hour.

8 The number of cars sold each day in May at V.G. Motors is shown in the frequency table.

Number of cars sold each day	1	2	3	4	5	6	7	8	9	10	11	12
Number of days	2	0	2	4	3	4	4	3	5	0	2	2

For the number of cars sold each day:
(a) Write down the mode.
(b) Write down the Median.
(c) Work out the range.
(d) Work out the Mean. Give your answer to 1 decimal place.

9 180 pupils are asked which is their favourite outdoor sport in the winter. The pie chart shows the results of the survey.

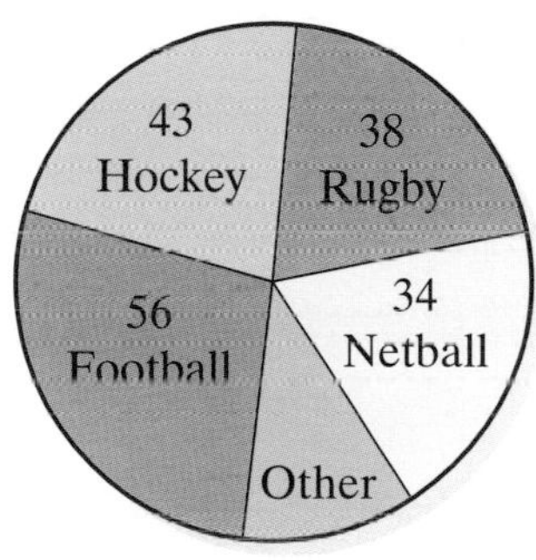

Diagram NOT accurately drawn

Jon is asked to make an accurate drawing of the pie chart.
(a) Work out the angle of the sector representing rugby.
A pupil is chosen at random.
(b) (i) Estimate the probability that the pupil's favourite sport will be hockey.
(ii) Estimate the probability that the pupil's favourite sport will be hockey or football or rugby.

10 There is a positive value of x which satisfies the equation:
$x^3 - x = 10$.
(a) Write down
(i) the nearest whole number below this value of x,
(ii) the nearest whole number above this value of x.
(b) Using a trial and improvement method, find this value of x. Give your answer correct to 2 decimal places.

11 **(a)** Copy the diagram overleaf on to graph paper. Reflect the quadrilateral **A** in the x axis. Label the reflection **B**.
(b) Rotate the quadrilateral **B** through 90° anticlockwise about the centre of rotation (0, 0). Label the image **C**.

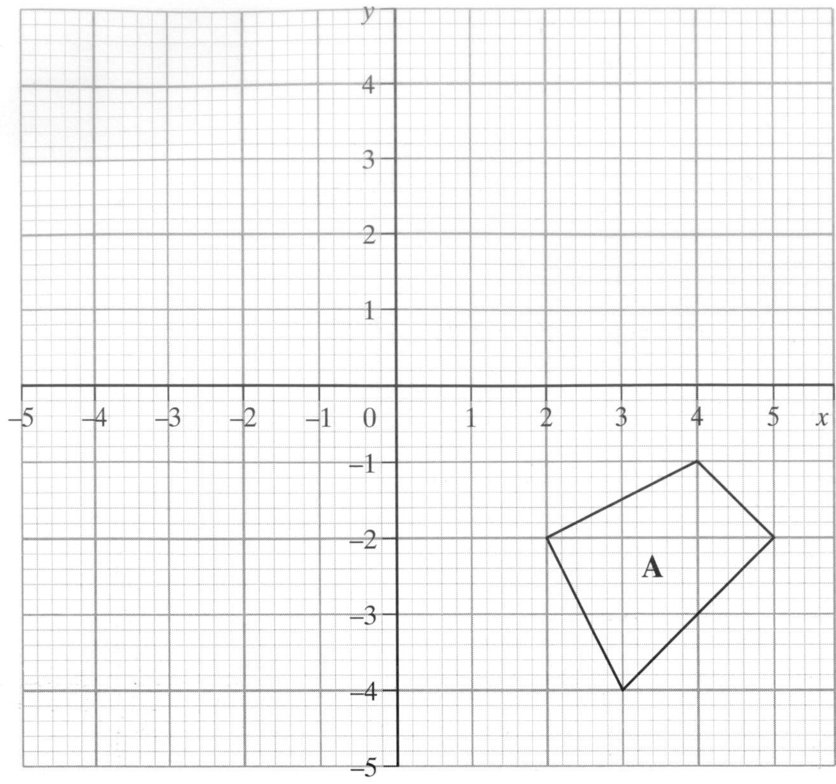

(c) Describe fully the single transformation which maps the quadrilateral **A** on to the quadrilateral **C**.

12 Tina and Julie each attempt to score a goal in netball. The probability that Tina will score a goal is 0.72.

(a) What is the probability that Tina will NOT score a goal?

The probability that Julie will score a goal is 0.6.

(b) Copy and complete the tree diagram below.

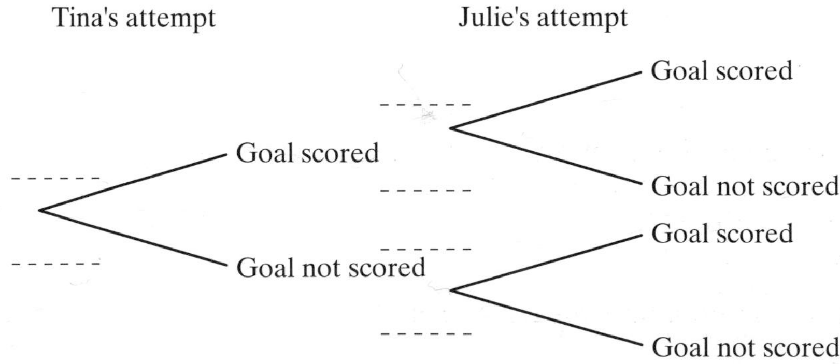

(c) Calculate the probability that:

(i) both Tina and Julie will score goals,

(ii) only one girl will score a goal.

13

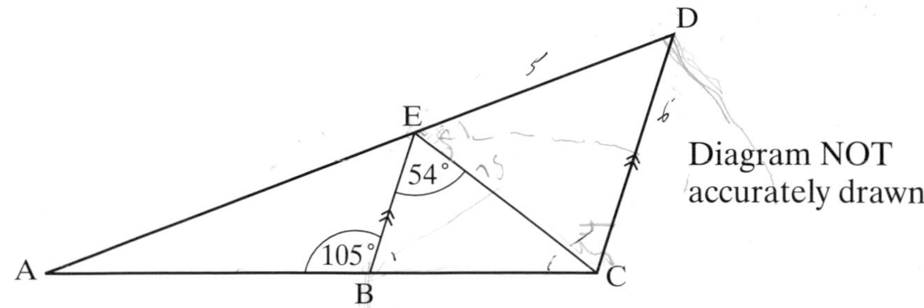

In the diagram BE is parallel to CD, angle ABE = 105° and angle BEC = 54°.

(a) Calculate the size of (i) angle EBC,
(ii) angle ECD.

(b) Given that AE = 10 cm, ED = 5 cm and CD = 6 cm calculate the length of EB.

14 Solve the inequality: $2x - 4 < 19$

15 Use the equation $y = x^3 - 2x^2 + 10$ to complete the table of values.

(a)

x	−3	−2	−1	0	1	2	3
y	−35					10	

(b) Draw the graph of $y = x^3 - 2x^2 + 10$.

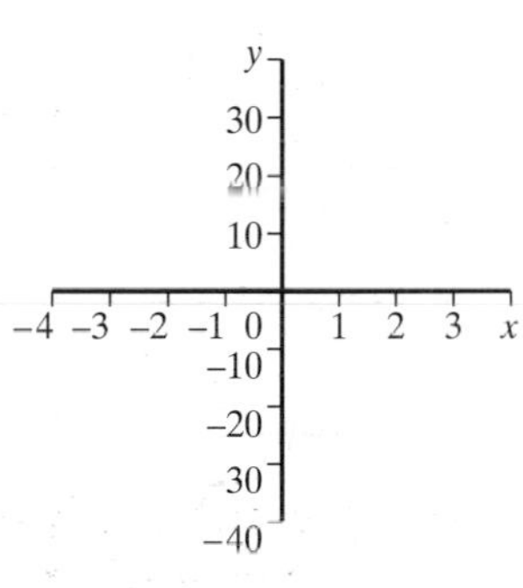

Use these values of x and y for your graph

16

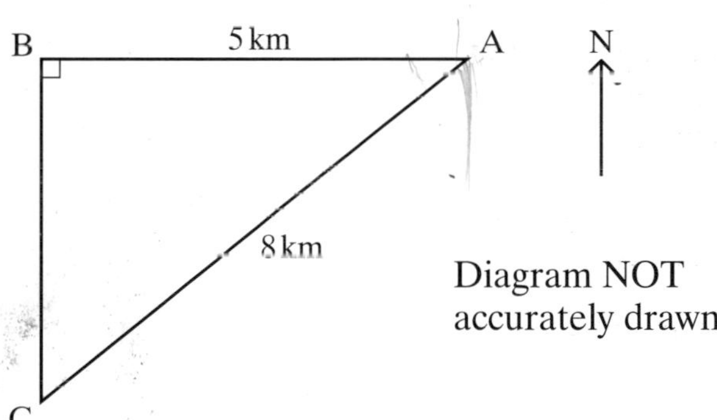

The points A, B and C mark the positions of three boats at sea. B is due north of C, BA = 5 km and AC = 8 km.

(a) Calculate the distance of B from C.

(b) Calculate the bearing of C from A.

17 Calculate the value of c from the simultaneous equations:

$$4c + d = 5$$
$$5c + 2d = 4$$

18 The marks gained by a group of 60 students in an examination are shown in the table.

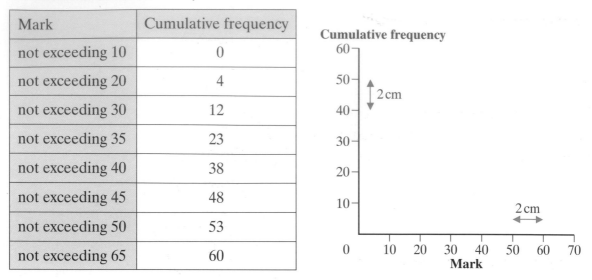

Mark	Cumulative frequency
not exceeding 10	0
not exceeding 20	4
not exceeding 30	12
not exceeding 35	23
not exceeding 40	38
not exceeding 45	48
not exceeding 50	53
not exceeding 65	60

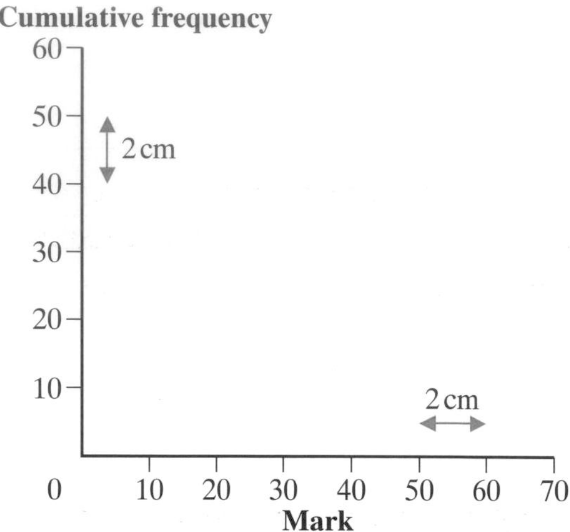

Draw a set of axes with 2 cm on the horizontal axis to represent 10 marks and 2 cm on the vertical axis to represent 10 students.

(a) On your grid draw a cumulative frequency graph to show the figures in the table.

(b) Use your graph to find an estimate for the number of students who gained more than 38 marks.

19 **(a)** Factorize completely: $6a^2 - 8a$

(b) Expand and simplify: $(2x - 3)(x + 2)$

Formulae Sheet: Intermediate Tier

Area of triangle $= \frac{1}{2} \times \text{base} \times \text{height}$

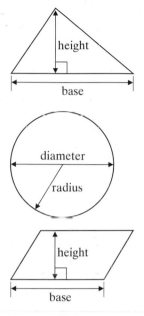

Circumference of circle $= \pi \times \text{diameter}$

$= 2 \times \pi \times \text{radius}$

Area of circle $= \pi \times (\text{radius})^2$

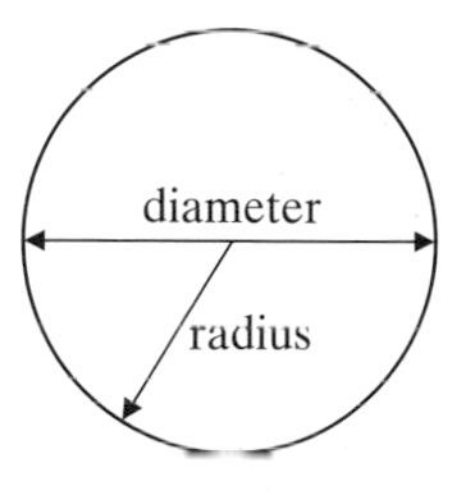

Area of parallelogram $= \text{base} \times \text{height}$

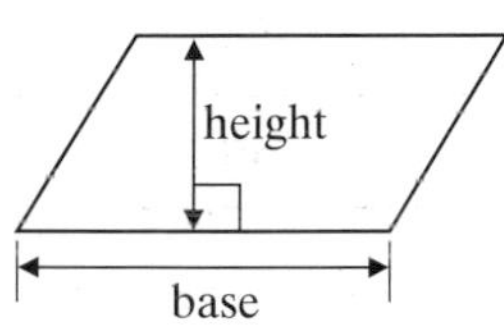

Area of trapezium $= \frac{1}{2}(a + b)h$

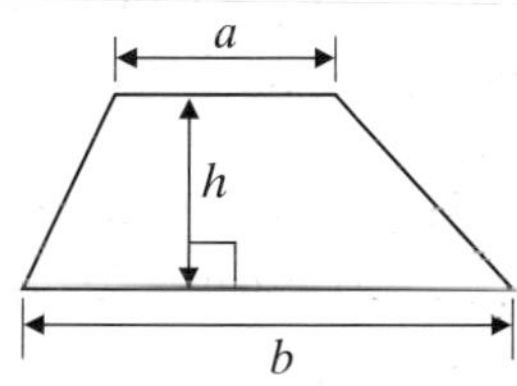

Volume of cuboid $= \text{length} \times \text{width} \times \text{height}$

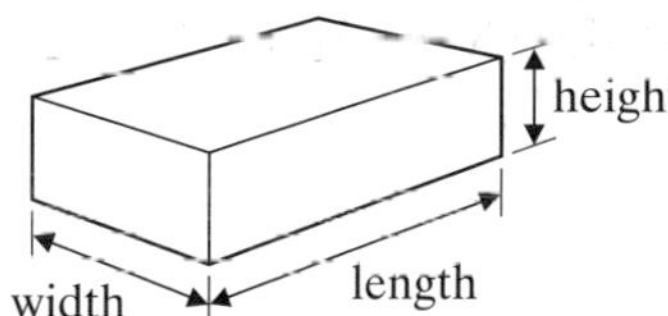

Volume of a cylinder $= \pi r^2 h$

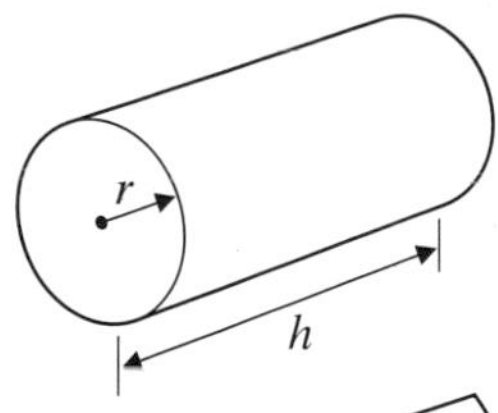

Volume of prism = area of cross section × length

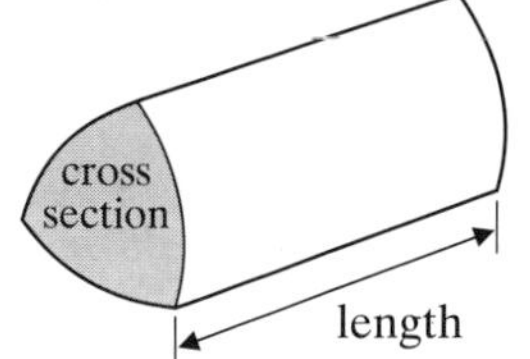

Pythagoras' Theorem

$$a^2 + b^2 = c^2$$

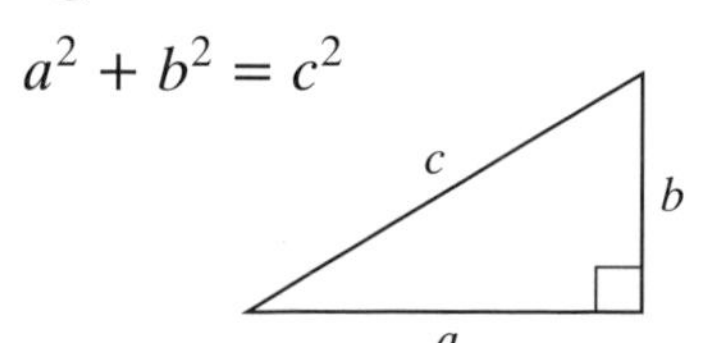

Trigonometry

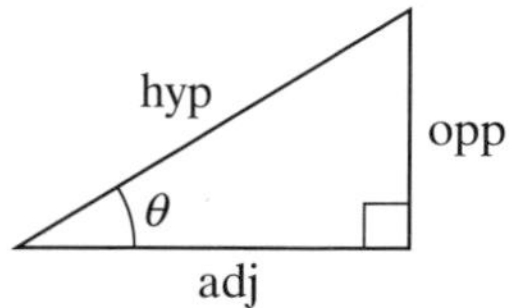

$$\sin\theta = \frac{\text{opp}}{\text{hyp}}$$

$$\cos\theta = \frac{\text{adj}}{\text{hyp}}$$

$$\tan\theta = \frac{\text{opp}}{\text{adj}}$$

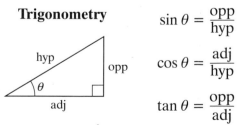

Answers

Unit 1 Number

Exercise 1A

1 (a) Two thousand three hundred and fifty two.
(b) Five thousand and seven.
(c) Twelve thousand three hundred.
(d) One hundred and three thousand, five hundred.
(e) Three hundred and five thousand, two hundred and three.
(f) Four million, forty thousand, four hundred and thirty.

2 (a) Nine hundred and ninety thousand, and ninety nine.
(b) Four hundred and fifty thousand, five hundred and forty.
(c) Six million, seven hundred and fifty thousand, eight hundred.
(d) Five million, two hundred thousand, four hundred and fifty.
(e) Seven million, eight hundred and four thousand, five hundred and sixty one.
(f) Eight hundred million, eight hundred thousand, eight hundred.

3 (a) 100 020 (b) 550 410 (c) 1 500 070
(d) 5 002 405 (e) 4 520 000 (f) 990 009 1 095 004

4 (a) 3 300 013 (b) 1500 (c) 2 500 000 (d) 5250
(e) 6750

Exercise 1B

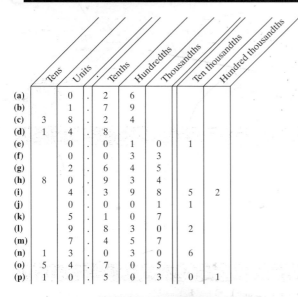

	Tens	Units	.	Tenths	Hundredths	Thousandths	Ten thousandths	Hundred thousandths
(a)		0	.	2	6			
(b)		1	.	7	9			
(c)	3	8	.	2	4			
(d)	1	4	.	8				
(e)		0	.	0	1	0	1	
(f)		0	.	0	3	3		
(g)		2	.	6	4	5		
(h)	8	0	.	9	3	4		
(i)		4	.	3	9	8	5	2
(j)		0	.	0	0	1	1	
(k)		5	.	1	0	7		
(l)		9	.	8	3	0	2	
(m)		7	.	4	5	7		
(n)	1	3	.	0	3	0	6	
(o)	5	4	.	7	0	5		
(p)	1	0	.	5	0	3	0	1

Exercise 1C

1 (a) 2.12 (b) 412.1 (c) 4.01 (d) 27
(e) 213 (f) 240

2 (a) 3710 (b) 0.2131 (c) 4920 (d) 0.0049
(e) 7.9 (f) 0.471

3 (a) 0.578 (b) 65 (c) 95.4 (d) 1.33
(e) 0.045 (f) 7.7 (g) 7990 (h) 1.01

Exercise 1D

1 4.101 m, 4.009 m, 4.0059 m
2 1.25 kg, 0.55 kg, 0.525 kg, $\frac{1}{8}$ kg
3 5.306 km, 5.305 km, 5.204 km, 5.202 km
4 9.99 t, 9.904 t, $9\frac{9}{10}$ t, 9.804 t
5 6.556 s, 6.554 s, $5\frac{3}{4}$ s, 5.623 s
6 2.02 *cl*, 2.0 cl, $\frac{1}{5}$ *cl*, 0.022 *cl*
7 6.306 km, 6.305 km, 6.204 km, 6.202 km
8 6.643 t, 6.448 t, 6.443 t, 4.512 t
9 $10\frac{4}{5}$ cm, 9.8 cm, 9.08 cm, 1.08 cm
10 8.88 m, 8.801 m, 8.8 m, 8.701 m

Exercise 1E

1	2910	2	227	3	9792	4	6696
5	181	6	49 572	7	135r2	8	27 897
9	502r8	10	69 865	11	736	12	431r2
13	10 848	14	333	15	10 656		

Exercise 1F

1 (a) 5°C (b) 3°C (c) 6°C (d) 10°C (e) 10°C
(f) 8°C (g) 5°C (h) 13°C

2 (a) –2°C (b) –3°C (c) –7°C (d) 3°C (e) 3°C
(f) –6°C (g) –9°C

3 (a) –12° C, –7° C, –5° C, –1° C, 0° C, 2° C, 4° C, 7° C, 9° C
(b) –9° C, –8° C, –3° C, –2° C, 0° C, 2° C, 5° C, 8° C, 10° C
(c) –7° C, –6° C, –4° C, –3° C, –1° C, 3° C, 5° C, 7° C, 8° C
(d) –8° C, –4° C, –3° C, –2° C, 1° C, 4° C, 6° C, 7° C, 9° C
(e) –9° C, –7° C, –5° C, –3° C, –1° C, 0° C, 4° C, 5° C, 7° C, 8° C

Exercise 1G

1 (a) 0 (b) –4 (c) –14 (d) –4
2 (a) +1 (b) +17 (c) –2 (d) +10
3 (a) –5 (b) +5 (c) –2 (d) –6
4 (a) –11 (b) +3 (c) +17 (d) –5
5 (a) –14 (b) +3 (c) –5 (d) –9

Exercise 1H

1–3

First number

–5	–4	–3	–2	–1	0	1	2	3	4	5	×
–25	–20	–15	–10	–5	0	5	10	15	20	25	5
–20	–16	–12	–8	–4	0	4	8	12	16	20	4
–15	–12	–9	–6	–3	0	3	6	9	12	15	3
–10	–8	–6	–4	–2	0	2	4	6	8	10	2
–5	–4	–3	–2	–1	0	1	2	3	4	5	1
0	0	0	0	0	0	0	0	0	0	0	0
5	4	3	2	1	0	–1	–2	–3	–4	–5	–1
10	8	6	4	2	0	–2	–4	–6	–8	–10	–2
15	12	9	6	3	0	–3	–6	–9	–12	–15	–3
20	16	12	8	4	0	–4	–8	–12	–16	–20	–4
25	20	15	10	5	0	–5	–10	–15	–20	–25	–5

Second number

4 (a) +10 (b) –12 (c) –8 (d) +15 (e) +3
(f) –6 (g) –20 (h) +4

Exercise 1I

1

	First number			
×	+5	+3	−6	−2
+2	+10	+6	−12	−4
+8	+40	+24	−48	−16
−3	−15	−9	+18	+6
−4	−20	−12	+24	+8

(Rows: Second number)

2

	First number			
÷	+6	−12	−18	+24
+3	+2	−4	−6	+8
−2	−3	+6	+9	−12
−6	−1	+2	+3	−4
+1	+6	−12	−18	+24

(Rows: Second number)

Exercise 1J

1 **(a)** −3 **(b)** −3 **(c)** +4 **(d)** +12 **(e)** −4 **(f)** −12
2 **(a)** −90 **(b)** +4 **(c)** +5 **(d)** −14 **(e)** −2 **(f)** +12
3 **(a)** −20 **(b)** +2 **(c)** −20 **(d)** +6 **(e)** +9 **(f)** −42
4 **(a)** +24 **(b)** −15 **(c)** −4 **(d)** +27 **(e)** 40 **(f)** +3
5 **(a)** +10 **(b)** −56 **(c)** +36 **(d)** +21 **(e)** −3 **(f)** −42

Exercise 1K

1 One hundred thousand, one hundred and one.
2 5500 **3** 3 750 000
4 374 214 390 002 539 999 542 372 642 137 735 102
5 3.91 km, 3.9 km, 3.671 km, 3.506 km, 3.451 km, 3.008 km
6 £875.00 **7** £52.00
8 **(a)** 3 **(b)** −20 **(c)** −5 **(d)** +11 **(e)** +1 **(f)** −9
9 1200 ft
10 **(a)** Archangel **(b)** 27°C
11 39
12 £3422
13 3404

Unit 2 Simple functions

Exercise 2A

(a) 210 mins **(b)** 345 mins **(c)** 480 mins **(d)** 120 mins
(e) 187.5 mins **(f)** 232.5 mins **(g)** 255 mins

Exercise 2B

1 **(a)** In → ×3 → −1 → Out

(b) **(i)** 5 **(ii)** 11 **(iii)** 2 **(iv)** 0.5 **(v)** 6.5
(vi) −4 **(vii)** −7 **(viii)** −16 **(ix)** 2.75 **(x)** 7.25

2 **(a)** In → +4 → ×2 → Out

(b) **(i)** 14 **(ii)** 20 **(iii)** 30 **(iv)** 9 **(v)** 13
(vi) 8.5 **(vii)** 10.5 **(viii)** 6 **(ix)** −4 **(x)** 8

Exercise 2C

1 **(a)** Out ← ÷2 ← −5 ← In

(b) **(i)** 7 **(ii)** 2 **(iii)** 5 **(iv)** 1 **(v)** 1.5
(vi) 3.5 **(vii)** −3 **(viii)** −4 **(ix)** −5 **(x)** 0.2

2 **(a)** Out ← +4 ← ÷2 ← In

(b) **(i)** 7 **(ii)** 14 **(iii)** 11 **(iv)** 5.5 **(v)** 8.5
(vi) −2 **(vii)** 3 **(viii)** 4 **(ix)** 5.25 **(x)** 9.25

Exercise 2D

(a) **(i)** 9 **(ii)** 9
(b) **(i)** 18 **(ii)** 18
(d) They are the same.

Exercise 2E

A and **H**, **B** and **C**, **D** and **E**, **F** and **G**

Exercise 2F

1 **(a)** $n \rightarrow 3n + 2$ **(b)** $n \rightarrow 3(n + 2)$ **(c)** $n \rightarrow \frac{n}{4} - 2$
(d) $n \rightarrow \frac{n-3}{3}$

2 **(a)** $n \rightarrow 4(n - 1)$ **(b)** $n \rightarrow \frac{n}{3} + 5$ **(c)** $n \rightarrow 4n - 1$
(d) $n \rightarrow \frac{n+2}{3}$

3
(a) In → ×5 → −2 → Out
(b) In → +1 → ×4 → Out
(c) In → ×3 → +4 → Out
(d) In → ÷4 → +3 → Out
(e) In → −2 → ÷2 → Out
(f) In → −4 → ×6 → Out

Exercise 2G

1

(a) 1 → 0, 2 → 2, 3 → 4, 10 → 18
(b) 1 → 5, 2 → 8, 3 → 11, 10 → 32
(c) 1 → 8, 2 → 10, 3 → 12, 10 → 26
(d) 1 → 0, 2 → 3, 3 → 6, 10 → 27
(e) 1 → 1.5, 2 → 2, 3 → 2.5, 10 → 6
(f) 1 → 2, 2 → 2.5, 3 → 3, 10 → 6.5

Exercise 2H

1 **A** and **H**, **B** and **D**, **C** and **E**, **F** and **G**

Exercise 2I

1 **(a)**

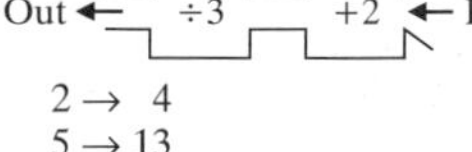

2 → 4
5 → 13
1 → 1
$\frac{1}{3}$ → −1

(b) Out ← ÷2 ← −3 ← In

4 → 11
1 → 5
2.5 → 8
−3 → −3

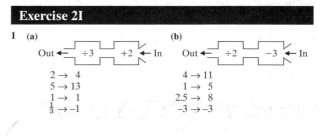

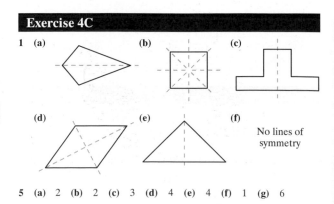

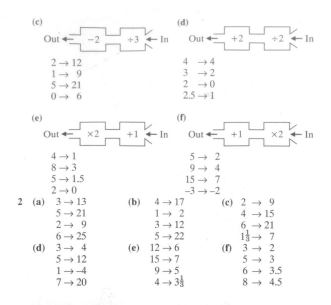

(c)

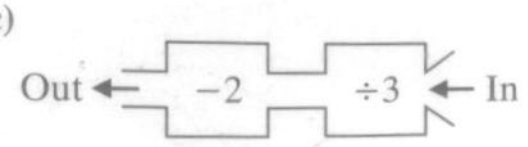

2 → 12
1 → 9
5 → 21
0 → 6

(d)

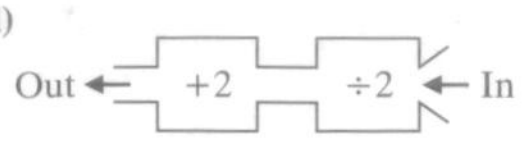

4 → 4
3 → 2
2 → 0
2.5 → 1

(e)

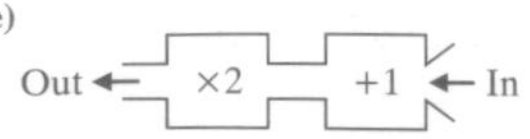

4 → 1
8 → 3
5 → 1.5
2 → 0

(f)

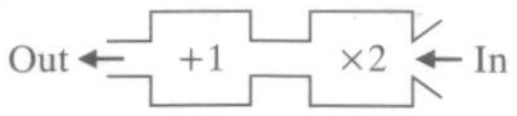

5 → 2
9 → 4
15 → 7
−3 → −2

2 **(a)** 3 → 13, 5 → 21, 2 → 9, 6 → 25 **(b)** 4 → 17, 1 → 2, 3 → 12, 5 → 22 **(c)** 2 → 9, 4 → 15, 6 → 21, $1\frac{1}{3}$ → 7
(d) 3 → 4, 5 → 12, 1 → −4, 7 → 20 **(e)** 12 → 6, 15 → 7, 9 → 5, 4 → $3\frac{1}{3}$ **(f)** 3 → 2, 5 → 3, 6 → 3.5, 8 → 4.5

Exercise 2J

1 **(a)** $n \to 2n + 6$ **(b)** $n \to 5n + 10$ **(c)** $n \to 3n - 6$
(d) $n \to 4n - 12$ **(e)** $n \to 4n + 2$ **(f)** $n \to 2n + 3$
(g) $n \to 2n - 1$ **(h)** $n \to 2n + \frac{3}{4}$ **(i)** $n \to 2n - \frac{1}{3}$
2 **A** and **H**, **B** and **D**, **C** and **E**, **F** and **G**

Exercise 2K

1 **(a)** $n \to 2n + 2$ **(b)** $n \to 3n + 6$ **(c)** $n \to 2n - 3$
(d) $n \to n - 1$ **(e)** $n \to \frac{n}{2} + 1$ **(f)** $n \to 4n$
(g) $n \to 2n - 2$ **(h)** $n \to \frac{n}{2} - \frac{1}{2}$
2 **(a)** $n \to 3n - 4$ **(b)** $n \to 2n + 1$ **(c)** $n \to n + 3$
(d) $n \to n - 4$
3 Pattern (ii). As the input goes up by 1 the output goes up by varying amounts.

Exercise 2L

1 **(a)** $2n + 5$ **(b)** $3n + 1$ **(c)** $4n - 7$
(d) $4n - 4$ **(e)** $3n$ **(f)** $n + \frac{1}{2}$

Unit 3 Probability 1

Exercise 3A

1

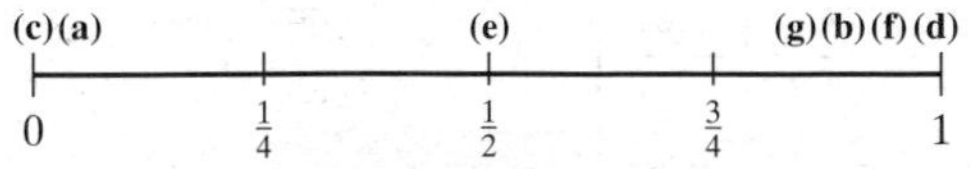

2

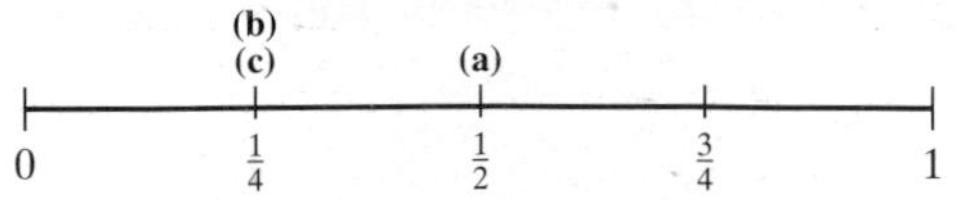

Exercise 3C

1 **(a)** $\frac{1}{6}$ **(b)** $\frac{1}{6}$ **(c)** $\frac{1}{2}$ **(d)** $\frac{2}{3}$ **(e)** $\frac{1}{3}$
2 **(a)** $\frac{1}{9}$ **(b)** $\frac{3}{9}$ **(c)** $\frac{5}{9}$ **(d)** $\frac{8}{9}$ **(e)** $\frac{4}{9}$
3 **(a)** $\frac{8}{16}$ **(b)** $\frac{4}{16}$ **(c)** $\frac{3}{16}$ **(d)** 0 **(e)** $\frac{1}{16}$
4 **(a)** $\frac{1}{52}$ **(b)** $\frac{13}{52}$ **(c)** $\frac{26}{52}$ **(d)** $\frac{1}{52}$ **(e)** $\frac{4}{52}$
(f) $\frac{48}{52}$ **(g)** 0
5 **(a)** $\frac{20}{5000}$ **(b)** $\frac{100}{5000}$ **(c)** $\frac{50}{5000}$ **(d)** $\frac{25}{5000}$
6 **(a)** $\frac{4}{30}$ **(b)** $\frac{10}{30}$ **(c)** $\frac{5}{30}$ **(d)** $\frac{2}{30}$ **(e)** $\frac{9}{30}$ **(f)** $\frac{20}{30}$
7 **(a)** $\frac{1}{18}$ **(b)** $\frac{2}{18}$ **(c)** $\frac{3}{18}$ **(d)** $\frac{3}{18}$ **(e)** $\frac{4}{18}$ **(f)** $\frac{2}{18}$
(g) $\frac{1}{18}$ **(h)** $\frac{1}{18}$ **(i)** $\frac{16}{18}$ **(j)** $\frac{14}{18}$ **(k)** $\frac{5}{18}$ **(l)** 0
8 **(a)** $\frac{1}{11}$ **(b)** $\frac{1}{11}$ **(c)** $\frac{2}{11}$ **(d)** $\frac{3}{11}$ **(e)** $\frac{4}{11}$

Exercise 3D

1 **(a)** $\frac{1}{6}$ **(b)** $\frac{5}{6}$ **(c)** $\frac{1}{6}$ **(d)** $\frac{5}{6}$
2 **(a)** $\frac{1}{3}$ **(b)** $\frac{2}{3}$ **(c)** $\frac{2}{3}$ **(d)** $\frac{1}{3}$
3 **(a)** $\frac{1}{9}$ **(b)** $\frac{4}{9}$ **(c)** $\frac{5}{9}$ **(d)** $\frac{4}{9}$ **(e)** $\frac{2}{9}$ **(f)** $\frac{3}{9}$
4 **(a)** $\frac{6}{20}$ **(b)** $\frac{14}{20}$ **(c)** $\frac{1}{20}$ **(d)** $\frac{19}{20}$ **(e)** $\frac{14}{20}$ **(f)** $\frac{11}{20}$
(g) $\frac{6}{20}$
5 **(a)** $\frac{4}{52}$ **(b)** $\frac{48}{52}$ **(c)** $\frac{12}{52}$ **(d)** $\frac{40}{52}$ **(e)** $\frac{8}{52}$
6 $\frac{4}{5}$
7 **(a)** $\frac{7}{20}$ **(b)** 8 **(c)** 5 **(d)** 7
8 **(a)** $\frac{1}{47}$ **(b)** $\frac{5}{50}$
9 **(a)** 0.4 **(b)** 0.85

Unit 4 2-D and 3-D shapes

Exercise 4A

1 **(a)** Square **(b)** kite **(c)** parallelogram
(d) right-angled triangle **(e)** trapezium
(f) rhombus **(g)** hexagon
(h) isosceles triangle **(i)** octagon
2 **(a)** equilateral triangle **(b)** pentagon
(c) regular octagon **(d)** isosceles triangle
(e) decagon
3 **(a)** square **(b)** trapezium **(c)** kite
4 **(a)** rectangle, square
(b) parallelogram, rhombus, rectangle, square
(c) rhombus, square
(d) parallelogram, rectangle, kite
5 **(a)** rectangle, square
(b) parallelogram, rhombus, rectangle, square
(c) rhombus, square, kite
(d) rhombus, square
(e) trapezium, parallelogram, rhombus, rectangle, square
6 **(a)** 133° **(b)(i)** 47° **(ii)** 47°
7 **(a)** 32° **(b)** 64°
8 **(a)** $15\,cm^2$ **(b)** $30\,cm^2$

Exercise 4B

2 **B** and **H**, **O** and **M**, **L** and **E**
3 **A** and **F**, **G** and **I**

Exercise 4C

1 **(a)**

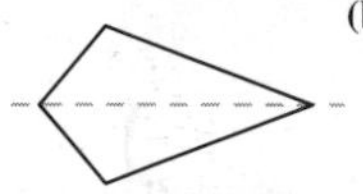

(b)

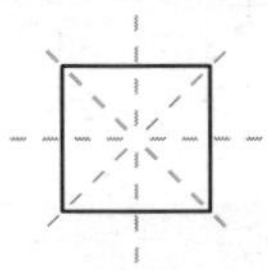

(c)

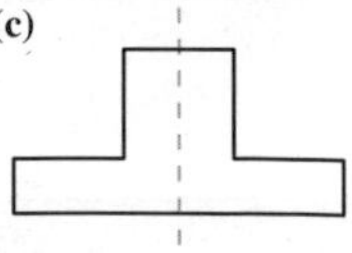

(d)

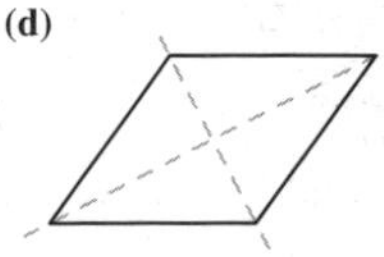

(e)

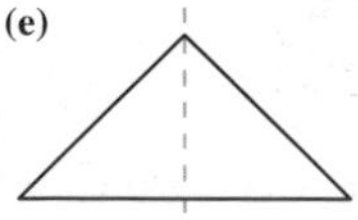

(f) No lines of symmetry

5 **(a)** 2 **(b)** 2 **(c)** 3 **(d)** 4 **(e)** 4 **(f)** 1 **(g)** 6

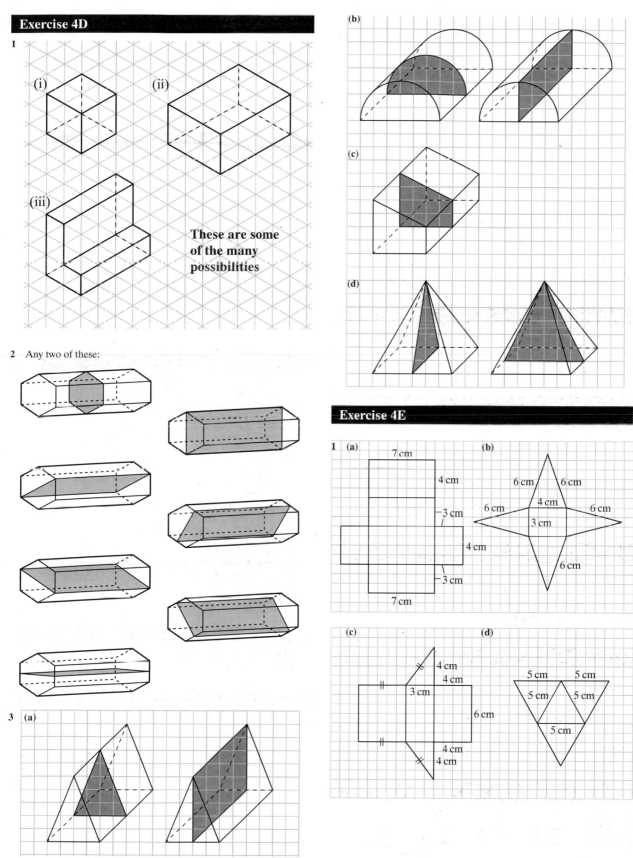

Exercise 4D

1

(i) (ii)

(iii)

These are some of the many possibilities

2 Any two of these:

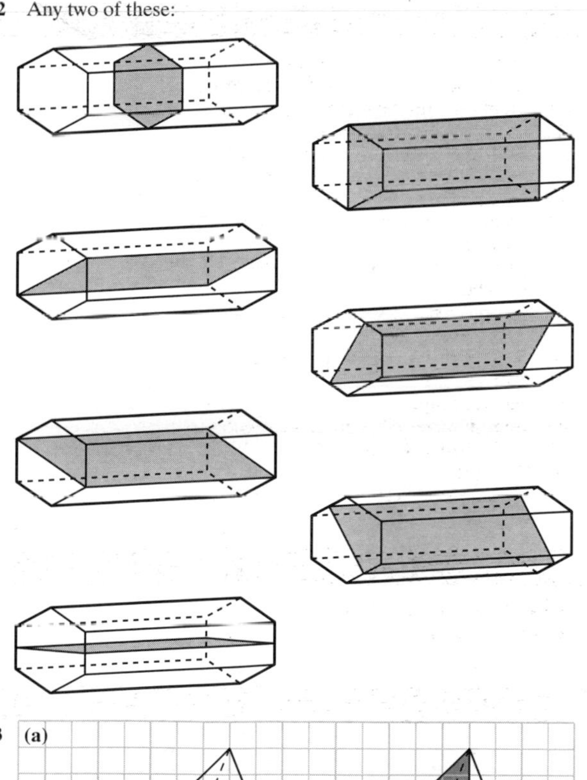

3 (a)

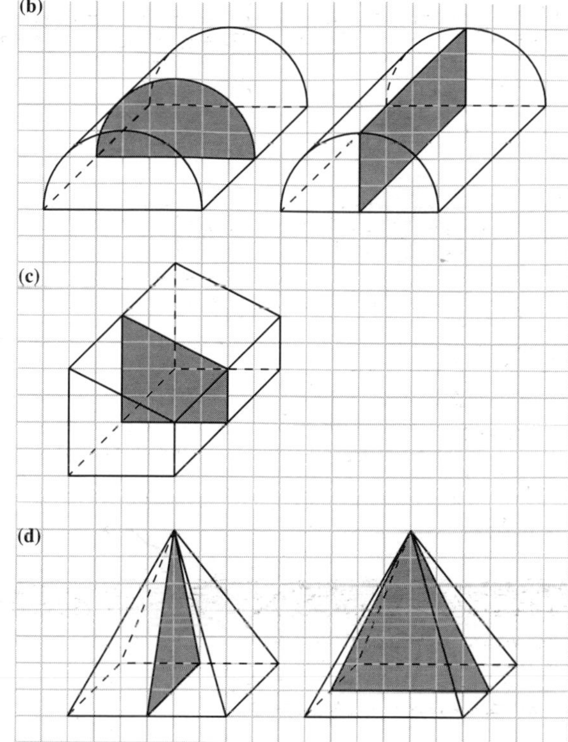

Exercise 4E

1

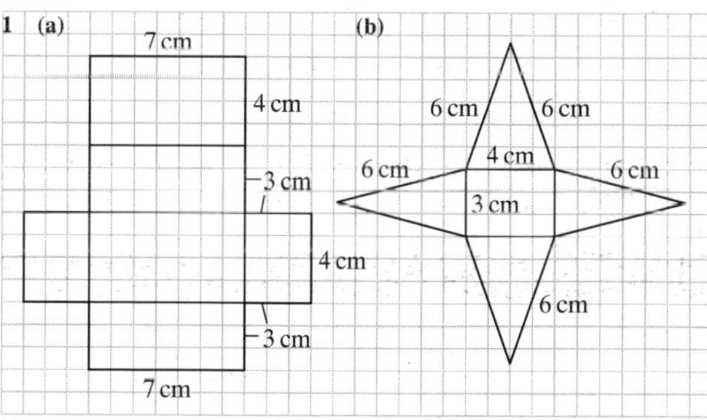

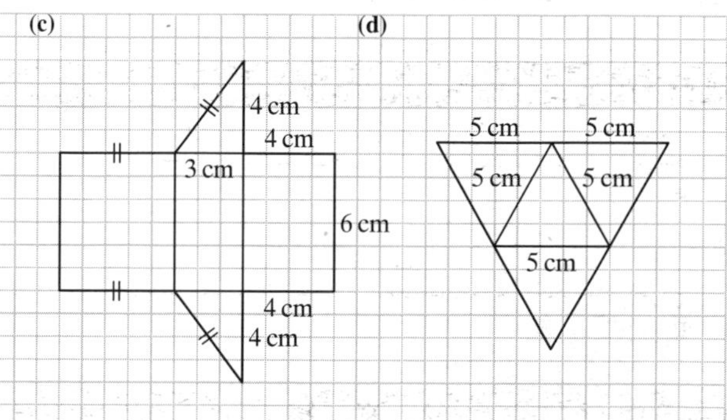

2 (a)

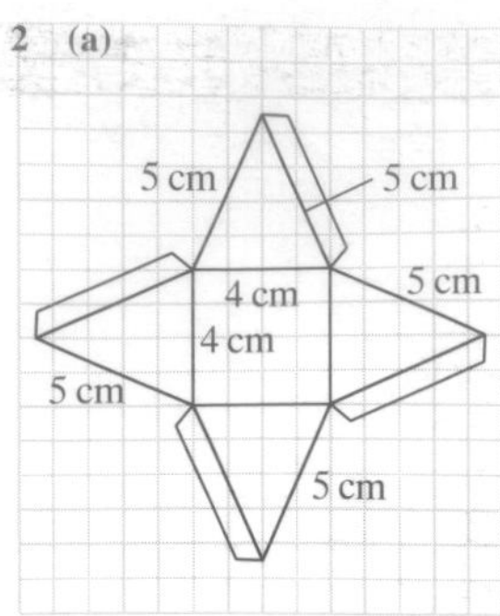

3 (a)

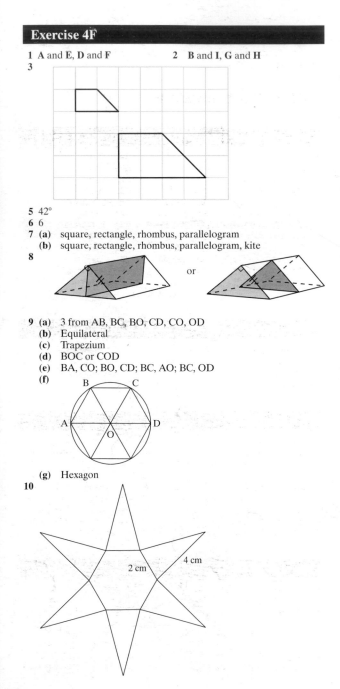

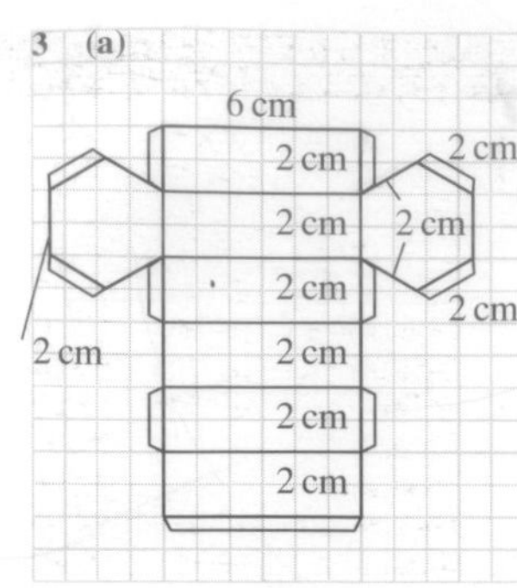

Exercise 4F

1 **A** and **E**, **D** and **F**

2 **B** and **I**, **G** and **H**

3

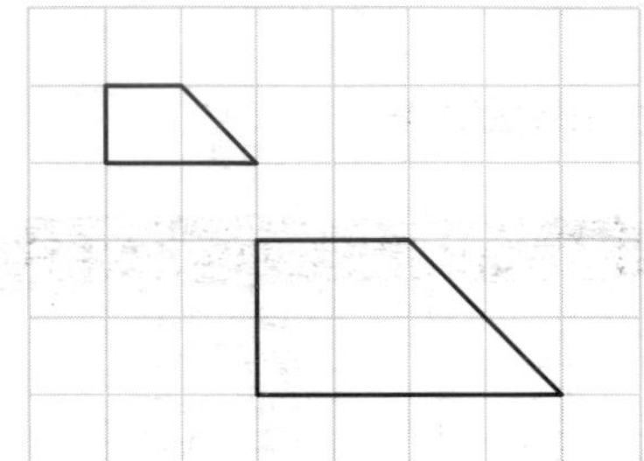

5 42°

6 6

7 **(a)** square, rectangle, rhombus, parallelogram
(b) square, rectangle, rhombus, parallelogram, kite

8

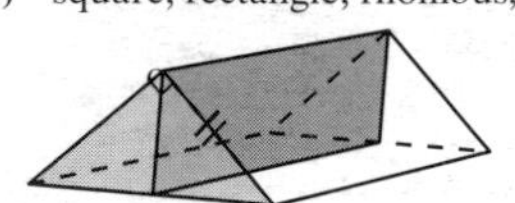

or

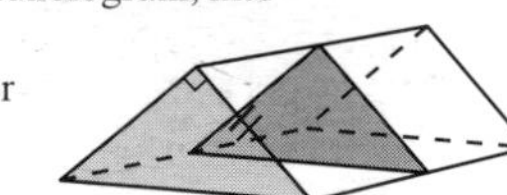

9 **(a)** 3 from AB, BC, BO, CD, CO, OD
(b) Equilateral
(c) Trapezium
(d) BOC or COD
(e) BA, CO; BO, CD; BC, AO; BC, OD
(f)

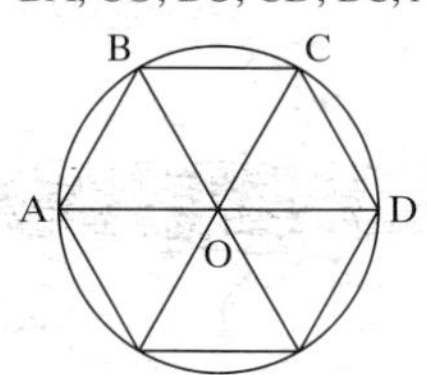

(g) Hexagon

10

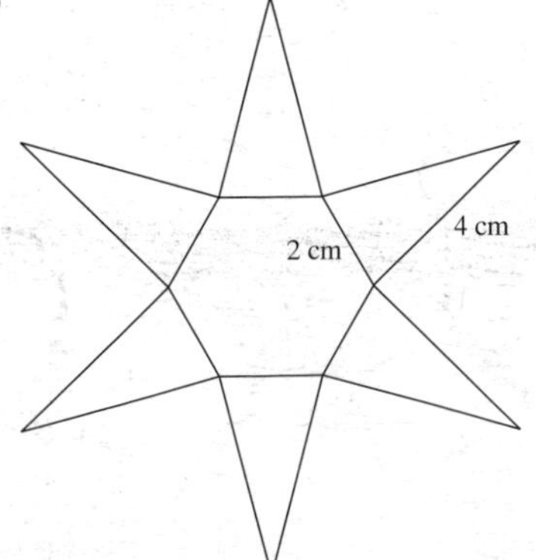

Unit 5 Measure 1

Exercise 5A

1 **(a)** 1.8 m **(b)** 1.2 m **(c)** 2.5 m **(d)** 1.5 m
2 **(a)** 3 m **(b)** 10 m **(c)** 4 m
3 **(a)** 7 m **(b)** 7 m **(c)** 0.9 m
4 **(a)** 3 m **(b)** 2.5 m **(c)** 10 m

Exercise 5B

Question	Metric	Imperial	Question	Metric	Imperial
(a)	570 ml	1 pint	**(e)**	300 ml	$\frac{1}{2}$ pint
(b)	300 ml	$\frac{1}{2}$ pint	**(f)**	5l	1 gallon
(c)	300 ml	$\frac{1}{2}$ pint	**(g)**	9l	2 gallons
(d)	100 ml	$\frac{1}{8}$ pint	**(h)**	90l	20 gallons

Exercise 5C

Question	Metric	Imperial	Question	Metric	Imperial
(a)	5 kg	11 pounds	**(f)**	200 g	$\frac{1}{2}$ pound
(b)	200 g	$\frac{1}{2}$ pound	**(g)**	500 g	1 pound
(c)	1 kg	$2\frac{1}{4}$ pounds	**(h)**	100 g	$\frac{1}{4}$ pound
(d)	100 g	$\frac{1}{4}$ pound	**(i)**	25/30 g	1 ounce
(e)	500 g	1 pound	**(j)**	2 kg	4.5 pounds

Exercise 5D

1 **(a)** Not sensible, 1.8 m
(b) Not sensible, 1.8 m
(c) Not sensible, 6 m by 5 m
(d) Not sensible, 2 kg
(e) Not sensible, 300 ml
(f) Could be sensible
(g) Sensible
(h) Sensible
(i) Sensible
(j) Not sensible, 200 ml
(k) Not sensible, 300 km
(l) Not sensible, 15 g
(m) Sensible
(n) Not sensible, 80 km/h
(o) Not sensible 500 ml
(p) Not sensible, 50+ l
(q) Sensible
(r) Sensible
(s) Not sensible, 50 litres
(t) Sensible

Exercise 5E

Question	Metric	Imperial
(a)	metres	feet
(b)	centimetres	inches
(c)	kilometres	miles
(d)	metres	feet
(e)	kilograms	pounds
(f)	grams	ounces
(g)	tonnes	tons
(h)	litres	gallons
(i)	millilitres	pints
(j)	millilitres	fluid ounces teaspoon
(k)	millilitres	fluid ounces
(l)	litres	gallons
(m)	minutes	minutes
(n)	seconds	seconds
(o)	hours	hours
(p)	days	days
(q)	metres	feet
(r)	millimetres	inches
(s)	kilograms	pounds
(t)	years	years

Exercise 5F

1 **(a)** Eleven o'clock **(b)** Quarter past nine **(c)** Ten to eleven **(d)** Five past three **(e)** Twenty to four **(f)** Twenty past twelve
2 **(a)** 10:00 **(b)** 22:00 **(c)** 09:30 **(d)** 21:30 **(e)** 20:20 **(f)** 08:20 **(g)** 07:00 **(h)** 20:00 **(i)** 15:30 **(j)** 04:40 **(k)** 01:08 **(l)** 13:08
3 **(a)** 17:50 **(b)** 05:50 **(c)** 23:00 **(d)** 08:00 **(e)** 08:15 **(f)** 20:45 **(g)** 14:55 **(h)** 06:40
4 **(a)** 8 am **(b)** 9:20 am **(c)** 9:30 pm **(d)** 1:10 pm **(e)** 12:10 pm **(f)** 12:20 am **(g)** 1:40 am **(h)** 8 am **(i)** 3:45 pm **(j)** 6 pm
5 **(a)** 4:30 pm **(b)** 9:10 pm **(c)** 11:55 pm **(d)** 2:02 pm **(e)** 6:25 am **(f)** midnight **(g)** midnight **(h)** noon **(i)** 10:55 am **(j)** 8:55 pm

Exercise 5G

1 3.8 **2** 44 **3** 30 **4** 37 **5** 3.4 **6** 46
7 190 **8** 4.3

Exercise 5H

1 11.1 **2** 4.6 **3** 24 **4** 3.6 **5** 7.3 **6** 29
7 167 **8** 52

Exercise 5I

1 5.3 cm **2** 6.4 cm **3** 1.3 cm **4** 0.7 cm
5 9.5 cm **6** 12.6 cm **7** 5.6 cm **8** 3.1 cm

Exercise 5K

1 **(a)** 120 minutes **(b)** 300 minutes **(c)** 150 minutes **(d)** 330 minutes **(e)** 375 minutes **(f)** 315 minutes
2 **(a)** 3 hours **(b)** 4 hours **(c)** $1\frac{1}{4}$ hours **(d)** 4 hours 20 minutes **(e)** 5 hours 25 minutes **(f)** $1\frac{1}{2}$ hours **(g)** 72 hours **(h)** 132 hours **(i)** 8 hours 20 minutes **(j)** 168 hours
3 3600 seconds **4** 1440 minutes **5** 31 536 000 seconds

Exercise 5L

1 **(a)** 10:45 **(b)** 10:00 **(c)** 11:55 **(d)** 10:10
2 **(a)** 09:50 **(b)** 11:20 **(c)** 12:30 **(d)** 08:55
3 **(a)** 12:20 **(b)** 13:25 **(c)** 14:30 **(d)** 08:50
4 **(a)** 15:15 **(b)** 20:00 **(c)** 01:35 **(d)** 05:30
5 **(a)** 09:40 **(b)** 11:25 **(c)** 07:55 **(d)** 08:50
6 **(a)** 08:05 **(b)** 10:50 **(c)** 09:40 **(d)** 08:10
7 **(a)** 07:25 **(b)** 09:10 **(c)** 05:40 **(d)** 06:35
8 **(a)** 02:05 **(b)** 04:45 **(c)** 23:15 **(d)** 19:45

Exercise 5M

1 **(a)** 11th Jan **(b)** 12th Mar **(c)** 13th June **(d)** 15th July **(e)** 20th Sept **(f)** 30th May **(g)** 5th July **(h)** 6th Sept
2 **(a)** 16th Feb **(b)** 17th Mar **(c)** 17th Apr **(d)** 21st Dec **(e)** 29th Nov **(f)** 2nd Oct **(g)** 6th Apr **(h)** 9th Dec
3 **(a)** 5th May **(b)** 6th July **(c)** 16th June **(d)** 1st Oct **(e)** 7th July **(f)** 19th June **(g)** 30th Dec **(h)** 4th Jan
4 Wednesday 10th April **5** Thursday 2nd May
6 Monday 13th May **7** Thursday 25th April
8 Friday 3rd May **9** 33 days
10 12 days **11** 35 days **12** 9 days

Exercise 5N

1 **(a)** 07:55 **(b)** 08:35 **(c)** 07:25 **(d)** 07:40

2

Coate	08:35	09:05	09:35
Piper's Way	08:40	09:10	09:40
Old Town	08:50	09:20	09:50
Drove Rd.	08:55	09:25	09:55
New Town	09:00	09:30	10:00
Bus Station	09:05	09:35	10:05

3

Bristol	08:10	08:25	08:40
Bath	08:30	08:45	09:00
Swindon	08:45	09:00	09:15
Didcot	09:05	09:20	09:35
Reading	09:15	09:30	09:45
London	09:40	09:55	10:10

4 07:45 **5** 08:35 **6** 09:15 **7** 08:10
8 **(a)** 30 mins **(b)** 20 mins **(c)** $1\frac{1}{2}$ hours **(d)** 30 mins **(e)** 35 mins
9 **(a)** 07:10 & 07:45 or 08:00 **(b)** 07:05 & 07:45 or 08:00 **(c)** 07:50 & 08:25 **(d)** 08:25 & 09:00 **(e)** 08:20 & 09:00 **(f)** 07:55

Unit 6 Approximation

Exercise 6A

1 **(a)** **(i)** 3410 **(ii)** 3400 **(iii)** 3000
(b) **(i)** 6940 **(ii)** 6900 **(iii)** 7000
(c) **(i)** 5370 **(ii)** 5400 **(iii)** 5000
(d) **(i)** 6100 **(ii)** 6100 **(iii)** 6000
(e) **(i)** 11 360 m **(ii)** 11 400 m **(iii)** 11 000 m
(f) **(i)** £31 300 **(ii)** £31 300 **(iii)** £31 000
(g) **(i)** 86 310 km **(ii)** 86 300 km **(iii)** 86 000 km
(h) **(i)** 63 940 t **(ii)** 63 900 t **(iii)** 64 000 t
(i) **(i)** £48 190 **(ii)** £48 200 **(iii)** £48 000
(j) **(i)** £33 730 **(ii)** £33 700 **(iii)** £34 000
(k) **(i)** 1300 m **(ii)** 1300 m **(iii)** 1000 m
(l) **(i)** 1180 m*l* **(ii)** 1200 m*l* **(iii)** 1000 m*l*
2 12 900 **3** 19 000 **4** £25 000

Exercise 6B

1 6 containers **2** 6 trips **3** 22 boxes
4 16 boxes **5** 13 trips **6** 5 tins
7 19 coins **8** 13 taxis **9** 5 bags
10 6 bags

Exercise 6C

1 **(a)** **(i)** 4.226 **(ii)** 4.23 **(b)** **(i)** 9.787 **(ii)** 9.79
(c) **(i)** 0.416 **(ii)** 0.42 **(d)** **(i)** 0.058 **(ii)** 0.06
2 **(a)** **(i)** 10.517 **(ii)** 10.52 **(b)** **(i)** 7.503 **(ii)** 7.50
(c) **(i)** 21.730 **(ii)** 21.73 **(d)** **(i)** 9.089 **(ii)** 9.09
3 **(a)** **(i)** 15.598 **(ii)** 15.60 **(b)** **(i)** 0.408 **(ii)** 0.41
(c) **(i)** 7.247 **(ii)** 7.25 **(d)** **(i)** 6.051 **(ii)** 6.05
4 **(a)** **(i)** 29.158 **(ii)** 29.16 **(b)** **(i)** 0.055 **(ii)** 0.05
(c) **(i)** 13.379 **(ii)** 13.38 **(b)** **(i)** 5.998 **(ii)** 6.00
5 **(a)** 5.617 **(b)** 0.0 **(c)** 0.9240 **(d)** 0.86 **(e)** 9.7

Exercise 6D

1 **(a)** **(i)** 0.06 **(ii)** 0.0618 **(b)** **(i)** 0.2 **(ii)** 0.165
(c) **(i)** 100 **(ii)** 96.3 **(d)** **(i)** 40 **(ii)** 41.5
2 **(a)** **(i)** 700 **(ii)** 735 **(b)** **(i)** 0.08 **(ii)** 0.0795
(c) **(i)** 6 **(ii)** 5.69 **(d)** **(i)** 600 **(ii)** 586
3 **(a)** **(i)** 0.01 **(ii)** 0.0145 **(b)** **(i)** 2000 **(ii)** 2220
(c) **(i)** 80 **(ii)** 76.2 **(d)** **(i)** 0.4 **(ii)** 0.380
4 **(a)** **(i)** 8 **(ii)** 8.38 **(b)** **(i)** 40 **(ii)** 36.0
(c) **(i)** 200 **(ii)** 187 **(d)** **(i)** 0.07 **(ii)** 0.0666

5 (a) (i) 90 (ii) 94.7 (b) (i) 900 (ii) 851
(c) (i) 6 (ii) 6.25 (d) (i) 0.06 (ii) 0.0626
6 (a) 0.098 (b) 54.88 (c) 8 (d) 3100 (e) 6000
(f) 53.0

Exercise 6E

1 (a) $234 \times 7 = 1638$ (b) $2152 \div 8 = 269$
(c) $1049 - 362 = 687$ (d) $966 + 97 \neq 1053$; 956
(e) $0.533 + 8.462 \neq 9.9095$; 1.4475
(f) $1.003 \times 1.2 \neq 1.236$; 1.03
2 (a) 8×8 (b) 64 (c) 65.0022
3 (a) $14 \div 7$ (b) 2 (c) 2.063 893
4 (a) 8×25 (b) 200 (c) 205.065
5 (a) $40 \times (6 + 6)$ (b) 480 (c) 447.12
6 (a) $\frac{7 \times 90}{0.2}$ (b) 3150 (c) 3685.4857
7 (a) 50×3 (b) 150 (c) 160.2729
8 (a) $\frac{200 \times 90}{50}$ (b) 360 (c) 305.050 56
9 (a) $2 \times (3 - 0)$ (b) 6 (c) 5.6316
10 (a) $(1000 \times 400) + 300$ (b) 400 300 (c) 441 572
11 (a) $\frac{30 + 40}{0.02}$ (b) 3500 (c) 3202.5316
12 (a) $\frac{0.7 \times 0.03}{0.03}$ (b) 0.7 (c) 0.651 8344
13 (a) $\frac{0.9 \times 8}{4 \times 0.3}$ (b) 6 (c) 5.334 753

Exercise 6F

1 (a) (i) 33.5 cm (ii) 34.5 cm
(b) (i) 64.5 g (ii) 65.5 g
(c) (i) 153.5 m (ii) 154.5 m
(d) (i) 19.5 *l* (ii) 20.5 *l*
2 (a) (i) 64.65 cm (ii) 64.75 cm
(b) (i) 17.55 m*l* (ii) 17.65 m*l*
(c) (i) 49.05 g (ii) 49.15 g
(d) (i) 43.95 *l* (ii) 44.05 *l*
3 (a) (i) 9.015 km (ii) 9.025 km
(b) (i) 6.105 s (ii) 6.115 s
(c) (i) 7.225 kg (ii) 7.235 kg
(d) (i) 0.425 s (ii) 0.435 s
4 (a) (i) 0.3235 km (ii) 0.3245 km
(b) (i) 0.1385 s (ii) 0.1395 s
(c) (i) 0.4545 kg (ii) 0.4555 kg
(d) (i) 0.8945 km (ii) 0.8955 km

Exercise 6G

1 9500 2 12 000 3 24 4 16
5 (a) 10.5 (b) 0.056 (c) 6.60 (d) 3.594
6 (a) 533 (b) 124.7 (c) 470 (d) 900
7 (a) $4.884 \div 1.5 = 3.256$ (b) $45 \times 1.25 = 56.25$
(c) $75.99 - 19.78 = 56.21$ (d) $26.19 + 83.27 = 109.46$
8 (a) 60×30 (b) 1800 (c) 88
9 (a) $\frac{100 - 20}{5}$ (b) 16
10 (a) 14.5 km or 14.499… (b) 13.5 km
11 (a) 20×30 (b) 600 12 5.15 km

Unit 7 Graphs of linear functions

Exercise 7A

1 (a) $y = x + 2$ (b)

x	0	1	2	3	4	5
y	2	3	4	5	6	7

(c)

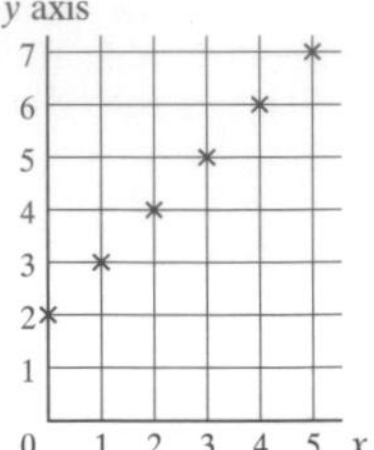

2 (a) $y = x + 4$

x	0	1	2	3	4	5
y	4	5	6	7	8	9

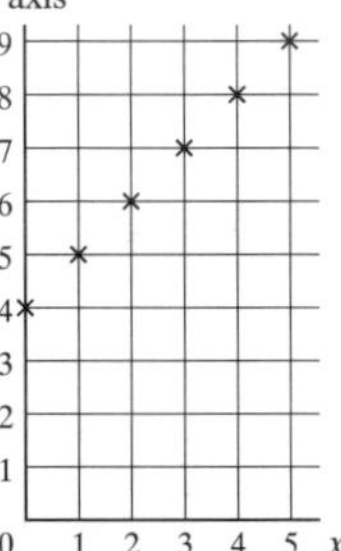

(b) $y = 2x + 3$

x	0	1	2	3	4	5
y	3	5	7	9	11	13

y axis

x axis

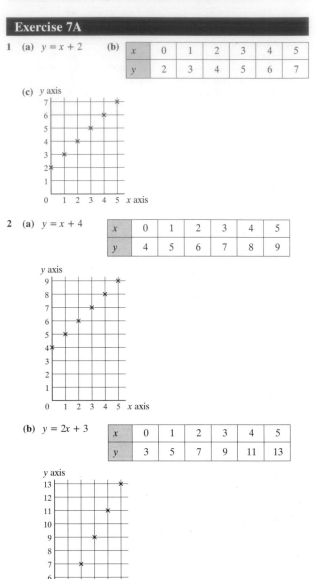

(c) $y = 3x + 2$

x	0	1	2	3	4	5
y	2	5	8	11	14	17

y axis

x axis

(d) $y = 2x$

x	0	1	2	3	4	5
y	0	2	4	6	8	10

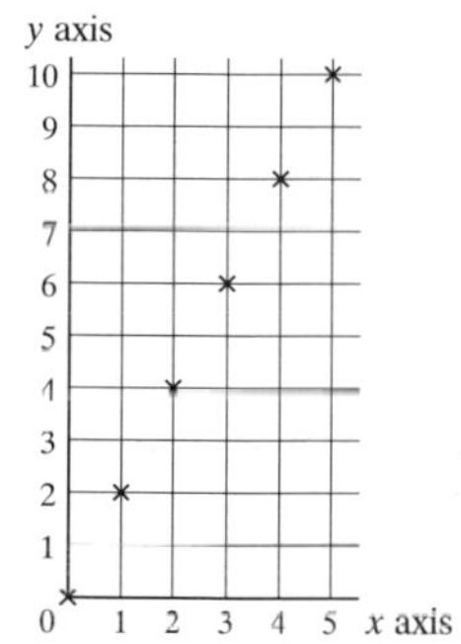

3 (a)

x	1	2	3	4	5
y	4	7	10	13	16

(b)

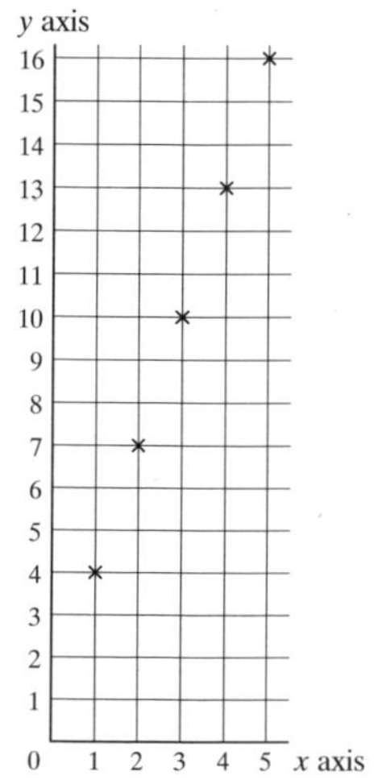

(c) $y = 3x + 1$

4 (a)

x	1	2	3	4	5
y	3	5	7	9	11

(b)

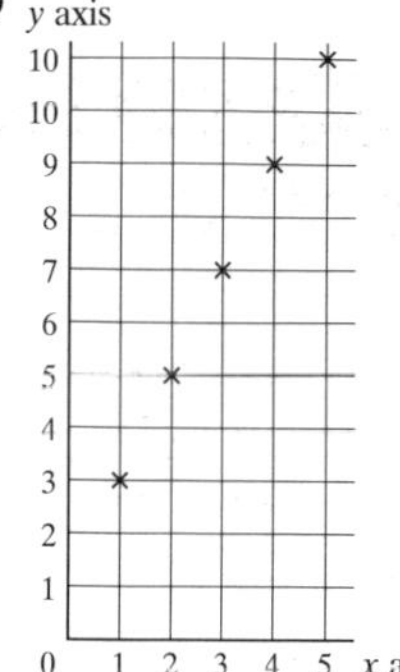

(c) $y = 2x + 1$

5 (a) (i)

x	1	2	3	4	5
y	3	5	7	9	11

(ii)

x	1	2	3	4	5
y	2	4	6	8	10

(b) (i) $y = 2x + 1$ **(ii)** $y = 2x$

6 (b) (i)

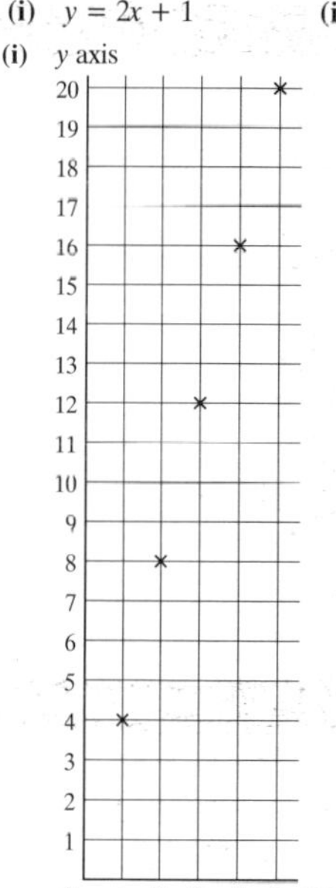

(ii)

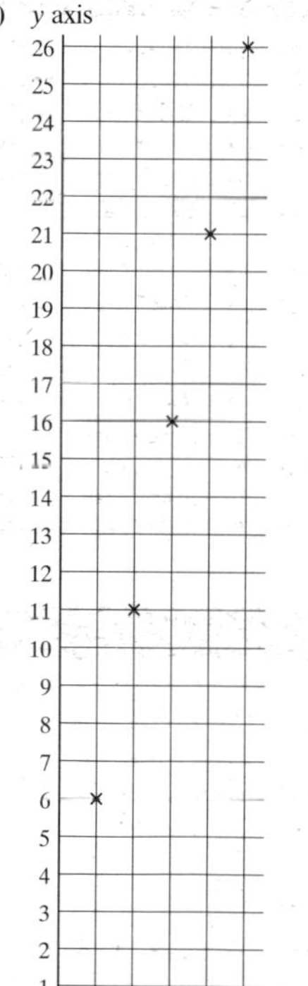

Exercise 7B

1 (a)

x	0	1	2	3	4
y	0	4	8	12	16

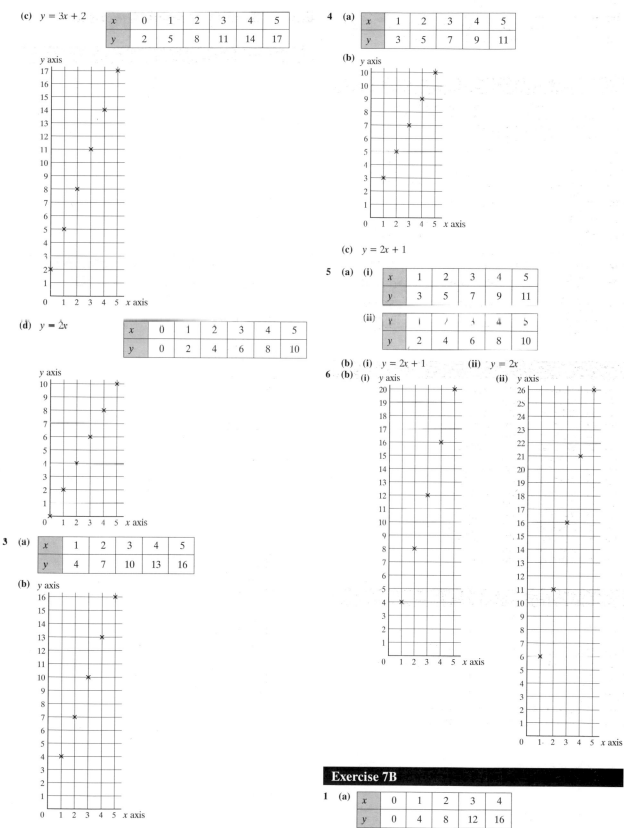

(b)

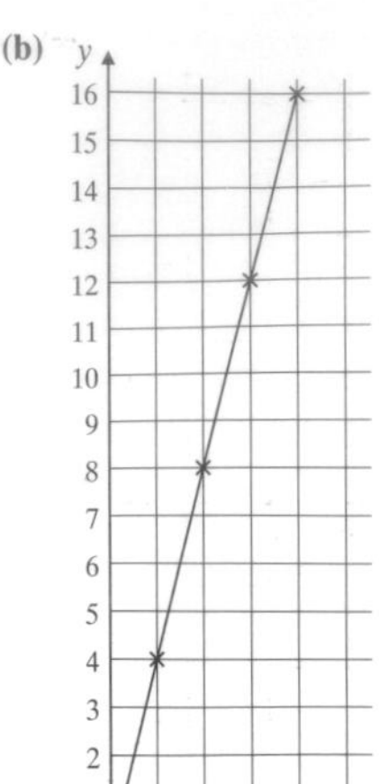

(c) 14 miles

2 (a)

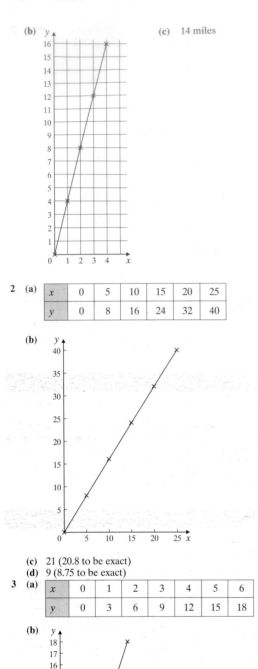

x	0	5	10	15	20	25
y	0	8	16	24	32	40

(b)

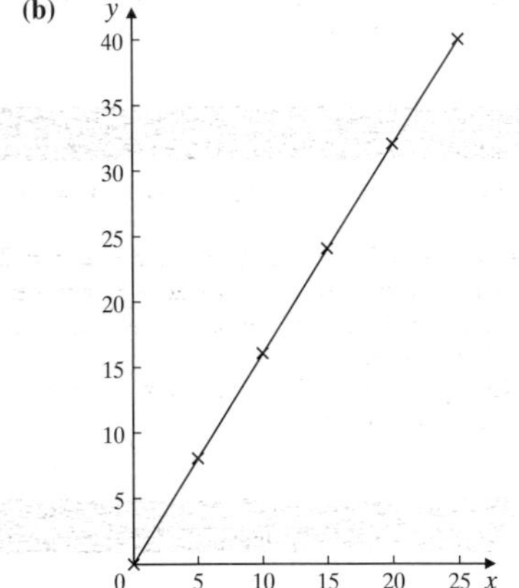

(c) 21 (20.8 to be exact)

(d) 9 (8.75 to be exact)

3 (a)

x	0	1	2	3	4	5	6
y	0	3	6	9	12	15	18

(b)

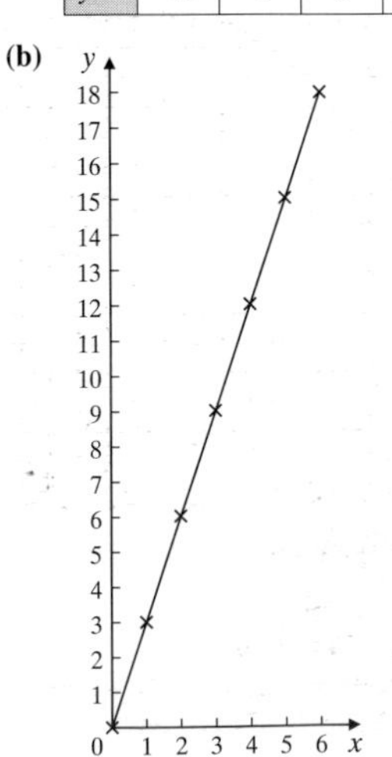

(c) 5 ($4\frac{2}{3}$ to be exact)

4 (a)

x	$\frac{1}{2}$	1	$1\frac{1}{2}$	2	$2\frac{1}{2}$	3	$3\frac{1}{2}$
y	1	$1\frac{1}{2}$	2	$2\frac{1}{2}$	3	$3\frac{1}{2}$	4

(b) A joint of lamb cannot weigh 0 kg.

(c)

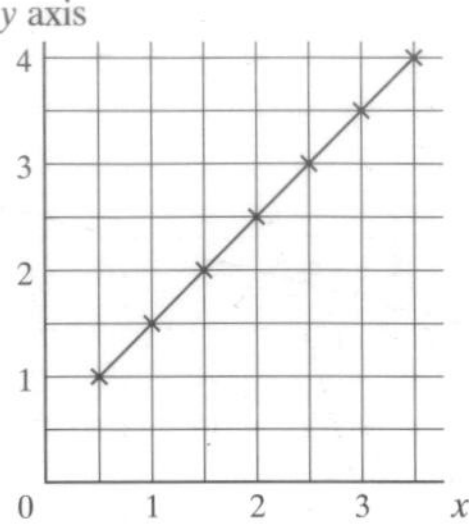

(d) About $2\frac{3}{4}$ hours

Exercise 7C

1 (a)

Litres L	0	10	20	30	40
Cost C in pounds	0	6.50	13.00	19.50	26.00

C axis

Cost(£)

L axis

Litres

(b) (i) £15 (£14.95 to be exact) (ii) 18.5 litres

2 (a)

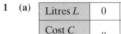

c	0	20	40	60	100
f	32	68	104	140	212

(b)

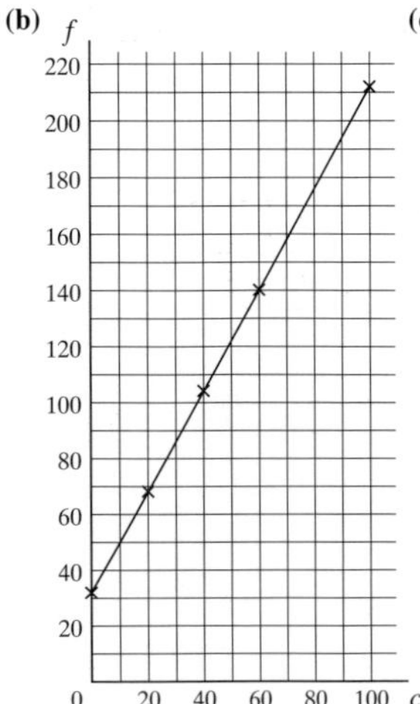

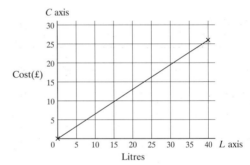

(c) (i) 91°F (91.4 to be exact)

(ii) 37°C

Exercise 7E

1 **(a)** $y = 3x + 1$ **(b)** $y = 3x - 2$ **(c)** $y = -2x + 2$
(d) $y = \frac{1}{2}x + 3$ **(e)** $y = -3x - 5$ **(f)** $y = -\frac{1}{3}x - 1$

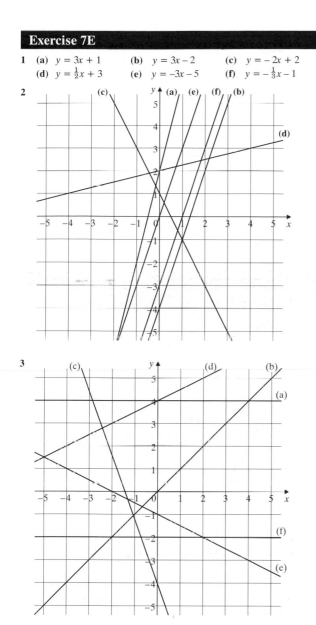

2

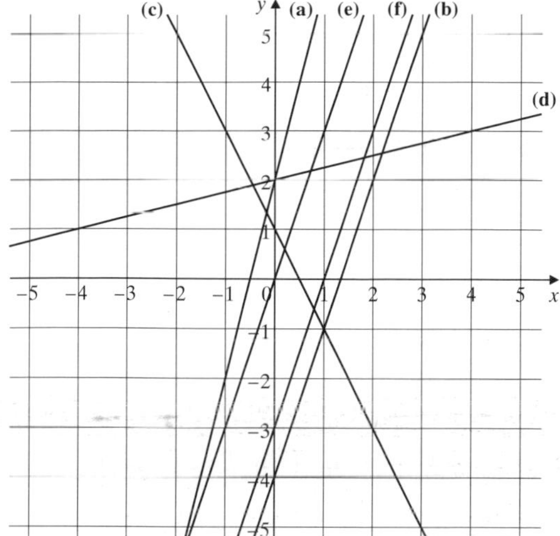

3

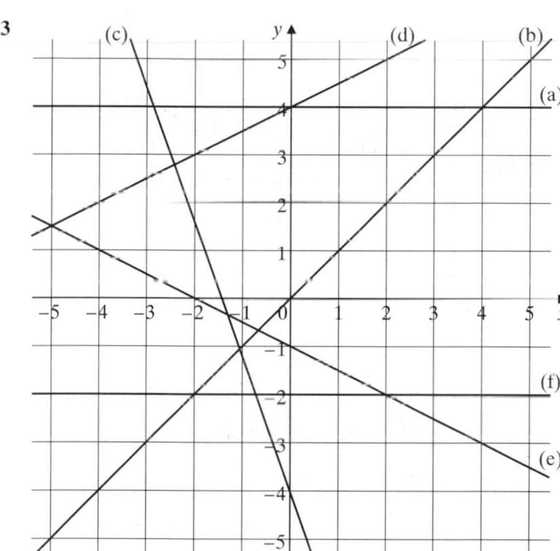

4 **(a)** $y = 3x + 2,\ y = 5x + 2$
(b) $y = 3x + 2,\ y = 3x - 3$

5 **(a)**

x	−2	−1	0	1	2	3
y	−5	−3	−1	1	3	5

(b)

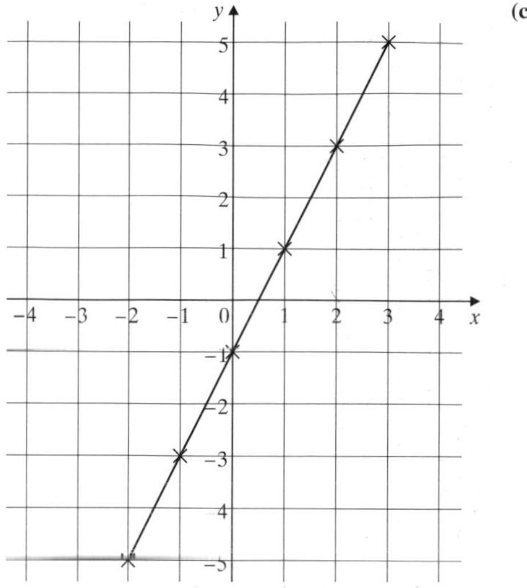

(c) 0.75

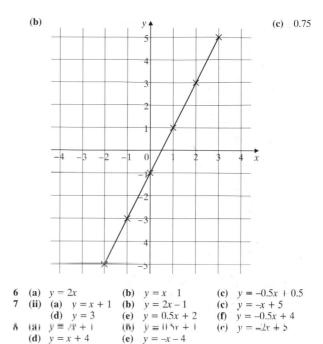

6 **(a)** $y = 2x$ **(b)** $y = x - 1$ **(c)** $y = -0.5x + 0.5$
7 **(ii)** **(a)** $y = x + 1$ **(b)** $y = 2x - 1$ **(c)** $y = -x + 5$
(d) $y = 3$ **(e)** $y = 0.5x + 2$ **(f)** $y = -0.5x + 4$
8 **(a)** $y = 2x + 1$ **(b)** $y = 0.5x + 1$ **(c)** $y = -2x + 5$
(d) $y = x + 4$ **(e)** $y = -x - 4$

Exercise 7F

1 **(a)** $x = 5$ **(b)** $x = 2$ **(c)** $x = 0.5$ **(d)** $x = -3$
(e) $x = 3$
2 **(a)** $x = -2,\ x = -1,\ x = 1,\ x = 2,\ y = -2,\ y = -1,\ y = 1,\ y = 2$
(b) $x = -2,\ x = 2,\ y = 3x + 3,\ y = 3x - 3,\ y = -3x + 3,\ y = -3x - 3$
(c) $y = x - 2,\ y = x - 1,\ y = x + 1,\ y = x + 2,\ y = -x - 2,$
$y = -x - 1,\ y = -x + 1,\ y = -x + 2$
3 **(a)** $y = x + 2$ **(b)** $y = 0.5x + 1$ **(c)** $y = 3x + 4$
(d) $y = x - 3$ **(e)** $y = -0.25x - 2$

Exercise 7G

1 Distance in kilometres from Braintree

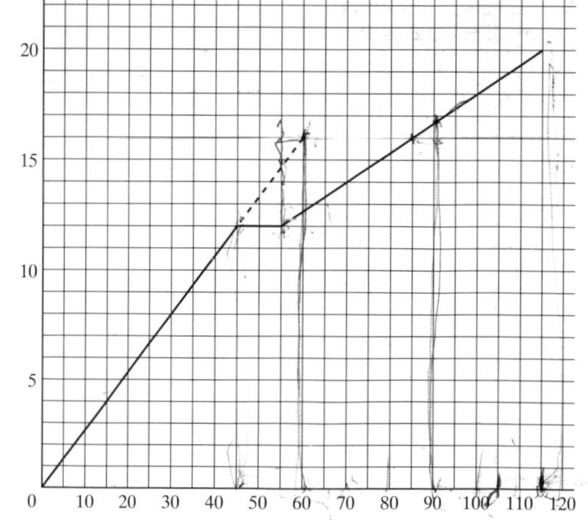

The whole journey takes 1 hour 55 minutes.

2 **(a)** 1000 metres or 1 km **(b)** 4 minutes
(c) Time to run 1500m = $\frac{1500}{9000}$ hour = $\frac{1}{6}$ hour = 10 minutes
On the graph join (8.40 am, 0) to (8.50 am, 1500).

3 (a) (i) 11.40 am (ii) 20 minutes (b) $12\frac{1}{2}$ miles
(c) Draw a line from (2.20 pm, 200) to (3.20 pm, 200). Then draw a line from (3.20 pm, 200) to (4.20 pm, 150) and continue this line to meet the Time axis at (7.20 pm, 0).

4 (a)

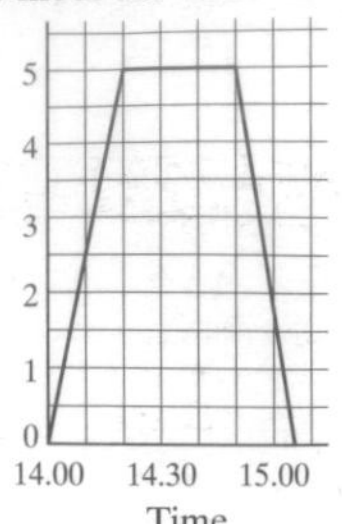

(b) 20 km/h

5

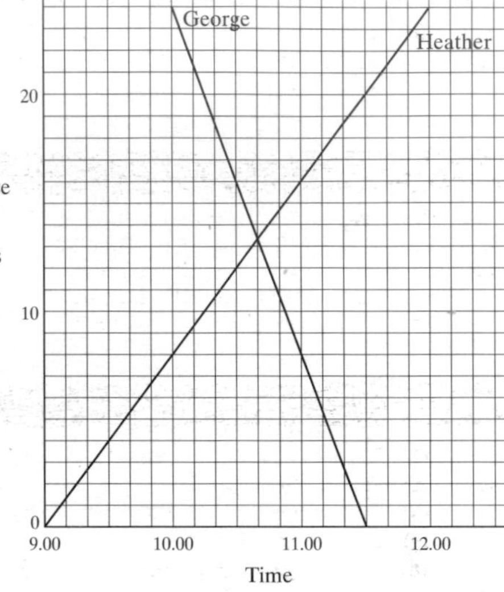

They meet at 10.40 am.

Unit 8 Collecting and organizing data

Exercise 8A

1

	Rock climbing	Mountain walking	Totals
Boys	**42**	5	**47**
Girls	7	20	**27**
Totals	**49**	**25**	**74**

2

	6	not a 6	Totals
Head	10	61	71
Tail	11	68	79
Totals	21	129	150

3

	Under 18	Over 18	Totals
Male	7	53	60
Female	12	28	40
Totals	19	81	100

Answer 28%

4

	Under 50	Over 50	Totals
Bus	173	7	180
Train	32	88	120
Totals	205	95	300

Answer 173

5

	Hotel	Caravan	Camping	Other	Totals
July	11	4	3	**2**	**20**
August	**22**	14	**8**	6	**50**
September	**16**	**7**	4	3	30
Totals	49	**25**	15	11	100

(b) (i) 50 (ii) 16

Exercise 8C

1 North Wales, New Forest, Devon
2 Northumberland, New Forest, Devon
3 North Wales, Peak District
4 North Wales, Peak District, Devon
5 4
6 Hang gliding, shooting
7 North Wales is longer and more exciting riding.
New Forest is shorter and cheaper, and would be easier for a beginner.

Exercise 8D

Qualitative: **(b)**, **(g)**, **(h)**.
Quantitative, discrete: **(e)**, **(i)**, **(j)**.
Quantitative, continuous: **(a)**, **(c)**, **(d)**, **(f)**, **(k)**.
(f) and **(k)** are continuous variables but they are usually treated as if they were discrete.

Exercise 8F

1 1–10 4; 11–20 5; 21–30 5; 31–40 8
2 (a) 1–5 2; 6–10 5; 11–15 7; 16–20 8; 21–25 13; 26–30 5
(b) 1–3 1; 4–6 1; 7–9 4; 10–12 4; 13–15 4; 16–18 4; 19–21 6; 22–24 5; 25–27 10; 28–30 1.
(c) Six intervals are best. There is no useful extra information from the ten intervals.
3 (a) 61.0–61.9 6; 62.0–62.9 9; 63.0–63.9 8; 64.0–64.9 5; 65.0–65.9 6; 66.0 and over 2.
(b) Length is a continuous variable.

Exercise 8G

1 Good **(a)**, **(e)**. Bad **(b)**, **(c)**, **(d)**.

Unit 10 Angles

Exercise 10A

1 45° **2** 134° **3** $a = 128°, b = 55°$ **4** 57° **5** 44°
6 (a) 25° **(b)** 130° **7** 32°
8 $a = 62°, b = 56°, c = 124°, d = 56°, e = 124°$
9 $a = 56°, b = 87°, c = 93°$
10 $a = 42°, b = 96°, c = 138°, d = 62°, e = 62°$
11 84° **12 (a)** 68° **(b)** 112° **(c)** 136°
13 $p = 132°, q = 66°, r = 66°, s = 114°, t = 66°, u = 114°$
14 $x = 47°, y = 123°$
15 $a = 13°, b = 54°, c = 54°, d = 72°$

Exercise 10B

1 (a) 101° **(b)** 79° **2** 125° **3** 144°
4 (a) 72° **(b)** 54°

Exercise 10C

1 **(a)** $x = 123°, y = 57°$ **(b)** $p = 39°, q = 141°$
(c) $a = 36°, b = 144°$ **(d)** $p = 137°, m = 43°$
2 **(a)** $x = 51°, y = 76°$ **(b)** $a = 62°, b = 62°, c = 33°$
(c) $a = 74°, b = 106°, c = 74°, d = 106°, e = 32°, f = 74°$
(d) $p = 48°, q = 132°, r = 48°, s = 48°$
3 **(i)** 64° **(ii)** 52°

Exercise 10D

1 43° **2** 29° **3** 38° **4 (a)** 66° **(b)** 24°
5 **(a)** 56° **(b)** 34°
6 **(a)** 34° **(b)** 56° **(c)** 68° **(d)** 68° **(e)** 22°

Exercise 10E

1 **(a)** 120° **(b)** 205° **(c)** 036° **(d)** 320°
2 **(a)** N, 72°, A, O **(b)** N, 110°, A, O **(c)** N, 160°, O, A **(d)** N, 70°, A, O

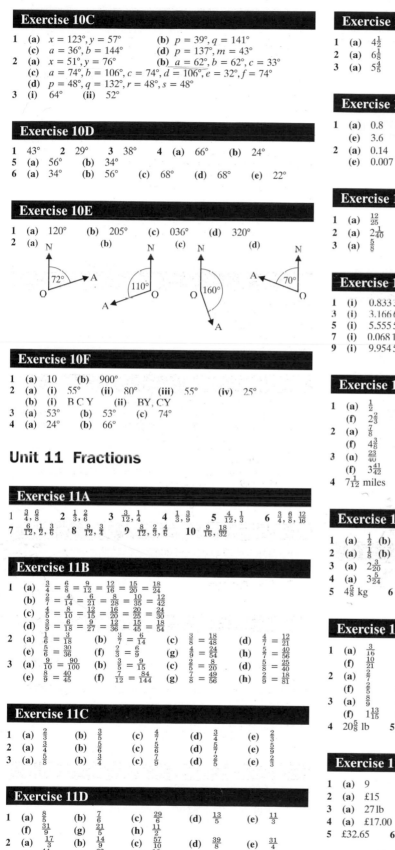

Exercise 10F

1 **(a)** 10 **(b)** 900°
2 **(a) (i)** 55° **(ii)** 80° **(iii)** 55° **(iv)** 25°
(b) (i) BCY **(ii)** BY, CY
3 **(a)** 53° **(b)** 53° **(c)** 74°
4 **(a)** 24° **(b)** 66°

Unit 11 Fractions

Exercise 11A

1 $\frac{3}{4}, \frac{6}{8}$ **2** $\frac{1}{3}, \frac{2}{6}$ **3** $\frac{3}{12}, \frac{1}{4}$ **4** $\frac{1}{3}, \frac{3}{9}$ **5** $\frac{4}{12}, \frac{1}{3}$ **6** $\frac{3}{4}, \frac{6}{8}, \frac{12}{16}$
7 $\frac{6}{12}, \frac{1}{2}, \frac{3}{6}$ **8** $\frac{9}{12}, \frac{3}{4}$ **9** $\frac{8}{12}, \frac{2}{3}, \frac{4}{6}$ **10** $\frac{9}{16}, \frac{18}{32}$

Exercise 11B

1 **(a)** $\frac{3}{4} = \frac{6}{8} = \frac{9}{12} = \frac{12}{16} = \frac{15}{20} = \frac{18}{24}$
(b) $\frac{2}{7} = \frac{4}{14} = \frac{6}{21} = \frac{8}{28} = \frac{10}{35} = \frac{12}{42}$
(c) $\frac{4}{5} = \frac{8}{10} = \frac{12}{15} = \frac{16}{20} = \frac{20}{25} = \frac{24}{30}$
(d) $\frac{3}{9} = \frac{6}{18} = \frac{9}{27} = \frac{12}{36} = \frac{15}{45} = \frac{18}{54}$
2 **(a)** $\frac{1}{6} = \frac{3}{18}$ **(b)** $\frac{3}{7} = \frac{6}{14}$ **(c)** $\frac{3}{8} = \frac{18}{48}$ **(d)** $\frac{4}{7} = \frac{12}{21}$
(e) $\frac{5}{6} = \frac{30}{36}$ **(f)** $\frac{2}{3} = \frac{6}{9}$ **(g)** $\frac{4}{9} = \frac{24}{54}$ **(h)** $\frac{5}{7} = \frac{40}{56}$
3 **(a)** $\frac{9}{10} = \frac{90}{100}$ **(b)** $\frac{3}{5} = \frac{9}{15}$ **(c)** $\frac{2}{5} = \frac{8}{20}$ **(d)** $\frac{5}{8} = \frac{25}{40}$
(e) $\frac{8}{9} = \frac{40}{45}$ **(f)** $\frac{7}{12} = \frac{84}{144}$ **(g)** $\frac{7}{8} = \frac{49}{56}$ **(h)** $\frac{2}{9} = \frac{18}{81}$

Exercise 11C

1 **(a)** $\frac{2}{3}$ **(b)** $\frac{3}{5}$ **(c)** $\frac{4}{7}$ **(d)** $\frac{3}{4}$ **(e)** $\frac{2}{3}$
2 **(a)** $\frac{3}{4}$ **(b)** $\frac{5}{6}$ **(c)** $\frac{5}{6}$ **(d)** $\frac{5}{7}$ **(e)** $\frac{5}{9}$
3 **(a)** $\frac{5}{8}$ **(b)** $\frac{3}{4}$ **(c)** $\frac{7}{9}$ **(d)** $\frac{2}{5}$ **(e)** $\frac{2}{3}$

Exercise 11D

1 **(a)** $\frac{8}{5}$ **(b)** $\frac{7}{6}$ **(c)** $\frac{29}{6}$ **(d)** $\frac{13}{5}$ **(e)** $\frac{11}{3}$
(f) $\frac{31}{9}$ **(g)** $\frac{21}{5}$ **(h)** $\frac{11}{2}$
2 **(a)** $\frac{17}{3}$ **(b)** $\frac{14}{9}$ **(c)** $\frac{57}{10}$ **(d)** $\frac{39}{8}$ **(e)** $\frac{31}{4}$
(f) $\frac{44}{5}$ **(g)** $\frac{63}{10}$ **(h)** $\frac{12}{5}$

Exercise 11E

1 **(a)** $4\frac{1}{2}$ **(b)** $2\frac{1}{4}$ **(c)** $2\frac{1}{3}$ **(d)** $3\frac{2}{5}$ **(e)** $2\frac{3}{4}$
2 **(a)** $6\frac{1}{8}$ **(b)** $5\frac{1}{4}$ **(c)** $3\frac{7}{10}$ **(d)** $7\frac{8}{9}$ **(e)** $4\frac{9}{11}$
3 **(a)** $5\frac{4}{5}$ **(b)** $4\frac{11}{12}$ **(c)** $4\frac{2}{7}$ **(d)** $3\frac{7}{11}$ **(e)** $7\frac{3}{7}$

Exercise 11F

1 **(a)** 0.8 **(b)** 0.75 **(c)** 1.125 **(d)** 0.19
(e) 3.6 **(f)** 0.52 **(g)** 0.625 **(h)** 3.425
2 **(a)** 0.14 **(b)** 4.1875 **(c)** 3.15 **(d)** 4.3125
(e) 0.007 **(f)** 1.28 **(g)** 15.9375 **(h)** 2.35

Exercise 11G

1 **(a)** $\frac{12}{25}$ **(b)** $\frac{1}{4}$ **(c)** $1\frac{7}{10}$ **(d)** $3\frac{203}{500}$ **(e)** $4\frac{3}{1000}$
2 **(a)** $2\frac{1}{40}$ **(b)** $\frac{49}{1000}$ **(c)** $4\frac{7}{8}$ **(d)** $3\frac{3}{4}$ **(e)** $10\frac{101}{1000}$
3 **(a)** $\frac{5}{8}$ **(b)** $2\frac{64}{125}$ **(c)** $\frac{13}{16}$ **(d)** $14\frac{7}{50}$ **(e)** $9\frac{3}{16}$

Exercise 11H

1 **(i)** 0.833 333 **(ii)** $0.8\dot{3}$ **2 (i)** 1.222 2222 **(ii)** $1.\dot{2}$
3 **(i)** 3.166 666 **(ii)** $3.1\dot{6}$ **4 (i)** 0.916 6666 **(ii)** $0.91\dot{6}$
5 **(i)** 5.555 555 **(ii)** $5.\dot{5}$ **6 (i)** 4.818 1818 **(ii)** $4.\dot{8}\dot{1}$
7 **(i)** 0.068 181 **(ii)** $0.06\dot{8}\dot{1}$ **8 (i)** 2.636 3636 **(ii)** $2.\dot{6}\dot{3}$
9 **(i)** 9.954 545 **(ii)** $9.9\dot{5}\dot{4}$ **10 (i)** 0.83 3333 **(ii)** $0.8\dot{3}$

Exercise 11I

1 **(a)** $\frac{1}{2}$ **(b)** $\frac{6}{7}$ **(c)** $1\frac{1}{5}$ **(d)** $1\frac{3}{5}$ **(e)** $3\frac{2}{9}$
(f) $2\frac{2}{3}$ **(g)** $1\frac{3}{4}$ **(h)** $1\frac{7}{8}$
2 **(a)** $\frac{7}{8}$ **(b)** $3\frac{5}{8}$ **(c)** $1\frac{3}{8}$ **(d)** $6\frac{5}{8}$ **(e)** $4\frac{1}{16}$
(f) $4\frac{3}{8}$ **(g)** $1\frac{1}{16}$ **(h)** $4\frac{3}{16}$
3 **(a)** $\frac{23}{40}$ **(b)** $\frac{11}{30}$ **(c)** $2\frac{29}{30}$ **(d)** $\frac{20}{21}$ **(e)** $3\frac{19}{42}$
(f) $3\frac{41}{42}$ **(g)** $5\frac{13}{15}$ **(h)** $2\frac{8}{9}$
4 $7\frac{1}{12}$ miles **5** $17\frac{1}{2}$ in. **6** $3\frac{11}{16}$ in. **7** $\frac{17}{30}$ **8** $1\frac{22}{35}$ lb

Exercise 11J

1 **(a)** $\frac{1}{2}$ **(b)** $\frac{1}{4}$ **(c)** $\frac{1}{2}$ **(d)** $\frac{3}{7}$
2 **(a)** $\frac{1}{8}$ **(b)** $\frac{3}{8}$ **(c)** $\frac{1}{8}$ **(d)** $2\frac{3}{8}$
3 **(a)** $2\frac{3}{20}$ **(b)** $2\frac{18}{35}$ **(c)** $5\frac{4}{15}$ **(d)** $3\frac{29}{72}$
4 **(a)** $3\frac{5}{24}$ **(b)** $2\frac{4}{9}$ **(c)** $3\frac{17}{40}$ **(d)** $3\frac{6}{35}$
5 $4\frac{5}{8}$ kg **6** $3\frac{1}{8}$ pint **7** $2\frac{1}{8}$ ft **8** $\frac{1}{12}$ **9** $2\frac{1}{8}$ km

Exercise 11K

1 **(a)** $\frac{3}{16}$ **(b)** $\frac{8}{15}$ **(c)** $\frac{4}{21}$ **(d)** $\frac{4}{15}$ **(e)** $\frac{2}{35}$
(f) $\frac{10}{21}$ **(g)** $\frac{3}{8}$ **(h)** $\frac{1}{5}$
2 **(a)** $\frac{2}{7}$ **(b)** $\frac{5}{14}$ **(c)** $\frac{2}{5}$ **(d)** $\frac{1}{6}$ **(e)** $\frac{1}{7}$
(f) $\frac{2}{5}$ **(g)** $3\frac{1}{2}$ **(h)** $\frac{13}{20}$
3 **(a)** $\frac{8}{9}$ **(b)** $\frac{14}{15}$ **(c)** $\frac{3}{8}$ **(d)** $3\frac{3}{4}$ **(e)** $\frac{5}{8}$
(f) $1\frac{13}{15}$ **(g)** 16 **(h)** 3
4 $20\frac{5}{8}$ lb **5** $14\frac{5}{8}$ min **6** 20 h **7** $9\frac{4}{5}$ h **8** $24\frac{1}{6}$ m^2

Exercise 11L

1 **(a)** 9 **(b)** 30 **(c)** 28 litres **(d)** 21 pints
2 **(a)** £15 **(b)** 3.704 kg **(c)** £2.64 **(d)** 62.05 litres
3 **(a)** 27 lb **(b)** £2.22 **(c)** 654.5 km **(d)** 280 people
4 **(a)** £17.00 **(b)** 168 toys **(c)** 720 cars **(d)** £37.15
5 £32.65 **6** £1.08 **7** 140 days **8** 21

Exercise 11M

1 (a) $\frac{4}{9}$ (b) $\frac{8}{15}$ (c) $\frac{9}{16}$ (d) 2
2 (a) $\frac{2}{9}$ (b) $\frac{1}{9}$ (c) $1\frac{1}{16}$ (d) $1\frac{3}{4}$
3 (a) $\frac{8}{9}$ (b) $7\frac{1}{2}$ (c) $6\frac{9}{10}$ (d) $1\frac{13}{20}$
(e) $\frac{3}{5}$ (f) $1\frac{1}{9}$ (g) $\frac{4}{9}$ (h) $\frac{9}{10}$
4 16 5 36 6 $11\frac{2}{11}$ days

Exercise 11N

1 4.95 t 2 289 cars 3 $\frac{2}{9}$ 4 $\frac{17}{45}$
5 $1\frac{3}{5}$ miles 6 605 7 $\frac{9}{16}$ 8 $\frac{2}{11}$

Exercise 11O

1 (a) $\frac{5}{9} = \frac{10}{18} = \frac{15}{27} = \frac{20}{36} = \frac{25}{45}$ (b) $\frac{2}{5} = \frac{4}{10}$
(c) $\frac{3}{8} = \frac{24}{64}$ (d) $\frac{8}{7} = \frac{40}{35}$
2 (a) $\frac{4}{5}$ (b) $6\frac{1}{3}$ (c) $\frac{1}{12}$ (d) $3\frac{1}{3}$
(e) 4 (f) $\frac{1}{13}$
3 (a) 0.875 (b) 2.75 (c) 4.36 (d) $0.\dot{7}$ (e) $2.8\dot{3}$
4 (a) $\frac{1}{25}$ (b) $2\frac{29}{40}$ (c) $5\frac{17}{25}$ (d) $\frac{3}{10}$ (e) $\frac{9}{20}$
5 $\frac{4}{5}$ kg 6 $8\frac{3}{8}$ ft 7 $3\frac{7}{8}$ miles 8 $4\frac{11}{16}$ ft 9 16 bags
10 $\frac{8}{9}$ 11 $4\frac{11}{12}$ in 12 $\frac{1}{8}$ 13 £18

Unit 12 Measure 2

Exercise 12A

1 (a) 300 cm (b) 3 cm (c) 600 cm (d) 10 cm
2 (a) 20 mm (b) 50 mm (c) 200 mm
3 (a) 5000 m (b) 3 m (c) 10 000 m (d) 20 m
(e) 60 000 m
4 (a) 5000 g (b) 40 000 g (c) 250 000 g
5 (a) 3 *l* (b) 8 *l* (c) 50 *l*
6 (a) 6000 m*l* (b) 40 000 m*l* (c) 350 000 m*l*
7 (a) 3 km (b) 45 km
8 (a) 2 kg (b) 3000kg (c) 50kg
9 8 000 000 10 1 000 000 11 4000 12 1 000 000

Exercise 12B

1 d, f, b, c, e, a 2 250 kg, 3000 g, 2 kg, 250 g, 25 g
3 5 mm, 4 cm, 50 mm, 20 cm, 75 cm, 2 m, 3 m = 3000 mm, 3 km, 4000 m
4 200 m*l*, 600 m*l*, 1 *l*, 2000 m*l*, 5 *l*

Exercise 12C

1 (a) 2.5 m (b) 3600 m (c) 0.75 m (d) 5 m
(e) 40 m (f) 0.005 m
2 (a) 4500 g (b) 400 g (c) 30 g (d) 5 g
3 (a) 35 cm (b) 250 cm (c) 0.5 cm (d) 8 cm
(e) 80 cm (f) 3.5 cm
4 (a) 3500 m*l* (b) 15 400 m*l* (c) 50 m*l* (d) 3 m*l*
5 (a) 35 mm (b) 7 mm (c) 0.8 mm (d) 5 mm
6 (a) 0.3 km (b) 0.05 km (c) 1.25 km (d) 0.075 km
7 (a) 0.25 *l* (b) 0.1 *l* (c) 0.05 *l* (d) 3.5 *l*
8 (a) 3.5 tonnes (b) 0.45 tonnes
(c) 0.05 tonnes (d) 0.003 tonnes
9 20 glasses 10 60 pieces 11 10 batches

Exercise 12D

1 (a) 2.4 cm, 25 mm, 3 cm, 50 mm, 57 mm, 6 cm
(b) 270 mm, 30 cm, 0.4 m, 45 cm, 500 mm, 1.2 m
(c) 2 m, 340 cm, 3500 mm, 370 cm, 4 m = 4000 mm
(d) 0.2 cm, 4 mm, 45 mm, 5 cm, 55 mm, 0.3 m, 36 cm
2 (a) 0.05 kg, 250 g, 0.3 kg, 500 g
(b) 3000 g, 4 kg, 4.5 kg, 5000 g, 400 kg, 0.5 t
3 (a) 250 m*l*, 0.3 *l* = 300 m*l*, 0.4 *l*, 500 m*l*
(b) 45 m*l*, 0.05 *l*, 360 m*l*, 0.4 *l*, 450 m*l*, 500 m*l*

Exercise 12E

1 640 km 2 $5\frac{1}{4}$ pints 3 67.5 litres 4 220 pounds
5 0.6 litres 6 6.7 gallons 7 0.875 pints 8 93.75 miles
9 1.76 pounds 10 2.625 pints

Exercise 12F

1 600 g of fat, 1000 g flour, 800 g of dried fruit
2 6.6 gallons 3 9.1 kg 4 10 cm 5 60 cm by 37.5 cm
6 They are the same
7 11 pounds of bread and 1.1. pounds of spread 8 2.86 litres
9 Hazel's guess was 5.06 pounds 10 7.7 pounds

Exercise 12G

1 (a) 35 spongs (b) 32 deltas (c) 336 spongs
2 (a) 72 dolts (b) 80 pings (c) 1200 dolts
3 (a) 20 farthings (b) 20 old pennies (c) 24 groats
(d) 192 farthings (e) 120 old pennies (f) 960 farthings

Exercise 12H

1 (a) 1 000 000 m^2 (b) 1 000 000 mm^2 (c) 1000 mm^3
(d) 1 000 000 000 mm^3
2 (a) 9 square feet (b) 27 cubic feet
3 (a) 0.8281 m^2 (b) 13.25 m^2
4 (a) 3840 cu. inches (b) 16.387 cm^3 (c) 62 926 cm^3
(d) 62.9 litres

Exercise 12I

1 (a) discrete (b) discrete (c) continuous
(d) discrete (e) continuous (f) continuous
(g) discrete (h) continuous (i) discrete
(j) continuous
2 (a) 2.65 cm, 2.75 cm (b) 3.85 cm, 3.95 cm
(c) 10.45 cm, 10.55 cm (d) 11.5 mm, 12.5 mm
(e) 24.5 mm, 25.5 mm (f) 35.5 mm, 36.5 mm
3 (a) 2.445 m, 2.455 m (b) 5.335 m, 5.345 m
(c) 3.995 m, 4.005 m (d) 22.5 cm, 23.5 cm
(e) 13.5 cm, 14.5 cm (f) 49.5 cm, 50.5 cm
4 12.05 s ≤ time < 12.15 s
5 (a) 22.345 s ≤ time < 22.355 s (b) 43.665 s ≤ time < 43.675 s
(c) 10.015 s ≤ time < 10.025 s
(d) 2 min 45.335 s ≤ time < 2 min 45.345 s
(e) 44.995 s ≤ time < 45.005 s (f) 49.995 s ≤ time < 50.005 s

Exercise 12J

1 (a) seconds (b) minutes (c) hours (d) minutes
(e) hours (f) minutes
2 (a) cm or m (b) mm (c) m (d) cm
(e) m (f) mm
3 (a) cm^2 (b) hectares (c) km^2 (d) m^2
4 (a) m*l* (b) *l* or gallons (c) litres or cubic metres
5 (a) metres (b) tape measure or trundle wheel
(c) nearest 10 cm or $\frac{1}{2}$ metre
6 (a) (i) seconds (ii) metres and centimetres
(b) tape measure or metre rule and stopwatch
(c) ± 1 cm and ± 0.1 s

Exercise 12K

1 12 miles 2 25 mph 3 5 hours 4 3.75 mph
5 7 mph 6 8 mph 7 $1\frac{1}{3}$ mph 8 $66\frac{2}{3}$ mph
9 20 mph 10 30 km/h

Exercise 12L

1 2700 kg m^{-3} 2 8960 kg m^{-3} 3 19 400 kg m^{-3}
4 8890 kg m^{-3} 5 10 505 kg m^{-3} 6 970 kg m^{-3}
7 7310 kg m^{-3} 8 7130 kg m^{-3} 9 11 400 kg m^{-3}
10 18 900 kg m^{-3}

Exercise 12M

1 0.000 325 m^3 2 900 kg 3 200 kg 4 0.0313 m^3
5 0.0714 m^3 6 8050 kg 7 3600 kg 8 0.127 m^3
9 0.002 87 m^3 10 0.000 0233 m^3

Exercise 12N

1 72 000 metres per hour 2 8.33 metres per second
3 1 mile per minute 4 54 kilometres per hour
5 72 kilometres per hour 6 1333 metres per minute
7 5.56 metres per second 8 2 160 000 km per hour
9 39 600 km per hour 10 27.2 metres per second

Exercise 12O

1 40 mph 2 70 mph 3 1 350 000 mph 4 61.25 mph
5 (a) 31.1 m/s (b) the bird
6 (a) 636.75 mph (b) 1.93 times
7 19.32g 8 362.9 kg 9 0.558 m^3
10 (a) 675 000 000 mph (b) 150 000 times

Exercise 12P

1 6 m 2 (a) \$641.75 (b) £61.35 3 9.40×10^{12}
4 404 g 5 (a) 99.5 m (b) (i) 14.75 s (ii) 14.85 s
6 36.3 kilometres per hour

Unit 13 Quadratic functions

Exercise 13A

1 (a) $n \to 2n^2 + 1$ (b) $n \to 3n^2 - 2$ (c) $n \to 3n^2 - 4$
(d) $n \to 2n^2 + 0.5$ (e) $n \to n^2 - 3$ (f) $n \to \frac{1}{2}n^2 - 1$

2 (a) $0 \to 1$, $1 \to 2$, $2 \to 5$, $3 \to 10$, $4 \to 17$, $5 \to 26$
(b) $0 \to 0$, $1 \to 3$, $2 \to 12$, $3 \to 27$, $4 \to 48$, $5 \to 75$
(c) $0 \to 2$, $1 \to 5$, $2 \to 14$, $3 \to 29$, $4 \to 50$, $5 \to 77$
(d) $0 \to -1$, $1 \to 1$, $2 \to 7$, $3 \to 17$, $4 \to 31$, $5 \to 49$

3 (a) $0 \to 3$, $1 \to 5$, $2 \to 11$, $3 \to 21$, $4 \to 35$, $5 \to 53$
(b) $0 \to 1$, $1 \to 5$, $2 \to 17$, $3 \to 37$, $4 \to 65$, $5 \to 101$
(c) $0 \to 3$, $1 \to 3.5$, $2 \to 5$, $3 \to 7.5$, $4 \to 11$, $5 \to 15.5$
(d) $0 \to 0.5$, $1 \to 1.5$, $2 \to 4.5$, $3 \to 9.5$, $4 \to 16.5$, $5 \to 25.5$

4 (a) (i) 0 (ii) 0 (iii) 0 (iv) 0 (v) 0
(vi) 1 (vii) 5 (viii) 1 (ix) $\frac{1}{2}$ (x) 1.5
(xi) −1 (xii) −5 (xiii) −1 (xiv) $-\frac{1}{2}$ (xv) −2.5
(b) They are the value of c in $n \to an^2 + c$

Exercise 13B

1 (a)

$n \to 2n^2 + 1$	1st diff	2nd diff
$0 \to 1$		
$1 \to 3$	2	
$2 \to 9$	6	4
$3 \to 19$	10	4
$4 \to 33$	14	4
$5 \to 51$	18	4

(b)

$n \to 3n^2 - 1$	1st diff	2nd diff
$0 \to -1$		
$1 \to 2$	3	
$2 \to 11$	9	6
$3 \to 26$	15	6
$4 \to 47$	21	6
$5 \to 74$	27	6

(c)

$n \to 2n^2 + 2$	1st diff	2nd diff
$0 \to 2$		
$1 \to 4$	2	
$2 \to 10$	6	4
$3 \to 20$	10	4
$4 \to 34$	14	4
$5 \to 52$	18	4

(d)

$n \to 2n^2 - 1$	1st diff	2nd diff
$0 \to -1$		
$1 \to 1$	2	
$2 \to 7$	6	4
$3 \to 17$	10	4
$4 \to 31$	14	4
$5 \to 49$	18	4

(e)

$n \to n^2 + 4$	1st diff	2nd diff
$0 \to 4$		
$1 \to 5$	1	
$2 \to 8$	3	2
$3 \to 13$	5	2
$4 \to 20$	7	2
$5 \to 29$	9	2

(f)

$n \to 3n^2$	1st diff	2nd diff
$0 \to 0$		
$1 \to 3$	3	
$2 \to 12$	9	6
$3 \to 27$	15	6
$4 \to 48$	21	6
$5 \to 75$	27	6

(g)

$n \to 4n^2 - 2$	1st diff	2nd diff
$0 \to -2$		
$1 \to 2$	4	
$2 \to 14$	12	8
$3 \to 34$	20	8
$4 \to 62$	28	8
$5 \to 98$	36	8

(h)

$n \to n^2 + \frac{1}{2}$	1st diff	2nd diff
$0 \to 0.5$		
$1 \to 1.5$	1	
$2 \to 4.5$	3	2
$3 \to 9.5$	5	2
$4 \to 16.5$	7	2
$5 \to 25.5$	9	2

(i)

$n \to \frac{1}{2}n^2 - \frac{1}{2}$	1st diff	2nd diff
$0 \to 0.5$		
$1 \to 0$	0.5	
$2 \to 1.5$	1.5	1
$3 \to 4$	2.5	1
$4 \to 7.5$	3.5	1
$5 \to 12$	4.5	1

(j)

$n \to -2n^2$	1st diff	2nd diff
$0 \to -0$		
$1 \to -2$	−2	
$2 \to -8$	−6	−4
$3 \to -18$	−10	−4
$4 \to -32$	−14	−4
$5 \to -50$	−18	−4

2 The output when the input is 0 is always c in $n \to an^2 + c$
3 The 2nd difference is always $2a$ in $n \to an^2 + c$

Exercise 13C

1 (a)

$n \to -2n^2 + 3n + 2$	1st diff	2nd diff
$0 \to 2$		
$1 \to 7$	5	
$2 \to 16$	9	4
$3 \to 29$	13	4
$4 \to 46$	17	4
$5 \to 65$	21	4

(b)

$n \to 3n^2 + 2n + 1$	1st diff	2nd diff
$0 \to 1$		
$1 \to 6$	5	
$2 \to 17$	11	6
$3 \to 34$	17	6
$4 \to 57$	23	6
$5 \to 86$	29	6

(c)

$n \to \frac{1}{2}n^2 - 2n + 6$	1st diff	2nd diff
$0 \to 6$		
$1 \to 4.5$	−1.5	
$2 \to 4$	−0.5	1
$3 \to 4.5$	0.5	1
$4 \to 6$	1.5	1
$5 \to 8.5$	2.5	1

(d)

$n \to -n^2 + 4n + 8$	1st diff	2nd diff
$0 \to 8$		
$1 \to 11$	3	
$2 \to 12$	1	−2
$3 \to 11$	−1	−2
$4 \to 8$	−3	−2
$5 \to 3$	−5	−2

2 The second difference is always $2a$ in $n \to an^2 + bn + c$

Exercise 13D

1 (a) $n \to 2n^2$ (b) $n \to 3n^2 + 4$ (c) $n \to 5n^2 + 1$
(d) $n \to \frac{1}{2}n^2 + 1$ (e) $n \to 4n^2$ (f) $n \to n^2 - 3$
(g) $n \to \frac{1}{2}n^2 + 2$ (h) $n \to 3n^2 + 0.5$
2 (a) $n \to n^2 + 3n + 1$ (b) $n \to 2n^2 - n + 2$
(c) $n \to n^2 + 2n - 1$ (d) $n \to 3n^2 - n - 2$
3 (a) $3n^2 + n + 2$ (b) $2n^2 + 7$ (c) $n^2 + 6$
(d) $2n^2 - 4$ (e) $1\frac{1}{2}n^2 + 1$ (f) $2n^2 - 5n - 1$
4 $2n^2$ 5 $n^2 + 3$ 6 $4n^2 + 4n - 3$

Exercise 13E

1 (a) $10n^2 + 3$ (b) $3n^2 + 3$ (c) $n \to 5n^2 + n + 2$
(d) $2n^2 - 3n$ (e) $-2n^2 - 1$ (f) $\frac{1}{2}n^2 - 3$
2 $n^2 + 4$ 3 For the sequence shown: $\frac{3}{2}n^2 + \frac{3}{2}n$
4 For the design of tower shown: $2n^2 - n$
5 11, $\frac{1}{2}n^2 + \frac{1}{2}n + 1$
6 1 1 white, n–1 black
2 $\frac{1}{2}n^2 + \frac{1}{2}n$ (the nth triangle number)
3 white: black = $1 : n - 1$
4 white: black = $n : \frac{1}{2}n^2 - \frac{1}{2}n$

Unit 14 Properties of numbers

Exercise 14A

1 (a) 31, 33, 35, 37, 39 (b) 121, 123, 125, 127, 129
2 (a) 62, 64, 66, 68 (b) 152, 154, 156, 158
3 (a) 6, 12, 18, 24, 30, 36, 42, 48, 54
(b) 8, 16, 24, 32, 40, 48, 56
4 (a) 1, 2, 3, 6, 9, 18 (b) 1, 2, 3, 4, 6, 8, 12, 24
(c) 1, 2, 5, 10, 25, 50
5 (a) 11, 13, 17, 19 (b) 41, 43, 47
6 (a) 8, 32 (b) 9, 15, 45 (c) 9, 15, 45 (d) 11, 23

Exercise 14B

1 (a) 64 (b) 343 (c) 144 (d) 1000
(e) 1, 4, 9, 16, 25, 36, 49, 64, 81, 100, 121, 144
(f) 1, 8, 27, 64, 125, 216, 343, 512
2 (a) (i) 1, 9, 49, 64 (ii) 1, 8, 64
(b) (i) 4, 16 (ii) 27, 125
(c) (i) 64, 81, 144 (ii) 64, 125
(d) (i) 81, 100, 169 (ii) 125, 216

Exercise 14C

1 (a) 169 (b) 12.25 (c) 1600 (d) 75.69
(e) 384.16 (f) 3294.76
2 (a) 216 (b) 13.824 (c) 8000 (d) −2.197
(e) 2406.104 (f) 47 437.928
3 (a) 11 (b) 15 (c) 130 (d) 1.7
(e) 0.7 (f) 5.8
4 (a) 15.91 (b) 48.38 (c) 4.29 (d) 92.07
(e) 5.43 (f) 1351.28
5 (a) 4.08 (b) 15.4 (c) 2.98 (d) 2.10
(e) 9.59 (f) 187

Exercise 14D

1 2.65 2 2.47 3 2.29 4 3.16
5 4.47 6 5.66 7 3.11 8 3.48
9 3.61 10 3.68 11 5.29 12 3.21

Exercise 14E

1 (a) 9 (b) 16 (c) 15 625 (d) 1
2 (a) 729 (b) 3125 (c) 0 (d) 6561
3 (a) 3375 (b) 2401 (c) 46 656 (d) 1000
4 (a) 16 (b) 216 (c) 59 049 (d) 73
5 (a) 1728 (b) 81 (c) 196 (d) 512
6 (a) 5 (b) 3 (c) 5
7 (a) 4 (b) 3 (c) 4
8 (a) 2 (b) 6 (c) 3
9 (a) 10 (b) 3 (c) 2

Exercise 14F

1 (a) 6^{11} (b) 8^8 (c) 2^6
2 (a) 4 (b) 6^3 (c) 7^4
3 (a) 4^5 (b) 5^2 (c) 3
4 (a) 5^{13} (b) 2^{11}
5 (a) 10^5 (b) 9^3
6 (a) 6^{11} (b) 5^6
7 (a) 3^8 (b) 4^6
8 (a) 6^3 (b) 5^5 (c) 4^2

Exercise 14G

1 (a) $2 \times 2 \times 2 \times 3$ (b) $2 \times 2 \times 2 \times 2 \times 2$
(c) $2 \times 3 \times 3$ (d) 13
2 (a) 4 (b) 2 (c) 6 (d) 6 (e) 7
3 (a) 12 (b) 12 (c) 14 (d) 30
4 (a) 60 (b) 144 (c) 850

Exercise 14H

1 (a) 6×10^5 (b) 3.5×10^4 (c) 5.4×10^3
2 (a) 2.5×10^4 (b) 7×10^3 (c) 2.36×10^5
3 (a) 4×10^7 (b) 1.21×10^6 (c) 5.4×10^4
4 (a) 324 000 (b) 57 500 (c) 8 040
5 (a) 2 000 000 (b) 256 000 (c) 30 600
6 (a) 2 700 000 (b) 16 000 000 (c) 8 090

Exercise 14I

1 (a) 9×10^{-3} (b) 8×10^{-2} (c) 4.5×10^{-1}
2 (a) 4.3×10^{-4} (b) 3.8×10^{-2} (c) 9.6×10^{-3}
3 (a) 9.4×10^{-6} (b) 8×10^{-4} (c) 7.77×10^{-5}
4 (a) 0.009 (b) 0.00074 (c) 0.0028
5 (a) 0.000 982 (b) 0.000 0465 (c) 0.005 61
6 (a) 0.000 000 55 (b) 0.000 134 (c) 0.006 502

Exercise 14J

1 (a) 7.15×10^3 (b) 1.106×10^6 (c) 6.048×10^{-3}
(d) 7.93×10^{-4} (e) 2.4×10^2 (f) 3.002×10^0
2 (a) 1.102×10^4 (b) 3.38×10^3 (c) 4.0666×10^3
3 4.55×10^{-11} 4 9.46728×10^{19}

Exercise 14K

1 (a) 5, 9, 27, 35, 37 (b) 9, 12, 27, 36 (c) 4, 8, 12, 16
(d) 5, 37 (e) 4, 9, 16, 36 (f) 8, 27
2 (a) 15 (b) 6 (c) 7
3 (a) 20 (b) 18 (c) 90
4 (a) 4.359 (b) 2.884
5 (a) 2197 (b) 625 (c) 7776 (d) 2401
6 (a) 4^9 (b) 4 (c) 4^{11}
7 (a) 1.496×10^8 (b) 2.5752×10^6
8 5×10^{-8}
9 11, 13, 17, 19 (any two)
10 (a) 5.94783×10^{21} (b) 36 100 000
11 3.818×10^3
12 2.5125×10^{-21}

Unit 15 Pythagoras' theorem

Exercise 15A

1 (a) (i) 16 (ii) 9 (iii) 25 (b) 25
(c) Area BADE = Area ACHI + Area CBFG
2 (a) (i) $6\frac{1}{4}$ (ii) 36 (iii) $42\frac{1}{4}$ (b) $42\frac{1}{4}$
(c) Area RPWX = Area QRST + Area PQUV

Exercise 15B

1 (a) 13 cm (b) 15 cm (c) 12.5 cm (d) 7.5 cm
2 (a) 11.4 cm (b) 35.5 cm (c) 7.2 m (d) 20.8 m
3 14.8 cm 4 5.8 km 5 54.7 m

Exercise 15C

1 (a) 9 cm (b) 24 cm (c) 7.5 cm (d) 10.5 cm
2 (a) 6.3 m (b) 35.5 cm (c) 8.7 cm (d) 21.2 cm

Exercise 15D

1 4.90 m 2 4.71 miles 3 12.4 cm 4 24.4 cm
5 12.4 m 6 36.1 m

Unit 16 Averages and spread

Exercise 16A

1 (a) 4.44, 3, 4 (b) 18.25 kg, 14 kg, 17 kg
(c) 2, 24 cm, 2.7 cm, 2.2 cm (d) £11.04, no mode, £7.75
2 £119.67 3 36 4 506 matches, 46.25 matches
5 156.18 cm 6 $x = 1$
7 (a) 5 or greater (b) 4 or smaller

Exercise 16B

1 (a) median 19 (b) range 11
2 2 hrs 20 min 3 £2250
4 9, 10 and 20; 7, 10 and a number between 10 and 19 inclusive.
5 4, 6, 6, 6, 6, 6, 8 is the easiest to obtain.

Exercise 16C

1 (a) 155 (b) 152 (c) 160
2 (a) 9 (b) 5 (c) 15
3 (a) 2 (b) 1 (c) 4
4 (a) 225 (b) 204 (c) 231.5

Exercise 16D

1 8 cm 2 10 °C 3 3 4 27.5 g

Exercise 16E

1 0, 20, 26, 12, 8, total f 45, total fx 66. Mean 1.47, Mode 1, Median 1
2 Mode 3, Median 3, Mean 3.35
3 Mode 0, Median 0, Mean 0.5
4 (a) 2 (b) 3 (c) 3.2
5 (a) 1 (b) 2.2 (c) 2

Exercise 16F

1 (a) 7 (b) 1 2 (a) 55 (b) 10
3 (a) 11 months (b) 5.5 months
4 (a) £8 (b) £2
5 (a) 4 (b) 1 6 (a) 5 (b) 3
7 (a) 5 (b) 1 8 (a) 8 (b) 2.75

Exercise 16G

1 (a) 13 (b) 6–10 (c) 30
2 (a) 61–100 (b) 69.34
3 11.79.
4 (a) $160 \le x < 165$ (b) 164.3
5 (b) 6–10 (c) 11–15 (d) 12.95

Exercise 16H

1 (a) 2, 9, 15, 19, 21, 22 (b) 2
2 (a) 9, 26, 60, 67, 69 (b) 21–30
3 21, 63, 127, 148, 150

Exercise 16I

1 Plot points (0, 2), (1, 9), (2, 15), (3, 19), (4, 21), (5, 22): join with a smooth curve.
2 (a) 2, 7, 16, 29, 50, 74, 107, 134, 152, 156, 157.
(b) Plot points (0, 2), (1, 7), (2, 16), (3, 29), (4, 50), (5,74), (6, 107), (7, 134), (8, 152), (9, 156), (10, 157): join with a smooth curve.
3 Plot points (10, 9), (20, 26), (30, 60), (40, 67), (50, 69): join with a smooth curve.
4 Plot points (120, 21), (140, 63), (160, 127), (180, 148), (200, 150): join with a smooth curve.
5 (a) 7, 19, 34, 70, 115, 143, 156, 163.
(b) Plot points (145.5, 7), (150.5, 19), (155.5, 34), (160.5, 70), (165.5, 115), (170.5, 143), (175.5, 156), (180.5, 163): join with a smooth curve.

Exercise 16J

1 (a) Plot points (20, 1), (25, 5), (30, 14), (35, 28), (40, 66), (45, 113), (50, 164), (55, 196), (60, 200): join with a smooth curve.
(b) (i) 44 mph (ii) 11 mph (iii) 71%
2 (a) 26, 45, 67, 82, 91, 96, 100.
(b) Plot points (40 000, 26), (52 000, 45), (68 000, 67), (88 000, 82) (120 000, 91), (160 000, 96), (220 000, 100): join with a smooth curve.
(c) £80 000
3 (a) 54, 172, 458, 1038, 1752, 2582, 2906, 2980, 2998, 3000.
(b) Plot points (10, 54), (20, 172), (30, 458), (40, 1038), (50, 1752), (60, 2582), (70, 2906), (80, 2980), (90, 2998), (100, 3000): join with a smooth curve.
(c) Median 47, Interquartile range 20
(d) 1625 fail
(e) 38

Exercise 16K

1 (a) 6 (b) $5\frac{1}{2}$ (c) 5 (d) 5.6
2 (a) £18.90 (b) 6.4 miles
3 (a) 3, 25, 86, 145, 208, 282, 335, 362, 365.
Plot points (0.5, 3), (5.5, 25), (10.5, 86), (13.5, 145), (16.5, 208), (20.5, 282), (25.5, 335), (30.5, 362), (35.5, 365) for last interval taken as 31°C to 35°C: join with a smooth curve,
(b) Median 15.25°C. Interquartile range 9°C
(c) between 12.3% and 15.1%

Unit 17 The tangent ratio

Exercise 17A

1 (c) Approximately 0.7

Exercise 17B

1 0.03492 2 0.1405 3 0.2308 4 0.4452
5 0.7399 6 1 7 1.557 8 2.618
9 3.951 10 10.57 11 20.44 12 572.9

Exercise 17C

1 17.74° 2 32.21° 3 41.98° 4 47.72°
5 60.94° 6 79.39°

Exercise 17D

1 (a) 22.6° (b) 53.1° (c) 16.3° (d) 36.9°
2 (a) 52.1° (b) 49.6° (c) 42.2° (d) 40.9°
3 52.0° 4 8.13° 5 56.3°

Exercise 17E

1 (a) 10.1 cm (b) 11.5 cm (c) 6.03 cm (d) 9.23 cm
2 (a) 7.55 cm (b) 15.6 cm (c) 2.58 cm (d) 10.2 cm
3 16.1 cm 4 2.00 m 5 3.25 m

Exercise 17F

1 16.7° 2 246 m 3 71.4° 4 54.5°
5 (a) (i) 31.0° (ii) 5.83 m (b) 61.9°
6 (a) 87° (b) 1908 m (c) 1911 m (d) 21 s

Unit 18 Graphs of more complex functions

Exercise 18A

1 (b)

x	−2.5	−1.5	−0.8	−0.6	−0.4	−0.2	−0.1	0	0.1	0.2	0.4	0.6	0.8	1.5	2.5
y	6.25	2.25	0.64	0.36	0.16	0.04	0.01	0	0.01	0.04	0.16	0.36	0.64	2.25	6.25

(a) Dotted line on graph.
(b) and (c). Solid line on graph.

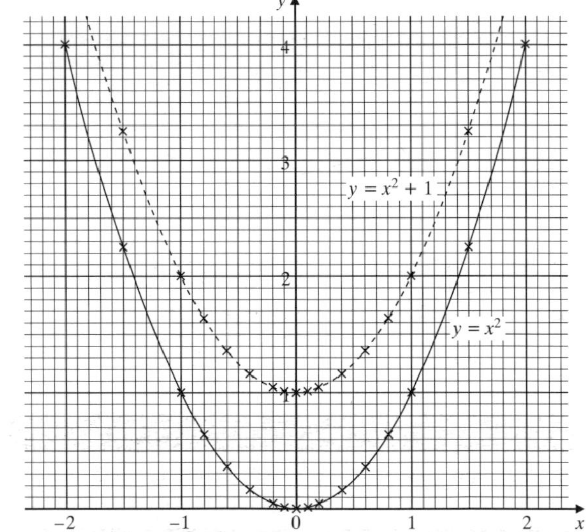

2

x	−3	−2.5	−2	−1.5	−1	−0.8	−0.6	−0.4	−0.2	−0.1	0	0.1	0.2	etc
y	10	7.25	5	3.25	2	1.64	1.36	1.16	1.04	1.01	1	1.01	1.04	

The graph of $y = x^2 + 1$ is shown by the dotted line in the answer to question **1**.

3 (c)

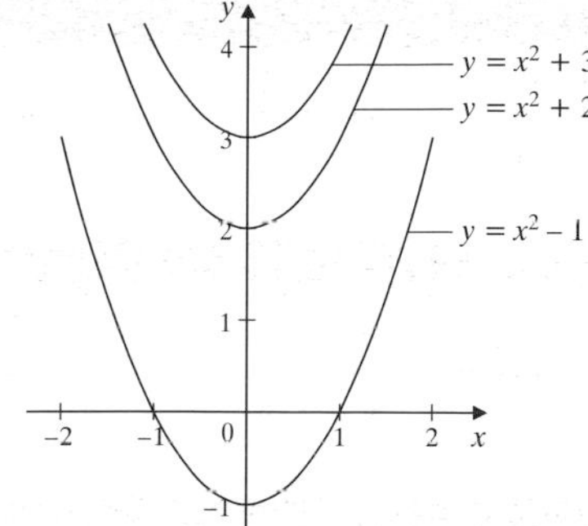

(d) The y axis is a line of symmetry for each graph of the type $y = x^2 + c$

(e) Each of these graphs cuts the y axis at the point $(0, c)$.

Exercise 18B

2 **(a)** A $y = x^2 + 2$, B $y = x^2$ **(b)** C $y = x^2 + 1$, D $y = x^2 - 1$ **(c)** E $y = 2x^2$, F $y = x^2$

(d) G $y = -x^2$, H $y = -x^2 + 1$ **(e)** I $y = x^2 + 1$, J $y = -x^2 + 1$ **(f)** K $y = 0.5x^2$, L $y = -2x^2$

(g) M $y = -2x^2 + 2$, N $y = -x^2 + 2$ **(h)** O $y = x^2 + 2$, P $y = -x^2 - 2$ **(i)** Q $y = x^2 - 3$, R $y = -2x^2 + 3$

3 **(a)** D **(b)** I **(c)** C **(d)** B **(e)** G **(f)** F
(g) E **(h)** A **(i)** H

4

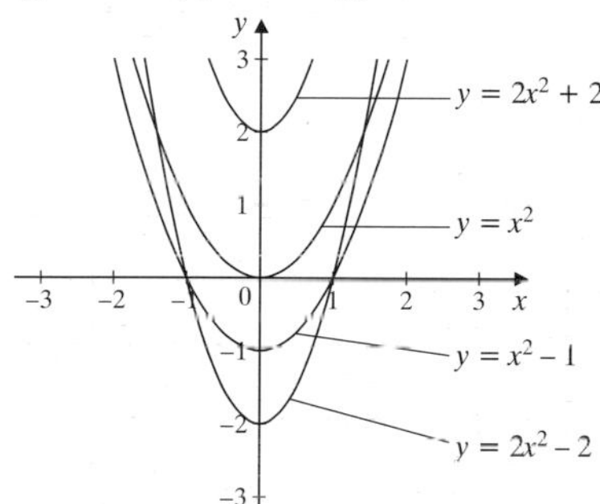

5 **(b)** **(i)** $y = 0.5x^2 + 1$ **(ii)** $y = -0.5x^2 - 1$
(c) **(i)** $y = 2x^2 - 3$ **(ii)** $y = -2x^2 + 3$
(d) **(i)** $y = -0.25x^2$ **(ii)** $y = -0.5x^2$
(e) **(i)** $y = x^2 - 2$ **(ii)** $y = -x^2 + 3$
(f) **(i)** $y = x^2 + 1$ **(ii)** $y = -3x^2$

Exercise 18C

1 **(a)** ±2 **(b)** ±4 **(c)** ±3 **(d)** ±7 **(e)** ±3 **(f)** ±6

Exercise 18D

1 **(b)** $x = 0$ **2** **(b)** $x = 0$ **3** **(b)** $x = 1$
4 **(b)** $x = 0$ **5** **(b)** $x = -1$ **6** **(b)** $x = 1.5$
7 **(b)** $x = -\frac{3}{4}$

Exercise 18E

1

x	−3	−2	−1	0	1	2	3	4
y	29	16	7	2	1	4	11	22

(a) **(i)** $x = -0.5$ or 2 **(ii)** $x = -1.5$ or 3
(iii) $x = 0.5$ or 1
(b) 0.875 **(c)** 0.75
(d) 0.5 is less than the minimum value for y.

2

x	−3	−2	−1	0	1	2	3	4	5
y	−16	−9	−4	−1	0	−1	−4	−9	−16

(a) **(i)** −1 or 3 **(ii)** 0 or 2 **(iii)** −2 or 4
(b) 0 **(c)** 1 **(d)** any value greater than 0.

3

x	−4	−3	−2	−1	0	1	2	3
y	−16	4	4	−8	−8	−4	4	16

(a) **(i)** $x = -3$ or 2 **(ii)** $x = -2$ or 1 **(iii)** −1 or 0
(b) −8.5 **(c)** −0.5 **(d)** any value less than −8.5

Exercise 18F

1 10.4 cm **2** 7.2 m by 5.6 m or 2.8 m by 14.4 m.

Exercise 18G

3 **(a)** A $y = x^3 + 2$, B $y = x^3$ **(b)** C $y = x^3 + 1$, D $y = x^3 - 1$ **(c)** E $y = 2x^3$, F $y = -x^3$

(d) G $y = 2x^3 + 1$, H $y = x^3 + 1$ **(e)** I $y = -x^3 - 2$, J $y = -x^3$ **(f)** K $y = \frac{1}{x}$, L $y = x^3$

(g) M $y = \frac{2}{x}$, N $y = \frac{1}{x}$ **(h)** O $y = \frac{1}{x}$, P $y = -\frac{1}{x}$ **(i)** Q $y = \frac{1}{x}$, R $y = \frac{1}{x} + 1$

4 **(a)** C **(b)** H **(c)** F **(d)** A **(e)** G **(f)** B
(g) D **(h)** I **(i)** E

5

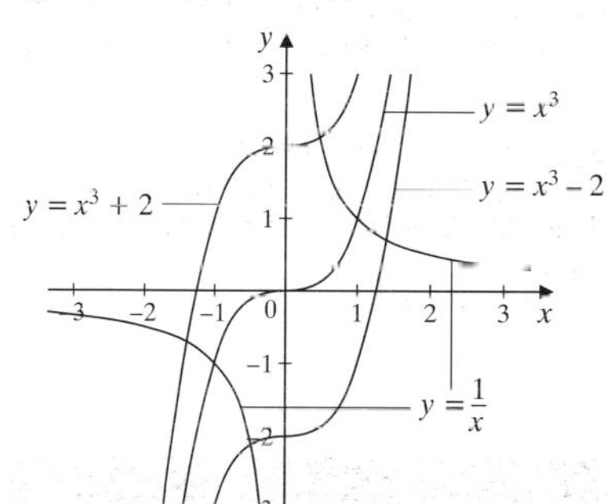

Exercise 18H

1 **(a)**

x	−3	−2	−1.5	−1	−0.5	0	0.5	1	1.5	2
x^3	−27	−8	−3.375	−1	−0.125	0	0.125	1	3.375	8
$2x^2$	18	8	4.5	2	0.5	0	0.5	2	4.5	8
y	−9	0	1.125	1	0.375	0	0.625	3	7.875	16

(b)

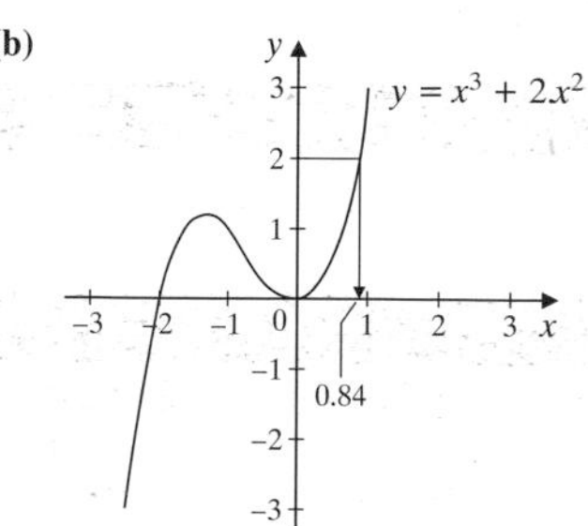

(c) $x = 0.84$

2 (a)

x	−2	−1.5	−1	−0.5	−0.1	0.1	0.5	1	1.5	2
$\frac{1}{x}$	−0.5	−0.67	−1	−2	−10	10	2	1	0.67	0.5
x^2	4	2.25	1	0.25	0.01	0.01	0.25	1	2.25	4
y	3.5	1.58	0	−1.75	−9.99	10.01	2.25	2	2.92	4.5

(b)

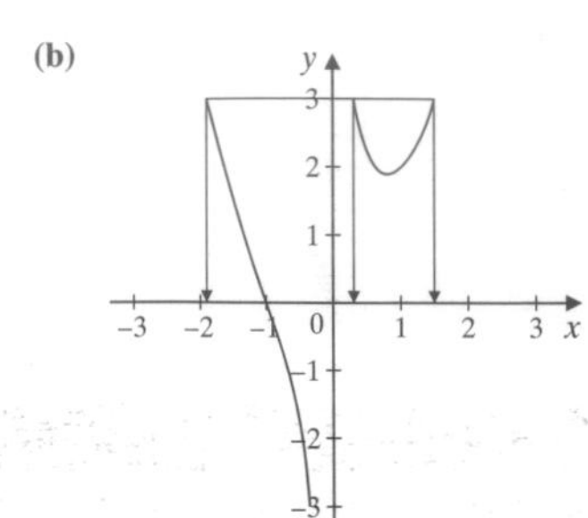

(c) $x = 0.35, -1.87, 1.53$

3

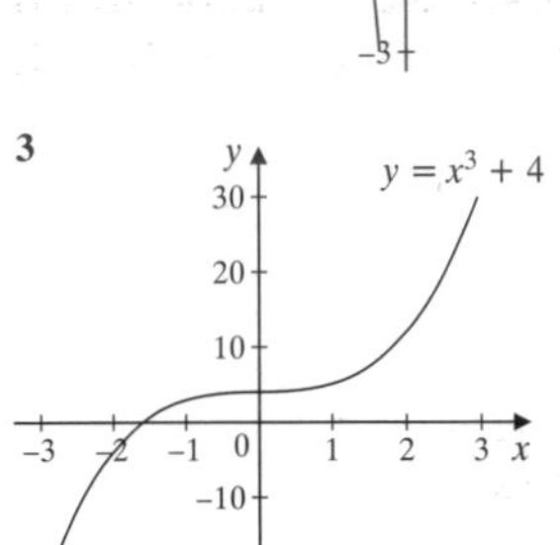

4

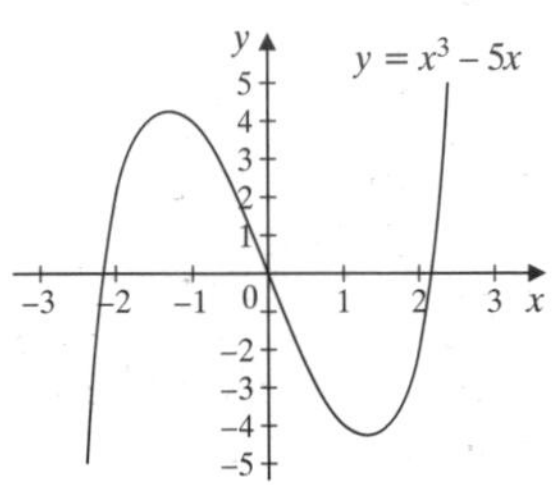

5

6

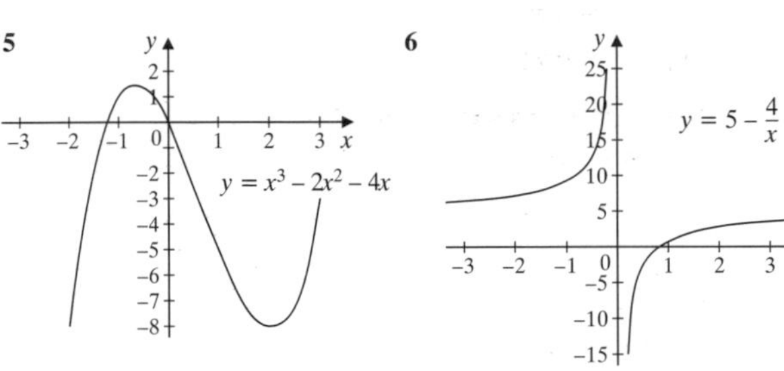

7

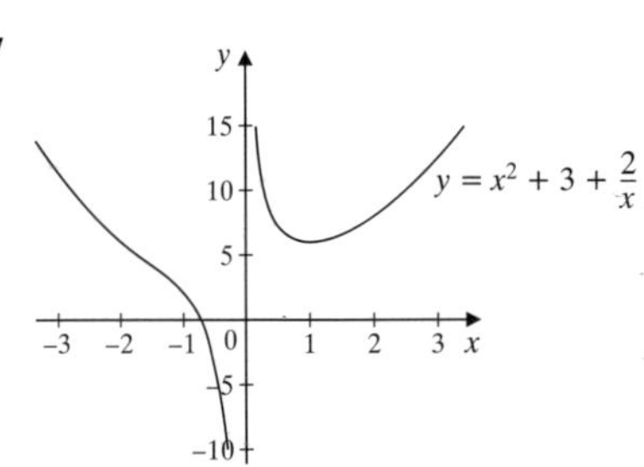

Exercise 18I

1 (a) $x = 1.18$ (b) $x = 1.14$ (c) 1.86 (d) 2.36
(e) 2.13 (f) 2.17

2 12.6 cm 3 5.7 cm × 11.4 cm × 17.0 cm

Exercise 18J

1 Car Y is bigger than car R.

2 Car Y is bigger than car R.
Car R has a greater maximum possible speed than car Y.

3 (a) (b) (c)

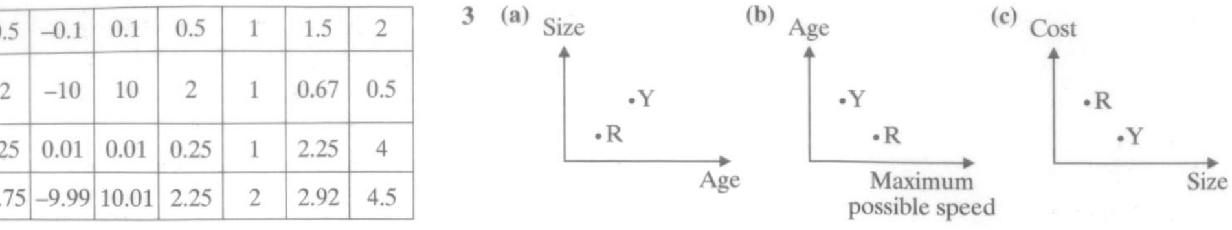

4 (a) a Siobhan b David c Kathleen d Maureen e Steve f Tom
(b) Kathleen

Exercise 18K

1 (a) E (b) A (c) B (d) C

2 (a) (b) (c) (d)

Height / Volume

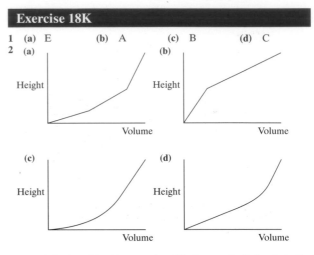

3 (a) The sound level increased rapidly then gradually levelled off.
(b) The record stopped suddenly.
Someone pulled out the plug of the record player or the record finished.

4 (a) B
(b) The speed of the ball is greatest immediately after kicking.
The speed decreases as the ball reaches its maximum height.
The speed increases as the ball falls to earth.
The ball stops suddenly when it hits the ground because it gets stuck in the mud!

5 (a) B (b) E

Unit 19 Probability 2

Exercise 19A

1 (a)

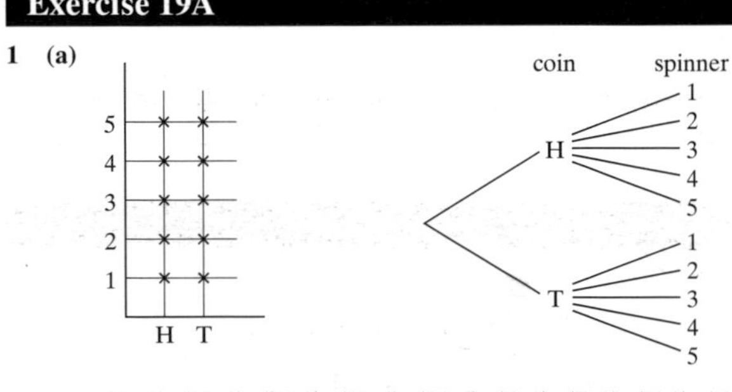

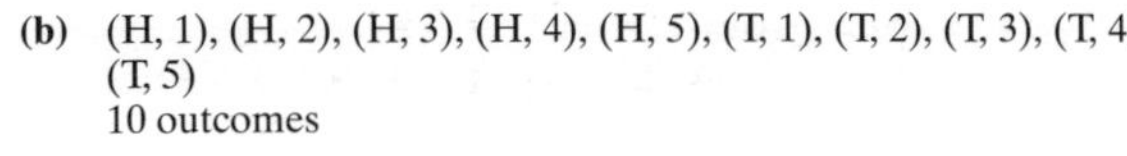

(b) (H, 1), (H, 2), (H, 3), (H, 4), (H, 5), (T, 1), (T, 2), (T, 3), (T, 4), (T, 5)
10 outcomes

2

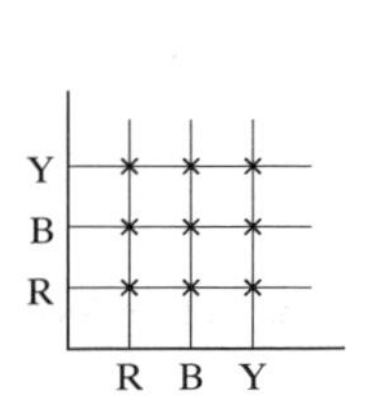

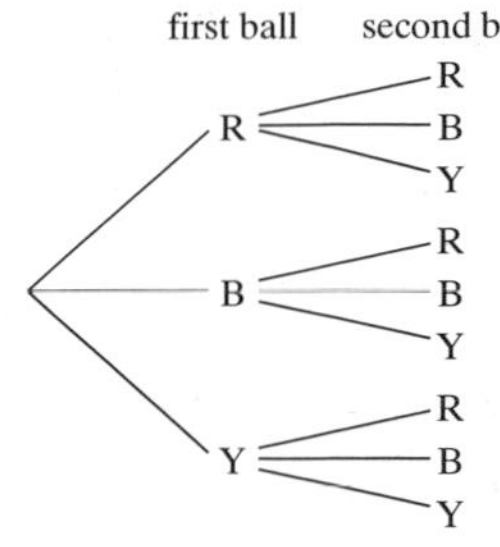

(b) (R, R), (R, B), (R, Y), (B, R), (B, B), (B, Y), (Y, R), (Y, B), (Y, Y)
9 outcomes

3 **(a)**

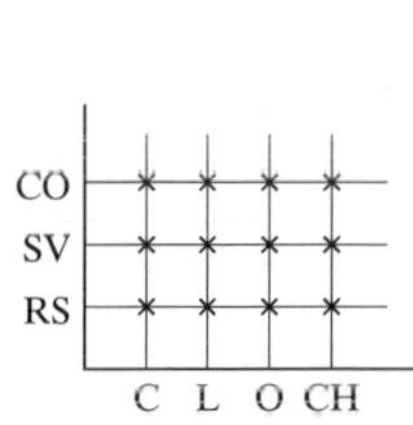

(b)

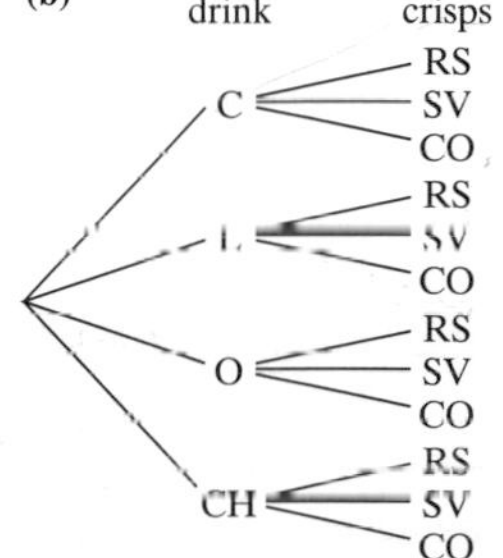

(c) (C, RS), (C, SV), (C, CO), (L, RS), (L, SV), (L, CO), (O, RS), (O, SV), (O, CO), (CH, RS), (CH, SV), (CH, CO)
12 outcomes

4 **(a)**

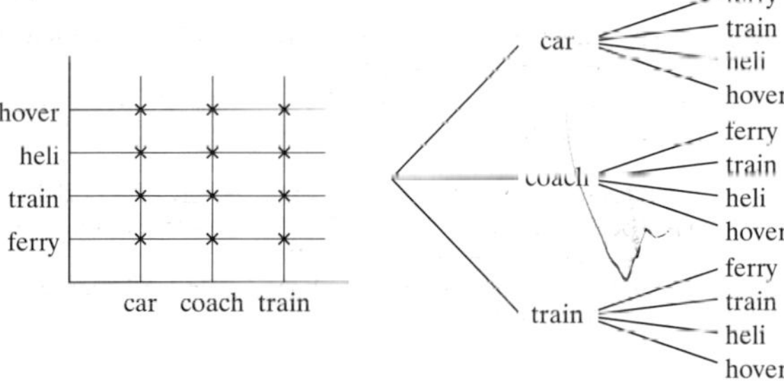

(b) 12 ways

Exercise 19C

1 $\frac{1}{12}$

2 $\frac{1}{36}$

3 **(a)** $\frac{1}{104}$ **(b)** $\frac{1}{8}$ **(c)** $\frac{1}{4}$ **(d)** $\frac{3}{26}$ **(e)** $\frac{1}{26}$ **(f)** $\frac{1}{52}$

4 **(a)** $\frac{3}{10}$ **(b)** $\frac{1}{5}$ **(c)** $\frac{1}{5}$ **(d)** $\frac{1}{10}$ **(e)** $\frac{1}{15}$

Exercise 19D

1 **(a)**

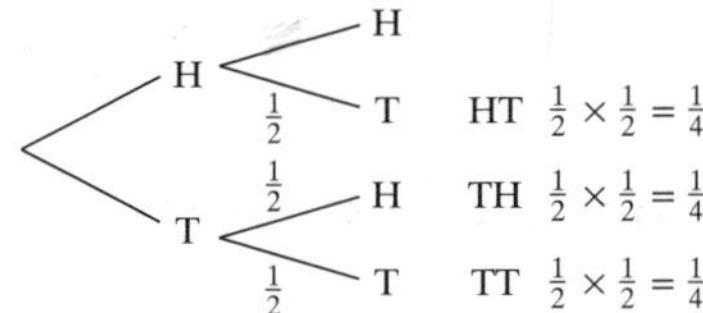

(b) **(i)** $\frac{1}{4}$ **(ii)** $\frac{3}{4}$ **(iii)** $\frac{1}{4}$

2 **(a)** Outcomes:
(RRR, RRG), RRB, RGR, RGG, RGB, RBR, RBG, RBB,
GRR, GRG, GRB, GGR, GGG, GGB, GBR, GBG, GBB,
BRR, BRG, BRB, BGR, BGG, BGB, BBR, BBG, BBB
All probabilities: $\frac{1}{3} \times \frac{1}{3} \times \frac{1}{3} = \frac{1}{27}$

(b) **(i)** $\frac{1}{27}$ **(ii)** $\frac{7}{27}$ **(iii)** $\frac{1}{9}$ **(iv)** $\frac{8}{27}$

3 **(a)** $\frac{1}{6}$ **(b)** $\frac{1}{6}$ **(c)** $\frac{3}{8}$ **(d)** $\frac{1}{8}$

4 **(a)** $\frac{1}{169}$ **(b)** $\frac{25}{169}$ **(c)** $\frac{144}{169}$

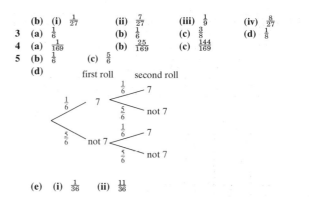

5 **(b)** $\frac{1}{6}$ **(c)** $\frac{5}{6}$

(d)

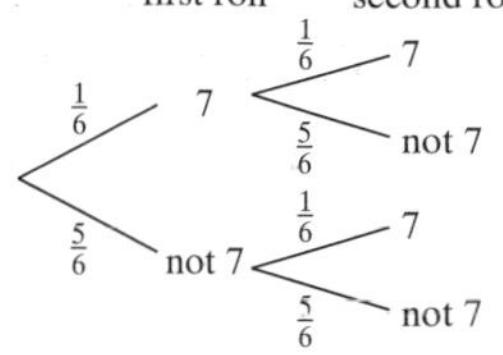

(e) **(i)** $\frac{1}{36}$ **(ii)** $\frac{11}{36}$

Exercise 19E

1 **(a)** (B, 1), (B, 2), (B, 3), (R, 1), (R, 2), (R, 3), (G, 1), (G, 2), (G, 3)
(b) $\frac{2}{5}$
(c) 0.8
(d) **(i)** 20 **(ii)** 20

2 **(i)** $\frac{6}{11}$ **(ii)** $\frac{5}{11}$

3 **(a)** **(i)** 6 **(ii)** 2
(b) $\frac{25}{200} (= \frac{1}{8})$

4 **(a)** $\frac{1}{4}$ **(b)** 0 **(c)** $\frac{0}{4}$

5 (H, 1), (H, 2), (H, 3), (H, 4), (H, 5), (H, 6)
(T, 1), (T, 2), (T, 3), (T, 4), (T, 5), (T, 6)

6 **(a)**

21	$\frac{21}{30} = 0.7$
27	$\frac{27}{40} = 0.68$
36	$\frac{36}{50} = 0.72$

(b) It is showing a trend towards 0.7

7 **(a)** $\frac{5}{8}$ **(b)** $\frac{7}{8}$

8 **(a)**

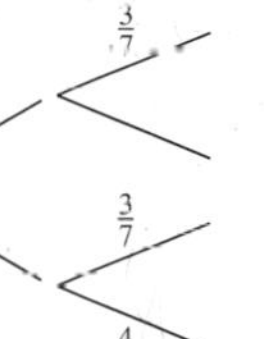

(b) $\frac{3}{14}$

9 **(a)** 0.14
(b)

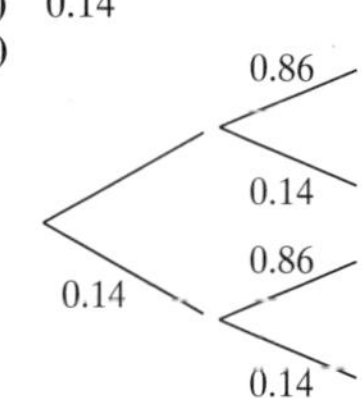

(c) 0.7396

10 **(a)** $\frac{1}{6}$ **(b)** $\frac{1}{3}$ **(c)**

2	3	4
3	4	5
4	5	6
5	6	7
6	7	8
7	8	9

(d) $\frac{1}{6}$
(e) A decrease. The new probability, P(4) $= \frac{3}{24}$ $(= \frac{1}{8})$ which is less than $\frac{1}{6}$.

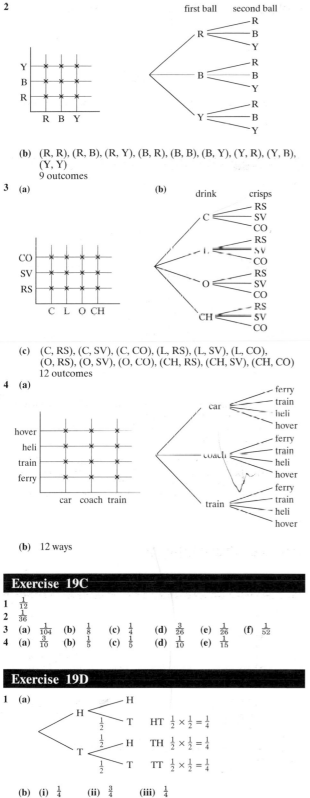

11 (a) (i) $\frac{1}{5}$ (ii) $\frac{4}{5}$

(b)

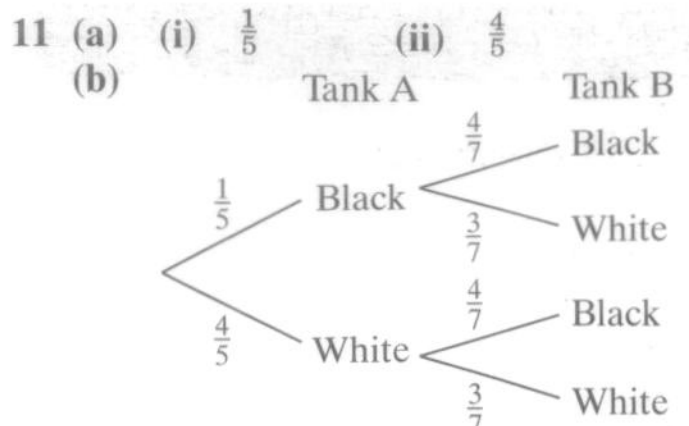

(c) (i) $\frac{12}{35}$
(ii) $\frac{19}{35}$

Unit 20 Lengths, areas and volumes

Exercise 20A

1 (a) (i) 24 cm (ii) 24 cm^2 (b) (i) 21 cm (ii) 26 cm^2
(c) (i) 37 cm (ii) 50 cm^2
2 (a) 15 cm^2 (b) 30 cm^2
3 (a) 86.8 cm^2 (b) 42.6 cm^2 (c) 94 cm^2
4 9 square inches
5 226.5 cm^2

Exercise 20B

1 (d) 2 (d) and 3 Approximately 3

Exercise 20C

1 (a) 15.7 cm (b) 21.0 m (c) 44.0 cm (d) 80.4 m
2 (a) 8.91 cm (b) 4.62 m
3 (a) 6.84 cm (b) 0.907 m
4 20.6 cm 5 239 m 6 605 cm

Exercise 20D

1 (b) Approximately 250 square units (c) Approximately 3

Exercise 20E

1 (a) 113 m^2 (b) 2730 cm^2 (c) 69.4 m^2 (d) 452 cm^2
(e) 11.3 cm^2
2 3180 cm^2 3 38.5 cm^2 4 161 m^2
5 (a) 8.14 m^2 (b) 3.08 m^2 6 3.52 cm 7 3.91 cm

Exercise 20F

1 84 cm^3
2 (a) 78 cm by 48 cm by 40 cm (b) 149 760 cm^3
(c) 18 920 cm^2 or 1.892 m^2
3 4.5 m^3
4 (a) 26 700 cm^3 (b) 3360 cm^3 (c) 7 (d) 3200 cm^3
5 (a) 47 250 cm^3 (b) 8430 cm^2
6 576 m^3 7 8.5 mm
8 7 cm 9 (a) 10 600 cm^3 (b) 2320 cm^2

Exercise 20G

1 (a) Length (b) Volume (c) Area (d) Length
(e) Area (f) Area

2

(a)			✓				
(b)		✓					✓
(c)	✓				✓	✓	
(d)				✓			

Exercise 20H

1 227
2 (a) 25 cm^2 (b) 154 m
3

		✓		✓	

4 (a) 36.9 m^2 (b) 295.2 m^3 (c) 0.32 m or 32 cm
5 (a) (i) 9 cm^2 (ii) 6 cm^2 (iii) 33 cm^2
(b) $A = 88n$
6 (a) 500 cm^3 (b) (i) 400 cm^3 (ii) 80%
(c) (i) 42 cm^2 (ii) 9.52 cm
7 (a) 113 cm^2 (b) 17.7 cm
8 88.0 m^2

Unit 21 Algebraic expressions and formulae

Exercise 21A

1 (a) 13 (b) 17 (c) −1 (d) 2.5 (e) 4
(f) 14 (g) $3\frac{2}{5}$ (h) 1.5
2 (a) 16 (b) 15 (c) 32 (d) 9 (e) 15
(f) 14
3 (a) 35 (b) 8 (c) 6 (d) 10 (e) 4
(f) −5
4 (a) 3 (b) 4 (c) 6 (d) 3 (e) 5
5 (a) (i)

	$2r + t$	t: 0	1	2	3	4	5
r	0	0	1	2	3	4	5
	1	2	3	4	5	6	7
	2	4	5	6	7	8	9
	3	6	7	8	9	10	11
	4	8	9	10	11	12	13
	5	10	11	12	13	14	15

(c) $4r + t$

Exercise 21B

1 (a) 101 (b) 47 (c) 14 (d) 147 (e) 23 (f) 6
2 (a) 19 (b) 33 (c) 27 (d) 20 (e) 16 (f) 7
3 (a) 44 (b) 10 (c) 16 (d) 20 (e) 30 (f) 3

Exercise 21C

1 (a) x^{10} (b) y^{11} (c) z^8 (d) w^{14}
2 (a) a^8 (b) b^6 (c) c^{10} (d) d^{11}
3 (a) p^3 (b) q^{10} (c) r^8 (d) t^4
4 (a) j^6 (b) k (c) m (d) n^2
5 (a) d^{12} (b) e^{10} (c) f^9 (d) g^{63}
6 (a) g^{24} (b) h^4 (c) 1 (d) 1
7 (a) $6x^5$ (b) $15y^{29}$ (c) $24z^9$
8 (a) $3p^5$ (b) $5q^2$ (c) $2r^4$
9 (a) $2187d^{14}$ (b) $64e^3$ (c) 1
10 (a) x^8 (b) y^9 (c) z^9
11 (a) a^6 (b) b^4 (c) 1
12 (a) $8d^{10}$ (b) $2e^4$ (c) $16f^4$
13 (a) $3p^{13}$ (b) $30q^{10}$ 14 (a) $6x^5$ (b) $4x^2$

Exercise 21D

1 (a) $2n + 6$ (b) $12p + 8$ (c) $2y^2 + 3y$ (d) $2x^2 + 10x$
(e) $3n - 6$ (f) $2p - 3$
2 (a) $4n + 12$ (b) $2p - 8$ (c) $5a + 5$ (d) $6x - 2$
(e) $20q - 12$ (f) $6r + 3s$ (g) $ab + 2a$ (h) $p^2 + pq$
(i) $2p^2 - p$
3 (a) $3x + 18$ (b) $4y - 8$ (c) $7t + 7$ (d) $12x + 8$
(e) $15y - 20$ (f) $6p + 2q$ (g) $x^2 + 3x$ (h) $x^2 + xy$
(i) $3y^2 - 2y$
4 (a) $2m + 10$ (b) $9n - 36$ (c) $8u - 8$ (d) $35x + 15$
(e) $4y^2 - 24y$ (f) $6x^4 + 15x^2$ (g) $20t^5 - 12t^3$
(h) $12x^5 + 28x^2y$ (i) $15y^4 - 20yx^2$

Exercise 21E

1 (a) $8r + 2$ (b) $2p - 6$ (c) $10x + y$ (d) $5m$
2 (a) $14a + 2b$ (b) $5p + q$ (c) $10r - 2s$ (d) $9p$
3 (a) $7x - y$ (b) $10m - 7n$ (c) 0 (d) $6p$
4 (a) $3a - 3b$ (b) $r^2 + r$ (c) $2mn$ (d) $3m + n$
5 (a) $r^3 + r$ (b) $3t^3 + 2t^2$ (c) $x^5 + x^3$ (d) $4y^3 - 2y^4$
6 (a) $3n + 2$ (b) $3n - 2$ (c) $2n - 4$ (d) $3p + 5r$
(e) $r - 2q$ (f) $2r - s$

Exercise 21F

1 (a) $a + 3b$ (b) $p + 5q$ (c) $2n - 1$ (d) $4s - 4r$
(e) $6y$ (f) $rs - 3r$
2 (a) $x - 2y$ (b) $11x - 3y$ (c) $2x^2 - x$
(d) $20y^2 - 23y + 6$ (e) $2x^2 - 9x + 10$ (f) $16y^4 + 9y^3$

Exercise 21G

2 (a) $ab + 3a + 4b + 12$ (b) $cd + 4c + 5d + 20$
(c) $xy + 6x + 3y + 18$ (d) $a^2 + 11a + 24$
(e) $b^2 + 11b + 28$ (f) $x^2 + 8x + 12$
3 (a) $2ab + 8a + 3b + 12$ (b) $3bc + 9b + 2c + 6$
(c) $4cd + 24c + 3d + 18$ (d) $2a^2 + 11a + 15$
(e) $3b^2 + 10b + 8$ (f) $4c^2 + 13c + 10$
4 (a) $ab - 3a - 4b + 12$ (b) $cd - 4c - 5d + 20$
(c) $xy - 6x - 3y + 18$ (d) $a^2 - 11a + 24$
(e) $b^2 - 11b + 28$ (f) $x^2 - 8x + 12$
5 (a) $ab + 3a - 4b - 12$ (b) $cd - 4c + 5d - 20$
(c) $xy + 6x - 3y - 18$ (d) $a^2 + 5a - 24$
(e) $b^2 - 3b - 28$ (f) $x^2 + 4x - 12$
6 (a) $2ab + 10a - 5b - 25$ (b) $3b^2 - 14b - 24$
(c) $3c^2 - 11c + 6$ (d) $3a^2 - 19a + 20$
(e) $3x^2 + 11x - 20$ (f) $2a^2 - 9a - 18$
7 (a) $2x^2 + 5xy + 3y^2$ (b) $3x^2 - xy - 4y^2$
(c) $5x^2 - 8xy + 3y^2$ (d) $6x^2 + 23xy + 20y^2$
(e) $6x^2 - 5xy - 25y^2$ (f) $12x^2 - 28xy + 15y^2$
8 (a) $x^2 + 6x + 9$ (b) $y^2 - 10y + 25$
(c) $4x^2 + 4x + 1$ (d) $9y^2 - 24y + 16$
(e) $9x^2 + 30xy + 25y^2$ (f) $36x^2 - 84xy + 49y^2$
9 (a) $3a^2 - 5a - 2$ (b) $12p^2 + 5p - 2$
(c) $3a^2 + 5a + 2$ (d) $12p^2 + 14p + 4$
(e) $2b^2 - 5b + 3$ (f) $8b^2 + 2b - 1$
10 (a) $2a + b + 2$ (b) $pq - p + q - 2$ (c) $3r^2 - 5r - sr + 2s$
(d) $4p^2$

Exercise 21H

1 (a) 5°C (b) 12°C (c) 53.6°F
2 (a) £2.50 (b) £47.50
3 (a) c is the cost in pounds so the 5 pence per mile travelled must be written in pounds, £0.05, in the formula.
(b) £32.50
4 (a) 70p (b) £1.22
5 (a) £30 (b) £40 (c) £110 (d) £145
6 (b) 352.93 francs
7 (a) 4 pence (b) It decreases
(c) (i) no, but it can be very close to 2 pence
8 It decreases.

Exercise 21I

1 (a) l goes in → ×2 → +1 → d comes out

(b) l comes out ← ÷2 ← −1 ← d goes in

(c) $\frac{d-1}{2}$ ← $d - 1$ ← d

so $l = \frac{d-1}{2}$

(d) 19
2 (a) $C = \frac{F-32}{1.8}$ (b) 24.4̇°C
3 (a) $d = \frac{c-2}{3}$ (b) $d = \frac{c-5}{4}$ (c) $d = \frac{c+6}{5}$
(d) $d = \frac{c-8}{7}$ (e) $d = 2(c-3)$ (f) $d = 3(c+4)$
4 (a) $x = \frac{y-5}{3}$ (b) $x = \frac{y+7}{4}$ (c) $x = \frac{y}{2} - 3$
(d) $x = \frac{y}{3} + 5$ (e) $x = 3y + 4$ (f) $x = 9y - 5$
(g) $x = 3(y-4)$ (h) $x = 2(y+7)$ (i) $x = \frac{6y+3}{2}$
5 (a) $b = \frac{a+3}{4}$ (b) $b = \frac{a}{3} - 2$ (c) $b = \frac{a}{2} + 3$
(d) $b = 4a + 3$ (e) $b = 2a - 4$ (f) $b = 22a - 3$
(g) $b = 2(a+3)$ (h) $b = \frac{a-2}{5}$
6 (d) $p = 2a + 2$, $a = \frac{p-2}{2}$
(e) $p = 2a$, $a = \frac{p}{2}$ (f) $p = 2a - 2$, $a = \frac{p+2}{2}$
(g) $p = 2a + 2(1-d)$ or $p = 2a + 2 - 2d$

$a = \frac{p - 2(1-d)}{2}$ or $a = \frac{p}{2} + d - 1$

$d = \frac{2a + 2 - p}{2}$ or $d = a + 1 - \frac{p}{2}$

Exercise 21J

1 (a) $2(x+3)$ (b) $2(3y+1)$ (c) $5(3b-1)$
(d) $2(2r-1)$ (e) $x(3+5y)$ (f) $4(3x+2y)$
(g) $4(3x-4)$ (h) $3(3-x)$ (i) $3(3+5g)$
2 (a) $x(3x+4)$ (b) $y(5y-3)$ (c) $a(2a+1)$
(d) $b(5b-2)$ (e) $c(7-3c)$ (f) $d(d+3)$
(g) $m(6m-1)$ (h) $x(4y+3)$ (i) $n^2(n-8)$
3 (a) $4x(2x+1)$ (b) $3p(2p+1)$ (c) $3x(2x-1)$
(d) $3b(b-3)$ (e) $3a(4+a)$ (f) $5c(3-2c)$
(g) $7x^3(3x+2)$ (h) $4y^2(4y-3)$ (i) $2d^2(3d^2-2)$
4 (a) $ax(x+1)$ (b) $pr(r-1)$ (c) $ab(b-1)$
(d) $q(r^2 - q)$ (e) $ax(a+x)$ (f) $by(b-y)$
(g) $3a^2(2a-3)$ (h) $4x^3(2-x)$ (i) $6x^3(3+2x^2)$
5 (a) $6ab(2a+3b)$ (b) $2xy(2x-y)$ (c) $4ab(a+2b+3)$
(d) $2xy(2x+3y-1)$ (e) $3ax(4x+2a-1)$ (f) $abc(a+b+c)$
6 (a) $5(x+4)$ (b) $2(6y-5)$ (c) $x(3x+5)$
(d) $y(4-3y)$ (e) $2a(4+3a)$ (f) $4b(3b-2)$
(g) $cy(y+1)$ (h) $3dx(x-2)$ (i) $3cd(3c+5d)$

Exercise 21K

1 (a) $(x+1)(x+3)$ (b) $(x+1)(x+2)$ (c) $(x+1)(x+11)$
(d) $(x+2)(x+3)$ (e) $(x+1)(x+4)$ (f) $(x+2)^2$
2 (a) $(x-1)(x-2)$ (b) $(x-1)(x-13)$ (c) $(x-1)(x-5)$
(d) $(x-2)(x-4)$ (e) $(x-3)^2$ (f) $(x-2)(x-6)$
3 (a) $(x+3)(x-1)$ (b) $(x+5)(x-1)$ (c) $(x+7)(x-1)$
(d) $(x+6)(x-1)$ (e) $(x+3)(x-2)$ (f) $(x+5)(x-3)$
4 (a) $(x-7)(x+1)$ (b) $(x-6)(x+1)$ (c) $(x-5)(x+3)$
(d) $(x-8)(x+1)$ (e) $(x-4)(x+2)$ (f) $(x-5)(x+4)$

5 (a) $(x-3)(x+3)$ (b) $(x-6)(x+6)$ (c) $3(x-2)(x+2)$
(d) $(x-5)(x+5)$ (e) $2(x-4)(x+4)$ (f) $3(x-3)(x+3)$
6 (a) $(p+1)(p+7)$ (b) $(q-1)(q-13)$ (c) $(r+6)(r-2)$
(d) $(a-4)(a+3)$ (e) $(b-7)(b+7)$ (f) $(c+6)(c-4)$
7 (a) $(d-8)(d+3)$ (b) $2(t-5)(t+5)$ (c) $(u+3)(u+12)$
(d) $(v-4)(v-9)$ (e) $(w+6)(w-5)$ (f) $(x-10)(x+2)$

Exercise 21L

1 (a) $y = 2x + 1$ (b) 4
2 20
3 (a) 1924 (b) $n = \frac{C-S}{x}$
4 2
5 5
6 (a) x^8 (b) y^4 (c) z^{24} (d) $15a^5$
(e) $7y^6$ (f) $64z^6$ (g) $6p + 23q$ (h) $3x^3 - 2xy$
7 $t = \frac{x}{uv}$
8 $k = \frac{p + qr}{q^2}$
9 $c = 18n + 5g$
10 (a) $2x^2 + 9x + 4$ (b) $2x(2x-3)$
11 $C = 27n$
12 (a) −28°C (b) 39 000 feet
13 (a) $2x^2 - 5x - 12$ (b) $5x(2x-1)$
14 (a) $(x+1)(x+7)$ (b) $(x-6)(x-4)$ (c) $(x-6)(x+2)$
(d) $(y+5)(y-2)$ (e) $(y-14)(y+1)$ (f) $(y+3)(y+8)$
(g) $(x-4)(x+4)$ (h) $2(x+1)(x+3)$ (i) $4x(x+3)(x-3)$

Unit 22 Percentages

Exercise 22A

1 (a) 0.45 (b) $\frac{9}{20}$ 2 (a) 0.6 (b) $\frac{3}{5}$
3 (a) 0.85 (b) $\frac{17}{20}$ 4 (a) 0.56 (b) $\frac{14}{25}$
5 (a) 0.69 (b) $\frac{69}{100}$ 6 (a) 0.06 (b) $\frac{3}{50}$
7 (a) 0.82 (b) $\frac{41}{50}$ 8 (a) 0.125 (b) $\frac{1}{8}$
9 (a) 0.44 (b) $\frac{11}{25}$ 10 (a) 0.675 (b) $\frac{27}{40}$
11 (a) 0.025 (b) $\frac{1}{40}$ 12 (a) 0.6225 (b) $\frac{249}{400}$
13 (a) $0.\dot{3}$ (b) $\frac{1}{3}$ 14 (a) 0.425 (b) $\frac{17}{40}$
15 (a) $0.55\dot{6}$ (b) $\frac{167}{300}$

Exercise 22B

1 75% 2 90% 3 148% 4 40% 5 45%
6 83% 7 49% 8 52.5% 9 36% 10 7.5%
11 87.5% 12 37.5% 13 $28\frac{1}{3}$% 14 18.75% 15 $41\frac{2}{3}$%
16 $33\frac{1}{3}$% 17 12.5% 18 40% 19 3% 20 140%
21 17.5% 22 17.6% 23 28.75% 24 $66\frac{2}{3}$% 25 0.8%
26 236% 27 $44\frac{4}{9}$% 28 60% 29 107% 30 15%

Exercise 22C

1 (a) 0.44, $\frac{9}{20}$, 49% (b) 60%, $\frac{5}{8}$, 0.64 (c) 38%, $\frac{2}{5}$, 0.41
(d) 0.64, 65%, $\frac{11}{16}$ (e) 0.6, 66%, $\frac{2}{3}$ (f) 0.7, $\frac{3}{4}$, 76%
2 47% 3 8% 4 45% 5 27%

Exercise 22D

1 £9 2 £0.96 3 6 g 4 £0.96
5 300 kg 6 18.5 m 7 126.5 g 8 15.75 *ml*
9 £8.20
10 (a) 1680 (b) 1820 11 36 12 £8625
13 33 14 100.8 miles 15 £1736

Exercise 22E

1 493 t 2 2312.5g 3 £175 4 £35.56
5 92 g 6 62 *ml* 7 £95.85 8 £26
9 £215 10 £13.504 11 £31.50 12 108.1 kg
13 £1820 14 368 15 76

Exercise 22F

1 60% 2 (a) 70% (b) 30%
3 (a) 37.5% (b) 62.5%
4 (a) 40% (b) 27% (c) 34% (d) 27%
5 30% 6 5% 7 15% 8 12.5% 9 12.5%
10 52.1%

Exercise 22G

1 25 cm 2 £125 3 £160 4 £64 5 £2400
6 £120 7 220 kg 8 £260

Exercise 22H

1 (a) 65% (b) 35% (c) 5%
2 (a) 4% (b) 10% (c) 23.75%
3 25% 4 31.25% 5 7.5% 6 27.3% 7 20%
8 $33\frac{1}{3}$%

Exercise 22I

1 (a) £35 (b) £8.75 (c) £8.05 (d) £46.90
(e) £3.47 (f) £12.86 (g) £4.98 (h) £1.08
2 (a) £468.83 (b) £129.25 (c) £88.11
3 (a) £114.89 (b) £177.87 (c) £41.70
4 £32.31 5 £15.03 6 £89.18 7 £14.10
8 £18.62 9 £55.32

Exercise 22J

1 (a) £148.80 (b) £16.80
2 (a) £1838.70 (b) £353.70
3 (a) £286.80 (b) £32.80
4 (a) £443.50 (b) £93.50
5 (a) £296.88 (b) £71.88
6 (a) £462 (b) £102

Exercise 22K

1 (a) £196.02 (b) £295.20 (c) £117.70 (d) £126.88
(e) £3355.28 2 2.22 years 3 £892.86 4 7.03%
5 1.62 years 6 £500

Exercise 22L and 22M

1 £94.19 2 £103.88 3 £62.59 4 £12 458.76
5 £243.34 6 £147.39 7 £26.89 8 £38.08

Exercise 22N

1 £83.80 2 £112.00 3 £797.50 4 £28.00
5 £139.83 6 (a) £122.20 (b) £85.54

Exercise 22O

1 £160 2 £79.90 3 £341 4 15% 5 £14.75
6 (a) £43.18 (b) £598.03 7 (a) £3 (b) 5%
8 (a) £450 000 (b) 4% less 9 £53.14

10 (a) £480.44 (b) £343.20 (c) £375

11 (a) (i) 0.375 (ii) 0.38 (b) 0.67
(c) 25%, 0.3, $\frac{3}{8}$, $\frac{1}{2}$, 0.6, 67%

Unit 23 Transformations

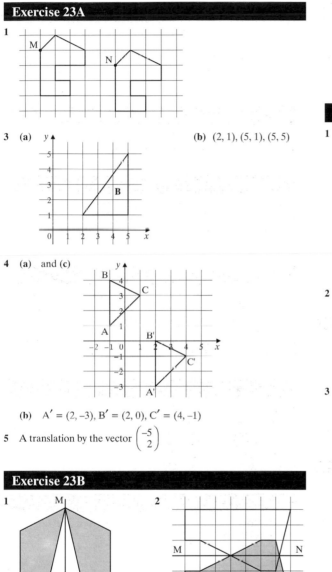

Exercise 23A

1

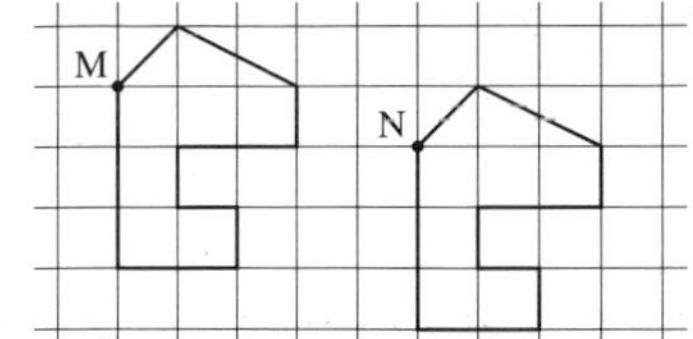

3 (a)

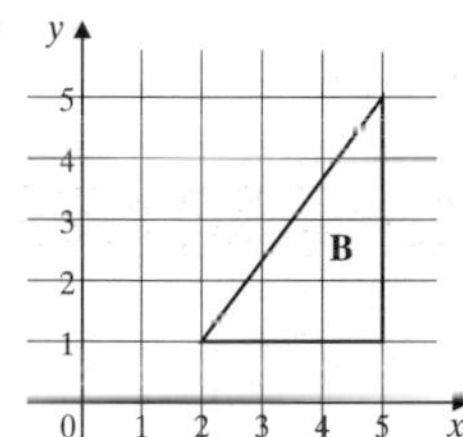

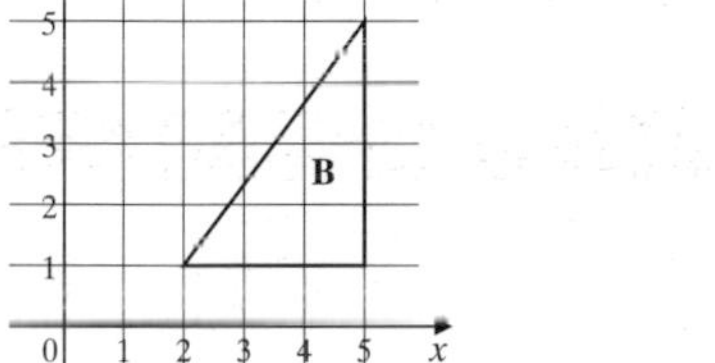

(b) (2, 1), (5, 1), (5, 5)

4 (a) and (c)

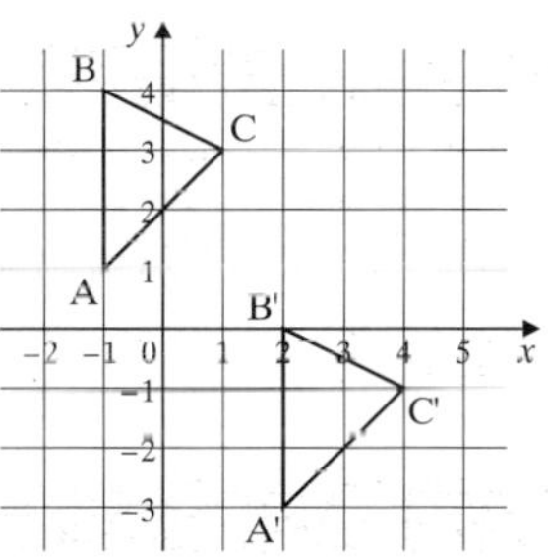

(b) A′ = (2, –3), B′ = (2, 0), C′ = (4, –1)

5 A translation by the vector $\begin{pmatrix} -5 \\ 2 \end{pmatrix}$

Exercise 23B

1

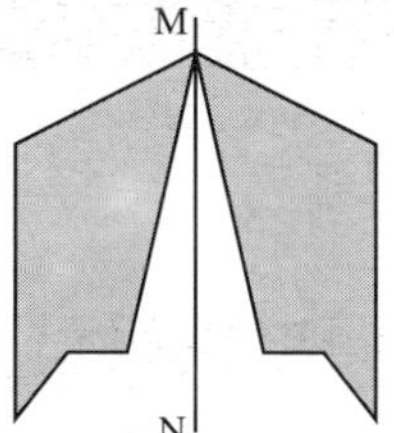

2

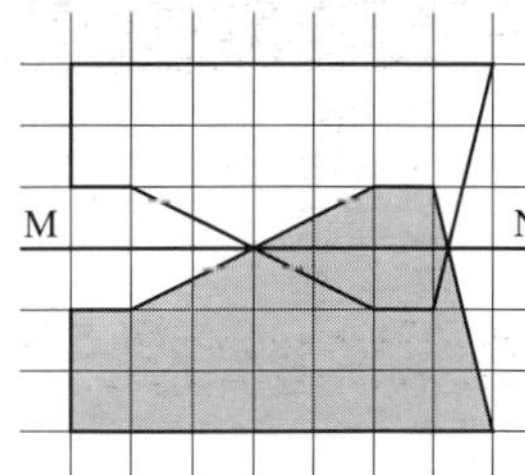

3

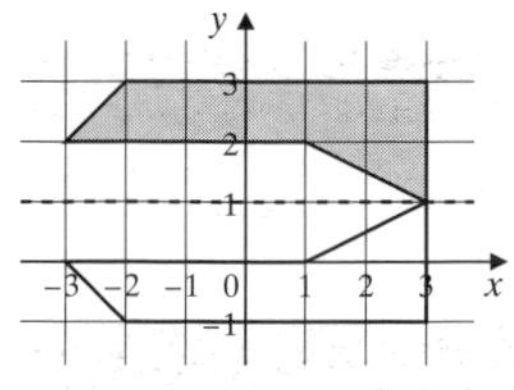

4

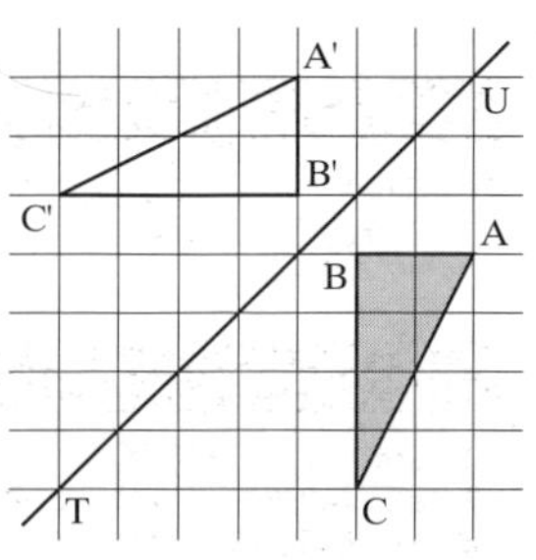

5

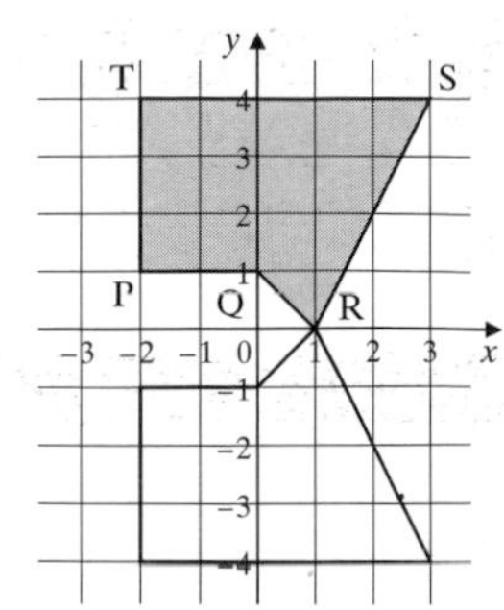

6 A reflection in the line $x = 2$

Exercise 23C

1 (a) (b) (c)

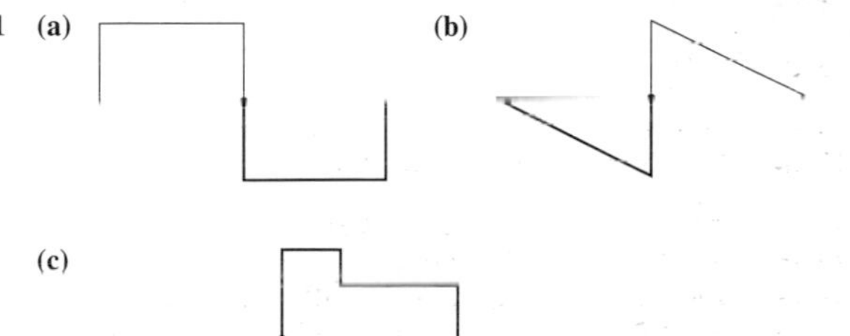

2 (a) (b) (c)

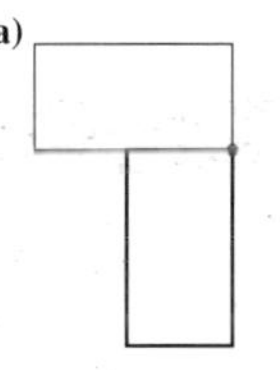

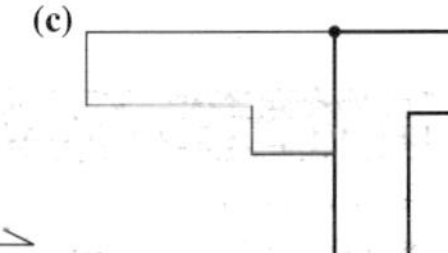

3

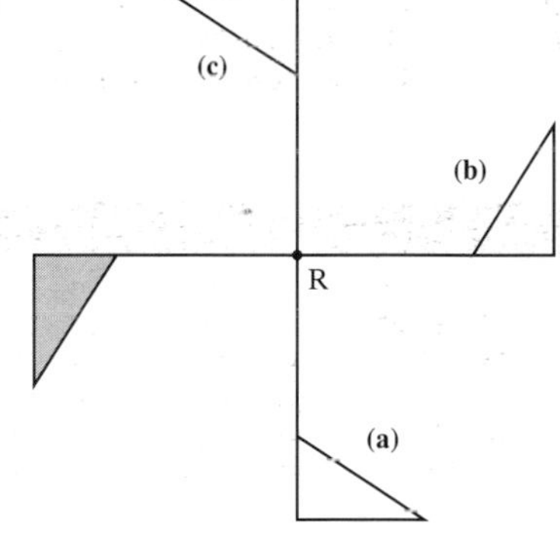

4

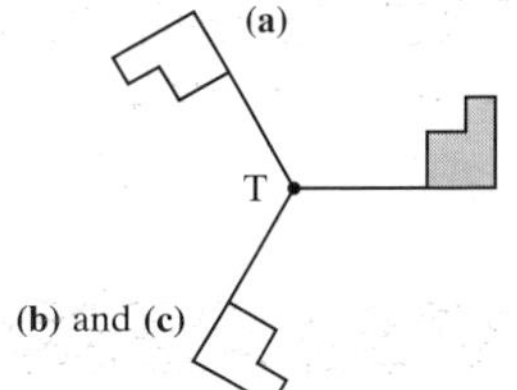

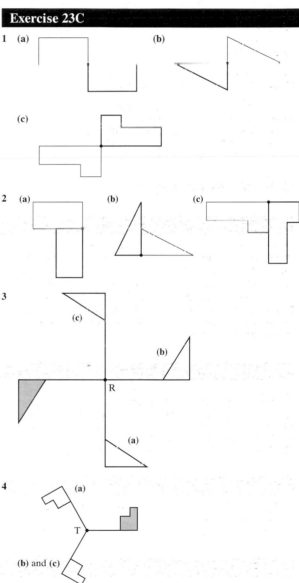

Exercise 23D

1 (a) (b)

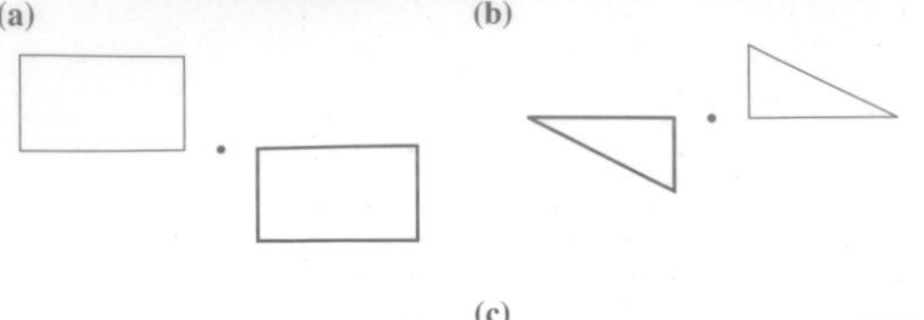

(c)

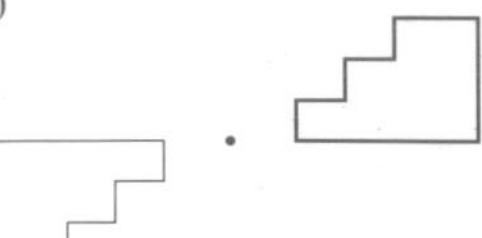

2 (a) (b) (c)

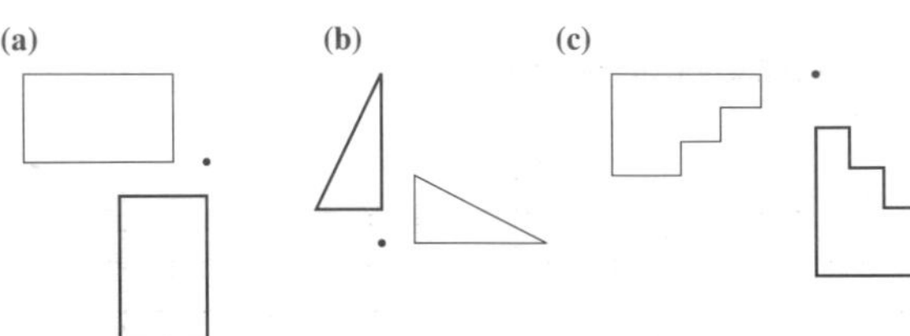

3

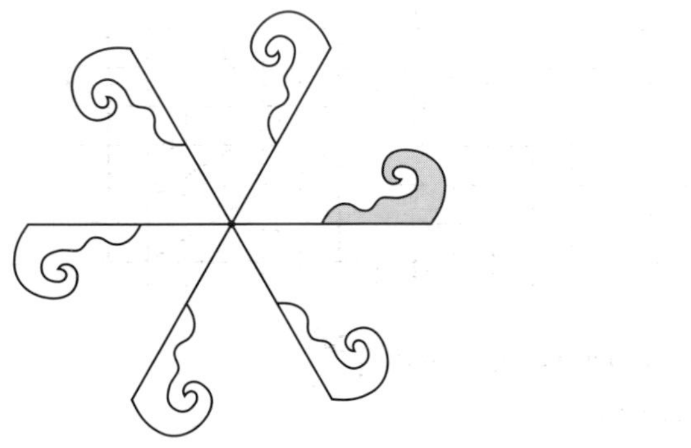

Exercise 23E

1

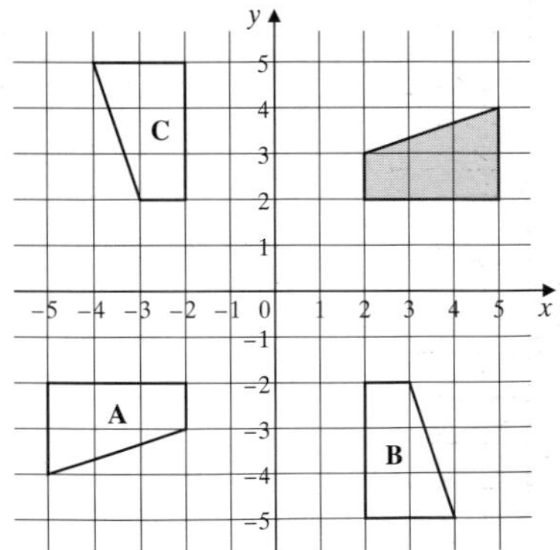

2

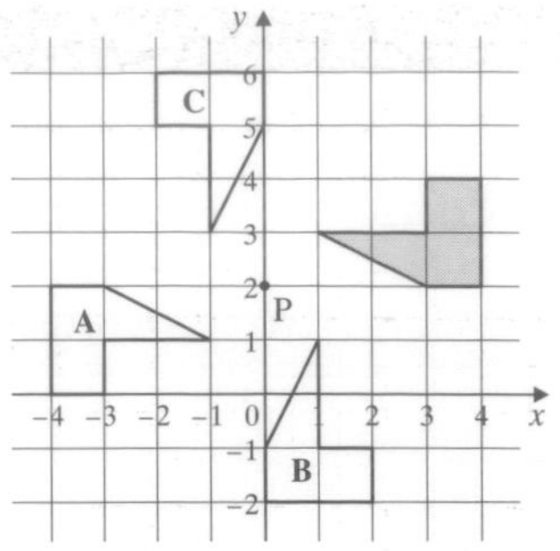

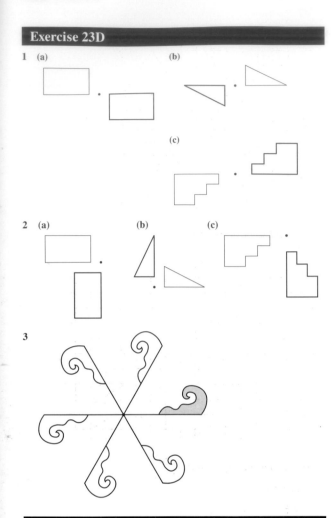

3 A rotation through 180° about the point (0, 0). (A half turn about (0, 0).)

Exercise 23F

1 These are some of the possibilities.

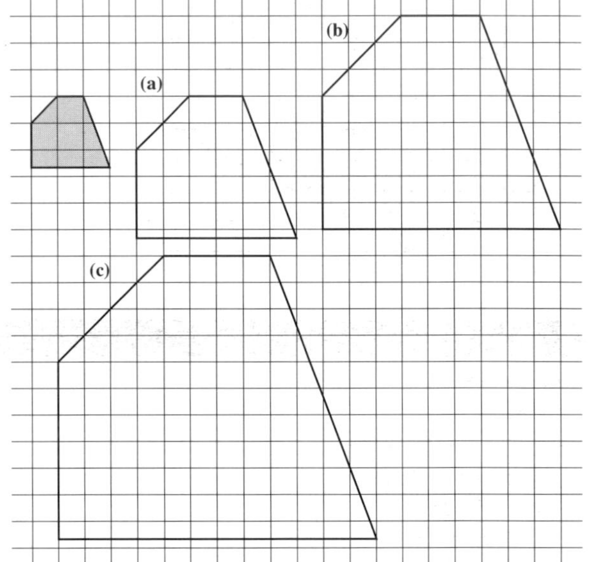

2

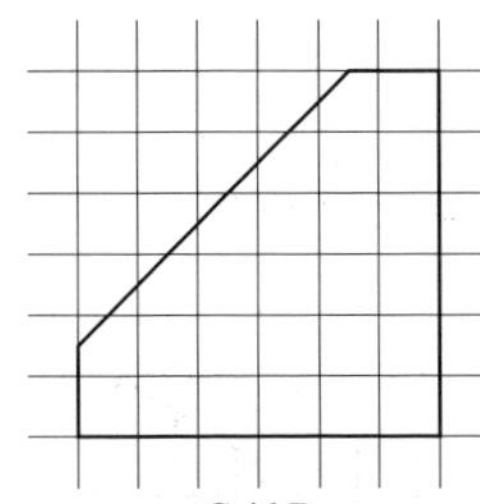

Grid B

3 4

Exercise 23G

1

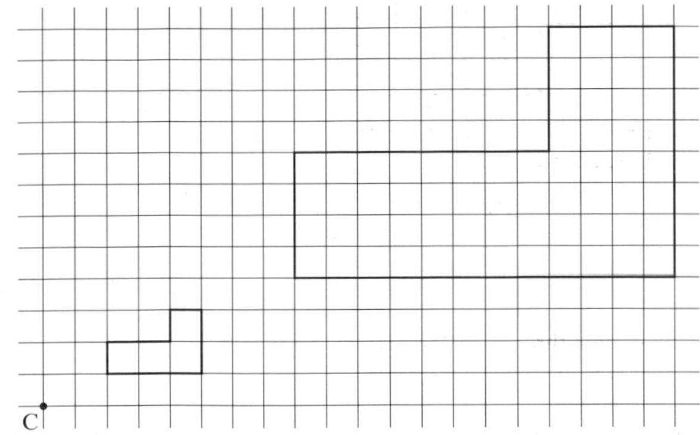

2 An enlargement by scale factor 2 and centre (7, 1).
3 An enlargement by scale factor $\frac{1}{2}$ and centre (7, 1).
4

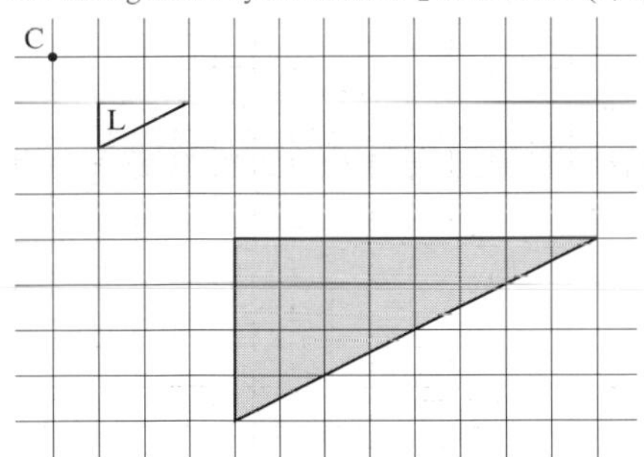

Exercise 23H

1 **(a)** and **(b)**

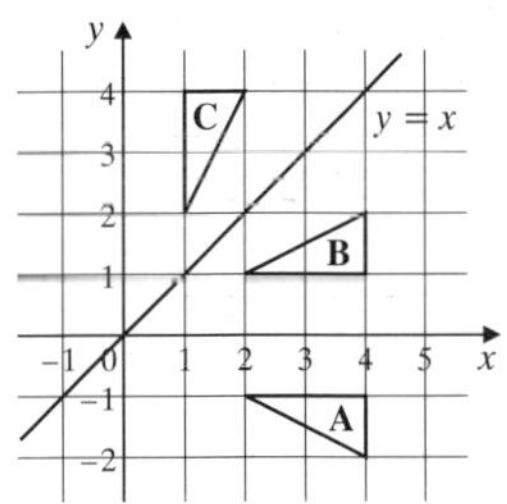

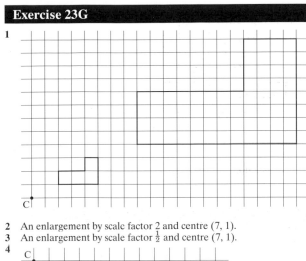

(c) A rotation through 90° anticlockwise about (0, 0).

2 **(a)** and **(b)**

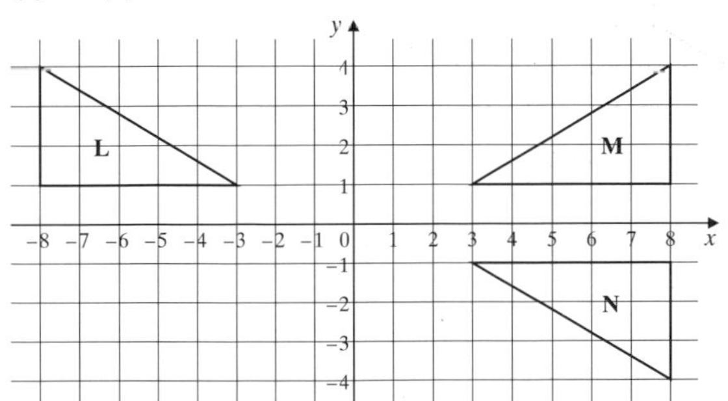

(c) A rotation through 180° about (0, 0).

3 **(a)** A reflection or a reflection and a translation.
(b) A translation.
(c) A reflection or a reflection and a translation.
(d) A rotation through 180° or a rotation through 180° and a translation.

4 **(a)**, **(b)** and **(c)**

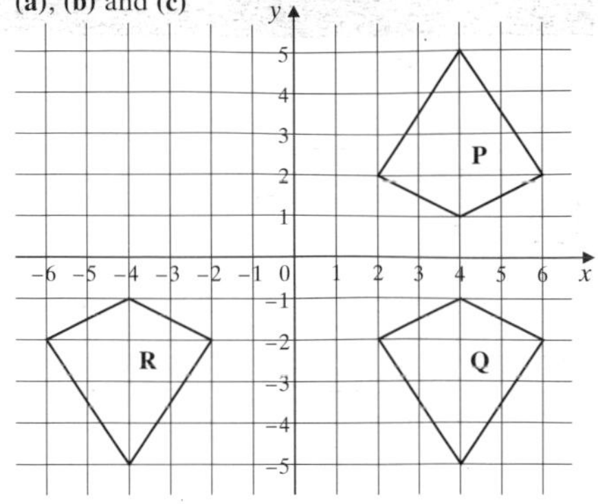

(d) A reflection in the y-axis.

5 **(a)** and **(b)**

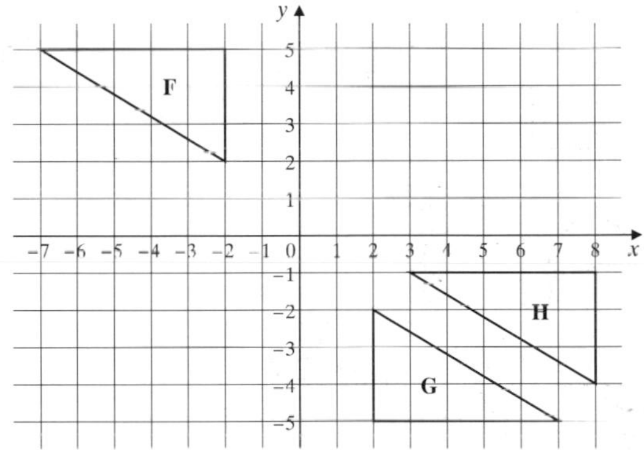

(c) A translation by the vector $\begin{pmatrix} 10 \\ -6 \end{pmatrix}$

6 **(a)** and **(b)**

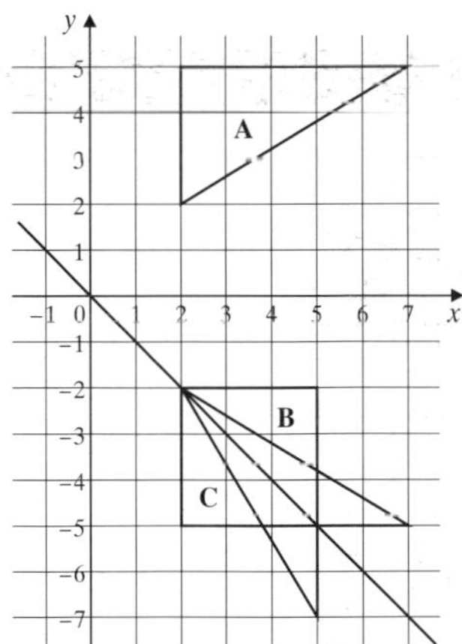

(c) A reflection in the x-axis.

Exercise 23I

1 (a) 2 (b) (6, 2)
2 (a)

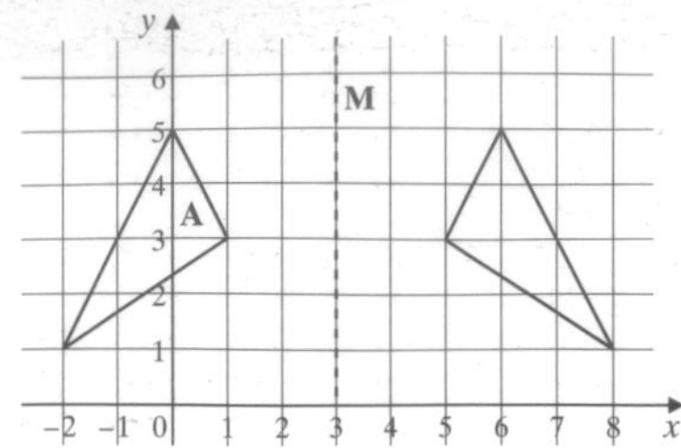

(b) (8, 1) (c) $x = 3$

3

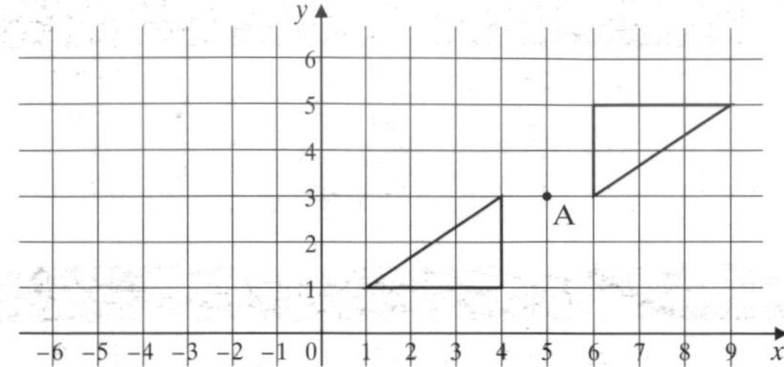

4 (a) and (b)

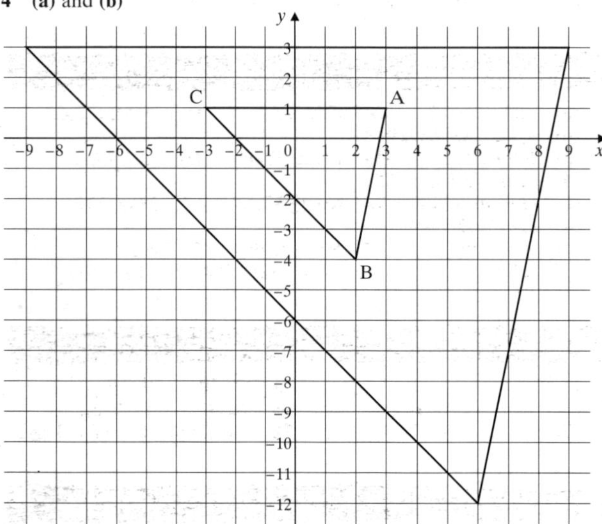

(c) (9, 3), (6, –12), (–9, 3)
5 (a) and (b)

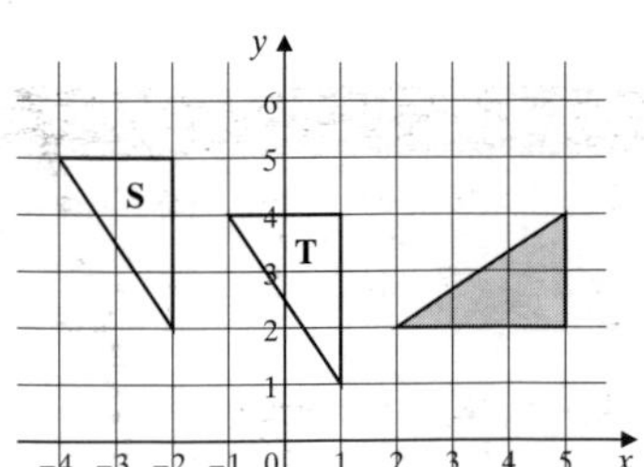

(c) A translation by the vector $\begin{pmatrix} 3 \\ -1 \end{pmatrix}$

6 (a), (b), (c) and (d)

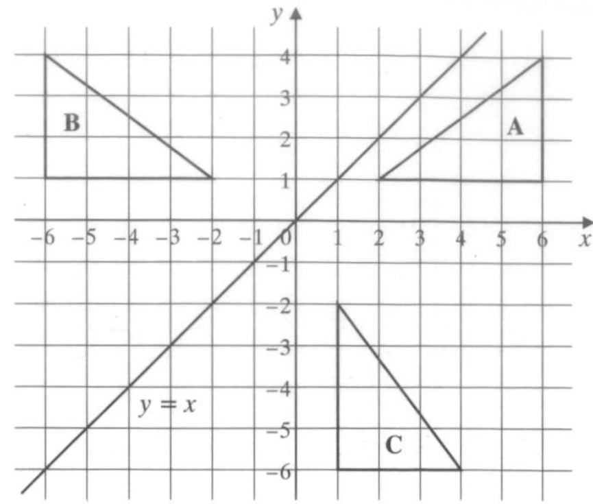

(e) A rotation through 90° clockwise about (0, 0).

Unit 24 Presenting data

Exercise 24A

1 (a) 50 (b) 35 (accept any integer from 31 to 39)
2 (a) Pictogram not appropriate
(b)

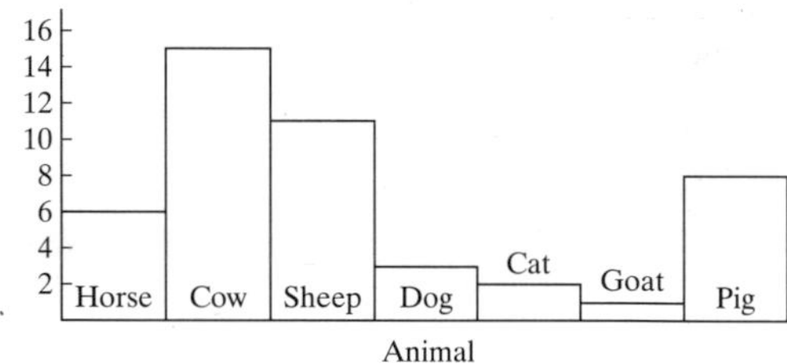

3 (a)

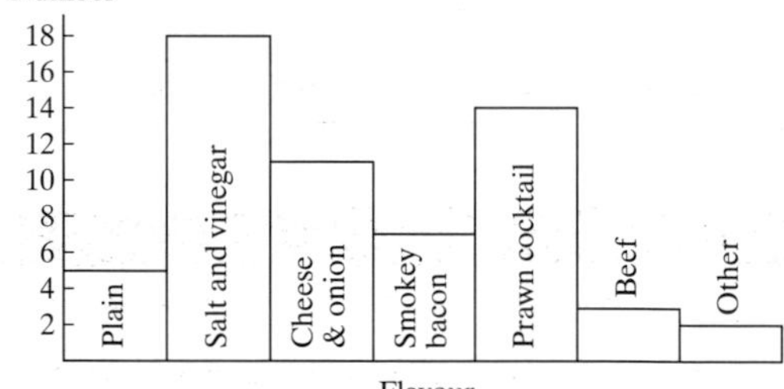

(b) 60
4 (a)

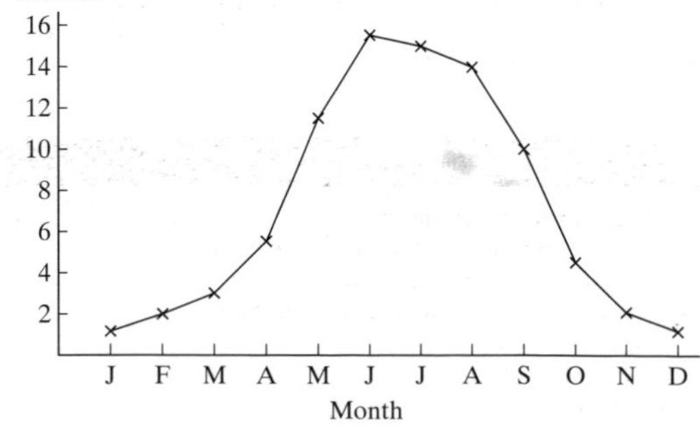

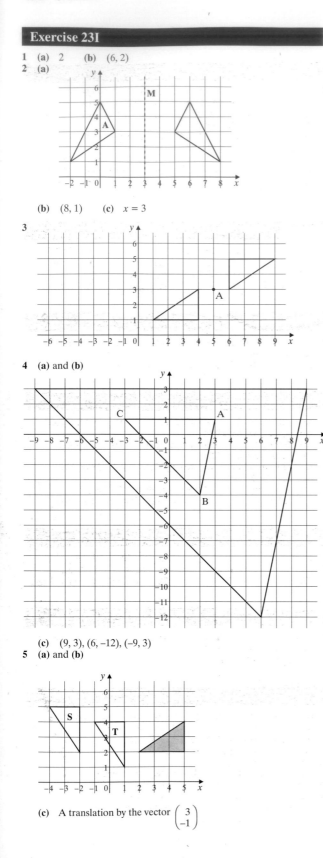

(b) 7.1 inches

5 (a)

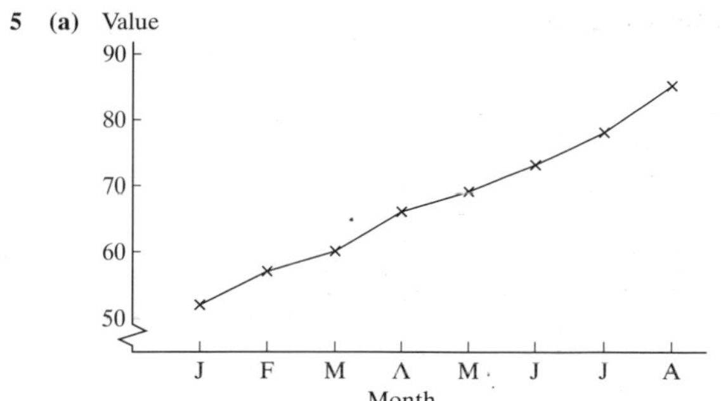

(b) 88–93 pence. This is called extrapolation. It is not very reliable.

Exercise 24B

1 (i)

Class interval (steepness °)	Tally	Frequency
1–10	III	3
11–20	~~IIII~~	5
21–30	IIII	4
31–40	~~IIII~~ I	6

(ii)

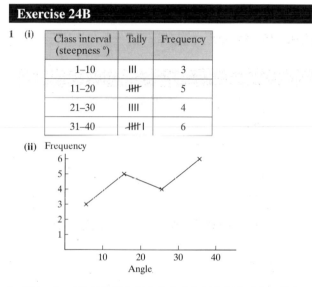

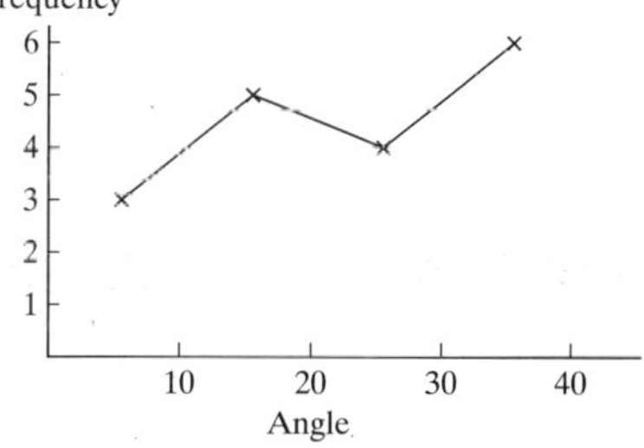

2 Mid points 4.5, 14.5, 24.5, 34.5, 44.5, 54.5, 64.5, 74.5 Mean 43.4
3 (a) 6 (b) 105 (c) 2 (d) 3.5

Exercise 24C

1 Angles: Conservative 158.4°, Labour 108°, Liberal Democrat 93.6°
2 (a) 58°
(b) Flour 120°, Butter 150°, Water 58°, Sugar 30°, Salt 2°
3 Silver 180°, copper 126°, zinc 54°
4 Bus fares 48°, going out 100°, clothes 120°, records 60°, other 32°
(c) $\frac{1}{3}$
5 Capital expenses 90°, BBC 1 126°, BBC 2 72°, Radio 72°
6 (a) 90, (b) 40°, (c) 0.22, (d) $\frac{3}{25}$
7 (a) 112 (b) 408

Exercise 24D

1 (c) High positive correlation
2 (b) There is no evidence of any correlation
3 (b) 1.3 amps (c) 6.5 ohms
4 (a) Mpg decreases as engine size increases
(b) Negative correlation
(d) About 45 mpg

Unit 25 Ratio and proportion

Exercise 25A

1 (a) 5 : 4 (b) 1 : 5 (c) 1 : 4 (d) 2 : 1
(e) 3 : 2 (f) 6 : 1 (g) 2 : 6 : 1 (h) 1 : 2 : 3
2 (a) 1 : 50 (b) 7 : 20 (c) 1 : 200 (d) 2 : 125
(e) 15 : 2 : 6 (f) 3 : 8
3 (a) 17 : 60 (b) 4 : 12 : 3 (c) 9 : 200 (d) 2 : 5
(e) 9 : 20 (f) 200 : 11
4 (a) 6 : 1 (b) 16 : 1 (c) 2 : 1 (d) 3 : 2
(e) 3 : 1 : 2 (f) 4 : 9 (g) 3 : 4 : 10 (h) 25 : 36
5 (a) 6 : 17 (b) 110 : 23 (c) 15 : 7 (d) 295 : 2
(e) 8 : 7 : 11 (f) 2 : 5 : 25

Exercise 25B

1 (a) 1 : 2.5 (b) 1 : 0.25 (c) 1 : 100 (d) 1 : 2.5
(e) 1 : 6.25 (f) 1 : 7.5 (g) 1 : 2.2 (h) 1 : 40
2 (a) 0.75 : 1 (b) 30 000 : 1 (c) 6 : 1 (d) 7.5 : 1
(e) 500 : 1 (f) 1000 : 1 (g) 33.3 : 1 (h) 0.2 : 1

Exercise 25C

1 (a) 2 (b) 66 (c) 16 (d) 2 (e) 8 (f) 7
(g) 4 (h) 8
2 3 kg 3 20 buckets 4 15 5 15 cm

Exercise 25D

1 (a) £4.26, £10.65 (b) £20, £25 (c) £9.44, £42.48
(d) £14.21, £56.84, £99.47
2 (a) 360 g, 240 g (b) 12 cm, 20 cm (c) 3.9 *l*, 19.5 *l*
(d) 6.3 m, 12.6 m, 15.75 m
3 (a) 13.68 m, 17.1 m (b) 45 cm, 30 cm (c) 18 kg, 30 kg
(d) £51, £102, £204
4 (a) 16 (b) 12 5 60°, 50°, 70° 6 400 g
7 £132, £176, £352 8 (a) 204 g (b) 153 g

Exercise 25E

1 £5.85 2 9 g 3 £24.50 4 70 p
5 840 6 96 p 7 £2.64 8 976 g
9 £2.25 10 2808 cm^3 11 720 g flour, 1080 g fat, 3 eggs.

Exercise 25F

1 3 days 2 5 hours 3 20 days 4 48 rooms
5 8 days 6 6 hours 7 14 8 15 days
9 $13\frac{1}{2}$ days 10 120

Exercise 25G

1 (a) 7 : 2 (b) 1 : 3 (c) 1 : 20 (d) 7 : 6 (e) 14 : 17
(f) 1 : 8 (g) 1 : 3 (h) 1 : 18 (i) 1 : 8
2 (a) 1 : 5 (b) 1 : 0.75 (c) 1 : 120 (d) 1 : 0.12
3 (a) 1.5 : 1 (b) 6 : 1 (c) 0.1 : 1
4 (a) 7 (b) 9
5 (a) 13.68 m, 17.1 m (b) £3.68, £5.52, £9.20
6 5 : 8 7 35 8 104
9 225° 10 45 11 5 days
12 (a) (i) 4 ounces (ii) 5 ounces (b) 27 cakes
13 7000 kg 14 35 feet

Unit 26 Accurate drawings, scales and loci

Exercise 26A

3 (b) 103° 4 (b) 1.6 cm

Exercise 26B

1 2 m
2 (a) 1.4 km (b) 17.4 cm
3 (a) (i) 12 500 cm (ii) 125 m
(b) (i) 6.3 cm (ii) 157.5 m (iii) 19 687.5 m^2
4 (a) 2.7 km (b) 258°
5 (b) (i) 2.35 km (ii) 080°

Exercise 26C

3 (c) (i) 14.5 km (b) 13.5 km

Exercise 26D

1 (a) 30° (b) 8 cm
2 (a) 10 cm (b) 3 cm (c) $c = 4$ cm, $e = 9$ cm
(d) $d = 2$ cm, $f = 10$ cm
3 (a) 51° (b) 12 cm 4 6.9 cm

Exercise 26E

1 (d) PA = 2.4 cm or 2.5 cm
2 Turn clockwise through 90°, move forward 40 m, move forward 50 m.
3 (b) 3.75 m 4 (b) 36.1 cm

Unit 27 The sine and cosine ratios

Exercise 27A

1 (g) They are about the same (between 0.6 and 0.7).
2 (g) They are about the same.

Exercise 27B

1 (a) 0.208 (b) 0.469 (c) 0.643 (d) 0.990
2 (a) 11.5° (b) 41.1° (c) 73.0°
3 (a) 5.42 cm (b) 10.0 cm (c) 10.2 cm (d) 21.7 cm
4 (a) 22.6° (b) 47.0° (c) 67.4° (d) 73.7°
5 8.68 m 6 30.0 cm

Exercise 27C

1 (g) They are about the same (between 0.8 and 0.9).

Exercise 27D

0.4384	64°	0.4384
0.5000	60°	0.5000
0.7986	37°	0.7986
0.8660	30°	0.8660

Exercise 27E

1 (a) 0.978 (b) 0.883 (c) 0.766 (d) 0.139
2 (a) 78.5° (b) 48.9° (c) 17.0°
3 (a) 7.19 cm (b) 4.73 cm
4 (a) 67.4° (b) 43.0° (c) 22.6° (d) 16.3°
5 (a) 20.2 cm (b) 48.3 cm 6 21.5 cm 7 72.1°

Exercise 27F

1 53.1 m 2 36.9° 3 64.3°

Exercise 27G

1 (a) (i) 50 km (ii) 42.4 km (b) (i) 53° (ii) 307°
2 5.52 m 3 80.6 m 4 (a) 8.60 km (b) 144°
5 44.5 m 6 41.4°
7 (a) 232° (b) 14° (c) 2.18 km (d) 8.73 km
8 80.8 m 9 168 10 12.9 m 11 14.2 m
12 (a) (i) 2.8867513(46…) m (ii) 2.89 m
(b) 2.5 m

Unit 28 Linear equations and simultaneous linear equations

Exercise 28A

1 (a) $1\frac{1}{2}$ (b) 3 (c) $\frac{1}{2}$ (d) 2 (e) $\frac{1}{4}$ (f) $2\frac{3}{4}$
2 (a) $c = 24h + 40$ (b)

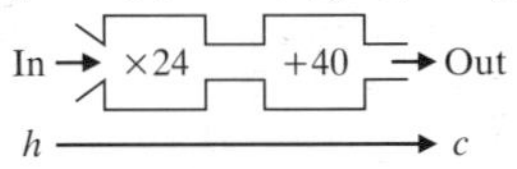

In → ×24 → +40 → Out
h → c

(c)

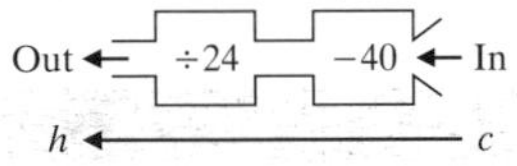

Out ← ÷24 ← −40 ← In
h ← c

(d) (i) $2\frac{1}{2}$ (ii) 4 (iii) 3 (iv) $1\frac{1}{2}$ (v) $2\frac{1}{4}$ (vi) $1\frac{3}{4}$
3 (a) $c = 18d + 5$ (b)

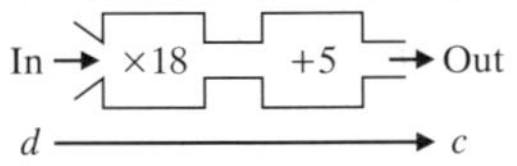

In → ×18 → +5 → Out
d → c

(c)

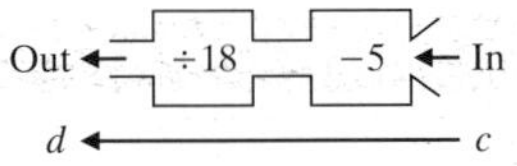

Out ← ÷18 ← −5 ← In
d ← c

(d) (i) 3 (ii) 5 (iii) $1\frac{1}{2}$ (iv) $4\frac{1}{2}$ (v) 2 (vi) 7
4 (a) $c = 5d + 38$
c is the cost, in pounds, of hiring the skip.
d is the number of days the skip is hired.
(b) (i) 3 (ii) 7 (iii) 4 (iv) 14 (v) 11 (vi) 9

Exercise 28B

1 (a) $h = 7$ (b) $d = 4$ (c) $d = 1$ (d) $h = 4$
(e) $h = 9$ (f) $d = 38$
2 12
3 (a) 3 (b) 8 (c) 28 (d) 47
(e) 64 (f) 11

Exercise 28C

1 (a) 3 (b) 8 (c) 28 (d) 47 (e) 64 (f) 11

2 (a) $d = 6$ (b) $h = 6$ (c) $h = 60$ (d) $d = 60$
(e) $q = 17$ (f) $r = 4$ (g) $m = 28$ (h) $r = 9$
(i) 33

Exercise 28D

1 (a) $r = 3$ (b) $p = 5$ (c) $s = -5$ (d) $m = 9$
(e) $d = 6$ (f) $g = -3$
2 (a) $2p + 4 = p + 9$ (b) $p = 5$ (c) 14
3 If £a is the cost of an adult ticket,
$2a + 2 = a + 5$
$a = 3$
An adult ticket cost £3.
4 If c pence is the cost of a can of drink,
$3c + 126 = 5c + 10$
$c = 58$
A can costs 58p.
5 $4x + 10 = 6x + 6$
$x = 2$
6 If £h is the amount the waiter was paid per hour,
$4h + 3 = 6h - 5$
$h = 4$
The waiter was paid £4 per hour.

Exercise 28E

1 (a) $p = 3$ (b) $x = 2$ (c) $t = 1.5$ (d) $h = 7$
(e) $m = 3$ (f) $x = 1$
2 (a) $p = 3$ (b) $q = 6$ (c) $s = 2.5$ (d) $n = -2$
(e) $k = 3$ (f) $y = 2.5$
3 (a) $8 + 2p = 28 - 6p$ (b) $p = 2.5$ (c) 13
4 (a) $45 - 2x = 30 + x$ (b) $x = 5$ (c) 35
5 (a) $15 - 3c = 12 - 2c$ (b) £3
6 (a) $70 - 60y = 60 - 20y$
(b) $y = \frac{1}{4}$. The volume of juice in one glass is 0.25 litres or 250cc.

Exercise 28F

1 (a) $h = -1$ (b) $p = 1$ (c) $q = 1\frac{1}{2}$ (d) $r = 2$
(e) $t = -3$ (f) $x = -2\frac{1}{2}$
2 (a) $m = 12$ (b) $g = 8$ (c) $n = 15$ (d) $x = 24$
(e) $p = 6\frac{6}{8}$

Exercise 28G

1 (a) (i)

x	−2	0	2	4
$y = 2x + 1$	−3	1	5	9

x	−2	0	2	4
$y = 4 - x$	6	4	2	0

(iii) $x = 1, y = 3$

(b) (i)

x	−2	0	2	4
$y = 2x - 5$	−9	−5	−1	3

x	−2	0	2	4
$y = 3 - 2x$	7	3	−1	−5

(iii) $x = 2, y = -1$

(c) (i)

x	−2	0	2	4
$y = x - 2$	−4	−2	0	2

x	−2	0	2	4
$y = 3x + 4$	−2	4	10	16

(iii) $x = -3, y = -5$
2 (a) $c = 10d + 30$ (b) $c = 15d$ (d) 6
3 (a) $t = 50m$ (b) $t = 25m + 600$ (d) £1200, 24 months
4 (a) $g = 40$ (b) $g = 0.01m + 16$, $g = 0.1m$
(d) Less than 178 minutes of calls in a month choose scheme C, 178 to 2400 minutes of calls in a month choose scheme B, more than 2400 minutes of calls choose scheme A.
5 If you expect to do less than $27\frac{1}{2}$ hours of skiing choose silver, if you expect to do more choose gold.
6 (a) 3500 pamphlets (b) £160

Exercise 28H

1 (a) $x = 9, y = 45$ (b) $x = 8, y = 64$ (c) $x = 11, y = 124$
(d) $x = 2, y = 10$ (e) $x = 2, y = 12$ (f) $x = 8, y = -12$
2 (a) $x = 2, y = 2$ (b) $x = 15, y = 36$ (c) $x = 3.5, y = 12.5$
(d) $x = 1.2, y = 0.4$ (e) $x = 3, y = 12$ (f) $x = 24, y = 27$

Exercise 28I

1 (a) $p = 2, q = 1$ (b) $x = 2.5, y = 1$
2 (a) $x = 1\frac{2}{3}, y = 3$ (b) $p = 3, q = -2$

Exercise 28J

1 (a) $x = 4, y = -2$ (b) $x = 2, y = \frac{1}{3}$ (c) $x = 7, y = -3$
2 (a) $x = -2, y = 4$ (b) $x = 2, y = -1$ (c) $d = 5, e = -2$
3 (a) $x = 5, y = -3$ (b) $p = 2, q = 3$ (c) $m = -3, n = -8$

Exercise 28K

1 (a) 4, 5, 6, 7 (b) −3, −2, −1, 0, 1, 2, 3, 4
(c) 4, 5, 6, 7 (d) −2, −1, 0, 1, 2, 3, 4
(e) −6, −5, −4, −3, −2 (f) −67, −66, −65
2 (a) $n < 2$ (b) $n \leqslant 6$ (c) $n < -3$
(d) $n > 3$ (e) $n > -3$ (f) $n \geqslant 5$
(g) $n < \frac{1}{3}$ (h) $n < -\frac{1}{2}$ (i) $n \leqslant -\frac{1}{2}$
3 (a) $n < 4$ (b) $x > 8$ (c) $x \geqslant 5\frac{1}{2}$
(d) $y < 4$ (e) $x < -3$ (f) $y > 5$

Exercise 28L

1 (a) $x = 1$ or 4 (b) $x = 1$ or 3 (c) $x = 2$ or 3
2 (a) $x = -1$ or −2 (b) $x = -2$ or −4 (c) $x = -2$ or −6
3 (a) $x = 1$ or −11 (b) $x = 4$ or −2 (c) $x = 2$ or −10
4 (a) $x = -4$ or +4 (b) $x = -7$ or +7 (c) $x = -9$ or +9
5 (a) $p = 2$ or 7 (b) $q = -3$ (c) $y = 5$ or −3
6 (a) $c = -3$ or −6 (b) $d = 3$ or −7 (c) $g = 2$ or 8

Exercise 28M

1 (a) $x = 6$ (b) $y = -2$
2 (a) $9x + 7$ cm (b) 4
3 3
4 (a) $4x + 20$ (b) $9x + 5 = 4x + 20$ (c) 3kg
5 (a) (i) $3x$ (ii) $x - 9$ (iii) $3x - 9$
(b) (i) $3x - 9 = 6(x - 9)$ (ii) 15
6 $x = 2$
7 $p = 2, q = -3$
8 (a) (i) $x = 7$ (ii) $y = -2$ (iii) $t = 13$
(b) (i) 14.4
(ii) $y = \frac{P}{2} - x$

9 (a) $x = 3$ (b) $p = 3, q = -3$
10 (a) $n < 3\frac{3}{4}$ (b) 3
11 (a) $x = -2$ or -7 (b) $x = -5$ or 2
12 (a) $y < 500$ (b) $x + y < 600$ (c) $y \geqslant 2x$

Unit 29 Interpreting data

Exercise 29A

1 All three forms had 5 absences for the week. Form B may have had the same person away all week whereas at least 5 from Form A had an absence during the week.
Form A: Median 0, Mode 0, Mean 1, Range 5
Form B: Median 1, Mode 1, Mean 1, Range 0
Form C: Median 0, Mode 0, Mean 1, Range 3
2 Although the mean suggests that the Hawks have the weaker players their higher range means that they may have some of the best players overall.
3 The members of the Tavistock are more closely matched for age than the members of the President if one looks at the evidence of the half at the middle of the range. Although the middle person of the President is younger than the middle person of the Tavistock the different ranges mean that they may also have some of the oldest members in the two clubs. There is not enough evidence to suggest that one club has older members than the other.
4 Whilst one might have expected that distant holidays would cost more, travel is only one aspect of the cost of a holiday. Length of holiday and quality of accommodation are also factors.
5 With one exception there is a high negative correlation.
Only 3 completed the full distance.
The winner averaged 68.25 seconds per lap.
6 (i)

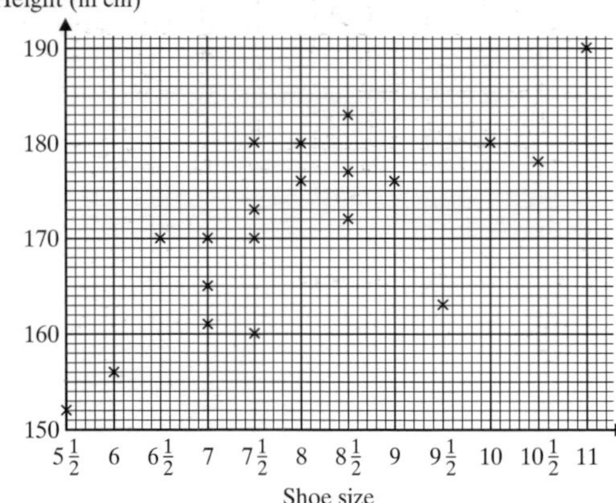

(ii) There is a low positive correlation between height and shoe size.
7 50 letters are sent to Vale Close and 60 to Wheeler Gardens.
Vale Close: Range 30, Mean 4.16, Median 2, Mode 2
Wheeler Gardens: Range 6, Mean 5, Median 5, Mode 5
One home contributes 60% of total letters delivered to Vale Close and this distorts the mean which will not be a good statistic when making comparisons.

Unit 30 Calculators and computers

Exercise 30A

1 7 3 → L EXE
4 9 → W EXE
L W → A EXE
2 L + 2 W → P EXE
Answers: 3577 cm^2, 244 cm
2 1 2 → R EXE
SHIFT π R x^2 → A EXE
2 SHIFT π R → C EXE
Answers: 452.389 cm^2, 75.398 cm.
3 1 5 → B EXE
9 → H EXE
(B H) ÷ 2 → A EXE
Answer: 67.5 cm^2
4 1 2 0 → L EXE
6 0 → W EXE
2 0 → H EXE
L W H → V EXE
Answer: 144 000 cm^3
5 5 → R EXE
1 2 → H EXE
SHIFT π R x^2 H → V EXE
Answer: 942.478 cm^3

Exercise 30B

1 "SIDE"
? → L
L x^y 3 → V
Answers: 125 cm^3, 216 cm^3, 343 cm^3
2 "FAHRENHEIT"
? → F
(F – 32) × 5 ÷ 9 → C
Answer: 30°C, 10°C, 20°C
3 "BASE"
? → B
"HEIGHT"
? → H
(B H) ÷ 2 → A
Answer: 52.5 cm^2

Exercise 30C

1 ? → L : L x^y 3 Answer: L = 4.64 cm
2 ? → L : 6 L x^y 2 Answer: L = 2.89 cm
3 Answer: 71.6°F
4 Answer: $x = 2.5$

Exercise 30D

1 5 EXE Ans + 5 EXE EXE ...
2 2 EXE Ans × 2 EXE EXE ...
3 1 0 EXE Ans – 1 EXE EXE ...
4 2 0 0 EXE Ans ÷ 1 0 EXE EXE ...

5 (-) 5 EXE Ans - 2 EXE EXE ...
6 3 EXE Ans x^y 2 EXE EXE ...
7 3 EXE 1 0 - Ans EXE EXE ...

Exercise 30F

1 $x = -1, x = 2$
2 $x = 0.5, x = 3$
3 $x = -1, x = 0, x = 1$
4 $x = -1.5, x = 1, x = 2$

Exercise 30H

1 length = 60 m, width = 30 m
2 7 red, 14 green, 10 brown stamps
3 base = 40 cm, height = 40 cm

Exercise 30I

1 width = 4.84 cm
2 Winford = £1.31, Barry = 86p, Syreeta = £2.37
3 base = 9.66 cm

Examination practice paper

1 30cm^2 **2** 8
3 **(a)** £1.60 **(b)** $\frac{2}{5}$ **(c)** 39 km
(d) Ahmed £1200, Dilys £900, Siobhan £600
4 **(a)** 3 **(b)** −1.5
5 **(a)** 300, 60 **(b)** 18 000 **(c)** 18 408, with working shown
6 **(a)** 49 **(b)** $d = 6n + 1$
7 **(a)** approximately 128 km **(b)** $53\frac{1}{3}$ mph
8 **(a)** 9 cars **(b)** 7 cars **(c)** 11 cars **(d)** 6.6 cars
9 **(a)** 76° **(b)** **(i)** $\frac{43}{180}$ **(ii)** $\frac{137}{180}$
10 **(a)** **(i)** 2 **(ii)** 3 **(b)** 2.31
11 **(a)** and **(b)**

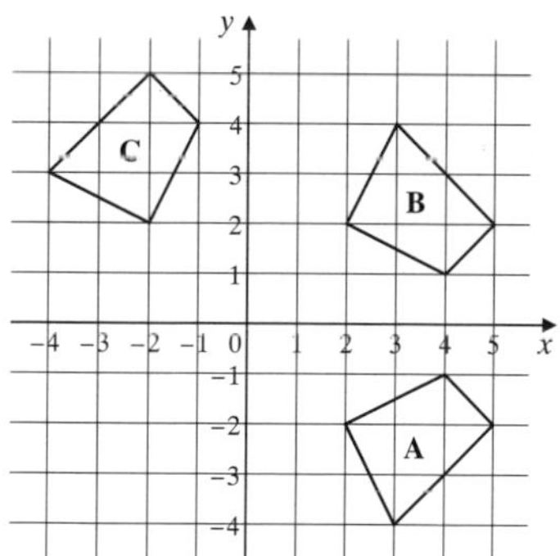

(c) Reflection in the line $y = x$.
12 **(a)** 0.28 **(b)**

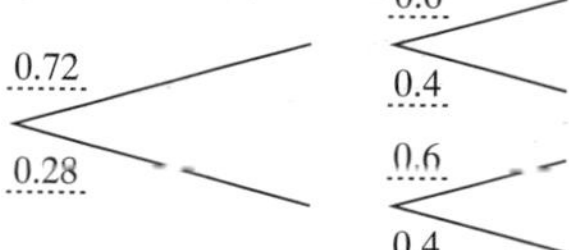

(c) **(i)** 0.432 **(ii)** 0.456

13 **(a)** **(i)** 75° **(ii)** 54° **(b)** 4 cm **14** $x < 11.5$
15 y: −6, 7, 10, 9, 19

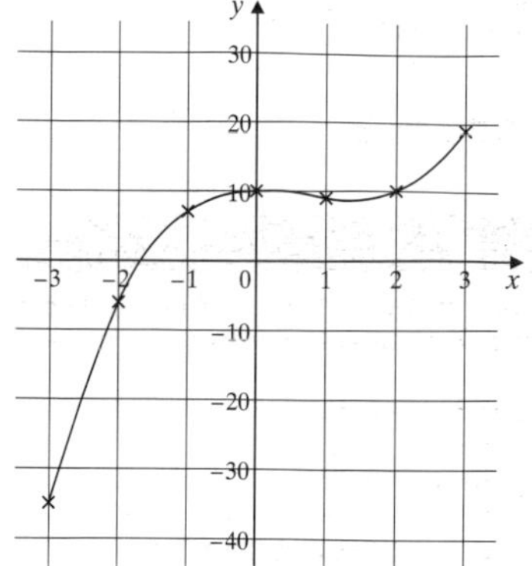

16 **(a)** 6.24 km **(b)** 219°
17 2
18 **(a)**

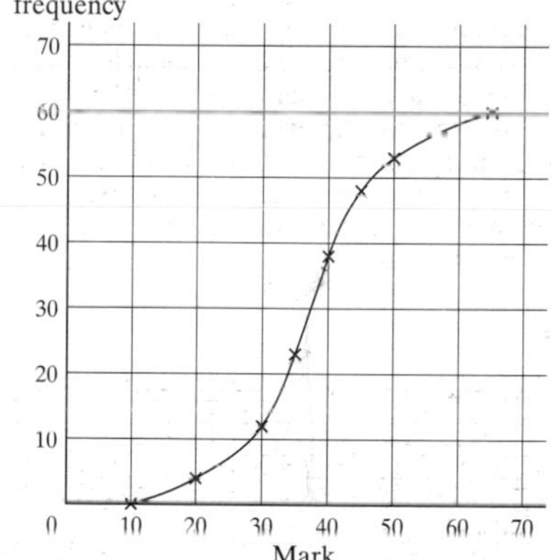

(b) 27
19 **(a)** $2a(3a - 4)$ **(b)** $2x^2 + x - 6$

Index

Algebraic expressions 291–311
  bracket removal 296–7, 299–301
  evaluating 291–4
  involving squares 293–4
  simplifying 297–9
Angles 121–36
  of depression 405
  of elevation 405
  and tangent ratio 229–31
Approximation 70–80
Arc 131
Areas 273–90
  converting units 159–60
Averages 201–25

Balance method, linear equations 415–16
Bar charts 356–7
Bearings 134–5
Brackets
  calculator operations 439
  in expressions 291
  multiplication 296–7, 299–301

Calculators 438–55
  see also Graphical calculators; Scientific calculators
Capacity, estimation 56
Chord 131
Circles
  area 279–80
  calculating angles in 131–3
  circumference 131, 277–8
Circumference 131, 277–8
Composite shapes 273–6
Compound interest 326–8
  calculator operations 439
  graphical calculators 448
Computers 438–55
Cones, properties 48
Congruent shapes 42–4, 343
Constant calculations 439
Continuous data 104, 217
Conversions, units 154–60
Correlations, scatter graphs 367–8
Cosine ratio 398–411
  applications 402–4
  and sine ratio 402
Credit, purchases 323–4
Cube numbers 179–80
Cube roots 181–2
Cubes 181
Cubic functions, graphs 244–7
Cuboids, volume 281
Cumulative frequency 214–15
  data interpretation 433–4
  graphs 216–25
Cylinders
  area of surface 282
  volume 282

Data
  continuous 104, 217
  discrete 104, 217
  interpreting 431–7
  organization 98–109
  presenting 355–72
  qualitative 103–4
  quantitative 103–4
  types of 103–4
  see also Grouped data
Data collection 98–109
  applications 107
Databases 102–3
Dates 64–5
Decimal places, rounding 73
Decimals 2–4
  calculator operations 438
  conversion to percentages 313
  division by 10, 100, 1000 4
  and fractions 142–3
  multiplication by 10, 100, 1000 3–4
  recurring 143–4
Denominator 137–53
Density 165–6
  investigation 110–20
Diagonals 110
  of quadrilaterals 40–2
Diameter 131
Digits 1–2
Dimensions 285–7
Direct proportion 379–80
Discrete data 104, 217
Distance–time graphs 93–6
Division, without a calculator 6–7
Dot patterns 118
Drawings, accurate 385–97

Enlargements 343–8
  centres of 345
Equations 412–30
  graphical calculators 449–50
  linear 413–27
  trial and improvement 249–50
  see also Quadratic equations; Simultaneous linear equations
Equilateral triangles, properties 40
Equivalent fractions 137–9
Estimation 55–8
  of calculations 75–6
  capacity 56
  length 55–6
  from scales 61–2
  weight 57–8
Even numbers 178

Factorization 307–8
  quadratic equations 428
  quadratics 308–9
Factors 178
Formulae 301–3
  rearranging 304–7
Fractions 137–53
  addition 144–5
  calculator operations 438
  conversion to decimals 142–3
  conversion to percentages 313
  division 149–50
  equivalent 137–9
  improper 140–1
  multiplication 147–8
  problem solving 150–2
  simplifying 139–40
  subtraction 146
Frequency distributions 104–6
  averages 207–8
  mean 208–9
  spread 209–11
Frequency polygons 360–2
Functions
  cubic 244–7
  graphs 81–92, 236–56
  inverse tangent 228
  linear 81–97
  notation 18–19
  reciprocal 244–8
  simple 15–27
  tables 81–5
  see also Quadratic functions

Generalizations 116–19
Gradients 89

Graphical calculators
operations 442–50
problem solving 445–7
saving formulae 444–5
Graphs
accurate 86–7, 247–8
applications 250–4
complex functions 236–56
cubic functions 244–7
distance–time 93–6
graphical calculators 448–50
interpretation 87–8, 250–4
line 357
linear functions 81–97
parallel lines 89, 92
quadratic functions 236–41
reciprocal functions 244–8
shapes 254–5
simultaneous linear equations 420–2
see also Scatter graphs; Straight line graphs
Grouped data 105–6
averages 211–13

Highest common factor 185
Histograms 357–9
Hypotenuse, Pythagoras' theorem 193–7

Imperial units, converting 157–8
Improper fractions 140–1
Independent events 257–9
Indices *see* Powers
Inequalities 412–30
solving 427–8
Input–output diagrams 19–20
Intercepts 89
Interest
compound 326–8
simple 324–6
Interquartile range 206–7
estimation 219
Inverse number machines 16–17, 20–21
linear equations 413–14
problem solving 412–13
Inverse proportion 381–2
Inverse tangent function 228
Investigations 110–20
Isosceles triangles, properties 40

Kites, properties 41

Lengths 273–90
estimation 55–6
and tangent ratio 231–3
Line of best fit 368–70
Line graphs 357
Line symmetry, two-dimensional shapes 45–6
Linear equations, solving 413–27
Linear functions, graphs 81–97
Linear graphs *see* Straight line graphs
Lines, measurement 62–3
Lines of reflection 336
Lines of symmetry 45–6
Loci 385–97
determination 390–2
Lowest common multiple 186

Mathematics, using and applying 110–20
Mean 201
Measures 55–69, 154–70
accuracy 160–3
comparing 168–9
compound 163–8
continuous 160–1
discrete 160–1
inaccuracies 77–8
time 59–60
units 58–9
Median 202–3
estimation 218
Memories, graphical calculators 442–3
Metric units, converting 154–60
Mirror lines 336
Mode 202
Multiples 178
Multiplication, without a calculator 6–7

Negative numbers 7–14
division 11
multiplication 10–11
subtraction 9–10
Nets, three-dimensional shapes 50–1
Number machines 15–20
equivalent 17–18
inverse 16–17
Number sequences
expressions for the *n*th term 25–7
graphical calculators 447
spreadsheets 450–1
Numbers 1–14
cube 179–80
even 178
odd 178
ordering 5
place value 1–2
prime 178
properties 178–92
rounding 70–5
square 179–80
see also Negative numbers
Numerator 137–53

Observations, recording 113–14
Odd numbers 178
Output–input diagrams 20–1

Parallel lines 39
calculating angles at 129–31
Parallelograms
area 273
properties 40
Patterns 114–15
Percentages 312–32
calculator operations 438–9
conversion to decimals 312
conversion to fractions 312
decrease 316–17
increase 316–17
problem solving 328–9
profit and loss 320–1
of quantities 315–20
Perimeter 273
Perpendicular lines 39
Pictograms 355
Pie charts 362–6
interpretation 364–6
Place value 1–2
Planes of symmetry 47–50
Polygons
calculation of angles 126–8
properties 39–42
Powers 294–6
calculation 183
calculator operations 440
division 184–5, 294–6
multiplication 184–5, 294–6
Predictions 114–15
Prime factor form 185
Prime numbers 178
Prisms
properties 48
volume 281
Probability 28–38, 257–72
combined events 261–5
equally likely outcomes 32–4
estimated 29–31
experiments 29–31
independent events 257–9
mutually exclusive events 34–6
Problem solving 111–13
Profit and loss, and percentages 320–1
Proportion 373–84
direct 379–80
inverse 381–2
Pyramids, properties 48

Pythagoras' theorem 193–200
calculator operations 440–1
formula 195

Quadratic equations
factorizing 428
problem solving 243–4
simple, solving 240–1
solving, using graphs 240–3
Quadratic functions 171–7
factorizing 308–9
graphs 236–41
method of differences 172–5
Quadrilaterals
calculation of angles 123–5
interior angles 123–5
properties 40
Qualitative data 103–4
Quantitative data 103–4
Quartiles 205–6
estimation 219
Questionnaires 107–8

Radius 131
Range 204
Ratios 373–84
dividing quantities 378
as fractions 376–7
unitary form 375–6
Reciprocal functions, graphs 244–8
Rectangles
areas 273–6
lengths 273–6
properties 40
Reflections 336–9
Relative frequency 259–61
Remainders, rounding 71–2
Results, tabulation 113–14
Rhombuses, properties 40
Right angled triangles, properties 40
Roots, calculator operations 440
Rotational symmetry, two-dimensional shapes 46–7
Rotations 339–43

Scalene triangles, properties 40
Scales 61–2, 385–97
in accurate drawings 387–9
Scatter graphs 366–70
correlations 367–8
data interpretation 434–5
lines of best fit 368–9
Scientific calculators
memory calculations 440
operations 438–41
Sequences
expressions for the *n*th term 25–7
see also Number sequences
Significant figures, rounding 74–5
Similar shapes 42–4, 343
Similarity, mathematical 392–5
Simple interest 324–6
Simultaneous linear equations
elimination 424–6
graphs 420–2
substitution 422–4
Sine ratio 398–411
applications 399–401
and cosine ratio 402
Speed 163–5
on a distance/time graph 94
Spread 201–25
Spreadsheets
operations 450–5
problem solving 451–3
Square numbers 179–80
Square roots 180, 182
Squares 180
properties 40
Standard form 186–9
calculations with 189–91
calculator operations 441
Straight line graphs 81–97
gradient–intercept form 89–91
Symbols, and generalizations 116–19
Symmetry 45–50

Tables
data organization 101–2
two-way 98–100
Tally charts, probability 29–31
Tally marks 104–5
Tangent 131
Tangent ratio 226–35
on calculator 227–8
Tessellations 123
Three-dimensional shapes 39–54
area 281–4
nets 50–1
planes of symmetry 47–50
representation on paper 47–8
volume 281–4
Time
calculations 63–4
measurement 59–60
Timetables 66–7
Transformations 333–54
combining 348–52
Translations 333–6
Trapeziums
area 274–6
properties 40
Tree diagrams 263–7
Trial and improvement
equation solving 249–50
graphical calculators 445–7
spreadsheets 453–5
square roots and cube roots 182
Triangles
areas 273–6
calculation of angles 121–2
interior angles 122
lengths 273–6
properties 40
Trigonometrical ratios 405–10
see also Cosine ratio; Sine ratio; Tangent ratio
Trigonometry, calculator operations 440–1
Two-dimensional shapes 39–54
Two-way tables 98–100

Units
choice of 58–9
converting 154–60, 167–8
imperial 157–8
metric 154–60
relationships between 159

VAT, calculations 322–3
Volumes 273–90
converting units 159–60

Weight, estimation 57–8